Biology of the invertebrates

Biology
of the
invertebrates

Cleveland P. Hickman, Ph.D.

*Department of Zoology,
DePauw University,
Greencastle, Indiana*

With 596 illustrations

Saint Louis

The C. V. Mosby Company

1967

To Frances

Who worked so faithfully with this book

Preface

The plan of this text is built around the concept that each major group of invertebrates has certain morphologic and functional features that have guided its radiation patterns throughout its long evolutionary development. Adaptation is the chief orienting factor in the evolution of all forms. An understanding of these basic adaptive features in the different invertebrate groups enables the student to determine how animals fit into their varied ecologic niches. In this way the student can appreciate better the structural and functional aspects of any particular invertebrate he may happen to study. Such a viewpoint also makes intelligible the bewildering diversity of animal forms. Comparative morphology and physiology must then represent the very essence of all revealing studies of any animal group.

Many restrictions are imposed upon a text of this kind in order to keep it within the size limits required of a one-semester course. Invertebrates have been widely studied by competent investigators in all parts of the world. This research has resulted in an enormous amount of revealing data covering nearly all aspects of invertebrate life—their phylogeny, their ecologic relationships, their evolutionary trends, and their physiologic reactions under controlled conditions. Invertebrate symposia with subsequent monographs are legion. To cover this material in a thoroughly adequate manner would require many volumes the size of this one. The aim of the present treatise is to restrict the coverage of this vast research material to those studies that give an interpretation of a broad morphologic understanding of the various invertebrate groups. It seems therefore quite logical in an introductory text on invertebrates to stress the structural aspects of animals. No one can appreciate the physiologic features of animals without understanding the limitations imposed by their basic adaptive structures. What animals can and cannot do is determined to a great extent by their evolutionary patterns of morphology.

This text has laid considerable emphasis on the classification of the invertebrates in the belief that the student can best orient himself to any particular group of invertebrates by having a fair idea of their general taxonomy. The attempt has been made to give the latest systematic presentations, although I well realize the constant flux of this discipline and that general agreement on such matters is nonexistent. This classification is presented early in the treatment of the groups so that the student can glean some idea of the diversification within the various groups.

Another major aim of the text has been to avoid a type presentation, but rather to give a broad coverage of a group as a whole. In no invertebrate group of any size can it be said that any one example or type covers all the characteristics that the student should know about that group. It is true, however, that some types have been emphasized more than others because such examples may reveal more factual material. Variations of basic structures are indicated as much as possible. All the larger groups of invertebrates present many exceptions to the general plan, and the student should be aware of those that are exceptionally interesting and that give an understanding of the potentiality of their basic adaptations.

The text is planned for zoology majors who have had at least a year of general zoology or biology and for those who are beginning graduate work in the field of zoology. Although a fairly extensive treatment of the groups is given, the text material may be covered in a semester by students who have had a good background in introductory zoology. Naturally, the number of class discussions per week will determine the length of time necessary to give an adequate coverage. It has been planned for at least three class periods each week during a semester.

The publication of so many excellent monographs and symposia on invertebrates in recent years has made the task of writing the text much easier than it would otherwise have been. These publications are listed under the annotated references at the ends of the various chapters. However, I have called upon specialists to review certain groups in order to benefit from their criticisms and suggestions. In every case, I am solely responsible for any errors or omissions that appear in the final draft of the chapters evaluated by these specialists. Restrictions of space prevented the incorporation of some of their suggestions, but their criticisms have been most helpful. I wish to acknowledge with gratitude the helpful suggestions and criticisms of the following persons: Dr. W. H. Johnson of Wabash College, who reviewed the protozoans; Dr. G. J. Bakus of the Allan Hancock Foundation and the University of Southern California, who reviewed the chapter on sponges; Dr. W. E. Martin of the University of Southern California, who reviewed the Platyhelminthes.

The Priapulida are now considered a phylum in their own right, and Dr. W. L. Shapeero of the University of Washington has given an appraisal of this group. The Arachnida, with special emphasis on the spiders, were reviewed by Dr. B. J. Kaston of San Diego State College; and the Mollusca by Dr. P. E. Dehnel of the University of British Columbia.

Dr. Warren Andrew of the Indiana University Medical School has been most helpful in loaning me several electron micrographs and photomicrographs of invertebrate structures; Dr. W. G. Bakus supplied several photographs of sponges; Dr. W. L. Shapeero furnished the photographs for the chapter on Priapulida; Encyclopaedia Britannica Films, Inc., allowed the use of many revealing photographs from their film records; the McGraw-Hill Book Company has kindly given permission to redraw certain figures from their copyrighted works; and Ward's Natural Science Establishment, General Biological Supply House, Inc., and Carolina Biological Supply Company also gave permission to use some of their photographs. I am also indebted to Dr. J. D. Costlow, Jr., for permission to redraw certain figures of *Sesarma cinereum* published in *Biological Bulletin*. Credit for these and other borrowed materials is given under the specific figures.

Illustrations for a work of this kind always present many problems. My wife Mrs. Frances M. Hickman has either made or supervised the making of the many line illustrations. Assisting her in this work were Miss Connie Hittle, Mrs. Barbara Poor, Mrs. Barbara L. Pickard, Mr. Bruce Gastineau, Miss Carole Thorlton, and Mr. Clifford M. Hickman. To these persons I wish to express my appreciation for their time-consuming work. I am especially indebted to Mrs. Hickman for attending to many other details of the entire manuscript besides the vast work of supervising the illustrations.

C. P. Hickman

Contents

Contents

Biology of the invertebrates

Introduction to the invertebrates

THE PRESSURE TO DIVERSIFY

At present, about 1,200,000 different species of animals have been named, and about 10,000 new species are added to the list each year. More than 90 percent of these species belong to the invertebrates. Although evolution of new species is a continuous process, the named species added to the list annually may result from the discovery of forms that have long been in existence but have only recently come to light. The fauna of the present is only a residue of the extinct faunas of the past. It is generally agreed that the numerous species that exist today represent only a small fraction of those that have existed in the long evolutionary history of animals. Although all major groups (phyla) of animals, with the exception of the phylum Chordata, belong to the invertebrates (and even some chordates may be considered invertebrates), the excess in the number of invertebrate species relative to the number of vertebrates is mainly because of the phylum Arthropoda, which contains at least 75 percent of all species.

The many types of animal life have had their origin in the variations to be found in any population unit. In every creature exists some minor differences that are not shared with others in its group. But whatever their differences, all creatures fall into certain natural groups of similar organisms that are called species. Localities naturally vary in the number of species and abundance of life they support, but most regions of the earth, when carefully investigated, will yield an amazing variety of forms. If the biologist were to study the fossil record, he would find that a vast change has occurred in most animal forms from geologic age to geologic age. There are excellent reasons, therefore, for believing that variants have been arising from the beginning of life. Many phylogenetic stocks developed into highly specialized groups and then became extinct. One group has often supplanted another group in the long evolution of life. Other groups have continued and flourished from the earliest times. Variations within the groups show an amazing diversity. Many stocks have given rise to numerous species within a relatively short time; others that show few species have remained virtually unchanged for millions of years.

With the possible exceptions of certain arid regions, frozen mountain peaks, restricted toxic sea basins, and a few others, every place on earth is represented by some form of life. Most species are adapted to a particular kind of environment that is restricted in size, food resources, habitat, and general conditions of existence. As populations increase, competition for these factors of existence increases, and adaptation pressure becomes keen and precise for those that survive. To escape from such competition those members of a population that may have suitable adaptations could move into new adjacent habitats and manage to survive. Such random dispersal of species occurs fairly commonly, and it explains one of the primary forces of distribution. Ecologic factors may play an important role in speciation in such cases. The rate of speciation depends to a great extent upon the presence of barriers for producing geographic isolates, the rate of genetic transformation of these geographic isolates, and the degree of opportunity afforded by vacant ecologic niches to new species. This syndrome of related conditions is often called opportunism in evolution.

EVOLUTIONARY AND ECOLOGIC PATTERNS OF INVERTEBRATES

Organic evolution is the result of the reaction between a progressive change in dynamic life and a progressively changing dynamic environment. Life shows an evolution from a less balanced relationship between the external and internal environment to a more closely adjusted relationship. Life as we now know it has been the outcome of a particular kind of biota within a particular kind of environment. It is impossible to understand the major evolutionary factors without at the same time considering the dynamics of the continually changing earth's crust and all the conditions of the external environment. Ecologic evolution is therefore a necessary corollary of biotic evolution. The environment has a broad meaning, because it includes the nonliving (physical) factors as well as all living things that in any way influence the organism (the biotic factors).

The geotectonic factor

The geotectonic factor refers to the structure of the earth's crust, its composition, its distribution, and its changes. Changes in the earth's crust have had profound effects upon the evolutionary pattern of animals. The earth's crust is characterized by two great, somewhat antagonistic forces—the elevating and leveling processes. These forces of elevation and leveling are continuous but do not always occur at the same intensity. Cycles of activity alternate with periods of minimum crustal disturbance. The dynamics of the geotectonic factors have been instrumental in changing and shifting physical conditions, such as soil, climate, and weather, and have been responsible for the production of varying ecologic conditions. Life has had to adapt itself to the ecologic conditions brought about by the continual moving and contraction of the earth's crust.

One of the most profound influences of the geotectonic factor is the breaking up of the earth's surface into extensive ecologic clines of widely variable physical conditions of climate, temperature, water, etc. This has not only been responsible for striking parallelisms between the features of the physical environment and morphologic variations but has also afforded a logical explanation for speciation. Most of the existing species owe their origin to geographic isolation. This isolation is a direct outcome of topographic shifting and changes. By such means biotic communities evolved, at first separately and then later by reuniting because physical barriers were broken down. Continual changes of physical conditions produced new biomes and therefore new opportunities for the evolution of new types. Diversity of topography means more ecologic niches for a more diverse life.

Extensive populations are continually being subjected to geographic variations. Spatially segregated populations invariably undergo differences from other populations of the same species with which they do not interbreed. The degree of differences between discrete populations depends upon the degree of geographic variations. Geographic variations necessitate the adaptation of each population to the area it occupies. There are isolating mechanisms other than geographic, but none have contributed more to our understanding of the evolutionary process than the geotectonic factor.

Species and speciation

Diversity of biologic systems is brought about by the slow processes of evolution under the guidance of the chemical and physical properties of the earth's crust. According to the scheme of the origin of life commonly held at present, a chemical pre-evolution involving the segregation of chemical constituents from many sources occurred. From simple compounds large macromolecules emerged, and under the influence of natural selection, certain aggregations of these molecules developed properties of life. At least three properties must have emerged during the chemical evolution that led to the production of living substance. First, a mixture of compounds had the power to absorb selected molecules from the environment. Second, some important compounds acquired the power of duplicating themselves. Third, some compounds served as catalysts or enzymes to facilitate the process.

Organisms are divided into discrete units that we call species. Speciation refers to that process whereby one species is split into two. The process of speciation may be thought of as either sudden or gradual. Some evolutionists believe that new species arose by sudden mutations, or saltation, that produced striking phenotypic effects in a single generation. With the exception of chromosome mutations involving a change in chromosome number (polyploidy), it is doubtful that this method of diversification is very common. There is no convincing evidence that new species have arisen in biparental organisms by gene mutations. Speciation is now regarded by most biologists as a gradual process, which was the original darwinian view. In the cline concept (J. S. Huxley) of the evolutionary process, the subdivisions of the cline, called demes, develop unique genetic characteristics. So long as the member of one deme can interbreed with that of another when the opportunity offers, there is no valid reason for considering the two demes separate species. However, genetic differences may occur to the point where fertile hybrids from two demes cannot be produced; then the two groups may be considered separate species. A species must be thought of as a group or a population, and speciation involves the members of a whole population and not merely a new type of organism or mutant form. Evolutionary change does not always involve an increase in the number of species or a splitting process. It is possible, in time, for one species to undergo a direct transformation into another species without the intervention of any splitting whatsoever. In such a case a new species has been formed without the multiplication of species. Evolutionary change or phyletic evolution should be distinguished from branching evolutionary lines or true speciation.

All major groups of animals may not have followed the same plan of speciation. This is especially the case with the extensive division of invertebrates. Up to the present time the speciation process is understood—and that is only partially—for a few groups of animals. In this text we can only point out one or two prominent mechanisms of the speciation process.

Isolating mechanisms and speciation

An isolating mechanism is any factor that tends to prevent interbreeding between groups of animals. Whatever method is involved to produce isolation must be considered the chief factor of speciation. The criterion of sterility, however, cannot be used as an absolute difference between species. Two different species may live side by side and have the power to interbreed and produce fertile offspring but rarely do so because of certain isolating mechanisms. There are, therefore, many devices that produce isolation mechanisms or properties that prevent interbreeding of species populations. Although spatial or geographic isolation is usually thought to be one of the most effective devices of isolation, most modern evolutionists do not consider this to be the most effective method. Biologic isolating mechanisms are now considered the chief basis for the effective prevention of interbreeding between species.

Biologic isolating mechanisms may be classified in various ways. Interbreeding between two species in the same region may be prevented by differences in the specific habitats of the two populations. This preventive method may be very effective among species that have limited mobility or among sedentary animals. Snails, for instance, may have soil preferences that hold them more or less to particular habitats, although different species lie fairly close together spatially. Even if such different species are completely fertile with each other, their habitat preferences normally prevent interbreeding. Seasonal differences in breeding can also be an effective barrier to the interbreeding of two species. One species may breed early and another late in the season, resulting in reproductive isolation. One of the most effective isolating mechanisms is based upon differences in behavior patterns (ethologic barriers). Much mating depends upon courtship displays, and appropriate stimuli between

3

male and female must be initiated to ensure specific mating. The courtship display of the male of one species may not arouse the mating response of the female of another species. Another important isolating factor is genetic isolation. Even if mates of different species copulate, they cannot produce fertile offspring. Each species seems to have a delicately integrated genetic system that fits it for a definite ecologic niche. This factor nearly always operates in time, because the longer two species are separated from each other by isolating mechanisms, the more incompatible their gametes become in functional relationships.

In any form of speciation, whenever genetic isolation is fully established between species, each will have its own evolutionary development, and hybridization will be subsequently impossible.

Evolution of communities and biomes

The many hundreds of thousands of animal species do not live in random mixtures but are assembled into groups with greater or lesser organizations and degrees of adjustments between the members and their environments. Two important aspects of group populations—communities and biomes—should be considered in the overall picture of evolutionary and ecologic patterns. All organisms meet the impact of their environments, not as single organisms but as members of populations that behave more or less as units. There are various degrees of population units, but the most important are the community and the biome. A biotic community is commonly defined as a natural assemblage of organisms or populations living together in a relatively uniform biologic area, self-sustaining and relatively independent of adjacent population assemblages. Certain modifications of this definition may be made for some communities, because it is a broad one and includes assemblages that do not always meet arbitrary distinctions. The community may be considered the natural unit of organization in ecology. A *major community*, such as a forest, is one that is self-sufficient as long as it receives sun energy from the outside; a *minor community*, such as a cave, depends to some extent on the energy supplied by adjacent communities. The evolution of the community may be considered as a

result of ecologic selection, by which organisms have been able to exist only when they fitted into some scheme of interdependence among the members and produced a self-sustaining unit. Communities vary greatly, but in general they contain only those species that fit into the ecologic conditions of the community and form a definite part of the web of interrelationships. Such an organization may be considered obligatory. The evolutionary history of any community must involve an extensive background and must have consisted of a slow process of gradually accumulated relationships. No doubt most communities started out by a few simple relationships, and as the community increased in complexity more and more of these unit relationships were involved. The dynamics of the earth's crust, referred to earlier, have been a responsible factor in forming congregations of species. Such changes could disrupt some existing communities and merge others. Communities have thus been in a flux from the beginning of life, and continuous change in their structure has been the general plan of their development. Various kinds of relationships have been evolved along with the evolution of communities, such as the predator-prey relationship (e.g., food chains), symbiotic relationships (mutualism, commensalism), parasitic relationships, and competitive relationships for the same food or other requirements. Each community develops a definite functional unity and characteristic pattern of energy flow. Also each community passes through orderly processes of change in which communities replace one another in a particular area in sequence—a general process commonly called ecologic succession.

The largest land community is the biome, which is characterized by a uniform climax vegetation and which is produced by the interaction of regional climates with regional biota. Although the names of the various biomes are associated with more or less specific plant formations (deciduous forest, coniferous forest, etc.), they are total community units comprising both plants and animals. The term *biome* has a broad meaning and includes the whole series of relatively transitory communities or seral stages as well as mature climax communities. A biome usually has a characteristic climatic condition involving temperature, humidity, and rainfall. Biomes may be of great areas, such as grasslands and deserts, or they may be relatively small, such as in mountainous countries where many biomes are often found close together. In the evolution of biomes each may have changed its dominant vegetation many times, even though the same ecologic conditions may have prevailed throughout. The origin and evolution of biomes are intimately associated with the great geologic changes in the physical environment of the earth's surface. Whenever the seral succession and development of communities have occurred through geologic periods, the climatically controlled regions with their communities become biomes. Terrestial biomes have undergone slower evolutionary changes than have biotic communities, but in the long geologic history of the planet, many characteristic biomes have appeared and disappeared. New biomes appear under the impact of great climatic changes, the colonization by plants and animals of regions where no life existed previously, and the succession of dominant vegetative forms that have changed the physical features of a given region. The fossil record plainly indicates that many regions of the earth which now have cold climatic conditions were once tropical or subtropical in nature. Tropical biomes have always existed to some extent, whereas many biomes in temperate and arctic regions have become extinct during geologic periods. Biomes continually undergo changes, although at a slow rate. Many changes are brought about by man himself. In certain regions he has enlarged some biomes and restricted others. Aside from man's influence, other factors produce additions and deletions in community structures and in the biome of which they are a part.

Paedomorphosis

The general term *paedomorphosis* refers to those conditions in which larval or immature features of ancestors become adult characters of descendants. During the evolution of an organism, it is possible for an adaptation that fits an early stage of a life history to its particular habitat to move into a later ontogenetic stage. Paedomorphosis is the idea that the adaptations to a larval or young life might profoundly influence the evolutionary course of the organism involved. Many terms (paedogenesis, neoteny, fetalization) have been used for this phenomenon, but they all refer broadly to sexual maturity in a larval or juvenile stage or to a change in relative rates of development of characters during phylogeny. The concept first introduced by W. Garstand years ago has been brought into sharper focus in recent years. The process has been fruitful in the production of evolutionary novelties. Man appears to be the result of such an evolutionary tendency. As an adult, he shows many of the fetal characteristics of apes. Selection for a particular larval adaptation might be strong enough to overcome a contrary selection in the adult life. Behavior as well as morphologic characters are influenced by paedomorphosis.

Among invertebrates, paedomorphosis has undoubtedly played an important role in evolution. A larval millipede with few segments is supposed to have served as a structural ancestor of insects. The burrowing acorn worm (Hemichordata) may represent the larval condition of an echinoderm. The wingless female glowworm is really the larval form of a firefly. Comparable cases of paedomorphosis have also been found among the ammonoids and brachiopods.

The concept of polymorphism

Many species, including both plants and animals, are represented in nature by two or more clearly distinguishable kinds of individuals. Such a condition is called *polymorphism*. This polymorphic variation may involve not only color but many other characters as well—physiologic as well as structural. The term has been used with many meanings, but the definition of the English geneticist E. B. Ford is generally accepted at present. His definition emphasizes the occurrence together in the same habitat of two or more distinct forms of a species in such proportions that the rarest of them could not have been maintained by recurrent mutation. This definition rules out seasonal and some other variations, such as the winter and summer pelage and plumage of certain mammals and birds. Polymorphism

5

always refers to variability within a population and is restricted to genetic polymorphism. It results when there are several alleles or gene arrangements with discontinuous phenotypic effects. It may be expressed by just two alternative types such as male and female dimorphism, or there may be many morphologic types within the species. The genetic pattern is well shown by the example of the ladybird beetle *Adalia bipunctata*, studied by N. W. Timofeeff-Ressovsky. In this genus some of the individuals are red with black spots while others are black with red spots. The black color behaves as a mendelian dominant gene and red as a recessive gene. The black and red forms live side by side and interbreed freely. Studies show that the black form is predominant from spring to autumn, and the red form is predominant from autumn to spring. It is thought that the changes are produced by natural selection, which favors the black form during summer and the red form during winter. For instance, more black forms, produced by dominant genes, die out during winter while the recessive red form survives. It is thus possible for the recessive gene, at least during part of the seasonal cycle, to occur more commonly than its dominant allele.

Sometimes an advantageous gene may spread through a population and tend to replace its allele. Such an example is industrial melanism in moths in certain industrial regions of England. In this case a mutant gene (melanism) of rather low frequency has a selective advantage over the normal form when the environment becomes black from pollution. Two polymorphic forms may exist side by side because of a balance of selective forces (balanced polymorphism) or because one may have a selective advantage and gradually replace the other (transient polymorphism).

Polymorphism has adaptive value in that it enables the adaptation of the species to different environmental conditions. Polymorphic populations are thus better able to adjust themselves to environmental changes and to exploit more niches and habitats. Without a doubt the potentialities of polymorphism are much greater than its realization, because every population must have many allelic series that are never expressed in the visible phenotype. Up to the present time there is no satisfactory explanation for the phenotypic uniformity of some species in contrast to the polymorphism of others.

Polymorphism is widespread throughout the animal kingdom, and often different forms have been mistaken for separate species. Some classic examples of polymorphism are the right-handed and left-handed coils of snails of the same species, the blood types of man and other animals (a biochemical distinction), sickle cell anemia in man, albinism in many animals, silver foxes in litters of gray foxes, and rufous and gray phases of screech owls in the same brood.

Regressive evolution

Regressive evolution is found to some extent among all groups of animals and may be defined as a loss in the internal stability of an organism. Organisms that show it have lost to some extent functional adaptations characteristic of their ancestors. Such loss of structural adaptations is usually manifested by vestigial organs that persist long after their functions have disappeared. Organisms are known that possess vestigial legs, eyes, wings, mouths, or other organs. The most logical explanation for the presence of such nonfunctional structures is that they have come from ancestors in which they were functional. Regressive evolution is probably caused by decreased or vanished selection pressure and by a convergent degeneration of homologous or analogous functional structure in different animals because of similar habitats.

Regressive evolution may not always involve the complete loss of function of an organ; it may be converted into another function. Some vestigial organs may not take on another function, but being harmless, they persist because they are correlated with a useful structure. Cave animals (troglobionts) represent one of the best examples of regressive evolution. Eyes and photoreceptor organs are reduced or absent in most cave beetles, millipedes, crayfish, isopods, and spiders, as well as in cave vertebrates. Some of the vestigial organs found in this group may be caused by mutations affecting the relative rate of growth, or by the selective value of low metabolism associated with growth retardation.

Regressive evolution may occur at any

level of biologic integration. The ameba may have regressed from more complex flagellates. Examples of regression among invertebrates are very numerous. Stages in life histories may have dropped out, examples being the coelenterates that may lack either the polyp or the medusa stage, wingless insects, and the extreme degeneration of bodily organs among many insects.

Extinction has also been a major factor in evolution. In all phylogenetic lines there has been an enormous turnover of organic patterns, so that the diversity of animals has been restricted. Some extensive groups (ammonites, trilobites, graptolites, etc.) are wholly extinct, and many present groups are mere shadows of their former diversity.

Invasion of land

It is generally agreed by zoologists that life originated in the sea, probably in the littoral regions. It is also thought that all the great groups, or phyla, arose in the sea. There are many divergent opinions on these matters, but the fossil record, fragmentary as it is, indicates that early life existed mostly in ocean waters. The types of body fluids in most animals is often advanced as further evidence for this view because of the similarity between animal blood and seawater; however, there are some authorities who do not consider this to be valid evidence. Although life may have originated in the sea, much evolution has occurred in fresh water and on land. Animals that are preadapted for such habitats spread to wherever there are vacant adaptive zones. It is known that various groups of aquatic arthropods invaded the land independently at least eight times. Invasion of the land, therefore, did not take place at any one time, and doubtless it is still occurring today.

The most successful invertebrate colonizers of the land are the arthropods and the mollusks (snails). Certain basic adaptive features of these groups made successful land invasion possible. The arthropods with chitinous exoskeletons and the snails with slime and coiled shells were admirably fitted for resisting the desiccation of land conditions. Other useful adaptations of these two groups for a land existence were highly efficient breathing systems, such as tracheae, book lungs, and lung devices. Burrowing invertebrates could also meet the challenge of a land existence. Land invasion no doubt occurred on a large scale as soon as a flourishing land flora was developed, such as that of the Devonian and Carboniferous periods. Early invaders of the land became dominant because of the lack of competition. By succession and spreading, animals explored and occupied new habitats.

Most migrations onto the land have occurred in places where there were gradual environmental changes, such as on ocean beaches, in estuaries, tidewater pools, etc. Conditions found in such places permitted experimental trials without fatal consequences. Abrupt changes from seawater to fresh water must have occurred rarely. A. S. Pearse, 1950, in *The Emigrations of Animals From the Sea* has summarized the various problems animals had to meet in their invasion of fresh water and land.

Influence of estuaries

An estuary is that zone where a stream or river meets the sea. It represents a mixture of fresh water from the river and salt water from the sea. Estuaries usually consist of an arm of the sea or the wide mouth of a river. Such a zone has unique environmental characteristics, such as brackish water, oscillating tidal currents, water mixing, and sedimentary deposits. It is a region of constant variations of temperature, variations in salt content of the water, and variations in bottom deposit. The instability of stream waters, as in volume, speed, and levels, is reflected in the estuaries at the mouths of rivers. Stratification of fresh water over the denser salt water also occurs there. Estuaries show many individual variations, depending upon the volume of water discharged by the stream, its swiftness, the topography of the surrounding land, wind currents, tides, etc.

In spite of their unstable conditions, estuaries represent a sort of threshold by which some animals pass from the sea to fresh water and land and vice versa. Most estuarine animals, however, are marine. All degrees of structural and physiologic adjustments to varying degrees of salinity are found in the organisms that inhabit estuaries. Some are able to adapt themselves

7

without difficulty to salty, brackish, or fresh water. One great problem is their ability to meet adequately the varying processes of osmosis in such environments. Most organisms established in estuaries have mechanisms for stabilizing their internal salt concentration by increasing their hydrostatic pressure through body contractions, by getting rid of excess water through excretory devices, by taking in excess salts, and by having an impermeable skin. Other devices of osmotic regulation are also known. A varied assortment of animals is found in many estuaries, often in associations not found elsewhere.

An estuary is a difficult passageway by which an organism may move to fresh water and land, and some authorities think that relatively few marine species became established in fresh water by migrating through estuaries. Some major phyla, such as echinoderms, have never been able to pass the barrier to a freshwater existence, although some are found in estuaries, because they have never been able to regulate their osmotic pressure sufficiently. Mollusks, on the other hand, have been more successful, and two of their six orders are found in fresh water or on land. It does seem, however, to be easier to go from marine to fresh water than in the reverse direction.

PALEOECOLOGY AND INVERTEBRATES

The study of the relationship of ancient animals to their environment and to each other is called paleoecology. The biota of the past had to face environmental conditions the same as their descendants do today. Paleoecology tries to reconstruct the nature of those environments in which fossil forms lived in the remote past. Interpretations of past conditions are based upon data obtained from fossils and from rock deposits in which fossils are found. All possible types of environments and ecologic relationships are involved, but marine environments are emphasized more than others because the paleontologic record is better known in marine deposits.

Many of the present ecologic concepts, such as communities, ecologic succession, food chains, etc., apply also to the ecology of the geologic periods. Other concepts may be vague because many organisms either do not fossilize or their composition undergoes radical alterations by the addition of substances foreign to them while they were living. Some fossil assemblages are also mixed and represent more than a single environment. Much information, however, can be obtained about them, such as their methods of locomotion, the temperature of their environments, the chemical makeup of their surroundings, the kinds of existence for which they were adapted (swimming, burrowing, creeping, etc.), the nature of catastrophic death, the relative abundance of certain forms, the extinction of others, and other data.

The most reliable source of information is that of the fossil-bearing rocks. The nature of the sediment and its manner of deposition often reveals a great deal of information about environmental conditions of the past. Specific types of sediment formation, such as shales, limestones, and sandstones, may yield data about turbidity, currents, landslides, etc., as well as information about the successions of fossils, the existence of geographic barriers that prevent mingling of contemporaneous animals, the correlation of individual fossil assemblages from widely different regions, the restricted occurrence of some species, and the wide distribution of others.

Hypotheses to explain the conditions of ancient life from the study of living creatures are not always trustworthy. Some animal lines have vastly changed their habits of living over long periods of time. Some are now found only in deep ocean water, whereas their ancient ancestors were largely shallow-water dwellers. Others were formerly pelagic, whereas their present descendants are relatively sessile. In most cases such hypotheses lack adequate means for testing. However, it seems to be true that most ecologic adaptations of animal groups were acquired early in their history and retained with minor changes.

FORM AND ORGANIZATION OF ANIMALS

Most animals have characteristic shapes and forms. This is especially true of multicellular organisms that, although they may undergo considerable changes in body form during their development, usually conform in the adult stage to a specific pattern. There are also some individual variations among the members of a species, but these are usually minor, such as size. Specific forms of the members of a species should be compared at the same stage of the life history. Among the protistans, however, variations of body form are more widespread because they are unicellular and reflect more the continually changing system of protoplasm during the life of the organism. Few protistans have a development that corresponds to that of metazoans. Usually among unicellular forms the life history consists of interdivisional stages that vary in form with a particular stage. The more complicated the life history of the protistan organism, the greater the body variation.

Body variations found among animals are usually grouped around a mean that is common for the species as a whole. The causes for these variations are either the hereditary makeup of the animals or environmental factors during their life histories.

What determines the form of animals?

Animals have a bewildering variety of forms. This diversity is expressed in shape, size, and general structural organization. Size varies from that of the smallest protistans to that of the largest whales. Variety in organic structures ranges all the way from the inconstant ameboid unicellular pattern to the bizarre structures of the Sargasso sea prawns or the echinoderms. As all animals have a unifying basic plan of structure and function, why do they have so many specific body plans? In our present stage of knowledge we can only speculate here and there as to why the animal assumes and maintains its own characteristic body plan.

Whatever the structural plan of an organism, it must be considered in the light of the unique properties of life itself. This uniqueness of the life process imposes certain requirements on the physical and functional makeup of the animal. Life is a dynamic process that can take place only in a certain complex organization. The animal, first of all, is a separate entity (colonies and monsters excepted) and has the power to maintain its characteristic form throughout life, although its body substance is continually undergoing change. It is an

open system for energy flow of materials from the outside. It is able to incorporate some of these materials into its own unique organization, and it uses others for energy purposes. In this metabolic process it forms waste substances that are discarded from the body.

This relationship between living organisms and their environment is expressed in patterns of adaptations. The animal has a characteristic life history and passes through stages of development and growth from the zygote to maturity. It undergoes many structural changes during its development and continues to do so throughout its life history. It has some power to regenerate lost parts with structures similar to those lost, so that animals of a particular species tend to retain the same mean size. The general activities and responses of the organism to its environment are coordinated into characteristic behavior patterns that make the animal a completely functional living unit. The dynamic quality of animals is displayed by their power of autonomous movement, which is performed by a variety of effector organs but chiefly by muscles.

Organisms have many ways of performing the same function, and this has resulted in many structural forms and patterns. The interaction of the organism and its environment with all the implications of natural selection has been a primary cause. Cumulative hereditary variability under the impact of natural selection, which works upon the restricted potentiality of the basic body plans of animals, has mainly determined organic form. The way that this operates to produce such a variety of forms is another matter. Physical and chemical principles of which we are still largely ignorant have operated throughout the evolutionary process. Most groups of animals have many structures whose presence cannot satisfactorily be explained; or, if a logical reason can be advanced, the method by which they evolved is unknown.

Physiologic and morphologic adaptations to varied habitats are generalizations of of wide application in the evolution of animals. By adaptive radiation a primitive group can move into many ecologic niches. Whenever there is a shift into a new niche, there is a basic adaptive feature of a group

9

that is modified for specialized purposes, e.g., the feathers or wings of birds that originated from reptiles. Adaptations to various forms of life usually involve morphologic changes, although some appear to be purely physiologic. Thus, the radially symmetric forms are best adapted for a sedentary or sessile life because the animals tend to grow equally in those directions in which the incidental forces of feeding are equal. Cephalocaudal differentiation and streamlining are characteristic of bilateral, actively moving animals. Along with this tendency the elongated serpentine form is popular for those animals that creep. Modifications of this plan are found in those that have flat or round bodies and those that have feeble locomotor powers. Segmentation of the body made possible a wide range of adaptive habits, because it created a more flexible construction and aided greatly in wriggling movements. The addition of locomotor appendages brought about much adaptive divergence in body forms so that animals could swim, dig, or run. Changes in jaw and feeding methods have been responsible for a variety of modifications of the head end and may be considered a primary factor in the varied patterns of body forms. Other factors that have played an important role in determining body form are the effects of the parasitic habits, the differential growth rates of body parts for specialization, the erect position, and the possession of shells.

Experimental morphogenesis throws some light on how these body plans are produced in the development of a specific form, but the overall picture can be obtained only by the integration of evolutionary, ecologic, and populational genetic factors. So far, little has been accomplished in this line of investigation. Throughout such a study, the three universal dimensions of living matter—development, function, and structure—must also be effectively integrated. Basically, the relatively new science of molecular biology may afford the key to many of the problems of morphology.

Among invertebrate metazoans there is one type of body plan around which many others are built. This is the saclike, radially symmetric form in which the cavity is surrounded by a double wall with an outer layer of cells for protection from the outside and an inner layer for digestion of food. A single opening to the outside serves as both mouth and anus. With the addition of tentacles for food gathering and protection, such a plan is found among the coelenterates, which are considered to be close to the ancestral base of metazoans. Digestion in such forms may be partly or wholly intracellular at first, but a better start is made toward the extracellular digestion of larger forms than is possible among unicellular organisms. Specialization of the cells of the inner and outer layers leads to (1) the formation of muscular and nervous elements for coordination and movement, (2) sensory elements for responses to the varied external and internal stimuli, (3) secretory cells that form protective noncellular layers of cuticle or calcareous shells, and (4) mesenchymal elements between the two layers.

Such a body plan has great possibilities for modification and specialization. The digestive tube may be much folded, branched, elongated, or shortened. The body form may be elongated and narrow or short and broad. This body plan is ideal for division of labor among communities of cells and is capable, with certain modifications, of attaining a variety of sizes. Although many such forms are sessile or restricted in movement, others are quite active swimmers.

The various body plans of the invertebrate Metazoa that have been built around, or derived from, a saclike or similar body plan include the flatworm type with bilateral symmetry and differentiated cephalocaudal axis, the roundworm type with tube-within-a-tube organization, the annelid type with segmented body, the arthropod type with specialized somites and jointed appendages, and the molluscan type with mantle and specialized foot.

Axial gradients and regeneration

Axial gradients refer to an axial organization in which there are differential regions of dominance that affect quantitatively the metabolic processes of the animal's body. Axial organization may be expressed in physiologic and developmental gradients of various kinds and also in the regeneration of parts. Axial gradients are usually most pronounced in the organization of lower types of animals, such as planarians, where the gradients were first established. In higher animals they appear to play a lesser part, except in very early developmental stages, because of the less plastic condition of the animals' differentiated tissues and body structures. The axial organization is built into the general plan of the body and is a property of protoplasm. In general, there is a dominant center of influence in the anterior part of the body and lesser fields of influence distributed over the body.

Axial gradients may express themselves by gradients of susceptibility and by processes of regeneration. In susceptibility, cells of different regions and types may be affected in different ways and rates by the same poison. This seems to be correlated with gradients of oxidative metabolism. Some cells are far more susceptible to poisons than others; the more active the metabolism of a cell, the more susceptible it is to the action of a poison. The power of regeneration varies greatly, depending mainly upon the level of animal organization, being found far less frequently in higher than in lower forms. Only very small parts of the body are regenerated in the adult condition of higher vertebrates. The simpler multicellular organisms may regenerate body organs or lost appendages, but most insects will not. A regenerated part may be of a different type than the original lost part. The eye of a crustacean may be replaced by an antenna. Usually the larger the part lost, the more rapid is the growth rate of the regenerating tissue. The process of regeneration commonly follows a definite sequence, although there are many variations. First, a regeneration blastema is formed from a mass of undifferentiated cells (neoblasts) that have come from the loss of differentiation in tissues near the lost part. During the growth of the blastema its cells undergo differentiation into the tissues that are to form the regenerated structures. Then the tissues are organized into a pattern that duplicates by differential growth the lost structure. Regenerated tissue is usually derived from the same kind of tissue in the parent body, but there are exceptions to this. Although much is known about the patterns of re-

generation in many groups of animals, no clear explanation can be given about the underlying reasons for this phenomenon.

Growth and body form

Differential growth is characteristic of all structures in the animal body. Under most conditions each tissue has a definite maximum rate of growth. Change in form and size are found throughout the life history of all multicellular animals. This not only occurs during the development of the animal but also during the adult condition. Growth may cease in mammals when they reach maturity, but in most invertebrates (except insects) growth continues in the adult but at a slower tempo. Growth tends to cease at a certain level in many terrestrial animals because land forms have more size restrictions than have aquatic organisms. The buoyancy of a watery medium permits large size, as in the whale. Some land forms such as reptiles continue to grow during adulthood. In a strict sense, body size never remains constant in most adult organisms because of loss of water and the relative increase of nonliving connective tissue. In many arthropods (insects) with chitinous exoskeletons, however, body size does not change in the adult.

Growth may take place by one or all of three types of growth changes. There may be an increase in *number* of structures, in *size* of structure, or in *spaces* between structures. Growth is mainly a molecular phenomenon; molecules are manipulated to form body structures. Molecules ready-made from the outside may be incorporated into the body or may be synthesized within the cells. They may increase in size by combining with other molecules to form macromolecules, and they may be separated from each other by spaces filled with fluid or cement substances. In this way cells increase in size, and by cell division they increase in number.

Most changes in body form are produced by differential growth of body structures. Growth involves both quantitative and qualitative changes. One organ or its part may grow faster or slower than another. It may also grow slower or faster than the body as a whole. When an organ is growing at the same rate as the mean growth rate of the body, it is called *isometric* growth.

11

If the organ's growth rate differs from the mean growth rate of the rest of the body, it is called *allometric* growth. Allometric growth is positive when the organ grows faster, negative when it grows slower than the body's rate. Allometry may be expressed on a logarithmic scale where the line gradient represents a growth coefficient, which is a relation of the relative growth rate of the organ to that of the body. Allometry factors may be an intrinsic part of the animal's pattern of body proportions, but they may be modified by ecogeographic principles. Body proportions seem to be very sensitive to natural selection factors that may be expressed by differences in temperature and climate. Ecogeographic rules apply to both vertebrates and invertebrates. Insects especially show adaptive patterns to geographic variations. Butterfly pupae from coastal southern California are larger and heavier than those of the same species from the Mojave Desert (W. Hovanitz). Beetles of the same species are larger and have wider abdomens in temperate central Europe than members along the warmer Mediterranean region (B. Rensch).

Growth gradients appear to be under the control of the axial organization, or the morphogenetic fields of development, but there are many unknown factors. It is the differential growth patterns that in the long run determine body form and proportions, although the exact mechanism is unknown.

THE PHYLOGENY OF INVERTEBRATES

Living matter is built upon a hierarchy of levels. The higher the level an organism reaches, the more energy it requires because of the greater demands of an organization that requires more integration and cooperation. The whole process of life from the beginning of its evolutionary development to its numerous present patterns exhibits this plan of hierarchy. Our concept of the origin of life and its evolution shows that atoms were organized into molecules, molecules into complex aggregates, macromolecules into cells, cells into organisms (unicellular and multicellular), and organisms into various taxons and community populations. At each level new properties are found above those of lower levels. In the animal kingdom we may divide the or-

ganisms into the following organization grades on the basis of the scheme just outlined:

Protoplasmic grade. Protozoa or acellular forms.

Cellular grade. Loose aggregation of differentiated cells, such as Porifera.

Cell-tissue grade. Aggregation of similar cells into definite patterns, such as Coelenterata.

Tissue-organ grade. Aggregation of tissues into specialized organs, such as Platyhelminthes.

Organ-system grade. Aggregation of organs to form systems with a basic body function, such as all higher animals.

Nature of the Protista

The first organisms were unicellular, and by evolutionary processes this type was elaborated and exploited to form the diverse patterns found in the extensive group that we call the Protista. The term *Protista* refers to all those forms that are usually unicellular, have nuclei, chromosomes, and mitotic cell division, do not have differentiated cells specialized for specific purposes, and are free living. It is true that certain cells (ova and sperm) of the multicellular animal may have a free-living existence for part of their life cycle but not for their whole life history. The Protista include the protozoa, algae, slime molds, and fungi. Some authorities also include the Monera (bacteria and blue-green algae), but this group lacks true nuclei and chromosomes. It is customary to consider the Protista as being acellular because their body is not divided into cells and is not strictly the equivalent of the metazoan cell. Some protistan cells may have many nuclei, but their cytoplasm is not divided into specialized parts with each part under the control of one of the nuclei.

The Protista, therefore, include many organisms of plantlike characters and many of animallike characters, but there is a basic protistan organization type throughout the group. Some are relatively simple with little specialization of parts, such as the slime molds and certain protozoans (amebas). Others have a number of cytoplasmic differentiations that correspond in some ways to the structural activities of the Metazoa, such as the organelles or intracellular organs of certain ciliates. Among the latter are found differentiations that correspond to skeletons, excretory organs, light-sensitive organs, conducting mechanisms, contracting structures similar to muscles, organs of locomotion, defense mechanisms, and parts of the alimentary system such as the mouth and anus.

The basic structural pattern of the protistans and the way their patterns can be modified indicates that they had enormous evolutionary potentialities. It is, therefore, logical to consider the Protista as the ancestors of all the Metazoa and the Metaphyta (the green, terrestrial, multicellular plants). Some reasons for this belief are that each metazoan in its embryonic development passes from an acellular to a cellular condition, and that the formation of a multicellular animal by the appearance of cell boundaries in a multinuclear protistan, or the aggregation of protistan cells to form colonies, is a logical way by which the Metazoa could have arisen.

Origin of Metazoa

It is impossible to link the multicellular organisms with any of the lower groups, although many speculations have been made about this problem. It is generally agreed that Metazoa arose from protistan ancestors, but evolutionists cannot state just which ones gave rise to multicellularity. The classic view has long held that multicellular organisms arose from protozoans, but there are many theories based upon the origin of metazoans from various protistan stocks. It is possible that different Metazoa arose not from one ancestor but independently from many kinds of protistans. Whatever its origin, the metazoan is more than a mere aggregation of cells. Its organization includes the whole body, and it behaves as a unit capable of living an independent existence in the animal kingdom. The multicellular organism is made up of cells that through specialization and division of labor have become unique and distinct parts of the whole organism. When such cells are separated from the body, they are no longer organisms themselves. Although some cells may survive for a period after removal from the body, their survival is limited (with few exceptions) unless they can regenerate into a whole or-

ganism. With their increased organization, metazoans acquire complex features not found in unicellular forms, such as distinct reproductive organs and distinct embryonic stages of development. However, organization is possible without cell division as is shown by the complexity of certain protistans. Even in multicellular organisms, when the zygote is prevented from dividing by certain chemicals, some differentiation and organization occurs to a certain point, as F. R. Lillie showed long ago with *Chaetoperus,* a marine polychaete.

Evolutionary trends in organisms are in general toward larger size. Complex organization requires in most instances larger body masses for efficient active lives. As we have already pointed out, complexity of structure imposes a minimum limitation on size. Larger size enables organisms to be less dependent upon environment, because much of the protoplasmic environment of the organism is remote from the fluctuating changes of the external environment. Limitations are also imposed upon large size, because an animal cannot continue to grow indefinitely. As an organism becomes larger, controlling restrictions of support, coordination, nutrition, and communication begin to operate.

The fossil record throws no light upon the nature of the early metazoans. The first metazoan fossils worthy of the name date from the early Cambrian period of the Paleozoic era, such as the trilobites. But trilobites had attained a high degree of complexity and must have had a background of simpler ancestors. Various theories such as the following have been proposed to account for the lack of Precambrian animal fossils: the Brooks theory, stating that early metazoans lacked a heavy calcareous shell in their active, free-swimming existence; the Daly theory, stating that there was insufficient calcium in the sea water of Precambrian times to form calcareous shells; and the Axelrod theory, stating that the littoral regions, where metazoans may have evolved, were subject to such drastic changes that fossilization could not occur. Recently, J. R. Nursall has made the interesting suggestion that a metazoan fauna probably did not exist for most of the Precambrian era. He postulates that there was a rapid diversification of metazoan forms

13

in late Precambrian times because of the addition of free oxygen to the environment. According to the scheme proposed earlier in this text on the origin of life, the early primitive organisms were heterotrophs, which obtained their nutrients dissolved in the sea and lived under anaerobic conditions. The evolution and development of autotrophic or photosynthetic organisms that were capable of utilizing sunlight for the reduction of carbon dioxide and the formation of carbohydrates meant that such organisms were no longer dependent upon sea nutrients. Nursall argues that the addition of free oxygen to the atmosphere by photosynthesis made possible in time oxidative metabolism, with all its advantages to both autotrophs and heterotrophs. This more efficient method of extracting energy by food breakdown made possible a greater range of organization, such as the formation of tissues and organs characteristic of the multicellular organism. According to this theory the transformation of a reducing atmosphere to an oxidizing one was all-important in the evolution of higher forms. The fossil record would then be a natural outcome of the greater diversity of animal life that resulted.

Theories concerning the origin of the Metazoa may be divided into the following four views: (1) the multicellular organism arose from a protistan colony through specialization and differentiation of cells; (2) the multicellular organism evolved from a multinucleated (syncytial) protistan, which became cellular by the development of membranes around the nuclei; (3) the multicellular organism came from plants, the Metaphyta, which developed heterotrophic characteristics; and (4) the multicellular organism had a polyphyletic origin from many ancestral stocks.

Origin of Metazoa from colonial Protozoa

There are many protozoan colonies, and some of these colonies can be fitted into logical series that show increasing organization. In some cases it is difficult to distinguish these colonies from a simple multicellular organism. *Volvox,* for instance, demonstrates a considerable organization beyond the unicellular condition. The spheroid type of protozoan colony is the

most abundant. These colonies may be arranged in steps to illustrate the evolutionary trend. The distinguishing characteristic of the Metazoa is that their cells are not all alike. A differentiation of the cells into two or more kinds must occur if the colonial theory is correct. In some simple protozoan colonies of few cells all the cells are alike. For example, in *Gonium, Pandorina,* and *Platydorina* any cell of the parent colony can form daughter colonies. The first differentiation is the loss by some cells of the power of reproduction, while others retain this power. In *Pleodorina illinoisensis* there are 28 reproductive cells and four somatic or sterile cells; in *Pleodorina californica* there are 32 somatic cells and about the same number of reproductive cells; and in *Volvox* the somatic cells greatly outnumber the reproductive cells. This theory, therefore, stresses the origin of the metazoans from hollow colonial flagellates. Additional evidence has been advanced in its support. Flagellates have probably given rise to the various protozoan classes and to the plants. Flagellate cells are widely distributed in many groups of animals (sponges, coelenterates), and flagellate sperm is the common type throughout the animal kingdom. G. S. Carter has pointed out the ease with which tissues of multicellular animals can be separated into cells in tissue cultures, sponges, etc., and the capacity of these cells to live relatively independent lives. Whether or not the early metazoan resembled the hypothetical gastraea of Haeckel or the solid stereogastrula of Metchnikoff would be of minor importance so far as the actual origin of the metazoan is concerned. L. H. Hyman thinks that the essential difference between a protozoan colony and the multicellular animal is the establishment of an axis with functional and morphologic differentiation (polarity). Transverse cleavage, which is not found in flagellates, greatly promoted such polarity in metazoans.

Since the phytoflagellate members of the family Volvocidae seem to be the most logical metazoan ancestors according to the colonial theory, the objection is sometimes raised that the loss of their cellulose walls and photosynthetic autotrophic nutrition would have to be explained in order to make the theory tenable. Another objection is that in many of this group of phyto-flagellates meiosis does not occur until after the zygote is formed (postzygotic) so that they are haploid instead of diploid. The colonial theory also does not explain the solid gastrula of the coelenterates, which should have been hollow according to the colonial theory. From our present knowledge, however, the colonial theory of metazoan origin seems to be the most logical of the theories proposed.

Syncytial theory of metazoan origin

The syncytial theory emphasizes the origin of Metazoa from multinucleated protistan cells. Such cells are not multicellular because their protoplasm is not divided into parts each under the control of one of the nuclei. However, if the various nuclei of a multinucleate cell were to become separated by cell membranes to form separate cells, such an organization would be quite similar to a multicellular body formed by the colonial method previously described. J. Hadži has greatly emphasized this theory in recent years, and he has had some able supporters, such as G. R. de Beer and E. D. Hanson. This theory primarily is based upon the resemblance between multinucleate ciliates and the acoelous flatworms (class Turbellaria). They resemble each other in that both have about the same size ranges, both are multi-nucleated, both are bilateral and ciliated, both ingest solid food in the same way, both have similar defense organs (the trichocysts of ciliates and the rodlike sagittocysts of turbellarians), and both lack a body cavity. Another resemblance between these two groups is their method of exchanging gamete nuclei. The characteristic conjugation of ciliates in which the migratory noncellular nuclei are exchanged between partners is not much different from the mutual injection of sperm into sex partners of acoelous flatworms. Both groups also have prezygotic meiosis, which follows the metazoan pattern.

Most biologists find objections to the syncytial theory, however plausible it seems. The theory makes the acoelous flatworms with bilateral symmetry the most primitive metazoans. It holds that the coelenterates with a primary radial symmetry are derived from them, not the reverse as is commonly held. L. H. Hyman has emphasized the position of coelenterates as the direct ancestors of Eumetazoa. They were the first animals in which ectoderm and endoderm were clearly differentiated. G. S. Carter also thinks that the simplest nervous system, the nerve net with its uncentralized arrangement, is an argument in favor of the colonial theory. The syncytial theory also fails to account for the flagellate sperm cell so characteristic of the metazoan pattern.

Origin of Metazoa from Metaphyta

The view that metazoans have arisen from the Metaphyta (plants) is held by a number of biologists. J. R. Baker, for instance, thinks that the transformation of plantlike protozoans to the cellular metaphytes is easy to explain because members of each group absorb nutriment from all sides equally. However, the metazoan has a different method of nutrition and requires the presence of a mouth. Some ciliates do have a definite mouth and gullet, but early stages of the metazoan probably do not require such a specialized structure; this could be a later development. Metazoans could have arisen from plantlike organisms when the latter acquired powers of locomotion, lost their photosynthetic powers, and became heterotrophic.

Polyphyletic origin of metazoans

It is agreed by biologists that no one view of metazoan origin satisfies all the requirements such a theory demands. Life may have arisen in different places and at different times on our planet. On this account many biologists think that the major groups may have evolved independently of each other. The patterns of similarity and the unified plan throughout the various groups could be explained on the basis that all had to use the same materials of their environment ("metabolic homology" of Nursall), that they faced similar conditions, that there are limitations imposed by the nature of the living substances, and that evolution is channeled in certain ways because of a particular physicochemical nature. This accounts for the homology of the nucleic acids that exist among the cells of all metazoans. It is possible that the metazoans could have arisen from

15

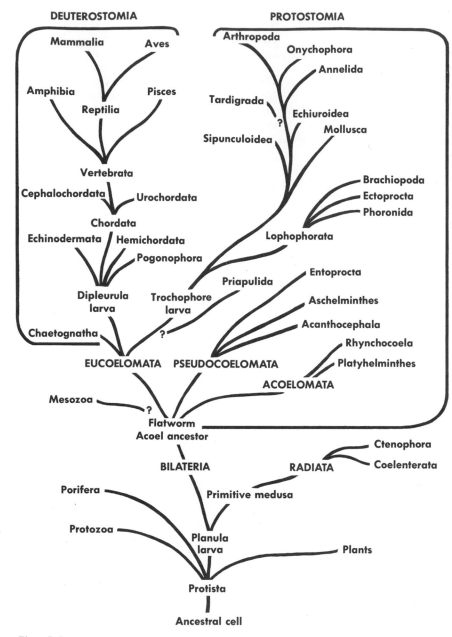

Fig. 1-1

Hypothetical phylogenetic tree showing relations of major groups (phyla) according to best evidence available. (From Hickman: Integrated principles of zoology, The C. V. Mosby Co.)

any level in the evolution of the Protista.

A hypothetical diagram of the possible relationships of the principal animal groups according to present evolutionary interpretation is shown in Fig. 1-1.

BASIC ADAPTIVE PATTERNS OF INVERTEBRATES

Each higher group, or taxon, of animals has some basic adaptation around which the evolution of the group has occurred (G.

G. Simpson). This basic adaptation, which is usually laid down early, determines to a great extent the amount and direction of evolutionary divergence and thus the number of ecologic niches for which the members of the group are fitted. Such adaptations may consist of a single outstanding characteristic, or each may involve several structures. In some cases there may be a certain basic adaptation for a class and another for a phylum. Many different groups may have similar adaptations, but one group may exploit the possibilities of the adaptation in question, and others may make little use of it. When animals change from one kind of environment to another, it is almost always made possible by some basic adaptive pattern. Within the new zone the nature of the adaptation will determine the degree of specialization for new ecologic niches. The adaptation may not be retained by all the taxa of a group. It may be lost entirely, and the nature of the original adaptation may be very obscure. The same basic adaptation may undergo an entirely different evolution in different closely related taxa, or it may evolve at a different rate in different groups. In general, the broader and less specialized the adaptation, the more likely it will be retained in the evolution of the group. Some distant and not closely related taxa have the same basic adaptation (convergent evolution). If two or more groups have many adaptations in common, such adaptations can usually be traced to a common basic adaptation or adaptations of a common ancestor.

The concept of basic adaptive patterns of invertebrates is of the utmost importance in understanding the evolutionary history of any group. It shows the trends and possibilities of the group and points the way for future development. It helps to explain the reasons why some animals are found in some regions and why others cannot exist there, to explain the presence of some of the coadaptations found in the lower taxa by the restrictions imposed from the basic adaptations of the higher taxa, and to explain why the phyla are basically different and how these differences arose as adaptations by the early members of each phylum. The concept of basic adaptive patterns is also very important in comparing the varied adjustments or adaptations of lower taxa of a group with the basic adaptation of the large taxonomic category. In the study of every organism this concept thus shows the importance of determining the nature of the basic adaptive feature. Such a determination is not always easy, because the selective forms of the environment are so involved in the long evolution of a group that the fundamental adaptive plan may be obscured by coadaptations of lower taxa to restricted ecologic niches. It is not enough to know the present adjustments of animals—one must determine the ecologic relationships of their ancestors. The fossil record, when sufficiently complete, may throw some light upon such paleoecologic information. In dealing with specific groups later in this text this important concept is emphasized throughout.

Adaptive patterns and adaptive radiation

Adaptive radiation is an evolutionary process by which a single relatively unspecialized phyletic line evolves into several descendant lines that are specialized for different niches or adaptive zones.

Radiate evolution is a broad term and refers to both physiologic and morphologic characters. Forms that are totally indistinguishable by morphologic criteria may have entirely different reactions to physiologic gradients. It is also common for two not closely related groups to have similar ecologic behavior patterns (convergent evolution), because a particular pattern of ecologic factors will select similar characteristics in the two groups by natural selection. Primitive characteristics also are likely to be best fitted for a good display of adaptive radiation patterns, because primitive characters are more general, more labile, and more capable of a variety of specializations. Some characters are far more labile than others and do not fit into the primitive category at all. Specific color patterns vary enormously throughout the animal kingdom, and it is impossible to state what the primitive pattern was like even if there should happen to be one.

Among invertebrates the insects represent the best illustration of adaptive radiation because no other group has equaled them in the patterns of evolutionary diversity. In a recent work (*A Classification of*

17

Living Animals by Lord Rothschild, 1961), some 29 orders and 700,000 species of insects are listed. The orders of insects represent a striking case of radiation, because the fossil record, incomplete as are all fossil records, partly indicates the way in which these orders emerged and became specialized for varied ecologic niches. The fossil record shows the progressive changes in structure that can be confirmed by morphologic and embryologic studies of existing forms. Probably originating as far back as the Mississippian period (350 million years ago), this amazing group has passed through three major evolutionary steps (F. M. Carpenter): the development of simple, functional, nonfolded wings from the thoracic wall, the development of wing articulations for folding, and the development of complicated metamorphoses. Insects have a very high potentiality for specialization, which has caused them to evolve species that are fitted for restricted ecologic niches, such as different parts of the same plant. A. E. Emerson has pointed out the variety of adaptive patterns among the Coleoptera (beetles), the largest order of insects. Their chief basic adaptive features are the thick, chitinous exoskeleton (as in the elytra, for example) and their complete metamorphosis. More than fifty ecologically adapted patterns can be listed among them, although some apply to the same species. Their varied adaptations involve behavior patterns, food habits, luminescent organs, locomotor defensive mechanisms, warning and concealing coloration, divided eye vision, reproductive patterns, acquatic adaptations, and many others. Some of these adaptive patterns may be widespread, and others may be very rare. Many phylogenetic branches may have evolved similar adaptations by convergence.

Invasion of new habitats

Wherever an animal enters a new habitat or niche, it faces a whole array of selection pressures and must be equipped with suitable characteristics if it is to meet successfully the conditions of the new environment. This means that the organism is in some way preadapted to the new niche in which it is now going to live. Any major shift of an animal into a new region usually involves a basic divergence of a basic adaptive character. Preadaptations need not be and seldom are complete for a major shift. Persistent habit over a long period within a particular habitat fits an animal to live better and increase its degree of successful adaptation. The successful invasion of the land by arthropods is mainly because of such preadaptations as the chitinous exoskeleton, segmented body, and jointed appendages. This type of morphology made possible specializations for efficient methods of locomotion and support. Terrestrial conquest is possible only to forms with strong skeletons or some sort of armor. The arthropodan type of integument, legs, and efficient striated muscle has produced one of the best forms of locomotion among invertebrates. Most successful evolutionary groups are explained by their ability to exploit such preadaptations in situations where they can have full deployment of their potentialities. Arthropods could not have undergone their amazing diversity in aquatic environments only.

Evolutionary novelties (E. Mayr) are those newly acquired morphologic or physiologic characters that enable an animal to fit into a new adaptive zone. C. Darwin and others have emphasized that the most important cause of the appearance of new structures is a change of function. Change of function alone is insufficient; there must also be inherent in the structural pattern of the animal the potentiality to perform the new function (preadaptation). The adaptive radiation of the arthropods, mentioned earlier, could take place only by the combination of their basic adaptive or preexisting structures into the adaptive pattern of the new habitat. Most evolutionary novelties are considered to be modifications of structures already present. It is possible, of course, that the right combination of genes or mutations could produce something new or a phenotype expression so novel that nothing like it existed before. The belief that novelties could thus suddenly emerge by a lucky mutation or combination of mutations (saltation) is not considered a valid premise in light of the theory of gradual evolution that is held by most biologists at present. Most mutations, moreover, have only a slight effect on the phenotype and simply replenish the gene pool. Preadaptations must be thought of as functional rather than morphologic shifts. Most preadapted structures can perform their functions before the need of the new functions arises, which is probably what L. Cuénot had in mind when he gave us the concept of preadaptation. Preadaptation may involve many traits, called generalized preadaptation, or a specific structure if the new niche is restrictively specialized. Whenever an old structure evolves toward the preadapted condition, it is modified by old selective forces until the new preadapted structure assumes its function; new selective forces now control its development in the new environment.

Basic adaptations and classification of invertebrates

Common characters in invertebrates are usually a result of basic adaptations. Throughout the phylogenetic tree the main branches are represented by a common basic structural plan within which has occurred a great variety of adaptive modifications. According to Mayr and others higher categories (orders, classes, phyla) are divided into lower categories such as families, which have a great variety of adaptations and usually occupy distinctive ecologic niches. According to this scheme the higher categories have few obvious adaptive characters because basic adaptations have been overlaid by the specific adaptations of the lower groups. Only general adaptive features are evident in higher taxa. For instance, it is easier to describe the adaptive patterns of each of the orders of insects than to explain those of arthropods in general.

The old typologic method of taxonomy is being replaced by methods emphasizing the population structure of species. Although type forms are convenient units for classification and are still used, the newer method tries not to force natural populations into artificial schemes. The clinal pattern for explaining evolutionary diversity shows that all populations of a species display one or more of three marked characteristics. These are (1) gradual changes in a population brought about by clinal variations, (2) geographically isolated populations, and (3) so-called hybrid zones of variable populations between two stable populations.

The character, or phenotypic, gradient of the cline (J. S. Huxley) is an outcome of differential selective factors of environmental variations to be found in the extensive range of a cline. These environmental factors vary according to gradients themselves and rarely show abrupt changes. Gene flow among adjacent populations of a cline tends to produce uniformity in the populations that share in the gene flow. Geographic isolates refers to a population that is prevented by barriers from sharing gene flow with other populations of the species. Almost any cline of extensive area will show such "pockets" of population. Such populations are powerful forces for incipient speciation. Contact belts or zones between phenotypically different populations offer opportunities for members of different populations to interbreed. Mayr calls this mixing of gene flow *allopatric hybridization*. Such populations of secondary intergradation may show any degree of differences in characters. Although most hybrid zones have been described for vertebrates, hybrid belts also involve invertebrates, such as those of insects (T. H. Hubbell) and snails (E. Mayr and C. B. Rosen).

In view of the previous concepts it is difficult to select a specimen of a population and designate it as a type. Species structure shows many variations that are determined by many factors. The taxonomist must understand these factors if a representative classification of a form is to be made.

From this standpoint of basic adaptations in relation to the preceding classification principles, it may be stated that a few key characters, which usually distinguish a major group, may show such variations under the impact of phylogenetic divergence that they tend to lose their analytic fitness for classification purposes. The classification of the larger groups is often based on a single or a few major characters, but the failure of the systematist to make a wide and comparative analysis of all variable characters that bear on the phylogeny of the forms being classified will usually result in an unnatural and misleading classification. A striking example of this principle is demonstrated by the classic case of the tunicate. The dramatic transformation during its individual history from a free-tailed tadpolelike larva to the sessile, soft, baglike adult that has lost many of its chordate characters made it impossible to correctly classify this form until its complete life history was known. Before that time tunicates were classified with the mollusks because of the superficial resemblance between the two groups.

PHYSIOLOGIC MECHANISMS OF INVERTEBRATES

All living systems must react to changes in their environment. Reactions may be quick, direct responses to stimuli, or they may be long-delayed responses to changes in the environment. Many such reactions are the outcome of a complex syndrome of causes and responses that partake of the nature of an adaptation. Organisms do not all respond in the same way to environmental changes. Each type of organism has its own characteristic adaptive patterns, which means that it has its own particular physiologic mechanisms. But all functions of an organism are based upon the methodical arrangements of structures, and the way these systems are put together in the final analysis determines the life process. The science of physiology tries to describe the processes that go on in the living organism and cannot be divorced from the structural components. However, physiologic mechanisms are more subject to variations with environmental change than are morphologic components. The way in which an animal adapts itself to a given environment depends upon its functional capacity. Its functional responses, however, are always determined by its genetic constitution and by its environment, but these two factors are not always equally effective. The same genotype may produce different phenotypes under varied environments, because the living system has the ability to modify its properties in accordance with changes in its environment. The vital functions of all animals must be adapted to environmental changes. Such adaptations are the result of the selection of the best adapted individuals, and favorable mutations must occur in order for natural selection to choose those individuals favorable for adaptations.

It is possible to classify organisms in various ways, such as morphologic, ecologic, and physiologic, depending upon the properties one is emphasizing. As C. L. Prosser has often pointed out, biologists have stressed the evolutionary trends of morphology more than they have those of physiology. Functional similarities and dissimilarities in the phylogeny of organisms are just as important in understanding evolution as are structural features. In the long and important chemical evolution that preceded the advent of living organisms, the groundwork for the basic plan of physiologic mechanisms was laid down. The whole scheme of our present concept of the origin of life involves physiologic aspects at nearly every step. Throughout the origin of complex carbon compounds under the influence of radiation energy, the synthesis of protein molecules, the formation of nucleoproteins and high-energy phosphate bonds, the electron transfer system of metabolism, the selective diffusion of organic molecules, the enzymatic action at all steps of the metabolic process, and other functional aspects have evolved during the preliminary biochemical evolutionary process. During the so-called organic evolution that gave rise to the great diversity of life as we now know it, there have been very few biochemicals added to organic life. Physiologic mechanisms have evolved early and were necessary prerequisites for living systems.

Physiologic regulation

Physiologic regulation is the adjustment an organism makes in controlling the output of its bodily processes. By such means every activity operates under influences that determine its rate and amount. The mechanisms by which quantitative responses by each property and component of the organism's body are made are, in most cases, triggered by specific detectors (E. F. Adolph). This indicates that detectors relay information to effectors, which in turn respond in a more or less specific way. Most regulations tend to restore the organism to normal conditions whenever its bodily states are disturbed by external stresses. Often delicate mechanisms of feedback are involved in these adjustments. To what extent an animal can restore itself depends upon its genetically determined limits of regulation. All organisms have large numbers of specific response mechanisms that are compressed into a very limited number of bodily structures or organs. A problem of all organisms is to regulate a maximal number of components with a minimal number of detectors and effectors.

Many regulative mechanisms maintain the constancy of internal states (homeostasis). Organisms show many variations in this respect. In some animals internal conditions change with the altered environment. This is illustrated by the body temperature of poikilothermic animals, which increases or decreases in conformity with the external environment. In others there is a relatively precise regulation of internal conditions in the presence of environmental change, so that such organisms can tolerate a wider range of environmental fluctuation but have a narrow range of internal conditions. Some animals are able to regulate certain functions and conform to the environment with respect to other functions. Physiologic division of labor operates in all regulative control of physiologic functions. One organ may be specialized for one aspect of a regulating mechanism, and another organ may be specialized for another role. Responses may be specific in some regulations and highly nonspecific in others. Regulative responses also vary with stages in the life history of an organism. Those of a caterpillar may be quite different from those of a butterfly. Some responses are quick acting, and others are delayed for long periods of time.

The numerous investigations concerning the physiologic differences of species and animal populations have centered upon two chief questions: (1) Are physiologic variations genotypic or phenotypic? (2) What is the mechanism involved in these variations? Organisms subjected to persistent environmental changes usually undergo compensatory changes. When a single environmental factor is involved, the compensatory change of the organism is called *acclimation;* when multiple environmental factors are considered, the compensatory changes are referred to as *acclimatization.* Acclimation is commonly done in the laboratory under controlled conditions. Acclimatization deals with a complex of environmental stresses such as climatic and seasonal changes. Many biologists consider that acclimatization has a wider meaning—that of genetic adaptation. Acclimation has been more widely studied because it is much easier to study the influences of one factor than of many. Whenever an organism adjusts at the same rate in a new environmental condition as in the old one, it is considered to have perfect acclimation.

Behavior patterns

Every living organism has built into its organization certain patterns of behavior. Behavior may be defined as externally directed activity originating from the stimulation of internal mechanisms. It often but not always brings about some change between the organism and its environment. Behavior directly or indirectly is determined or influenced by mechanisms involving a sequence of stimulation and response. A reaction may be initiated by a stimulus, but its nature depends upon the type of organism involved. Animals have different mechanisms of response depending upon their effectors (muscles, glands, sol-gel relations, stinging organelles, etc.). Reactions may be initiated by external stimulation, or they may also arise in the organism spontaneously or automatically. Sometimes the same reaction is produced by stimuli of many kinds. Some behavior patterns are very simple and involve only local reactions of certain parts of the body; others are concerned with centralized reactions of the whole organism. All behavior patterns vary with the general physiologic condition of the organism. A hungry hydra, for instance, will react toward food stimuli quite differently from a satiated specimen.

Behavior patterns vary all the way from the simple taxes or trial-and-error movements of Protista to the highly complicated patterns in those organisms with well-coordinated nervous systems. Many of the simpler metazoan forms have behavior similar to that of the Protista. Many different types of stimulation may produce the same reaction in both protozoans and metazoans, but the latter have many more types of reaction. Perhaps most behavior has some adaptive significance, but such adaptation is not necessarily perfect. Everything the animal does—food getting, defense and

21

offense tactics, courtship display, shelter seeking, and scores of other activities—involves behavior in some form. Invertebrates display a wide range of behavior adaptations that are correlated with their structural organization. As we go up the scale of organization levels, we find that uncentralized behavior tends to be replaced by centralized control in which there is a definite pattern of receptor organs, conductors, association centers, and effector systems. In coelenterates there is very little centralized behavior, and most of their reactions are localized because their nerve net acts mainly as a conducting system. As H. S. Jennings pointed out long ago, some of their reactions appear to be random and spontaneous while others, such as the swimming of the medusae, may be regarded as a simple form of central control. Flatworms have advanced in central control with their so-called "brain" and ladder type of nervous system. When stimulated, reactions of the whole organism usually take place. Planarians have some capacity for learning—perhaps the first group that may be said to have this faculty. Both flatworms and the more highly organized annelid worms can be trained in simple ways, such as being conditioned to master the right turns in elementary mazes. Echinoderms with a highly modified nerve net, including associative neurons and reflex arcs, have better coordinated reactions than coelenterates and may display unified action in some behavior patterns. Many of their actions seem to be aimless or of the trial-and-error variety.

Among the invertebrates, however, it is in the arthropods that we find the most complicated patterns of behavior. This is particularly true of the large group of insects. These organisms have adapted themselves to so many ways of life and new environments barred largely to other invertebrates, that they have developed a central and coordinated control far beyond that of most others in the invertebrate kingdom. Their receptor system and nervous connections are specialized for quicker conduction and response, and the addition of the power of flight has made possible the development of greater speed and distance of travel. Their compound eyes and antennary sense organs are admirably adapted for perception of the environment. Their brain controls the tone of their muscles and the sensitivity of the whole body. But the common form of insect behavior is innate with combinations of chain behavior, simple reflexes, and some degrees of learning. Chain behavior, in which each action acts as a stimulus to the next step, is very common among them. However, they do not operate by instinct alone, because their behavior can be modified. It may be said, therefore, that innate structural behavior patterns and reflexes of great complexity, with learning of the simplest conditional reflexes, have been built into the insect's nervous system in an evolution of hundreds of millions of years.

Pigment

Pigmentation of some kind is found in almost all invertebrates. It may be permanent or it may be changeable. Pigmentation has many functions such as for protection, concealment, regulation of light, formation of vitamins, mating reactions, humidity adjustments, and many others. In some cases pigmentation may be purely incidental to physiologic processes. It may be produced by the deposition of organic pigments (biochromes), or it may result from structural coloration or schemochromes (color effects produced by diffraction, interference, or scattering of light rays by physical surfaces). Structural colors may be altered or destroyed mechanically, but no chemical substance can be extracted from surfaces that display such coloration. Diffraction and interference colors are also iridescent, i.e., the visible colors of the spectrum will vary according to the angle with which the object is seen.

Diffraction is chiefly produced by a surface that is broken up into a form of grating. When a beam of white light strikes the units of such a grating, spectra that have an iridescent effect appear. The moving ciliary combs of ctenophores provide such a surface and are responsible for the beautiful colors found in these creatures. *Interference* is far more common than diffraction in the animal kingdom and is produced whenever light rays are reflected from surfaces of very thin multiple layers separated by other layers of materials of contrasting refractile indices. A soap bubble, the color of which changes as the distance between layers change, is a good example of interference of light. Among invertebrates the transparent, thin wings of flies and dragonflies, the scales of the wings of Lepidoptera and Coleoptera, the carapace of many crustaceans, and others represent this type of coloration. *Scattering* is produced by the dispersal of the shorter wavelengths by very small particles, such as the blue color of the sky. In the invertebrates the blue color of some dragonflies and wood lice appears to be caused by interference, although this type of coloration is far more common among vertebrates.

Pigments or biochromes are definite chemical compounds that have the power to impart color to animals. Biologic pigments may be suspensions, colloids, or even true solutions. A pigment transmits some but not all the wavelengths of visible light. If a pigment absorbs all the incident light, it is black; if it absorbs all the shorter wavelengths of visible light except the red, the color of the pigment is red, and so on with the other wavelengths of light. The most common biologic pigments are the carotenoids, melanin, and guanine, but there are many others (quinones, flavins, anthocyanins, hemoglobin, chlorocruorin, etc.). We are mainly interested in the first three. Carotenoids or lipochromes are very common among invertebrates and produce red, orange, and yellow colors. They are found in beetles, coelenterates, sponges, crustaceans, and echinoderms. These pigments are commonly found in branched chromatophores, known as xanthophores. Melanin is fairly common among invertebrates and is responsible for black or brown coloration wherever it is found. This pigment is usually in the form of small granules that are mainly found in branched cells known as chromatophores or melanophores, but it is sometimes found in unbranched ectodermal cells. Melanogenesis is influenced by many factors, such as movement, hormones, humidity, low temperatures, etc. A group of pigments closely related to melanin are the ommochromes, which isolate the ommatidia of the compound eye in their optical activity. These pigments are usually brown but may be other colors. These pigments are also found in invertebrates other than the arthropods. Guanine is the purine base of

one of the nucleotides of the nucleic acids (DNA and RNA). It is found, therefore, in all cells, but only when it accumulates abundantly in granular or crystal form does it enter into the coloration of animals. Such animals give a white or silvery light because they reflect all incident light. This pigment is usually found in special cells (guanophores). It has a restricted distribution among invertebrates, being found in cephalopod skin, which displays iridescence by light interference in its cells (iridocytes).

Pigment cells are often unicellular, and changes in coloration are produced when the pigment is dispersed in the branched cells (colored effect) or concentrated in the center of the cell (blanching). In some crustaceans the pigment unit is multicellular and may contain many different pigments, but only one color is found in a cell. In some mollusks, especially in cephalopods, the pigment cell is enlarged or constricted by radially disposed muscles. This is the only type of pigment cell controlled directly by nervous action in the invertebrates; in the other types, color changes are affected by neurohumors through the internal medium. The direct nervous control is probably responsible for the rapidity of color changes in cephalopods.

Color changes in invertebrates are caused by many kinds of stimuli and are usually adaptive in nature. Many crustaceans become dark at night and pale during the day, although there are one or two exceptions. Color of background is a common stimulus; most crustaceans will become dark on a black background and pale on a white background. Light, temperature, and humidity also influence color changes.

Biologic clocks

A physiologic mechanism that has been studied extensively in recent years is the biologic clock. A biologic clock refers to an automatic timing device that is built into the behavior pattern of animals in such a way that they can utilize the natural cycles of their physical environment to the best advantage. Such timing devices have been the outcome of the organism's adaptation to the rhythmic nature of its external environment. These internal clocks are now known to play important roles in many aspects of animal behavior and physiology. Biologic clocks have been studied and demonstrated in most major groups of organisms, with the possible exception of some primitive forms such as bacteria and blue-green algae. Timing devices are known to be involved in migratory activities, bird migration, orientation problems, diurnal and nocturnal activities, breeding cycles, seasonal cycles, color transformations, etc.

Although biologic clocks have evolved and are synchronized under the impact of external cycles, they are not altogether dependent upon the persistence of external rhythms. Most biologic clocks are built around circadian rhythms, i.e., the 24-hour cycle of the day. Organisms usually establish their rhythmic activities both externally and internally to a given order or sequence, and do not function at the same rate over the daily cycle. By such means they can adapt their activities to the regularly recurring changes in the environment. There are also other rhythms or cycles that are correlated with the lunar phases, tidal phases, and even animal phases. Carefully performed experiments have demonstrated that biologic clocks are based on intrinsic processes and are a definite part of the animal's organization. This is strikingly shown by experiments in which animals that normally have rhythms correlated to daily changes in their environment will still have these same rhythms even in the absense of external stimuli. For instance, fiddler crabs normally become dark in color by the dispersal of their pigment in pigment cells at daybreak and become pale in the evening by concentration of their pigment to the center of pigment cells. They thus have a dark color during the day in contrast to the lighter one at night. When kept continuously in a darkroom for long periods of time, the crabs retained their dark-light rhythm synchronized with the outside day-night cycle without noticeable variation. However, it is possible to reset the clock by subjecting the crabs to certain external conditions. It was found by F. A. Brown, Jr., that if the crabs were left for six hours in the darkroom in seawater near the freezing point and then warmed to room temperature, the clock stopped or slowed, so that when the crabs resumed their 24-hour cycle, the rhythmic change was six hours slow. Furthermore, the crabs showed no tendency to return to the original rhythm and remained at the reset time. The same investigator also was able to reset the clocks by illumination effects at critical times in the daily cycle.

Among invertebrates timing devices are probably most highly evolved in honeybees, although these organisms have been more extensively studied than other forms. Bees have the capacity to determine their direction by the sun and can make suitable corrections for the shifting of the sun's position at various times of the day. They thus share with birds a compass mechanism for determining correct orientations.

An explanation of the precise way organisms adjust themselves to the rhythmic cycles of their environment is impossible from our present state of knowledge. Biologic clocks are inherited and are relatively independent of temperature, chemicals, drugs, and other inhibitors. It is not known whether the clock is localized or involves the makeup of the whole organism. It appears to be a metabolic mechanism under enzyme-controlled metabolic reactions and thus requires a certain amount of energy for its operation. However, the usefulness of the clock to the living organism can be demonstrated in multiple ways.

Bioluminescence

Interesting effector organs among invertebrates are those capable of producing light. The power to produce living light is found in most major groups of organisms. It is found in the Protozoa (Sarcodina and Dinoflagellata) and in virtually all metazoan phyla, both marine and terrestrial, such as Coelenterata, Annelida, Arthropoda (Crustacea, Insecta), Mollusca, and some others. Although the power to produce light has evolved several times in organic forms, the mechanism of light generation is very much the same in all forms. The functional significance of light production is not apparent in all cases, but it appears to serve a useful function for the attraction and recognition between sexes of the same species, for protection against predators, and for the attraction of prey. Emission of light appears to provide no survival value for the organism in some species.

The mechanism of light production involves the coordinated action of water, inorganic ions, oxygen, two organic substances call *luciferin* and *luciferase,* and the high-energy bond, adenosine triphosphate (ATP). Light production is a chemical reaction in which luciferin is oxidized in the presence of the enzyme luciferase. Both luciferin and luciferase differ in composition in different species, although they are probably similar in chemical composition, both being proteins. Extracts of luciferin will not luminesce by themselves, but if ATP is added to luciferin, ATP complex is formed. In the presence of water, oxygen, and magnesium ions this complex emits light when luciferase is added. In this process oxygen is used up and ATP is reduced to adenosine diphosphate (ADP). Some forms (ctenophores) will luminesce in the complete absence of dissolved oxygen but may derive their oxygen from some bound form. It is evident that all animals do not produce light in the same way, because a multiplicity of processes are involved.

In most animals the production of light is not a continuous process but is usually produced intermittently by nervous stimulation of specialized cells in light-producing organs. However, the control or stimulation is not the same in all organisms. The energy emitted in light production falls within the visible spectrum but may range across a narrow or broad band. The light rays may be of any length, but yellow and blue are more common. More than one color may be given out by different luminous organs in some animals. The intensity of the light emitted varies with different animals, being brightest in the ctenophore *Mnemiopsis.* So far as is known no heat is associated with the light, and therefore it is often called "cold light."

Ciliary feeding mechanisms

Ciliary, or filter, feeders are common among invertebrates and are found to some extent in larval forms of some vertebrates. This is a primitive feeding method commonly used by many animals for collecting food and getting it into the mouth. That so many animals have met this need in much the same manner indicates that a great deal of convergent evolution has taken place in the mechanisms of ciliary feeding. Forms not closely related often use similar methods. The method, which varies somewhat with different groups, consists essentially of ciliary currents induced by cilia, hairs, or setae that draw food particles into the mouth, often with the assistance of mucus that collects food particles into stringy masses. It is the typical feeding method of most sessile organisms, but is also found in those with active locomotion.

In some protozoans and rotifers currents of water are produced by the beat of the cilia on the disk, and food particles are carried into the mouth or gullet. In ciliates such as *Paramecium* the mechanism of food collecting is assisted by the currents of water induced by the strong cilia in the oral groove. The disk of rotifers consists of two incomplete rings of cilia that create vortices, and accepted food particles pass between the two rings of cilia into the mouth while rejected food is cast away in places where the rings are incomplete. Most metazoan invertebrates make use of ciliated surfaces and mucus in food collecting. Particles of food are collected by the sticky mucus and conveyed to the mouth and inside the body by cilia. The lophophore of tentacles in Ectoprocta, Entoprocta, Brachiopoda, and others utilizes this type of filter feeding. Water currents are driven into the crown of the lophophore between the tentacles, which are provided with cilia for carrying the food into the mouth. Ciliary currents and mucous secretions are used for carrying food along the tentacles of tube-dwelling annelids and the ambulacral groves of crinoids. Many mollusks, such as the freshwater clam, have elaborated a very efficient method of filter feeding. Protochordates, which may be considered the only invertebrates with gill slits, have a variant form of the same method. In the classic *Amphioxus* the wheel organ and other ciliary bodies draw currents of water into the mouth and pharynx, where mucus secreted by the endostyle collects the food particles into stringy masses or nets that are carried by ciliary action through the hyperpharyngeal groove into the intestine. In the intestine the food is digested and absorbed with the mucus. In most filter-feeding devices the suspended particles that are not food or those that are too large are sorted out and discarded.

The transport of the gut food cord has

25

been reviewed recently by J. E. Morton. Transportation through the intestine of most filter feeders involves some peristalsis, but chiefly it depends upon ciliary movements. The gut cord is usually rotated by a rod or ciliated esophagus that aids in circulating the food particles in the stomach and shedding them from the cord for extracellular enzymatic digestion. Many ciliary feeders also retain a great deal of intracellular digestion that requires a sorting of food particles suitable for phagocytosis.

Filter-feeding forms are generally omnivorous because they must depend mainly upon planktonic organisms that contain both plant and animal forms, although some do make a selection.

Annotated references

Ager, D. V. 1963. Principles of paleoecology, New York, McGraw-Hill Book Company. *An excellent introduction to the ecologic conditions under which animals and plants lived in the past geologic ages.*

Carter, G. S. 1961. A general zoology of the invertebrates, ed. 4. London, Sidgwick & Jackson, Ltd., Publishers. *This work is not intended as a text of invertebrates but represents a fine appraisal of the many aspects of invertebrate morphology and physiology.*

Hedgpeth, J. W. 1957. Treatise on marine ecology and paleoecology, vol. 1. New York, Geological Society of America. *A pretentious treatise on various ecologic aspects of animal life.*

Marcus, E. 1958. On the evolution of the animal phyla. Quart. Rev. Biol. 33:24-58. *An evaluation of the present status of animal phylogeny.*

Mayr, E. 1963. Animal species and evolution. Cambridge, Harvard University Press. *A masterly analysis of the present basic concepts of evolutionary biology; perhaps the most outstanding treatise of its kind published in the last decade.*

Morton, J. E. 1960. The functions of the gut in ciliary feeders. Biol. Rev. 35:92-140.

Nursall, J. R. 1959. Oxygen as a prerequisite to the origin of the Metozoa. Nature (London) 183:1170-1172.

Pearse, A. S. 1950. The emigrations of animals from the sea. Washington, D.C., The Sherwood Press. *An attempt to explain how animals met and overcame problems in the invasion of the land.*

Reid, G. K. 1961. Ecology of inland waters and estuaries. New York, Reinhold Publishing Corp. *An introduction to the chemical and physical factors that operate in fresh water and estuaries and their bearing upon biota.*

Rensch, B. 1960. Evolution above the species level. New York, Columbia University Press. *A modern, synthetic theory of evolution, based upon systematics, comparative morphology, and paleontology.*

Rothschild, L. 1961. A classification of living animals. New York, John Wiley & Sons, Inc. *Includes an index of orders, suborders, and many genera.*

Simpson, G. G. 1961. Principles of animal taxonomy. New York, Columbia University Press. *A useful, up-to-date account of the principles underlying classification. No specific treatment is given of animal taxa.*

Phylum Protozoa

It is impossible to state just what the earliest organisms were like at the beginning of life, but from our present knowledge of evolution we are justified in believing that an ancestral protistan type of cell was an innovation of the greatest importance in biologic evolution. The term "Protista" is used by many biologists to refer to those organisms (either plant or animal) whose specializations and differentiations are restricted to a single cell. Protista may have one or more true cell nuclei with distinct nuclear membranes in contrast to some primitive forms that do not (Monera). It is not always possible to draw a sharp line of demarcation between the unicellular and the multicellular forms. The protistans do not form a natural group of organisms, but they form a convenient one. Although they have not followed the plan of complication and differentiation followed by multicellular animals and plants, they have in some cases become highly specialized within the limitations of a unicellular pattern. Since protistans are not equivalent to the single cell of multicellular organism, it is best, perhaps, to call them acellular organisms.

The term "Protozoa" is usually restricted to those protistans that have no chlorophyll and whose nutrition is holozoic, saprozoic, or symbiotic. These are the animallike organisms in contrast to the plantlike forms of the Protista. Hard and fast lines of distinction between the protistans in this respect are not always made, however. Protozoans are also a convenient, not a natural, group of organisms. Within the Protozoa there is an enormous diversity of form and complexity. Although protozoans may be considered primitive, it is doubtful whether

the performance of all functions of a protozoan's life within the confines of one cell, instead of within numerous differentiated cells, is simple. Most protozoans are unicellular, but some are colonial and show some differentiation and division of labor among their cells. Protozoans as a group have exploited about all the known possibilities of the unicellular type of existence.

CLASSIFICATION

For many years zoologists have followed a traditional taxonomy in the classification of protozoans, but within the past decade many changes have occurred. No one system of protozoan taxonomy, however, has become stabilized, and the following one represents a tentative scheme based upon the work of some of our leading protozoan taxonomists. It has been customary to rank the protozoans as a single phylum with each of the four groups as a class, but some authorities think that each of the four groups, or classes, should be given phylum rank, making Protozoa a superphylum.

Phylum Protozoa. Unicellular (acellular) or colonial; mostly microscopic; all types of nutrition; most symmetries represented; locomotor organelles of cilia, flagella, or pseudopodia; 30,000 to 40,000 species.
Subphylum Plasmodroma. Monomorphic nuclei; locomotor organs of flagella or pseudopodia, or absent.
    Class Mastigophora (Flagellata). Locomotor organelles of flagella or pseudopodia.
    Subclass Phytomastigina (Phytoflagellata). With chromatophores; a few lack chromatophores.

27

Order Chrysomonadida. With yellow or brown chromatophores; no gullet; one to three flagella; solitary or colonial; siliceous cysts. *Uroglena, Dinobryon.*

Order Cryptomonadida. Usually with one to two yellow-brown chromatophores; usually with gullet; nutrition holophytic, saprophytic, or symbiotic; two flagella. *Chilomonas, Cryptomonas.*

Order Dinoflagellida. With two flagella, one around the body, the other longitudinal; body covered by cellulose plates or naked; brown, yellow, or green chromatophores; free living or parasitic. *Ceratium, Noctiluca.*

Order Phytomonadida. Solitary or colonial; two to eight flagella; no gullet; usually with green chromatophores; cellulose membrane in some. *Eudorina, Volvox, Chlamydomonas.*

Order Euglenida. Body slender; one to two flagella in gullet; chromatophores green or none; food reserve (starch or paramylum bodies); stigma in some. *Euglena, Peranema.*

Order Chloromonadida. Two flagella; usually many green chromatophores; stigma absent. *Gonyostomum, Vacuolaria.*

Subclass Zoomastigina. No chromatophores.

Order Rhizomastigida. One or two flagella; pseudopodia. *Mastigamoeba, Histomonas.*

Order Protomonadida. One or two flagella; body plastic or ameboid; some with collar; mostly parasitic. *Trypanosoma, Leishmania, Protospongia.*

Order Polymastigida. Three to eight flagella usually; axostyle or axostylar filaments; often many nuclei; mostly parasitic or commensal. *Chilomastix, Giardia.*

Order Trichomonadida. Three to six flagella; axostyle; uninucleate or multinucleate. *Trichomonas, Tritrichomonas.*

Order Hypermastigida. Many flagella; complex cytoplasm; uninucleate; symbiotic. *Trichonympha, Lophomonas.*

Order Opalinida. Flattened body; covered with cilia; multinucleate; symbiotic. *Opalina.*

Class Sarcodina. Locomotion by pseudopodia; no definite pellicle; uninucleate or multinucleate; mostly holozoic.

Subclass Actinopoda. With radiating axopodia; floating or sessile.

Order Helioflagellida. With both axopodia and flagella. *Tetradimorpha.*

Order Heliozoida. Spherical; radiating axopodia; no central capsule. *Actinophrys, Actinosphaerium.*

Order Radiolarida. Mostly spherical; central capsule of pseudochitin; radiating axopodia; latticelike skeleton of silica or strontium sulfate. *Acanthometra, Thalassicolla.*

Subclass Rhizopoda. No axopodia; variety of pseudopodia; mainly creeping forms.

Order Proteomyxida. Radiating, branched, and fusing protoplasmic processes; chiefly parasitic. *Vampyrella, Pseudospora.*

Order Mycetozoida. Plasmodium or pseudoplasmodium; slime molds. *Arcyria, Dictyostelium.*

Order Amoebida. Short pseudopodia (lobopodia); naked, usually with thin pellicle; some with flagellate stages. *Amoeba, Entamoeba.*

Order Testacida. One-chambered test of silica or calcium carbonate with single aperture; filopodia. *Arcella, Difflugia.*

Order Foraminiferida. Slender, branched pseudopodia; simple or chambered test of calcium carbonate or chitin with one to many openings. *Globigerina, Discorbis.*

Class Sporozoa. No locomotor organs; reproduction by asexual and sexual phases; saprozoic; internal parasites.

Subclass Telosporidia. Spores with no polar capsules; infective sporozoite.

Order Gregarinida. One-celled spores formed directly by zygote; extracellular parasites; life cycle of both schizogony and sporogony or sporogony alone. *Gregarina, Monocystis.*

Order Coccidia. Schizogony and sporogony in life cycle; intracellular parasites; spores with one to many walls. *Eimeria, Hepatozoon.*

Order Haemosporidia. Intracorpuscular parasites; alternate schizogony and sporogony; naked sporozoites. *Plasmodium, Babesia.*

Subclass Cnidosporidia. Spore with one to four filaments in polar capsule and containing sporoplasms; spore often of many cells.

Order Myxosporida. Spore large and covered by chitinous bivalve shell; parasites of lower vertebrates. *Myxidium, Coccomyxa.*

Order Actinomyxida. Spore with three valves; three polar capsules; parasite in coelom or gut of annelids. *Triactinomyxon, Synactinomyxon.*

Order Microsporida. Spore shell of one piece; one or two polar filaments; intracellular parasites in arthropods and fishes. *Nosema, Coccospora.*

Order Helicosporida. Small barrel-shaped spore; one thick filament; three sporoplasms. *Helicosporidium.*

Subclass Acnidosporidia. Simple spores; no polar filaments; spore with single sporozoite.

Order Sarcosporidia. Crescent-shaped spore; many spores in cyst; muscle parasites. *Sarcocystis.*

Order Haplosporidia. Few spores in cyst. *Haplosporidium.*

Subphylum Ciliophora. Cilia present in adult or young stages; tentacles in adults of some; mostly two kinds of nuclei (macronucleus and micronucleus).

Class Ciliata

Subclass Holotricha. Cilia usually over entire body surface.

    Order Gymnostomatida. Body usually large; no buccal ciliation. *Didinium, Prorodon.*

    Order Suctorida. Stalked, sessile forms; tentacles at distal end; ciliation only in young stages. *Podophrya, Trichophrya.*

    Order Chonotrichida. Vase shaped; cilia only around funnel; ectocommensal. *Spirochona, Stylochona.*

    Order Trichostomatida. No buccal ciliation; vestibulum into cytostome present. *Colpoda, Balantidium* (only ciliated protozoan parasitic in man).

    Order Hymenostomatida. Uniform body ciliation; definite buccal ciliation or undulating membrane; dorsal zone of membranelles. *Paramecium, Tetrahymena.*

    Order Astomatida. No cytostome; body ciliation uniform; parasitic in invertebrates. *Anoplophrya, Hoplitophrya.*

    Order Apostomatida. Mostly commensals on marine crustaceans; complex life histories; unique rosette near mouth; spiral ciliary rows on body. *Foettingeria, Spirophrya.*

    Order Thigmotrichida. Cytostome with buccal ciliation in some; thigmotactic cilia for attachment to host; in mantle cavity of mollusks. *Boveria, Hemispeira.*

    Order Peritrichida. Enlarged ciliated disk at apical end; restricted ciliation; often attached by a stalk. *Vorticella, Carchesium.*

Subclass Spirotricha. Compound ciliary structures (cirri) on ventral surface of body and buccal organelles; adoral zone of membranelles.

    Order Heterotrichida. Buccal ciliation usually well developed; pigments in some; body ciliation ventral or lacking; adoral zone of membranelles well developed. *Stentor, Bursaria.*

    Order Oligotrichida. Cilia reduced or absent; usually conspicuous adoral zone of membranelles at anterior end. *Halteria, Strombidium.*

    Order Tintinnida. Trumpet-shaped body in lorica; often conspicuous oral membranelles. *Tintinnopsis, Codonella.*

    Order Entodiniomorphida. Cilia reduced or absent; adoral zone of membranelles; endocommensals; specialized internal structures. *Epidinium, Entodinium.*

    Order Ctenostomatida (Odontostomatida). Carapaced and compressed; sparse ciliation; adoral membranelles. *Saprodinium, Epalxis.*

    Order Hypotrichida. Flattened; cilia or cirri only on ventral surface. *Kerona, Stylonychia, Euplotes.*

BASIC ADAPTIVE FEATURES AND EVOLUTION

The structural feature in protozoans that has probably been most effective in guiding and restricting their adaptive evolution has been the differentiation of the cortical region or the ectoplasm. This outer layer of the cytosome is differentiated in various degrees among the different Protozoa and is involved not only with determining the body shape but also with the development of food-getting apparatus and the types of nutrition, the mechanism of body movement (fibrils and myonemes), and with locomotion (pseudopodia, cilia, and flagella). The ectoplasmic surface may be naked with little differentiation of pellicle or cuticle, thus fitting the animal for the direct absorption of dissolved substances (saprozoic nutrition); but when the ectoplasm differentiates into hard and impermeable coverings, the holozoic mode of nutrition with its specialized food-catching organelles, definite mouth opening (cytostome), cytopharynx, food vacuoles, etc. becomes necessary. Locomotion by pseudopodia, cilia, flagella, and general gliding is brought about by the differentiation of the cortical region. Neuromotor systems of longitudinal ectoplasmic fibrils connecting basal bodies of cilia are found in some ciliates. Sense perception is a general property of the ectoplasm, which often develops sense organelles such as simple eyespots, or stigmata, and more complex receptors.

Not the least of the evolutionary novelties engendered by the ectoplasm are the protective devices that are found throughout the protozoan kingdom. Encasements, tests, and shells, as well as elaborate pellicles and secreted membranes on the ectoplasmic surface, are found throughout the phylum. Organelles of defense and offense such as trichocysts and toxicysts are present in certain ciliates and flagellates. Polar capsules with their filaments for host attachment represent an interesting evolutionary novelty in some sporozoans.

PHYLOGENETIC RELATIONSHIPS

From an evolutionary point of view little of certainty is known about the origin and relationships of the Protozoa. As a phylum they rank among the most primitive of all animal groups, but whether they arose from one ancestral group or from many is not known. As already stated, protozoans probably do not form a natural group at all but must be regarded as a polyphyletic assemblage, the members of which display about the same level of organization, although with marked degrees of complexity within that level.

Relationships among the four classes of protozoans are obscure at present. It is thought that the Mastigophora may be the most primitive class, although the Sarcodina were long considered to be most primitive because of the apparent simplicity of their protoplasmic structure. However, chlorophyll-bearing organisms such as green flagellates (Mastigophora) could have lived without holozoic nutrition, which is characteristic of ameboid organisms (Sarcodina). Holophytic flagellates could, therefore, by loss of chloroplasts give rise to the animallike flagellates. But some of the most recent schemes of the origin of life assign photosynthesis to a much later stage of biologic evolution. The view that because Sarcodina sometimes have flagellate young stages they represent primitive characteristics is not considered altogether valid, because experimental work has shown that certain ameboid forms can be made to develop flagella when treated a certain way. The presence of flagella thus may not necessarily denote a primitive condition.

The Sporozoa, entirely parasitic, may have arisen from the Mastigophora and the Sarcodina, while the highly complex Ciliophora could also have arisen from flagellates because of the similarity between flagella and cilia, but this relationship is problematic. It is generally agreed that the various sporozoan orders had separate origins, but they too could have arisen from mastigophoran or sarcodinian ancestors.

FOSSIL RECORD

Protozoan fossils do not reveal a great deal about the evolution of the phylum. Most protozoan fossils belong to the orders Radiolarida and Foraminiferida, because the members of these two orders are provided with shells or tests that fossilize fairly easily. Radiolarian fossils have been found in Precambrian rocks, but they show us little about the nature of the earliest protozoans, which were probably without

shells and were not preserved. The early foraminiferans, which are the most abundant of all the protozoan fossils, did not produce calcareous shells until the Jurassic period; before this their tests were largely composed of sand or other foreign substances. Most of the largest forams became extinct in the remote past. They were important in the formation of chalk, limestone, and marble, and their tests make up a large part of the sediment covering the ocean floor.

Other groups of Protozoa that were fossilized to some extent were the dinoflagellates, the silicoflagellates, and a few test-bearing ciliates. Many protozoan fossils bear remarkable resemblance to modern species. Most of their fossils are of marine origin.

The study of protozoan fossils has practical importance. Many protozoans were sensitive to temperature changes of the oceans, and their cycles of abundance or decrease indicate climatic changes of past geologic periods and can be used to predict future climatic cycles. But one of their most important utilitarian aspects is the information they yield about oil deposits. This is especially true of foraminiferans that have played a role in the formation of hydrocarbons. By examination of borings and castings from wells and quantitative measurements of the fossils, it has been possible to locate geologic traps or pockets of oil.

ECOLOGIC ASPECTS

Protozoans are especially suited for moist conditions, but they may be found in a dormant state of encystment wherever life can exist. Protozoans have many means of dispersal or distribution because they are small and active, and their cysts can be carried by air or water currents, the feet of birds, the digestive systems of animals, and in innumerable other ways.

Protozoans possess great adaptibility and acclimation to a wide variety of habitats and have occupied an enormous range of ecologic niches. They are found in water everywhere, from the arctic regions to fairly hot springs with temperatures of more than 60° C. Many have the power to acclimate themselves by gradual change to temperatures and other environmental conditions far beyond their usual range. In dry regions (deserts, arid soils, mountain elevations, etc.) their cysts are viable for years. They are found in both fresh and salt water but are more abundant in standing water than in running water. Some are definitely pelagic and others are benthonic. They may be found at all depths of the sea.

Limiting factors necessarily vary with different species. Moisture seems to be necessary for reproduction in all species, although many live encysted for a long time in extreme dessicating conditions. All species, perhaps, have certain optimum ranges of restricting factors. For temperature many species thrive best within the range of 10° to 25° C. In the cyst state, however, they can withstand much lower temperatures—even freezing in some cases—although freezing conditions are fatal in most instances. Most species favor a pH of neutrality or one that is slightly alkaline. Adaptation to the salt content of water naturally varies with marine and freshwater forms, but many protozoans can be acclimated gradually either way. Some ciliates, such as *Prorodon*, are found in Great Salt Lake, where the salt content is more than 30 percent. Nutritional requirements are also limiting factors, such as certain minerals, amino acids, vitamins, and sugars—but these requirements vary greatly. Some protozoans synthesize their own food (photosynthesis), and some depend upon symbionts. They all require molecular oxygen or oxygen from some other source.

All forms of relationships are found in Protozoa. Many types of symbiosis, both useful and harmful, are found in the ecologic interactions of Protozoa. Mutualism, or a state of mutual benefit to both partners, is well illustrated by zoochlorellae and zooxanthellae, which live in certain protozoans. The same relationship is also found between termites and their flagellates. Commensalism, in which one partner receives benefit without harm to the other, is well shown by *Kerona* and *Trichodina*, which use the hydra's body surface as a substratum—although these species may be ectoparasitic. Parasitic forms are found in all classes of Protozoa, and one class, Sporozoa, is exclusively parasitic.

GENERAL FEATURES

Most protozoans are microscopic, but some may be 2 to 3 mm. long, and are visible to the naked eye. The smallest may not be more than 2 microns long; the largest are certain foraminiferans that may exceed 70 mm.

The body may be very plastic and without a limiting pellicle, as in the ameba, which has only a thin cell membrane; but many protozoans have a body whose rigidity is determined by surface and internal structures. These factors determine the form, which varies greatly throughout the phylum. All varieties of symmetries are found, but strict bilateral symmetry is uncommon because of spiral torsion. The kinds of adjustment protozoans make to their habitats are often correlated with their shape. Radial symmetry and conical shape is the rule among sessile forms such as the vorticellids and their relatives; spherical symmetry or its modifications are more common among floating types, for example *Volvox*. Creeping forms are usually flattened. Many protozoans are asymmetric.

Besides the cell membrane, protistans often have other body coverings of nonliving secreted materials. These range from a variety of pellicles to rigid tests or shells. Some secreted coverings consist of organic materials such as cellulose or tectin and may be gelatinous in structure. They often contain embedded materials such as minerals, sand grains, or diatom shells. Dinoflagellates may have a hardened armor of cellulose plates in elaborate designs. Tests and shells contain mostly inorganic substances. Foraminiferans build shells of calcium carbonate. Radiolarians may have complex internal skeletons of silica or strontium sulfate.

The protoplasm of protozoans is usually divided into distinct regions—a relatively clear ectoplasm and a somewhat opaque endoplasm. This differentiation is best seen in some ameboid forms in which the colloidal reversibility of ectoplasm and endoplasm is evident.

The ectoplasm contains many structures and, as already stated, is chiefly responsible for the varied evolutionary trends of the phylum. Among the structures the ectoplasm bears are the trichocysts and toxicysts of ciliates, the nematocysts of some dinoflagellates, and the polar capsules of the Cnidosporidia. Some of these are offensive and defensive organelles, and others may be used for anchoring the organism

Fig. 2-1

Electron micrograph of cross section through some of flagellatae of *Pseudotrichonympha.* (×140,000.) (Courtesy I. R. Gibbons, Harvard University, Cambridge.)

to the substrate. Trichocysts are minute oval-shaped bodies in the deeper layer of the pellicle and are arranged at right angles to the body surface. When stimulated, they discharge long filaments through pores in the pellicle (Fig. 2-40, *C* to *E*). The polar capsules of cnidosporidians and the nematocysts of dinoflagellates discharge spirally coiled threads that resemble those of coelenterate nematocysts. The peculiar sucking tentacles of the order Suctorida are also ectoplasmic structures as are the various types of locomotor organelles such as pseudopodia, flagella, and cilia.

Ciliary arrangement varies with the species. In some species the cilia are arranged in rows and spirals originating in the region of the mouth and proceeding to the posterior region. Many cilia may be grouped together to form compound organelles, such as membranes, membranelles, and cirri. Typically each cilium has a basal granule (kinetosome) from which a filament (basal fibril or kinetodesma) extends into the cyto-

plasm, joining with other filaments to form a longitudinal bundle running parallel to the row of cilia (Fig. 2-39). These ectoplasmic fibrils form the neuromotor apparatus, which conducts stimuli and coordinates locomotor activities. In some complex ciliates fibrils radiating out from a central organelle, or motorium, control movements of fused cilia called cirri.

Both cilia and flagella show (by the electron microscope) a similar structure—an outer sheath enclosing a matrix in which an axoneme extends to a granule. The axoneme consists in most cases of two central and nine peripheral fibrils (Fig. 2-1). Some cilia and flagella are as long as 150 microns (*Trichonympha*), but others are only 3 to 4 microns long.

Pseudopodia are retractile extensions of the body and exist in several forms, such as the lobopodia with broad and rounded tips, axopodia with axonemes in their slender bodies, and filopodia (rhizopodia), which are also slender, tapering, without axonemes, and tending to branch and fuse (Fig. 2-2). Other types of pseudopodia include the filamentous myxopodia that branch and anastomose into networks.

The ectoplasmic cortex also includes myonemes or contractile fibrils found in certain ciliates and sporozoans. Another organelle associated with movement is the undulating membrane of the trypanosomes and some others.

Endoplasmic inclusions consist of chromatophores, mitochondria, stigmata, nuclei, food vacuoles, contractile vacuoles, and others. Chromatophores are common in phytoflagellates, which, strictly speaking, do not belong to Protozoa. Chromatophores contain chlorophyll that may be masked by other colored pigments. Pyrenoid bodies are often associated with chromatophores and may function in starch formation. Starch-related carbohydrates known as paramylum bodies are found as food reserves in many phytoflagellates including *Euglena*. Light-perceiving organelles, such as stigmata, are also characteristic of many phytoflagellates, while more complex photoreceptors (ocelli) are present in some dinoflagellates. Symbiotic bacteria and green flagellates occur in many Protozoa.

Mitochondria, which are of great importance in cellular metabolism, are very small

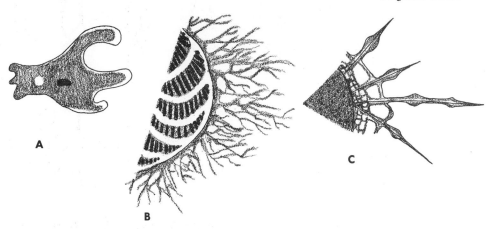

A

B

C

Fig. 2-2

Types of pseudopodia. **A,** Lobopodia, as in *Amoeba.* **B,** Portion of foraminiferan showing rhizopodia. **C,** Portion of heliozoan showing axopodia. Each axopodium contains axoneme surrounded by cytoplasmic sheath.

rodlike or spherical bodies that have been described in many species of Protozoa and may be found in all Protozoa. Another common cytoplasmic body, the Golgi apparatus, appears to be present in some protozoans according to studies with the electron microscope. Dictyosomes (disk-shaped organelles) and parabasal bodies (long cylindric structures usually attached to a centriole by a filament) exist in some classes of Protozoa. They are probably secretory in function, the same as the Golgi apparatus.

The contractile vacuole is found in most freshwater protozoans as well as in some marine and parasitic species. These vacuoles perform their function by a rhythmic cycle, periodically swelling in volume, then collapsing to discharge their fluid contents to the outside (Fig. 2-3). Fluid enters the vacuoles in various ways—by collecting canals, by fusion of cytoplasmic vacuoles, and by secretion or diffusion through the vacuolar membrane. There is often more than one contractile vacuole in a particular species, and the discharge pore may or may not be in a specific place. They are mostly osmoregulatory in function, but they may have other functions, including a slight excretory one.

Protozoa have various devices for obtaining their food. In saprozoic feeding, food in solution simply diffuses through the body wall. In holozoic feeding, which seems to be the most common method, solid particles pass through temporary or permanent cytostomes, and the food is digested intracellularly in food vacuoles. Some protozoans synthesize their own food by photosynthesis (autotrophic or holophytic); others make use of symbiotic algae living within them. Combinations of these methods may be found in the same species. Suctoridans have unique sucking tentacles by which the liquid contents of their prey are drawn into food vacuoles (Fig. 2-42).

Protozoans other than the Ciliophora have only one kind of nucleus, but there may be several nuclei in the same organism. In addition to chromosomes a nucleus usually contains an endosome (karyosome), which is a central mass of chromatin material (Fig. 2-4, *H, I*). Electron microscopic studies indicate that the nuclear membrane consists of two membranes, each about 70 to 80 Å thick and separated from each other by a space of 300 to 400 Å. Many pores up to 800 Å in diameter are found in the membrane. The inner and outer membranes meet at the boundaries of the pores. The Ciliophora have two kinds of nuclei—the micronucleus and the macronucleus. The macronucleus, the larger of the two, is concerned mainly with the metabolic activities of the organism, but it also has a regenerative capacity; on the other hand the micronucleus is concerned with the genetic functions of the organism. There are usu-

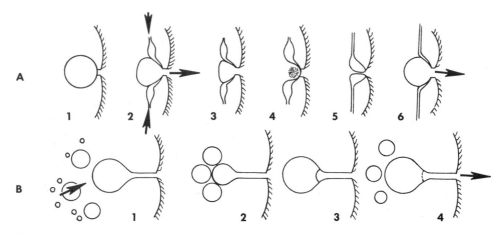

Fig. 2-3

Diagram of operation of two types of contractile vacuoles. **A,** In *Paramecium multimicronucleatum*, vacuole in **1** is full, with membrane closing pore; in **2** and **3** pore is open, vacuole emptying, collecting canals filling; **4,** pore is closed; **5** and **6,** vesicles fuse to form contractile vacuole. **B,** In *Paramecium trichium*, contractile vacuole is fed by vesicles, has no collecting canals; vacuole empties by permanent tube and pore (many species lack tube). **1,** Vacuole full; secondary and tertiary vacuoles forming; **2** and **3,** vacuole empties, then refills by fusion of secondary vacuoles formed by fusion of tertiary vacuoles; **4,** primary vacuole full again. (Modified from King.)

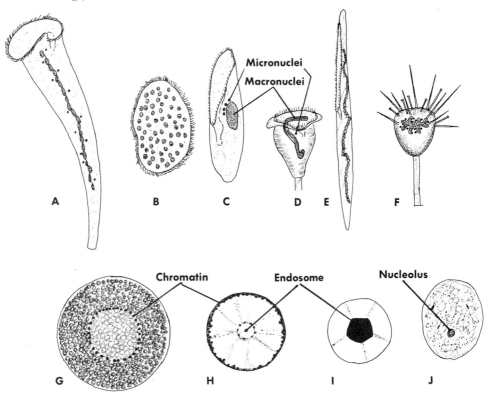

Fig. 2-4

Types of nuclei. **A** to **F,** Ciliophorans with both micronuclei and macronuclei (except **B**). **A,** *Stentor.* **B,** *Opalina* with many vesicular nuclei and no micronuclei; shows more affinity to flagellates than to ciliophorans. **C,** *Paramecium multimicronucleatum.* **D,** *Vorticella.* **E,** *Spirostomum.* **F,** *Ephelota,* a suctoridan. **G** to **J,** Types of vesicular nuclei. **G,** *Endamoeba.* **H,** *Entamoeba.* **I,** *Endolimax.* **J,** Typical vesicular nucleus with nucleolus. Endosomes contain chromatin, nucleoli do not.

Fig. 2-5

Binary fission in protozoans. **A** to **C**, Sarcodinians. **D** and **E**, Ciliates. **E** to **H**, Flagellates. **A**, *Amoeba proteus,* typical mitotic division. **B**, *Arcella* extrudes cytoplasm and one of its two nuclei; cytoplasm secretes new shell. **C**, *Euglypha.* **D**, *Stentor,* transverse fission. **E**, *Vorticella,* longitudinal fission. In **D** and **E** micronuclei divide mitotically; macronuclei divide amitotically. **F**, *Euglena.* **G**, *Chlamydomonas,* multiple fission. **H**, *Ceratium* divides diagonally, each half regenerating missing parts; apical horn of one may remain attached to girdle of another, forming chains, with original halves forming ends of chains.

ally not more than two of each kind of nuclei, but some protozoans have more. Protozoan nuclei vary a great deal with the group and the species. They may be of almost any shape, such as oval, crescent, ribbonlike, or beaded (Fig. 2-4).

Both asexual and sexual methods of reproduction are found in Protozoa. Asexual reproduction is present in all protozoans and is the only method in many. Reproduction involves division (fission) of the body and is usually preceded or accompanied by nuclear division. The most common asexual method is simple binary fission that is usually mitotic (i.e., involving precise chromosome distribution) and may be transverse, longitudinal, or oblique (Fig. 2-5). There are variant forms of fission. Ordinary binary fission results in two daughter cells about equal in size; budding, in organisms unequal in size; plasmotomy, division of multinucleate forms into multinucleate progeny without division of nuclei; and schizogony (multiple fission), formation of a number of uninucleate buds from a multinuclear parent. Some organelles may be self-reproducing, such as blepharoplasts of flagella, basal granules (kinetosomes) of cilia, and parabasal bodies of trypanosomes.

Sexual reproduction is found in some protozoans and includes such processes as syngamy, conjugation, and autogamy. Syngamy involves the fusion of two gametes that may be similar (isogametes) or dimorphic (anisogametes). This process usually involves meiosis, which may occur in the formation of the gametes or after their fusion (postzygotic). Conjugation is an exchange of gametic nuclei between two animals that adhere together temporarily, followed by about three divisions of the micronucleus (Fig. 2-44). In conjugation a zygote nucleus, or synkaryon, is formed in each conjugant. Autogamy is more restricted than conjugation and involves similar nuclear behavior except that there is no exchange of gametic nuclei. Instead there is a fusion of gametic nuclei in the same individual that produces the gametes.

The life cycle of protozoans, which may be very complex, often involves encystment at some stage (Fig. 2-6). The process varies greatly among the protozoans and is absent in a few species. In general, encystment involves an accumulation of reserve food, loss of water, a rounding up of the organism, dedifferentiation and loss of organelles, and a secretion of an enclosing wall of chitin, mineral salts, keratin, or

Fig. 2-6

Some protozoan cysts.

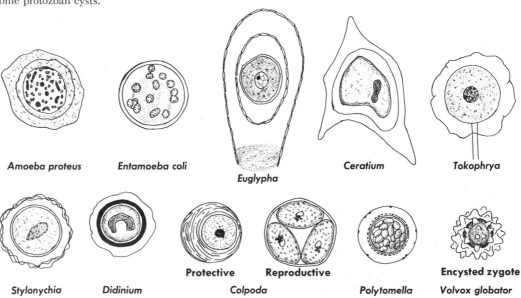

Amoeba proteus   Entamoeba coli   Euglypha   Ceratium   Tokophrya

Stylonychia   Didinium   Protective   Reproductive   Polytomella   Encysted zygote
                           Colpoda   Volvox globator

other materials. Cysts vary greatly in form. Encystment has many advantages, such as providing the protozoan with protection against desiccation, extreme temperatures, and harsh environmental factors and with increase in longevity, widespread distribution, etc. Some cysts survive for years. Reproductive phases, such as fission, budding, and syngamy, may occur in the cysts of some species. No encystment has been found in *Paramecium*, and it is rare or absent in marine forms.

CLASS MASTIGOPHORA

The class Mastigophora is made up of members that bear at some stage (usually the adult stage) one or more flagella. They represent a large heterogeneous assemblage of species and are regarded as being closer to the primitive ancestral stock of acellular forms than any other protozoan class. Often they are regarded as a sort of connecting link between animals and algae. Of all protozoans they have the most varied characteristics of size range, life cycles, types of reproduction, modes of living, and types of nutrition. Many are free living, but others are parasitic. They have a widespread distribution, and some can exist in regions devoid of other forms of life if physical conditions are not too harsh. Stagnant pools contain them wherever carbon dioxide is abundant. They are the most abundant members of both freshwater and marine plankton. A few species can live in both fresh water and sea water if the transfer is gradual. Most of them are solitary and free swimming, others are sessile and stalked, and others form colonies of varied structures and relationships.

The Mastigophora may be divided into two subdivisions or subclasses, the Phytomastigina and the Zoomastigina. Members of the former are often referred to as the phytoflagellates or plantlike forms, and those of the latter as the zooflagellates or animallike forms. The principal differences between the two groups are their manners of nutrition and reproduction. Phytoflagellates mostly have chromatophores that contain the chlorophyll necessary for photosynthesis, and their nutrition is holophytic. Starch or paramylum is their chief anabolic food product. Zooflagellates lack chromatophores, and they have animal

starch or glycogen. Their nutrition is either holozoic or saprozoic. Some phytoflagellates also have sexual stages that are lacking in nearly all zooflagellates. Phytoflagellates, moreover, are usually provided with a pellicle or cellulose cell wall and rarely have more than two flagella. It is thought that zooflagellates have been derived from phytoflagellates by the loss of pigment in the latter.

In the evolution of the flagellates it seems that the loss of chlorophyll was one of the first changes, followed by changes to a saprozoic, holozoic, or symbiotic method of nutrition. Colorless heterotrophs occurred frequently by loss of plastids. Actually, such changes can be produced by artificial methods—for example, the production of colorless euglenas by treatment with streptomycin. Present primitive zooflagellates are usually free living, holozoic, and resemble colorless flagellate algae. The collared flagellate *Protospongia* (order Protomonadina), for instance, resembles certain flagellate algae and is of interest because of its possible affinity with the sponges. The evolutionary trend among the zooflagellates has been toward a parasitic life, some possessing complex life histories. Although most of the small primitive members of this group have only one or two flagella, some of the highly specialized symbiotic species have hundreds of flagella attached to ribbon-shaped kinetosomes—e.g., *Trichonympha*, the symbiont of termites.

Colony formation is another trend in the Mastigophora. Some are simple aggregates of nonmotile cells in a gelatinous matrix; others are free swimming and are composed of hundreds and even thousands of cells. These larger colonies show some differentiation into somatic and reproductive cells, such as in *Volvox*. Colonial forms may be spherical, flattened, linear, tubular, dendroid, etc. Some are compact colonies and resemble certain stages in the embryology of the Metazoa. Certain authorities suggest that ancestral protozoans were similar to the simpler flagellates of the present time and gave rise on the one hand to algae and higher plants and on the other hand to colorless flagellates, sarcodinians, and other protozoans. The relationship between flagellates and the Sarcodina must be a close one, because some flagellates lose their

37

flagella and become wholly ameboid in their movements.

General features

The most common feature of mastigophorans is the presence of one or more flagella, although this organelle is absent in a few of them. The form of these animals may be oval, spherical, elongated, etc., usually with definite anterior and posterior ends. Only a cell membrane or a very thin pellicle is present in those that have free ameboid movement or can change their body shape. Many, however, have firm pellicles that may be ridged in various ways. In addition, calcareous or siliceous shells and armors of considerable variety are common in the group. Differentiation between ectoplasm and endoplasm is usually not distinct. Some species have a pit or groove (cytopharynx) at the anterior end that serves as the insertion of the flagella but is probably not for food intake. Chromatophores or chloroplasts of various shapes are found in the colored species. The chromatophore may consist only of chlorophyll, which may be hidden by red, brown, or other pigments. Hematochrome, a reddish pigment, may be scattered through the cytoplasm. It may shield the chromatophores from certain rays, and it is often concentrated in the cup forming the stigma or eyespot of some species. Pyrenoids, the protein bodies concerned with starch formation, are found in association with the chloroplasts.

Contractile vacuoles are found in many flagellates, especially freshwater forms. The contractile vacuole is usually formed by the fusion of small vacuoles and discharges into the cytopharynx, or reservoir, if one is present.

In some dinoflagellates there are nematocysts, similar to those in coelenterates, and also trichocysts, the organelles so common among ciliates.

Most flagellates have a single nucleus, but a few (e.g., *Giardia*) have two. The nucleus may have an endosome (karyosome) and may be quite large in some species and small in others.

Locomotion

The typical flagellum is made up of a longitudinal axoneme enclosed in a sheath. The electron microscope reveals that the axoneme is made up of a bundle of 11 fine fibrils, two of which are central; nine are present in a ring around the other two (Fig. 2-1). The fibrils are enclosed in a spiral sheath continuous with the cell membrane. The nine outer fibrils may each be made up of two or more finer fibrils. In some flagella, by special preparations, numerous small lateral mastigonemes, which may increase the flagellar surface in movement, can be seen extending from the flagellar sheath. The flagellum originates from the blepharoplast (kinetosome), a kind of basal granule just inside the pellicle that seems to be essential for the movement of both flagella and cilia. The blepharoplast may function as a centriole in cell division, but in other cases there may be a separate centriole fused to the nuclear membrane. The blepharoplast appears to have genetic continuity and is connected to the centriole by a filament, the rhizoplast (Fig. 2-13). Some flagellates also have one or more parabasal bodies, which vary in shape and are connected by fine fibrils to the blepharoplast. Another body found in trypanosomes and some other flagellates is the kinetoplast, which is connected to the blepharoplast. The functions of parabasal bodies and kinetoplasts are obscure at present.

The mechanism of flagellar movement is not yet fully understood. Its method of use is not the same in all flagellates. An early theory (Bütschli) emphasized a spiral turning of the flagellum like a propeller, serving to pull the organism forward. The undulating motion necessary for this action passes from the base to the top of the flagellum, and spiral rotation of the body ordinarily occurs along with the flagellar action. Some flagellates have a rowing stroke in which the flagellum is held rigid and concave in the direction of the stroke. It then bends back like a cilium when it recovers its position, so that it offers less resistance to the water.

Most flagellates have one to four flagella, although the symbionts of termites may have hundreds. They may have various functions, such as steering, anchoring, pushing, or pulling. The undulating membrane of some parasitic species has a border formed from a flagellum. Flagella may originate from almost any part of the body—anterior end (most common), posterior end, lateral surface, or cytopharynx.

Nutrition

The Mastigophora make use of every type of nutrition except chemosynthesis. The chlorophyll-bearing flagellates are almost entirely holophytic, while the colorless forms may be saprozoic or holozoic or both. Some species may use all three types of nutrition *(Ochromonas)*. *Euglena gracilis* is holophytic in the light but saprozoic in the dark. Ameboid phases of flagellates engulf their food much like the Sarcodina. In most cases holozoic flagellates ingest their food at the anterior end near the base of the flagellum by a mouth (cytopharynx), or some kind of depression. Internal skeletal rods (trichites) may reinforce the mouth and gullet, although this type of internal skeleton is far more common in ciliates.

Precise experimental investigation on the nutritional requirements of protozoans seems to show that these requirements are simpler for flagellates than for any other protozoan group. This is especially the case with the chlorophyll-bearing forms. In those that have lost their plastids, food requirements are more exacting (S. H. Hutner and L. Provasoli, 1951). It is apparent that in the evolution of microorganisms the primitive, simple plantlike protozoans can synthesize their proteins with nitrates; some colorless (saprozoic) species require ammonium salts, and other colorless flagellates require amino acids and peptones. Thus there has been a physiologic loss of function along with morphologic evolution (W. H. Johnson, 1941).

Life cycle and reproduction

Most flagellates reproduce asexually by longitudinal division. In dinoflagellates, fission is transverse or oblique. Mitotic processes vary greatly within the group. Sexual reproduction is mainly restricted to some of the phytoflagellates and complex polymastigotes. In their life cycle there is usually a cyst stage. Multiplication may also occur by multiple fission and, in some, reproduction may take place within the cyst. Multiple fission is most common

in the trypanosomes and dinoflagellates.

Binary fission usually begins with the division of the basal body or a centriole. The fate of the flagella is not the same in all species at binary fission. In some they may be lost entirely and new ones may be regenerated in the daughter cells. When there is only one or a few flagella, each flagellum may split longitudinally (rare) or, more commonly, a second flagellum grows out from the basal body, which divides in fission. In multiflagellate forms the flagella are distributed in approximately equal numbers to each daughter cell, each of which then regenerates new flagella from basal granules to complete its normal number. In armored species at cell division the theca may be divided between the daughter cells, or one cell may receive the whole theca, and the naked cell regenerates a new one. Sometimes the theca is lost entirely, and the daughter cells have to regenerate new ones. A spindle is formed within the nucleus in some cases, with the halves of the basal body acting as centrioles if the latter are lacking. In other cases in place of a spindle there may be only a strand connecting the centrioles. Usually the dividing mechanism (spindle and centrioles) as well as the chromosomes develop from the endosome. There are some variations of this plan. Chromosomes are usually constant for a particular species and behave as chromosomes do in other forms. The division of the nucleus is followed by that of the cytopharynx (if present), and the organism divides posteriorly from the anterior tip. In some dinoflagellates, fission is incomplete resulting in a chain of individuals, e.g., *Ceratium* (Fig. 2-5). Mitosis in termite flagellates has been extensively studied by L. R. Cleveland.

In those flagellates that have sexual reproduction, the gametes may be morphologically alike (isogametes), or they may be unlike (anisogametes). In the latter case microgametes (small and motile) and macrogametes (large and nonmotile) are recognized. The sexual fusion of two gametes is called syngamy. The phytomonac genus *Chlamydomonas* is a good example of isogamy, although some of its species have heterogamy. *Volvox* in its varied reproduction produces both eggs and sperm and is an example of heterogamy. Meiosis

A

B

Fig. 2-7

A, *Dinobryon sertularia* (order Chrysomonadida); each cell is enclosed in vaselike test, bears two unequal flagella, and usually has two lateral yellow-brown chromatophores; cells are 30 to 40 microns long. **B,** *Chilomonas paramecium* (order Cryptomonadina); lacks chloroplasts; has trichocysts at base of cytopharynx; oval bodies are starch grains; widely used in nutritional studies; 20 to 40 microns long.

among flagellates may be prezygotic or postzygotic.

The life cycle varies among the different flagellates. Cyst formation is common with many of them, especially among the holozoic species. It is not found in the chlorophyll-bearing species to any extent. Stages in the same life cycle may show polymorphism, in which individuals show distinct differences from each other. Intracystic formation, in which secondary cysts are formed inside of primary ones, may also occur, especially in dinoflagellates. Palmella, or ameboid stages, in which individuals lose their flagella and become balllike, are found in the life history of many flagellates, especially dinoflagellates. By fission this stage sometimes forms a colony-like aggregation in a matrix of mucus and may remain in this condition for some time.

Subclass Phytomastigina

The subclass Phytomastigina is made up of the plantlike flagellates, or phytoflagellates. Most of them are characterized by bearing chromatophores of various pigments, such as chlorophyll, carotin, and xanthophyll, although some may lack chloroplasts (*Chilomonas*, Fig. 2-7, *B*). These pigments may be represented in most colored species but in different proportions, so that chloroplasts (green chromatophores) contain more of the chlorophyll; and xanthoplasts (yellow chromatophores) have more of the xanthophyll than of other kinds (*Dinobryon*, Fig. 2-7, *A*). However, some chromatophores may consist entirely of chlorophyll, as in members of the Euglenida and Phytomonadida. Those that have chlorophyll can make their food by photosynthesis and are nutritionally independent except for a few outside requirements (salts and vitamins).

This subclass is no doubt made up of the most primitive members in the class Protozoa and bears a close relationship to algae. As a group the members display a great range of structure and physiology. Many are solitary, but others are colonial. Although most possess flagella, some are nonflagellated or ameboid at some stage or throughout their existence. The green phytoflagellates are almost always autotrophic, but others have saprozoic and

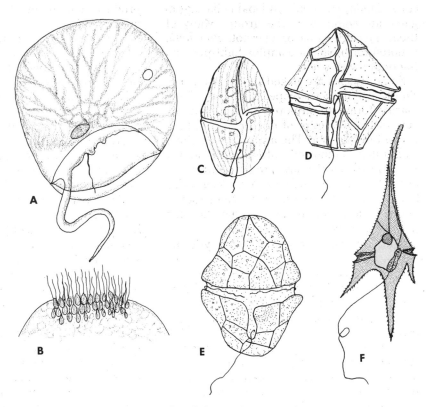

Fig. 2-8

Order Dinoflagellida. **A,** *Noctiluca scintillans;* noted for phosphorescence in sea; 200 to 2,000 microns long. **B,** *N. scintillans* budding; buds become isogametes that fuse in pairs to form zygotes. **C,** *Gymnodinium costatum;* typical unarmored dinoflagellate; related species *G. brevis* causes certain "red tides." **D,** *Gonyaulax;* responsible for "red tides" off California coast; 50 microns long. **E,** *Glenodinium cinctum,* with both epitheca (anterior to girdle) and hypotheca (posterior to girdle) made up of plates; 45 microns long. **F,** *Ceratium hirudinella;* has one apical and two or three basal horns; many varieties, depending upon depth of water in which they are found; 95 to 700 microns long.

holozoic nutrition. Some members are symbionts in other organisms.

Phytoflagellates have a wide distribution in both fresh and salt water. Green flagellates make up one of the most important members of plankton. They are abundant in some stagnant pools and ponds. Except in the cyst form they require moisture of some kind in order to exist. They also form important food chains for many other organisms. A few may be parasitic, such as certain ectoparasitic dinoflagellates on the gills of fishes and other forms.

As type forms in this subclass, we shall select members of three common orders, Dinoflagellida, Euglenida, and Phytomonadida. A study of these three orders will give a fair conception of the range of organization in this subclass.

Order Dinoflagellida

The dinoflagellates represent an unusual group of protozoans that are found primarily in marine water, although some species occur in fresh water. Some have chro-

matophores of various colors, and others are colorless. Their chief characteristic is the arrangement of the two flagella, one of which usually runs in an encircling groove transverse to the body axis and the other in a longitudinal groove directed backward for propelling the animal. The transverse flagellum causes the organism to rotate. Dinoflagellates are usually of fixed shapes and bizarre forms (Fig. 2-8). The encircling groove, or girdle, divides the animal into two parts—the epicone and the hypo-

41

cone. Chain, ameboid, and palmella aggregates are common in the group. Many of them have a stigma or eyespot. *Pouchetia* is noted for having a complex light-perceiving organ with a lens.

Some species are naked or enclosed in a simple cellulose envelope, but most of the marine forms are armored with a cellulose coat of two valves or of one or many plates cemented together. The armor is sometimes elaborately embossed, often with spines. Unarmored species are often brightly colored. Some, too, such as *Noctiluca* (Fig. 2-8, *A*) are phosphorescent. Nematocysts and trichocysts are found as organelles in a number of species.

Most dinoflagellates have holophytic nutrition, but the colorless ones may be ameboid and holozoic. Some may entrap their prey by branched pseudopodia extruding through theca pores. Some are ectoparasitic or endoparasitic in a nonflagellate encysted condition.

One of their characteristic structures is the pusule system organelle, which consists of vacuoles connected by canals to the exterior. The system is noncontractile and may serve for the intake of fluid. Two of these organelles may be present, one connected to each flagellar orifice. The exact function of the pusule system is unknown.

Reproduction is by oblique or transverse binary fission (Fig. 2-5, *H*). Usually each daughter cell receives part of the armor and secretes the remaining part, but in some cases the entire armor is lost. There may be multiple fission in the encysted condition. Encystment is rare among clorophyll-bearing species. Little is known about sexual stages in dinoflagellates, although they may occur.

Dinoflagellates are mostly free living and have a wide distribution. They make up much of the plankton in both fresh and marine water. One of the most common species is *Ceratium* (Fig. 2-8, *F*), which bears three long spines. Its species are found in both fresh and salt water. In fresh water its chromatophores are usually green.

Sometimes certain marine species of dinoflagellates appear in enormous numbers (up to 25,000,000 to 50,000,000 per liter) and produce the "red tides" off the coasts of many regions, especially Florida and southern California. These organisms produce a toxin highly fatal to fishes and other marine life. The toxin produces its injurious effect upon the nervous system. The genus *Gonyaulax* (Fig. 2-8, *D*) is mainly responsible for the California outbreaks and the genus *Gymnodinium* (Fig. 2-8, *C*) for those in Florida.

Order Phytomonadida

Protozoans of the order Phytomonadida are mostly grass green, but a few are colorless. This is a large group of about one hundred genera, and they closely resemble typical plants. Two flagella are found in most, although some have more and a few have only one. Unicellular species are more common than the colonial forms. Their size is small and their body is usually oval or elongated and enclosed in a cellulose membrane. There is no gullet. Their chlorophyll is the same as that of higher plants, and their pyrenoids have starch as the reserve material. They are provided with a stigma and two contractile vacuoles. Some are stained red with the pigment hematochrome. Their nutrition is chiefly holophytic although some are mixotrophic. Colorless species are saprozoic. Reproduction is asexual (longitudinal fission) and sexual. Encystment and palmella stages are common in many species. The central nucleus divides mitotically with typical chromosome behavior.

Colonial Phytomonadida may be irregularly flat or spherical. Most colonies have 4 to 128 cells, but some species of *Volvox* may have several thousands. Individual zooids in a colony typically have two flagella and have most of the other structures found in solitary species. The zooids may be loosely connected, but they are chiefly held together in a common cellulose membrane or embedded in a mucilaginous jelly. Familiar genera of colonial species are *Gonium* (4 to 16 cells, Fig. 2-9, *A*, *B*), *Pandorina* (16 cells, Fig. 2-9, *C*), *Eudorina* (32 cells), and *Pleodorina* (32 to 128 cells, Fig. 2-9, *D*). In all of these except *Pleodorina*, each zooid is capable of both asexual and sexual reproduction. The zooids at the anterior pole of *Pleodorina* are sterile. Asexual reproduction takes place by the repeated fission of each zooid to form a colony, which is set free by the rupture of the parent. Sexual reproduction

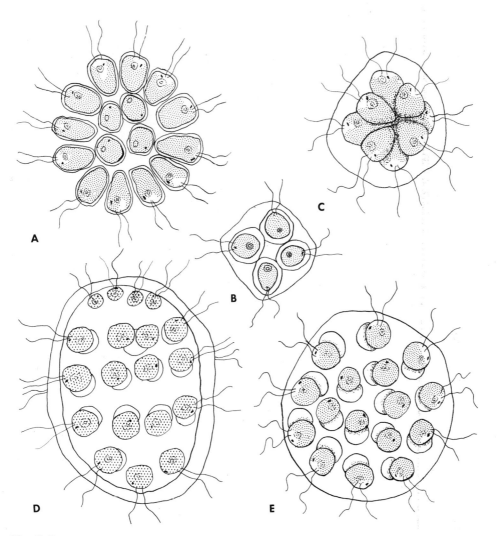

Fig. 2-9

Order Phytomonadida. **A,** *Gonium pectorale;* usually 16 zooids; fresh water; colony up to 90 microns in diameter. **B,** *Gonium sociale;* four zooids; each may give rise to daughter colony by cell division, or each may serve as isogamete; fresh water; cells 10 to 22 microns long. **C,** *Pandorina morum;* 16 cells; each cell divides four times to form new colony; colony 20 to 50 microns or more in diameter. **D,** *Pleodorina illinoisensis;* four small anterior zooids sterile; other 28 zooids capable of both asexual and sexual reproduction; colony up to 450 microns in diameter. **E,** *Eudorina elegans;* 32 cells; each forms new colony; colony 40 to 150 microns in diameter.

may occur by the zooids becoming free and serving as gametes, or gametes may be formed by fission of the zooids. The gametes may be isogamous or anisogamous. After encystment the zygote becomes a free flagellate that divides to form a colony, or the zygote may hatch directly into a small colony.

The most striking colonial form is the genus *Volvox.* The most familiar species is *Volvox globator* (Fig. 2-10). It is a hollow sphere about 1.3 mm. in diameter with many thousands of biflagellate zooids. The zooids are embedded in a gelatinous matrix, and adjacent cells have cytoplasmic connections between them (Fig. 2-11). The cells in these colonies are always green, with the exception of the sexually differen-

43

Fig. 2-10

Volvox colonies (order Phytomonadida); 1,000 to 3,000 cells in hollow ball; 350 to 500 microns in diameter.

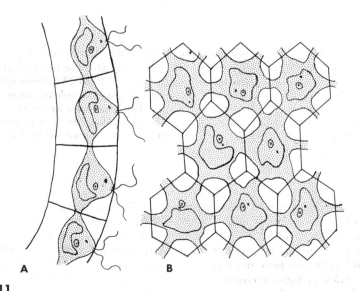

A   B

Fig. 2-11

Portion of colony of *Volvox globator* (order Phytomonadida) showing protoplasmic connections between zooids. **A,** Side view. **B,** Surface view.

tiated cells. The majority of the zooids each has a pair of flagella, a stigma, and chromatophores. Some zooids are gonidia that form new colonies asexually by multiple fission. These colonies remain in the hollow of the parent colony until set free. Other zooids enlarge to form macrogametes or eggs, and others, by repeated division, produce small biflagellate microgametes or sperm. Eggs are liberated into the hollow colony where they are fertilized by the sperm to form zygotes with thick, spiny shells. The zygotes eventually hatch into new colonies. *Volvox globator* is monoecious, and male, female, and asexual reproductive zooids are found in the same colony; but in some species the sexes are separate (dioecious).

Order Euglenida

The order Euglenida is made up of forms that usually show an anteroposterior elongation with a definite shape (Fig. 2-12). The pellicle, often ridged or striated, may be soft enough for contortions or too rigid for change of shape. Euglenida have one or two flagella, which may be equal or unequal in length. A stigma of red hematochrome granules is found at one side of the cytopharynx, but the stigma is absent in colorless species. Many species have green chromatophores (never masked by other pigments), which may be irregular, circular, or stellate in shape. Hematochrome is found in a few. Pyrenoids are sometimes associated with the chromatophores, and their reserved food supply is paramylum (a starchlike polysaccharide), which is stored in definite bodies. A cytostome and cytopharynx (gullet), from which the flagellum or flagella emerge, is present at the anterior end. In holophytic forms the gullet is not concerned with obtaining food but serves as a passageway for fluid or waste and for the flagella, which are usually attached to its wall by two roots. In holozoic species the cytostome and gullet serve for food intake as well (Fig. 2-13).

The lower part of the gullet widens into a reservoir, into which the large contractile vacuole discharges its contents. The contractile vacuole is formed each time after discharge by the fusion of many small vacuoles. Green members are almost entirely holophytic, but some absorb soluble

Fig. 2-12

Euglena viridis showing flagellum; 50 to 60 microns long. (Courtesy Ward's Natural Science Establishment, Inc., Rochester, N. Y.)

organic matter (saprozoic); most of them under certain conditions can become wholly saprozoic. The colorless species are holozoic or heterotrophic and live upon bacteria and other small organisms. Reproduction in the order occurs by asexual longitudinal fission in the free or encysted condition. Fission may occur in the cysts of some, producing palmella stages. Sexual reproduction has never been fully established, although a primitive form of such has been reported in one or two species.

Euglenida are widespread in almost all quiet surface waters, although the green species are found mostly in fresh water, where they form typical blooms.

This order takes its name from its most characteristic family, the Euglenidae. There are several species of *Euglena* (Figs. 2-12, 2-13), and they vary a great deal in structural features. The following are the most common species that one is likely to find in fresh water: *Euglena viridis* (60 mi-

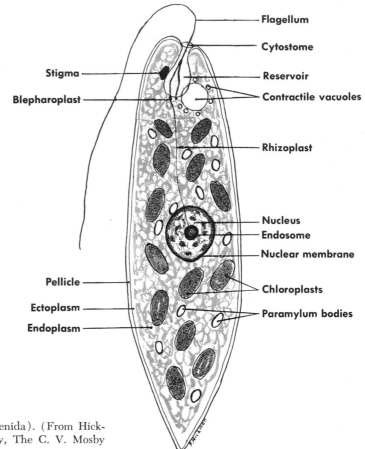

Fig. 2-13

Structure of *Euglena* sp. (order Euglenida). (From Hickman: Integrated principles of zoology, The C. V. Mosby Co.)

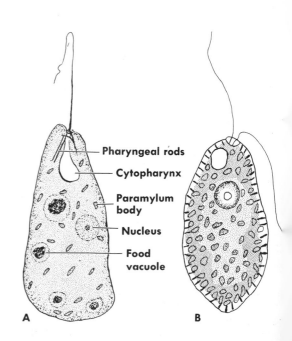

Fig. 2-14

A, *Peranema trichophorum* (order Euglenida); colorless euglenoid; one flagellum (not seen) is attached to pellicle; 20 to 70 microns long. **B**, *Vacuolaria virescens* (order Chloromonadida); nucleus large; many chromatophores; commonly found in acid bog waters but are poorly known; 50 to 150 microns long.

crons), with a spindle-shaped but plastic body and stellate arrangement of chromatophores from a central point; *Euglena spirogyra* (100 microns), with a cylindric but changeable body and spiral arrangement of tiny knobs; *Euglena oxyuris* (500 microns), with a very large body and spirally twisted pellicle; *Euglena gracilis* (50 microns), with an elongated oval body and fusiform chromatophores; and *Euglena rubra* (35 microns), with a cylindric body and numerous red hematochrome granules.

Of the colorless members of the order, one of the most familiar is the genus *Peranema* (Fig. 2-14, *A*), which has an elongated body with a more or less truncated posterior end and long tapering flagellum. Two rods near the reservoir are used in the ingestion of prey. It occurs very commonly and has been much used in experimental nutrition studies.

The rarely found members of the order Chloromonadida (Fig. 2-14, *B*) bear a superficial resemblance to the Euglenida.

Subclass Zoomastigina

The Zoomastigina lack chromatophores and vary in their organization from simple to complex. They do not possess starch bodies or paramylum, and they often have more than two flagella, but some have none. Some have pseudopodia as well as flagella. A parabasal body of debatable function is often present. Cells are usually naked or have delicate membranes; most are small. Many form colonies that show a variety of forms. Nutrition is holozoic, saprozoic, or parasitic. The Zoomastigina are found in both fresh and marine waters in both free-living and parasitic form. Asexual reproduction is by longitudinal fission; sexual reproduction is unknown. Encystment is common among them. Because of these and other characteristics these flagellates belong to the animal division of the Mastigophora.

This subclass may have arisen from the Phytomastigina by loss of chromatophores and by other changes. Some of the Phytomastigina show variations in color and nutrition not far removed from typical members of Zoomastigina.

The following orders and some of their members are of the most interest from the standpoint of this text.

Fig. 2-15

Trypanosoma gambiense (order Protomonadida) scattered among human red blood cells; carried by the tsetse fly; it causes African sleeping sickness; 22 microns long.

Order Protomonadida

The Protomonadida have one or two flagella, their body usually has no definite pellicle, and they are often ameboid. Free-living forms are holozoic, while the many parasitic species are saprozoic. In addition to longitudinal fission, multiple fission is found in some parasitic forms.

The trypanosome (genus *Trypanosoma*, Fig. 2-15) is a common parasite in the blood and fluids of vertebrates and is carried from host to host by bloodsucking invertebrates in which it undergoes a series of changes in its life history. *Trypanosoma gambiense* (or the similar *Trypanosoma rhodesiense*) causes the dreaded African sleeping sickness. Its vector is the tsetse fly (*Glossina*). The flagellate is elongated with pointed ends and a flagellum arising from a basal granule near the parabasal body. The basal portion of the flagellum forms the outer margin of the undulating membrane that runs along one side of the body. The parasites do their chief damage by invading the nervous system, resulting in lethargy, coma, and death. There are many other species of pathogenic or nonpathogenic trypanosomes that infect different species of vertebrates. One of these, *Trypanosoma lewisi*, is nonpathogenic in the rat and has been much studied. This flagellate undergoes multiple fission in the stomach of a

47

Fig. 2-16

Proterospongia (Protospongia), a colonial choanoflagellate;
by repeated division of one cell, spores are formed, each
of which may form new colony of 6 to 60 cells (order Protomonadida). (From Hickman: Integrated principles of
zoology, The C. V. Mosby Co.)

Fig. 2-17

Codosiga botrytis (order Protomonadida), a choanoflagellate. **A,** Colony. **B,** Single zooid; cells 10 to 22 microns
long.

flea and changes to trypanosome form before being discharged in the feces. Rats are
infected by licking their fur, where the
feces are deposited by fleas. Chagas' disease of man in the tropics is caused by
Trypanosoma cruzi, which is transmitted by
a bug *(Triatoma).* In this disease the heart
and skeletal muscles show swellings caused
by cystlike bodies of the parasites.

Another dangerous parasite of this order
is *Leishmania,* which is probably transmitted by sandflies *(Phlebotamus).* Stages
in the life history of the parasite are found
in both the vector and man, where it causes
kala-azar, a disease of the liver, spleen,
and related organs of the reticuloendo-
thelial system.

An interesting nonparasitic group of this
order is the choanoflagellates, which have
a thin protoplasmic collar around the base
of the single flagellum (Figs. 2-16, 2-17).
They include the colonial *Proterospongia*
(Protospongia, Fig. 2-16), which forms a
gelatinous mass with the flagellated collared membranes on the outside and ameboid individuals embedded in the interior.
Particles of food are attracted by the flagellum to the outside of the base of the collar, where they adhere and are transferred
to a vacuole in the protoplasm. This organism has been regarded as a possible
link between the unicellular protozoans and
the sponges because of the unique collared
cells (choanocytes) lining internal cavities
of the sponges. However, *Proterospongia*
may have no phylogenetic significance
(L. H. Hyman).

Order Hypermastigida

The members of the order Hypermastigida are the most complex flagellates, both
in their structure and modes of division.
They live in the alimentary canals of termites, cockroaches, and wood roaches,
where they often form a classic symbiotic
relationship between the host termite and
the flagellates. They have many flagella that
originate in the very complex blepharoplasts and related structures in the anterior
part of the body. Their method of nutrition is holozoic or saprozoic. Termites and
cockroaches eat wood, which is digested
for the host by the flagellates. Without their
flagellate symbionts, the host is unable to
utilize the wood diet and will die. The

flagellates benefit by obtaining food and lodging (L. R. Cleveland). At each molt the flagellates are shed by the termites. Reinfection occurs when recently molted individuals lick the anus of infected individuals (termite) or eat the cysts passed in the feces (roaches).

Trichonympha (Fig. 2-18) is the common genus of this order that is found in termites; *Lophomonas* is a genus that lives in the domestic cockroach.

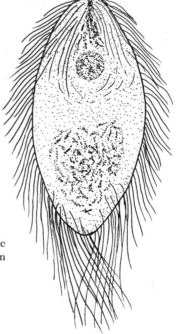

Fig. 2-18

Trichonympha agilis (order Hypermastigida), the classic symbiont of termites; 55 to 115 microns long. (Drawn from photograph of living trophozoite.)

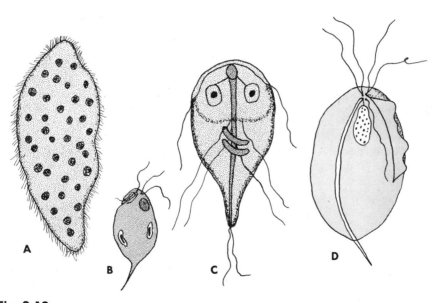

Fig. 2-19

A, *Opalina* sp. (order Opalinida); common parasite in gut of frogs and toads; 100 to 840 microns long. **B,** *Chilomastix mesnili* (order Polymastigida); commensal flagellate in human colon; related species found in other vertebrates; no clinical significance; trophozoite 10 to 15 microns long. **C,** *Giardia* (order Polymastigida); stained trophozoite is common intestinal parasite of man causing digestive disturbances and irritations; cysts common in feces. **D,** *Trichomonas vaginalis* (order Trichomonadida); common human parasite; may cause severe irritation in vagina and male urogenital tract; related species found in mouth and colon. (**C** modified from Jahn.)

Order Opalinida

Opalina (Fig. 2-19, *A*) is the most familiar member of the order Opalinida. It is found in the rectum of frogs and toads and is very common. Its nutrition is entirely saprozoic because it has no cytostome. It reproduces by binary fission and has many nuclei. Cysts are passed out of the host and are eaten by tadpoles in which they hatch to form anisogametes. After fusion of the gametes the zygote gives rise to the adult by nuclear division.

Until recently the taxonomic status of *Opalina* has been in doubt. It had always been classified among the ciliates but is now placed among the flagellates because its several nuclei appear to be all alike, and its plane of cell division is like that of flagellates, not ciliates (J. O. Corliss).

Members of the order Polymastigida (Fig. 2-19, *B*, *C*) are also found in the digestive tract of animals and elsewhere.

CLASS SARCODINA (RHIZOPODA)

The extensive protozoan class Sarcodina is chiefly characterized by ameboid movement that involves the formation of cytoplasmic extensions called pseudopodia, which are also used for food intake. Some sarcodinians at certain stages develop flagella. Most of them creep or float around, although a few are sessile. They have no pellicle or a very thin one, so that the body is plastic unless it is enclosed with a skeleton of some sort. They are mostly solitary or free living, but some are parasitic and colonial. In their phylogeny their affinities to the Mastigophora are evident because some flagellates have ameboid stages and some sarcodinians have flagellate stages or flagellate gametes. The flagellate order Rhizomastigida includes *Mastigamoeba*, which resembles amebas but also has a flagellum (Fig. 2-20).

The fossil record indicates that the sarcodinians are probably the oldest of protozoans because foraminiferan and radiolarian shells date back to Precambrian times. The only older fossils that have been found are those of algae and fungi.

Sarcodinians are found in both fresh and marine water. Many are almost exclusively freshwater forms, such as the shelled amebas, and others such as the radiolarians are exclusively marine. A number of species

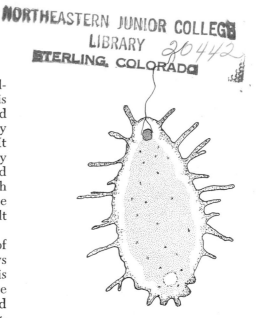

Fig. 2-20

Mastigamoeba aspera (order Rhizomastigida); often considered borderline form between flagellates and Sarcodina because they possess both flagella and pseudopodia; 150 to 200 microns long.

live in both salt and fresh water. The foraminiferans and radiolarians are plankton forms, and as they die their shells sink to the ocean floor to form the bottom ooze. Other members of this group are not restricted to the surface but live at considerable depths. Some species of amebas are able to live in moist surface soils.

The Sarcodina are divided into two subclasses—the Actinopoda, or those with axopodia (raylike pseudopodia with axial filaments), and Rhizopoda, or those that lack axopodia but have various types of pseudopodia, such as lobopodia, filopodia, and rhizopodia.

General features

The Sarcodina as a group show less organization in some particulars than the flagellates. For example, their shape is less definite and often without symmetry of any kind, although some may have spherical or other symmetry. Naked forms may change shape constantly because of temporary pseudopodia. Although a pellicle is poorly developed or absent altogether, the cytoplasm is usually differentiated into ectoplasm and endoplasm. In place of a specialized cuticle, shells, tests, and skeletons are secreted by the cytoplasm. These may contain silica and chitin strengthened by the addition of inorganic salts and foreign substances. Openings in the shells permit the extension of pseudopodia. Internal skeletons are present in radiolarians. The endoplasm contains the nucleus or nuclei, food vacuoles, granules, and contractile vacuoles. Most have only one nucleus, but some are multinucleated.

The protoplasmic extrusions (pseudopodia) represent one of the most characteristic features of this class. There are several types of pseudopodia, depending to some extent upon the order. The lobopodium type is broad and cylindric with rounded tips and composed of both ectoplasm and endoplasm; the ectoplasmic filopodium is slender with sharp tips; the rhizopodium is often much branched and forms extensive networks; and the axopodium type is usually straight and raylike with a central axial rod (axopodium).

Locomotion

The most characteristic locomotion of the class Sarcodina is ameboid movement. Although this form of locomotion typically belongs to the order Amoebida, nearly all sarcodinians use some modification of it. Ameboid movement is not the same in all amebas but varies from species to species. In some species there may be protoplasmic flow without the formation of typical pseudopodia. *Amoeba proteus* is often taken as the type example of ameboid locomotion. In this species the rigid pseudopodia may appear without restriction of size; in active movement the animal appears to flow into a pseudopodium, which appears to direct the locomotion. At present the theory that is most logical is based upon the view that the protoplasmic flow is dependent upon the sol-gel reversibility of the cytoplasm. The real driving force is the pressure exerted by the less fluid plasmagel, the external layer of cytoplasm. When this layer contracts in the formation of a pseudopodium, the more fluid inner plasmasol flows into that region where the pressure of the plasmagel is lessened. This movement causes the beginning pseudopodium at that point to protrude as the plasmasol flows into it. When the plasmasol reaches the tip of the pseudopodium, it tends to "fountain" back peripherally in places where it be-

comes a part of the plasmagel just under the pellicle. At the same time the plasmagel at the temporary posterior end is changing into plasmasol, which now flows anteriorly. Recent studies with the electron microscope fail to show any fibrillar structures that could account for protoplasmic streaming in the ameba, although ameboid movement is considered a type of contraction similar to muscle contraction. At the molecular level, however, the endoplasm is thought to contain long protein chains that undergo contraction.

There may be more than one mechanism of ameboid movement. The tail-contraction or Mast's theory just described is considered by some authorities to be too simple, and in its place a theory has been proposed that involves the pulling forward of the cytoplasm by a contraction force at the tips of the pseudopodia (front-contraction theory). Evidence indicates that the endoplasmic axial core has about the same viscosity as the ectoplasmic tube, instead of being much less as in Mast's theory. The chief regions of low viscosity and places where there is a rapid flow of cytoplasm are zones around the axial endoplasm and the region where the endoplasm is being formed from the posterior ectoplasm. Strands of freely movable cytoplasm move forward in the axial endoplasm to the anterior fountain zone where they diverge outward and join the ectoplasmic tube. The endoplasm anchored to the ectoplasmic tube contracts, everts, and pulls the axial endoplasm forward. Continuous streaming movements are kept up by the propagated contraction along the ectoplasm. The hyaline cap is formed from water squeezed from the endoplasm. This water eventually moves backward to the tail in the channel just beneath the plasmalemma.

Neither one of the foregoing mechanisms explains the reticulopodia formation of foraminiferans and radiolarians. Some workers have proposed an unknown active shearing force or antiparallel force to explain such movement. All streaming movements of the cell are at present poorly understood.

Nutrition

Nutrition in Sarcodina is holozoic, food consisting of almost any small organisms such as other protozoans, algae, bacteria,

51

diatoms, etc. There are no permanent organelles for food intake, which may occur at any region of the body. A pseudopodium forms a food cup by flowing around and enclosing the food object. The food vacuole so formed is engulfed or sucked into the cytoplasm. Engulfment of the prey may take place by two methods: (1) circumfluence, in which the encircling pseudopodium remains in close contact with the food, and (2) circumvallation, in which the pseudopodium by an enlarged cup surrounds not only the prey but also some water along with it. The first method is commonly employed by shelled forms with filopod pseudopodia, the second by naked amebas. Those with threadlike pseudopodia (axopodia and rhizopodia) such as foraminiferans and radiolarians capture their prey in a network arrangement. These pseudopodia produce a sticky and paralyzing substance that sticks to the prey. Intracellular digestion within the food vacuole occurs through enzymatic action.

Life cycle and reproduction

The Sarcodina show many types of life cycles. Asexual reproduction takes place by binary fission, which varies in the different groups. Sexual reproduction occurs in all the orders but is uncommon among naked amebas. Encystment occurs among some but is absent in others. The nucleus may be single or multiple.

Division is accompanied by true mitosis with spindle, chromosomes, and centrioles (usually). The number of chromosomes varies in those studied from a few to hundreds (*Amoeba dubia*). In most cases the nuclear membrane persists during cell division. Division is usually simpler in the naked Sarcodina than in the shelled species. In some shelled amebas the shell divides into two parts, and each daughter cell receives one part and forms a new half. *Arcella vulgaris*, which has two nuclei, at fission extrudes part of the cytoplasm and a nucleus through the shell aperture just before fission. The extruded cytoplasm secretes a new shell, and when the two-shelled animal divides, each daughter has a shell (Fig. 2-5, *B*). A variation of this fission is found in *Euglypha*, which has a test composed of secreted scales and spines. Before fission an individual stores up an

extra supply of these platelets, which are used to form a new test by the extruded cytoplasm (Fig. 2-5, *C*).

Life cycles are known for a few of the Foraminiferida. They have two phases, one asexual and the other sexual. There are also two types of individuals (dimorphic) in each species, based mainly upon the size of the initial chamber (proloculum) of the test. The megalospheric type (gamont) has a large proloculum, one nucleus, and is relatively small in size; the microspheric type (schizont) has a small proloculum, many nuclei, and is relatively large. This dimorphism results from a unique reproductive cycle in which the asexual and sexual generations alternate. In a typical life history (although there are some variations) a schizont or microspheric individual (Fig. 2-21, *A*) becomes multinucleated and by multiple fission (asexual phase) produces many small amebalike young, each of which secretes a megalospheric shell (Fig. 2-21, *B*) and becomes a gamont after escaping from the parent shell. Pairs of gamonts attach (Fig. 2-21, *C*), and in time the gamonts undergo sporulation and release many flagellated anisogametes (Fig. 2-21, *D*). These fuse in pairs (sexual phase) to form zygotes that develop into schizonts with microspheric shells (Fig. 2-21, *E*).

The life cycle of Heliozoida, or sun animalcules, is well known for certain genera, especially *Actinosphaerium* and *Actinophrys* (Fig. 2-22, *A*). These show some variations from other Sarcodina. Both asexual and sexual reproduction occur. In *Actinosphaerium*, which is multinucleated, the nuclei divide mitotically, and eventually the organism divides by plasmotomy to form two organisms. The sexual cycle at first involves the disintegration of most of the nuclei and the encystment of the organism. Within the cyst each nucleus with some cytoplasm forms a secondary cyst. Then each organism within a cyst divides into two daughter cells that undergo two typical maturation divisions to produce gametes, which unite to form the zygote. The latter, after a period of encystment, hatches into a young heliozoan that eventually acquires a multinuclear condition.

Life cycles of radiolarians are still obscure. It is known that asexual reproduction involves binary fission in which the

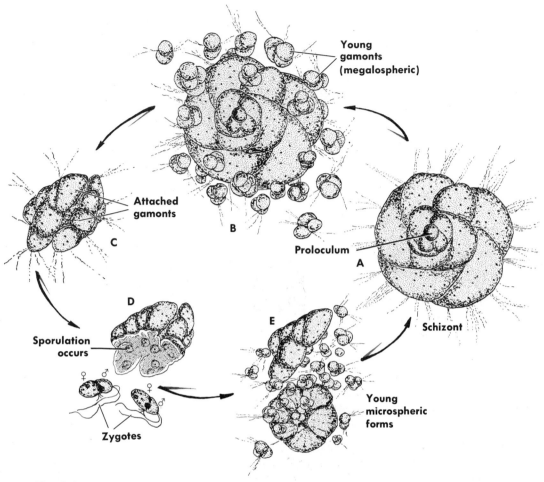

Fig. 2-21

Life cycle of *Discorbis* (order Foraminiferida); see text for description of stages. **A,** Schizont, or microspheric individual, produces by multiple fission (asexual) many amebalike forms that secrete megalospheric shells and become gamonts. **B,** Release of gamonts from parent schizont. **C,** Gamonts mature and pair. **D,** Attached gamonts produce biflagellated anisogametes that fuse in pairs (sexual) to form zygotes. **E,** Development of zygotes into schizonts with microspheric shells, each of which grows into mature schizont, **A.**

skeleton is divided, and the daughter cells each regenerate the missing half; or one daughter cell receives the whole skeleton, and the other daughter cell regenerates a new skeleton. True mitosis with hundreds of chromosomes is typical. In sexual reproduction, the occurrence of which is not completely known, flagellate microspores and macrospores may be produced, or they may be isospores. It is not known definitely whether or not these unite in sexual union.

Subclass Actinopoda
Order Helioflagellida

The Helioflagellida have both axopodia and flagella either at the same time or in one phase of a dimorphic cycle. It is not a large group but is found in both marine and fresh water. The group may throw some light on the phylogeny of the Actinopoda, indicating relationship with the Mastigophora. Many protozoologists assign certain of its genera, such as *Tetradimorpha*

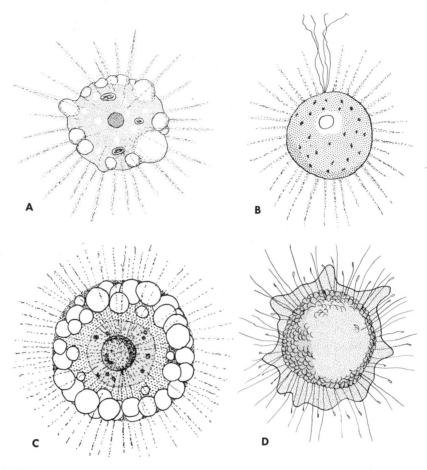

Fig. 2-22

A, *Actinophrys* (order Heliozoida); pseudopodia contain axial filaments (axopodia); this genus has no test, but many genera are provided with one; 40 to 50 microns in diameter. **B,** *Tetradi-morpha radiata* (order Helioflagellida); swimming stage; body 27 to 38 microns in diameter; flagella 38 to 57 microns long. **C,** *Thalassicolla nucleata* (order Radiolarida); has no skeleton but many radiating axopodia; 5 mm. in diameter. **D,** *Vampyrella lateritia* (order Proteomyxida); with filopodia it punctures cellulose walls of algae and sucks out contents; 30 to 40 microns in diameter.

(Fig. 2-22, *B*) and *Actinomonas*, to the Mastigophora.

Order Heliozoida

The members of the well-known order Heliozoida are characterized by having a more or less spherical form with radiating axopodia (Figs. 2-22 A, 2-24, A). These pseudopodia are usually characterized by having rows of granules along them. In some the axonemes of the axopodia converge on a central granule. The cytoplasm in some is differentiated into a highly vacuolated ecto-plasm with contractile vacuoles and a less transparent endoplasm with few granules. The inner and outer cytoplasm are not separated by a central capsule. Many of them have a siliceous skeleton or test; some have a one-piece test with pores through which the axopodia are extended. This test may have a latticelike arrangement with spicules. Some are enclosed by a gelatinous mantle in which spicules of silica and foreign objects are embedded. The nucleus may be single or multiple.

Heliozoidans are holozoic and live upon

small animals, which they trap with axopodia that are supposed to contain a paralyzing substance. The prey may be pulled back by the shortening of the axopodia, or the axial filaments may disappear and the pseudopodia surround the prey and carry it into the body. Most heliozoidans are found in fresh water in which they float, or they may roll in contact with a substratum by successive contractions of axopodia.

The most common genera are *Actinophrys* (Fig. 2-22, *A*), which has no skeleton and *Clathrulina,* which has a latticed test of tectin.

Order Radiolarida

The order Radiolarida is the oldest known group of animals and contains chiefly pelagic marine organisms. They are among the largest of protozoans, some of which may be several millimeters in diameter. The variations in the different species have centered around their skeleton (Fig. 2-23), which has undergone diversified

specializations. They have a central capsule enclosed by a central capsule membrane that separates the inner from the outer cytoplasm and is composed of chitin or tectin. It is usually spherical, ovoid, or lobate and is perforated for cytoplasmic continuity. The intracapsular part is concerned with reproduction; the extracapsular part, with nutrition and hydrostatic functions. Contractile vacuoles are not found. The extracapsular part, or calymma, consists of a mucilaginous substance that forms the walls of large vacuoles of fluid (Fig. 2-22, *C*). Pseudopodia are of the axopodium or filopodium type, but axonemes are not always present. Skeletal parts are composed of strontium sulfate or siliceous materials. Spines often radiate out from the center of the body through the central capsule (Fig. 2-24, *B*). Latticework test of spherical or other shapes is fused with the spines and lies at the surface of the body. In some species the rods and spines are outside the central capsule. Most types

Fig. 2-23
Types of radiolarian skeletons; note great variety of forms representing all symmetries. (Courtesy General Biological Supply House, Inc., Chicago.)

Fig. 2-24

A, *Actinosphaerium,* a heliozoan. B, *Tessaraspis,* a radiolarian from marine plankton. (From Encyclopaedia Britannica film, "Protozoa: One-Celled Animals.")

of symmetry are found in the group, as Haeckel long ago discovered.

The central capsule contains the nucleus and often many oil globules. Some species are multinucleated.

Radiolarians are chiefly holozoic, feeding upon small organisms, microplankton, etc. The food is caught by the pseudopodia and passed into the deeper regions of the cytoplasm for digestion. Some species have symbiotic zooxanthellae that may furnish the products of holophytic nutrition to the host.

Most species live within the upper 1,500 to 2,000 feet of the sea, although some have been found much deeper. When they die, their shells sink to the floor of the sea to form bottom sediments or ooze. Their shells can withstand greater pressures than those of the foraminiferans so that the ooze of the deepest oceans is largely made up of radiolarian shells.

Some authorities separate the order into two subdivisions. The term "Acantharia" is applied to those few with geometrically arranged spicules of strontium sulfate; the true "Radiolarida" is the term applied to those with an odd assortment of skeletons composed of other substances.

Subclass Rhizopoda
Order Proteomyxida

The members of the order Proteomyxida are poorly defined because they are not well known, and they show many variations. In some species the mature forms are plasmodia; in others they are ameboid uninucleate organisms. Their pseudopodia are filopodia, which usually anastomose to form branches. Their nearest relatives seem to be the Mycetozoida. Most of them are found as parasites on algae or other plants in either marine or fresh water. Some parasitize eel grass. The formation of a motile pseudopodium by the aggregation of individuals before encystment occurs in some. Asexual reproduction is by binary fission and multiple fission in the encysted condition, resulting in biflagellate swarmers. Gametes and zygotes are produced in the life cycle of some members. Filamentous tracks along which the individuals glide are often secreted.

Some common genera are *Vampyrella* (Fig. 2-22, *D*), *Pseudospora,* and *Biomyxa.*

Order Mycetozoida

Organisms of the order Mycetozoida are commonly called slime molds and show a remarkable resemblance to fungi, because they put forth sporangia with spores. They seem to exist on the borderline between Protozoa and Protophyta, and they have been the subject of intensive investigation by J. T. Bonner in recent years because of their interesting life history and primitive nature. Three or four subgroups are recognized in this order, each of which apparently has a different ancestry. It has been suggested that they evolved from soil amebas. They resemble plants in having cellulose walls, and they are like amebas in having ameboid stages and similar methods of ingesting food. They are holozoic or saprozoic in their nutrition. They have contractile vacuoles and often have pigments of various colors. Most are free living, but some are parasites of plants. Most of them live on decaying vegetable matter, an old rotten log in moist surroundings being a favorite locality. In their mature stages they are either a plasmodium (Fig. 2-25, *A*) or a pseudoplasmodium. Streaming movements to and away from the periphery are found in the plasmodia. Under dry or other unfavorable climatic conditions the plasmodium divides into cysts, each with a dozen or so nuclei and surrounded by a wall (sclerotium, Fig. 2-25, *B*). When revived, the contents of the cyst fuse and produce plasmodia. Lack of food causes the plasmodium to develop sporangia from lobular masses (Fig. 2-25, *C*, *D*). The walls of the sporangia reach down to the substratum, where they may spread out as networks that serve as supporting structures. Spores are formed in the sporangia by mitosis and become covered with a cellulose membrane. When the spor-

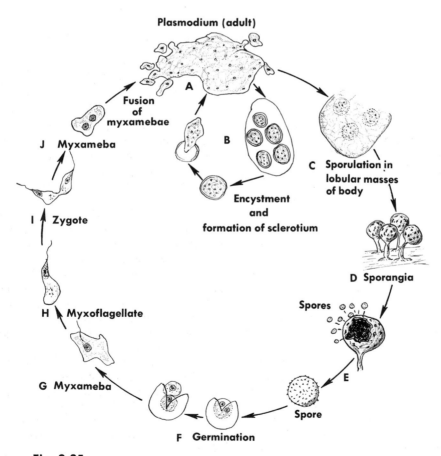

Fig. 2-25

Life history of mycetozoan such as *Physarum* sp. See text for description.

Fig. 2-26

Sporangium of *Arcyria denudata* (order Mycetozoida); fibrous network (capillitium) bearing spores is supported by cuplike base on stalk. On left, sporangium wall has broken and capillitium is expanded; sporangia are 2 to 3 mm. high.

angia disintegrate, the spores are scattered by the wind (Figs. 2-25, *E,* 2-26). Spores germinate into myxamebae, which undergo ameboid movement and later form myxoflagellates or swarmers (Fig. 2-25, *F* to *H*). Myxoflagellates may serve as gametes and undergo syngamy to form ameboid zygotes, or they may feed, grow, multiply by binary fission, and encyst. In either case they eventually form myxamebae (Fig. 2-25, *I, J*) that by growth and nuclear division produce a small plasmodium. Fusion of these plasmodia may produce the large plasmodia.

In the Acrasina, or cellular slime molds, the small myxamebae may exist as solitary individuals feeding and undergoing binary fission. Sometimes they aggregate (possibly under the influence of acrasin or evocator secreted by certain myxamebae) and form a pseudoplasmodium in which there is no protoplasmic fusion. This pseudoplasmodium can move as a unit and may increase in size by fission of its amebas. Eventually the pseudoplasmodium assumes an upright condition and forms a pseudosporangium with base, stalk, and spores. Sexual reproduction does not occur.

Order Amoebida

The members of the order Amoebida are considered the most characteristic and the best known in the class Sarcodina. Their size varies from tiny forms of 3 to 4 microns diameter to the large members of 3 mm. diameter. They typically form lobopodia, which display ameboid movement involving a flow of protoplasm. In some there may be protoplasmic movement without the formation of pseudopodia. Their shape is irregular and constantly changing. They may have a delicate pellicle, although there is little cortical differentiation. The ectoplasm is hyaline, while the endoplasm is granular. Both these layers are usually found in the pseudopodia. A flagellate stage may be found in some dimorphic species (soil amebas), but most have a monomorphic life cycle. Binary fission is the common method of reproduction, although multiple fission may also occur. Their nuclear division is mitotic with spindles and chromosomes. The spindle is often intranuclear. Sexual reproduction is doubtful. Encystment is common. Contractile vacuoles are present in freshwater species but are mainly absent from marine and parasitic forms.

Amebas are found in all kinds of fresh, salt, and brackish waters, in most soil, and in the digestive tracts of invertebrates and vertebrates.

The order is divided by some authorities into three groups or families. Family Dimastigamoebidae includes in their life history a dominant ameboid stage, a transitory biflagellate stage, and a cyst. This family includes the soil amebas, fecal amebas, and some others. Under certain conditions the ameboid phase may be transformed into the flagellate phase. *Naegleria,* or *Dimastigamoeba,* is the best known genus.

Family Amoebidae includes the familiar genus *Amoeba* of several species. They are free living and are monomorphic in their life history. A single contractile vacuole is found. They are mostly naked but may have a delicate pellicle. The various species differ with respect to type of pseudopodia. *Amoeba proteus* (Fig. 2-27), which may reach a diameter of 600 microns, has large lobopodia with longitudinal ridges and a disk-shaped biconcave nucleus. In its endoplasm are many truncate or other shaped crystals. *Amoeba dubia* is another familiar species and is somewhat smaller than *Amoeba proteus.* It usually has many lobopodia with smooth surfaces and an oval nucleus. Its few endoplasmic crystals are large (of different types), and it may have more than one contractile vacuole. Other species one may encounter in cultures are *Amoeba discoides* with few smooth pseudopodia, often confused with *Amoeba proteus; Amoeba (Thecamoeba) verrucosa* with short, blunt pseudopodia and wrinkled body surface; and *Amoeba limax* with no definite pseudopodia and rounded body. The very large amebas are represented by the genus *Pelomyxa* (Fig. 2-28), formerly and often still called *Chaos*, which reaches a size of 3 to 5 mm. and can easily be seen with the naked eye. *Pelomyxa carolinensis* moves by means of pseudopodia, as does *Amoeba proteus; Pelomyxa palustris* moves by protoplasmic waves and with little change in shape.

The third family of amebas is the Endamoebidae, which are parasitic or endocommensal in the digestive tracts of invertebrates and vertebrates. One or two are highly pathogenic. There are two genera often confused because of similarity of spelling: *Endamoeba* is the genus found in cockroaches and termites; *Entamoeba* is the one commonly found in vertebrates. *Entamoeba coli* is found in the intestine of man and monkeys. This species is small with blunt and granular pseudopodia. Mature cysts contain eight nuclei. It may be considered a commensal, but heavy infections result in gastrointestinal disturbances. *Entamoeba gingivalis* is a species living in the mouth. The most harmful member of this genus is *Entamoeba histolytica* (Fig. 2-29), which produces amebiasis or amebic dysentery in man. In its life history the trophozoite, which is about 20 to 40 microns in diameter, lives on the intestinal tissues and blood of man causing ulceration of the colon. By binary fission the trophozoite gives rise to small precystic stages that eventually form a cyst (5 to 20 microns diameter) with four nuclei. Dysenteric feces may contain trophozoites, but normal feces

Fig. 2-27

Amoeba proteus (order Amoebida); animal is preparing to extend three new pseudopodia to the left.

Fig. 2-28

Comparison in size of *Pelomyxa* (1 to 5 mm. long) and *Amoeba proteus* (up to 600 microns long); several paramecia are also shown. (Courtesy Carolina Biological Supply Co., Burlington, N. C.)

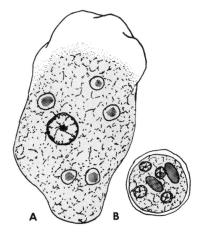

Fig. 2-29

Entamoeba histolytica (order Amoebida). **A,** Mature organism (trophozoite); 15 to 35 microns long. **B,** Cyst; dark, rodlike structures are chromatoid bodies.

may have only the cysts. Man becomes infected by ingesting cysts in drinking water. When the cyst breaks up in man, a single tetranucleate ameba hatches and divides mitotically to form eight uninucleated trophozoites.

Order Testacida

The ameboid forms of the order Testacida are enclosed in a one-chambered test that is made of siliceous materials or pseudochitin plus foreign substances (sand) and secreted plates embedded in a gelatinous matrix. Some of the tests have two layers. Some tests are flexible, and others are firm. They have lobopodia or filopodia that extend, become attached, and pull the body forward. A single aperture is provided for the extrusion of the pseudopodia. The endoplasm is granular or vacuolar and contains food vacuoles, contractile vacuoles,

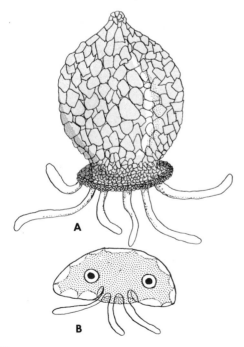

Fig. 2-30

A, *Difflugia urceolata* (order Testacida); test covered with sand grains; 200 to 230 microns long. B, *Arcella vulgaris* (order Testacida); test circular and domelike; 30 to 100 microns in diameter.

one or more nuclei, and often numerous extra nuclear chromidia. Asexual reproduction is by longitudinal or transverse fission in which usually one daughter cell receives the parental shell and the other secretes a new shell (Fig. 2-5, *B*). In hard tests, part of the cytoplasm exudes and forms a new shell before division occurs. Multiple fission and encystment may occur. Sexual reproduction is by ameboid anisogametes that copulate (syngamy). Testacidans live mostly in fresh water, although a few are marine. Some are found in moist soil, moss, etc.

Difflugia (Fig. 2-30, A, up to 500 microns long), a familiar genus, has a pyriform shell of foreign particles cemented together. *Arcella* (Fig. 2-30, B, to 250 microns diameter) has a transparent, bowl-like test of chitin or siliceous plates embedded in tectin. Another common genus is *Euglypha* (Fig. 2-5, *C*), which has an oval test of siliceous scales in longitudinal rows and is often provided with one or more spines.

Order Foraminiferida

Some authorities think there are as many as 20,000 species in the order Foraminiferida. They are characterized by having rhizopodia or myxopodia (Fig. 2-2, *B*), and a one-chambered or multichambered test that may be calcareous or siliceous with various substances, such as sand or sponge spicules. These substances are cemented together by pseudochitinous or gelatinous materials. Foraminiferans are among the largest of protozoans, some reaching a diameter of more than 100 mm., although most are in the range of 0.5 to 10 mm. The tests are of various shapes—oval, tubular, branched, spiral, etc. Most shells are multichambered or multilocular consisting of a series of successively larger chambers that are separated internally by calcareous septa with pores or canals connecting the chambers (Fig. 2-31). The cytoplasm is found in all the chambers and is continuous through the septal pores. One or more nuclei are found in the endoplasm. By passing through the mouth or pores of the test the cytoplasm forms a layer (ectoplasm) over the test. The ectoplasm and endoplasm are connected by pores in the test. As the animal grows, successive chambers are added to the initial chamber, the proloculum.

Foraminiferans capture their prey by means of their pseudopodial network, which exhibits active streaming movements.

Most foraminiferans are found in marine or brackish water; only a few are freshwater forms. A few are pelagic or sessile, but most are creeping bottom dwellers (benthonic). A third of the ocean bottom is covered with *Globigerina* (Fig. 2-32) ooze, which is made up mainly of the accumulation of the tests of this common foraminiferan. Their tests are rarely found in ocean water deeper than 4,000 meters, because at greater depths their tests dissolve in the larger concentration of carbon dioxide. Foraminiferans have left an impressive fossil record starting about the close of the Devonian period. They have formed important rock strata, such as the limestone used in the great pyramids of Egypt. They are also important in detecting oil-bearing strata.

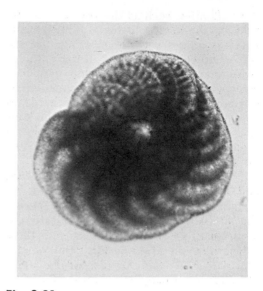

Fig. 2-31

Foraminiferan shell, *Elphidium* sp.; 3 to 4 mm. in diameter.

CLASS SPOROZOA

The class Sporozoa is made up entirely of endoparasites. Their cosmopolitan nature is shown by the fact that their hosts are distributed among all the animal phyla. They are distinguished from all other protozoan classes by their lack of all organelles of locomotion, such as pseudopodia, cilia, or flagella. Some are of the greatest importance to man. The malaria parasite causes more illness and death than any other disease agency. Many serious disorders among animals other than man are caused by these parasites. Hyperparasitism or the infection of another parasite by them is also found. They show an amazing degree of host specificity—a particular sporozoan species may infect only one kind of host. As a group, they do not show a close bond of homogeneity but must be considered an assortment of organisms that have few affinities with each other. About the only character they have in common is their parasitic habit and their spore formation in some stage of their life history.

Since the Sporozoa are such a heterogeneous group, it is probable that each subclass and order had a separate origin. The characteristics of certain stages in their life history may give a clue in some cases to

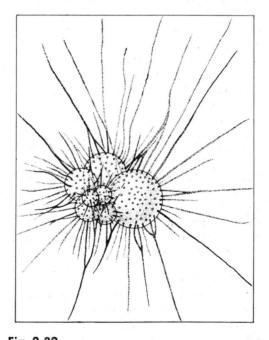

Fig. 2-32

Globigerina bulloides (order Foraminiferida); chambers spirally arranged and spherical in shape; rhizopoda. (Courtesy General Biological Supply House, Inc., Chicago.)

their affinities, such as the presence of flagella on the microgametes of Telosporidia, which is supposed to indicate flagellate ancestry. Ameboid movement of many sporozoans may indicate relationship with Sarcodina. Spore formation, so characteristic of Sporozoa, is also found in both Mastigophora and Sarcodina. Perhaps the four classes of Protozoa are polyphyletic, as suggested by many authorities (L. H. Hyman, G. A. Kerkut).

The taxonomy of the Sporozoa is difficult, and authorities are not in agreement on certain taxa. At the present time the scheme that probably meets with the greatest favor is the one that divides the class into three subclasses: the Telosporidia, the Cnidosporidia, and the Acnidosporidia. This classification is based mainly upon the characteristics of the spore.

General features

The Sporozoa have a great variety of shapes. This variation is not restricted to groups of species but is found in stages of the life history of a given species. Their method of infecting hosts is usually by means of spores enclosed in hard walls, or sometimes the transmission is by naked young. An intermediate host such as mosquitoes, leeches, flies, and other vectors is used in some cases.

Sites of infection may be body spaces, intestine, bladder, coelomic cavity, blood cells, muscle cells, and other organs.

Organelles are uncommon in Sporozoa. The cytoplasm has one nucleus in young stages but becomes multinucleated about the time of multiple fission. Differentiation of ectoplasm and endoplasm is common in the group. Myonemes and adhesive organs are present in gregarines.

Locomotion

All locomotor organelles are absent in the adult stage, but microgametes are often flagellated. Certain stages exhibit ameboid, gliding, and squirming movements. Cytoplasmic fibrils (myonemes) present in some may explain the sinuous motion in those that have such fibrils. Ameboid movement appears to be fairly common in the active stages of some species of *Plasmodium*. Many of their movements are difficult to explain.

Nutrition

There are no organelles for the capture and ingestion of food in Sporozoa. Nutrition is mostly saprozoic, or by absorption of liquefied substance from the host over most of the body surface, except in a few forms in which absorption may occur at the anterior end. However, recent work by M. A. Rudzinska and W. Trager shows that a certain species of malaria plasmodia can ingest hemoglobin in small solid particles by ameboid movement. It has also been shown that trophozoites of *Nosema* (Fig. 2-37), a microsporidian, can ingest solid bits of their host's tissues.

Life cycle and reproduction

There is an asexual and a sexual phase in the life cycle of the Sporozoa, but there is a great deal of diversity in the life cycles of the different forms. Some groups, such as the gregarines (Fig. 2-33), may restrict their reproduction to the sexual phase. Typically, in the asexual phase the vegetative trophozoite attains full size and becomes a schizont, which by multiple fission (schizogony) forms agametes or merozoites. The merozoites either reinfect the host and produce another generation of schizonts, or they may develop directly into microgametes, which can produce a zygote or oocyst by fertilization (sexual reproduction). The oocyst undergoes a series of multiple fissions to form sporoblasts and sporozoites (sporogony or spore formation), which may be naked young or walled spores.

Only the zygote is diploid; all other phases are haploid. If there are two different hosts, the life cycle usually involves schizogony in one and sporogony in the other.

In some species the life cycle may not involve sporogony at all, and the infective stage is an ameboid sporoplasm, not a sporozoite. Life histories are very incompletely known for many Sporozoa.

Subclass Telosporidia

The subclass Telosporidia contains some common parasites characterized by having spores that lack polar capsules and that produce one to many sporozoites. In some cases they give rise to naked sporozoites instead of spores. Their life histories have

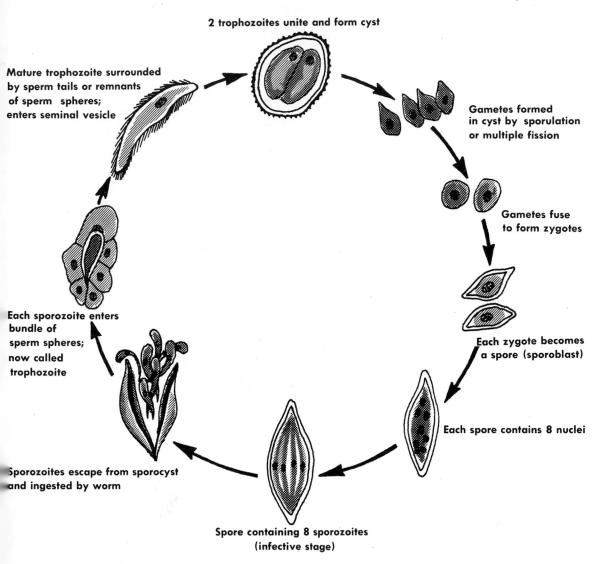

2 trophozoites unite and form cyst

Mature trophozoite surrounded by sperm tails or remnants of sperm spheres; enters seminal vesicle

Gametes formed in cyst by sporulation or multiple fission

Gametes fuse to form zygotes

Each zygote becomes a spore (sporoblast)

Each sporozoite enters bundle of sperm spheres; now called trophozoite

Each spore contains 8 nuclei

Sporozoites escape from sporocyst and ingested by worm

Spore containing 8 sporozoites (infective stage)

Fig. 2-33

Life cycle of *Monocystis* (order Gregarinida); common sporozoan parasite in seminal vesicles of earthworms. (From Hickman: Integrated principles of zoology, The C. V. Mosby Co.)

both asexual and sexual phases, although schizogony is lacking in most of the gregarines, and they increase only by sporogony.

The order Gregarinida includes some common parasites of arthropods and annelid worms. Two gregarines often adhere end to end to form what is called syzygy. In such unions the anterior member becomes the female, the posterior, the male. Usually when a spore enters a host, the emerging sporozoites enter the epithelial cells of the digestive system. When they become trophozoites, they are restricted mainly to the gut lumen.

A common gregarine genus is *Monocystis* (Fig. 2-33), which parasitizes the seminal vesicles of oligochaetes. *Gregarina rigida*, common in the gut of certain grasshoppers, is another gregarine.

The order Coccidia has a wide distribution in both vertebrates and invertebrates. Most of them attack the epithelium of the digestive tract and glands. Both asexual

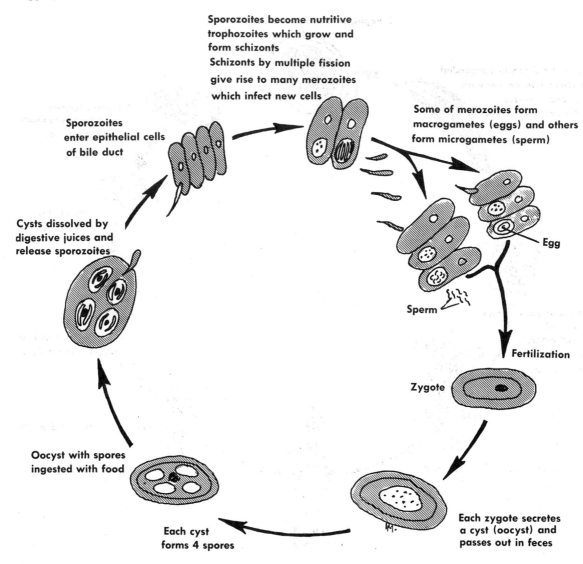

Sporozoites become nutritive trophozoites which grow and form schizonts
Schizonts by multiple fission give rise to many merozoites which infect new cells

Sporozoites enter epithelial cells of bile duct

Some of merozoites form macrogametes (eggs) and others form microgametes (sperm)

Egg

Sperm

Cysts dissolved by digestive juices and release sporozoites

Fertilization

Zygote

Oocyst with spores ingested with food

Each zygote secretes a cyst (oocyst) and passes out in feces

Each cyst forms 4 spores

Fig. 2-34

Diagram of life cycle of *Eimeria stiedae* (order Coccidia); parasite of rabbits. (From Hickman: Integrated principles of zoology, The C. V. Mosby Co.)

schizogony and sexual sporogony are found. The genus *Eimeria* (Fig. 2-34), which includes many species, is a common parasite of the bile duct and liver of rabbits and of the intestines of chickens. This order has a very wide host range, being found in cattle, pigs, frogs, fishes, etc. These parasites may be very destructive.

The best known members of the order Haemosporidia are the four species that cause malaria in man, but there are many other species, some of which infect other vertebrates. Members of this group are intracellular parasites of vertebrate blood corpuscles. Their life history always involves two hosts—a vertebrate and an invertebrate. Asexual reproduction (schizogony) takes place in the blood of vertebrates, and sexual reproduction, or sporozoite formation, occurs in the alimentary canal of a bloodsucking invertebrate. Since they always remain within the body of one or the other host, the parasites have no cyst wall, and naked sporozoites (the infective forms)

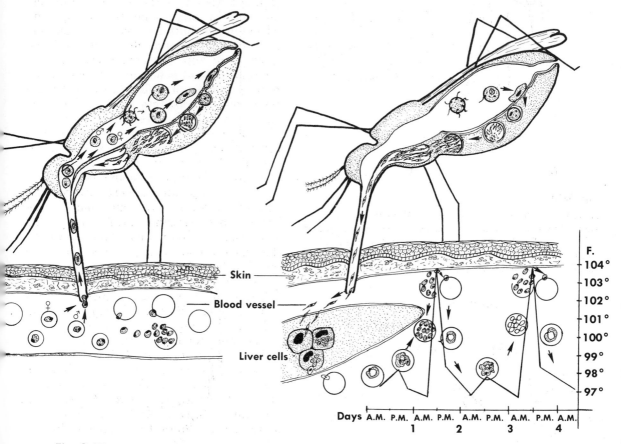

Skin

Blood vessel

Liver cells

Days A.M. P.M. A.M. P.M. A.M. P.M. A.M. P.M. A.M.
1 2 3 4

F.
104°
103°
102°
101°
100°
99°
98°
97°

Fig. 2-35

Life cycle of *Plasmodium vivax* (order Haemosporidia); malarial parasite. Left, *Anopheles* mosquito ingests infected blood. Right, mosquito injects sporozoites into man; fever cycle of infected subject shown at lower right. (From Hickman: Integrated principles of zoology. The C. V. Mosby Co.)

hatch directly from the zygote. All the true malarial parasites are placed in the genus *Plasmodium* (Fig. 2-35). The vector that carries malaria for mammalian hosts is the *Anopheles* mosquito; those vectors for birds are mosquitoes of the genera *Aedes* or *Culex*. Certain other genera, such as *Haemoproteus* and *Leucocytozoon*, closely related to *Plasmodium* cause malaria in birds and reptiles. Certain flies serve as vectors for the parasites of these genera. The paroxysm of malaria consisting of chills and high fever corresponds with the liberation of merozoites and their toxins from corpuscles. This schizogonic cycle varies with the different species of *Plasmodium* responsible for human malaria. In *Plasmodium vivax* (benign tertian malaria) the cycle is every

48 hours, in *Plasmodium malariae* (quartan malaria) every 72 hours, in *Plasmodium ovale* every 48 hours, and in the highly malignant *Plasmodium falciparum* (tertian malaria) every 48 hours.

Babesia bigemina, the cause of Texas cattle fever, was the first demonstration of the transmission of a protozoan parasite by an arthropod vector (T. Smith and F. S. Kilbourne, 1893). The life history of the parasite in cattle and the tick was first worked out by E. W. Dennis (1932).

Subclass Cnidosporidia

The sporozoans of the subclass Cnidosporidia usually have spores with polar capsules, each containing a coiled filament that by inversion can anchor the spore to

65

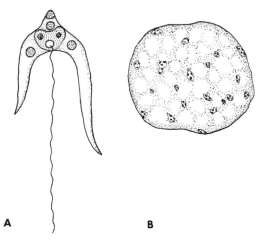

Fig. 2-36

A, *Synactinomyxon tubificis* (order Actinomyxida); spore stage; found as parasites in annelids, especially in gut of tubificidae. B, *Myxidium serotinum* (order Myxosporida); trophozoite stage; this sporozoan is common in gall-bladder of certain toads and frogs. (Modified from Kudo.)

Fig. 2-37

Life cycle of *Nosema bombycis* (order Microsporida); cause of pébrine, fatal disease of silkworms. When spore, **A**, with coiled filament and sporoplasm, is ingested by worm, filament is extruded, **B**, and sporoplasm is freed, **C**, from other part of spore and invades gut epithelial cell, **C**, where, by binary fission or budding, many uninucleated amebas are formed and, **D**, may enter any tissue in body. In time, multinucleated cells, **E**, arise and develop into characteristic spore, **A**, made up of sporoplasm, spore envelope, and polar capsule.

its host. Each spore may contain one to four capsules. Spores in this subclass also contain one or more ameboid sporoplasms, which in the host become amebulas and later become trophozoites that feed and grow on the host. The cnidosporidian spore (in some orders) is unique in being formed from a number of cells instead of from a single one, a condition that may indicate an affinity with the Mesozoa. The method of multiplication in the group is both schizogonic and sporogonic, but schizogony is very restricted in this subclass. Details of their life cycles vary in the different orders.

The Cnidosporidia are exclusively parasites of the lower vertebrates and invertebrates; none parasitize man. There is no secondary or intermediate host. However, they have economic importance for man's interests because their infections may seriously affect silkworms, honeybees, and fishes. Four orders are recognized: Myxosporida (Fig. 2-36, *B*), Actinomyxida (Fig. 2-36, *A*), Microsporida, and Helicosporida.

The more common members of this subclass are *Nosema bombycis* (Fig. 2-37), the cause of pébrine disease of the silkworm, and *Unicapsula muscularis*, found in muscles of halibut fish and often producing epidemics. The control of *Nosema* was a result of classic experiments by L. Pasteur.

Subclass Acnidosporidia

These sporozoans do not have polar filaments in their spores, each of which contains one sporozoite. It is a subclass of doubtful status, because its members are incompletely known, and their development seems to be different from that of most other Sporozoa. There are two orders, Sarcosporidia and Haplosporidia. The Sarcosporidia are muscle parasites in higher vertebrates such as pigs, sheep, horses, and man (few cases). The common genus is *Sarcocystis* (Fig. 2-38, *B*), which may infect the muscles of the throat, heart, and other regions. Infection is usually through the mouth. The Haplosporidia are parasites of invertebrates and fish. It is the least known group of the Sporozoa. They have very simple spores. The amebulae form characteristic plasmodia, which break up into uninucleate bodies, each of which forms a spore. The characteristic genus is *Haplosporidium* (Fig. 2-38, *A*), which infects the

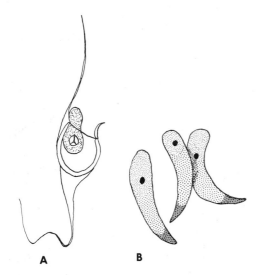

A   **B**

Fig. 2-38

A, *Haplosporidium chitonis* (order Haplosporidia); spore stage; spore develops into multinucleated plasmodium in amphineuran host; plasmodium then produces uninucleated sporoblasts that develop into spores. **B,** *Sarcocystis* (order Sarcosporidia); spores; this group is not well understood, and some authorities think members may be form of fungi. (**A** redrawn from Kudo: Protozoology, Charles C Thomas, Publisher.)

liver, connective tissue, and gut epithelium in invertebrates and lower vertebrates.

Subphylum Ciliophora

CLASS CILIATA

The ciliates represent one of the most homogeneous groups among the protozoans. They are also distinguished by their wide distribution and the ease with which they can be found in water that will support any life. More than 6,000 species have been described, and doubtless many more exist. Their distinctive characteristics are their cilia (present in some stage) for locomotion and for food getting and the presence of two kinds of nuclei—a large macronucleus and a smaller micronucleus. The ciliates are larger than most other protozoans, although their range in size is from 10 or 12 microns to 3,000 microns or 3 mm. long.

A variety of forms is found in ciliates. Free-swimming organisms may be spherical or elliptic, while creeping forms tend to have a flattened shape. Some species have a kind of radial symmetry, and others approach bilateral symmetry. Most of them are free living and solitary, but some are sessile, colonial, ectocommensal, or endocommensal. Most are colorless, but a few are brightly colored such as the different species of *Stentor.* Color may be caused by chromatophores or by symbiotic bacteria. The color of *Blepharisma,* for instance, is in the pellicle. This can be observed when the pellicle is shed in a strychnine sulfate solution. Ciliates are found in both freshwater and saltwater habitats.

Perhaps no group of animals has been more widely used for experimental purposes than the ciliates. This use is perhaps because of the ease with which they can be obtained and cultured, their rapid multiplication, and the many fundamental biologic problems that they pose. Although many ciliates are simple protozoan organisms, some are the most complex animals to be found among unicellular forms. Some ciliates appear to have exploited nearly all the potentialities to be found within the restrictions of a single membrane or cell.

Classification of ciliates has undergone many changes since their discovery by Leeuwenhoek in 1676. At the present time the scheme of the French investigator E. Fauré-Fremiet and the American investigator J. O. Corliss is widely accepted by many protozoologists. Their scheme is based upon the probable evolutionary pattern of the group. Chief specific structures that are used in the taxonomic arrangements of ciliates are the ciliary patterns and the nature of the cytostome. Although there is only one class, there are two subclasses—Holotricha and Spirotricha—and subordinate orders.

In recent years, Corliss, a world authority on Ciliophora, has proposed a phylogenetic tree of the class showing possible relationships among its numerous orders. The fossil record of ciliates yields little or no evidence to support any scheme of phylogeny, but there are certain indirect evidences that have proved useful, such as the data obtained from comparisons of life histories, cytostomes, infraciliature, etc. Corliss and others have laid great emphasis on changes in the somatic and buccal ciliation in the evolution of the group. As mentioned elsewhere, the four classes of Protozoa are probably polyphyletic, and each class has originated by convergent evolution from several stocks. Ciliates pose peculiar problems of nuclear dimorphism, sexual phenomena, and complex infraciliature that makes them especially difficult to relate to the other groups. Their kinship to the flagellates is apparent in the similarity of flagella and cilia and the apparent homology of kinetosomes and other structures of the two groups.

Fig. 2-39

Portion of pellicle and infraciliature of *Paramecium.* (Redrawn from Corliss: The ciliated Protozoa, Pergamon Press, Inc.)

General features

Most ciliates have a distinct ectoplasm and endoplasm. From the ectoplasm the pellicle, cilia, infraciliature, and trichocysts originate; from the endoplasm the nuclei, contractile vacuoles, food vacuoles, pigment, etc., originate. The endoplasm undergoes rotation, or cyclosis. The pellicle may be very thin and hardly distinguishable. In a few species it may be differentiated into an armor of calcareous grooves. Longitudinal and diagonal grooves in the pellicle indicate places of attachment of ciliary rows. The pellicle may also have a pattern of various figures bounded by ridges.

The pellicle has been most thoroughly studied in *Paramecium,* in which, according to C. F. Ehret and E. L. Powers (1959), the outer stratum of the pellicle is made up of ciliary corpuscles, each composed of an outer and inner peribasal membrane. One or two cilia arise from a pit in the center of each corpuscle (Fig. 2-39).

Cilia are short, slender, and hairlike. They are usually arranged in longitudinal or diagonal rows. The electron microscope reveals that they, like flagella (Fig. 2-1), have two central and nine peripheral fibrils. They may clothe the entire surface (somatic ciliation), or they may be restricted

Fig. 2-40

A, Left, intact cirrus; right, cirrus unraveled into cilia by acid treatment. **B,** *Stylonychia,* using cirri for locomotion. **C,** Undischarged trichocyst. **D,** Portion of discharged trichocyst. **E,** Diagrammatic portion of paramecium with both discharged and undischarged trichocysts. **F,** Structure of membranelles of *Stentor* with fibrillar attachments. (Modified from Hyman.)

to certain regions (oral ciliation). Compound ciliary organelles are complex structures formed by the compounding or fusion of cilia to form a sheet (undulating membrane), a triangular or rectangular block of cilia two to four rows wide (membranelle, Fig. 2-40, *F*), or the fusion of a tuft of cilia (cirrus, Fig. 2-40, *A, B*). Undulating membranes and membranelles help propel food into the cytopharynx and may also aid in locomotion. Membranelles are found in a specialized zone leading to the cytostome.

In connection with the ciliation, just underneath the pellicle is the infraciliature, composed of the basal granules (kinetosomes) of the cilia and their associated kinetodesmal fibrils (Fig. 2-39). The cilia and their kinetosomes are arranged in rows. The kinetosomes of a row and the fine fibrils (kinetodesmata) that connect them and run anteriorly in a bundle parallel to the row make up what is known as a kinety. All ciliates seem to have kinety systems, even those that are without cilia at some stage. Kinetosomes appear to be self-duplicating and can give rise to cilia, fibrils, and trichocysts. The silver line system of staining by impregnation with silver (first developed by B. M. Klein in 1926) has been important in the study of the infraciliature and trichocysts. More recently, electron microscopic studies have revealed more of the ultrastructure of these organelles.

The fibrillar system, often known as the neuromotor apparatus, was first described in detail by R. G. Sharp (1914) in his classic experiments on *Epidinium* (*Diplodinium*, Fig. 2-51), a ciliate symbiont of cattle. He described a central motorium near the cytostome from which the fibrils radiated to connect with the basal granules or kinetosomes of the cilia. The neuromotor system is apparently a motor-coordinating system for ciliary movement.

Trichocysts (Fig. 2-40, *C* to *E*), another distinctive character of ciliates, are restricted mainly to the subclass Holotricha. They are small rodlike or oval bodies in the ectoplasm at right angles to the body surface. They may be distributed all over the body, or they may be limited to certain regions such as the anterior end. When discharged, they turn inside out as long filaments, which pass through the pellicle. Upon extrusion, the trichocyst hardens ex-

cept for the tip, which remains sticky for attachment. The stimulus for discharge seems to be mechanical touch, but other modes, e.g., chemical and electric, are known. Their functions are not always clear, but they may be offensive and defensive. The trichocysts of some ciliates are known to paralyze some organisms. A number of different types of trichocysts are recognized. The electron microscope reveals them as tack-shaped barbs with long, finely striated shafts.

Some ciliates are capable of contractile movements—either of the whole body, as in *Stentor* or *Spirostomum,* or of their stalks, as in *Vorticella* or *Carchesium.* Myonemes, contractile fibrils in the ectoplasm, bring about these movements. Myonemes are mostly of ectoplasmic origin, although in peritrichs they appear to be derived from both ectoplasm and endoplasm. They usually run lengthwise of the body near the grooves where cilia are attached, although in some, such as *Stentor*, they are also wound spirally around the gullet. In contractile stalks the fibrils are spirally arranged and bring about the peculiar bobbing motion of these attached forms.

Most ciliates have a mouth (cytostome) usually associated with a buccal cavity (cytopharynx, Fig. 2-41) with compound ciliary organelles. The mouth may be in a lateral or ventral position. The region around the cytostome is the peristome and is specialized for water currents. It may be an oral groove or some other specialization. A funnellike cytopharynx often extends from the peristome (and cytostome) down into the endoplasm. Special cilia and membranelles are found in connection with the peristome for creating water currents. Myonemes encircling the cytopharynx of many ciliates facilitate swallowing.

Contractile vacuoles with one to many collecting canals (Figs. 2-3, *A,* 2-41) are found throughout the Ciliophora. Some ciliates have no collecting canals at all but are fed by smaller, secondary, and tertiary vacuoles (Fig. 2-3, *B*). Most contractile vacuoles are fixed in position, open by a permanent pore to the exterior, and are of constant number for the species. Some marine as well as freshwater ciliates may have contractile vacuoles.

Two kinds of nuclei are the rule in the

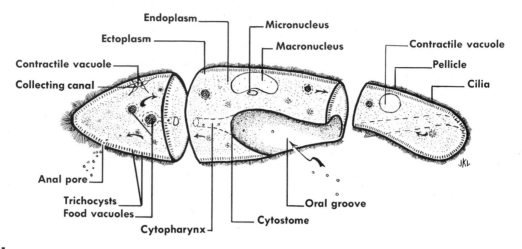

Fig. 2-41

Diagram of structure of *Paramecium*. (From Hickman and Hickman: Laboratory studies in integrated zoology, The C. V. Mosby Co.)

majority of Ciliophora (Fig. 2-4). Usually there is one of each kind present, although there may be more. The smaller, or micronucleus, contains chromosomes and has a generative function. It undergoes mitosis like any metazoan cell except that centrioles are often absent. The micronucleus is usually ovoid or rounded. The larger macronucleus has somatic or metabolic functions and does not undergo mitosis but divides by amitosis. It is usually single and may be oval, round, crescent, or other shapes. The macronucleus is known to have genic control over certain hereditary characters, and it arises from the micronucleus.

Two other cytoplasmic organelles of almost universal presence in ciliates are (1) mitochondria, spherical or rodlike structures, and (2) Golgi apparatus, which may appear as networks, spherules, or rings. The former of these two cytoplasmic inclusions furnish important teams of enzymes in cellular metabolism; the latter is apparently involved in secretion.

Locomotion

Ciliates are among the most active of all protozoans, and their locomotory mechanism is very efficient. Cilia produce movement by a rowing action, each cilium producing a lash like an oar, involving both an effective stroke and a recovery stroke. The effective stroke is made with the cilium outstretched to offer as much resistance as possible; in the recovery stroke the cilium is bent and brought back in position like the arm of a swimmer, with the least amount of resistance. The cilia are coordinated in their beat by the neuromotor system, because the numerous cilia must beat together. Most ciliates move in a spiral path that is generally characteristic for the species. Various theories try to account for this spiral rotation on its longitudinal axis. H. S. Jennings thought that the body form and the stronger beat of the oral cilia were chiefly responsible; others think that the spiral movement really results from the oblique strokes of the cilia working together in the same direction. Cilia are also used for crawling and walking (e.g., *Oxytricha* and *Euplotes*). Many forms have large cirri that have originated from the fusion of tufts of adjacent cilia (Fig. 2-4, A, B). Some cilia may also be sensory in function as in the order Thigmotrichida. Contractile movements brought about by myonemes have already been discussed.

Nutrition

Most ciliates are holozoic and are the most expert food catchers among the protozoans. Many of them are provided with a cytostome at the anterior end, and as they move through the water they come in contact with food, which is either swept into the mouth by special cilia or mem-

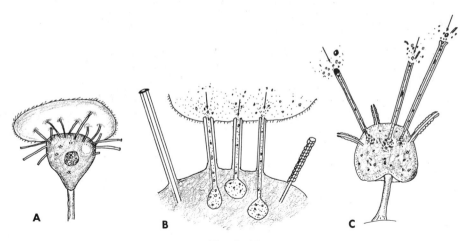

Fig. 2-42

A, *Tokophrya* feeding on ciliate. B, Tentacles of *Tokophrya;* left, extended; middle, feeding on contents of ciliate; right, contracted. C, *Choanophrya* feeding on organic particles in water.

branelles or is seized directly. Preoral chambers in the form of grooves, depressions, vestibules, or buccal cavities provided with undulating membranes or membranelles aid in sweeping the food down the gullet into the endoplasm where food vacuoles are formed. This arrangement is common among the current feeders. Many ciliates are raptorial and ingest prey even larger than themselves. *Didinium,* for instance, has a proboscis for seizing paramecia and then engulfing them (Fig. 2-45, A). The sessile suctoridans, while adhering to their prey with their knobbed, tubelike tentacles, can paralyze them with a hypnotoxin. The contents of the prey are then sucked through the tentacular tubes and digested in the body (Fig. 2-42).

Ciliates live on a great variety of foods, such as bacteria, other protozoans, algae, diatoms, etc. *Paramecium* has an especial fondness for bacteria and may consume millions in a single day. Some ciliates are more fastidious in their food selection than others. Some, like *Didinium* (Fig. 2-45, A) prefer paramecia and rarely seize other kinds. Those that practice food selection may choose their prey by chemical attraction; many are restricted by the limitations of their food-getting mechanisms.

Ciliates have no digestive tube, and when a food vacuole is formed at the base of the cytopharynx or other region, it follows a definite circuit induced by the cyclosis of the endoplasm (Fig. 2-41). A food vacuole consists of the food particle, a film

of water, and some endoplasmic secretions; its size is somewhat constant for a given species. In the digestive process, the reaction at first in the vacuole is acid (about pH 4) and then gradually becomes alkaline as digestion proceeds. Proteolytic amylases and other enzymes have been detected in certain cases. Digestion takes place rapidly and may be completed in 20 to 30 minutes. The indigestible part, or fecal material, may be discharged through a special opening, the cytoproct, or anal pore.

Some parasitic ciliates are saprozoic, but others do not differ from free-living holozoic forms in their nutrition.

Life cycles and reproduction

The reproductive life cycle of Ciliophora involves asexual reproduction, a type of sexual reproduction, and encystment. True sexual reproduction with fusion (syngamy) of free gametes probably does not occur in this extensive group, but conjugation with meiosis and chromosome recombinations do occur, a process that certainly represents sexual phenomena. Some species also have variant forms of conjugation, such as autogamy and cytogamy.

Asexual reproduction is mostly transverse binary fission, except in the Peritrichida, where it is longitudinal (Fig. 2-5, *D, E*). **71**

Biology of the invertebrates

Fig. 2-43

Binary fission in *Paramecium* showing elongation and constriction of macronucleus before division. (From Hickman: Integrated principles of zoology, The C. V. Mosby Co.)

Fission involves both micronuclei and macronuclei. The micronucleus divides first by a mitotic process with spindle and chromosomes as already mentioned. On the other hand, the macronucleus divides amitotically simply by elongation and then constriction in the center; no mitosis or chromosomes are involved in the process (Fig. 2-43). However, the ciliate macronucleus is known to be highly polyploid and contains many genomes produced by repeated endomitosis. There are many variations in nuclear behavior among the different ciliate species.

Budding occurs in some ciliates where small daughter cells arise from the outer surface of the parent body; or the budding may be internal (Suctorida) in a brood pouch from which the young ciliated individuals escape at the end of development.

In conjugation, which is the sexual phenomenon in ciliates, a pair of conjugants come together, become sticky, and adhere together at the mouth region, where there is a protoplasmic fusion or bridge. Changes in each conjugant now occur in both macronucleus and micronucleus; the former degenerates early or late in the process and is absorbed by the cytoplasm (Fig. 2-44). The micronucleus usually undergoes three preparatory divisions, the first two divisions being mitotic. All but two of the daughter

micronuclei now degenerate. One of the two surviving nuclei, or pronuclei, becomes the stationary, or female, micronucleus, while the other forms the wandering, or male, micronucleus. The so-called male micronucleus of each partner now migrates across the protoplasmic bridge and fuses with the stationary nucleus of the other to form a synkaryon in each conjugant or partner. After the two conjugants separate and become exconjugants, the synkaryon in each then divides a variable number of times, depending on the species, to form products, some of which remain micronuclei and others of which develop into macronuclei. The final result of the synkaryon divisions is to form the nuclear conditions characteristic of the species. In this restoration to the normal condition the cytoplasm may also undergo division to distribute the correct number of nuclei if the synkaryon divides more than once, or in the case of species with many macronuclei and micronuclei, the synkaryon in each exconjugant merely divides several times without cytosomal divisions until the normal condition is reached. The pattern of conjugation varies greatly among Ciliophora. In some (vorticellids) the conjugation union is permanent instead of being temporary. Hereditary mating types in which populations of a species do not conjugate among themselves but only with those of a complementary group are found in some ciliates.

In autogamy there is a reorganization involving the union of two nuclei both of which have come from the same parent. The micronuclear changes are about the same as those in conjugation. The two micronuclei (*Paramecium aurelia*) divide three times producing two functional and many degenerating nuclei. The two functional nuclei then unite in a paroral cone and form a synkaryon, while the original macronucleus disappears. The synkaryon divides twice into four micronuclei, two of which transform into new macronuclei and two of which remain as micronuclei. When the cytosome divides and separates the macronuclei, each of the micronuclei also divides so that the original condition of one macronucleus and two micronuclei is restored.

Still another variant form of conjugation is cytogamy. In this process two individual

Fig. 2-44

Sexual reproduction, or conjugation, in *Paramecium caudatum*.

ciliates come together as in conjugation; there is no mutual fertilization, but within each partner there is a fusion of two gametic nuclei produced in the same individual, forming a synkaryon as in autogamy.

Various factors may induce conjugation, such as starvation, sudden darkness in light conditions, low temperatures, the presence of certain salts, etc. The process of conjugation may be beneficial in producing nuclear reorganization and heritable variation and may be useful in rejuvenation of species. Whatever value conjugation may have in this way, however, does not apply to all ciliates, for some survive without the process. Conjugation is definitely restricted to certain types.

Encystment occurs in many protozoans, and Ciliophora are no exception (Fig. 2-6, *F* to *I*). There are many variations in the process among the ciliates. Precystic changes in the organism usually occur before a cyst wall is secreted. Gelatinous materials for the ectocyst membrane sometimes accumulate in the peripheral cytosome. Starch and glycogen may accumulate, but food vacuoles are ejected. Locomotor organelles are mainly reabsorbed. The fluid content of the organism is lessened and the cytosome becomes denser. Environmental conditions, such as crowding, lack of food, accumulation of waste products, lack of essential nutrients, dessication, distilled water, rich feeding, etc., are inducements to encystment. The cysts display a great variety in form and size and in their methods of formation. Some are spherical and smooth, some are warty or covered with knobs, and some are colored. The ectocyst is composed of a hard substance that in some species seems to be a polysaccharide in composition; in others it appears chitinous or keratin-like. Excystment, or the emergence from the cyst, involves many changes, such as a regeneration of organelles and an internal reorganization. Organelles, such as contractile vacuoles and cilia, first appear. Cyclosis starts and the organism grows

larger. The membrane becomes thinner and finally disappears. The cyst itself is often ruptured by the absorption of water and organic substances into the cytoplasm, or it may be dissolved by enzymes.

Subclass Holotricha
Order Gymnostomatida

The Gymnostomatida is considered the most primitive of all the orders of Ciliophora; members are numerous and widespread. They are found in both fresh and salt water, the sands of intertidal zones being a favorite habitat. Many of them are large (2 mm. or longer). The simple cilia are usually distributed all over the body, but there are no cilia in the buccal area. The cytostome may be at or near the anterior end, at the lateral region, or on the ventral surface. Rodlike trichites reinforce the cytopharynx. A few of these organisms are harmless commensals, but most of them are carnivorous or herbivorous. There are many families and genera in this order, the most familiar genera being *Didinium* (Fig. 2-45, *A*), which has an expansible cytostome used in catching paramecia and other ciliates; *Coleps,* which has a barrel-shaped body and ectoplasmic plates; *Loxophyllum,* which is flask shaped with trichocysts and chain nuclei; *Dileptus,* which has a long neck with rows of trichocysts and a round mouth with trichites; and *Prorodon,* which is ovoid or cylindric with a terminal contractile vacuole.

Order Suctorida

The Suctorida are often considered as a separate class of Protozoa because of their

Fig. 2-45

A, *Didinium nasutum* (order Gymnostomatida); proboscis armed with trichocysts is efficient organ for seizing paramecia. **B,** *Podophrya fixa* (order Suctorida). **C,** *Spirochona* (order Chonotrichida); asexual reproduction by lateral budding is common in this group.

A   B   C

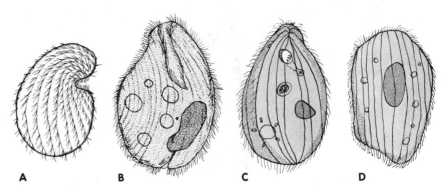

Fig. 2-46

A, *Colpoda cucullus* (order Trichostomatida). Divides only in encysted stage; 40 to 110 microns long. B, *Balantidium coli* (order Trichostomatida); only parasitic ciliate in man; note cytopyge, or cell anus, at posterior end; 40 to 80 microns long. C, *Tetrahymena geleii* (order Hymenostomatida); genus *Tetrahymena* has been widely used in physiologic experiments on growth and metabolism; 40 to 60 microns long. D, *Anoplophrya orchestii* (order Astomatida); often found in gut of sand flea, *Orchestia;* 6 to 68 microns long.

highly specialized tentacles and other structures. Cilia are present only in the young. These ciliates have a pellicle and sometimes a lorica. Their tentacles serve as mouths when they become fastened to prey and suck out the prey's protoplasm (Fig. 2-42). One kind of tentacle is suctorial and bears knobs on the end; another kind is sharp for piercing. Sucking may be effected by expansion of the body surface.

Most species are stalked, and young are produced by both external and internal budding. Binary fission and encystment also occur. Sexual reproduction involves fusion of conjugants. An infraciliature is found throughout their life history. Common genera are the following: *Podophrya* (Fig. 2-45, *B*), which have tentacles over the entire body surface; *Acineta*, which have tentacles usually arranged in two fascicles and a lorica; and *Ephelota*, which have a stout stalk and both suctorial and prehensile tentacles. Suctoridans are frequently attached to hydroids, bryozoans, and the algae on the backs of turtles.

Order Chonotrichida

Members of the order Chonotrichida are mostly ectocommensals on marine crustaceans. The group is not large. The body is commonly vase shaped with an apical peristome that is provided with a relatively complicated ectoplasmic funnel. This funnel contains rows of cilia leading to the cytostome and cytopharynx. *Spirochona* (Fig. 2-45, *C*) and *Stylochona* are common genera.

Order Trichostomatida

Ciliates of the order Trichostomatida, like the gymnostomes, have no buccal ciliation but have a vestibulum that passes from the outside of the body to the cytostome. A few species are endocommensals in domestic animals, but most are found wherever free-living protozoans live. The little *Colpoda* (Fig. 2-46, *A*), with its vestibulum in the middle of the flattened ventral side and its convex left border, is one of the most familiar examples of the order. It has been used frequently in nutrition experiments. *Balantidium coli* (Fig. 2-46, *B*), with oval body, anterior peristome, and poorly developed cytopharynx, is a common parasite in the intestine of pigs and is the only ciliate that is parasitic in man. This species, which man may acquire by ingesting cysts from pigs, may cause balantidiasis, a disease of the large intestine characterized by ulceration and severe dysentery; it can be fatal.

Order Hymenostomatida

Ciliates of the order Hymenostomatida usually possess a ciliation of an undulating membrane on the right side of the buccal cavity and an adoral zone of membranelles on the left side. There are variations of this plan among the different species. This

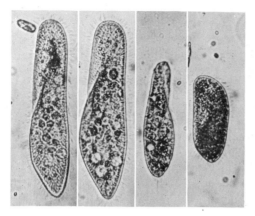

Fig. 2-47

Four common species of *Paramecium* photographed at same magnification. Left to right: *P. multimicronucleatum*, *P. caudatum*, *P. aurelia*, and *P. bursaria* (order Hymenostomatida). (Courtesy Carolina Biological Supply Co., Burlington, N. C.)

order includes some of the best known and most studied genera among the protozoans, such as *Paramecium* (Fig. 2-47) and *Tetrahymena* (Fig. 2-46, *C*). The former is studied in all zoology laboratory courses as a ciliate type and has been the object of intensive investigations in sexual phenomena, mating types, taxonomy, and genetics. The latter is widely used for nutritional studies because it can be grown in media free from other organisms (axenic cultures). Other common genera of this order include *Frontonia*, with an oval to ellipsoid body, long vacuolar canals, and uniform distribution of fusiform trichocysts; and *Colpidium*, with an elongated, kidney-shaped body and lateral cytostome.

Order Astomatida

All members of the order Astomatida lack a mouth or cytostome. They are parasitic forms found mostly in oligochaetes. Some species are provided with holdfast organelles such as suckers or other devices. Asexual reproduction is by transverse fission and may also involve budding. The group is ill defined and may be secondarily degenerate forms. Some authors suggest making them a suborder of Thigmotrichida. *Anoplophrya* (Fig. 2-46, *D*), a common genus, has an oval or ellipsoid body, dense ciliation, and is parasitic in the gut of earthworms and other forms.

Order Apostomatida

The ciliates of the order Apostomatida are characterized by having rosettelike cytostomes, spiral ciliary rows, and complex life histories. Most of them are commensals on marine crustaceans. In their life histories different developmental phases with division of labor among them are correlated with the molting cycles of their hosts. The genera *Foettingeria* and *Spirophrya* are two common examples of the order.

Order Thigmotrichida

Members of the order Thigmotrichida may or may not have a cytostome. They take their name from the thigmotactic cilia with which they attach themselves to their hosts, which are usually mollusks. Their buccal ciliation, when present, is often located at or near the posterior end. Some species have larger and longer cilia on one side than the other. Some of their structures are modifications associated with their parasitic habit. Their common habitat is the mantle cavity or gills of clams. Some have tentacles for sucking out the contents of their hosts' epithelial cells. They show affinities to both hymenostomes and peritrichs. *Ancistruma mytili*, with ovoid and crescent-shaped body, lives in the mantle cavity of *Mytilus*. Another common genus is *Boveria* (Fig. 2-48, *C*), with conical body and posterior cytostome, which lives in the shipworm *Teredo*.

Order Peritrichida

Forms of the order Peritrichida are characterized by a disklike anterior region with an adoral zone of membranelles and cilia that wind counterclockwise when viewed from the anterior end. Many species look like an inverted bell attached to a stalk. Most are sessile and attached as ectocommensals to animals and plants. Stalked forms have a free-swimming stage called a telotroch, which makes possible a wider distribution. Asexual reproduction is by binary fission, and conjugation is common. With the exception of the adoral zone, the body is devoid of cilia. These ciliates may be solitary or colonial. The best known examples of peritrichs are the solitary *Vorticella* (Figs. 2-48, *A*, 2-49, *A*) and the colonial *Epistylis*. Both are stalked. *Vorticella* has an inverted, bell-shaped body and con-

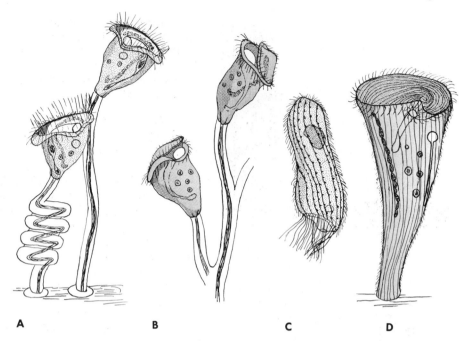

A   B   C   D

Fig. 2-48

A, *Vorticella* (order Peritrichida); 35 to 150 microns long, depending on species. B, *Carchesium polypinum* (order Peritrichida); stalks contract individually; 100 to 125 microns long. C, *Boveria teredinidi* (order Thigmotrichida); cytostome at posterior end; on gills of *Teredo navalis;* 27 to 173 microns long. D, *Stentor coeruleus* (order Heterotrichida); 1 to 2 mm. extended.

tractile stalk and is common in both fresh and salt water. *Epistylis* has a vase-shaped body and noncontractile stalk. It may form large colonies. Another stalked form is *Carchesium* (Fig. 2-48,*B*), which is similar to *Vorticella* but is colonial. Each stalk, however, can contract independently. A common motile peritrich is *Trichodina,* which is ectozoic on hydras and parasitic in or on fish and amphibians. It has a low, barrel-shaped body with a posterior circlet of cilia by which it glides. It may cause serious infections in fish.

Subclass Spirotricha
Order Heterotrichida

The order Heterotrichida is a large group of the subclass Spirotricha and contains many ectocommensals and endocommensals of both invertebrates and vertebrates, although they are not found in man. Ciliation is more or less uniform over the body except in the adoral zone of membranelles or undulating membranes. In a few species, ciliation is lacking altogether. Pigments of various colors may be found in their cytoplasms. Bodies are of various shapes, including oval and elongated forms, but are not depressed. Some species are quite large. The order includes many in-

teresting types that are frequently used in cultures. One of these is *Stentor* (Figs. 2-48, *D*, 2-49, *B*), with trumpet-shaped or cylindric body, a peristome encircled by a row of membranelles, a spirally coiled cytopharynx, and a beadlike macronucleus. Capable of great contraction because of its myonemes, it can extend 1 to 2 mm. in length. Some of its species are blue. *Stentor* is often used in morphogenetic investigations. *Blepharisma* is pink—a rare color in ciliates. *Spirostomum* is an elongated, cylindric form that may reach a length of 3 mm. It has well-developed myonemes and is highly contractile. *Nyctotherus,* with an oval, compressed body, is a common commensal in the intestines of frogs and cockroaches.

Order Oligotrichida

Members of the order Oligotrichida have scanty cilia, as the name implies. The body is usually spherical or fusiform, and the

77

A

B

Fig. 2-49

A, *Vorticella,* living (order Peritrichida). B, *Stentor* (order Heterotrichida). (**A** from Hickman: Integrated principles of zoology, The C. V. Mosby Co.; **B** from Encyclopaedia Britannica film, "Protozoa: One-Celled Animals.")

adoral zone of membranelles at the anterior end is well developed. All members of this order are free living. *Halteria* (Fig. 2-50, *A*) is a familiar form that often can be recognized by the jerky movements that it makes with its long bristles.

Order Tintinnida

Members of the order Tintinnida are conical or trumpet shaped and live in secreted shells or loricas. They are mostly pelagic, but a few are found in brackish or fresh water. Their adoral zone of membranelles often extends out from the lorica. Other cilia are scanty. They have left the only known ciliate fossil record. *Tintinnopsis* (Fig. 2-50, *B*) has a lorica that is often covered with foreign bodies and may be found in fresh or salt water.

Order Entodiniomorphida

The honor of being the most complex of all ciliates belongs to the members of the order Entodiniomorphida. The body is somewhat elongated, oval, and asymmetric. Members have no external ciliation except for one or two zones of membranelles. There may also be one or two tufts of specialized cilia. Along the right ventral side of some species is a row of skeletal plates. Posterior spines occur in some. A tough pellicle encloses the body of the animal, and

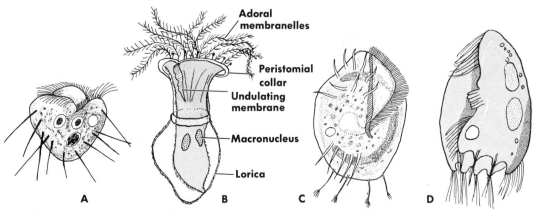

Adoral membranelles

Peristomial collar

Undulating membrane

Macronucleus

Lorica

A   B   C   D

Fig. 2-50

A, *Halteria* (order Oligotrichida); 25 to 50 microns long. B, *Tintinnopsis* (order Tintinnida); diagrammatic, with lorica in optical section; 100 microns long. C, *Euplotes* (order Hypotrichida); 70 to 90 microns long. D, *Epalxis mirabilis* (order Ctenostomatida); 35 to 45 microns long. (**B** redrawn from Jahn and Jahn: How to know the Protozoa, William C. Brown Co., Publishers.)

internal structures are numerous and complex. Besides the cytostome, there is a gullet, rectum, and anus. Myonemes are common, and there is an extensive neuromotor system with a motorium ("nerve center"). In addition, there are the regular organelles of the ciliate.

These organisms are exclusively endocommensals in the stomach (rumen and paunch) of herbivorous animals such as cattle, sheep, goats, and others. They are present in enormous numbers (10 billion to 50 billion in a single animal) and were once thought to aid in the digestion of their host's food. However, as E. R. Becker (1932) showed, herbivores can survive just as well without them; but the protozoans cannot survive without their hosts. This finding indicates that the protozoans are strictly harmless commensals. Some are found in the colon of higher mammals including apes. *Epidinium* (Fig. 2-51) and *Ophryoscolex* are common genera.

Order Ctenostomatida

Members of the order Ctenostomatida bear carapaces and are sparsely ciliated. Their adoral zone has eight membranelles, and their cilia are restricted to a few rows on the carapace. Their bodies are highly

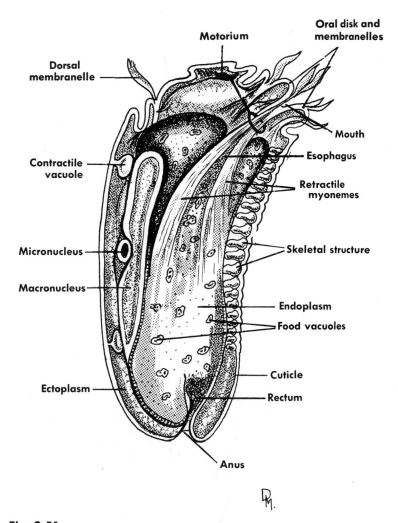

Fig. 2-51

Epidinium (Diplodinium) ecaudatum (order Entodiniomorphida); shown in longitudinal section; 130 microns long. (From Hickman: Integrated principles of zoology, The C. V. Mosby Co.)

compressed. This is an insignificant group that lives in sapropelic habitats, i.e., the black bottom slime of foul waters rich in carbon dioxide and decaying nitrogenous products. Some species are found in sewage tanks, but there are both freshwater and saltwater forms. The common genera are *Saprodinium* and *Epalxis* (Fig. 2-50, *D*).

Order Hypotrichida

Members of the order Hypotrichida are common wherever protozoans occur. They are oval and strongly flattened dorsoventrally, with the ventral side specialized for creeping. On the ventral surface the cilia are replaced by cirri that are designated according to location—frontals, marginals, etc. The dorsal surface usually bears sensory bristles with only a few cilia. The peristome and its adoral zone of membranelles are well developed. In some species the buccal area may occupy a large part of the ventral surface. This order represents a group that has reached a high degree of specialization in the evolution of ciliates.

The following genera are familiar to all who study protozoans: *Stylonychia* (Fig. 2-40, *B*), with an ovoid shape and three caudal bristles; *Oxytricha*, similar to *Stylonychia* but without caudal bristles; *Euplotes* (Fig. 2-50, *C*), with ovoid body and four caudal bristles; and *Kerona*, with a kidney-shaped body and six oblique rows of ventral cirri but no caudal bristles. *Kerona* is ectozoic, or parasitic, on hydra, where it is often seen creeping on the body and tentacles.

Annotated references

Allen, R. D. 1962. Amoeboid movement. Sci. Amer. **206**:112-122. *The newer interpretation of ameboid movement.*

Cleveland, L. R. 1925. Method by which *Trichonympha* ingests solid particles of wood. Biol. Bull. **48**:282-287. *In this and other papers Cleveland has described his classic studies on the symbiosis between termites and roaches and their intestinal Protozoa.*

Conn, H. W. 1905. Protozoa of the fresh waters of Connecticut. Hartford, State Geol. & Natur. Hist. Surv. Bull. **2**:1-120.

Corliss, J. O. 1961. The ciliated Protozoa; characterization, classification, and guide to the literature. New York, Pergamon Press, Inc. *An excellent evaluation of the class Ciliata. One of*

the most important recent studies on the Protozoa.

Edmondson, W. T. (editor). 1959. Ward and Whipple's fresh-water biology, ed. 2. New York, John Wiley & Sons, Inc. *Many useful keys to freshwater Protozoa are found in this important handbook.*

Ehret, C. F., and E. L. Powers. 1959. The cell surface of *Paramecium*. Int. Rev. Cytol. **8**:97-133.

Ericson, D. B., and G. Wollen. 1964. The deep and the past. New York, Alfred A. Knopf, Inc. *A study of forams in an understanding of deepsea stratigraphy.*

Gibbons, I. R., and A. V. Grimstone. 1960. On flagellate structure in certain flagellates. J. Biophys. Biochem. Cytol. **7**:697-718.

Gojdics, M. 1953. The genus Euglena. Madison, University of Wisconsin Press. *A comprehensive account of the taxonomy and morphology of the genus.*

Grasse, P. P. (editor). 1952. Traite de zoologie. Paris, Masson et Cie. *Parts 1 and 2 of volume 1 of this comprehensive treatise are devoted to the phylogeny, general features, and other aspects of the Protozoa together with a detailed treatment of the subphylum Plasmodroma.*

Grimstone, A. V. 1961. Fine structure and morphogenesis in Protozoa. Biol. Rev. **36**:97-150. *This article brings up to date the present state of knowledge on the organization of the protozoans.*

Hall, R. P. 1953. Protozoology. Englewood Cliffs, N. J., Prentice-Hall, Inc. *A good introductory text on the Protozoa.*

Hirshfield, H. I. (editor). 1960. Biology of the Amoeba. New York, New York Academy of Sciences. *An entire treatise by many specialists is devoted to the many aspects of this classic protozoan.*

Hutner, S. H., and A. Lwoff (editors). 1951-1955. Biochemistry and physiology of the Protozoa, vols. 1 and 2. New York, Academic Press Inc. *A comprehensive account of the physiology and chemistry of the group.*

Hutner, S. H., and L. Provasoli. The phytoflagellates. In Hutner, S. H., and A. Lwoff (editors). 1951-1955. Biochemistry and physiology of protozoa, vol. 1. New York, Academic Press Inc.

Hyman, L. H. 1940. The invertebrates; Protozoa through Ctenophora, vol. 1. New York, McGraw-Hill Book Company. *An extensive section of this fine treatise is devoted to the morphology and physiology of the Protozoa. Knowledge about the group is brought up to date in volume 5 (1959).*

Jahn, T. L., and F. F. Jahn. 1949. How to know the Protozoa. Dubuque, Iowa, William C. Brown Company, Publishers. *A useful manual for the identification and description of protozoan forms.*

Jennings, H. S. 1906. Behavior of the lower organisms. New York, Columbia University Press. *A classic study that always has its appeal.*

Johnson, W. H. 1941. Nutrition in the Protozoa. Quart. Rev. Biol. **16**:336-48.

Johnson, W. H. 1956. Nutrition of Protozoa. Ann. Rev. Microbiol. **10**:193-212.

King, R. L. 1925. The contractile vacuole of *Paramecium multimicronucleata*. J. Morphol. **58**:555-557.

King, R. L. 1928. The contractile vacuole of *Paramecium trichium*. Biol. Bull. **55**:59-69.

Kirby, H. 1950. Materials and methods in the study of Protozoa. Berkeley, University of California Press. *A useful manual for collecting, cultivating, and preparing Protozoa for study.*

Kudo, R. R. 1961. Protozoology, ed. 5. Springfield, Ill., Charles C Thomas, Publisher. *An authoritative work that stresses taxonomy.*

Mackinnon, D. L., and R. S. J. Hawes. 1961. An introduction to the study of Protozoa. New York, Oxford University Press, Inc. *An up-to-date account with excellent illustrations.*

Manwell, R. D. 1961. Introduction to protozoology. New York, St. Martin's Press, Inc. *This introductory study stresses the biologic aspects of the protozoans with less emphasis on the taxonomy of the group. An excellent text for learning the ways of these small forms.*

Mayr, E. (editor). 1957. The species problem. Washington, D. C., American Assn. for the Advancement of Science. *One of the papers is by Professor T. M. Sonneborn, who presents a fine analysis of the present status of mating types and the concept of the syngens.*

Pennak, R. W. 1953. Fresh-water invertebrates of the United States. New York, The Ronald Press Company. *An excellent up-to-date section on freshwater Protozoa with keys of the common genera. Introductory accounts of protozoans in general are especially worthwhile.*

Pettersson, H. 1954. The ocean floor. New Haven, Yale University Press. *A description of the role the forams and radiolaridans have played in building up the sediment carpet of the ocean floor.*

Phleger, F. B. 1960. Ecology and distribution of recent Foraminifera. Baltimore, The Johns Hopkins Press.

Pitelka, D. R. 1963. Electron-microscopic structure of Protozoa. New York, Pergamon Press, Inc.

Rudzinska, M. A. and W. Trager, 1957. Intracellular phagotrophy by malaria parasites; an electron microscope study of *Plasmodium lophurae*. J. Protozool. **4**:190-199.

Sleigh, M. A. 1963. The biology of cilia and flagella. New York, Pergamon Press, Inc. *An up-to-date analysis of the movement of those organs from the viewpoint of their comparative anatomy and function. Many revealing diagrams of structural organization and some excellent electron micrographs.*

Tartar, V. 1961. The biology of Stentor. New York, Pergamon Press, Inc.

Wichterman, R. 1953. The biology of Paramecium. New York, McGraw-Hill Book Company. *One of the finest and most exhaustive monographs ever published on a single genus of the Protozoa.*

Chapter 3

Phylum Mesozoa

The Mesozoa are wormlike animals that are endoparasites in the bodies of certain marine invertebrates. Since their discovery in 1839, they have been found as parasites in cephalopods, flatworms, rhyncocoels, brittle stars, annelids, and clams. The members of this phylum are considered the simplest multicellular animals, and their taxonomic status is a subject of perennial controversy among students of the group. One common interpretation considers their simplicity as a secondary adaptation to a parasitic life and that they should be placed as a subdivision (class) under Platyhelminthes; an alternative view emphasizes their primitive nature and that they are a well-defined group meriting phylum status in their own right. They are small forms, the largest not exceeding 9 mm. in length; most are much smaller than this, and some species are under 1 mm. in length.

CLASSIFICATION

Class Moruloidea

Order Dicyemida (Rhombozoa). Elongated, symmetric, vermiform body; single layer of flat cells or syncytium (usually ciliated) enclosing a central axial cell or cells giving rise to reproductive cells (agametes); two reproductive phases (nematogen and rhombogen); nematogen phase gives rise to vermiform larva; rhombogen phase produces infusoriform larva; life cycle consists of sexual (primary host) and asexual generations in intermediate host; cell constancy; all members are endoparasites in cephalopods. *Dicyema, Pseudicyema, Dicyemennea.*

Order Orthonectida. Asexual stage is a mul-

tinucleated ameboid plasmodium; plasmodium asexually gives rise to males and larger females; hermaphroditic or dioecious; inner cell mass of many cells gives rise to sex cells; internal fertilization; ciliated larva. *Rhopalura, Stoecharthrum.*

BASIC ADAPTIVE FEATURES

There are so many obscure points about the life cycles and systematic relationships of this phylum that it is impossible to indicate what adaptive features have been followed in their evolutionary development. Although they are considered the simplest in body structure of all multicellular animals, this simplicity does not extend to their life cycles, which are amazingly complex and still incompletely known. All of the Mesozoa are adapted in certain ways to a parasitic existence, which may explain somewhat their simplicity of structure—but it may be true that they are primitive in structure without having undergone the degeneration associated with parasitism. Perhaps their most striking adaptation is their reproductive cycle of metagenesis involving asexual reproductive phases, such as stem nematogens and primary nematogens that give rise to vermiform larvae, and the sexual rhombogen phase that produces the infusoriform larva (product of a fertilized egg). The plasmodium of the orthonectids may correspond to the axial cells of dicyemids, because in both groups agametes give rise to either larvae or sexually mature forms. Although the life cycle for the dicyemids is incompletely known, such diverse reproduction may have significance in their parasitic relationships to the host. The position of the reproductive cells in the interior may indicate a pattern that

most metazoans have followed in their evolution.

PHYLOGENETIC RELATIONSHIPS

The view once held that Mesozoa formed
an intermediate link between the protozoans and the metazoans has been in doubt
for many years. Some mesozoan characteristics seem to indicate a relationship to
Protozoa, such as the presence of cilia, the
differentiation of cells into somatic and reproductive types, and the phagocytic surface layer of cells. Another view that has
been held by many is that mesozoans are
really degenerate flatworms. Aside from the
parasitic habit and the resemblances between the infusoriform larva and the miracidium, there appears to be little evidence
of flatworm affinities. Most diversity of
opinion hinges upon whether or not mesozoans are simply primitive in structure or
are degenerated parasites with the secondary simplicity of a higher metazoan group.
If they are considered primitive, this would
indicate that the first metazoans had a solid
rather than a hollow gastrula. Early investigators, such as E. Van Beneden, and
later ones, such as M. Hartmann and L. H.
Hyman, have stoutly maintained that Mesozoa is a well-defined, primitive group and
is not the result of parasitic degeneration.
Other than these views, nothing is known
about their exact phylogenetic status. They
have left no fossil record.

GENERAL STRUCTURAL FEATURES AND LIFE HISTORIES

Details of structure as well as life histories vary in the two orders of Mesozoa.
In the order Dicyemida, the common form
of the parasite (primary nematogen) is an
elongated cylindric body with the posterior end somewhat pointed and the anterior end relatively thick and blunt (Fig.
3-1). It is found exclusively in the kidneys
of cephalopods and is about 8 or 9 mm.
long in some species, shorter in others.

The organism is made up of 25 cells
arranged in a single layer of large, ciliated
cells (the somatoderm or somatic cells) enclosing one or more elongated axial cells.
The somatoderm of the head contains
eight or nine polar cells that form the cap
(calotte). This cap consists of two circlets
or tiers of cells, with four cells in the an-

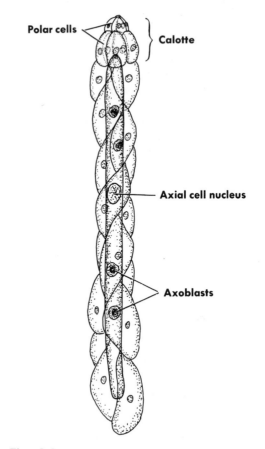

Fig. 3-1

Primary nematogen of *Dicyema* (order Dicyemida).

terior circlet and four or five cells in the
other circlet. The other somatoderm cells
(10 to 17 in number) form the trunk and
are constant in number for the species.
These cells may be arranged more or less
spirally.

The elongated axial cell contains, in
addition to its own nucleus, reproductive
cells called agametes that have been
formed without maturation. In some species there appears to be an earlier stage
(stem nematogen) than the primary nematogen. These stem nematogens usually
have three axial cells arranged in linear
series in the long axis, and they may also
have a different number and arrangement
of somatic cells (B. H. McConnaughey).

Axoblasts or germ cells in the stem nematogen give rise to ordinary or primary nematogens that replace the stem nematogens
as the population of organisms increases.

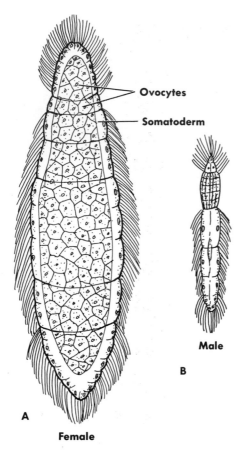

Ovocytes

Somatoderm

Male

B

A

Female

Fig. 3-2

A, Female and, **B,** male orthonectid *(Rhopalura)* (order Orthonectida).

As soon as the primary nematogens have completed their differentiation and become vermiform larvae they leave the mother nematogen and increase the infection in the kidney of the cephalopod host. Primary nematogens keep on increasing until the host attains sexual maturity or until there is a heavy population of parasites; the parasite is then transformed into a new phase called the rhombogen. From infusorigens, or hermaphroditic individuals, which remain in the axial cell of the rhombogen, eggs and sperm are produced. The fertilized egg gives rise to free-swimming ciliated larvae, the infusoriform larvae. These larvae are discharged into the sea with the cephalopod urine, and their fate is unknown. There are variant accounts of this process among the authorities.

The order Orthonectida shows several differences from the preceding order. This parasite has been found in a number of invertebrates, such as flatworms, mollusks, annelids, and brittle stars. The asexual stage in their life history consists of a multinucleated ameboid plasmodium that causes damage to the host by spreading. After they multiply by fragmentation, the plasmodia give rise asexually to males and females. Usually only one sex comes from the agamete of a plasmodium, but sometimes both sexes may arise from the same plasmodium. Some sexual forms are hermaphrodites. Males are smaller than females.

In structure, they consist of a single layer of ciliated epithelial cells surrounding an inner mass of sex cells (Fig. 3-2). The epithelial cells form rings around the body, each ring consisting of rows of cells. The rings give an appearance of segmentation. The cilia on the anterior group of rings (the cone) are directed forward; those on the rest of the body point backward. The male has fewer rings than the female but has the same body regions. The inner cell mass consists of eggs in the female and sperm in the male. Hermaphroditic forms have a testis anterior to the egg mass.

The males and females escape from their hosts and swim in the sea. The male fertilizes the female by discharging his sperm through a genital opening in the female. After insemination, the eggs develop in the female into ciliated larvae. When liberated from the female, the larvae infect new hosts of the same kind. The larvae have superficial layers of ciliated cells and an inner mass of germinal cells. In the host the larvae disintegrate, and each germinal cell gives rise to a plasmodium.

Annotated references

Caullery, M. 1912. Le cycle evolulif des orthonectides. Proceedings of 8th International Congress of Zoology at Graz (1910), pp. 765-774. *An active investigation of the orthonectids.*

Frenzel, J. 1892. Untersuchungen über die Mikroskopische Fauna Argentiniens. Arch. Naturgesch. **58:**66-96. *An account of the strange and unique animal Salinella which consists of a single layer of cells surrounding a digestive cavity with a mouth at one end and an anus at the other. It has no internal cells and does not fit* *into any known metazoan phylum. It has not been found since its original discovery.*

Hyman, L. H. 1940. The invertebrates; Protozoa through Ctenophora, vol. 1, chap. 4. New York, McGraw-Hill Book Company. *The most comprehensive American account of the morphology and phylogeny of the Mesozoa.*

Hyman, L. H. 1959. The invertebrates; smaller coelomate groups, vol. 5. New York, McGraw-Hill Book Company. *The author reaffirms her stand that the Mesozoa is a well-defined phylum and not a degenerate flatworm.*

Lameere, A. 1916-1919. Contributions a la connaissance des Dicyemides. Bull. Sci. Fr. Belg. **50**:1-35; **51**:347-390; **53**:234-275. *This is one of the best accounts of the order Dicyemida by one of the leading French investigators of the Mesozoa.*

McConnaughey, B. H. 1951. The life cycle of the dicyemid Mesozoa. Univ. Calif. Publ. Zool. **55**:295-336.

McConnaughey, B. H. The Mesozoa. In Dougherty, E. C. (editor). 1963. The lower Metazoa; comparative biology and phylogeny. Berkeley, University of California Press. *The most recent account by the foremost American student of the group. The author points out the resemblance between the Mesozoa and the parasitic flatworms and Aschelminthes.*

Stunkard, H. W. 1954. The life history and systematic relations of the Mesozoa. Quart. Rev. Biol. **29**:230-244. *This investigator presents evidence to show that the Mesozoa are degenerate flatworms, being derived from a remote ancestor of all flatworms.*

Van Beneden, E. 1876. Recherches sur les Dicyemides. Brussels Acad. Roy. Belg. Bull. Cl. Sci., **41**:1160-1205; **42**:35-97. *The famous Belgian cytologist was one of the first to study this group of animals discovered in 1839, and he considered them intermediate between the Protozoa and the Metazoa.*

Phylum Porifera

The sponges are multicellular organisms of the incipient tissue level of organization. Their whole structural organization is different from that found in other phyla. They consist of two or more types of specialized cells, but they have no organs or mouth, and certain of their cells are capable of independent existence for a few days. The body has numerous pores, canals, and chambers through which water circulates and openings through which water passes to the outside. Certain internal cavities are provided with collar cells (choanocytes) which, by the beating of their flagella, keep currents of water moving through the various canals and chambers. The sponges are almost all sessile and aquatic organisms that have relatively simple responses, little contractility, and little irritability. For supporting their body structure, most have a unique skeletal system of spicules or organic fibers or a combination of both spicules and fibers.

With the exception of one family, they are all marine forms that exist from the intertidal zone to a depth of about 9,000 meters. More than 5,000 species have been described, but their taxonomy is very much in a state of flux.

CLASSIFICATION

Although they are multicellular organisms, sponges are so atypical that they are often placed in a subkingdom of their own (the Parazoa). Classification within the phylum is difficult, and sponge authorities are far from agreement in regard to certain subdivisions. The major groups or taxa are subdivided mainly on the kind of skeleton structure. Subdivisions of these major taxa are based on various morphologic characteristics.

Class Calcarea (Calcispongiae). The members of the class Calcarea all have spicules of calcium carbonate and large choanocytes. This type of sponge is rather small (mostly under 10 cm. in height), is often solitary, is grouped into clusters, or consists of anastomosing tubules. Many have vase-shaped bodies that are radially symmetric. Each individual has a terminal osculum encircled by a collar of extended monaxon spicules that give it a peculiar fringed appearance. Sometimes the osculum is protected by a sieve membrane. All three levels of sponge architecture—asconoid, syconoid, and leuconoid —are found in this class (Fig. 4-1). Calcareous sponge spicules are of three types: monaxonid (one ray), triradiate (three rays), and quadriradiate (four rays, Fig. 4-2, A). These sponges are found chiefly in shallow seawater down to depths of 200 meters (a few are found deeper). Many are found at depths of less than 10 meters. Wherever found they are attached by their bases to some hard substratum.

The class Calcarea is divided into two subclasses, Calcinea and Calcaronea, and a number of orders.

Subclass Calcinea. Larva parenchymula-like; flagellum (in choanocyte) independent of nucleus; some triradiate spicules with equal rays. *Clathrina, Dendya, Leucascus.*

Subclass Calcaronea. Amphiblastula larva; flagellum (in choanocyte) arises from nucleus; triradiate spicules with one ray longer than other two. *Leucosolenia* (Fig. 4-4, C), *Scypha.*

Class Hyalospongiae (Hexactinellida). The glass sponges vary in size from a few inches to more than 4 feet in length. They are radially symmetric sponges of varied shapes, such as cylindric, urn shaped, or funnel shaped. The bodies are either directly attached by their bases or by stalks of root spicules to a substratum. Their chief distinguishing features are the skeleton of siliceous spicules, commonly six rayed (Fig. 4-3), which are often bound together into a

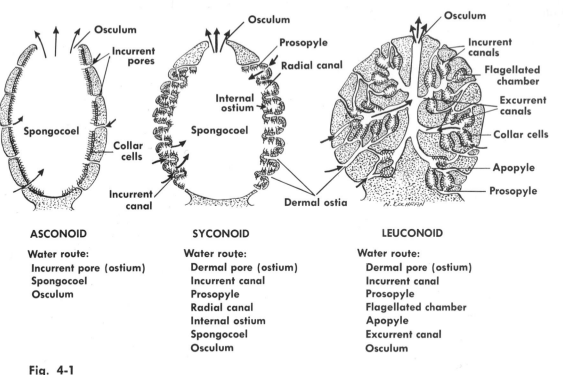

ASCONOID

Water route:
Incurrent pore (ostium)
Spongocoel
Osculum

SYCONOID

Water route:
Dermal pore (ostium)
Incurrent canal
Prosopyle
Radial canal
Internal ostium
Spongocoel
Osculum

LEUCONOID

Water route:
Dermal pore (ostium)
Incurrent canal
Prosopyle
Flagellated chamber
Apopyle
Excurrent canal
Osculum

Fig. 4-1

Three types of sponge structure. (From Hickman: Integrated principles of zoology, The C. V. Mosby Co.)

lattice network forming a glasslike structure (Fig. 4-5) and the trabecular net of living tissue produced by the fusion of the pseudopodia of many types of amebocytes. Within the trabecular net are thimble-shaped chambers lined with choanocytes and often opening into the spongocoel. The osculum is unusually large and may be covered over by a sievelike plate of silica. There is no epidermis of pinacocytes or typical mesenchyme, and both the external surface and spongocoel are lined with the trabecular net, which may be slightly modified to form outer and inner surfaces that are perforated with pores for the passage of water through the sponge wall. Because of the rigid skeleton and lack of contractility, muscular elements (myocytes) appear to be absent. The general arrangement of their chambers fits glass sponges into both syconoid and leuconoid types (Fig. 4-1), although some authorities describe them as subleuconoid. In species with thick and much-folded walls, there may be deeper lying flagellated chambers, and the pattern just described may be more complicated. Thus the body wall typically has the following regions: outer surface, subdermal trabecular net, flagellated chambers, subgastral trabecular net, inner surface, and spongocoel. This class of sponges

lives primarily in deep water, usually at depths of 200 to 5,000 meters, although some have been found under antarctic ice at depths of 20 meters.

The class Hyalospongiae has two subclasses, Amphidiscophora and Hexasterophora, each of which contains a number of orders.

Subclass Amphidiscophora. Spicules in trabecular net not fused to form a rigid network; amphidisk spicules present; anchored by basal tufts to soft bottom sediments. *Hyalonema, Monorhaphis.*

Subclass Hexasterophora. Spicules in trabecular net often fused to form a rigid network; amphidisk spicules absent; usually fixed to substratum by base. *Hexactinella, Euplectella* (Figs. 4-4, *B*, 4-5), *Aphrocallistes* (Fig. 4-6).

Class Demospongiae. This is the largest class of sponges, both in number of species and in extent of distribution. They also have the most complicated morphologic patterns. They are characterized by having a skeleton of one-rayed to four-rayed siliceous spicules, of spongin fibers (Fig. 4-15), of both, or of neither. Some sponges with both siliceous and calcareous elements have recently been reported (W. D. Hartman). Their flagellated chambers have small choanocytes, and their canal system is of

Fig. 4-2

Some types of spicules. **A**, Calcarea. **B**, Demospongiae.

Fig. 4-3

Some spicules from hexactinellids (Hyalospongiae).

the leuconoid type (Fig. 4-1, *C*). Mesenchyme is well developed, and the incurrent and excurrent canal systems may be complex. The spongocoel is often lacking, but a large, common central canal may lead to the osculum. By repeated folding the whole sponge becomes irregular and indefinite in shape with the interior containing a maze of water channels. An epidermal epithelium pierced with pores and oscula covers the surface. Incurrent canals branch irregularly through the mesenchyme, and there may be subdermal spaces beneath the dermal membrane. Incurrent canals open into the small flagellated chambers by small apertures (prosopyles). The flagellated chambers in turn open by apopyles into excurrent canals, which unite with other canals to form larger tubes that finally reach the oscula. The leuconoid type has many variations, because it is a type that permits larger size and a more efficient water circulating system.

The Demospongiae vary in size from forms

Fig. 4-4

A, *Spongilla,* a freshwater sponge (class Demospongiae). **B,** *Euplectella,* a glass sponge (class Hyalospongiae). **C,** *Leucosolenia,* a calcareous sponge (class Calcarea).

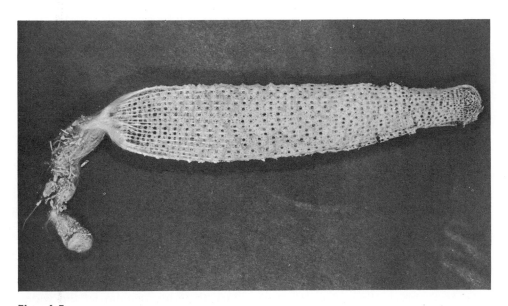

Fig. 4-5

Dried skeleton of glass sponge *Euplectella.*

only a few millimeters in diameter to those which are more than 2 meters across. Shapes are highly variable as is to be expected in organisms that are so irregular in their growth. They may be encrusting forms (Fig. 4-7), may be upright and branching, or may be shaped like vases, fans, or cushions. This class contains over 80 percent of all sponge species, and they are found from the intertidal zone down to the abyssal zone. Some species live in brackish water,

and one family (Spongillidae) occurs in freshwater ponds and lakes. Shallow-water Demospongiae may be beautifully colored in orange, yellow, blue, or red. Spongillidae are of a greenish hue because of the presence of zoochlorellae.

According to W. D. Hartman, this class has two subclasses—Tetractinomorpha (Tetractinellida) and Ceractinomorpha (which includes the Monaxonida and Keratosa)—and 10 orders.

89

Fig. 4-6

Left, *Aphrocallistes vastus,* an orange-colored glass sponge (Hyalospongiae). Right, *Craniella villosa,* a typical tetractinellid sponge (Demospongiae). From Friday Harbor, Washington. (Courtesy G. J. Bakus.)

Fig. 4-7

Mycale adherens encrusting scallop shell *(Hinnites)* (Demospongiae). From Smith Island, Washington. (Courtesy G. J. Bakus.)

Subclass Tetractinomorpha. With siliceous tetraxon spicules; little or almost no spongin; no skeleton in some; amphiblastula and parenchymula larvae. *Cliona* (Fig. 4-9), *Suberites* (Fig. 4-8), *Craniella* (Fig. 4-6), *Tethyla, Oscarella.* **Subclass Ceractinomorpha.** With siliceous monaxon spicules; spongin common; no skeleton in some; parenchymula (stereogastrula) larva. *Halisarca, Spongia, Spongilla* (Fig. 4-4, *A*), *Halichondria, Haliclona, Mycale* (Fig. 4-7).

BASIC ADAPTIVE FEATURES

The one adaptive feature that has been most responsible for the evolutionary history of sponges is their water-current system. Any advancement in the structural complexity of sponges is centered upon an increase in the efficiency of water currents that enter and leave the sponge. Sponges feed upon bacteria, small planktonic organisms, and minute particles of detritus filtered from the water, and it is important that the used water should be separated from the fresh supply.

Water enters the flagellated chambers through openings (prosopyles) of the inhalant canals. In freshwater sponges the average diameter of the flagellate chamber is about 40 to 60 microns. Water passes from the flagellate chambers into the exhalant system through apertures called apopyles. Choanocytes are usually clustered near the prosopyles with their collars so oriented as to direct their currents toward the apopyles. Because of choanocyte activity and the greater size of the outlets of the flagellated chambers than that of their inlets, a fall in pressure occurs between the prosopyles and apopyles. Water is thus drawn in through the inhalant canals and propelled toward the apopyles and exhalant canals. The leuconoid type of sponge structure allows a large size because it develops more chambers for capturing food and for gaseous exchange. A more advanced organism and greater size in the evolution of sponges is made possible by this union of many channels and many flagellated chambers.

To separate the food-free outflow water with its excretory products from the fresh intake water laden with food, it is necessary that the osculum jet the water away as far as possible from itself to prevent the foul water from reentering the sponge. This is accomplished by a chamber of pressure that is built up in the exhalant canals by the pumping action of the flagellated chambers (where the choanocytes have their collars pointed toward the apopyles of the exhalant canals) and by regulation of the size of canals as well as oscular openings and subdermal spaces. If the osculum is decreased in size, for example, the jet issuing from it will increase in velocity and throw the water farther away from the sponge, just as the water issuing from a garden hose will increase in velocity when the nozzle size is diminished.

PHYLOGENETIC RELATIONSHIPS

The Porifera differ from all members of the Metazoa in so many ways that they are considered a blind branch of the animal kingdom with no direct relationship to the true metazoan forms. They are therefore often placed in a separate subkingdom, the Parazoa. However, many authorities think that sponges have descended from the choanoflagellates (order Protomonadida of the Mastigophora) because of the similarity between the collar cells of this protozoan to the choanocytes so characteristic of sponges. As evidence for this relationship, *Proterospongia,* a colonial flagellate (Fig. 2-16), has been advanced. As described, this colonial flagellate consists of a number of collar cells embedded in a gelatinous matrix and could very well have served as an ancestor of sponges. But the exact taxonomic status of *Proterospongia* has been in doubt because some zoologists consider it a fragment of an actual sponge. In recent years a few species of *Proterospongia* have been described, and it is now thought that the genus is an actual colonial flagellate. However, the choanocytes of larval sponges have flagella but do not acquire collars until the flagellate cells migrate inward. It is, therefore, very doubtful that *Proterospongia* could have served as a sponge ancestor.

Sponges do have some protozoan characteristics, such as the phagocytic method of nutrition and the secretion of their skeletal spicules by amebocytes. There are also some resemblances between the embryonic development of certain sponges and that of colonial flagellates such as *Volvox.* Both undergo developmental stages in which the flagellate layer of cells has the flagella pointing inward and later, by inversion, has them pointing outward. Sponges also bear resemblances to coelenterates in the calcareous or horny nature of their skeletons, the presence of flagellate cells and mesenchyme, a stereoblastula stage, amebocytes (interstitial cells) for forming sex cells, and in other ways. But there are just as many differences between the two groups, and the similarities may be due to convergence.

The embryology of sponges sheds little light upon their relationships because their developmental stages are so different from those of true metazoans. As L. H. Hyman points out, it is very difficult or impossible to homologize the embryology of Metazoa with that of sponges.

The relationship of the different classes of sponges to each other is as vague and uncertain as is the relationship of sponges to other groups of animals. It will be recalled that the Calcarea have all three types of canal systems—asconoid, syconoid, and leuconoid. Demospongiae have only the leuconoid type, but evidence points strongly toward the origin of this class from a rhagon ground plan that consisted of a simple conelike structure with flagellated chambers opening into a spongocoel bearing a single osculum at the summit. From this asconoid type, folds in the choanocyte layer lead to a transitory syconoid stage. Further changes in location and arrangement of the flagellated chambers and canals lead to the leuconoid stage. However, the leuconoid type in Calcarea was evolved independently, and the presence of this type in calcareous sponges does not indicate a close relationship to Demospongiae.

FOSSIL RECORD

Although most sponges are not preserved well as fossils because their spicular skeleton tends to separate into fragments, a fossil record of sponges extends from late Precambrian to Recent times.

All three classes of living sponges have fossil records. Sponge fossils have been most abundant in certain Jurassic, Cretaceous, and Tertiary formations. The Calcarea are recorded from Devonian to Recent times, although a few date back to the Cambrian.

Most sponge fossils are of the pharetrone type in which the spicules are united in a rigid network. The glass sponges (Hyalospongiae) have been found in most formations from Cambrian to Recent, although they reached their greatest abundance in Cretaceous and Jurassic periods. Well-preserved specimens have been recovered from the Devonian period. Demospongiae show a very fine fossil record from Precambian to Recent times. Purely horny sponges are not preserved as fossils, but most Demospongiae also have siliceous spicules which do fossilize. Most fossils of this class have lithistid skeletons (order Lithistida), or skeletons with knobby, siliceous spicules and rigid, stony frameworks.

ECOLOGIC RELATIONSHIPS

Ordinarily, few animals eat sponges because of their spicules and the bad taste of the sponge's bodily substance. Some sponges are actually toxic. However, coral reef fishes prey upon most species of sponges (G. J. Bakus, 1964). A few sponges with horny skeletons may be eaten by turtles. Sponges also have regular predators in nudibranchs, chitons, and gastropods. Freshwater sponges (*Spongilla*, Fig. 4-4, A) are parasitized by the larvae of spongeflies (order Neuroptera) that live in them. Myriads of different animals live in the natural cavities or on the surface of sponges in different sorts of biologic association. These animals include arthropods, annelids, nematodes (which may eat sponge cells), hydroids, zoanthids, and many others. Certain crabs *(Dromia)* fasten sponges or pieces of sponge to their backs for protective purposes. *Euplectella* (a glass sponge) harbors and imprisons certain shrimp for life. Some freshwater sponges are symbiotic with zoochlorellae (an algae), which may manufacture sugars that are utilized by the sponge cells. The siliceous sponge *Suberites ficus* (Fig. 4-8)

often lives on a snail shell occupied by a hermit crab and may completely enclose both shell and crab except for the shell opening. In regions where this association occurs such sponges will probably not grow unless their larvae become attached to a shell inhabited by a crab.

Some sponges may do injury to other organisms. The larvae of the boring sponge *Cliona* (Fig. 4-9) settle on the shells of pelecypods, burrow through, and occupy channels in the shell interior. The method of boring is not known. The mollusk is frequently weakened and may become susceptible to infection. Oysters are often so victimized. Sponges that are unable to burrow may occupy the burrows of the boring sponges.

M. W. deLaubenfels, who made an extensive study of marine sponge distribution, found that one of their favorite habitats is offshore from the mouth of a river. In some cases a particular species is abundant in a habitat where no other sponges are present.

The English investigator G. G. Bidder has worked out the relation of sponges to currents of water. He found that sponges grow more rapidly if they are elevated 10 to 20 cm. above their substratum because the water currents are more vigorous there, or because the sponges can avoid contamination from sediments. Apparently for this reason, many sponges are stalked.

GENERAL MORPHOLOGIC FEATURES

The structure of a sponge is best understood by studying the asconoid type or the embryologic development of a freshwater sponge. In the asconoid type of sponge (Fig. 4-1, A) the vase-shaped and radially symmetric body consists of a wall enclosing a cavity, the spongocoel, which opens at the summit by an osculum. The wall has both an outer and inner epithelium between which there is mesenchyme. The outer epithelium or epidermis is made up of a single layer of flat cells, the pinacocytes; the inner epithelium, which lines the spongocoel, contains the choanocytes also arranged in a single layer. Between the epithelial layers is the mesenchyme of skeletal spicules, various amebocytes, and a gelatinous matrix. Within the wall are tubular cells (porocytes), each of which extends

Fig. 4-8

Suberites ficus containing hermit crab. Sponge grows over and dissolves snail shell, leaving crab encased in sponge for shelter (Demospongiae). From San Juan Island, Washington. (Courtesy G. J. Bakus.)

Fig. 4-9

Cliona celata, sulfur sponge, or boring sponge, on oyster shell.

from the external surface to the spongocoel. Water is drawn through these pores by the beat of the flagella of the choanocytes into the spongocoel and passes out through the osculum. The bore of the ostia and osculum can be regulated by myocytes (modified pinacocytes), which form circlets around these openings. The simple asconoid type of sponge thus described is of restricted occurrence because the inefficient extraction of food particles as described in a former section imposes size limitations.

The syconoid type of canal system overcomes some of these restrictions. This type is produced by the outpushing of the walls of the asconoid type to form radial canals (Fig. 4-1, *B*). These radial canals fuse and are arranged with incurrent (inhalant) canals lying between them (Fig. 4-10). By this arrangement the incurrent canals open to the outside by dermal ostia or pores and their blind inner ends lie between the radial canals; the radial canals open into the spongocoel by internal ostia and their blind outer ends lie between the incurrent canals. Between the radial and incurrent canals, the wall has small pores (the prosopyles) which allow the water to pass from the incurrent canals into the radial canals. In this

way a wall is produced that contains alternating radial and incurrent canals. The inhalant canals are lined with pinacocytes, and the radial canals are lined with choanocytes, while the spongocoel is now lined with an epithelium of endopinacocytes (Fig. 4-10) instead of choanocytes (the asconoid pattern). In the syconoid type the water flows through dermal ostia, incurrent canals, prosopyles, radial canals with choanocytes, internal ostia, spongocoel, and osculum.

The leuconoid type (Fig. 4-1, *C*) is best understood by examining the developmental stages of a freshwater sponge in a gemmule, the asexual reproductive body characteristic of these sponges. A young sponge just hatched from a gemmule appears like a miniature adult sponge. In these juvenile sponges various cell types are found in the inhalant canals, such as archaeocytes, wandering amebocytes, gland cells, pinacocytes, choanocytes, etc. (Fig. 4-11). In later stages mesenchyme and skeletal elements appear as the chief supports of the sponge body.

Epithelium lining
inhalant canals
(pinacocytes)

Dermal ostium

Inhalant canal

Radial canal

Amebocyte

Choanocytes
lining radial canals

Amphiblastula larva

Mesenchyme

Epithelium
lining spongocoel
(endopinacocytes)

Spongocoel

Fig. 4-10

Cross section through wall of *Scypha* showing canal system and cell structure. (Photomicrograph
of stained slide.) (From Hickman: Integrated principles of zoology, The C. V. Mosby Co.)

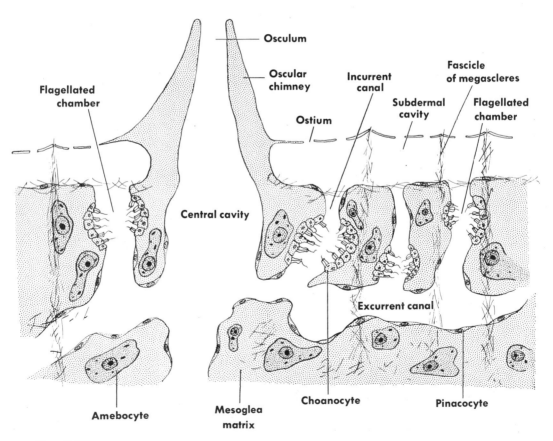

Flagellated
chamber

Osculum

Oscular
chimney

Incurrent
canal

Fascicle
of megascleres

Ostium

Subdermal
cavity

Flagellated
chamber

Central cavity

Excurrent canal

Amebocyte

Mesoglea
matrix

Choanocyte

Pinacocyte

Fig. 4-11

Section through peripheral portion of freshwater sponge (diagrammatic).

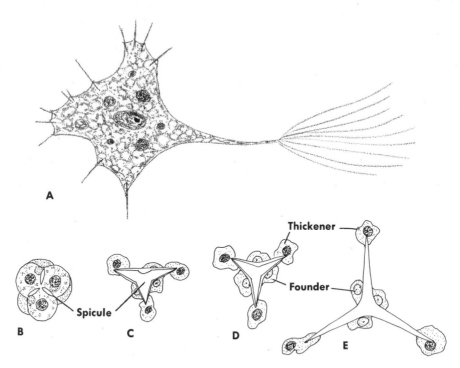

A

Thickener

Founder

Spicule

B

C

D

E

Fig. 4-12

A, Lophocyte. B to E, Secretion of triradiate spicule. B, Group of six scleroblasts have started three rays. C to E, Further development of spicule with three founder cells at base and three thickeners at tips. (A modified from Pavans de Cecatty, 1955; B to E modified from Woodland, 1905.)

Since sponges have reached the incipient tissue level of differentiation, many cell types are to be expected. Most of them are differentiated for various functions, but their terminology is confusing because different names have been assigned to some that have the same function in different sponges. The early larva (amphiblastula) is composed of both flagellated and nonflagellated cells. The nonflagellated cells give rise to pinacocytes, scleroblasts, and porocytes; the flagellated cells form choanocytes, archaeocytes, and amebocytes. With one or two exceptions most sponge cells have developed with slight modifications from a primitive undifferentiated ameboid cell. Of the various cells found in sponges, the chief ones and their functions will be described.

Pinacocytes are flat, polygonal cells forming the epidermis, the lining of the inhalant and exhalant cavities (syconoid sponges), and also the lining of the larger canals and spaces of the leuconoid type. They have the ability to contract and can reduce the surface area of a sponge. They also can be differentiated into spindle-shaped, contractile myocytes which form circlets around the ostia and oscula for regulating water passage. A modification of pinacocytes are the porocytes, tubular cells containing central canals that act as incurrent pores in asconoid sponges. Porocytes may occur also as transient structures in siliceous sponges and have been described in freshwater sponges (Spongillidae).

The mesenchyme contains many types of ameboid cells, such as collencytes, star-shaped cells that are found among the inhalant canals (Fig. 4-13); scleroblasts that secrete the spicules (Fig. 4-12, B to E); spongioblasts that form spongin; archaeocytes or undifferentiated embryonic cells that give rise to sex cells; and gland cells that are derived from amebocytes and secrete mucus.

The most highly differentiated cells of the sponge are the collar cells, or choanocytes, whose flagella create the currents of water through the sponge. Each is made up

95

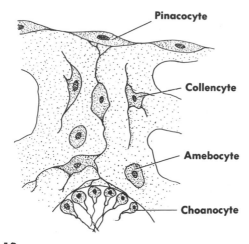

Fig. 4-13

Types of sponge cells. Some authors have suggested a nervous function for collencytes.

Fig. 4-14

Structure of collar cell based on electron microscope studies. Left, transverse section through collar showing protoplasmic tentacles and flagellum (center). Right, longitudinal section showing portion of cell with its protoplasmic tentacles. (Modified from Rasmont et al., 1957.)

of a spherical, oval body surmounted by a contractile, cytoplasmic collar with a long flagellum extending from the base of the collar (Fig. 4-14). Choanocytes vary in size in the different types of sponges, being largest in the Calcarea.

A new type of cell (lophocyte, Fig. 4-12, *A*) has been described for some siliceous, freshwater sponges. It is an ameboid cell with a tuft of fibrils at one or both ends and occurs in connection with the pinacocyte epithelium of the subdermal cavity.

Its function is unknown, but it may secrete fibrillar bundles.

Over the years, sponge investigators have described cells which bear some resemblance to nerve cells. O. Tuzet and M. Pavans de Ceccatty (1953) have recently revived interest in the concept by describing what they consider to be nerve cells. Most students, however, are skeptical concerning physiologic evidence of a nervous system in sponges. C. L. Prosser (1960), who worked on both marine and freshwater sponges, concluded that there was only local contraction of the myocytes in reaction to stimuli and that there was no evidence of true conduction. The whole problem has been reviewed by W. C. Jones (1962).

The skeleton is one of the most typical structures of sponges, being absent in only a few genera. From a taxonomic viewpoint, the skeleton is one of the most useful diagnostic characteristics for classifying sponges. The skeleton consists of spicules (Figs. 4-2, 4-3), spongin (Fig. 4-15), or both. Spicules or sclerites are crystalline in structure and consist of rays or spines radiating from a point. They are secreted by scleroblasts (Fig. 4-12, *B* to *E*), a kind of mesenchyme cell. Both calcareous and siliceous spicules have a core of organic material around which is deposited either calcite ($CaCO_3$) in calcareous sponges or silica (SiO_2nH_2O). Traces of other minerals (manganese, zinc, copper, etc.) also occur.

Spicule shapes and sizes vary greatly and an extensive terminology has been developed to describe them. According to size, they are commonly divided into the larger macroscleres or megascleres that make up the supporting framework of the sponge and smaller microscleres, which are scattered through the mesenchyme. This distinction does not apply to all sponges (e.g., calcareous sponges), however. On the basis of their number of axes and rays, spicules are divided into many types. Monaxons are straight or curved spicules that are formed by growth along one axis. They have pointed, knobbed, or hooked ends. Tetraxons (quadriradiates) consist of four rays each pointing in a different direction. Sometimes this type loses rays and becomes three rayed, two rayed, or one rayed. The triradiate spicule is the most common spic

Fig. 4-15

Spongin fibers.

ule in Calcarea. The rays may be equal or unequal in length. Triaxons (hexactinals) have three axes meeting at right angles producing six rays. Many modifications of this type are found, such as a reduction in rays, curving and branching of rays, and the development of hooks, spines, and knobs on their ends or elsewhere. Polyaxons or asters have several rays radiating from a central point and are found chiefly among the microscleres. Spicules may be detached from each other, or they may form a loosely jointed framework. In some cases they form a very firm and rigid latticework.

Spongin (Fig. 4-15) is the fibrous skeleton found along with siliceous spicules in many sponges, or it may make up the entire skeleton in others (horny or bath sponges). In species that have siliceous spicules spongin often serves to hold the spicules together. Spongin is a scleroprotein, as is also the familiar keratin of hair and fingernails, and is secreted by spongioblasts in the form of separate rods that fuse together to form long fibers.

PHYSIOLOGY

Most known physiologic phenomena in sponges involve their water-current systems, because sponges have practically no locomotion and very restricted contractile powers. The general plan and dynamics of the water-current system were discussed in a former section. Some contraction is found in the majority of sponges, and it is probably limited to the contractile powers of the pinacocytes, myocytes, and collencytes. Most of the activities of sponges, however, center upon the regulation of the water currents on which they depend for their nutrition. By means of myocytes around the oscula and dermal pores they are able to narrow or enlarge these openings and thus regulate the water flow. In an undisturbed condition most sponges have their orifices wide open in both quiet and running water, although there are some individual differences. As a rule the dermal pores are not as sensitive as the oscula to injurious conditions such as unoxygenated and foul water, harmful chemicals, extreme temperatures, exposure to air, and so forth. In freshwater sponges, mechanical touch or stroking may not cause closure of the dermal pores or oscula. Their most sensitive region appears to be the edge of the osculum.

Contraction of the pinacocytes can produce a decrease in the entire body size of a sponge, especially in the asconoid type. In Porifera with oscular tubes (e.g., certain freshwater species) the tube may lengthen under certain conditions and shorten under others. There is little or no evidence of conductivity from one region of a sponge to another; contractions are believed to be direct responses to stimuli. Some transmission of excitatory states may occur, however, through contractile tissue.

The chief problem of the sponge is to move food particles to the choanocytes. This process is rather simple in the asconoid sponge in which the water current passes directly through the porocyte to the choanocytes lining the spongocoel. In the leuconoid type the problem is more involved, because there are more openings, canals, and chambers through which the water must pass. The whole incurrent system acts as a sieve, and only the smallest particles can reach the choanocytes, because prosopyles have diameters of only a few microns. The collars of the choanocytes trap the small food particles, which are passed into the cell body and digested or passed on to amebocytes where digestion occurs (calcareous sponges). In other sponges particles of food small enough to get through the dermal pores are ingested by the specialized amebocytes (archaeocytes and collencytes) that form a reticulum in the inhalant canals. It is probable that certain particles too large for the dermal pores are ingested by the pinacocytes of the epithelial surface. Digestive enzymes, however, are more common in the choanocytes than they are in the amebocytes (Hartman, 1960).

Egested waste is discharged by the amebocytes either into the water currents of the exhalant canals or to the dermal epithelium for voiding. Gaseous exchange of oxygen and carbon dioxide occurs between the amebocytes and the water flowing through the canal systems.

REPRODUCTION AND REGENERATION

Both asexual and sexual reproduction are found in sponges. Asexual methods involve

Fig. 4-16

A, Reduction bodies of calcareous sponge. **B,** Section through reduction body showing mass of amebocytes enclosed in epithelium.

reduction bodies, gemmules, and budding. Reduction refers to masses of many kinds of amebocytes with epidermal covering that persists after the disintegration of the parent sponge. These reduction bodies (Fig. 4-16) can develop into complete sponges when conditions become favorable.

Gemmules occur in all freshwater sponges and some marine sponges. Freshwater gemmules originate as clumps of food-laden amebocytes (archaeocytes) around which is secreted a hard layer by other amebocytes (Fig. 4-17). Scleroblasts also add spicules between the outer and inner spongin of the hard coat. The sponge forms large numbers of these gemmules in the fall, and when the parent sponge disintegrates the gemmules can withstand adverse conditions. In the spring the cells within the gemmule escape to the outside through an outlet, the micropyle (Fig. 4-17, *D*), and form a sponge. Gemmules of marine sponges are also enclosed by spongin with or without spicules. In some species of Demospongiae gemmules without spongin develop into flagellated larvae like those from fertilized eggs.

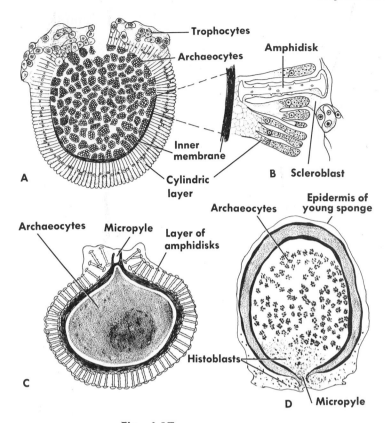

Fig. 4-17

Gemmule formation in freshwater sponge. **A,** Young gemmule of *Heteromyenia* in which trophocytes and cylindric layer are secreting inner membrane. **B,** Portion of cylindric layer of same into which scleroblast is placing its amphidisk. **C,** Completed gemmule of *Heteromyenia*. **D,** Gemmule of *Spongilla* hatching. (**A** to **C** modified from Evans, 1901; **D** modified from Brien, 1932.)

In budding, masses of archaeocytes migrate to the tips of spicule clumps that project from the surface. Later these buds become detached and form new sponges.

Sexual reproduction, which may not occur in tetractinellid sponges, involves germ cells, ova, and sperm. Germ cells may arise from archaeocytes, other amebocytes, or from choanocytes. The ova grow at the expense of other amebocytes or special nurse cells (trophocytes). After reaching full size the ova undergo maturation. The various stages of spermatogenesis occur during the development of the sperm, which may arise by the transformation of an amebocyte or a choanocyte. The sperm fertilizes an egg with the help of a choanocyte that loses its collar and flagellum and acts as a carrier for the sperm (Fig. 4-18). The sperm loses its tail, enlarges, and is transferred to the egg after the carrier cell fuses with the ovum. In some other sponges, sperm are carried by water currents. Fertilization and early development occur in situ. Both dioecious and hermaphroditic

sponges are found, but the majority of sponges are hermaphroditic.

Most sponges have remarkable powers of regeneration. Fragments may grow into complete sponges, but this process is a long one. Suspensions of sponge cells prepared by squeezing pieces of sponge through bolting cloth into seawater can reorganize or reunite into functional sponges (H. V. Wilson). In this reorganization the various types of cells migrate to their appropriate positions in the new organism, or some types of cells are formed anew from amebocytes. Mixed cell suspensions of two species may form a temporary aggregation but later separate, so that each cell mass is composed exclusively of one species or the other.

Fig. 4-18

Carrier cell with sperm near egg.

EMBRYOLOGY

The embryology of sponges shows variations in the different classes. These major differences chiefly revolve around the manner of formation of the two types of larvae—the amphiblastula (mainly calcareous sponges) and the parenchymula (Demospongiae). The amphiblastula is hollow; the parenchymula, or stereogastrula, is solid. In calcareous sponges, such as *Scypha*, the egg after fertilization remains in the mesenchyme of the parent and there undergoes development (Fig. 4-20). Segmentation, which is holoblastic, produces first a ring of eight similar cells, each of which divides horizontally into a small and a large cell (Fig. 4-19). The eight large cells so produced are destined to form the future epidermis; the eight small ones lying next to the maternal choanocytes will form choanocytes. The future choanocyte cells divide rapidly, while the future epidermal cells remain undivided. This produces a blastula with blastocoel. An opening in the middle of the large cells (macromeres) serves for ingesting maternal cells. Each small cell (micromere) acquires a flagellum on its inner end next to the blastocoel. Then a process called inversion occurs in which the embryo turns inside out through its mouth so that the flagellated cells are now on the outside. Most of the surface of the larva is made up of these flagellated cells, but the posterior part contains the large nonflagellated cells. This amphiblastula larva breaks out of the mesenchyme and passes with the water current through the osculum of the parent. After the larva swims around for a short time, the gastrula is formed either by overgrowth of the larger nonflagellated cells or by invagination of the flagellated cells into the interior. The micromeres are now located inside the gastrula and the macromeres are on the outside, which is just the reverse process of gastrulation in the Metazoa. The amphiblastula attaches itself by the blastopore end and begins to grow.

In the early development of sponges a

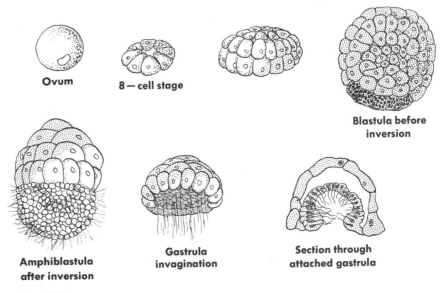

Ovum

8 — cell stage

Blastula before inversion

Amphiblastula after inversion

Gastrula invagination

Section through attached gastrula

Fig. 4-19

Development of calcareous sponge (*Scypha*).

Fig. 4-20

Portion of cross section of *Scypha* showing eggs in early cleavage stages.

so-called olynthus stage of an asconoid type develops (Fig. 4-21). Depending on the species, this olynthus stage may remain as an asconoid type, or it may differentiate later into a syconoid or leuconoid structure. In the parenchymula (stereogastrula), or solid type of larva, the outer flagellated cells lose their flagella, migrate into the interior, and transform into choanocytes. In some cases the formerly flagellated cells may degenerate after reaching the interior, and the choanocytes are formed anew by the archaeocytes (H. Meewis, 1939).

The parenchymula (Fig. 4-22 *A, B*) differs chiefly from the amphiblastula in having most of its surface (except the posterior region) ciliated and in having the interior filled with amebocytes that are formed by a proliferation of cells from the blastula wall. Most of the ameboid cells eventually migrate to the outside and form the dermal epithelium while the flagellated cells are moving into the interior.

Although the leuconoid type may pass through developmental stages that resemble the asconoid and syconoid structures

Fig. 4-21

Olynthus stage in development of calcareous sponge. It has ascon organization.

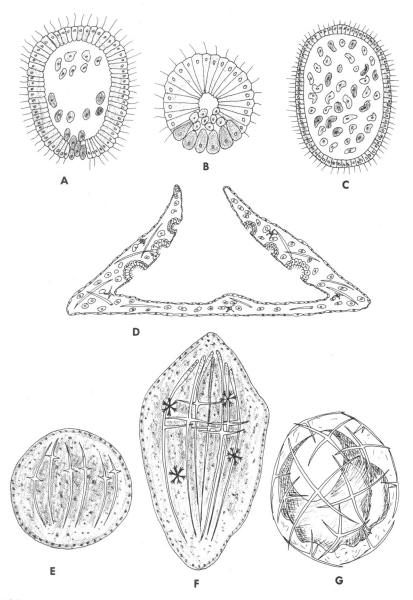

Fig. 4-22

Some types of sponge larvae. **A** to **C**, Parenchymula (stereogastrula) larvae. **A**, Larva of *Clathrina* showing unipolar immigration. **B**, Newly hatched larva of *Leucosolenia*. **C**, Completely ciliated larva of horny sponge. **D**, Vertical section of rhagon stage. **E** to **G**, Larval stages of *Farrea* (Hexactinellida). **G**, Osculum and flagellated layer are forming. (**E** to **G** modified from Okada, 1928.)

before attaining the adult leuconoid condition, many Demospongiae as well as other leuconoid sponges are derived directly from a simple rhagon type of canal system. The rhagon (Fig. 4-22, *D*) consists of a broad base and a narrow summit with a relatively large spongocoel that opens to the exterior by an osculum at the top. Its walls are thick with rounded chambers that open into the spongocoel by large apopyles and open to the outside by prosopyles of inhalant canals. In the wall between the chambers and subdermal spaces is the mesenchyme. The leuconoid type is developed from the rhagon by outfoldings of the flagellated chambers and by the formation of excurrent channels. The rhagon with its flagellated chambers and canals is more advanced in its organization than olynthus, but none of the adult Demospongiae remain in this condition. Many variations of the leuconoid type may have arisen independently several times in the evolution of sponges.

Few developmental stages of the Hexactinellida have been studied. Y. Okada (1928) has studied the development in *Farrea sollasii* in which he describes the cleavage of the fertilized eggs as developing into a stereogastrula (Fig. 4-22, *E* to *G*). The embryo consists of an outer layer of closely packed cells and a central jelly-like mass of ameboid cells, some of which later become choanocytes arranged around a central cavity. Cross-shaped tetractinal spicules appear at the surface before the larva leaves the adult sponge. After the larva settles down, the sponge assumes a tubular form with an osculum.

Both the hollow amphiblastulae and the solid stereogastrulae have a brief free-swimming existence. The free-swimming period varies greatly; in some species it may last for a few days and in others for only a few hours. Usually the larvae swim with the anterior end directed forward, but sometimes they may swim with the posterior end forward. A calcareous larva, such as that of *Leucosolenia* (Fig. 4-22, *B*), which has most of the body surface ciliated when newly hatched, may gradually increase its nonciliated region at the expense of the ciliated portion until both areas are about equal before the larva becomes attached. Bakus (1964) has shown that when the parenchymula of *Tedania gurjanovae* becomes attached to a substratum by its anterior end, its cilia become motionless in a few minutes, and the larva undergoes a radical metamorphosis that involves a change into a platelike, amorphous mass of irregular cells before assuming the adult structural features.

Annotated references

Bakus, G. J. 1964. Morphogenesis of *Tedania gurjanovae* Koltun (Porifera). Pacific Sci. 18(1):58-63. *A description of larval metamorphosis is given in addition to adult morphology.*

Bakus, G. J. 1964. The effects of fish-grazing on invertebrate evolution in shallow tropical waters. Allan Hancock Foundation Publications (occasional papers, No. 27). Los Angeles, University of Southern California Press. *The author presents evidence that the grazing of reef fishes has been a potent force in the survival and distribution of many shallow-water sponges.*

deLaubenfels, M. W. 1936. Sponge fauna of the Dry Tortugas with material for a revision of the families and orders of the Porifera. Washington, D. C., Carnegie Institution of Washington, Tortugas Laboratories, pub. 30. *An important systematic work on American sponges.*

Hartman, W. D. 1960. Porifera. In McGraw-Hill Encyclopedia of Science and Technology, vol. 10, pp. 513-519. New York, McGraw-Hill Book Company. *A concise account of the basic morphology and physiology of sponges.*

Hyman, L. H. 1940. The invertebrates; Protozoa through Ctenophora, vol. 1. New York, McGraw-Hill Book Company. *The section on Porifera represents one of the best accounts of the group. In volume 5 of this treatise (1959) the section on Porifera is brought up to date.*

Jewell, M. Porifera (section 11). In Edmondson, W. T. (editor). 1959. Ward and Whipple's fresh-water biology, ed. 2. New York, John Wiley & Sons, Inc. *A taxonomic key to the freshwater sponges of the United States.*

Jones, W. C. 1962. Is there a nervous system in sponges? Biol. Rev. 37:1-150. *A notable review of this controversial subject in which the author refutes the idea of sensory and ganglionic cells in sponges, but believes that excitatory transmission is restricted to contractile tissue. A comprehensive bibliography is included.*

Lackey, J. B. 1959. Morphology and biology of a species of *Protospongia*. Trans. Amer. Micr. Soc. 78:202-206. *Ever since Kent (1880) described the new genus* Protospongia, *or* Proterospongia, *as a possible transition between the choanoflagellates and sponges, some biologists have cast doubt upon the identity of his single specimen, considering it simply as a sponge fragment. But in recent years the genus has been rediscovered and appears to be a typical choanoflagellate.*

Levi, C. 1956. Etude des Halisarca de Roscoff; embryologie et systematique des demosponges. Arch. Zool. Exp. Gen. 93:1-184. *An important study on the embryology and histology, and a proposed new classification of the Demospongiae.*

Meewis, H. 1939. Contribution a l'etude d'embryogenese des Myxospongidae. Arch. Biol. (Liege) 50:3-66.

Minchin, E. A. Porifera. In Lankester, E. R. (editor). 1900. Treatise on zoology, part 2, pp. 1-178. London, Adam & Charles Black, Ltd. *A work that will always be useful for the basic structure of sponges.*

Okada, Y. 1928. Development of *Farrea sollasii.* Tokyo Univ. Faculty Sci. J., section IV, vol. 2, part 1, pp. 1-27. *One of the few accounts of the embryology of the Hexactinellida.*

Pavans de Ceccatty, M. 1955. Le systeme nerveus des eponges calcaires et siliceuses. Ann. Sci. Nat. Zool. series 11, **17**:203-288. *A description of bipolar and multipolar cells with long processes that connect structures has been advanced as evidence for the presence of nerve cells in sponges.*

Pennak, R. W. 1953. Fresh-water invertebrates of the United States, chap. 3. New York, The Ronald Press Company. *An account of the biology and taxonomy of the freshwater sponge family Spongillidae.*

Tuzet, O. The phylogeny of sponges according to embryological, histological, and serological data, and their affinities with the Protozoa and the Cnidaria. In Dougherty, E. C. (editor). 1963. The lower Metazoa; comparative biology and phylogeny, pp. 129-165. Berkeley, University of California Press. *The author believes that the sponges are intermediate between the protozoans and the coelenterates and should be regarded as the most primitive living metazoans.*

Wilson, H. V., and J. T. Penney. 1930. The regeneration of sponges (Microciona) from dissociated cells. J. Exp. Zool. **56**:73-148. *A repetition and extension of the early classic investigations of Wilson in this field.*

Phylum Cnidaria (Coelenterata)

The members of the phylum Cnidaria have reached the tissue grade of organization and belong to the radiate phyla of the Eumetazoa. They have primary radial symmetry (biradial in some), one opening (mouth) into the enteron, which may be simple or modified by diverticula or canals, and a body wall composed of two distinct layers—epidermis and gastrodermis (from ectoderm and endoderm) with a structureless mesoglea between them. In some members there may be the beginning of a third germ layer, the mesoderm. The body parts are built concentrically around an oral-aboral axis that extends from mouth to base and that gives the characteristic radial symmetry. Arrangement of bodily parts may be indefinite or built around a definite number—four or six or a multiple thereof. Typically, with few exceptions they all have extensible tentacles that encircle the oral end and possess diagnostic stinging organelles (nematocysts).

Polymorphism (more than one kind of form in one species) is characteristic of the group, although it is absent in one class. The individuals of the polymorphic forms are (1) the cylindric polyp attached at the aboral end, the free end provided with mouth and tentacles, and (2) the free-swimming medusa with a bell-shaped or saucer-shaped gelatinous body provided with marginal tentacles and with a centrally located mouth on a projection of the concave side.

The phylum is a large one; its members are exclusively aquatic and mostly marine. They include jellyfish, sea anemones, corals, hydras, and hydroids. Individual organisms may be single or in colonies.

CLASSIFICATION

The classification of coelenterates varies with different students of the group with little agreement among them except for some of the major taxa.

Phylum Cnidaria (Coelenterata). Body with radial or biradial symmetry; individual either a sessile polyp or free-swimming medusa; stinging nematocysts; tentacles about the mouth; presence of mouth but no anus; only one cavity (enteron); reproduction usually asexual in polyps, sexual in medusae; freshwater or marine; 9,600 species (L. Rothschild).

Class Hydrozoa. Both polyp and craspedote medusa (possessing a velum) in life cycle; gastrovascular cavity without stomodeum or nematocysts and lacking partitions; sex cells in epidermis.

Order Hydroida. Polyps well developed; solitary or colonial with sense organs of ocelli and ectodermal statocysts, usually with free medusae budded off.

Suborder Anthomedusae (Gymnoblastea). Hydranths without hydrotheca (athecate); gonophores naked; medusae tall, without statocysts, and with gonads on manubrium. *Tubularia* (Fig. 5-17), *Hydra* (Fig. 5-22), *Clava* (Fig. 5-18), *Bougainvillia* (Fig. 5-14).

Suborder Leptomedusae (Calyptoblastea). Hydrotheca present (thecate); coenosarc covered with horny perisarc; gonophores in gonotheca; gonads on radial canals; medusae usually with statocysts; both polyp and medusa well developed. *Obelia* (Fig. 5-11), *Sertularia* (Fig. 5-29), *Plumularia*.

105

Suborder Limnomedusae. Polyps small, naked, and sessile; gonads on walls of stomach or radial canals; medusae with velum, hollow tentacles, and statocysts. *Gonionemus* (Fig. 5-35), *Craspedacusta* (Fig. 5-36).

Order Milleporina. Colonial hydroids; calcareous skeleton with pores for protrusion of polyps; polyps dimorphic; dactylozooids hollow with capitate tentacles; medusae without enteron or tentacles. *Millepora* (Fig. 5-31).

Order Stylasterina. Dactylozooids solid without tentacles; gonophores are degenerate sporosacs; colonial; calcareous skeleton. *Stylantheca, Allopora.*

Order Trachylina. Polyp reduced or absent; craspedote medusae with statocysts, tentaculocysts, and entodermal statoliths; tentacles usually above bell margin.

Suborder Trachymedusae. Bell margin smooth; gonads on radial canals; solid tentacles; no polyp stage. *Liriope* (Fig. 5-33), *Olindias, Aglantha.*

Suborder Narcomedusae. Medusae with margin scalloped by peronia; solid tentacles attached above margin; mouth opens into stomach, which is broad and often lobed; no polyp stage. *Cunina, Aegina* (Fig. 5-34).

Suborder Pteromedusae. Bipyramidal medusae; four swimming lobes. *Tetraplatia.*

Order Siphonophora. Swimming colonies of several types of polyps and medusae attached to a stem or float; oral tentacles absent; only undeveloped and attached medusae. *Physalia* (Fig. 5-39), *Velella* (Fig. 5-40), *Porpita.*

Class Scyphozoa. Medusa is main stage in life cycle; no true velum; no stomodeum; gastrovascular system with gastric tentacles and pouches; mesoglea extensive and cellular; gonads endodermal in gastric cavity; marginal tentaculocysts with endodermal statoliths; polyp stage absent or reduced consisting of a scyphistoma that produces medusae directly or by transverse fission; medusae mostly dioecious.

Order Stauromedusae. Sessile, polyplike medusae; attached by aboral stalk; medusae develops directly from scyphistoma; marginal sense organs absent or modified tentacles present. *Haliclystus* (Fig. 5-44), *Lucernaria.*

Order Cubomedusae. Bell cubical with four tentacles or four groups; bell margin bent in to form a velarium; four flattened sides. *Tripedalia, Carybdea* (Fig. 5-45, A).

Order Coronatae. Margin scalloped; bell surrounded by circular furrow above margin; tentacles on gelatinous expansions (pedalia). *Nausithoe, Periphylla* (Fig. 5-45, B).

Order Semaeostomae. Corners of mouth with four frilly lobes (oral arms); margin scalloped; tentacles along margin or grouped into bunches. *Aurelia* (Fig. 5-41), *Cyanea* (Fig. 5-46), *Chrysaora* (Fig. 5-45, C).

Order Rhizostomae. Oral lobes fused; mouths numerous in oral lobes; tentacles absent. *Cassiopeia, Rhizostoma.*

Class Anthozoa. Polyps exclusively; medusae absent; mouth with stomodeum (gullet); siphonoglyph usually present; oral end expanded into oral disk; gastrovascular cavity divided into compartments by complete or incomplete septa with nematocysts; mesoglea cellular (connective tissue); endodermal gonads in septa; skeleton present or absent.

Subclass Alcyonaria. Polyps with eight pinnate tentacles; eight single complete septa; one ventral siphonoglyph; endoskeleton present; colonial.

Order Stolonifera. Polyps separate and connected by stolons or basal mat; skeleton of separate spicules or spicules fused into tubes. *Tubipora* (Fig. 5-49), *Clavularia.*

Order Telestacea. Colonies of long axial stems each with lateral polyps; calcareous spicules generally united. *Telesto* (Fig. 5-50, A), *Coelogorgia.*

Order Alcyonacea. Coral soft; polyps fused into fleshy mass at lower ends; polyps protrude at oral ends only; skeleton of separate calcareous spicules, not axial. *Alcyonium* (Fig. 5-50, E), *Anthomastus, Xenia.*

Order Coenothecalia. Calcareous skeleton of nonfused spicules of aragonite; erect cylindric cavities for the polyps. *Heliopora* (Fig. 5-50, C, D).

Order Gorgonacea. Skeleton of gorgonin or calcareous spicules or both; polyps short and borne on the sides of skeletal axis. *Gorgonia* (Figs. 5-51, 5-52), *Corallium.*

Order Pennatulacea. Colony of one long axial polyp and of many lateral dimorphic polyps; colony embedded in coenenchyme; skeleton of calcareous spicules. *Renilla* (Fig. 5-53), *Pennatula.*

Subclass Zoantharia. Tentacles usually simple and not branched; skeleton solid if present; solitary or colonial.

Order Actiniaria. Skeleton absent; septa paired often in multiples of six; polyp columnar with usually muscular wall; usually one or more siphonoglyphs; solitary; aboral end usually on pedal disk. *Metridium* (Fig. 5-55), *Actinia, Edwardsia.*

Order Ptychodactiaria. Filaments lacking ciliated areas; mesenteries in irregular cycles; capitate tentacles absent; solitary. *Ptychodactis, Dactylanthus.*

Order Corallimorpharia. Resembles corals, but no skeleton; capitate tentacles radially arranged; filaments without ciliated areas; colonies sheetlike. *Corallimorphus, Corynactis.*

Order Scleractinia (Madreporaria). Calcareous exoskeleton; siphonoglyph absent; solitary or colonial; polyps small; reef formers. *Fungia, Astrangia* (Fig. 5-60), *Orbicella*.

Order Zoanthidea. Skeleton absent; no pedal disk; septal pairs usually of one complete and one incomplete pair; ventral siphonoglyph; solitary or colonial; often commensal. *Zoanthus, Parazoanthus, Epizoanthus*.

Order Antipatharia. Skeleton horny and stemlike with branches; polyps on stem; complete septa single; tentacles six or eight in number; two siphonoglyphs. *Antipathes, Dendrobrachia, Parantipathes*.

Order Ceriantharia. Polyps slender without pedal disks; tentacles numerous in two whorls; septa complete and numerous; one siphonoglyph; tube dwellers; solitary. *Cerianthus*.

BASIC ADAPTIVE FEATURES

There is a fundamental plan of structure throughout the coelenterate group. This basic plan consists of a single sac with one opening and walls of two cell layers with the body parts concentrically arranged around an oral-aboral axis. Between the two cell layers (ectoderm and endoderm) there is a mesoglea of gelatinous matrix, which may or may not contain cells. Such a body has primary radial symmetry, although it may be modified in a biradial or bilateral direction (Anthozoa), and it bears a remarkable resemblance to the gastrula stage of the metazoan plan. However complex a coelenterate may be, it never deviates from this plan. Both medusa and polyp are constructed on the same scheme (Fig. 5-1), and each has undergone modifications of this pattern to fit its particular environment. Whatever interpretation one may make about the status of the polyp or medusa in the life history, polymorphism probably does not imply that coelenterates are evolving toward either phase, but that a balance has been reached in their populations under existing environmental conditions. Such widespread dimorphism throughout the coelenterate group (with the exception of class Anthozoa) allows for adjustment to a much wider variety of environments. The presence of both a sessile phase and a floating phase has made possible a benthonic (bottom) as well as a pelagic (open water) existence. The presence of two (sometimes more) forms in a single species of this phylum has in this way enabled organisms to avoid some of the restrictions imposed on their evolutionary pattern by radial symmetry and a generally diploblastic and saclike structure. Their lack of organs with the consequent loss of division of labor has been compensated for, to a degree, by the evolutionary

Fig. 5-1

Diagrammatic comparison of polyp and medusa forms. (From Hickman: Integrated principles of zoology, The C. V. Mosby Co.)

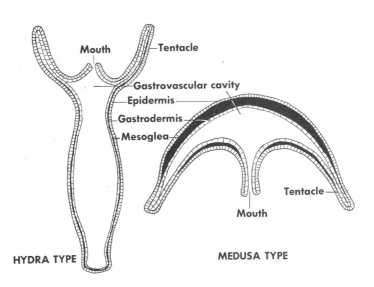

Mouth — Tentacle
Gastrovascular cavity
Epidermis
Gastrodermis
Mesoglea
Tentacle
Mouth
HYDRA TYPE   MEDUSA TYPE

development of different individuals with diversified functions.

Another interesting aspect of coelenterate architecture, insofar as the hydroid polyp is concerned, is their constant turnover and renewal of cells at different levels. This circumstance indicates that such a morphologic organization cannot be considered a stable entity. *Hydra,* in which this phenomenon has been studied more than in other genera, shows a proliferating region behind the tentacles that gives rise to new cells replacing those shed at the base of the polyp and at the ends of the tentacles. It is not known how general this regression-replacement process is among coelenterates other than the hydra family (Hydridae), although S. Crowell has shown that the old hydranths of *Campanularia* undergo resorption and replacement regularly. Ecologic factors may influence this process as well as intrinsic factors (P. Tardent). Such a process indicates that a hydroid polyp is morphologically active throughout its existence and that the process may play a vital part in its basic adaptive nature.

PHYLOGENETIC RELATIONSHIPS

The theory of the evolutionary pattern of coelenterates commonly held is that the earliest forms were free-swimming medusoid jellyfish and that the hydroid stages were simply larval stages in their life histories. According to the colonial theory and the revised blastea theory, the metazoan planuloid ancestor is supposed to have been similar to the planula larva of coelenterates. This hypothetical planuloid ancestor was believed to have been somewhat oval, radially symmetric, and solid in structure, with ciliated cells on the outside for locomotion and a solid mass of cells on the inside for nutrition and reproduction. A mouth was absent, and food could be engulfed by the external cells and passed to the inside. This ancestor, by acquiring tentacles and methods for capturing food, could have developed into a medusoid form with a floating or swimming existence. The paleontologic record bears out this theory to some extent because medusae have been found in much earlier geologic formations (Precambrian) than have hydroids. According to this theory, by Cam-

brian times a sessile polypoid fitted for a bottom-dwelling existence appeared in the life cycles of some medusae, and led to many lines of Hydrozoa. L. H. Hyman has stressed the order Trachylina as best representing the most primitive coelenterate forms because the actinula larva of this group develops directly into the adult medusa, their ontogeny tends to repeat the phylogeny of other coelenterates, and they have only one type of nematocyst. Hydra with four kinds of nematocysts would not be considered primitive according to this theory. Hyman has long argued that the hydroid colony is a persistent larval stage.

An alternative view of the origin of the coelenterates places the class Anthozoa as the basic stock and claims that the evolutionary history of the group has developed from the anthozoans to the classes Scyphozoa and Hydrozoa. Evidence for this theory stresses the importance of the polypoid condition, which is the sole one in Anthozoa; the tendency toward bilateral symmetry in this class; and the view that the coelenteric outpocketings of Anthozoa gave rise to the coelomic sacs of the bilateral phyla (enterocoelous theory). This view suggests that the coelenterates have arisen from turbellarian flatworms because both have an ectodermal stomodeum and suggests that the nematocysts of coelenterates have arisen from the sagittocysts of turbellarians. Adherents of this theory believe that an anthozoan could have arisen if a rhabdocoelid turbellarian had adopted a sessile habit and become fixed at its oral end. Hyman has answered some of these arguments by pointing out that the coelenteric outpocketings of Anthozoa are not formed in the same way as coelomic sacs but are ingrowths of septa to increase the digestive surface, that transformations of radial into bilateral symmetry have occurred many times in the animal kingdom, and that if the Anthozoa are the most primitive coelenterates it is very difficult to account for medusae in the other coelenterate classes. Her conclusions are that the coelenterates must be regarded as the ancestral stock of all the other eumetazoan groups because of their type of organization, the absence of anus, coelom, organs, and a well-defined mesoderm.

The whole problem seems to center upon

the nature of the earliest metazoan form, whether the polyclad flatworm or the coelenterate is the more primitive. Present knowledge does not justify a definite answer to this question.

FOSSIL RECORD

Coelenterates have one of the longest fossil records in the animal kingdom. Representatives of all classes have been found as fossils, although some have left better records than others. Those without skeletons or hard parts naturally have left far fewer fossils than corals, for example. Only under the most fortunate circumstances have jellyfishes been preserved, such as those in the famed Burgess Shale of British Columbia. Some Precambrian fossil medusoids have been found, which gives evidence for the theory that the medusa is more primitive than the polypoid stage that, according to the fossil record, came later in Cambrian times.

Of the hydrozoans, the orders Milleporina and Stylasterina with their calcareous skeletons have left the best fossil records. Fossils of both orders are found in Tertiary and Cretaceous deposits. Most hydrozoans have soft parts only and have left few fossils, although some extinct orders of this class that had skeletons are present in certain Mesozoic deposits.

By far the best fossil record is left by members of the subclass Alcyonaria (Figs. 5-2, 5-3) of the anthozoans. To this group belong the corals, which are important components of many rock formations from Ordovician to present times. Common types of such fossils are the sea pens, the sea fans, blue corals, and the organ-pipe corals. The other subclass (Zoantharia) of the anthozoans that includes corals as well as sea anemones have also left many coral fossil records, but the sea anemones (order Actiniaria) have left no distinctive fossils because of their lack of hard parts. Two orders of corals, Rugosa (Fig. 5-2) and Tabulata, have left extensive fossil records dating back to the Ordovician period.

GENERAL MORPHOLOGIC FEATURES

As mentioned in the introduction, coelenterates have two morphologic types, the polyp (hydroid) and the medusa (jellyfish). Each of these phases can be derived from

Fig. 5-2

Colonial rugose coral fossils from Devonian period.

Fig. 5-3

Large scleractinian coral fossil; such corals usually date from Mesozoic era.

the other. The presence of two different and distinct individuals in the group is an example of polymorphism, a condition that is widespread throughout the phylum and that is carried in some taxa of the phylum to a far greater extent than anywhere else in the animal kingdom. Polymorphism, however, shows many variations among the coelenterate classes. It is most striking in Hydrozoa, in which polyp and medusa stages are fairly well balanced; it is present in Scyphozoa, in which there is a **109** distinct tendency to suppress the polyp phase and emphasize the medusa; and it is entirely absent in Anthozoa, in which only the polyp form is found. Polymorphism, as pointed out in a previous section, has adaptive value because it promotes ecologic diversity of habitat distribution. As E. Mayr (1963) has emphasized, the advantages of this morphologic pattern are so great that one wonders why it is not more widespread in the animal kingdom.

The term *polymorphism,* so widely used by zoologists in reference to the coelenterates, has a somewhat different meaning here than among other groups, because it refers to division of labor among diversified individuals of a species. The term *alternation of generations,* wherein sexual and nonsexual forms succeed each other, has largely been discarded in describing the life histories of those coelenterates with medusoid and polypoid stages. The polyp is considered a persistent larva and the medusa is considered an adult. But there are also other types of so-called polymorphism in the coelenterates, such as *Hydractinia,* in which a colonial pattern of sexual and nonsexual individuals is found together; the same is true of the Siphonophora. In many Scyphozoa a single polyp may produce several medusae, and the blastostyle of a colony of *Obelia* buds off many medusae. There are many other variations on this theme in this extensive phylum. In some coelenterates it is very difficult to distinguish between a colonial system and an individual system. The problem of individuality, therefore, enters the picture in fine distinctions.

Polyps are usually sessile, although some have limited sliding or creeping movements, such as hydras and sea anemones; hydras may also move by a somersaulting method. A polyp is usually radially symmetric but may tend in some cases toward biradial or bilateral symmetry. It has a longitudinal oral-aboral axis through the cylindric trunk, or stem. The aboral end, or base, is specialized in various ways for attachment to a substratum. The base may be in the form of an adhesive pedal disk, rootlike stolons, or simply a pointed end. The oral or free end bears a mouth, usually surrounded by a set of varying numbers of tentacles, and it may be expanded into a vase-shaped hydranth or an oral disk. The mouth may be circular as in hydras, or it may be elongated as in anthozoan polyps and bear ciliated grooves called siphonoglyphs at one or both ends. The wall of the polyp is made up of an outer epithelial wall (the epidermis) and an inner epithelial layer (the gastrodermis) with a mesoglea of gelatinous substance or mesenchyme between the two epithelial layers. The central cavity of the cylindric body or trunk is the gastrovascular cavity or enteron. In hydroid polyps the enteron is a simple tube; in scyphozoan and anthozoan polyps the cavity is partly divided and its surface is greatly increased by septal ridges that may, in anthozoans, form complete partitions in part of the gastrovascular cavity.

The medusa individual is built on basically the same coelenterate plan as the polyp but is specialized for a free-swimming or floating existence. It is usually bell shaped or bowl shaped with a mouth at the end of a suspended stalk, or manubrium, on the underside (Fig. 5-4). The aboral surface is the convex side of the umbrella and is called the exumbrella; the oral side is the concave side, or subumbrella. The mouth leads into the gastrovascular stomach that may be a simple chamber, or its periphery may be divided into four perradial pouches by four interradial septa. From the stomach four or more radial canals run through the umbrella to the ring or circular canal in the bell margin. Centrifugal canals may lead off from the ring canal and pass throughout the length of the tentacles. Sense organs such as eyespots, statocysts, etc. are often found along the ring canal, on the bases of the tentacles, or on marginal specializations of the bell. The arrangement of the radial canals, tentacles, and sense organs gives a tetramerous radial symmetry to most medusae. Both the exumbrellar and subumbrellar surfaces are covered with epidermis while the stomach, manubrium, and the various canals are lined with gastrodermis. Between the epidermis and gastrodermis there is a thick jelly layer, the mesoglea, which may or may not contain cells. The mesoglea is usually much thicker in medusae than in polyps.

The medusae of class Hydrozoa contain

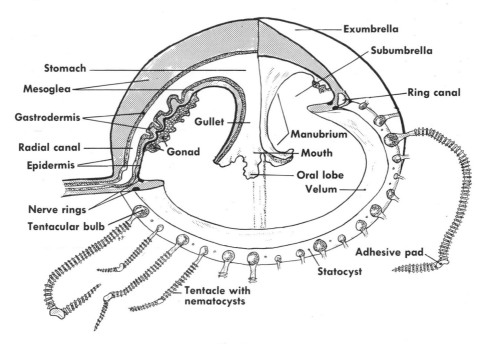

Fig. 5-4

Diagram of structure of *Gonionemus*, a hydrozoan medusa. (From Hickman: Integrated principles of zoology, The C. V. Mosby Co.)

a circular shelf, the velum (Fig. 5-4), which projects inward from the subumbrellar margin of the bell and partly reduces the subumbrellar space. Such medusae are called craspedote medusae in contrast to the acraspedote, scyphozoan medusae that lack a velum.

Swimming in medusae is accomplished by a sort of jet propulsion in which the subumbrellar muscles contract suddenly and force the water from the subumbrellar space. This expulsion propels the medusa in an aboral direction. The umbrella is returned to its original form by the elasticity of the thick mesogleal layer and the cycle is repeated. The swimming movement results from coordination of the nerve net and the marginal sense organs. The medusa thus has two main functions—locomotion and sexual reproduction—and its many modifications involve one or the other of these two functions. In some cases it may become a mere float by loss of tentacles and other specialized structures; in other forms it may serve only in a reproductive capacity.

The body form of the medusa is determined to a great extent by the firm, resilient mesoglea that is much more abundant in the jellyfish stage than in the polyp. The body form of the latter depends partly

upon the rigidity of its tissues and partly upon the water in the gastrovascular cavity. Large polyps are often provided with ciliated grooves in the mouth region for conducting water into the cavity. When the polyp is expanded, water performs the duties of a skeleton by giving rigidity to the body. Water in the body of the polyp is regulated by the action of circular and longitudinal muscles in the body wall. When water in the gastrovascular cavity is trapped by the closure of the mouth, the polyp can become shorter and broader by contracting the longitudinal muscles; when the circular muscles contract, water is expelled or squeezed from the mouth or body pores, and the body becomes extended and thin.

Tentacles represent one of the most specialized structures in coelenterate morphology, although they may be absent in both polyp and medusa stages. Throughout the group tentacles may be divided into two categories: (1) capitate, or those that are short with a small cap provided with ne-

111

matocysts, and (2) filiform, or those that are elongated with nematocysts generally placed along their entire length in diversified arrangements (warts, rings, etc.). Either or both kinds may be present in the same species; tentacles display a large diversity in number, arrangement, and structure. This diversity is not restricted to differences between polyp and medusa phases but also extends to differences within each phase. Tentacles may be hollow or solid; when hollow the tentacular canal may be continuous with the gastrovascular or ring canal, or it may be separated by a partition. Solid tentacles are filled with a gastrodermal core of vacuolated cells. Tentacles are usually single, but in a few species they are branched. They may be arranged in one or more circlets, or they may have an irregular arrangement. They may be definite in number for a particular species, or they may be indefinite in number and in-

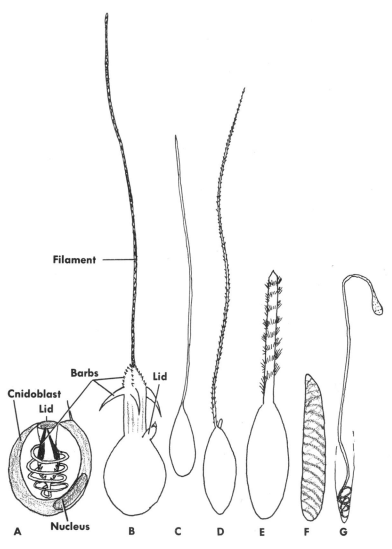

Fig. 5-5

Types of nematocysts. **A,** Cnidoblast with nematocyst, penetrant. **B,** Discharged penetrant (stenotele). **C,** Glutinant without spines (atrichous isorhiza). **D,** Glutinant with spines (holotrichous isorhiza). **E,** Microbasic amastigophore of anemone *Sagartia.* **F,** Spirocyst of anemone. **G,** Same as **F,** unraveling (not discharged). (Redrawn from Hyman: The invertebrates; Protozoa through Ctenophora. McGraw-Hill Book Company.)

crease with age. Especially in the medusa phases tentacles are usually liberally provided with sensory organs besides nematocysts. Specialized sense organs are often found in their enlarged bases (tentacular bulbs). The bases may also function to produce nematocysts and aid in digestion. In some cases the tentacular bulb is the only part of the tentacle present.

Stinging organelles

One of the diagnostic features of coelenterates are certain stinging organelles, or capsules, that are used for food gathering and for defense against enemies. These organelles are divided into two kinds, nematocysts and spirocysts. Nematocysts are of many forms (Figs. 5-5, *A* to *E*, 5-6) and are widely distributed throughout the phylum; spirocysts are all alike (Fig. 5-5, *F*, *G*) and are restricted to the subclass Zoantharia of Anthozoa. Nematocysts are produced from special cells called cnidoblasts, which are transformed interstitial cells. Nematocysts may be produced in regions where they are to be used, or they may develop in other locations, the cnidoblasts migrating by ameboid movement to

their definitive sites. The nematocysts on the tentacles of hydroid polyps originate on the hydranth body or stem; in medusae the basal enlargements of the tentacles serve as sites of formation. In Hydrozoa nematocysts are restricted to the outer epidermis; in the other two classes they are found in both epidermis and gastrodermis. In both polyps and medusae certain regions of the body are favorite locations for nematocysts. They are most common on tentacles where they are grouped into rings, ridges, and knobs. In the tentacles of hydroid polyps such as hydras, they form clusters known as batteries. They are far more common in the oral than in the aboral region, and they are totally absent where the body has an exoskeleton. In Scyphozoa and Anthozoa they are common on the gastric filaments, septal filaments, and acontia. Some nematocysts are only a few microns long after discharge, but others may reach a length of more than 1 mm.

The cnidoblast (Figs. 5-5, *A*, 5-6, 5-7), which forms the nematocyst, is an oval or pear-shaped cell with a basal nucleus; it is attached to the epidermis by a slender stalk. The double-walled capsule of the

A   B   C   D   E

Fig. 5-6

Nematocysts of *Hydra littoralis*. **A**, Penetrant. **B**, Streptoline glutinant. **C**, Stereoline glutinant. **D**, Volvent. **E**, Discharged volvent attached to copepod bristle. (Courtesy Carolina Biological Supply Co., Burlington, N. C.)

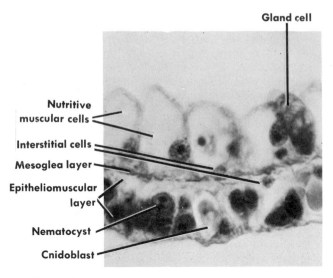

Gland cell

Nutritive
muscular cells

Interstitial cells

Mesoglea layer

Epitheliomuscular
layer

Nematocyst

Cnidoblast

Fig. 5-7

Portion of cross section of body of hydra. (From Andrew: Textbook of comparative histology, Oxford University Press, Inc.).

nematocyst is first secreted by the cnidoblast, and later the tube or thread becomes differentiated and coiled inside this capsule. The capsule has a small lid, or cap, directed to the outside. The nematocyst is placed near the free surface of the cnidoblast. A bristlelike structure, the cnidocil or trigger, projects from the tip of the undischarged nematocyst. A cnidocil is probably a modified flagellum, since it has the characteristic nine peripheral elements. In an anemone nematocyst the trigger is actually a flagellum. Although there are 17 major categories of nematocysts (R. Weill), all are discharged by eversion of the thread tube to the exterior. The various kinds of nematocysts can be divided into two main divisions: those that have threads with closed ends (astomocnidae), and those that have threads with open ends (stomocnidae). The first type is used for attachment or as a lasso to catch prey; the other type is used for penetration and injection of toxins into prey. The toxins are probably complex proteins in nature.

When a nematocyst is discharged, it cannot be used again. A discharged nematocyst consists of the old capsule, or bulb,

and a thread tube that often bears spines and thorns at its base. Nematocysts are useful in determining the taxonomic status of coelenterates. Most coelenterates have three or four types of nematocysts, but in the primitive order Trachylina and some others they are all of one type. Hydra has four kinds of nematocysts: desmonemes (volvents), stenoteles (penetrants), holotrichous isorhizas (glutinants with spines), and atrichous isorhizas (glutinants without spines) (Figs. 5-5, 5-6). The first two types are discharged by food stimulation; the third type responds to mechanical stimuli other than food; and the last type responds to contact with the substratum and is used for attachment when the animal is walking on its tentacles. Nematocysts have been called "independent effectors" because their discharge appears to be independent of nervous excitation pathways, at least in many species studied. However, G. O. Mackie and others have shown that nonnervous conduction is possible in nerve-free epithelia such as the membranes of epitheliomuscular cells. Contact with the cnidocil, or trigger, is involved in some discharges, but in many cases chemical stimulation (as from food) is necessary to lower a threshold before the trigger operates. The mechanics of the actual process of discharge seem to involve an intake of water because of increased permeability of the capsule wall and, in some cases, probably involve contraction of the cnidoblast. This increased pressure on the contents of the capsule forces open the lid (operculum) and causes the thread tube to evert.

The spirocysts are thin-walled capsules of one cell layer in thickness (Fig. 5-5, *F, G*). They contain a long, unarmed tube of uniform diameter that everts when discharged. Within the body of the tube are bundles of rodlets running parallel to the long axis of the tube (J. A. Westfall). Spirocysts stain with acid dyes, whereas nematocysts have an affinity for basic dyes. The chief content of spirocysts is mucoprotein or glycoprotein. The exact function of spirocysts and their methods of discharge are unclear. Since they have no flagellum, a chemical stimulus has been suggested for their discharge. They are restricted mainly to the oral disk and tentacles of sea anemones.

MORPHOLOGY AND PHYSIOLOGY OF BODY SYSTEMS

Some systems, such as respiratory and excretory systems, are entirely lacking in the coelenterates, and the circulatory and digestive systems are combined into one—the gastrovascular system. Respiration and excretion are effected by the individual cells without any specialized structures or organelles.

The epithelial system is represented by the epidermis, or outer epithelium, and by the gastrodermis, the inner epithelium (Fig. 5-7). Epidermis is derived from ectoderm. The epidermis usually consists of a single layer of cells that vary from flat squamous to tall columnar types. In some cases the epithelium is a syncytium. It may be ciliated or flagellated in most polyps and in some medusae. The bases of the epithelial cells reach to the mesoglea, to which they may be fastened by pseudopodial processes. Many kinds of specialized cells are found in the epidermis. In epitheliomuscular cells the bases may be drawn into strands containing myonemes or contractile fibers that run in a longitudinal direction in or near the mesoglea. In some groups (Trachylina, Scyphozoa, and Anthozoa) the bases lack contractile extensions because the independent myoneme bundles may be embedded in the mesoglea or near it. Other cells found in the epidermis are the cnidoblasts with nematocysts; gland cells that are mucus producing and are especially common on the tentacles and pedal disk; elongated and branched sensory cells that are attached at their bases to the general nerve plexus; and small, rounded, undifferentiated interstitial cells, that are general factotums in producing various types of cells (sex, cnidoblasts, etc.) as needed.

The gastrodermis, derived from endoderm, is constructed on the same plan as the epidermis, and it shares some of the same kinds of cells. It lines the gastrovascular cavity and has two major functions to perform: (1) the movement of food materials about the gastric cavity by means of its flagellate cells and (2) digestion of food both extracellularly and intracellularly. The chief cells found in the gastrodermal layer are the large nutritive-muscular cells whose bases are drawn into contractile extensions containing myonemes that run in a circular direction near the mesoglea (Fig. 5-7). Nutritive-muscular cells are generally columnar, highly vacuolated, and contain food vacuoles. Their free ends usually bear two flagella to each cell. In some coelenterates (Anthozoa) the gastrodermal muscles run in a longitudinal direction as well as in a circular direction. Other types of gastrodermal cells are gland cells (some of which secrete enzymes) with abundant secretion granules; sensory nerve cells similar to those of the epidermis; and small interstitial cells. Cnidoblasts are found in the gastrodermis in such specialized regions as gastric filaments, septal filaments, and acontia but are absent in the gastrodermis of hydrozoans.

The mesoglea between the epidermis and gastrodermis varies greatly in different taxa of the phylum. It also varies in the polyp and medusae stages; in the latter it makes up the greater part of the animal. In Hydrozoa it is almost entirely acellular, but in the other classes the mesoglea contains fibers and cells (collenchyme) forming something that resembles a third germ layer. In all medusae the extensive mesoglea has a content of almost 95 percent water. In the medusae of all classes the mesoglea is sharply marked off from epidermis and gastrodermis by a very thin jelly layer. The mesoglea may be thought of as a sort of skeleton, and in some anthozoans it may serve as the origin and insertion of muscle cells.

The digestive system, as already mentioned, is a part of the gastrovascular system. Digestion may be described as partly extracellular and partly intracellular. Glandular cells in the gastroderm produce proteolytic enzymes that are discharged into the gastric cavity where they partially break down the food into small particles. These particles are then engulfed by gastrodermal cells of all types and not merely by the nutritive-muscular cells. Within the food vacuoles so formed the digestive process is finally completed. The digested products are then diffused to all parts of the organism. Epidermal cells cannot engulf food materials.

All members of the phylum are carnivorous and strictly herbivorous diets are unknown in the group. However, some xeniid

115

corals apparently do not feed and are thought to depend on their algal symbionts for nutritional purposes. Most coelenterates cannot digest starches. The nematocysts are effective weapons in immobilizing prey, and the tentacles manipulate the food to the mouth region where ciliary action and muscular movements force it into the enteron.

Occasionally throughout the phylum symbiotic algae (zooanthellae) are found that, by photosynthesis, produce by-products that are incorporated into the protoplasm of the coelenterate. In some anthozoans, such as reef-forming corals, this accessory food supply may form an important item in their economy. The green hydra *(Chlorohydra)* gets its color from gastrodermal zoochlorellae *(Chlorella).* In some symbiotic relationships, the apparent advantages may be largely in favor of the algae, but it may be assumed that the coelenterate also derives some benefit.

Although the gastrovascular cavity is a relatively simple sac in many polyps of Hydrozoa, it becomes more complicated in both polyp and medusa of the other classes. In polyps it may be subdivided by septa, and in medusae it consists of a central stomach with radiating canals that join the circular, or marginal, canal. The endodermal tentacles or gastric filaments in Scyphozoa are the chief sites of enzyme secretion and, to some extent, of intracellular digestion as well. Anthozoans are provided with a sinuous cord, the septal filament, along the free edge of each septum, and these filaments have gland cells that secrete digestive enzymes into the gastrovascular cavity. Both gastric filaments and septal filaments are liberally supplied with nematocysts.

In coelenterates the muscular system is in the simplest condition found among true metazoan animals. The muscular system in simple hydroid polyps consists of an outer sheath of epidermal, longitudinal fibers at the bases of epidermal epitheliomuscular cells and an inner sheath of circular fibers at the bases of gastrodermal cells. These sheaths are not continuous sheets but are rather networks of anastomosing strands. As previously mentioned these muscle fibers are parts of epithelial cells in both sheaths. Such a muscle arrangement

makes possible contraction and extension of the cylindric body of a sessile, radial animal.

In all medusae and in most members of Scyphozoa and Anthozoa the musculature appears to be a subepithelial layer except in the tentacles where the primitive sheath is largely retained. The muscle fiber (myoneme) is always in a separate part of the cell from that portion containing the nucleus, and the connection between the two portions may be drawn into one or more long strands (depending on the number of myonemes). This arrangement may give the appearance of a separate muscle layer where the epidermis is a thick one, as in many of the larger coelenterates. In some cases the epitheliomuscular cells lie entirely below the surface of the epithelium—for example in the swimming muscle of large scyphomedusae. The deep-lying tissue may actually be enclosed in mesoglea and may become partially isolated from the superficial layer.

In medusae the swimming muscles of the subumbrella are well-developed circular and radial bands. Muscle cells are elongated and, in the circular fibers of medusae, are striated. In anthozoans and scyphozoans, in which muscle fibers form independent bundles, the mesoglea is closely applied to the muscles and may actually enfold them.

Skeletons are of two types in coelenterates: (1) the mesoglea and (2) secreted epidermal exoskeleton. The mesoglea has already been mentioned as a type of skeleton that may give considerable support and rigidity to the body of coelenterates, especially in the medusae. The secreted exoskeleton of the epidermis exists in a great variety of types ranging all the way from the chitinous tubes (periderm or perisarc) of hydroids to the calcareous skeletons of corals. In hydrozoan polyps especially, the tubular skeleton of chitin gives rigidity against wave action in habitats where colonial hydroids are found. Such a skeleton may form a cup (hydrotheca) around the hydranth, or it may be restricted to the stem, or it may be absent altogether (as in hydras). In stony corals the hard, calcareous exoskeleton lies outside the polyp's body and exists in various patterns of skeletal vertical ridges or septa radiating from the center to the periphery. The axial skeleton, another type, is found in sea pens and gorgonians (Anthozoa). This skeleton has an axial rod of sclerified proteins derived from invaginated ectoderm or from the mesoglea. Such a skeleton is tough and flexible. Sometimes the axis is a rigid structure of calcareous spicules cemented together with calcium carbonate. In the common sea anemone the fluid in the gastrovascular cavity acts as a hydrostatic skeleton.

The nervous system of coelenterates has been the subject of many investigations over the years, and many new concepts about it have originated from time to time. Since coelenterates comprise the lowest metazoan phylum that possesses a nervous system and since the classic nerve net they possess is considered to be one of the most primitive types, interest in its morphology and physiology has never waned. The system consists of an unpolarized network or plexus of bipolar and multipolar neurons and their neurites, together with the neurites of epidermal sensory cells that unite with the plexus. The chief nerve plexus lies just beneath the epidermis outside the muscular sheath. A similar but usually less developed plexus is found in a subgastrodermal position. Both plexuses may be regarded as one system in some forms, because neurite connections between the two nets may be found in the mesoglea. In other cases the two plexuses have little or no contact and behave as separate entities. *Velella,* for instance, has two distinct plexuses. One of these is made up of continuous giant fibers (syncytial or closed system, Fig. 5-8), and the other consists of discontinuous neurons and is known as the open system (Mackie). Other studies have shown two nerve nets in *Aurelia* and some others—the subumbrella net that controls the simultaneous contraction of circular and radial muscle, and a diffuse net in the epidermis that controls local reactions. The nerve net in the much-studied hydra is still customarily described as a continuous net with nerve cell bodies at the angles; but synaptic or open systems have been described in other hydrozoans, in sea anemones, and in scyphomedusae. The neurosensory cells in the epithelium may make synaptic junctions

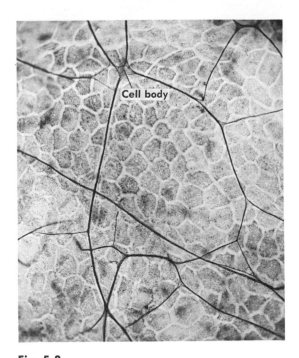

Fig. 5-8

Portion of syncytial giant fiber system of *Velella.* This form is provided with two nervous systems—one of syncytial (continuous) giant fibers and one of nonsyncytial (discontinuous) neurons. (Courtesy G. O. Mackie, University of Alberta, Edmonton.)

with the general nerve net as S. Leghissa has shown in the anthozoan *Actinia.* In colonial forms the nerve net may be continuous from one member to another in the whole colony, but there are many variations of this pattern. Response to stimuli may involve the whole colony, or it may be restricted to a localized region.

Theoretically, a stimulus at any one point of a nerve net can be transmitted to all points of the system. However, local activities, e.g., locomotion, feeding, etc., are possible and involve only a part of the response system. Whether synaptic or continuous, the nerve net differs from the majority of nervous systems in being able to conduct equally well in all directions, because polarization is either lacking or is very restricted. Independent effectors are common in coelenterates; the action of nematocysts, cilia, and chromatophores, for example, may be largely or entirely independent of nervous elements. In medusae

117

Fig. 5-9

Medusa of *Sarsia gemmifera*, a gymnoblastic hydroid. Asexual reproduction occurs by budding along manubrium. Height of parent bell is 2 to 4 mm.

coordination of swimming is produced by the balance organs, or statocysts, of the bell margin. Light sensitivity may be generalized, as in *Hydra* (L. M. Passano), or localized in ocelli, as in *Sarsia* (Fig. 5-15).

Both asexual and sexual reproduction are common throughout the phylum. Most coelenterates are dioecious, although there are a few exceptions. Sex cells may develop from interstitial cells in either the epidermis or the gastrodermis. With few exceptions the gonads are restricted to medusae or sessile gonophores. Gonophores are medusa buds that do not develop to a free stage. In some coelenterates the gonads are transient organs, and their location on the body varies. In hydromedusans the gonads may appear on the manubrium or in the endoderm beneath the radial canals; in hydroid polyps they may occur almost anywhere. Scyphozoan gonads are located on the floor of the stomach, and germ cells escape by way of the mouth. In anthozoans the gonads are located on the septa that subdivide the coelenteron. In all cases ducts and accessory organs are absent. Fertilization usually occurs in the surrounding water, but in some species the eggs are fertilized in situ, where they develop to a late stage.

In asexual reproduction polyps may bud from stems, stolons, or other polyps, and medusae may bud from hydranths, stolons, or other medusae. In hydrozoans, where both polyp and medusa stages are usually well represented, most medusae bud from hydroid colonies, but they may also bud from other medusae (*Sarsia*, Fig. 5-9). A rare method of asexual reproduction in hydrozoans is by means of frustules —small, elongated, planulalike but nonciliated bodies that are budded off from a polyp or stolon and creep about on the bottom until they eventually develop into new polyps or colonies. In the Anthozoa

Fig. 5-10

Strobila of *Aurelia*. Note layers of ephyrae. (Photograph of stained slide.)

Phylum Cnidaria (Coelenterata)

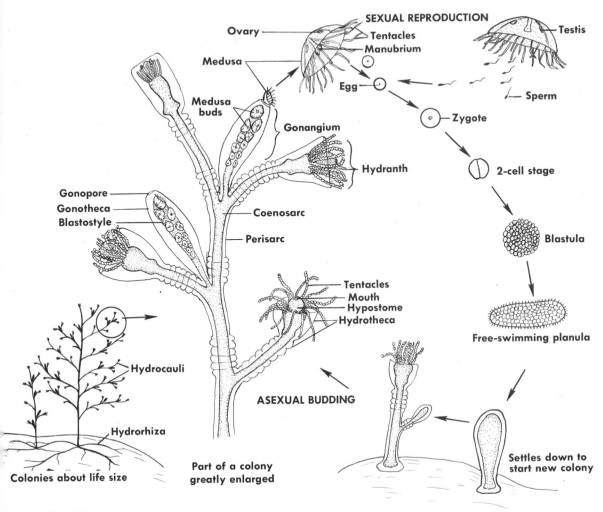

Fig. 5-11
Life cycle of *Obelia*. (From Hickman: Integrated principles of zoology, The C. V. Mosby Co.)

polyps undergo both transverse and longitudinal fission. Transverse fission is also common in the development of the medusa from the larval stage in Scyphozoa, and it may also occur in the polyp of Hydrozoa. The scyphistoma larvae, common in many scyphozoans, may give rise to medusae directly by budding off the side or by strobilation or may send out stolons that bud off other scyphistomae. A scyphistoma in process of strobilation gives rise by transverse fission to ephyrae (Fig. 5-10). Medusae sometimes arise by direct asexual budding from other medusae, as in the Anthomedusae, but no polyps are derived directly from medusae by budding.

Polyps have great powers of regeneration, and most parts cut from a parent stock will develop into a new polyp. Gradients of regeneration are found in polyps similar to those present in planarian worms. Much of this regenerative capacity is lost in the medusa stage.

Although there are some differences in the developmental stages of coelenterates, a certain basic plan is followed (Fig. 5-11). Cleavage follows fertilization and a ciliated blastula is formed. The gastrula may be formed by an infolding of one end of the blastula, or it may be formed by the inwandering of surface cells so that a second layer is formed. In all cases a stere-

119

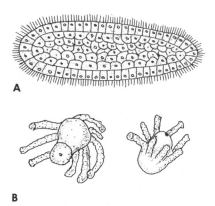

Fig. 5-12

A, Planula larva in longitudinal section, with outer layer of ectodermal cells and inner core of endodermal cells; characteristic of many coelenterates. B, Actinula larvae of *Tubularia*. (Sketched from life.)

ogastrula results. The stereogastrula elongates into the planula larva (Fig. 5-12, *A*), which is provided with cilia and is free swimming. In a short time the planula becomes attached to a substratum by its anterior end or by its side and forms mouth and tentacles at its posterior end. From such a polyp a colony may form by growth and budding. Some variations of this pattern occur. The planula in many hydroids (Tubulariidae and others) develops tentacles and a mouth and becomes an actinula, which resembles a short, stalkless polyp (Fig. 5-12, *B*). The actinula creeps around, attaches itself, and becomes either a polyp or a medusa. The larvae of medusae that have no polypoid stage develop directly into new medusae.

CLASS HYDROZOA

The members of Hydrozoa may be either polymorphic, wholly polypoid, or wholly medusoid in their life histories. They have a tetramerous or polymerous radial symmetry and differ from the Scyphozoa and Anthozoa by having no subdivisions of the gastrovascular cavity, no nematocysts in the digestive cavity, and no stomodeum. Other differences are the presence of a velum and the presence in the medusa of highly specialized sense organs differing from rhopalia. A large diversity of form exists within the group. A typical polyp consists of an attached base, a stem, and a terminal hy-

dranth. Solitary forms are usually anchored to a soft substratum by short, unbranched roots or by modified stolons. In the freshwater polyp, the hydra, the end is an adhesive pedal disk. The base in colonial forms is made up of stolons (rhizomes) that form an anastomosing rootlike structure (hydrorhiza, Fig. 5-11) fastened to a substratum. The stolons give rise to buds that form the new individuals of a colony. The main stalk of a colony is called the hydrocaulus. The stolons and hydrocaulus are made up of a living hollow tube (coenosarc) that is usually covered by a chitinous tube (periderm or perisarc) secreted by the epidermis. The coenosarc has both epidermis and gastrodermis separated by a mesolamella and encloses a gastrovascular cavity that extends throughout the colony. The hydranth is usually vaselike and bears an elevated part, the hypostome or manubrium, in which the terminal mouth is situated. Around the base of the hydranth and the mouth there is usually a circlet of tentacles, but other arrangements of tentacles are also found. In the Gymnoblastea (Anthomedusae) the hydranths lack a periderm (athecate); in the Calyptoblastea (Leptomedusae) each hydranth is enclosed in a secreted cup of periderm, the hydrotheca (thecate).

The hydrozoan medusa has tetramerous radial symmetry and may be bell shaped, dome shaped, or have other shapes. From the center of the subumbrella hangs the quadrangular manubrium that may bear lobes and oral tentacles provided with nematocysts. A stomach, or gastric cavity, is found at the base of the manubrium, but variations of this plan exist. Four radial canals, 90 degrees apart, usually radiate from the stomach to the ring canal in the bell margin. Some forms may contain more radial canals that may also branch. The gastrovascular cavity includes all these canals as well as the stomach and manubrium. A velum is present, although in some cases, e.g, *Obelia*, it may be rudimentary (Fig. 5-30).

The margin of the circular bell is usually unscalloped and bears the sense organs and tentacles. Sense organs are commonly represented by ocelli (Fig. 5-15) and statocysts (Fig. 5-32). Tentacles may be few or numerous and, in a few species, may be branched. They may be either solid or hollow extensions of the ring canal. The base of each tentacle is enlarged to form the tentacular bulb that may bear an ocellus or other sensory structures. The bulbs also serve as sites of nematocyst formation.

Diversity of body form among hydrozoans is chiefly because of variations between the hydroid and medusoid generations. Some hydrozoans have no medusoid stages, and others have no hydroid stages. Still others may have both generations combined and present in the same specimen. This composite nature is well illustrated in the Siphonophora where many different types of polypoid and medusoid components are found together in the same individual. The basic adaptive nature of the phylum, as already mentioned, plays a part in this evolutionary pattern. The typical balanced system of hydroid and medusoid generations found in many Hydrozoa (Figs. 5-11, 5-13) permits existence in varied assortments of environments. The polyp fitted for a sessile existence and the medusa with a swimming adaptation promote a wide distribution of the species. But a pure medusa form without a polyp-

oid stage (e.g., *Liriope,* Fig. 5-33) can live far out at sea where a polyp could not exist. On the other hand, a purely sessile life in a favorable situation could lead to suppression of the medusoid stage and the persistence of the polyp form.

The Hydrozoa are commonly divided into five orders, each of which has certain distinctive characteristics. They are Hydroida, Milleporina, Stylasterina, Trachylina, and Siphonophora.

Order Hydroida

The order Hydroida includes most of the hydrozoans. It includes the suborders Limnomedusae, Anthomedusae, and Leptomedusae. In the Limnomedusae the polyps are minute, sessile, and entirely naked. They may or may not bear tentacles. They produce other polyps and medusae by budding. The medusae have hollow tentacles. Well-known examples are *Gonionemus* and *Craspedacusta.*

The Anthomedusae (Gymnoblastea) include species without a protective cup (athecate) around the hydranths and gonozooids, e.g., *Eudendrium* and *Bougainvillia* (Fig. 5-14). The Leptomedusae (Calyptoblastea) include species that are thecate, or have a hydrotheca cup around the hydranth and a gonotheca cup around the gonozooid, e.g., *Obelia* (Fig. 5-11) and *Campanularia* (Fig. 5-28, *B*). Gymnoblastic hydroids usually begin as juveniles with few tentacles on their hydranths; as they grow they add more tentacles (Fig. 5-16). On the other hand, the hydranths of calyptoblastic hydroids do not grow after emerging from a bud, do not add tentacles, and are absorbed by the colonies after a few days. The medusae of the Anthomedusae (Fig. 5-9) possess tall bells, manubrial gonads, tentaculer bulbs, usually with ocelli (Fig. 5-15), no statocysts, and few tentacles. The medusae of Leptomedusae usually have saucer-shaped or bowl-shaped bells, gonads on the radial canals, statocysts (but lack eyespots), and many tentacles (Fig. 5-35). Some leptomedusans do not have free medusae. Many morphologic variations exist within these two suborders.

In the life histories of the suborders Anthomedusae and Leptomedusae there is typically both a polyp and a medusoid stage, but there is a distinct tendency to-

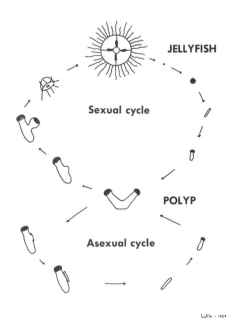

JELLYFISH

Sexual cycle

POLYP

Asexual cycle

Lytle - 1959

Fig. 5-13
Life cycle of freshwater hydrozoan, *Craspedacusta sowerbyi.* (Courtesy Charles F. Lytle.)

Fig. 5-14

Bougainvillia, a calyptoblastic hydroid. Left, portion of colony. Right, medusa.

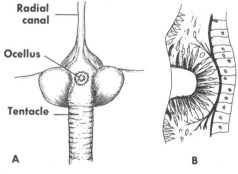

Fig. 5-15

A, Base, or bulb, of marginal tentacle of *Sarsia tubulosa*, bearing ocellus. **B,** Section through ocellus of *Sarsia*. Pit is filled with transparent lens and lined with pigmented epithelial cells and nerve cells. (**A** modified from Russell.)

ward suppression of the medusoid stage in many members of these suborders. Such suppression may involve rudimentary medusae attached to the polyp, sessile gonophores, reproductive undeveloped medusae (sporosacs) on the polyp, and even complete loss of the medusoid generation.

In the typical life history the fertilized egg (zygote) produced by the medusa develops into a planula larva. The ciliated planula larva swims around, attaches itself to a substratum, and develops a mouth and tentacles at its free end. It is now a polyp and by developing stems, stolons, and other polyps, begins a hydroid colony (Fig. 5-16). In some hydroids (*Tubularia*) the planula larva remains in the gonophore, develops into an actinula larva with mouth and tentacles, becomes free to creep around, and finally transforms into a polyp. A colony of polyps or hydranths

Fig. 5-16

Development of hydroid and medusa from planula larva. Left, development of *Eudendrium,* a gymnoblastic hydroid that has no free medusa stage. Right, development of *Aglaura,* a trachyline medusa with no attached polyp stage.

gives rise to two types of individuals (dimorphia)—gastrozooids for nutrition and gonophores or buds that develop into medusae. Since most Hydroida are dioecious, the medusae produced by a particular colony are all of the same sex. Gonophores may arise from the main stem or hydrocaulus, from a blastostyle stalk, from the hydrorhiza, or from the gastrozooid directly. Some of these variations will be described in the following accounts of some common genera of hydroids.

In members of the gymnoblastic type the perisarc does not extend beyond the base of the polyp and does not form a hydrotheca.

Suborder Anthomedusa (Gymnoblastea)

Some familiar gymnoblastic genera are:

Tubularia. Tubularian colonies are made up of large polyps with long stems. They may consist of single, unbranched individuals, or branching may occur from stolons that do not form a network. The hydranth bears two whorls of solid tentacles, the

123

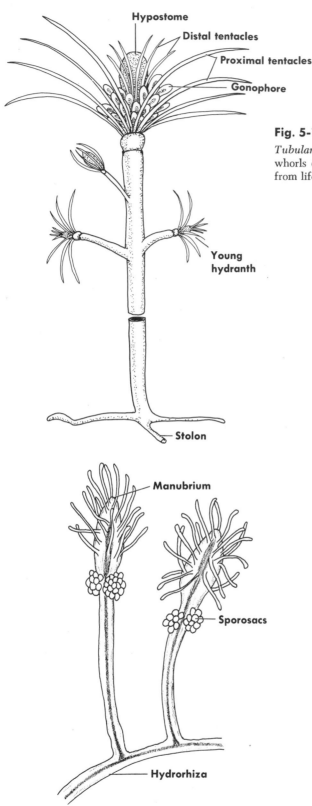

Hypostome

Distal tentacles

Proximal tentacles

Gonophore

Fig. 5-17

Tubularia crocea, a gymnoblastic hydranth, with two whorls of tentacles and clusters of gonophores. (Sketched from life.)

Young hydranth

Stolon

Manubrium

Sporosacs

Hydrorhiza

Fig. 5-18

Clava; polyps about ¼ inch tall with filiform tentacles (Gymnoblastea).

basal circlet of large tentacles and oral circlet of smaller tentacles around the mouth (Fig. 5-17). The sessile gonophores grow in grapelike clusters from stems attached between the two circlets of tentacles. The medusae always remain attached to the parent polyp, and their zygotes develop into planula larvae in the subumbrella before leaving as actinula larvae (Fig. 5-12) to start a new colony.

Clava. The elongated hydranths of these clublike polyps possess 15 to 30 filiform tentacles scattered over them (Fig. 5-18). The hydranths spring from a hydrorhiza. The undeveloped medusae or reproductive buds (sporosacs) are attached in clusters just beneath the tentacles and never become free.

Corymorpha. This is a solitary hydroid about ½ inch long (Fig. 5-19). The hydranth has two circlets of filiform tentacles with branching gonophores attached between them. The upper circlet of small tentacles surrounds the mouth at the top of the tall hydranth. The stem, which is narrow at the top and broader at the base, terminates in a branched, rootlike structure attached to sandy or muddy bottoms. This stem has a number of small canals instead of a single gastrovascular cavity, and it is especially adapted for support by being filled with gastrodermal cells. The medusae that develop from the gonophore buds are free swimming, and each is provided with a single trailing tentacle. *Corymorpha* has no asexual reproduction.

Eudendrium. This is a striking example of a bushy, much-branched colony (Fig. 5-20). The hydranth is provided with a single circlet of filiform tentacles (20 to 32) surrounding a funnel-shaped hypostome. The male and female gonophores arise from the gastrozooids and differ from and digest food for the colony. Reproductive zooids (gonozooids) are short with no mouth or tentacles, although they possess nematocysts. They bear gonophores that produce sporosacs, as there is no medusa stage. Some zooids are male and others are female. The defensive zooids (dactylozooids) are most abundant near the margin of the colony and are of two kinds, the spiral zooids with capitate tentacles and the tentaculozooids that are elongated and few in number. Sensory zooids resemble the dactylozooids but have no nematocysts and are provided with sensory components.

Hydra. These athecate forms belong to the family Hydridae. There are 15 species that belong to the family in the United States, most of which are members of the

Fig. 5-19

Corymorpha, a gymnoblastic hydroid. **A,** Polyp. Height is about 5 cm. **B,** Medusa (called *Steenstrupia*). (Redrawn from Hyman: The invertebrates; Protozoa through Ctenophora. McGraw-Hill Book Company.)

each other in appearance. No medusa generation occurs.

Hydractinia. This genus is a polymorphic, colonial form found on rocks and especially on shells occupied by hermit crabs. Several types of hydroid individuals are connected at the base by a network of stolons (Fig. 5-21). At least four types of zooids exist—nutritive zooids, reproductive zooids, defensive zooids, and sensory zooids. Each of these types has its own distinctive features. Nutritive zooids (gastrozooids) are tube shaped with a terminal mouth surrounded by filiform tentacles. They ingest

Female gonophores

Male gonophores

Fig. 5-20

Eudendrium (Gymnoblastea). **A,** Part of colony, with female gonophores. (Sketched from life.) **B,** Male gonophores.

Fig. 5-21

Portion of colony of *Hydractinia*, with three types of individuals connected at base by network of stolons. Left, gonozooid. Center, gastrozooid, shown between two spines. Right, dactlyozooid.

genus *Hydra*. (Fig. 5-22). Two species, *Chlorohydra viridissima* and *Pelmatohydra oligactis*, are worldwide in distribution; the others are restricted to North America. They are solitary in habit, possess no medusoid stages, and are distinguished by complete absence of a perisarc and the presence of hollow tentacles. When extended, the body varies in length from 2 to 25 mm. depending on the species. Hydras are strictly freshwater forms and are usually attached to a substratum of some sort (vegetation, leaves, stones, etc.) by a pedal disk of glandular cells.

The body consists of a long column and a distal region, the hypostome, that bears the mouth at its tip and a circlet of extensible tentacles at its base (Fig. 5-22). Five or six tentacles are usually present, but there may be more and sometimes fewer than this number. The column is usually divided into a stout distal part where the

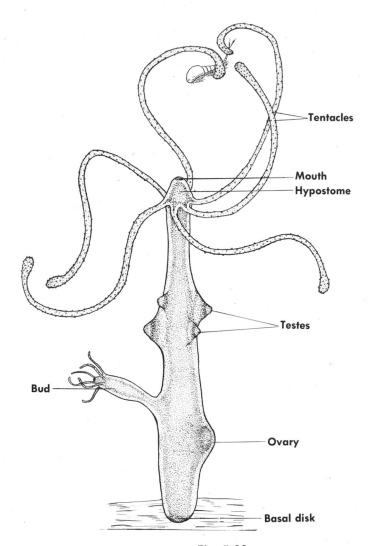

- Tentacles
- Mouth
- Hypostome
- Testes
- Bud
- Ovary
- Basal disk

Fig. 5-22

Generalized structure of hydra. Most hydras are dioecious. (From Hickman: Integrated principles of zoology, The C. V. Mosby Co.)

stomach is located and a short proximal stalk that terminates in the pedal disk.

The body wall is composed externally of a layer of epidermis and internally of a layer of gastrodermis lining the gastrovascular cavity (Figs. 5-7, 5-23, A). Between these two layers is the secreted noncellular mesoglea. Epitheliomuscular cells form most of the epidermis. The bases of these cells terminate in contractile fibrils (myonemes) next to the mesoglea and form a longitudinal muscular layer, or sheath. The nutritive-muscular cells of the gastrodermis are also provided with contractile fibrils that form a circular layer of muscle. Sensory cells are present in the epidermis, and interstitial cells are found

in both epidermis and gastrodermis. The elongated sensory cells, which are generalized receptors for touch, temperature, etc., are connected with processes of the nervous system that form a nerve net lying at the base of the epidermis or in the mesoglea. The four kinds of nematocysts found in a hydra were described in the section on stinging organelles (Fig. 5-6). They are found throughout the epidermis except on the basal disk. Nematocysts are especially abundant on the distal column and

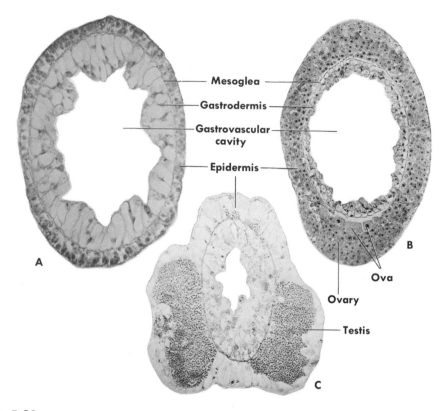

Mesoglea
Gastrodermis
Gastrovascular cavity
Epidermis
A
B
Ova
Ovary
Testis
C

Fig. 5-23

Photomicrographs of cross sections through hydras. **A,** Normal individual with typical epidermis. **B,** Female with epidermis thickened to form ovary with developing ova. **C,** Male with testes formed in epidermis.

A   B   C

Fig. 5-24

Living hydra in process of eating *Daphnia*. At right, hydra has swallowed *Daphnia* and has captured small protozoan. (From Hickman: Integrated principles of zoology, The C. V. Mosby Co.)

on the tentacles. Each nematocyst organelle is contained in a modified interstitial cell, the cnidoblast, and they are used as defensive and food-getting devices (Fig. 5-24).

Budding is the most common method of asexual reproduction. The first buds usually originate near the junction of the gastric and stalk region, and successive buds appear spirally toward the distal region. The bud, or new hydra, at first has a common gastrovascular cavity with the parent since it starts as an outpouching of the wall on the side of the parent. The bud later becomes cylindric, develops tentacles (Fig. 5-22), and eventually pinches off at the base so that the new hydra becomes a separate individual. Hydras may also reproduce asexually by transverse or longitudinal fission, but such fission does not occur in normal individuals; it is found only in those that suffer unusual conditions of injury or depression.

Sexual reproduction is mainly seasonal, occurring in autumn or early winter when water temperature is dropping, or in spring or summer for certain species. Hydras may be either dioecious or hermaphroditic; most American species are dioecious. In hermaphroditic species the ovaries are proximal and the testes are distal to the gastric region. Sometimes the ovaries and testes of hermaphrodites develop simultaneously, or they may develop at different times. The gonads develop from cell aggregations in the epidermis. Clumps of interstitial cells merge to form a single ovum in a rounded swelling called the ovary (Figs. 5-23, *B*, 5-25, *C*); the testes (Figs. 5-23, *C*, 5-25, *A, B*) are conical elevations provided in some species with a nipple through which the sperm escape. In dioecious species testes or ovaries may be located throughout the gastric region. Males far outnumber females.

When mature, the ovary ruptures through the epidermis exposing the egg (Fig. 5-26), which remains attached throughout fertilization and early development. The egg may be fertilized by sperm from the same or from another hydra. During late cleavage the embryo secretes around itself the embryonic theca of chitin or other material. These thecated embryos are sticky, and when they drop off from the parent, they become attached to a substratum and complete their development. Such embryos are highly resistant to adverse conditions of drying and freezing. After a dormant period of several weeks

A   B   C

Fig. 5-25

A, Hydra with testes. (From stained slide.) **B,** Living hydras, mostly males with testes. **C,** Living hydras, mostly females with mature ovaries and developing eggs. (**B** and **C** courtesy General Biological Supply House, Inc., Chicago.)

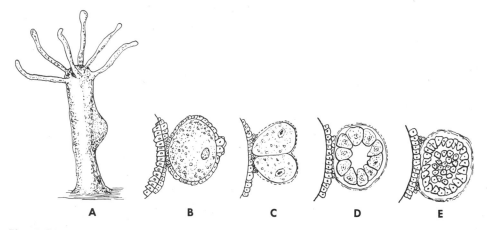

Fig. 5-26

Early stages in development of hydra (diagrammatic). **A,** Female with ovary. **B,** Fertilized ovum. **C,** Cleavage. **D,** Blastula. **E,** Stereogastrula with outer ectoderm and inner endoderm.

Fig. 5-27

Cordylophora lacustris with attached medusoid gonophores. This freshwater hydroid forms colonies 1 to 2 inches high.

the theca ruptures and the juvenile hydra emerges equipped with tentacles and gastrovascular cavity. Sexual reproduction in many species may be induced by placing them in a refrigerator for two or three weeks—feeding should continue during this period.

Besides the 15 species of hydra, the only freshwater coelenterates in the United States are a colonial hydroid, *Cordylophora*

lacustris (Fig. 5-27), with attached medusoid gonophores, and a freshwater jellyfish with its polyp stage, *Craspedacusta sowerbyi* (Fig. 5-36). *Cordylophora* belongs to the family Clavidae of the order Hydroida, and *Craspedacusta* belongs to the family Petasidae of the order Trachylina.

Cordylophora. This is a branching, colonial hydroid colony (Fig. 5-27) consisting of a basal hydrorhiza fastened to substrata of sticks and rocks. It has been found in certain inland rivers of the middle west and in many other parts of the world. This form seems to prefer brackish inlets or estuaries, in which it reaches its largest growth. Its appearance is usually sporadic. The colonies attain a height of 10 to 100 mm.—the smaller sizes live in fresh water. The hydranths are naked with 10 to 20 filiform tentacles arranged irregularly over them. The gonophores or sporosacs are bulbous bodies located below the hydranths. Few gonophores are produced on colonies in fresh water. Mature ova remain on the female gonophores where they are fertilized by sperm that swim from the male gonophores. The embryo develops in situ on the gonophore to the planula stage and then escapes to form a new colony. There is no true medusa. Most of the hydranths disintegrate in the fall or early winter leaving only a few basal portions of the colony to start new colonies in the spring.

Suborder Leptomedusae (Calyptoblastea)

The Calyptoblastea include those hydroids that have a protective periderm or perisarc cup around the hydranths (hydrothecae) and around the gonozooids (gonothecae). Most members of this suborder have no free medusae. The Leptomedusae or jellyfish of this group usually possess flattened or saucer-shaped bells with gonads on the radial canal, statocysts, and numerous tentacles. Most of them lack ocelli on the tentacular bulb. Some of the more common members of this group are:

Plumularia. This colonial form originates from a creeping hydrorhiza and is made up of plumelike, feathery branches bearing small, sessile, bell-like hydrothecae arranged on one side only (Fig. 5-28, *C*). It also bears nematophores provided with nematocysts and adhesive cells that are used to ensnare prey. The hydrothecae are too small for the polyps to be completely retracted within them.

Sertularia. In this colony the hydrothecae are arranged on opposite sides of the branching stems (one pair to each internode), and they are large enough to enclose the polyps when retracted (Figs. 5-28, *A*, 5-29). The colony may grow to a height of about ½ to 2 inches. The gonothecae are large and vaselike. The lid, or operculum, of the hydrotheca is made up of two flaps. These forms are most commonly found on floating seaweeds.

Campanularia. The cup-shaped hydrothecae are borne at the ends of branches in this form (Fig. 5-28, *B*). Gonophores are sessile and may produce either free medusae or sporosacs. Medusae are provided with lithocysts on the margin of the umbrella, and gonads are attached to the radial canals. In some species the gonangia are much larger than the hydrothecae. Colonies are usually ½ to 1 inch in length.

Obelia. This colonial genus contains many species and has a wide distribution throughout the world. Colonies are attached to rocks and shells sometimes as deep as 40 fathoms. This animal is one of the most frequently studied in general zoology courses because its life history is a classic example of so-called metagenesis,

Fig. 5-28

Some calyptoblastic hydrozoans. **A,** *Sertularia cornicina;* left, portion of stem and one gonophore; right, natural size. **B,** *Campanularia verticillata;* left, portion of stem with hydrothecae and gonophores; right, natural size. **C,** *Plumularia corrugata;* left, portion of stem with small hydrothecae and large female gonophores; right, about natural size. (Modified from Fraser, 1937.)

Fig. 5-29

Sertularia, colonies attached to bit of seaweed (preserved).

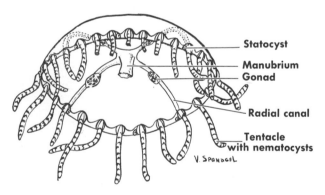

Fig. 5-30

Medusa of *Obelia*. Although hydrozoan, velum is rudimentary.

which involves an asexual generation alternating with a sexual generation.

The colony (Fig. 5-11) is usually quite bushy and may grow to a height of from less than an inch to more than a foot. The branched stem bears flowerlike hydranths with gonangia arising from axils of the branches. The medusae are free swimming and originate from medusoid buds on the

blastostyle, the central stalk of the gonangium. The branching stem is attached to the substratum by a rootlike hydrorhiza. The stem consists of an inner, hollow coenosarc with epidermal, mesogleal, and gastrodermal layers. The coenosarc cavity is a part of the gastrovascular cavity, which is continuous throughout the colony. Around the stem is the horny perisarc. The hydranths are the asexual polyps and resemble hydras in structure. Each hydranth is enclosed in a cup-shaped or vase-shaped hydrotheca, which is a continuation of the perisarc. Each hydranth or polyp has about 20 solid tentacles.

The gonangium is the reproductive polyp; it is made up of a central clublike blastostyle enclosed in a perisarc sheath, the gonotheca. The blastostyle bears on its surface many small medusoid buds. When mature, these medusoid buds escape through the constricted opening, the gonopore, at the top of the gonotheca. The sexes of the medusae are separate in *Obelia*.

The bell of the medusa is about 1 mm. in diameter when the medusa escapes from the blastostyle and usually bears 16 to 24 tentacles; when mature, the medusa may attain a diameter of 5 mm. and possess many tentacles, but the velum is rudimentary (Fig. 5-30). Sperm and eggs are shed into seawater when the jellyfish become sexually mature. The zygote develops into a ciliated planula larva that attaches to a substratum, develops a mouth with tentacles, and becomes a polyp. From this asexual hydroid form develop the stolons, stems, and other polyps to start a new colony.

Suborder Limnomedusae

The Limnomedusae may have hollow or solid tentacles and a minute polyp stage. The polyps of Limnomedusae give off nonciliated planulalike frustules that creep about and develop into polyps. Medusae also arise from gonophores that are budded from the sides of the polyps. Two common Limnomedusae are *Gonionemus* (Fig. 5-31) and the freshwater form *Craspedacusta* (Fig. 5-32). *Gonionemus* has hollow tentacles that bear adhesive pads for clinging to seaweeds (Fig. 5-4); *Craspedacusta* has solid tentacles.

Statocyst

Manubrium
Gonad

Radial canal

Tentacle
with nematocysts

V. SPONOGEL

Fig. 5-31

Gonionemus, exumbrellar view, preserved specimen (Limnomedusae). Note well-developed gonads beneath radial canals and adhesive pads on tentacles. Polyp stage of *Gonionemus* is small, buds off frustules to form polyps, and has gonophores that give rise to medusae.

Craspedacusta sowerbyi is the only freshwater medusa, or jellyfish, in North America. It has been found sporadically in artificial bodies of water located in most of our states. This jellyfish appears to have a wide distribution and may have originated from marine ancestors in certain river basins of China. A mature medusa has the typical bell shape and is about 15 to 20 mm. in diameter (Fig. 5-32, *B*). There are from 50 to 400 or 500 tentacles arranged in three (sometimes more) sets. The bell margin is provided with many statocysts, and there is a thick velum. Nematocysts of one kind are abundant around the mouth, at the margin of the bell, and on the tentacles. Swimming movements are produced by rhythmic contractions of the bell. Most of the medusae of a locality are of one sex only (monosexual populations). The four gonads are convoluted masses on the subumbrella on or near the radial canals. Eggs and sperm are discharged into the water where fertilization occurs.

A   B

Fig. 5-32

Craspedacusta sowerbyi, a freshwater limnomedusan. **A,** Polyp, naked and without tentacles; 0.5 mm. long. **B,** Medusa (preserved specimen); 15 to 20 mm. in diameter. Resembles *Gonionemus,* but tentacles are more varied in length and lack adhesive pads. (**A** courtesy Charles F. Lytle; **B** courtesy Carolina Biological Supply Co., Burlington, N. C.)

The zygote develops into a colony of just a few individual hydroids. The naked polyps, or hydranths, are only about 0.5 mm. long, are devoid of tentacles, and can creep around on a substratum to feed on small organisms (Fig. 5-32, *A*). Debris often collects on the polyp because of a sticky secretion. A colony of polyps may reach a size of 2 or 3 mm. Three methods of asexual reproduction occur in the hydroid stage (Fig. 5-13). By budding, new polyps are formed from the parent and may remain attached to form a colony; or planula-like buds (frustules) may constrict off and develop into polyps that creep about and form a colony. A third method is the formation of polyp buds that develop into free-swimming medusae. C. F. Lytle has shown that the production of the three kinds of buds is differentially affected by feeding rates. At high feeding rates, for example, more frustules and fewer of the other two kinds of buds are formed. The medusa at first is very small and has only eight tentacles, but the number of tentacles increases rapidly as the medusa matures.

Order Milleporina

The members of the order Milleporina are the stinging corals of shallow tropical seas. They are rarely found below a depth of 30 meters. Their structure is similar to that of hydroids with the addition of a calcareous skeleton, and they are often brightly colored. They make up part of the fauna of coral reefs and form leaflike calcareous growths which attain a height of 1 to 2 feet. Their skeleton is covered with a thin layer of tissue pitted with pores, through which the bodies of the polyps are extended. These pores open into cavities and interconnecting tubes crossed by hori-

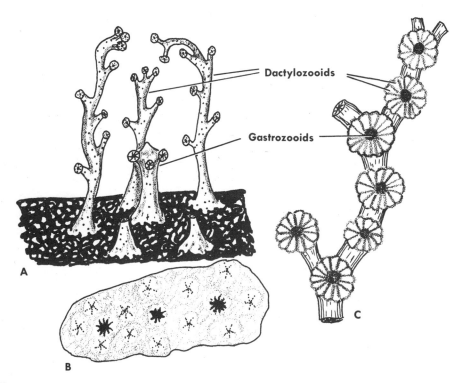

Fig. 5-33

A, Group of polyps of *Millepora* (order Milleporina). Gastrozooid is surrounded by five dactylozooids (two are cut off). **B,** Portion of surface of dry *Millepora,* magnified to show three gastropores surrounded by smaller dactylopores. **C,** Portion of corallum of *Astylus* (order Stylasterina). Each cyclosystem on branch has deep central gastropore surrounded by circlet of slitlike dactylopores. This genus, as its name implies, lacks spines.

zontal calcareous plates. The minute polyps are said to cover the coenosteum like a layer of white felt. The two types of polyps are the gastrozooids with knobby tentacles and a mouth, and the dactylozooids, which bear two or three kinds of nematocysts and short, capitate tentacles but no mouth. Gonophores bud from the coenosarc tubes and develop medusae that disintegrate after releasing sex cells. *Millepora* (Fig. 5-33, *A, B*) is the only genus in this order.

Order Stylasterina

The Stylasterina resemble the Milleporina and are often included with them in a single order, the Hydrocorallina. They are found mostly in tropical seas and are brightly colored. Like the millepores their calcareous skeleton is covered by tissue that bears pores opening into ramifying tubes. The gastrozooids are found in deep cups along the edges of the branches or only on one face of the colony (Fig. 5-33, *C*). Gastrozooids also differ from those of millepores by having, in most genera, a spine, or style, at the base of each cup. The other type of polyp (dactylozooid) is without tentacles or mouth, but is provided with nematocysts. Eggs and sperm are produced by sporosacs on the surface of the colony, from which the planula larvae escape. The order is represented by such genera as *Stylaster, Stylantheca* (California), and *Cryptohelia*.

Order Trachylina

Members of the order Trachylina are medusae that differ from other hydrozoan jellyfish in possessing gastroderm lithocysts, or balancing organs (Fig. 5-34), and in almost completely lacking the polypoid stage.

The three kinds of medusae found in this order are sometimes considered as separate orders. They are the Trachymedusae, the Narcomedusae, and the Pteromedusae.

The Trachymedusae are found in the open seas and have solid tentacles. *Liriope* is a common example (Fig. 5-35). Their gastrovascular system contains four to eight radial canals beneath which are the epidermal gonads. Along the margin of the bell are the statocysts. Development is direct—the egg gives rise to a swimming planula that becomes an actinula larva by the

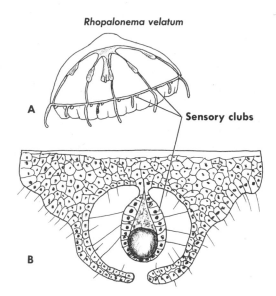

Fig. 5-34

A, *Rhopalonema velatum,* a trachymedusan, showing sense organ at right of each tentacle base. **B,** Sensory club with single concretion nearly enclosed in capsule *(Rhopalonema).* In young medusa, sensory club is free. Later, ectodermal capsule grows from margin and finally completely encloses club.

Fig. 5-35

Liriope scutigera (Trachymedusae) lacks hydroid stage. Bell is about ¾ inch in diameter, with pink tentacles and yellow-green manubrium. Common along Atlantic coast.

Fig. 5-36

Aegina citrea (Narcomedusae) with tentacles attached above bell margin. Deep-water form (order Trachylina). Hardy reports that in aquarium it remains almost motionless, with tentacles stretched upward. (×2½.)

formation of a mouth and tentacles. The actinula transforms directly into a medusa.

Narcomedusae differ from Trachymedusae in having lobed stomachs, tentacles attached above the margin of the bell, and an absence of peripheral canals (Fig. 5-36). They also have lithostyles or sense clubs hanging from the bell margin, and their gonads are located in the gastric pockets.

Pteromedusae is represented by *Tetraplatia*, an unusual medusa found in marine plankton. It is slender and bipyramidal in shape, with a groove about the equator from which extend four swimming lobes, each with two statocysts. These lobes apparently represent the velum. The upper pyramid is the bell; the lower one is the manubrium, with the mouth at the lower pole.

The order Trachylina is of great interest in the evolutionary development of coelenterates because members usually lack a polypoid stage and because their direct mode of development (planula-actinula-medusa) is supposed to indicate a primitive condition. From the primitive actinula larva other larvae may have budded off and, in time, developed into the polyp or hydroid form, which, with many modifica-

tions, became an established part of their life history.

Order Siphonophora

Members of the order Siphonophora are large floating colonies of modified polypoid and medusoid components; several different types exist. The various components may be connected by a stem or coenosarc, or they may be compactly grouped together. Such colonies represent the highest degree of polymorphism to be found among the coelenterates. It is thought that siphonophores evolved from trachyline ancestors with a swimming actinuloid stage and an adult medusoid stage, and that the

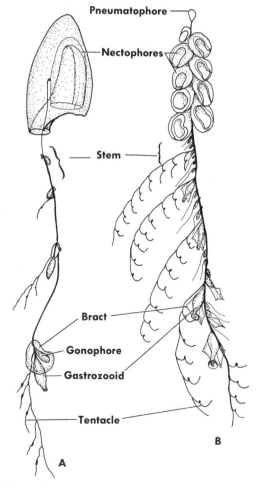

Fig. 5-37

Two types of siphonophore colony. **A,** Calycophora. **B,** Physonectae.

merger of these two stages produced the siphonophoran colony. Both polypoid and medusoid components are found in several modifications (Fig. 5-37), but few are strictly hydroid forms. The commonest polypoid components are the gastrozooids with a mouth and one hollow tentacle armed with nematocysts for the capture and the digestion of food; the palpons, similar to gastrozooids but simpler, serving as accessory digestive organs; and the gonozooids with or without a mouth but with no tentacle and bearing clusters of gonophores for reproduction. The medusoid components are made up of the swimming bells (highly modified medusae without mouth and tentacles) for locomotion; bracts—thick, gelatinous, many-shaped structures with a gastrovascular cavity for streamlining, protection, and flotation; and gonophores, basically medusalike, for carrying the sex cells. The float or pneumatophore, formerly considered to be an altered medusa, is now regarded as an aboral invagination, and the bracts may be altered tentacles instead

Fig. 5-39

Physalia physalia, the Portuguese man-of-war, is best known of siphonophores. This one has caught fish. (Courtesy New York Zoological Society.)

of altered medusoids. On the basis of swimming bells and floats, the Siphonophora are often divided into the following groups: Calycophora with swimming bells (nectophores), Physonectae with both floats and swimming bells, and Cystonectae with only floats. *Stephalia* (Fig. 5-38), a classic example of a form with swimming bells, belongs to the Physonectae.

One of the most familiar of siphonophores is the Portuguese man-of-war *(Physalia,* Fig. 5-39). This colonial form (a cystonect) has a float that may reach a diameter of 12 inches or more. The stem is rudimentary beneath the float. A gas gland secretes into the float a gas composed of nitrogen, oxygen, carbon monoxide, and argon. Excretory pores may open to the outside from the float. This form lacks the swimming bells and bracts characteristic of many siphonophores, but it possesses the other components. Lacking swimming bells,

Fig. 5-38

Stephalia (Physonectae of order Siphonophora). Note ring of swimming bells (nectophores) at base of float.

137

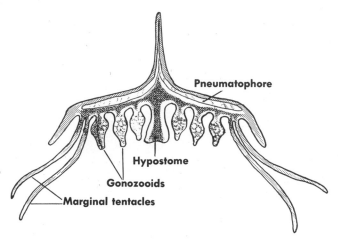

Fig. 5-40

Diagrammatic section of *Velella,* the purple sail, a siphonophoran that is thought to be essentially individual hydranth, except for having gonozooids to carry medusa buds (Chondrophora).

Physalia is carried along by wind and wave action. Whenever a fish comes in contact with the dangling, trailing dactylozooids, it is paralyzed by the nematocysts and drawn up by the tentacles to the region of the gastrozooids. The lips of the latter spread over the fish and form a sort of bag in which digestion begins. Nematocysts are large, numerous, and very virulent. They are found on most members of the colony, although the float and parts of the gastrozooids are deficient in mature nematocysts. Each of the cnidoblasts is provided with a cnidocil. The nature of the toxin found in the nematocysts has been recently studied by C. E. Lane, who found it to be a simple protein consisting of a few toxic peptides. He also found that the toxin is synthesized by gastroderm cells and passes to the nematocyst (in the epidermis) through the mesogleal layer. *Physalia* is very dangerous to bathers in southern waters.

Another group of polymorphic floating colonies is the Chondrophora, which includes *Velella* and *Porpita.* Although this group is usually included under Siphonophora, some taxonomists now consider it to be, in its own right, an order or suborder of the Hydroida. These colonies are probably the most modified polymorphic forms of all.

Velella, for example, has a flat, disklike float with air chambers and a vertical extension that acts as a sail (Fig. 5-40). The stem is a flat coenosarc forming part of the float. Beneath the disk is a large central gastrozooid surrounded by gonozooids that bear the medusiform gonophores. On the margin of the disk are the dactylozooids, or fringing tentacles. The gastrovascular cavities of the various zooids communicate with gastrodermal canals above the central gastrozooid, forming a sort of excretory system. The air chambers of the disk open to the outside by pores and canals. Gonophores are set free in reproduction, but they quickly disintegrate after the discharge of the sex cells.

Regarding the siphonophores, G. O. Mackie (1963) makes the interesting observation that they are the most complex coelenterates to have fully explored the possibilities of colonialism. By doing so, they have escaped some of the limitations and restrictions imposed by a diploblastic body plan. By converting whole individuals into organs, siphonophores have reached the organ grade of construction. Higher animals have reached this higher grade by using mesoderm (lacking in siphonophores) in a triploblastic arrangement for the formation of organs.

CLASS SCYPHOZOA

The class Scyphozoa consists of members that have emphasized the medusa stage in the typical coelenterate life history of polypoid and medusoid structures. They include the scyphomedusae and medusalike polypoids with distinct four-part radial symmetry (tetramerous) and a gastrovascular cavity divided by four longitudinal septa. The polypoid stage is usually reduced (scyphistoma) or absent. Diversity in their life histories is shown by some that are polyplike and sessile throughout their life cycle, and by others that are always pelagic and lack the sessile polyp stage. In general the scyphomedusae are of large size and the scyphopolyps are of small size. Scyphomedusae differ from hydromedusae in possessing a mesoglea with cells (a true cellular layer), gastric tentacles or oral lobes about the mouth, division of the gastrovascular cavity into a central stomach and four gastric pouches, scalloped or

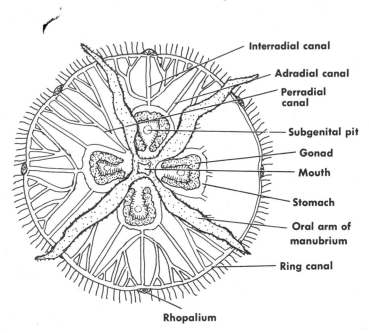

Labels (clockwise from top):
Interradial canal
Adradial canal
Perradial canal
Subgenital pit
Gonad
Mouth
Stomach
Oral arm of manubrium
Ring canal
Rhopalium

Fig. 5-41

Subumbrellar view of *Aurelia*, a scyphomedusan (semi-diagrammatic) (order Semaeostomae).

notched bell margin (lappets) with sensory organs between the lappets, and no velum. In some members, including *Aurelia,* a velarium that is analogous to the velum exists.

In most scyphozoans (scyphomedusae and scyphopolyps) the parts around the oral-aboral axis are symmetrically repeated in fours or some multiple of four (Fig. 5-41). The mouth is foursided, and the axes running from the four corners of the mouth are called perradii. In the scyphomedusae interradii occur between the perradii. The gastric pouches and oral arms lie on the planes of the perradii, whereas the septa lie on the planes of the interradii. When the marginal bodies are four in number, they may be at the ends of either the perradii or interradii; when there are eight marginal organs, they are found at the ends of both perradii and interradii. When the number exceeds eight, the marginal organs are located on the adradii, which lie between each perradius and interradius.

The scyphomedusae vary in shape in the different groups of Scyphozoa; they are dome shaped, cone shaped, or saucer shaped. The medusa consists of an upper umbrellar part and lower oral arms. The umbrella, as in hydromedusae, has an upper convex surface (exumbrella) and a lower concave surface (subumbrella). Nem-

atocysts are found in both surfaces of the bell in definite regions. In most orders the bell margin is notched or scalloped into lappets. Sense organs (tentaculocysts or rhopalia), four or some multiple of four in number, are found between the lappets (Fig. 5-42). A sense organ, all of which are based on the same plan throughout the group, is composed of a statocyst or vesicle containing a concretion (statolith) and an ocellus that may contain the typical parts of the vertebrate eye (cornea, lens, retina, etc.). Sense organs are usually found in the niches between lappets.

Tentacles may be solid or hollow, are usually definite in number (few or many) for a species, and may occur on the lappets, in niches between the lappets, or on the subumbrellar surface. They are provided with numerous nematocysts of two or three types. In some of the orders four interradially located subgenital pits, or shallow depressions, located on the subumbrellar surface may function in respiration.

The endoderm-lined manubrium with its terminal mouth is found in the center of the subumbrella. The mouth is four cornered, and each of its angles may be drawn into

139

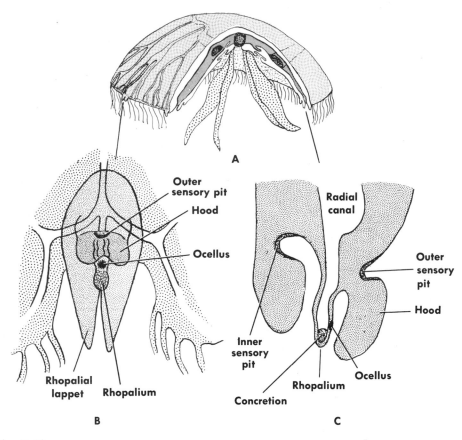

Fig. 5-42

Structure of rhopalium, or sense organ, of *Aurelia* (diagrammatic). **A,** *Aurelia,* with part of body removed, showing location of rhopalia. **B,** Outer or aboral view of rhopalium. **C,** Radial section of rhopalium.

a frilly oral arm, which is liberally supplied with nematocysts. (The oral arms are fused and the central mouth is closed in the order Rhizostomae; in place of the mouth many suctorial mouths open by canals into the interior.) The mouth leads to the large gastrovascular system. Usually four septa composed of gastrodermis and mesoglea divide the gastrovascular cavity into a central stomach and four perradial gastric pouches. Gastric filaments of mesogleal and gastrodermal derivation are found on the free inner edge of each septum. The filaments bear glands and nematocysts. In some orders this arrangement of the gastrovascular system is not found in adults but is restricted to the scyphistoma, or larval stage. From the periphery of the stomach many radial canals, simple or branched, run to

the bell margin where they join the ring canal if present (Fig. 5-41).

Muscles are mainly epidermal and are restricted to the subumbrella and tentacles. The coronal, or ring muscle band, of the subumbrella serves to contract the umbrella in swimming. Muscles of tentacles are largely longitudinal fibers and are used in the extension and contraction of tentacles in catching prey.

Present evidence seems to indicate that there are two nerve nets in scyphomedusae. One of these is the main subumbrellar net, or plexus, which controls pulsation of the bell by activating simultaneously the muscles necessary for locomotion. The other, more diffused nerve net, with cell bodies in both subumbrellar and exumbrellar epidermis, controls local reactions of food ingestion and may also inhibit the bell pulsations. Recent investigations seem to indicate that the nervous system is synaptic and not continuous. There is no marginal nerve ring such as that found in hydromedusae, except in one order, the Cubomedusae.

Most Scyphozoa are dioecious. The gonads are formed from endodermal (gastrodermal) cells just below the gastric filaments. In medusae with septa the gonads are arranged on both sides of each septum, forming eight gonads altogether. In most medusae the ripe sex cells rupture into the gastrovascular cavity and reach the outside through the mouth. The zygotes may develop, in seawater or in the folds of the oral arms, into coeloblastulae at first and later develop into ciliated planulae. After attachment, the planula develops into a scyphopolyp, or scyphistoma (Fig. 5-43, *A*) that undergoes asexual budding and finally matures into a strobila (Fig. 5-43, *B*). The strobila asexually produces ephyrae (Fig. 5-43, *C*), which are shed as young, free-swimming medusae and grow into adult medusae. Radial cleavage is characteristic of the group.

The five living orders of Scyphozoa are Stauromedusae, Cubomedusae, Coronatae,

Fig. 5-43

Three stages in life cycle of *Aurelia*. **A**, Scyphistoma. **B**, Strobila, composed of layers of budding ephyrae. **C**, Ephyra. (From stained slides.)

Samaeostomae, and Rhizostomae. A brief description of these orders and their common genera is herewith presented.

Order Stauromedusae

Stauromedusae are sessile scyphozoans that possess a type of combined polyp and medusa form. The medusoid part is made up of a cuplike bell (calyx) that is eight sided and bears eight groups of capitate tentacles and eight sensory bodies (rhopalioids or anchors). The polyp part is usually a stem that terminates in a pedal disk, which is attached to a substratum. The whole often forms a trumpet-shaped or goblet-shaped body. The four-cornered mouth is situated at the center of the calyx, and on each side of the quadrangular manubrium is located a subumbrellar funnel into the interior. The gastrovascular cavity is continued into the arms, tentacles, and rhopalioids. Although sessile, most Stauromedusae can move about by attaching and releasing their pedal disks and anchors.

Haliclystus, or the "clown" (Fig. 5-44), is one of the most familiar genera of this order.

Order Cubomedusae

The bell of the Cubomedusae has four flattened sides and a relatively cuboid form. A gelatinous, leaf-shaped blade, or pedalium, is present at the base of each ex-

umbrellar ridge. Each pedalium bears a tentacle or cluster of tentacles provided with nematocysts. Above the margin in the center of each flat side (i.e., perradially) is located a sensory organ (rhopalium). Each rhopalium has a statocyst and six ocelli. The short, quadrangular manubrium that connects the mouth with the stomach is present in the center of the subumbrellar cavity. An extension of the subumbrella forms a velarium. The nervous system features a marginal nerve ring that connects with the sensory organs, an arrangement not found in other Scyphozoa. Reproduction is typically scyphozoan, and there may be a polypoid stage—such a stage has been described in some members. The best known genera are *Carybdea* (Fig. 5-45, *A*) and the "fire medusae," *Chiropsalmus.* Most members of the group can give dangerous stings.

Order Coronatae

Medusae of the order Coronatae are dome shaped, conical, or flattened, but the exumbrella is divided by a horizontal coronal furrow into two parts—an upper domelike disk and a lower coronal part. The coronal part has thick, gelatinous pedalia separated from each other by grooves that point toward the centers of marginal lappets. Usually each of the pedalia is provided with a tentacle. Sensory organs (rhopalia) are found at the ends of those pedalia that have no tentacles. There are two stomachs—an upper central stomach and a coronal stomach, which communicate through gastric ostia.

The members of this group are found chiefly in deep marine waters (abyssal) and usually are known only from deep-sea dredgings. Some members, however, such as *Nausithoe,* are found in the surface waters of warm seas. *Periphylla,* (Fig. 5-45, *B*), is a deep-sea form.

Order Semaeostomae

Medusae of the order Semaeostomae are the most familiar ones of the Scyphozoa and are the ones commonly studied in zoology classes. The bell is flat to dome shaped, and its margin is scalloped into many lappets. In the niches between the lappets are the sensory organs (rhopalia). Tentacles are distributed in different places

Fig. 5-44

Haliclystus, the "clown" (order Stauromedusae).

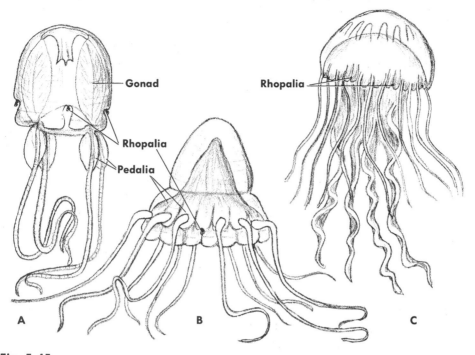

Fig. 5-45

Three scyphomedusans. **A,** *Carybdea* (order Cubomedusae). **B,** *Periphylla* (order Coronatae). **C,** *Chrysaora* (order Semaeostomae).

according to species. They are located along the exumbrellar margin in *Aurelia;* in the grooves between the lappets in *Pelagia;* and on the subumbrella in *Cyanea* (Fig. 5-46). The tentacles are short in *Aurelia,* but long in most other genera. The oral arms are conspicuous structures in most members, being frilly, leaflike, and provided with ciliated grooves and nematocysts. The stomach is cross shaped and lacks septa and gastric pouches in the adults, but has numerous gastric filaments. From the stomach numerous simple or branched radial canals run to the bell margin where they connect with sense organs and tentacles. A ring canal is absent in most members. Gonads are located in the floor of the stomach and discharge their products through the mouth.

The life history is the typical metagenesis pattern of planula, scyphopolyp, strobila, and ephyra (Fig. 5-43). All are dioecious, except the striking and beautiful *Chrysaora* (Fig. 5-45, *C*). In *Pelagia* the planula transforms directly into an ephyra medusa.

Fig. 5-46

Cyanea, the largest jellyfish (order Semaeostomae). (Courtesy C. P. Hickman, Jr.)

Biology of the invertebrates

Most Semaeostomae are coastal forms, and the order includes the largest coelenterate, *Cyanea* (Fig. 5-46). Specimens of this genus taken from northern waters have bells 8 feet in diameter and 800 or more tentacles that are 100 to 200 feet long.

Order Rhizostomae

The chief distinctive features of the Rhizostomae are the fusion of the oral arms and the lack of marginal tentacles. The bell varies in shape from a distinct bowl or dome to those that are flat and concave on top. The central mouth is usually obliterated by the fusion of the eight oral arms. In its place are many suctorial mouths connected to the complicated brachial canals that run to the central stomach. From the cruciform stomach numerous radial canals in the form of networks run to the periphery of the bell, which may or may not have a circular canal. Filamentous appendages loaded with nematocysts are found on the arms. Life histories are similar to those of the Semaeostomae.

Cassiopeia is the most familiar American form and is common around Florida. *Rhizostoma* has a wide distribution in shallow waters of the tropical and subtropical regions.

CLASS ANTHOZOA

The Anthozoa are characterized by having an exclusively polypoid, attached form; a flat, oral disk with hollow tentacles; a mouth, usually with one or more siphonoglyphs, or ciliated grooves, leading into a true stomodeum lined with ectoderm; an enteron partitioned longitudinally into radial compartments by vertical endodermal septa or mesenteries with nematocysts on the inner margin; a cellular mesoglea or connective tissue; endodermal gonads on the septa; and presence or absence of a skeleton. They may be solitary or colonial and include the sea anemones, sea fans, sea pansies, sea pens, corals, and some others. Externally the polyp exhibits the characteristic radial symmetry of the coelenterate, but internally it presents a distinct bilateral tendency that is definitely primary as revealed by the embryologic record. According to their symmetry Anthozoa may be divided into those that are octamerous, or built around a plan of eight (Alcyonaria, Figs. 5-47, *B*, 5-48) and those that are hexamerous or polymerous, or built on a plan of six or multiples of six (Zoantharia, Figs. 5-47, *A*, 5-57).

The general morphology of the group includes the oral disk with an oval or slit-

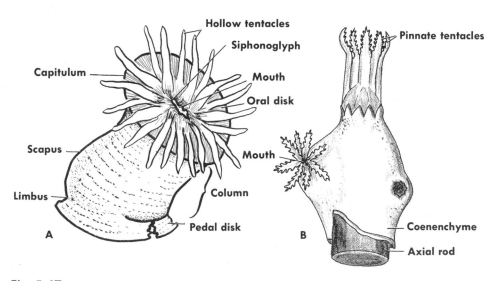

Fig. 5-47

Anthozoan polyps. **A,** Sea anemone *Bunodosoma* (Zoantharia). **B,** Portion of soft coral *Gorgonia* (Alcyonaria, order Gorgonacea).

144

like mouth in its center. The mouth bears a ciliated groove at one or both ends, the siphonoglyph, and opens into the gastrovascular cavity by the pharynx, the lining of which appears to be ectodermal. The siphonoglyph aids in driving water into the gastrovascular cavity for respiratory purposes. The tentacles vary in the two subclasses. In the Alcyonaria eight pinnate tentacles arise from the margin of the oral disk (Fig. 5-47, *B*). These rather thick tentacles bear short projections, the pinnules, arranged in a row on each side of the tentacles giving the whole a feathery appearance. In the zoantherians the simple tubular tentacles are arranged in one or more circles to form a tentacular crown (Fig. 5-47, *A*). A pedal disk is found at the basal end of the body. That part of the body between the pedal and oral disks is called the column.

As already mentioned, the gastrovascular cavity is partitioned by longitudinal mesenteries, or septa, provided on one side with longitudinal retractor muscles. These mesenteries are really vertical folds of the mesoglea and gastrodermis of the body wall, radiating inward toward the pharynx, and connecting to the oral disk at the top. Septa that reach from the wall to the pharynx are called complete or primary septa. *Metridium* (Figs. 5-55 to 5-57) usually has six pairs of primary septa. Pairs of primary septa associated with the siphonoglyphs are called directives. Below the pharynx the inner edges of the septa are free. Between the pairs of primary septa may be successively shorter cycles of paired incomplete septa that do not reach to the pharynx, known as secondary, tertiary, and quaternary septa. The free edge of each incomplete mesentery forms a sort of sinuous cord called the septal filament (Figs. 5-55, 5-56), which bears nematocysts and gland cells for digestion. In some forms two septal filaments (asulcal) are ectodermal derivatives from the stomodeum and are provided with flagellate cells for driving water toward the mouth (Fig. 5-48). In many anemones the lower ends of the septal filaments are prolonged as free threads (acontia), which may protrude through the mouth or through the cinclides (pores in the column for the emission of water) when the body contracts.

The mesoglea in Anthozoa is a mesenchyme consisting of a jelly matrix and stellate cells. The muscular system of epidermal longitudinal fibers and gastrodermal circular fibers varies in the different orders but is usually not well developed. Septa possess both circular gastrodermal fibers and longitudinal gastrodermal fibers (retractors).

Skeletal structures (when present) are external or internal. The external skeleton, such as the calcareous exoskeleton of corals, is formed from the secretions of ectodermal cells. Internal skeletons, such as those of the soft corals, are sclerites or calcareous spicules secreted by ectodermal scleroblasts in the mesoglea.

The nervous system is made up of subepidermal and gastrodermal plexuses, which in most cases form a continuous nervous connection.

Both sexual and asexual reproduction occurs in anthozoans. Gonads develop on all septa except the two asulcal ones. Sex cells are formed by the interstitial cells of the gastrodermis. Both dioecious and monoecious forms are found. Zygotes develop into planulae or polyps. Asexual reproduction may involve fission and budding.

The class Anthozoa is usually divided into two subclasses, Alcyonaria (Octocorallia) and Zoantharia (Hexacorallia), each of which contains a number of orders. The distinction between the two subclasses is based chiefly upon the nature of the tentacles, septa, siphonoglyphs, and skeletons. Several evolutionary lines are recognized in the two groups, but the order Antipatharia of the subclass Zoantharia is considered to contain primitive living anthozoans because of their simple organization of septa, tentacles, mesoglea, and siphonoglyph.

A brief résumé of the two subclasses and their orders is presented here.

Subclass Alcyonaria

Alcyonarian polyps have octomerous radial symmetry with a distinct tendency toward bilateral symmetry (Figs. 5-47, *B*, 5-48). Only one strongly developed siphonoglyph (ventral) is present. Some forms are dimorphic (e.g., small siphonozooids without tentacles and regular autozooids). They are colonial, and the gastrovascular cavi-

Fig. 5-48

Diagram of cross section through pharynx of *Alcyonium* to show octomerous septal arrangement typical of alcyonarian polyps.

Fig. 5-49

Tubipora, the organ-pipe coral (order Stolonifera). (From Hickman: Integrated principles of zoology, The C. V. Mosby Co.)

ties of the various polyps of a colony are interconnected by complex canal systems, or solenia, of the common mesogleal mass (coenenchyme) in which the polyps are embedded (Fig. 5-50, *E, F*). An endoskeleton of horny material or calcareous spicules is secreted by ectodermal cells or by ectodermal scleroblasts.

Order Stolonifera

Stoloniferan polyps arise singly from a creeping stolon that forms a thin, flat mat for a colony, and there is no coenenchymal mass. The polyp is cylindric and thin walled and the oral end, or anthocodium, is retractile into a nonretractile anthostele usually protected by spicules. Polyps are connected by solenial tubes of the stolons and sometimes by crossbars. Their skeleton (when present) is composed of calcareous spicules, which, in the common organ-pipe coral *Tubipora* (Fig. 5-49) found in coral reefs, are fused together into tubes. Polyps never bud from the wall of a primary polyp. Another common genus is *Clavularia.*

Order Telestacea

The members of this group form branching colonies by lateral budding from a primary polyp that arises from a creeping stolon. Their spicules or sclerites may be scattered singly or fused into tubes. *Telesto* (Fig. 5-50, *A, B*) is the best-known member.

Order Coenothecalia

The blue corals, present on certain coral reefs, have calcareous skeletons composed of crystalline fibers of aragonite that are fused onto lamellae. The polyps occupy numerous wide, cylindric cavities while the erect solenial systems are found in smaller cavities. A flat coenenchyme with a network of solenia connecting polyps and erect solenial tubes is found on the surface. The skeleton grows by the pushing up of polyps and solenia to successive higher levels. *Heliopora* (Fig. 5-50, *C, D*) is a common blue coral of coral reefs.

Order Alcyonacea

The Alcyonacea are the fleshy or soft corals that have the polyps embedded in a gelatinous coenenchyme from which retractile anthocodia or oral ends protrude. In some species the anthocodia are nonretractile. Dimorphic forms are present in a few species. The polyp base may be protected by spicules and is called a calyx. The skeleton consists of isolated calcareous spicules, or sclerites, that are scattered over the coenenchyme. The colony may be

146

Fig. 5-50

Some Alcyonarian corals. **A,** *Telesto* (order ,Telestacea). **B,** Enlarged portion of *Telesto*. **C,** *Heliopora* (order Coenothecalia). Single zooid with adjacent coenenchymal tubules (skeleton removed). **D,** Diagram of architecture and mode of growth of colony of *Heliopora*. Numbers indicate calyx of mother zooid, **1,** and calices of successively formed zooids. **E,** Small colony of *Alcyonium* (order Alcyonacea). **F,** Section through coenenchyme of *Alcyonium* showing expanded and contracted polyps and solenial network. (**A** redrawn from Hyman: The invertebrates; Protozoa through Ctenophora, McGraw-Hill Book Company; **B** to **D** modified from Bourne, 1895; **F** modified from Hickson, 1895.)

mushroom shaped or plantlike in form. *Alcyonium* (Fig. 5-50, *E*, *F*) and *Xenia* are common genera; most members are found at considerable depths in warm oceans.

Order Gorgonacea

The Gorgonacea are horny corals that have a gorgonin axial skeleton and are often found in fanlike or featherlike colonies (Figs. 5-51, 5-52). The colony may branch in a radial direction or in one plane (sea fan). The axial rod (Fig. 5-47, *B*) consists of an outer cortex and an inner medulla. Around the cortex is the axial epithelium (ectodermal or mesogleal in origin), which secretes the axial skeleton. The axial skeleton in some members (*Paragorgia, Corallium*) contains calcareous spicules; in others (*Gorgonia, Paramuricea*) the skeleton is spiculeless. A shallow layer of some

Fig. 5-51

Small piece of *Gorgonia,* preserved with polyps expanded (order Gorgonacea). (×2.)

147

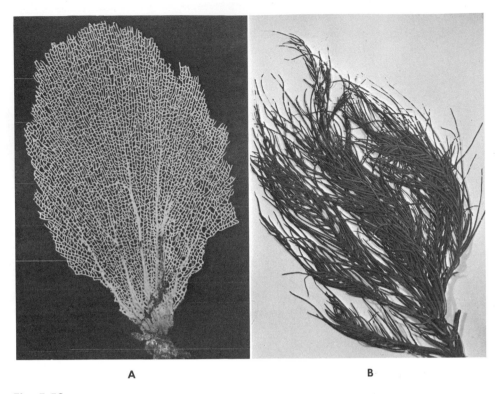

A   B

Fig. 5-52

Gorgonian soft corals, dried. **A,** Sea fan *Gorgonia.* **B,** Sea plume. These specimens are about 15 inches tall.

form of coenenchyme with polyp tubes, solenia, and calcareous spicules covers the central axial rod. In some ways the gorgonians are the most striking of all corals. They have a wide distribution, especially in the warmer seas, and add much color to coral reefs.

Order Pennatulacea

The members of these corals are the sea pens (Fig. 5-54), sea feathers, and sea pansies (Fig. 5-53). They have one long, primary axial polyp with many secondary lateral polyps that arise as direct buds from the primary polyp. The body consists of a distal rachis bearing many polyps and a proximal peduncle without polyps. No stolons are present, and the lower end of the peduncle (sometimes enlarged) is embedded in the soft substratum of the sea floor. The rachis may be a radially symmetric, club-shaped body over which the polyps are scattered, or it may be bilater-

ally symmetric with the polyps restricted to lateral positions. Modifications of the last plan exist, such as the presence of polyps on the dorsal surface and a polyp-free central surface. All members of the order are dimorphic with typical autozooids that may or may not be retractile and siphonozooids without tentacles, retractor muscles, or gonads. The gastrovascular cavity of the primary polyp is divided by partitions into four longitudinal canals enclosing a horny skeletal axis. A spongy network of solenia is found around the canals. The cavities of the secondary polyps communicate with the longitudinal canals by solenia. Special gastrodermal muscles (both circular and longitudinal) are found in the peduncle and, to some extent, in the rachis for circulating the water. Most of the colonies are provided with a horny, calcareous, unbranched axial skeleton, and the coenenchyme contains smooth calcareous spicules of many shapes and forms.

The Pennatulacea are found in warm coastal waters on soft substrata. Many have been obtained from fairly deep dredgings. Common genera are *Renilla*, the sea pansy (Fig. 5-53), *Pennatula*, and *Funiculina*.

Subclass Zoantharia

Members of the subclass Zoantharia of Anthozoa differ mainly from those of the subclass Alcyonaria in having simple tubular tentacles (mostly retractile), mesenteries (complete or incomplete) in sixes or multiples of six, usually siphonoglyphs in both edges of the stomodeum, a skeleton (when present) not of mesogloeal calcareous spicules, and a solitary as well as a colonial existence. These anthozoans are monomorphic, and the number of tentacles varies from six to many hundreds. The septa have a distinct bilateral or biradial arrangement and correspond (are coupled) on each side of the plane of symmetry that bisects the mouth (Figs. 5-55, 5-57). In those with two siphonoglyphs the symmetry is biradial, because two planes at right angles can each produce two similar halves; in those with one siphonoglyph only one such plane can produce two similar halves. In some members the septa are always found in pairs close together. Two pairs of complete septa, one at each constricted end of the mouth, are called directives and are characteristic of sea anemones and some others. This subclass contains far more variations in most morphologic features than does the subclass Alcyonaria.

Order Actiniaria

Actiniaria are the most widely distributed of all the anthozoans, being found in coastal waters from warm to frigid regions. They are commonly called sea anemones because of their flowerlike appearance (Figs. 5-47, *A*, 5-55). They are solitary and sessile forms that live below the low-tide mark attached to a substratum by their pedal disk. They are not immovably fixed, however, for they can glide on their pedal disks by waves of muscular contraction. Varieties of movement are found in the group, and a few can swim by using their tentacles.

The body is cylindric and divided into oral disk, column, and base. The circular fold between the column and oral disk di-

Fig. 5-53

Renilla, the sea pansy (about life size). Polyps grow on only one side of the rachis. Long peduncle is attached to substratum (order Pennatulacea).

Fig. 5-54

Sea pen, preserved specimen (order Pennatulacea). **149**

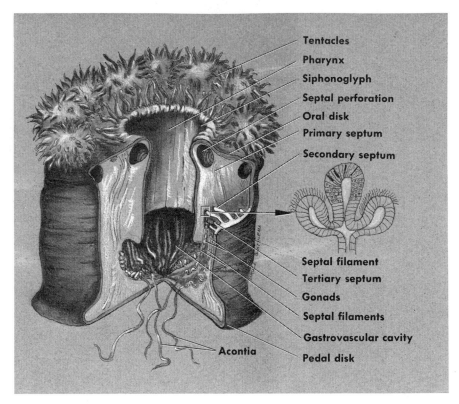

Fig. 5-55

Metridium cut to show pharynx and septal arrangement. Inset, section through septal filament showing its central cnidoglandular band and outer ciliated bands (Zoantharia, order Actiniaria).

vides the animal into an upper capitulum and a lower scapus (Fig. 5-47, A). A deep groove, or fossa, may be found between the collar and base of the capitulum. Between the pedal disk and column, the junction is called limbus. In extreme contraction a marginal sphincter muscle at the base of the capitulum may function to close the upper end of the scapus over the retracted oral disk. The oral disk is flat, usually circular, and bears the tentacles and mouth, which is present in a smooth region called the peristome.

Tentacles with nematocysts may be few in number, or they may be numerous and cover most of the oral disk. They may be arranged in cycles or radiating rows. When the number of tentacles is definite, the number is usually some multiple of six and doubles in each successive cycle after the innermost cycle. There are thus six primary tentacles (innermost and oldest), six secondary tentacles, 12 tertiary tentacles, 24 quaternary tentacles, etc. The primary tentacles are usually the largest, tentacle size decreasing toward the marginal region.

In most sea anemones the septa are in pairs (Figs. 5-55, 5-57). The space between the members of a pair is the entocoel, while the space between pairs is the exocoel. The retractor muscles of a pair of septa project into the entocoel except in the directives, where the retractors project into the exocoel. Although many variations exist, the pairs of septa occur in cycles or multiples of six. The first cycle consists of six pairs of primary septa that are complete and reach the stomodeum. Two pairs of these, one at each end of the pharynx, are directives and there are two pairs on each side between the directives (Fig. 5-57). A second cycle of six pairs is made up of incomplete secondary septa, each pair of which is situated in an exocoel. In the third cycle, 12 pairs of incomplete tertiary septa occur in the 12 exocoels formed by the secondary septa, and so on if additional cycles are present. Complete septa are provided, below the oral disk and near the pharynx, with holes (stoma) for water flow between the interseptal chambers. Marginal stoma near the column may also be present.

The septal or mesenteric filaments already described are made up in sea anemones of three tracts, or lobes (Fig. 5-56). The middle lobe (cnidoglandular) is provided with nematocysts and enzyme-secreting gland cells and is found in all septa below the stomodeum. The lateral lobes bear ciliated cells for water circulation and alveolar tracts of phagocytic cells for digestion. Since the functions of the septal filaments are performed by different parts of the same filament and not by different filaments as in Alcyonaria, some variations exist in the distribution of the tracts in the various sea anemones.

Muscles in sea anemones are specialized for many different kinds of movement, such as the retractor muscles of the septal fila-

Fig. 5-56

Septal filament of sea anemone, *Metridium,* with trefoil arrangement of free edge. Central cnidoglandular band is flanked on each side by flagellated band. (From Andrew: Textbook of comparative histology, Oxford University Press, Inc.)

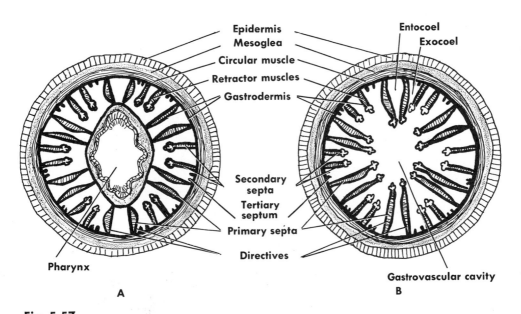

Epidermis
Mesoglea
Circular muscle
Retractor muscles
Gastrodermis
Entocoel
Exocoel
Secondary septa
Tertiary septum
Primary septa
Directives
Pharynx
Gastrovascular cavity

A   B

Fig. 5-57

Diagram of transverse sections through actiniarian polyp such as *Metridium.* **A,** Through pharynx. **B,** Below pharynx.

151

ments for shortening the polyp, the circular muscles of the wall mesoglea for extending the polyp, the transverse muscles of septal filaments near the stomodeum for opening the mouth, the muscles of the tentacles, etc. Most of the muscles are gastrodermal in origin.

The nematocysts of sea anemones include both types, spirocysts and nematocysts proper. The former are restricted to the tentacles and oral disk, while the latter are found everywhere. Several kinds of the nematocysts proper are found.

The gonads are bands on the septa behind the septal filaments (Fig. 5-55). They may be present on all filaments or on just certain filaments. Some species may be dioecious and others monoecious. Asexual reproduction by fission, budding, and pedal laceration occurs in the group. Fission may be either longitudinal or transverse. Fertilization may occur in the gastrovascular cavity, and development may occur in septal chambers, or it may occur in the sea.

Total cleavage may be equal or unequal and gives rise to a coeloblastula. By in-

gression or invagination the blastula is converted into a ciliated planula larva. All sea anemones in their development pass through a phase called the Edwardsia stage because of its similarity to the primitive *Edwardsia*, a small, burrowing sea anemone. In this stage eight septa with bilateral symmetry occur similar to the eight mesenteries or macrosepta of *Edwardsia*. In a later stage (Halcampoides) two couples of septa develop and pair with the four lateral septa to form six complete pairs, the basic plan of sea anemones. Additional paired septa may form patterns characteristic of the different species.

Order Scleractinia (Madreporaria)

The order Scleractinia is made up of the true or stony corals. They are chiefly responsible for the coral reefs and islands of the warm coral seas. They may be solitary but most are colonial, and they are attached to a firm substratum. They possess a hard, calcareous exoskeleton secreted by the epidermis and found outside the polyp body. In general the polyp (usually small) has the same basic plan as the typical sea

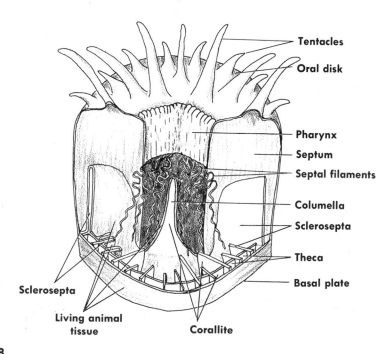

Fig. 5-58

Diagram of polyp of stony coral (order Scleractinia) cut away to show internal structure.

anemone (Fig. 5-58). A pedal disk and cinclides, however, are absent. The typical oral disk bears tentacles in cycles of six so arranged that there is a tentacle over each interseptal cavity. The tentacles may be found in alternating cycles of the hexamerous pattern similar to that found in Actiniaria. Outer cycles, however, may not have their regular number of tentacles because of irregularities in the formation of septa. The tentacles, which vary in size and length, usually bear nematocysts in some form of cluster.

The mouth is circular or oval surrounded by a peristome. There are no siphonoglyphs. The septa show many variations of the hexamerous plan. In some members, the primitive arrangement is similar to that of *Edwardsia*, i.e., four single complete septa, four incomplete septa, and two pairs of directives. But corals often possess alternating cycles of incomplete septa to form the hexamerous pattern of 6, 6, 12, 24, etc., pairs. Usually only three cycles of septa are present. The septal filaments bear only the cnidoglandular tract and may protrude through the mouth during ingestion and digestion of food. Septal muscles are poorly developed, and stoma are lacking.

The skeleton of corals is secreted by the epidermis of the polyp base and the lower part of the column. After a basal plate of skeleton is formed by the polyp base, the epidermis may secrete a colloidal mass in which calcareous crystals are precipitated. In this process the epithelium is thrown into radial folds and a circular fold that are responsible for the formation of the radial vertical walls (sclerosepta) and the skeletal cup (theca). These epithelial folds also project upward into the septal spaces of the gastrovascular chamber into which the radiating scleroscepta fit. The structure of the skeleton of a typical coral (there are many variations) may exhibit the following structures: (1) the corallum, or the skeleton of the colony (called corallite for the individual coral cup); (2) the basal plate between the zooid and substratum; (3) the scleroseptia, or radial plates of calcium carbonate, that reach from the periphery toward the center of the coral cup; (4) the theca, or wall of the cup, that encloses the aboral region of the polyp; (5) the columella, or central skeletal mass, that may arise from the basal plate or from the union of trabecular extensions of the scleroseptia; (6) the costae, or longitudinal ribs, on the outer surface of the theca, which may represent the peripheral edges of scleroseptia; (7) the epitheca, or a second wall, that may arise from the basal plate and may be separated from the theca by the costae; (8) the pali, or ridgelike projections, between the inner edges of the scleroseptia and the columella; and (9) the dissepiments, or horizontal and oblique calcareous partitions, between the scleroseptia.

Most true corals are colonial and may form masses of various shapes, such as spherical masses, branches, plates, etc. The thecae of a colony may be widely spaced or close together. Colonies usually arise by budding or division from a single, sexually producing polyp. Superficially the corallum appears to lie within the polyp, but morphologically it is entirely outside the polyp body; the polyp is merely molded upon the skeleton. The surface of the colony between the thecae is occupied by a sheet of living tissue (coenenchyme), which is an extension of the polyp walls above the theca. The coenenchyme thus connects together all the members of a colony and contains a gastrovascular cavity that is continuous with the gastrovascular cavities of individual polyps. The lower epidermal surface of the coenenchyme, which is made up of both epidermis and gastrodermis, secretes the skeletal parts between the thecae.

Most corals, especially the reef-forming ones, prefer tropical waters not over 50 to 100 meters in depth, but there are exceptions. The symbiotic zooxanthellae that are common in reef corals may impose this restriction of depth. Some of the common colonial stony corals are the branching ivory coral *Oculina* (Fig. 5-59) with widely separated thecae; *Astrangia* (Fig. 5-60) with closely placed thecae and protruding polyps, very common along the North Atlantic coast; *Orbicella* with massive form, a common reef builder of the West Indies; *Acropora* with branches and small cylindric cups; and the brain coral (*Meandrina*) with rows of confluent thecae that produce a surface of curved depressions and ridges. Solitary corals are best represented by *Carophyllia* and *Balanophyllia*. Perhaps the most abundant source of reef-forming cor-

153

Fig. 5-59

Oculina, the ivory coral; cluster about 4 inches tall. Inset at right is closeup of some of cups (order Scleractinia).

als is the Great Barrier Reef of Australia where more than 200 species have been described.

As already mentioned, reef-forming corals have a symbiotic relationship with unicellular algae or zooxanthellae (Dinophysidae). These plants are found in specialized carrier cells in the gastrodermal epithelium. The revealing work of T. Goreau and others indicates that the zooxanthellae are actively involved in coral skeletogenesis by promoting the mechanism of calcification. Investigations show how the process of calcium deposition is speeded up by photosynthesis of the zooxanthellae, which removes the excess CO_2 formed at the site of mineralization. Excess CO_2 in the form of H_2CO_3 tends to decrease the velocity of the reactions necessary for coral formation. In this process calcium ions (Ca^{++}) in seawater first combine with bicarbonate ions ($HCO_3{}^{-}$) of metabolic origin to form calcium bicarbonate ($Ca[HCO_3]_2$) and then calcium carbonate ($CaCO_3$) which is deposited in the coral framework. In ad-

dition to assisting in coral skeletogenesis zooxanthellae also supply oxygen and, according to some authorities, food as well. It is thought that these algae must have played an important role in the growth and evolution of shallow-water corals by promoting the rapid deposition of calcium to offset the constant erosion of coral material under the impact of the severe battering of shore wave action.

Order Zoanthidea

Although most members of the order Zoanthidea are colonial, some solitary species exist. They are best described as skeletonless, anemonelike anthozoans without a pedal disk. Their body is divided into a capitulum and scapus and is often encrusted with detritus such as sand grains, sponge spicules, foram shells, etc. that may be embedded in the surface and mesoglea. The oral disk bears two circlets of unbranched tentacles. Their most unique feature is the arrangement of the septa. Only the sulcal (ventral) pair of directives is

Fig. 5-60

Astrangia danae, a scleractinian coral, polyps extended from their corallites. This beautiful little coral grows in colonies up to 3 inches across, encrusted on rocks and shells in sheltered places. (Courtesy General Biological Supply House, Inc., Chicago).

Order Ceriantharia

These anthozoans bear some resemblance to anemones in that their bodies are cylindric, muscular, and smooth. By mucus secreted from ectodermal cells each polyp forms a sort of sheath or tube, of sand, nematocysts, and detritus in which it is enclosed up to the oral disk. The sheathed animal lies buried in the sandy bottom with only the oral disk and two circlets of tentacles protruding. Other than this sheath there is no protective skeleton. The polyp is provided with one dorsal siphonoglyph, which also forms a groove (hyposulculus) in the pharynx. A pedal disk is lacking. The septal or mesenteric arrangement is unique in that only one cycle of single complete septa exists, although bilaterally they are coupled. They increase continually by the addition of new couples to the ventral interseptal space only, so the number of septa is indefinite. The directives are the three most dorsal couples. Independent muscle fibers (longitudinal) form a layer borne on the mesoglea and are not connected to epidermal cells. Septal filaments with adhesive acontioids are also present.

Cerianthus, the most familiar form, is common on sandy bottoms in both American and European waters, and is found in both deep and shallow water.

complete. The other septa form pairs of one complete septum and one incomplete septum so that in the entire polyp there is only one pair in which the two members are complete (the sulcal directives). In the colonial forms polyps are united by stolons with solenia. A common colonial form, *Epizoanthus,* is found epizoic on other corals and snail shells inhabited by hermit crabs. Although most abundant in warm tropical waters, this order has a wide distribution.

Order Antipatharia

The order Antipatharia consists of the black or thorny corals, most abundant in the deeper waters of the tropic and subtropic zones. They usually form slender, branching, plantlike colonies several feet tall. A basal plate of the main stem attached to a substratum is usually present. The polyps, which are arranged on various parts of the branches, are short, cylindric bodies each possessing a circlet of six nonretractile tentacles provided with clusters of nematocysts. Two slightly differentiated siphonoglyphs are found in the stomodeum. Adjacent polyps of a colony are united by a coenenchyme but have no common gastrovascular cavity. Their body surface is ciliated, and their body musculature is weakly developed. The polyps are mostly dioecious. *Antipathes* is one of the most familiar genera.

Annotated references

Berrill, N. J. 1957. The indestructible hydra. Sci. Amer. **197:**48-58. *A study of the hydra's structure and regenerative capacity.*

Borradaile, L. A., and F. A. Potts (revised by G. A. Kerkut). 1958. The Invertebrata, New York, Cambridge University Press. *This standard work gives considerable treatment to the coelenterates.*

Brien, P. 1951. Contribution a l'etude des hydres d'eau douce. Bull. Soc. Zool. France **76:**277-296.

Buchsbaum, R. 1948. Animals without backbones. Chicago, University of Chicago Press. *Many fine illustrations of coelenterates in this semipopular treatise.*

Buchsbaum, R., and L. J. Milne. 1960. The lower animals; living invertebrates of the world. Garden City, Doubleday & Company, Inc. *Superb illustrations of hydroids, jellyfishes, and corals are given in Chapter 3.*

Bullock, T. H., and G. A. Horridge. 1965. Structure and function in the nervous system of invertebrates. San Francisco, W. H. Freeman & Co., Publishers. *A comprehensive summary of what is known about the form and function of the nervous system of invertebrates.*

155

Burnett, A. L. 1959. An immortal's nature. Natur. Hist. **68**:498-507. *This article describes the renewal of cells in hydra from experiments of P. Brien.*

Crowell, S. 1953. The regression-replacement cycle of hydranths of *Obelia* and *Campanularia*. Physiol. Zool. **26**:319-327.

Crowell, S. (editor). 1965. Behavioral physiology of coelenterates. Amer. Zool. **5**:335-589. *An excellent symposium by many specialists on the present status of the physiologic aspects of this group. Some of the papers also discuss the ctenophores and echinoderms.*

Darwin, C. 1962. The structure and distribution of coral reefs. Berkeley, University of California Press. *A reprint of the classic study by the great naturalist.*

Fraser, C. M. 1937, 1944. Hydroids of the Pacific and Atlantic coasts of Canada and the United States. Toronto, University of Toronto Press. *These two monographs, one for each coast, represent a comprehensive taxonomic study of the hydroids with extensive keys and figures.*

Goreau, T. 1961. Problems of growth and calcium deposition in reef corals. Endeavour **20**:32-39. *A summary of the recent concept involving the role of zooxanthellae in coral formation.*

Hand, C. 1959. On the origin and phylogeny of the coelenterates. Syst. Zool. **4**:191-202. *A summary of the planuloid ancestral theory of coelenterate origin.*

Hardy, A. C. 1956. The open sea. Boston, Houghton Mifflin Company. *Beautiful color plates of jellyfishes are included.*

Hyman, L. H. 1940. The invertebrates; Protozoa through Ctenophora, vol. 1. New York, McGraw-Hill Book Company. *A comprehensive and authoritative treatise with extensive bibliographies and revealing illustrations. Volume 5 (1959) of this work summarizes the investigations on the coelenterates since 1940.*

Lankester, E. R. (editor). 1900. Treatise on zoology; part 2, The Porifera and Coelenterata. London, Adam & Charles Black, Ltd. *The account of the coelenterates by G. H. Fowler and G. C. Bourne in this outstanding treatise will always be of use to students of this group, although many investigations and interpretations have been made in the past sixty years.*

Lenhoff, H. M., and W. F. Loomis. 1961. The biology of hydra and of some other coelenterates. Coral Gables, University of Miami Press. *The record of a noteworthy symposium discussing the structure of hydra and the results of research on various problems of coelenterate patterns.*

Loomis, W. F. 1959. The sex gas of hydra. Sci. Amer. **200**:145-156. *An account of the factors that influence sex in hydra.*

MacGinitie, G. E., and N. MacGinitie. 1949. Natural history of marine animals. New York. McGraw-Hill Book Company.

Mackie, G. O. 1960. The structure of the nervous system in *Velella*. Quart. J. Micr. Sci. **101**:119-131. *A description of the two types of nervous systems—the syncytial and the nonsyncytial—found in certain coelenterates.*

Mackie, G. O. Siphonophores, bud colonies, and superorganisms. In Dougherty, E. C. (editor). 1963. The lower Metazoa; comparative biology and phylogeny. Berkeley, University of California Press. *The author discusses some of the difficulties in distinguishing between individuality and colonial patterns of animals and shows how the members of the siphonophore colony are integrated and controlled by the "colonial will."*

Marcus, E. 1958. On the evolution of the animal phyla. Quart. Rev. Biol. **33**:24-58. *An appraisal of the present status of the origin of the various animal groups.*

Mayer, A. G. 1910. Medusae of the world. 3 volumes. Washington, D. C., Carnegie Institution of Washington. *A comprehensive and authoritative monograph on jellyfish.*

Mayr, E. 1963. Animal species and evolution. Cambridge, Harvard University Press. *An excellent synthesis of our present knowledge of the processes of evolution.*

Moore, R. C., C. G. Lalicker, and A. G. Fischer. 1952. Invertebrate fossils. New York, McGraw-Hill Book Company. *Chapter 4 discusses fossil coelenterates and modern coelenterates.*

Payne, F. 1924. A study of the freshwater medusa, *Craspedacusta ryderi*. J. Morphol. **38**:387-430. *An excellent account of this interesting freshwater coelenterate.*

Pennak, R. W. 1953. Fresh-water invertebrates of the United States. New York. The Ronald Press Company. *One chapter of this important reference treatise is devoted to the freshwater coelenterates. Keys, illustrations, and specific descriptions are included.*

Russell, F. S. 1953. The medusae of the British Isles. New York, Cambridge University Press. *A magnificent monograph of the British jellyfishes with full text descriptions and excellent plates.*

Smith, F. G. W. 1948. Atlantic reef corals. Coral Gables, University of Miami Press.

Smith, R. I., et al. 1954. Intertidal invertebrates of the central coast. Berkeley, University of California Press. *An excellent manual, mostly including keys and illustrations, of the invertebrates of the California coast by many specialists.*

Tardent, P. 1963. Regeneration in the Hydrozoa. Biol. Rev. **38**:293-333.

Totton, A. K., and G. O. Mackie. 1960. Studies on *Physalia physalia* (L). Discovery Reports **30**:301-

407. *An exhaustive account of the morphology, behavior, and histology of this species.*

Uchida, T. On the interrelationships of the Coelenterata, with remarks on their symmetry. In Dougherty, E. C. (editor). 1963. The lower Metazoa; comparative biology and phylogeny. Berkeley, University of California Press. *The author's views fall into line with the planuloid ancestry that Hand and Hyman have stressed. Uchida believes that this planuloid ancestor gave rise to two groups—those with radial symmetry (Hydrozoa and Scyphozoa) and those with bilateral symmetry (Anthozoa).*

Wells, J. W. Coral reefs. In Hedgepeth, J. W. (editor). 1957. Treatise on marine ecology and paleoecology. Washington, D. C., Geological Society of America. Memoir 67:609-632.

Westfall, J. A. 1964. Fine structure and development of nematocysts in the tentacles of *Metridium*. Amer. Zool. 4:435.

Yonge, C. M. 1931. A year on the Great Barrier Reef. London, William Collins Sons & Co., Ltd.

Yonge, C. M. Ecology and physiology of reef-building corals. In Buzzant-Traverso, A. A. (editor). 1958. Perspectives in marine biology. Berkeley, University of California Press.

Phylum Ctenophora

The phylum Ctenophora, formerly included within the coelenterates as a class, is made up of a group of jellyfish commonly known as comb jellies. They share with the coelenterates a position in the radiate phyla, and they are also at the tissue level of organization. They are entirely marine and mostly pelagic in habit. Members derive their phylum name by possession of eight meridional rows of comblike plates that are used for locomotion. A few are modified for a creeping existence.

Ctenophores bear many resemblances to coelenterates, including gelatinous mesenchyme, the general radial symmetry of body structures around an oral-aboral axis, the gastrovascular system in the form of canals, the lack of a cavity except the digestive cavity, and the lack of organ systems. But they have certain distinctive features of their own that set them off as a separate group. Some of these structures may indicate an advancement in organization over the coelenterates; others are merely unique adaptive devices for ctenophoran existence. In general structure, the comb jellies resemble medusae, especially scyphomedusae. Their body wall is composed of an epidermis and a gastrodermis with a collenchyme between. The presence of collenchyme represents a clear advancement over hydroids in that it contains assorted cells such as amebocytes, connective tissue cells, and true muscle cells. The symmetry of ctenophores is definitely biradial, which is usually an indication of a step or grade toward the bilateral symmetry that higher animals possess. Instead of nemato-cysts (found only in one species) most ctenophores possess colloblasts, or adhesive cells, on tentacles for catching their prey.

Skeletal structures, excretory organs, and respiratory organs are entirely lacking. Their mosaic type of development is also different from that of the coelenterates, which have an indeterminate type of cleavage. Ctenophores also have a distinctive larval form (cydippid) with definite bilateral features. Polymorphism, so common among the coelenterates, is not present in this phylum, which is monomorphic throughout.

The shape, or body form, of ctenophores shows considerable variation. Many have a football shape with modifications such as pyriform, globular, and bell shapes. Lateral and dorsoventral compressions are also present, producing a definite ribbon shape in some.

As a group ctenophores are perhaps the most beautiful animals of the sea. Their transparency, the delicacy of their glasslike structure, their iridescence by day and luminescence at night have given them a distinct beauty rarely found in the animal kingdom.

CLASSIFICATION

Fewer than 100 species of ctenophores have been described to date, although some new species have been added in the last decade or so. Ctenophores are classified on the basis of their tentacles, body form, oral lobes, gastrovascular divisions, and body compressions. On this basis two classes and five orders make up the phylum at the present time.

Phylum Ctenophora. Biradial modification of radial symmetry; ellipsoid, spherical, or ribbon shaped; eight rows of ciliated comb plates at some stage; ectoderm, endoderm, and ectomesoderm (mesoglea); gastrovascular cavity with one opening (mouth), a large stomodeum, and many branches; tentacles (in most) with colloblasts in place of nematocysts (except in one species); nervous system of a subepidermal plexus with concentrations under the comb plates; endodermal gonads in walls of gastrovascular canals; hermaphroditic reproduction; mosaic development; cydippid larva.

Class Tentaculata. Tentacles in some form with or without sheaths; tentacles two or more in number, may or may not be retractile.

Order Cydippidea. Spherical or oval-shaped body; two-branched retractile tentacles; gastrovascular branches ending as blind sacs. *Pleurobrachia* (Fig. 6-1), *Mertensia*, *Hormiphora*.

Order Lobata. Two flaplike oral lobes and four auricles; numerous tentacles, two of which are usually long; meridional canals anastomose around oral end. *Mnemiopsis* (Fig. 6-6), *Bolinopsis*.

Order Cestida. Bodies long and ribbonlike because of compression; reduced chief tentacles with sheath; two rows of small tentacles on oral edge. *Cestum* (Fig. 6-7, *A*), *Velamen (Folia)*.

Order Platyctenea. Bodies vertically flattened because of compression in the oral-aboral plane; with two tentacles and sheath; comb rows found only in larva. *Coeloplana*, *Ctenoplana*.

Class Nuda. Without tentacles; gastrovascular canal with fine branches anastomosing to form a network.

Fig. 6-1

Pleurobrachia (order Cydippidea), a common ctenophore; about ¾ inch in diameter. (From Hickman: Integrated principles of zoology, The C. V. Mosby Co.)

Order Beroida. Laterally compressed helmet-shaped bodies; mouth and pharynx wide; gastrovascular canal with many side branches; tentacles absent at all stages. *Beroë* (Fig. 6-7, *B*).

BASIC ADAPTIVE FEATURES

The basic structures that have guided the evolutionary development of the ctenophores are the arrangement of the comb plates, or rows, and the general biradial symmetry. Both these features are found with modifications throughout the group. The main features of their morphology are arranged around the oral-aboral axis that extends from the mouth to the sense organ (statocyst). The comb plates give a radial symmetry, but the tentacle sheaths and the gastrovascular canals give them a biradial symmetry in which the morphologic structures are arranged with reference to two planes at right angles to each other. These planes are determined by the nature of the gastrovascular cavity along the main central axis. The first part of the cavity leading from the mouth is the pharynx, or stomodeum, which is flattened or compressed from side to side. The pharynx extends about two-thirds of the way toward the aboral pole and opens into the true stomach, which is also compressed but in a plane at right angles to that of the pharynx. The long axis of the pharynx lies in the sagittal plane; the compressed stomach, gastrovascular canals, and tentacle sheaths lie in the transverse plane. The whole plan of the ctenophoran body is arranged with reference to these two planes (Fig. 6-3).

Since the comb plates are the principal organs of locomotion, they have largely determined the distribution of morphologic structures such as the eight meridional canals of the gastrovascular cavity under the comb rows and the nerve strands of the subepidermal plexus in the same place. The comb plates are fitted for a pelagic and planktonic existence where feeble movements are sufficient. Only in such highly modified ctenophores as *Cestum* is the swimming action of the plates supplemented by the sinuous movement of the ribbonlike body, or in the Platyctenea where creeping locomotion is evident.

159

PHYLOGENETIC RELATIONSHIPS

Although many zoologists in the past considered the ctenophores as a class under Coelenterata, there are valid reasons for separating the two groups into different phyla. Some of the resemblances and differences of these two groups have already been indicated in the introduction to the Ctenophora. That both coelenterates and ctenophores have arisen from the same basic stock seems to be a logical suggestion in the light of their resemblances. The presence of nematocysts in one species of ctenophores *(Euchlora rubra)* is regarded not as a mere accidental development brought about by eating hydroids but as a part of the true nematocyst structural pattern of this particular species. This factor and others might suggest that the ctenophores have arisen from a trachyline ancestor. It will be recalled that the order Trachylina represents a very primitive group that may have given rise to the various coelenterate stocks (L. H. Hyman). *Hydroctena,* an aberrant trachyline medusa, has a ctenophoran form that includes an aboral sense organ. The biradial symmetry so characteristic of Ctenophora is easily derived from the tetramerous radial symmetry of hydromedusae. Only *Gastrodes,* a parasite of certain tunicates and a member of the order Platyctenea, has a planula larva, but this one example may indicate a relationship with the Coelenterata.

Another theory of long standing concerns the possible relationship between the ctenophores and the polyclad turbellaria. This theory is based mainly upon the resemblance of such creeping ctenophores as *Coeloplana* and *Ctenoplana* to turbellarian worms. G. A. Kerkut in recent years has listed many resemblances between *Coeloplana* and the Polycladida. The view held at present, however, is that these resemblances are results of convergent evolution brought about in these ctenophores when they assumed a creeping mode of life and are not evidences of relationships.

Within the Ctenophora, the order Cydippidea is considered the most primitive and the least modified of the ctenophoran plan. The other orders supposedly evolved along independent lines at a later time.

GENERAL MORPHOLOGIC FEATURES

Ctenophoran morphology is perhaps best understood in the most typical and least modified members such as those belonging to the order Cydippidea. The ctenophores of this order most familiar to American and British zoologists are *Pleurobrachia* (Fig. 6-1) and *Hormiphora,* which resemble each other except in a few details. These genera are oval shaped or egg shaped and possess transparent bodies. The body wall contains an outer epidermis, which may be syncytial or cellular, of cuboid or columnar cells and an inner endodermal epithelium with collenchyme (mesoglea) between the two layers. The mouth is situated at one pole and a sense organ at the other pole.

On the surface of the body are eight rows of comb plates arranged meridionally and equally spaced. These plates start near the sense organ and extend for about four-fifths of the distance to the oral pole. Each plate consists of a transverse row of fused cilia borne upon modified ectodermal cells, and the plates are arranged in succession and united as a ciliary tract to form a complete comb-plate row (Fig. 6-2). In locomotion the beat in each row starts at the

Fig. 6-2

Portion of comb row showing three plates, each composed of transverse rows of long fused cilia.

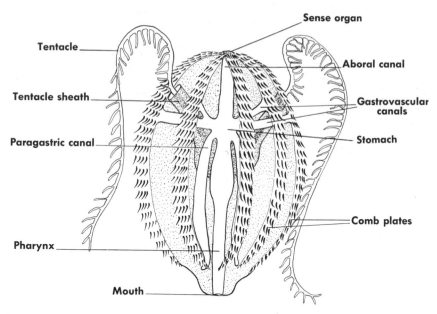

Fig. 6-3

Diagram of *Pleurobrachia* showing major structures. (From Hickman: Integrated principles of zoology, The C. V. Mosby Co.)

aboral end and, as each plate beats in succession, proceeds in a wave to the oral end causing the animal to move with the mouth in front. The direction of the wave is reversible. The synchrony and coordination of the beat are controlled by nervous impulses from the statocyst through nervous connections.

Two tentacles are found in most ctenophores, situated at opposite ends of the transverse or tentacular axis (Fig. 6-3). The base of each tentacle is fastened to the bottom of a pouch or sheath into which the tentacle may be retracted. When fully extended, the highly extensible tentacle may be much longer than the body. The tentacle is solid, composed mainly of mesoglea and longitudinal muscle strands, and covered with epidermis. The sheath is an invaginated epidermal pouch that bears at its bottom the formative tissue for the tentacles and the colloblasts. The tentacle has many lateral branches that are covered with special adhesive cells (colloblasts or lasso cells). Each colloblast (Fig. 6-4) is composed of a sticky, crescent-shaped body that is fastened on its concave side by two filaments, one of which is spirally twisted and contracted around a stiff, cen-

Fig. 6-4

Colloblast.

161

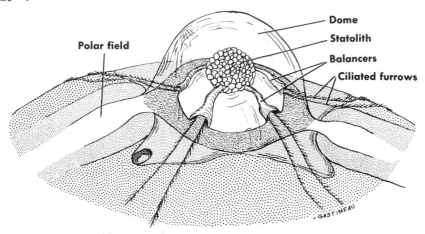

Fig. 6-5

Statocyst enlarged to show details. (Modified from Chun.)

tral filament. Food (small organisms, ova, etc.) is captured by the sticky colloblasts of the tentacles, which are drawn over the lips of the mouth where ingestion of food occurs. Tentacles are not only used for catching prey, but they also serve as balancing organs when the ctenophore is floating. The colloblast may correspond to the nematocyst of coelenterates, but these two organelles are not homologous because they have a different origin.

The sense organ, or statocyst (Fig. 6-5), is located at the aboral pole and is somewhat complicated in structure. Its general structure consists of a cyst containing a centrally located statolith, which is composed of fused calcareous bodies. The floor of the statocyst is composed of ciliated epidermal and secretory cells. The statolith is supported on four pillars of fused cilia (the balancers) located interradially on the sensory floor. Two ciliated furrows lead from the base of each balancer to the pair of comb rows in the same quadrant. These tracts may carry impulses to the comb rows from the sense organ. The dome-shaped cover of the statocyst is formed of fused cilia. On each side of the statocyst in the sagittal plane is a ciliated area of unknown function called the polar field.

The gastrovascular system consists of an extensive canal system that is closely involved with the biradial symmetry of the group. The slitlike mouth opens into a long tubular pharynx or stomodeum (ecto-

dermal lining) that is flattened in the tentacular, or transverse, plane and lies directly in the oral-aboral axis. Its walls are much folded, and most digestion occurs here. Digestion in Ctenophora is both extracellular and intracellular. The pharynx extends upward for about two-thirds of the way toward the aboral pole and opens through a short esophagus into the stomach (infundibulum). The stomach is lined by endoderm and is flattened in the sagittal plane at right angles to the tentacular plane.

From the stomach the digested food products are distributed to the body by vertical and horizontal sets of canals. The vertical canals consist of two blind pharyngeal, or paragastric, canals, one on each side of the stomodeum, that end near the mouth, and a single aboral canal that runs toward the aboral pole. This aboral canal, just below the statocyst, divides into four short excretory canals that end in small sacs, or ampullae. Each sac lies in one of the angles formed by the intersection of the sagittal and tentacular planes. Two of these sacs (anal canals) lying diagonally opposite to each other open by pores to the surface; the other two sacs end blindly. The horizontal set of canals is made up of those canals that serve to connect the stomach with the eight meridional canals, which are located beneath the comb rows. From each side of the stomach in the tentacular plane, a large transverse canal gives off horizontally a tentacular canal to the tentacular sheath and two interradial canals. Each interradial canal bifurcates so that there are four canals on either side of the body. Two of the four canals on each side are adjacent to the tentacular plane (subtentacular), and two are adjacent to the sagittal plane (subsagittal). Each of the eight canals so formed passes to the underside of a comb row to produce, orally and aborally, a long meridional canal that extends the length of each comb row.

Ctenophores are hermaphroditic, and male and female gonads occur close to each other in the meridional canals on their branches. The bandlike gonads are formed from endodermal epithelium lining the meridional canals; the male gonad is on one side, and the female gonad is on the other side of each canal. In the canals the ovaries are always found on the side nearest the sagittal or the tentacular plane (perradial), and the spermaries are found on the interradial side of the wall. In some species (e.g., *Euchlora*) gonads are found only on four of the light meridional (subtentacular) canals. Eggs may be fertilized in situ, either by sperm carried in by gastrovascular canals or by adjacent sperm (self-fertilization). In most cases, however, the mature germ cells are shed into seawater where fertilization occurs. Fertilized eggs in the canals are shed directly through the epidermis over the meridional canals and not through the mouth. *Coeloplana* and *Ctenoplana* appear to be the only members with definite genital ducts (for sperm).

In their embryology ctenophores are the only animals that have biradial cleavage, and their development follows a biradially symmetric scheme. At the eight-cell stage four blastomeres are large and four are smaller. These cells are so arranged that the large blastomeres form a central mass with two smaller ones at each side. The long axis at this stage later becomes the tentacular plane of the adult. Succeeding divisions result in an increase of micromeres (the smaller blastomeres) so that a ring of these blastomeres is formed on the concave aboral surface of the large macromeres, which divide much more slowly. As the micromeres continue to divide they spread increasingly over the surface of the macromeres as a single layered sheet (an epibolic process). During this process the macromeres invaginate into the interior so that gastrulation involves both epiboly and invagination. The micromeres become the epidermis, and the macromeres become the endoderm; thus the cleavage is determinate (mosaic), and all the early blastomeres are required to form a complete organism. In further development the cells of the collenchyme apparently come from the ectoderm; the mesenchyme is thus an ectomesoderm. The musculature comes from cells in the collenchyme that are not epitheliomuscular cells. The characteristic and unique comb rows arise from interradial bands on the ectoderm where cells divide rapidly. From the aboral ectoderm the sense organ and polar bands are also derived. The young larval form is called a cydippid larva and has many features of the adult belonging to the order Cydippidea. In other orders the larva undergoes various modifications before becoming an adult.

Most ctenophores display luminescence. The luminous materials are granules secreted by endodermal cells in the walls of the meridional canals often in or near the gonads. Ctenophores emit their light by flashes and control its production by nervous stimulation. External light seems to inhibit luminescent action, for they do not usually flash until they have been in the dark for several minutes.

CLASS TENTACULATA
Order Cydippidea

The chief characteristics of the order Cydippidea were described in the previous section. As already mentioned the members of this order retain the characteristics of the larva until the adult stage is attained. They are often considered to be the most typical and least modified of all ctenophores. They are globular or egg shaped and possess two tentacles that have lateral branches covered with colloblasts. Their gastrovascular canals are simple, end blindly, and do not form a peripheral canal system. In some members the body is compressed in the sagittal plane. The comb rows are mostly equal in length.

Familiar examples are *Pleurobrachia*, (Fig. 6-1), *Hormiphora*, and *Euchlora* (the genus with nematocysts).

Order Lobata

The body of ctenophores in the order Lobata is compressed in the tentacular plane **163** and is helmet shaped. A large contractile lobe is found on each side of the oral end in the sagittal areas of the body. These lobes cause the subsagittal comb rows to be longer than the subtentacular ones. From the ends of the latter comb plates four auricles or lappets with ciliated edges extend above the mouth, a pair on each side. The tentacle sheaths of the larva disappear during metamorphosis, and the reduced tentacles of the adult are located on each side of the mouth. In addition, numerous accessory tentacles are found in ciliated auricular grooves that extend from the mouth to the auricles. In the gastrovascular system the four interradial canals arise directly from the stomach, and transverse canals are lacking.

Common examples of the order are the genera *Bolinopsis*, *Mnemiopsis* (Fig. 6-6), and *Ocyropsis*. The first two are common along the Atlantic coast.

Fig. 6-6

Mnemiopsis (order Lobata). (Photograph by Roman Vishniac, courtesy Encyclopaedia Britannica Films, Inc.)

Order Cestida

Members of this order of ribbon-shaped ctenophores are compressed in the tentacu-

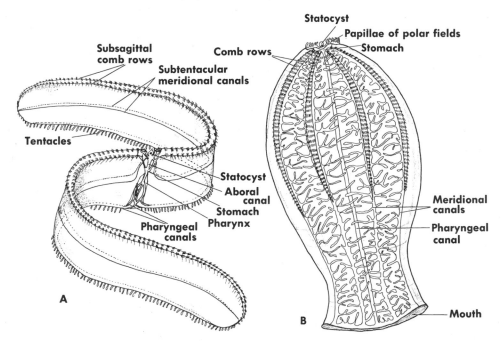

Fig. 6-7

A, *Cestum veneris* (order Cestida) commonly called "Venus' girdle." Common in European and tropical waters (Florida). **B,** *Beroë* (order Beroida). No tentacles or tentacle sheaths. (**B** redrawn from Hyman: The invertebrates; Protozoa through Ctenophora, McGraw-Hill Book Company.)

lar plane and elongated in the sagittal plane. They may be more than a meter long. The subsagittal comb rows extend over the entire length of the aboral surface, while the subtentacular plates are rudimentary or reduced to only a few. The tentacle sheaths and the filamentous tentacles are shifted orally toward the mouth. Two rows of short tentacles extend in tentacular grooves from the mouth to the extremities of the body. The subtentacular meridional canals run down the middle of the elongated body and unite with the subsagittal and paragastric canals, all of which run horizontally.

Cestum or "Venus' girdle" (Fig. 6-7, *A*) is the familiar example. *Velamen* is the other genus and occurs off the eastern American coast.

Order Platyctenea

Members of the order Platyctenea are the most highly modified of all ctenophores. Much of this modification centers around their creeping or sedentary methods of existence. Their body is flattened in the oral-aboral axis and elongated in the tentacular axis, so they really have dorsal and ventral surfaces. The gastrovascular system is shortened, and part of the oral (ventral) surface is everted pharynx. The canals from the stomach anastomose to form a peripheral network. Comb rows may or may not be present. The gonads are present in the meridional canals, and each testis opens to the surface by a duct and pore. They possess tentacle sheaths and retractile tentacles as well as a statocyst.

The most striking examples are *Coeloplana* and *Ctenoplana* found chiefly off the coasts of Indo-China and Japan; *Coeloplana* has also been found off the coast of Florida.

CLASS NUDA
Order Beroida

These bell-shaped or cone-shaped ctenophores have no trace of tentacles or tentacle sheaths at any stage of their development. They have a wide mouth with a greatly enlarged stomodeum (pharynx), and the body is compressed in the tentacular plane. In some members the comb rows may extend the full length of the

organism, although in *Beroë* they do not reach this far. The eight meridional canals unite with the paragastric canals and send out numerous diverticula, which anastomose to form a peripheral network all over the body. The polar fields are fringed with branched papillae.

The widely distributed genus *Beroë* (Fig. 6-7, *B*) has a pinkish cast and may reach a length of several inches in colder waters, although its size is much smaller off the New England coast.

Annotated references

Bourne, G. C. Ctenophora. In Lankester, E. R., (editor). 1900. Treatise on zoology. London, Adam & Charles Black, Ltd. *A good basic description of the morphology of ctenophores.*

Hyman, L. H. 1940. The invertebrates; Protozoa through Ctenophora, vol. 1. New York, McGraw-Hill Book Company. *One of the best general accounts of the ctenophores. Discusses the morphology, physiology, phylogeny, and classification of the group. Well illustrated and provided with an extensive bibliography.*

Hyman, L. H. 1959. The invertebrates; smaller coelomate groups, vol. 5. New York, McGraw-Hill Book Company. *The chapter entitled "Retrospect" summarizes recent work on the Ctenophora.*

Komai, T. A note on the phylogeny of the Ctenophora. In Dougherty, E. C., (editor). 1963. The lower Metazoa; comparative biology and phylogeny. Berkeley, The University of California Press. *The author thinks that the Ctenophora should be considered a subphylum under phylum Coelenterata and that they are more closely related to the Hydrozoa than to any other group.*

Komai, T. 1951. The nematocysts in the ctenophore *Euchlora rubra*. Amer. Natur. 85:73-74. *The author believes that the nematocysts, which exist in this species instead of colloblasts, have been acquired by eating medusae and are not derived from a natural development within the animal.*

Mayer, A. C. 1912. Ctenophores of the Atlantic coast of North America. Washington, D. C., Carnegie Institution of Washington, Pub. No. 162. *A technical account with many plates and figures.*

Picard, J. 1955. Les nematocysts du ctenaire *Euchlora rubra*. Recueil Trav. Stat. Marine Endoume, Bull. No. 9, fasc. 15, pp. 99-103. *The nematocysts are restricted to the epidermis along longitudinal tracts and are not acquired by eating medusae; they are formed in the epidermis of the tentacle bases.*

Chapter 7

Phylum Platyhelminthes

embers of the large phylum Platyhelminthes are known as flatworms.
Platyhelminthes represents one of
the dozen or so major phyla of the animal
kingdom. They are bilaterally symmetric,
triploblastic, nonsegmented, dorsoventrally
flattened worms that are also characterized
by lack of anus (usually), coelom, or hemocoel, and possess no true circulatory or
respiratory systems or skeleton. Other characteristics are the presence of an excretory
system of flame-bulb protonephridia, a
complex, usually hermaphroditic reproductive system, and a solid mesenchyme (parenchyma) filling spaces not occupied by
organ systems. Within the group a large
diversity of morphologic features as well
as of ecologic habits exists, although all
have some common features that justify the
inclusion of members within the same phylum. Much of this diversity of structure
results from the widespread parasitic habits that are found throughout the phylum.
Members within the phylum illustrate all
stages from free existence to partial and
complete dependence on other members of
the animal kingdom.

In the evolutionary blueprint of the animal kingdom the phylum Platyhelminthes
occupies an unique position. They intro-
duce certain morphologic features that,
with some refinement and modification,
become the adaptive structural characters
of all higher groups. Among these important contributions are bilateral symmetry,
true triploblastic organization in which

mesoglea is replaced by a cellular, endomesodermal layer, a subepidermal musculature suggestive of the muscles of more advanced animals, an excretory system for a
more demanding metabolism, and the start
of a centralized nervous system of the ladder type in place of the diffused nerve net
of radially symmetric animals. It is of physiologic interest that flatworms are considered by animal behaviorists as the lowest
group that can be studied for basic concepts of behavior and learning. Not the
least of the flatworm contributions to the
blueprint of the animal kingdom is their
organ-tissue architecture in which a tendency occurs for an anatomic unit to be
made up of several tissues. This tendency
definitely points the way toward the complexity of higher forms.

CLASSIFICATION

Some 15,000 species of flatworms have
been listed to the present time. Students of
this group differ a great deal concerning its
taxonomy, and several schemes have been
proposed for its classification including
those of L. H. Hyman, B. Dawes, J. G.
Baer, G. R. La Rue, and others. This disagreement is not merely restricted to taxa
of lower levels but involves those of class
rank as well. However, the scheme here
followed is one that corresponds with the
opinion of many zoologists.

Phylum Platyhelminthes. Body bilaterally symmetric, dorsoventrally flattened, acoelomate; soft
and vermiform; body covered by ciliated epithelium or cuticle; some provided with suckers and
hooks for parasitic existence; digestive system usually incomplete (gastrovascular) or absent; ex-

cretory system of flame-bulb protonephridia; body spaces filled with parenchyma (mesenchyme); no true circulatory or respiratory systems; reproductive system complicated and usually hermaphroditic; development direct or with metamorphosis of larval stages; free living, commensal, or parasitic habits.

Class Turbellaria. Mainly free living, from 5 mm. to 50 cm. long; cellular or syncytial epidermis usually ciliated and with rhabdoids; body undivided with ventral mouth; gastrovascular cavity (usually); no suckers; simple life cycles.

Order Acoela. Body small (1 to 4 mm.) with mouth and pharynx but lacking intestine; digestive parenchyma; delimited gonads and oviducts absent; no protonephridia; small cerebral ganglia and many longitudinal nerves; marine. *Convoluta, Anaperus.*

Order Rhabdocoela. Body length up to 15 mm.; intestine straight without diverticula; protonephridia and oviducts usually present; compact gonads; cuticular organ in place of soft penis; nervous system of two longitudinal nerves; freshwater, terrestrial, or marine. (This order is sometimes divided into the orders Catenulida, Macrostomida, and Neorhabdocoela.) *Stenostomum, Microstomum, Mesostoma* (Fig. 7-11).

Order Alloeocoela. Body up to 40 mm. long and usually cylindric; plicate pharynx; intestine with short diverticula; numerous testes; complex protonephridial system; freshwater, marine, or terrestrial. (This order is sometimes divided into the orders Gnathostomulida, Lecithoepitheliata, Archoophora, Holocoela, and Seriata.) *Plagiostomum, Monocelis.*

Order Tricladida. Body from 3 to 500 mm. long and usually elongated; with plicate pharynx and triclad intestine; one anterior and two posterior branches; numerous rhabdoids; two or more eyes; usually numerous testes and one pair of ovaries; with yolk glands; female apparatus with one or two bursae; male apparatus with a penis papilla; freshwater, marine, or terrestrial. *Dugesia, Bipalium, Bdelloura* (Fig. 7-4).

Order Polycladida. Body usually broadly flattened or oval, up to 150 mm. long; plicate pharynx with intestine of many branches; mouth near middle of body; usually many eyes; nervous system with numerous radiating nerve ends; ovaries and testes numerous; yolk gland lacking; one or two gonopores; Müller's larva in some; marine. *Notoplana, Stylochus* (Fig. 7-16).

Class Trematoda. Body undivided and covered with a tegument of living cells, forming a sort of epidermis; one or more suckers; digestive tract mostly two branched; one ovary; life cycles

may be simple and direct or complex with alternation of generations; mostly hermaphroditic but some dioecious; almost exclusively ectoparasitic or endoparasitic.

Order Monogenea (Heterocotylea) Diminutive oral sucker or none; anterior adhesive organs; body 5 to 25 mm.; posterior end with adhesive disk (haptor) usually provided with hooks; intestine usually double and branched; duplex excretory system with anterior, dorsolateral pores; simple ovary; simple life cycle and direct development; mostly ectoparasites on vertebrates. *Polystoma* (Fig. 7-17), *Gyrodactylus.*

Order Aspidobothria (Aspidogastraea). Oral sucker and anterior adhesive organs absent; with large ventral sucker or with a ventral row of suckers, hooks absent; one excretory pore (posterior); mostly endoparasites with simple life cycle. *Stichocotyle, Aspidogaster.*

Order Digenea (Malacocotylea). Usually with two suckers, one anterior around mouth and one ventral; hooks absent; single excretory pore; uterus long with many eggs; complex life cycles of many larval stages in one or more intermediate hosts before metamorphosis to adult; chiefly endoparasites. *Fasciola* (Fig. 7-18), *Opisthorchis* (Fig. 7-19), *Schistosoma* (Fig. 7-20).

Class Cestoda. Body with outer covering of living cells (tegument) connected to deeper cells and permeated by pore canals; no digestive system at any stage; usually an anterior organ (scolex) specialized for attachment with bothria, bothridia, acetabula, or hooks; body usually of few to many proglottids, or segments; each proglottid with one or two complete hermaphroditic reproductive systems; embryo hooked; complicated life cycles, usually involving two or more hosts.

Subclass Cestodaria. Undivided body; no scolex; one set of reproductive organs; ten-hooked larva; endoparasites of primitive fishes, often in coelomic cavity.

Order Amphilinidea. With protrusible proboscis; long uterus. *Amphilina.*

Order Gyrocotylidea. With holdfast organ at posterior end; direct uterus to pore. *Gyrocotyle* (Fig. 7-23).

Subclass Eucestoda. Body elongated and usually divided into few to many proglottids (segments); anterior end a scolex bearing adhesive organs; six-hooked larva. Five major orders are here presented.

Order Tetraphyllidea (Phyllobothrioidea). Body segmented with a scolex bearing four bothridia, often with hooks. *Phyllobothrium* (Fig. 7-26, A).

Order Proteocephaloidea. Body segmented with scolex bearing four lateral acetabula and apical sucker or gland. *Proteocephalus* (Fig. 7-26, *B*).

Order Trypanorhyncha. Body segmented with a scolex bearing two or four bothria and four protrusible proboscides armed with spines. *Haplobothrium.*

Order Pseudophyllidea. Body segmented or unsegmented with a scolex bearing two to six shallow bothria; or scolex may be lacking. *Dibothriocephalus (Diphyllobothrium)* (Figs. 7-27, 7-28).

Order Cyclophyllidea (Taenioidea). Body segmented with scolex bearing four deep acetabula, often with an apical rostellum armed with hooks. *Taenia* (Figs. 7-29 to 7-31).

BASIC ADAPTIVE FEATURES

The Platyhelminthes is the lowest group of the animal kingdom to have established the creeping method of locomotion and bilateral symmetry. These two features are related because movement in a definite direction has resulted in a vermiform pattern of body structure as the organism is drawn out along a single axis. Through contact during locomotion with fresh tracts of medium and other stimuli, one end of a radially symmetric body has become more specialized than the rest. This is the beginning of a head (cephalization) and tail differentiation; nervous coordinating centers and sensory organs are concentrated at the anterior end for controlling locomotion and for correlating the activities of the animal with the environment. Along with the head and tail differentiation, the ventral side became specialized for contact and locomotion with the substratum and the dorsal part became specialized for concealment and protection. In this way a radially symmetric form such as a planula larva could have become bilaterally symmetric, thus originating the bilateral condition.

As evidence for this occurrence, the planuloid-acoeloid theory has been supported by many zoologists. According to this theory, a remarkable resemblance exists between the primitive order Acoela and this hypothetical planuloid ancestor. Among the primitive characteristics of the Acoela is the presence of a syncytial and ciliated epidermis, musculoepithelial cells, a solid mass of cells in the interior, a central mouth on the ventral side, the parenchymal ingestion and intracellular digestion of food, modification of the subepider-

mal nerve plexus, a statocyst in or near the brain, and the derivation of germ cells from ameboid cells of the interior mass. The Acoela lack a basement membrane beneath the epidermis, an excretory system, distinct gonads, and a digestive cavity. All these features, with minor modifications, are found at the level of coelenterate organization. This finding indicates that with the acquisition of the changes induced by the bilateral condition, as mentioned, it is not difficult to bridge the gap between the radially symmetric planuloid ancestor and the bilaterally symmetric acoeloid form.

The flatworms have introduced many other features in addition to bilateral symmetry. One of the most distinct changes is the development of a definite cellular mesenchyme (mesoderm) in place of the mesoglea of coelenterates. Although the mesoglea of some coelenterates contains cellular elements (ectomesoderm) and, in ctenophores, may actually have mesenchymal muscle fibers, in general the mesoglea in those groups is made up of a jellylike substance. In certain Platyhelminthes (Turbellaria), however, the middle layer between epidermis and gastrodermis consists of a mesenchyme (parenchyma) that has originated primarily from the embryonic endoderm. Thus the parenchyma is really an endomesoderm in contrast to the ectomesoderm of coelenterates and ctenophores. The structure of flatworm mesenchyme varies, but in most members it appears to be a syncytium with many ameboid cells. From the mesenchyme the muscular, reproductive, and excretory systems arise. The nervous system in some flatworms sinks into the mesenchyme.

The replacement of the bulky, jellylike mesoglea with cellular elements has made possible less bulk and a vermiform body. The addition of a definite mesoderm greatly increases metabolic and energy demands so that greater food intake is required by the flatworm. Its creeping habit and vermiform body have determined the evolutionary trends of the group. The majority have taken up a parasitic existence for which their body's form and slow movement are well adapted. Such a parasitic habit has produced many morphologic changes that involve loss (of enteron and many sense organs) and specialization (adhesive organs, suckers, alternation in life cycles, cuticular modifications). Such modifications produce patterns that superficially appear to be distinct from the typical organization of a platyhelminth found in the class Turbellaria; but basically all patterns are variations on the same theme of body structure and functional behavior.

PHYLOGENETIC RELATIONSHIPS

Although many different theories exist to account for the origin of flatworms, the primitive nature of certain types indicates that they are more closely related to coelenterates than to any other of the basic metazoan stocks. The view taken of the planuloid-acoeloid theory of flatworm origin described in the last section is shared by many zoologists but not by all. Some alternative views have considered the Platyhelminthes to be more primitive than Coelenterata (J. Hadži, 1951), and others have suggested that flatworms are an advanced group that has lost structures characteristic of higher levels of organization such as an anus, coelom, circulatory system, etc. (E. Marcus, 1958). It is unnecessary to describe here the reasons advanced in support of the alternative theories because so many objections against them have been offered by the great majority of zoologists. At the present time it cannot be stated with certainly just which group is the most primitive of the Metazoa because of the lack of transition types.

Within the phylum the interrelationships indicate that all members directly or indirectly originated from a stem similar to the order Acoela (Fig. 7-1). In the class Turbellaria three orders (Alloeocoela, Polycladida, Rhabdocoela) appear to have developed directly from the Acoela on the basis of morphologic evidences. The order Tricladida shows a close affinity to the Alloeocoela because many members of the latter order grade into the triclads. The parasitic classes are thought to have developed from free-living members of the phylum. Some of the turbellarians, such as the rhabdocoels, tend toward a parasitic existence by being endocommensals. Some stages in the life cycles of trematodes also resemble a rhabdocoel. Cestodes appear to have developed independently from parasitic rhabdocoels and are therefore not closely related to the other parasitic class, the trematodes.

GENERAL MORPHOLOGIC FEATURES

Although flatworms are basically flattened dorsoventrally, as the name suggests, and in general have a vermiform appearance, considerable diversity of form exists within the phylum. This diversity is not restricted to differences between the three classes but also applies to members of the same class. Some species are only moderately elongated with segments (proglottids) that form tapering or ribbonlike organisms. Still others have a broad leaflike form. In addition to these typical shapes many odd and bizarre forms are also to be found in a group that counts many thousands of species. Since many flatworms are generally transparent, their immediate color may be due to ingested food; but in some species the color is normally brown, gray, blackish, with occasional brighter colors. The bilateral vermiform condition has stressed a head end in contrast to a less differentiated posterior region, but exceptions exist where posterior features are more prominent than those of the head.

Most flatworms have organs of adhesion which may be glandular, muscular, or in the form of suckers and hooks. Most organs of attachment and adhesion are found in the head region, although they may also occur in the posterior region or in other regions of the body. Parasitic members, especially, are usually well provided with such adhesive devices, but they may also be found among free-living individuals.

The body covering varies with the class. Turbellarians have a definite, one-layered epidermis, which is cellular or syncytial and usually bear cilia in tracts or over the entire body (Fig. 7-2). Rod-shaped bodies (rhabdites) are found in the cells and, when discharged in the water, may form gelatinous sheaths around the body for protection. Irritants may be responsible for their discharge. Epithelial cells may be large and flat or columnar (cuboid) with round nuclei.

Below the epidermis is a thin, noncellular basement membrane which may serve for the attachment of muscles. This basement membrane is scanty or absent in cer-

169

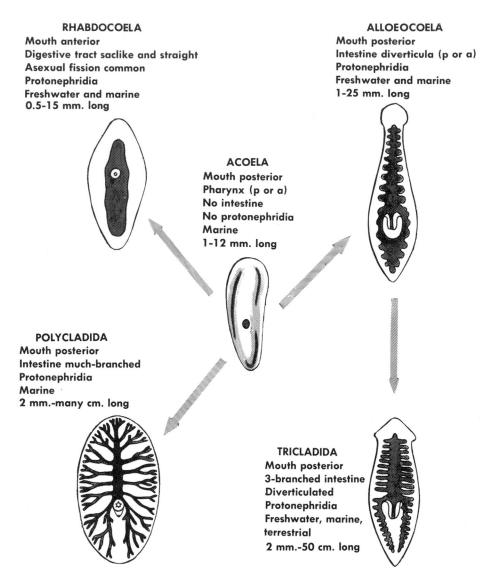

RHABDOCOELA
Mouth anterior
Digestive tract saclike and straight
Asexual fission common
Protonephridia
Freshwater and marine
0.5-15 mm. long

ALLOEOCOELA
Mouth posterior
Intestine diverticula (p or a)
Protonephridia
Freshwater and marine
1-25 mm. long

ACOELA
Mouth posterior
Pharynx (p or a)
No intestine
No protonephridia
Marine
1-12 mm. long

POLYCLADIDA
Mouth posterior
Intestine much-branched
Protonephridia
Marine
2 mm.-many cm. long

TRICLADIDA
Mouth posterior
3-branched intestine
Diverticulated
Protonephridia
Freshwater, marine,
terrestrial
2 mm.-50 cm. long

Fig. 7-1

Orders of class Turbellaria showing chief diagnostic characters. (**p** means present; **a** means absent.) (From Hickman: Integrated principles of zoology, The C. V. Mosby Co.)

tain parts of the body (sensory organs). In some cases the epidermal cell nulcei sink into the parenchyma and retain connection with the epidermis by long strands of cytoplasm.

In the parasitic classes Trematoda and Cestoda, studies with the electron microscope have completely changed the classic concepts of their cuticle. It is now known that their body covering (tegument) consists of syncytial, living protoplasm (not an inert, lifeless secretion) that represents extensions of deeper-lying nucleated protoplasm or cells (Fig. 7-3). The outer surface of the tegument is folded into many small extensions (microtriches), and pore canals, which open to the exterior, penetrate through it into the parenchyma. These newer morphologic discoveries explain many functional aspects once considered obscure. The microtriches facilitate absorption of food by increasing the sur-

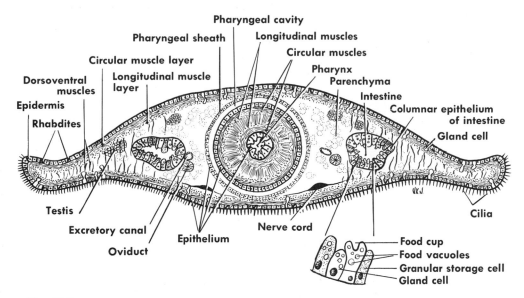

Fig. 7-2

Cross section through pharyngeal region of planarian. (From Hickman: Integrated principles of zoology, The C. V. Mosby Co.)

Fig. 7-3

Diagram of section through typical tegument of cestode as revealed by electron microscope.

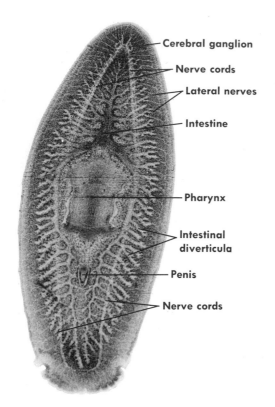

- Cerebral ganglion
- Nerve cords
- Lateral nerves
- Intestine
- Pharynx
- Intestinal diverticula
- Penis
- Nerve cords

Fig. 7-4

Ladder type nervous system of turbellarian *Bdelloura*, a marine triclad. (Stained preparation.) (From Hickman: Integrated principles of zoology. The C. V. Mosby Co.)

face area and, by interlocking with the microvilli of the host's mucosa, they may partially act as holdfast organs. Pore canals could also help absorb substances in solution. Finally, the presence of living protoplasm might explain the ability of the worm to resist digestion by the host because of the constant renewal of the outer tegument by its deeper layer of cells. It will be noted that the tegument lies on a basement membrane, below which are the circular and longitudinal muscle layers. Beneath the muscle layers are dark, elongated cells the extensions of which supposedly form the tegument. Variations in the structure of the tegument are known to occur in the different regions of the body, both within the same species as well as between species.

A cuticle is almost entirely lacking in turbellarians because of the cilia. Subepi-

dermal unicellular glands of many kinds are common in free-living flatworms and secrete slime trails and adhesive devices.

A skeleton of any kind is lacking in the phylum, although relatively hardened parts exist, such as spines, hooks, and suckers that are differentiations of the epidermis or tegument. Such hardened parts are made up of scleroprotein (cuticularized), and chitin is almost nonexistent.

The parenchyma, or mesenchyme, that fills the body spaces of all flatworms varies in different platyhelminths. In origin it appears to be chiefly endomesoderm. Its general structure is that of a netlike syncytium of cells with long, irregular processes and small granules. The syncytium may be formed by the anastomosis of branched mesenchymal cells. There are numerous fluid-filled interstices scattered in the syncytium through which free ameboid cells wander. These ameboid cells are useful as formative cells in regeneration of injured parts and in reproduction. The parenchyma, in addition, serves in the transportation of food and in excretory functions.

The nervous system appears to be derived directly from coelenterates, at least in primitive flatworms; it consists essentially of a subepidermal network and an aggregation of nerve cells at the anterior end to form cerebral ganglia (brain) in free-living forms. Other modifications of the nerve net pattern involve the sinking of the nervous system into deeper regions (mesenchyme) of the body and the formation of longitudinal cords of which the two ventral ones are the most prominent (Fig. 7-4). Transverse connections between the longitudinal cords form the characteristic ladder type of nervous system among flatworms (Figs. 7-4, 7-12).

Sense organs are common in free-living flatworms and in the larval stages of the parasitic classes. In the adults of trematodes and cestodes they are restricted to a few tangoreceptors and free sensory nerve endings. In turbellarians the sense organs take the form of eyes, otocysts, ciliated pits, tentacles, chemosensory receptors, and statocysts. The most common sensory organ is the tangoreceptor, or tactile cell, that terminates in bristles or hairlike structures. Taste and rheotactic receptors have a wide body distribution and enable the animal to detect food juices and changes in the flow of water over the surface of the body. Ciliated pits with long cilia and bristles are the location of sensory cells. Certain areas on the head region are provided with ciliated grooves that bear special chemosensory receptors (auricular organs).

Eyes, or ocelli, are very common among the turbellarians (Fig. 7-5); usually there is a single pair, but there may be more. They usually consist of pigment cups sunk into the mesenchyme in which photosensitive cells (Fig. 7-6) are located. The retina (photosensitive) consists of bipolar nerve cells with rounded, club-shaped distal endings projecting into the cup, their proximal endings joining the central nervous system. A lens is absent, but the epidermis over the eye is not pigmented and may serve as a sort of cornea. Many modifications of this pattern exist. In this inverse type of eye the light has to first pass through the mass of nerve fibers before reaching the sensitive retina.

A digestive system is present in all flat-worms except those of the order Acoela and the class Cestoda. The mouth, which serves for both ingestion and egestion, is found either anteriorly or ventrally. In simple forms the digestive sac is straight without diverticula, but in others it is branched. The stomodeal pharynx is typically a muscular tube and may or may not

Fig. 7-5

Cross section through anterior end of planarian showing eyes as pigmented cups. Structure between eyes is anterior branch of intestine. (From Andrew: Textbook of comparative histology, Oxford University Press, Inc.)

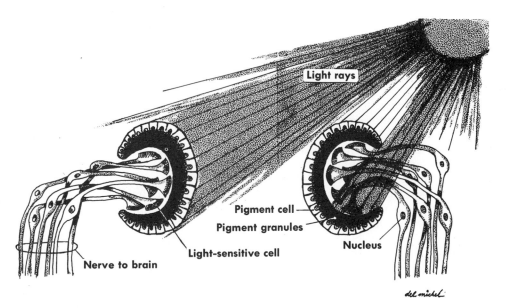

Fig. 7-6

Ocelli, or eyes, of planarian (diagrammatic). Pigment cup allows light to enter open side parallel to long axis of light-sensitive cells. Planarian determines light direction from stimulation of light-sensitive cells. (From Hickman: Integrated principles of zooolgy. The C. V. Mosby Co.)

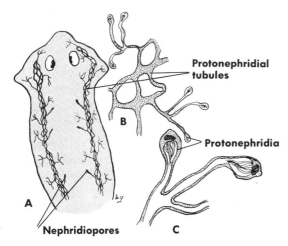

Protonephridial
tubules

B

Protonephridia

A

bg

Nephridiopores   C

Fig. 7-7

Excretory system of flatworm such as planarian. **A,** Two canals with their network of tubules in anterior part of body. **B,** Portion of one canal system enlarged to show network of tubules and protonephridia (flame cells). **C,** Two protonephridia enlarged.

be protrusible (Figs. 7-8, 7-12). It occurs in a variety of types such as simple, bulbous, and plicate. The digestive tract is lined with a single, nonciliated layer of cells that are phagocytic and digestive in function. With the exception of the pharynx the digestive system appears to have little or no muscular layer. Digestion is known to be both extracellular and intracellular.

Throughout the phylum, with the exception of the order Acoela, the typical protonephridial excretory system is found. It usually consists of main canals, which run down either side of the body and which break up into smaller and smaller branches that terminate in flame bulbs. The main canals open to the exterior by nephridiopores the positions of which vary (Fig. 7-7, A). The terminal part of a main canal may be enlarged to form a bladder just before the pore. A flame bulb, or protonephridium (Fig. 7-7, C), is made up of a cell with branched processes and a capillary in which cilia from the bulbous free end of the cell vibrate to produce the characteristic "flame." A single cell may supply cilia to several capillaries in some forms. Flame bulbs are best seen in the cercaria of trematodes. The tubes and flame bulbs run throughout the mesenchyme. The smaller

branches of the tubular excretory system are ciliated, while the main canals are usually not. In the process of excretion the cells of the capillary wall appear to pass fluids and substances into the lumen of the tube, while the action of the flame bulb is to maintain a hydrostatic pressure that keeps excreted substances moving down the tube. The function of the excretory system seems to be osmoregulation of body fluids and, possibly, some excretion as well.

Flatworms lack respiratory and circulatory systems. Exchange of respiratory gases takes place by diffusion through the body wall in turbellarians. Among parasitic members anoxybiotic respiration occurs in which glycogen is used and carbon dioxide and fatty acids are given off. Some facultative parasites may be oxybiotic and make use of the small amount of oxygen in the gut.

Platyhelminthes reproduce both asexually and sexually. Asexual reproduction usually involves fragmentation or binary fission. By such methods some turbellarians produce, temporarily, long chains of individuals. Trematodes, in their larval stages, undergo polyembryony by which individuals are asexually increased. Tapeworms bud off proglottids asexually from the neck region of the scolex, and some (e.g., *Echinococcus*) produce numerous larvae by internal or external budding.

Most flatworms are hermaphroditic, and their reproductive systems are the most complex in the animal kingdom. Sex cells are developed from certain free cells of mesenchyme and migrate to regions where gonads are formed. (In the primitive form, Acoela, no gonads or oviducts exist, and the germ cells are arranged in longitudinal rows of eggs and sperm.) In the reproductive system (Fig. 7-8), testes are usually numerous, but only one or two ovaries are present as a rule. One unique feature of the female system is that the yolk is added by vitelline glands to the eggs after the latter leave the ovary, instead of yolk material becoming a part of the egg structure within the ovary as in other animals. The yolk, or vitelline, glands may discharge into the oviducts either directly or by special yolk ducts.

To ensure cross-fertilization a copulatory apparatus or complex is usually present.

This consists mainly of a genital antrum for receiving the male penis and sacs to store the sperm from the sex partner. The oviducts may or may not unite before entering the complex. The female complex, therefore, usually consists of a branched or rounded ovary from which runs a short oviduct that is joined by the common yolk duct and a short duct from the seminal receptacle. The muscular Laurer's canal also joins the oviduct between the ovary and the entrance of the common yolk duct. Laurer's canal (often absent) may open to the outside and may function in copulation in some unknown manner. The oviduct widens to form the ootype, which is surrounded by Mehlis' glands. These glands were formerly thought to secrete the shell, but the shell material is now known to come from yolk cell granules. The ootype is the place where the finished eggs are produced. Along each side of the body are the numerous yolk glands (vitellaria), which are connected by ducts to one main transverse duct from either side. These two main ducts form a common duct (often with an enlarged yolk reservoir) before entering the ootype or the oviduct nearby. From the ootype the much-coiled uterus (a continuation of the oviduct or ovovitelline duct) extends to the common genital antrum, or the uterus may open separately to the exterior.

The male part of the complex consists of a protrusible penis or eversible cirrus and single or paired vesicles (spermiducal) for storing sperm. The sperm ducts, which carry the sperm from the testes, may unite before entering the copulatory apparatus. The spermiducal vesicles are dilated portions of the sperm ducts; when they are present seminal vesicles are usually absent and vice versa. The lumen of the common sperm duct is called the ejaculatory duct and opens at the end of the penis. In addition a prostatic apparatus may be present consisting of gland cells that open directly or by way of the prostatic vesicle into the ejaculatory duct. The penis is pear shaped and muscular; at rest it opens into the genital atrium, but in copulation it is pushed through its own gonopore into the gonopore of its sex partner. The penis often bears a stylet or spines; sometimes its place is taken by an eversible cirrus formed from

Fig. 7-8

Reproductive system of turbellarian. Male structures are shown on left, female on right; but in life, both systems are paired.

the terminal part of the ejaculatory duct. In trematodes the male copulatory organ is usually a cirrus.

Both male and female systems are highly variable in the flatworms, and modifications of the plan just described are numerous throughout the group. For instance, a common gonopore or separate gonopores for the male and female systems may exist. Gonopores may be located ventrally (the usual place), or they may be lateral or even dorsal. A common genital antrum or separate ones may also exist. In some turbellarians a genitointestinal canal is found between the reproductive system and the intestine, and the sex cells are discharged through the mouth. A separate vaginal or bursal pore for copulation only is found in some members.

Although cross-fertilization by mutual insemination is the rule among flatworms, self-fertilization sometimes occurs. During copulation the ventral surfaces of the sex partners are closely applied together so that their gonopores are opposite to each other. Then the penes or cirri are each pushed into the gonopore of the other for

Fig. 7-9

Cell lineage, polar view, as found in spiral determinate cleavage characteristic of protostomes (polyclads, annelids, mollusks, ascidians, etc.). In such cleavage, fate of blastomeres is determined early, so that removal of one early blastomere will result in defective larva. **A,** Third cleavage, resulting in micromeres and macromeres. **B,** Second quartet has formed; first quartet has divided. **C,** Third quartet has formed; second quartet divided again. One quadrant of cells, composed of macromeres 1B and its descendants, is shaded. (See text for explanation.)

the mutual exchange of sperm. Hypodermic impregnation, in which sperm are injected directly through the epidermis, may occur in some turbellarians and cestodes. Eggs are laid either in gelatinous masses (Acoela and Polycladida), or the egg mass is enclosed in a capsule. Capsules are often deposited in cocoons within which juveniles develop (most Turbellaria). Eggs of trematodes and cestodes usually emerge from the hosts and hatch into free-swimming larvae that enter the intermediate host. In some trematodes and many cestodes the eggs must be eaten before hatching occurs. Some turbellarians produce a thin-shelled (summer) egg with few yolk cells and thick-shelled, dormant (winter) eggs that can withstand the rigors of winter. The summer egg is self-fertilized and may develop in the body of the parent.

Except in the Acoela and the Polycladida, which lack yolk glands, the eggs are ectolecithal and the yolk is contained within yolk cells; but in the Acoela and Polycladida the egg is endolecithal with the yolk enclosed in the ova. The type of development is determined primarily by the differences between these two types of eggs. The most typical and least modified development is that of the endolecithal egg. In this egg the cleavage is of the spiral determinate type similar to that of annelids and mollusks.

In spiral cleavage the egg divides into four equal blastomeres in the first two meridional cleavages. These blastomeres are called A, B, C, D. The third division is unequal and at right angles to the first two and results in four large macromeres and four small cells forming the first quartet of micromeres. These micromeres are designated 1a, 1b, 1c, 1d, and the macromeres are 1A, 1B, 1C, 1D (Fig. 7-9, *A*). In successive cleavages, second, third, etc. quartets of micromeres are given off by the macromeres. Micromeres of the second quartet are numbered 2a, 2b, 2c, and 2d, whereas the macromeres become 2A, 2B, 2C, and 2D. When a third quartet is given off (3a, 3b, 3c, 3d), the macromeres become 3A, 3B, 3C, 3D, etc. (Fig. 7-9, *B, C*). In this scheme lower case letters represent micromeres; capital letters represent macromeres.

As the original quartets divide, their

subsequent divisions are represented by exponents (Fig. 7-9, *C*); thus the two daughter cells of 1a become 1a^1 and 1a^2. When these two daughter cells divide, more exponents are added. In this way the daughter cells of 1a^1 become 1a^{11} and 1a^{12}, and those of 1a^2 will be 1a^{21} and 1a^{22}. The division of 1a^{21} produces 1a^{211} and 1a^{212}. The exponent 1 is given to the cell nearer the animal pole. The macromeres are located at the vegetal pole. It will be noted that all the blastomeres named a are derived from blastomere A of the original four blastomeres (A, B, C, D) and occupy about one quadrant of the embryo. The number before the letters designates the quartet from which the cell is derived, and the exponent indicates the number of subsequent divisions after the formation of a particular quartet of cells. The lower the number the nearer the micromere is to the animal pole; the macromeres are found at the vegetal pole. Cleavages are oblique and alternate right and left. It is thus possible to follow the origin of any particular cell.

The germ layers are formed when the third quartet of micromeres is given off. The first three quartets and the cells derived from them form the ectoderm and the ectomesoderm. In typical spiral cleavage, four macromeres (4A, 4B, 4C, 4D) and three micromeres of the fourth quartet (4a, 4b, 4c) produce the endoderm of the enteron by invagination. Micromere 4d is a large cell called the mesentoblast (M), which gives rise to the endomesoderm and contributes a few cells to the endoderm.

When the embyro is a blastula, it may be a coeloblastula with little yolk or a stereoblastula with much yolk. Gastrulation occurs partly by epiboly and partly by invagination. The blastopore closes, and the mouth is formed near the blastopore by a small stomodeal invagination that later becomes incorporated with the enteron.

In the polyclads the 4d cell gives rise to both the endoderm (4d^1) and the endomesoderm (4d^2), whereas the macromeres 4A, 4B, 4C, and 4D and micromeres 4a, 4b, and 4c are utilized as food material. Most of the mesodermal structures are formed from the endomesoderm.

In the acoels, cleavage, although spiral, differs from typical spiral cleavage in that a single vertical cleavage of the egg results in two blastomeres, A and B, which produce the micromeres in duets rather than in quartets. Gastrulation occurs by epiboly of cells from the first three duets, with cells 4A, 4B, 4a, and 4b forming the interior of the stereogastrula. The stomodeum forms near the site of the blastopore, but no enteron forms, and the endoderm and mesoderm never become distinct.

In the ectolecithal development of triclads, alloeocoels, and rhabdocoels the presence of yolk cells among the blastomeres alters the developmental pattern considerably. The fate of the various cells cannot be followed and the germ-layer formation is omitted.

In some flatworms development is direct, but many (marine polyclads) produce characteristic larvae such as Müller's or Gotté's larvae. These larvae will be discussed under descriptions of the various groups.

CLASS TURBELLARIA
Order Acoela

These marine worms are considered to be the most primitive members of the phylum. They range in length from 1 to 12 mm. and are somewhat oval to elongate in form.

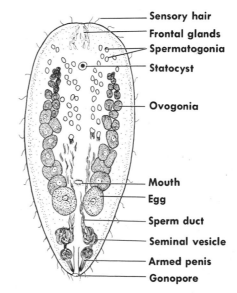

Fig. 7-10

Childia spinosa (order Acoela). This primitive form has epidermal musculature similar to that of coelenterates. (Modified from Graff, 1911.)

They have little color except what they acquire from symbiotic algae. The ciliated epidermis is often syncytial, and the bases of the epidermal cells may bear contractile elements that form a muscle layer. One or two statocysts and some frontal glands are usually found at the anterior tip (Fig. 7-10). Sense organs may also include sensory bristles and one or two pairs of eyes. The mouth is usually found near the middle of the ventral side and leads into a syncytial parenchymal mass that makes up the interior. There is usually no digestive system, and an excretory system is lacking. Digestion is by phagocytic cells of the mesenchyme. The nervous system consists of some poorly developed ganglia and several pairs of longitudinal nerves that lie subepidermally or deeper. As previously mentioned, the hermaphroditic reproductive system contains no gonads or oviducts, but sperm ducts are present. Scattered clusters of mesenchyme cells directly form sex cells that are arranged in longitudinal tracts of eggs and sperm. Both male and female copulatory mechanisms are present. Single or paired seminal or spermiducal vesicles open into the male canal of the penis (often two or four in number), which may be provided with prostatic glands. Sperm is discharged through the male gonopore near the posterior end, or the male canal may unite with the female canal. A female canal, or vagina, may join the common antrum, or a separate female gonopore may be present. In the absence of female structures copulation may occur by hypodermic impregnation in which sperm are injected directly through the epidermis of the sex partner. Fertilized eggs are discharged through the mouth, gonopore, or body rupture. Development is direct, and the young worms are similar to the adult in form.

The Acoela live under stones, in the bottom muck, or among algae. Some are pelagic and others are ectocommensal. *Convoluta* and *Amphiscolops* are two well-known genera.

The phylogenetic significance of Acoela has already been mentioned.

Order Rhabdocoela

In the newer classification of Turbellaria, the Rhabdocoela is now broken up into three orders—Catenulida, Macrostomida,

and Neorhabdocoela. The length of these worms ranges from 0.3 to 15 mm., and they include freshwater, marine, and terrestrial species. The body is elongated to an oval, plump shape. The ciliated epidermis is cellular or syncytial and is provided with rhabdites. The worms usually lack the frontal glands, but their body surface has sensory bristles or hairs. A statocyst is usually lacking. They often bear one or more eyes of the epidermal pigment-spot type. The nervous system usually consists of a bilobed brain and two main longitudinal nerves with few transverse connectives. The rhabdocoels have a simple, unbranched digestive tract with few or no diverticulations and a simple or bulbous pharynx. The excretory system is of the protonephridian type. The reproductive system is made up of compact gonads (a pair of testes and one or two ovaries), a pair of yolk glands, and the copulatory complex. Mutual insemination normally occurs, and the eggs (single or multiple) are enclosed in a capsule when laid. Yolk glands are lacking in many species.

The order Catenulida is made up of colorless freshwater forms with simple pharynx, a single median protonephridium, no yolk glands, and usually no sex organs. The nervous system contains a brain and four pairs of longitudinal nerves. Reproduction is mainly asexual by binary fission and the formation of zooid chains. In some members one or more ovaries may exist without ducts, and a single testis with a duct modified into a copulatory organ that opens through an anterior, dorsal pore may be present. In such cases the endolecithal eggs are discharged by rupture of the body wall. *Stenostomum* is a common freshwater genus.

Members of the order Macrostomida have paired protonephridia and a single pair of longitudinal nerves. Yolk glands are lacking, but the usual hermaphroditic reproductive system is often present. Chains of zooids are formed by asexual methods. The common freshwater genus *Microstomum* is often provided with nematocysts obtained by eating hydras.

Most rhabdocoels belong to the order Neorhabdocoela and have a bulbous pharynx, paired protonephridia, sexual reproduction, yolk glands, ectolecithal eggs, and ventral gonopores. The mouth may be located at the anterior end or near the middle of the body. Some members are provided with a protrusible proboscis.

The extensive group of neorhabdocoels is broken up into subgroups or suborders such as the Dalyellioida, the Typhloplanoida, the Kalyptorhynchia, and the Temnocephalida.

The Dalyellioida are characterized by a dolioform (barrel-shaped) pharynx with the mouth near the anterior end. The principal genus is *Dalyellia,* common in fresh waters.

The Typhloplanoida usually have a rosulate pharynx (sometimes dolioform) with the mouth near the middle of the body. *Mesostoma* (Fig. 7-11) is a common freshwater genus throughout the world.

The Kalyptorhynchia have a rosulate pharynx, but they are also provided with a pouch at the anterior end possessing a protrusible glandulomuscular proboscis by which they are able to capture their prey. *Gyratrix* is a common genus in both fresh and marine water.

The Temnocephalida are ectocommensals on crayfish and other forms in tropical and subtropical waters. They differ from most rhabdocoels in possessing tentacles and adhesive organs; also most species lack cilia. *Temnocephala* is a typical genus.

Order Alloeocoela

As a group the alloeocoels are intermediate in their characteristics between the Acoela and the Tricladida. They range in length between 1 mm. and 40 mm. They are mostly of an elongated and cylindric shape, and are found in freshwater, saltwater, and terrestrial habitats. Their chief characteristics are a plicate pharynx, a diverticulated enteron, three or four pairs of longitudinal nerves with transverse connections, a pair of protonephridia each with one to three branches, and a reproductive system of paired ovaries, many testes, and a penis. Eyes may or may not be present. The group ranges between the primitive characteristics of Acoela and the more specialized and complex structures of the triclads, which were supposedly derived from the alloeocoels.

The best known genus is *Plagiostomum,* which occurs in both fresh and salt water

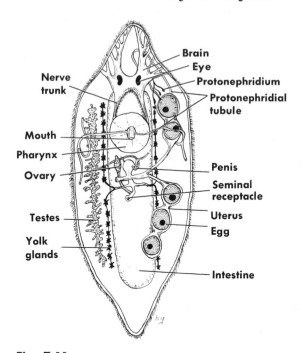

Fig. 7-11

Mesostoma (order Rhabdocoela), a common freshwater form whose summer eggs hatch within body. Testes shown only on left; uterus only on right.

in Europe and America. The largest genus is *Baicalarctia* from the famed Lake Baikal.

Order Tricladida

These worms range in length from 2 mm. to more than 50 cm. Their body is elongated, usually flattened, and provided with many mucus glands. The epidermis is ciliated on the ventral surface (rarely elsewhere) and bears many rhabdites. Adhesive glandulomuscular organs are common on the ventral side of the anterior end. Eyes are lacking in cave forms only. The mouth is located posterior to the ventral middle surface and opens into the pharyngeal cavity (Fig. 7-12). The worms possess a plicate and tubular pharynx attached anteriorly and a three-branched, diverticulated intestine consisting of one anterior branch and two posterior ones. Some have more than one pharynx (polypharyngy) and many mouth openings. The excretory system consists of a network of protonephridial tubules with numerous nephridiopores on each side of the body. The female reproductive system (Fig. 7-8) consists of **179**

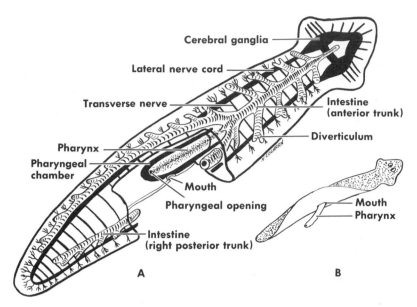

Cerebral ganglia

Lateral nerve cord

Transverse nerve

Intestine (anterior trunk)

Diverticulum

Pharynx

Pharyngeal chamber

Mouth

Pharyngeal opening

Intestine (right posterior trunk)

Mouth

Pharynx

A

B

Fig. 7-12

A, Diagram of digestive and nervous systems of planaria; cutaway section shows ventral mouth. **B,** Pharynx extended through ventral mouth. (From Hickman: Integrated principles of zoology, The C. V. Mosby Co.)

Spermatids

Sperm

Spermatocytes

Spermatogonia

Fig. 7-13

Section through testis of *Dugesia* showing sperm cells in different stages of development.

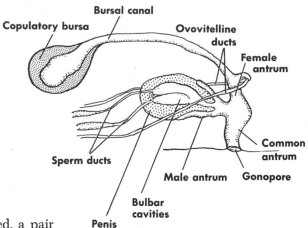

Fig. 7-14

Copulatory organs of planarian.

two small ovaries anteriorly located, a pair of ovovitelline ducts with numerous yolk glands, the female antrum, and usually one or two copulatory bursae. The male system (Fig. 7-8) has few to many testes (Fig. 7-13) laterally located, a sperm duct on each side connected to the testes by sperm ductules, a pair of spermiducal vesicles or enlarged parts of the sperm ducts, and a male antrum containing the copulatory organ (penis) into which the sperm ducts enter singly or after fusion (Fig. 7-14).

In copulation, which occurs by mutual insemination, the sperm first enter the copulatory bursa before traveling up the ovovitelline ducts to fertilize the eggs near the ovaries (Fig. 7-14). The fertilized eggs collect yolk from the yolk glands as they pass down the ovovitelline ducts and finally enter the male antrum where a capsule, or cocoon, is formed around them. Each capsule (Fig. 7-15) containing several fertilized eggs is attached by a stalk to some object after discharge through the gonopore and hatches in about two weeks into juvenile worms. Asexual reproduction by fission is common in some triclads, and in some, such as the land planarian (*Bipalium*), fragmentation and regeneration is the usual method.

Classified according to habitat, there are three well-recognized suborders of this order.

The Maricola are rather small marine forms that occur under stones along the coastlines of most seas and are incapable of asexual reproduction. *Bdelloura*, a common ectocommensal on the horseshoe crab *Limulus (Xiphosura)*, is a familiar genus.

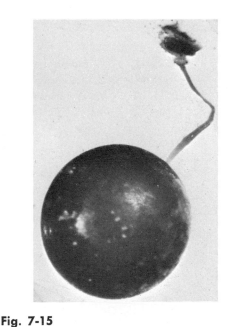

Fig. 7-15

Egg capsule (cocoon) of planarian. Capsule is formed in male antrum and contains many eggs and yolk cells. Eggs hatch into juvenile worms in two to three weeks. (Courtesy Carolina Biological Supply Co., Burlington, N. C.)

The Paludicola, or freshwater forms, are usually larger than the Maricola and are found in streams, ponds, and lakes of the temperate zones. Lake Baikal in Siberia is unusually rich in species of this group. To this group belong the familiar planarians of which there are many species in America, Europe, and Asia. *Dugesia tigrina* is well known to all zoologists and reproduces both sexually and asexually depending upon weather and temperature conditions.

To the Terricola belong the land planarians which live on the forest floors under leaf mold, logs, etc. They cannot endure complete submersion in water, although they must have humid conditions. They are found mostly in tropical and subtropical regions, although a few have been introduced into the temperate zones. *Bipalium*, a large worm 8 or 10 inches long, has often been found in greenhouses in the United States. Some of its species reproduce entirely by fragmentation, but one or two species reproduce sexually in California. In their natural habitats of the tropics the Terricola reproduce both sexually and asexually.

Order Polycladida

These marine flatworms derive their name from their enteron, which has many diverticula radiating from the central main stem. In length they vary from 2 mm. to more than 15 cm. Their body is much flattened and often broadly leaflike. Their main habitat is on the bottom of littoral zones, although some members are pelagic and swim down to considerable depths. A few are commensals on shells of mollusks and hermit crabs. Their color varies from the transparency of pelagic species to the bright hues of those in warm waters. Many eyes and usually some tentacles are present. They lack statocysts and frontal glands; adhesive organs are rare. The ciliated cellular epidermis is provided with numerous glands and rhabdites. The nervous system is made up of a brain anterior to the pharynx and a number of radiating nerves, two of which are usually larger than the others. The mouth is located near the middle of the body and opens into the plicate pharynx. Yolk glands are absent, but testes and ovaries are numerous. Other parts of the reproductive system are similar to the flatworm plan (Fig. 7-16). Insemination may be hypodermic or regular, but self-fertilization does not occur. The endolecithal eggs are fertilized just before laying. Sperm usually collect first in Lang's vesicle, a bursa with a long stalk. Eggs are laid in gelatinous masses that become enclosed in capsules. In some polyclads the egg develops into Müller's larva, which may indicate an evolutionary link between the turbellaria and the ctenophores on the one hand or with the annelids on the other. The larva is provided with a series of ciliated lobes that are lost when it assumes the creeping habits of the adult. As already described, the embryology of polyclads is of the spiral determinate type and resembles that of mollusks and annelids.

Three of the best known and most widely distributed genera are *Notoplana* and *Stylochus* (Fig. 7-16) found on both the Atlantic and Pacific coasts, and *Planocera*, a pelagic form.

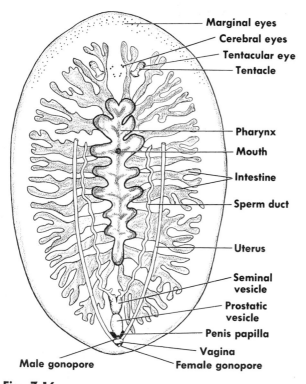

Fig. 7-16

Stylochus ellipticus, a common polyclad of both Atlantic and Pacific coasts. (Modified from Pearse, 1938.)

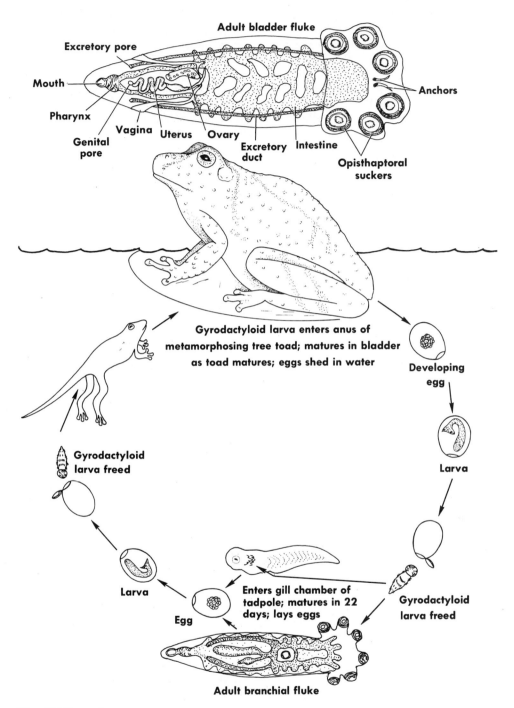

Fig. 7-17

Life history of *Polystoma nearcticum* (order Monogenea). This bladder fluke lives in urinary bladder of tree toads *(Hyla versicolor, H. cinerea);* sheds eggs into urine. Larvae develop in water and attach to external gills of young tadpoles where, in three weeks, they mature neotenically into branchial flukes. When larvae from eggs produced by either bladder fluke or neotenic branchial fluke attach to older tadpoles, neoteny does not occur; larvae enter bladder by way of cloaca, develop slowly, maturing as toad matures, in two or three years. (Modified from Olsen, 1962.)

CLASS TREMATODA
Order Monogenea (Heterocotylea)

The members of this group of trematodes are mostly ectoparasites on the gills, skin, and external orifices of fishes, a few amphibians, turtles, and a few other hosts. They are provided with distinctive anterior and posterior adhesive organs called, respectively, prohaptor and opisthaptor (posthaptor). The prohaptor consists of small lateral suckers and adhesive glands and sometimes an oral sucker surrounding the mouth; the opisthaptor usually has many hooks. The distinctive characteristics of the order are a single host in the life cycle, sexual reproduction, and direct development. Body shapes vary but are typically flattened and leaflike. The excretory pores are paired and lie near the anterior end. The pharynx is a muscular organ, and the enteron is bifid, often with diverticula. There are separate genital openings for the male and female reproductive systems. Cross-fertilization is the rule, although self-fertilization may also occur. They feed on both mucus and blood of the host. The egg capsules are provided with filaments for attachment to hosts. Monogeneids have a high host specificity and are very sensitive morphologically to the position of their microhabitats on the host.

The Monogenea are usually divided into two groups, Monopisthocotylea in which the opisthaptor is a single sucker or disk with anchor and marginal hooks, and the Polyopisthocotylea with multiple suckers and cuticularized clamps. *Gyrodactylus,* a common genus on the gills of freshwater fishes, is an example of the Monopisthocotylea; and *Polystoma*, which lives in the urinary bladder of frogs, is an example of the Polyopisthocotylea.

Polystoma (Fig. 7-17) has one of the best-known life histories, although it is not typical of all monogeneids. The adult fluke lives in the urinary bladder of frogs and breeds in the spring; its eggs in the urine are discharged into the water. The egg hatches into a larva with a hooked opisthaptor, attaches itself to the gills of a tadpole, and grows as the tadpole develops. When the frog metamorphoses, the young fluke may enter the host's esophagus and pass down to the bladder where it completes its development and becomes sexually mature in about two to three years. The bladder fluke form may infect the frog by way of the anus instead of the esophagus. In some cases, however, the fluke may attach itself to a young tadpole, mature neotenically, and reproduce the first year. Such neotenic forms never get into the bladder and never fully mature.

Order Aspidogastraea (Aspidobothria)

The Aspidogastraea were formerly included under the order Digenea. They are endoparasitic in mollusks, fishes, turtles, and skates and are mostly characterized by very large opisthaptors or suckers divided by septa into longitudinal rows of depressions (alveoli). Such a sucker may occupy most of the ventral surface. The alveoli are important in taxonomic procedures. An oral sucker may be absent or weakly developed. In general anatomy the Aspidogastraea resemble the Digenea, but their development is direct, as in Monogenea.

Aspidogaster, common in the pericardial chamber of freshwater clams, is a well-known genus. Only one host is necessary in the life history.

Order Digenea (Malacocotylea)

This extensive group of endoparasitic trematodes is characterized by having more than one host in their life histories. The adults are sexual and usually have vertebrates of all classes except cyclostomes for their definitive hosts. The asexual larval stages are passed in intermediate hosts, usually mollusks, rarely annelids. The life history may be very complicated and involve two to four hosts for complete development. In most cases the adults are hermaphroditic, but a few are dioecious. In the definitive host the adults usually occupy the digestive tract and the derivatives or appendages of the tract, such as the gallbladder and its ducts, the liver, the lungs, the bladder, and kidneys. Some live in blood vessels and cavities (coelom and head). Aquatic animals harbor more digenetic trematodes than do terrestrial forms.

Certain unique morphologic features of the adults in this group exist. No opisthaptor is found at the posterior end as in other trematodes. The mouth is usually anterior

Fig. 7-18

Stages in life cycle of sheep liver fluke, *Fasciola hepatica* (class Trematoda, order Digenea). Not enlarged to same scale. **A,** Adult (up to 30 mm. long). **B,** Egg (130 to 150 microns long). **C,** Miracidium. **D,** Sporocyst. **E,** Redia. **F,** Cercaria (250 to 350 microns long). **G,** Metacercaria. (Courtesy Carolina Biological Supply Co., Burlington, N.C.)

and opens into an oral sucker that may be poorly developed or lacking. In some members, the mouth is ventral without a sucker. In place of the opisthaptor there is often a ventral sucker, the acetabulum, usually highly muscular with a raised rim. It operates mainly on the principle of a vacuum and not by glandular secretions. It may be found at various locations on the body such as anterior to the middle of the ventral surface (Distomata), posterior end, or it may be absent. It is often of great diagnostic value in taxonomic determinations. The length of the adults is usually 20 to 25 mm., but some are smaller and others are larger than this. The Digenea as a whole show an enormous variety of modifications.

In their complex life histories development is indirect. Development of the egg may begin before it leaves the host, or it may be delayed until later. The egg (Fig. 7-18, *B*) usually divides into propagation and somatic cells, forming a ball of cells. From the ball of cells the first larval stage, the ciliated miracidium, develops (Fig. 7-18, *C*). The miracidium enters an intermediate host and becomes a germinal sac, the sporocyst (Fig. 7-18, *D*), which contains, among other cells, germ balls or germinal cells. The germ balls may develop into daughter sporocysts, or they may produce a generation of the next larval stage, the

rediae (Fig. 7-18, *E*), which differ from sporocysts in having a pharynx and saclike gut. The rediae may produce a second generation of rediae, or the redial stage may be absent altogether. From the daughter sporocysts or from the rediae, the cercariae develop (Fig. 7-18, *F*). The number of cercariae that emerges from the intermediate host may be small or large. Reproduction in the sporocysts and rediae appears to be by mitosis of segregated germinal cells or balls without sexual phenomena, a process called polyembryony. The cercaria consists of an oval-shaped body and a simple or forked tail (lacking in some) and it has many of the structures of the adult fluke. After leaving the intermediate host it encysts on vegetation or on a second intermediate host. When the encysted larva or metacercaria, a juvenile fluke (Fig. 7-18, *G*), is eaten by a vertebrate, it is transformed into the adult fluke. Some cercariae (blood flukes) are able to penetrate the skin directly. Many variations of the life cycle are found in this group in which the number of species is constantly increased as a result of investigations and in which the taxonomy is in a state of flux and confusion at the present time.

Of the many members of this extensive order, some of the more important parasitic genera are: *Fasciola* (Fig. 7-18) found in

185

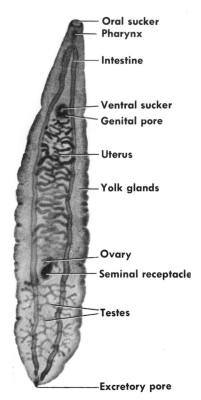

Oral sucker
Pharynx
Intestine
Ventral sucker
Genital pore
Uterus
Yolk glands
Ovary
Seminal receptacle
Testes
Excretory pore

Fig. 7-19
Opisthorchis, the human liver fluke (order Digenea).

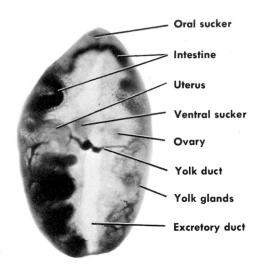

Oral sucker
Intestine
Uterus
Ventral sucker
Ovary
Yolk duct
Yolk glands
Excretory duct

Fig. 7-21
Paragonimus westermani (order Digenea), found chiefly in man and some other mammals, produces paragonimiasis. Adults up to ½ inch long discharge eggs into sputum or feces. Free-swimming miracidia enter snail and pass through sporocyst and redia stages. Cercariae leave snail, enter viscera and muscles of freshwater crabs, and encyst in soft tissues. Human infection occurs from eating raw crabs or by drinking contaminated water. (AFIP No. 52-1862.)

Fig. 7-20
Adult male and female *Schistosoma mansoni* in copulation. Male has long sex canal that holds female (darker individual) during insemination and oviposition. Man is usually primary host; certain snails are intermediate hosts. (AFIP No. 56-3334.)

the bile ducts of sheep, goats, and other domestic animals with pond snails and vegetation as the intermediate hosts; *Opisthorchis* (Fig. 7-19), in the bile ducts of mammals (including man), birds, and other vertebrates with certain snails and fishes as the intermediate hosts; *Schistosoma* (Fig. 7-20), in the blood vessels of birds and mammals (including man) with pulmonate snails as the intermediate host; *Paragonimus* (Fig. 7-21), in the lungs of mammals (Fig. 7-22) with operculate snails and crayfish or crabs as intermediate hosts; and *Fasciolopsis* in the intestine of man, pigs, and dogs, with snails and water nuts (*Trapa natans*) as intermediate hosts. The first intermediate host is nearly always a mollusk, but W. E. Martin (1944, 1952) has found two examples of a polychaete worm serving as the first intermediate host.

Classification of the trematodes has been based primarily upon certain features such as the arrangement of the reproductive system, the position and nature of the suckers,

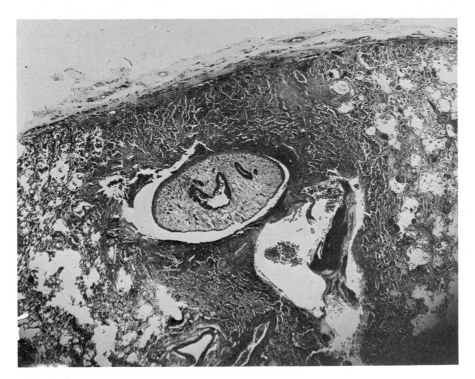

Fig. 7-22

Paragonimus fluke (order Digenea) in lung tissue. (AFIP-ACC No. 496822.)

the type of miracidia and cercariae, the nature of the epithelial lining of the bladder, and the arrangement of the excretory system.

CLASS CESTODA (CESTOIDEA)
Subclass Cestodaria

The subclass Cestodaria is made up of a few endoparasites of primitive fishes. They differ mainly from other cestodes in being unsegmented, in not forming proglottids, and in having a larva (oncosphere or lycophore) with 10 hooks that is usually found in crustaceans. They also occur as parasites in the coelomic cavity as well as in the intestine. Instead of a scolex they may bear a protrusible proboscis with large frontal glands. In others the posterior end is provided with a holdfast organ, or rosette. They are hermaphroditic with the sexual phase in the vertebrate host.

The best-known genera are *Amphilina*, a parasite in the coelom of the sturgeon *Acipenser*, and *Gyrocotyle* (Fig. 7-23) in the intestine of chimaeroid fishes.

Subclass Eucestoda

The Eucestoda are the true tapeworms whose bodies are chiefly divided into segments, or proglottids, and whose larvae bear six hooks. The adults are endoparasites in vertebrate intestines, and their life cycle involves one or two intermediate hosts that may be either invertebrate or vertebrate. The anterior end is usually modified into a scolex, or holdfast organ, followed by a short, undivided neck. Tapeworms range in length from 1 mm. to many feet, and the proglottids may number few to many thousands. The chain of proglottids (the strobila) gradually increases in breadth and length posteriorly, so that the broadest and longest proglottids are at the posterior end, and the smallest and least differentiated proglottids are just behind the neck, from which the proglottids proliferate asexually (Fig. 7-24). The scolex, which is modified in different species (Fig. 7-26), is a generally solid structure of muscle and mesenchyme and bears the organs of attachment (suckers, hooks, etc.), nephridial

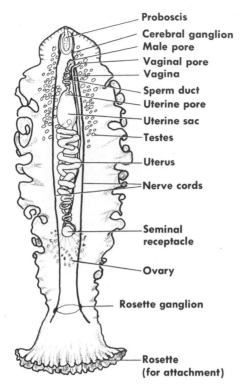

Proboscis
Cerebral ganglion
Male pore
Vaginal pore
Vagina
Sperm duct
Uterine pore
Uterine sac
Testes
Uterus
Nerve cords
Seminal receptacle
Ovary
Rosette ganglion
Rosette (for attachment)

Fig. 7-23

Gyrocotyle (subclass Cestodaria). Adults are parasitic in chimaeroid fishes.

Fig. 7-24

Ruminant tapeworm *Moniezia expansa* (subclass Eucestoda). Note small scolex and slender neck proglottids at upper left.

canals, and a sort of brain. The body is covered with a living tegument as already described in a former section. Through each proglottid and the length of the strobila runs a pair of longitudinal lateral nerves. The nerves are connected by commissures in each proglottid. A pair of longitudinal lateral excretory canals in dorsal and ventral arrangement on each side of the proglottid runs through the length of the body. Flame bulbs are connected to the four main excretory canals by a system of fine canals. With five or six exceptions all cestodes are hermaphroditic.

The reproductive systems are progressively developed from anterior to posterior ends of the strobila (Fig. 7-25) with the male system maturing before the female system (protandry). Each proglottid contains a full set of reproductive organs and, in some cases, two complete sets. The general plan of the reproductive system is similar to that found in other flatworms with many diverse arrangements. The genital ducts (gonoducts) of both sexes usually open into a common antrum, which may be double if the reproductive systems are double. There is a single genital opening, or gonopore, for each common antrum.

Fertilization may take place within a single proglottid (self-fertilization), between proglottids in the same strobila, or between proglottids of different worms. Hypodermic insemination may occur in those that lack a vaginal opening. Copulation occurs by eversion of the cirrus into the vagina. Self-fertilization appears to be the most common method. The egg is fertilized in a region of the oviduct where the ovum, with yolk cells, becomes enclosed in a shell. Within the uterus the eggs develop into the oncosphere larval form with three pairs of hooks. The posterior proglottids become distended (gravid) with embryos (Fig. 7-25) and are shed from the strobila to the outside of the host. In some members only the shelled embryos are shed. After being eaten by an intermediate host, the oncosphere escapes from its membrane and undergoes further development. Two intermediate hosts are usually required, one of which is a crustacean and the other a fish or other vertebrate (Fig. 7-28). Many variations of this plan exist. The embryo attains entrance to the definitive vertebrate

Fig. 7-25

Proglottids from three sections of tapeworm *Taenia pisiformis* showing progressive sexual maturity. Left to right: immature proglottids from anterior region, mature proglottids from middle portion, and gravid proglottid from posterior end.

host when the latter eats the intermediate host. Usually the postoncosphere development involves a procercoid larval stage in the first intermediate host and a plerocercoid stage in the second intermediate host. The plerocercoid develops many of the structures of the adult such as a scolex, thickened cuticle, and nervous and excretory systems. Strobilation, however, does not occur until it is eaten by the final vertebrate host. However, this pattern of development is modified in certain orders.

Tapeworms vary greatly in length of life. Some large, human tapeworms such as *Dibothriocephalus latus* (order Pseudophyllidea) and *Taenia saginata* (order Cyclophyllidea) may live 30 to 35 years, or sometimes for as long as the host lives. Many tapeworms live less than a year, and some live only a few days. Tapeworm infection may produce no visible symptoms, but diarrhea, abdominal pain, abnormal appetite, and even convulsions may occur. Diagnosis of infection is made by fecal examination for proglottids or eggs, x-ray films, skin tests, etc. Some progress has been made experimentally in cultivating larval and adult tapeworms outside of the body, but the process is very difficult.

Order Tetraphyllidea (Phyllobothrioidea)

In these tapeworms the scolex is provided with four broad, leaflike muscular structures (bothridia) of many diverse forms symmetrically arranged around the anterior region of the elongated scolex. Hooks are also found on the scolex of some members. Tetraphyllids are small, intestinal parasites of elasmobranch fishes and are usually less than 3 or 4 inches long with a few hundred proglottids. The sexually immature proglottids are shed from the body and become sexually mature in the intestine of the host. Each proglottid contains a single reproductive system of each sex that may open by a genital pore on each side. A complete life history is unknown, **189**

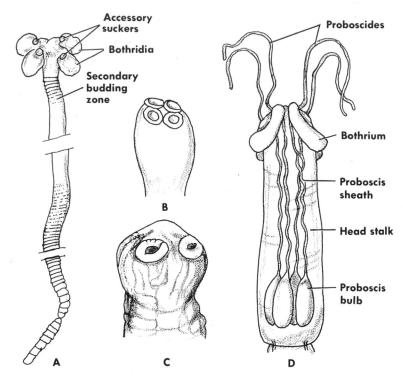

Fig. 7-26

A, *Phyllobothrium dornii* proliferates in usual manner at rear end of neck; then later starts forming proglottids in opposite direction just behind scolex. Small portions omitted from drawing (order Tetraphyllidea). B, *Proteocephalus coregoni* scolex; has no apical sucker though most species in this genus do; parasitic in coregonid fishes (order Proteocephaloidea). C, *Corallobothrium giganteum* scolex; its four suckers are facing forward; has been found in siluroid fishes in Mississippian drainage system (order Proteocephaloidea). D, *Gilquinia squali;* parasitic in spiny dogfish *Squalus.* This order (Trypanorhyncha) has eversible tentacles, or proboscides, as well as bothria. (Modified: A, Curtis, 1906; B, Wardle, 1932; C, Essex, 1927; D, Hyman, 1940.)

but larval forms have been found in various invertebrates and some marine fishes.

Phyllobothrium (Fig. 7-26, A) is one of the most familiar genera and has been extensively studied.

Order Proteocephaloidea

The tapeworms of this order are intestinal parasites of freshwater fishes, amphibians, reptiles, and elasmobranchs. They are short (a few inches in length), slender, and are distinctly segmented. The scolex, or holdfast organ, bears four cup-shaped suckers (acetabula) of varying form, and many species have an apical organ or degenerate sucker at the tip of the holdfast. A rostellum with hooks is found in the genus *Gan-*

gesia. The mesenchyme of the proglottid is divided into cortical and central regions, as in the order Tetraphyllidea, and there are other anatomic similarities between the two orders. The life cycle involves the ingestion of the oncosphere with its membranes by copepods *(Cyclops),* in the body cavity of which the larva develops into procercoid and plerocercoid stages, although the latter stage may occur in the definitive host. The definitive vertebrate host (freshwater fishes, amphibians, and reptiles) becomes infected by eating parasitized *Cyclops* or by eating small vertebrates that have fed on parasitized copepods. *Proteocephalus* and *Corallobothrium* are among well-known species (Fig. 7-26, B, C).

Order Trypanorhyncha (Tetra-rhynchoidea)

This order of tapeworms is characterized by having four spiny, eversible proboscides of the scolex (Fig. 7-26, *D*). The elongated scolex is divisible into a bothrial region with one to four suckers (often called bothridia but which, because of their weak muscularity, should probably be considered bothria) and a head stalk with the proboscis apparatus consisting of four spiny proboscides. Each proboscide is contained in a sheath and ends with a muscular proboscis. The proboscides, or tentacles, are everted by muscular contractions of bulbs, which force fluid against their inner ends, and then are pulled back by retractor muscles. The tapeworms are usually under 4 inches in length and are chiefly parasites in the spiral valve of elasmobranch fishes and in the intestine of some ganoid fishes. The life history is incomplete for the marine species, but larval forms of the procercoid or cysticercoid types have been found in marine invertebrates and teleost fishes.

Haplobothrium, an aberrant genus found in the common freshwater fish *Amia*, lacks the suckers and has some other features not characteristic of the order. Its life history has been worked out and indicates that the larval stages involve *Cyclops* and the teleost fish *Ameiurus*. (R. A. Wardle and J. A. McLeod consider *Haplobothrium* a member of Pseudophyllidea.)

Order Pseudophyllidea

These widely distributed tapeworms are parasitic in all classes of vertebrates. The chief diagnostic character is a scolex usually bearing two shallow grooves (bothria) arranged in a dorsal and ventral position to each other. In some species the scolex bears a circle of hooks. Some members are monozoic with bodies not divided into proglottids. The genital openings, or gonopores, are often found near the ventral or dorsal midline instead of on the lateral margins. The uterine pore, in some cases, is separate from the male pore. One of the best known genera is *Dibothriocephalus latus* (*Diphyllobothrium*, Figs. 7-27, 7-28), the broad tape-

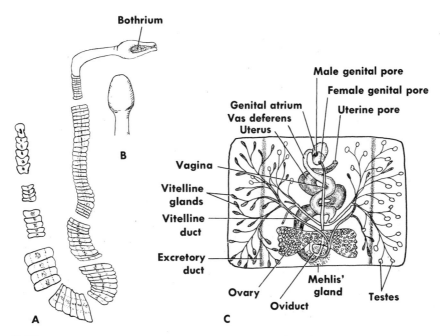

Fig. 7-27

Dibothriocephalus latus, the fish tapeworm (order Pseudophyllidea). **A**, Adult worm showing narrow side of scolex with bothrium and part of strobila. **B**, Flat side of scolex. **C**, Mature proglottid.

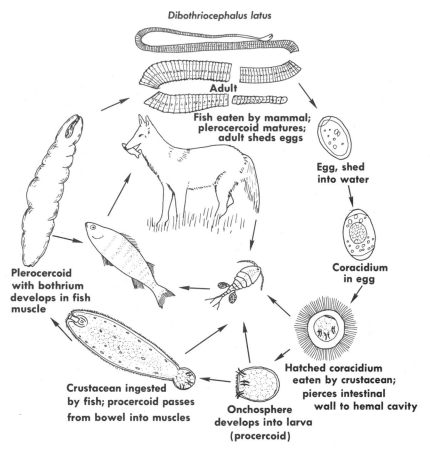

Dibothriocephalus latus

Adult

Fish eaten by mammal; plerocercoid matures; adult sheds eggs

Egg, shed into water

Coracidium in egg

Plerocercoid with bothrium develops in fish muscle

Hatched coracidium eaten by crustacean; pierces intestinal wall to hemal cavity

Crustacean ingested by fish; procercoid passes from bowel into muscles

Onchosphere develops into larva (procercoid)

Fig. 7-28

Life cycle of broad tapeworm *Dibothriocephalus latus,* common human parasite in Russia and Siberia, Finland, and many other places, including our Great Lakes region. Other mammal hosts are usually dogs, cats, pigs (Russia), and bears (Canada). Intermediate hosts are certain species of *Cyclops* and *Diaptomus* and freshwater fish such as pike, perch, lawyer, trout, and ruff. If infected fish is eaten by another fish, plerocercoid travels to muscles again; it does not mature sexually unless it reaches intestine of mammal host.

worm of man and of some fish-eating mammals. The life cycle of this tapeworm is well known (Fig. 7-28). The egg capsule hatches into a ciliated embryo (coracidium) that is eaten by the first intermediate host, a copepod (*Cyclops* or *Diaptomus*). In the body cavity of the copepod the coracidium develops into a procercoid larva. When the copepod host is ingested by the second intermediate host (usually a fish, but other vertebrate classes may be involved), the procercoid develops into a plerocercoid larva. When the definitive host eats the second intermeditae host, the worm develops into the adult form, which may reach a

length of 60 feet with a strobila numbering up to 4,000 proglottids.

Order Cyclophyllidea (Taenioidea)

The tapeworms of this order are found in the intestine of warm-blooded vertebrates (birds and mammals), although they may also occur in reptiles and amphibians. The characteristic scolex bears four cup-shaped suckers (acetabula) and a muscular rostellum with a crown of hooks (Fig. 7-29). In some members the rostellum may be withdrawn into a rostellar receptacle, or it may be absent altogether. The worms vary in length from 1 or 2 mm. to several feet,

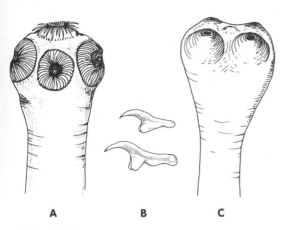

A   **B**   **C**

Fig. 7-29

A, Scolex (holdfast) of *Taenia solium* showing row of apical hooks in addition to suckers. **B,** Enlarged view of short and long hooks (side view) of *Taenia solium*. **C,** Scolex of *Taenia saginata,* which is provided only with suckers.

but most are only a few inches long. New proglottids are budded off just posterior to the scolex and, as they are pushed back, become sexually mature and larger (Figs. 7-24, 7-25). With the exception of one genus *(Dioecocestus),* they are all hermaphroditic. One or two sets of sex organs are present in each proglottid, and both reproductive systems share a common gonopore and antrum that usually lie in the lateral margin (Fig. 7-30). Usually no uterine opening exists in this order. The ova may be fertilized by sperm from the same or from a different proglottid and are collected together in a uterus, ultimately filling the proglottid with ripe egg capsules. Ripe cestode eggs contain onchosphere or hexacanth larvae with six hooks. Ripe proglottids containing the infectious eggs are passed out of the gut of the host along with fecal material.

Nerve cord

Excretory canal

Sperm duct

Genital pore

Vagina

Testes

Uterus

Ovary

Mehlis' gland

Yolk gland

Fig. 7-30

Mature proglottid of dog tapeworm *Taenia pisiformis* (order Taenioidea). (Courtesy General Biological Supply House, Inc., Chicago.)

Fig. 7-31

Piece of "measly pork" showing cysts of bladder worms (cysticerci) of *Taenia solium*. Bladder worm cysts of *Taenia saginata* have similar appearance.

Only one intermediate host (sometimes omitted) is required in the life cycle of the Cyclophyllidea. After an intermediate host (invertebrate or vertebrate) ingests the eggs, the oncosphere is freed from its membranes and penetrates the intestinal wall into the coelom, hemocoel, liver, or other parts where it develops into some type of metacestode such as a cysticercoid. A cysticercoid usually has the scolex retracted into a vesicle and is provided with a tail. Some metacestodes of this order have the scolex invaginated (introverted), lack the tail appendage, and form a bladder worm called a cysticercus (Fig. 7-31). This type of metacestode is most common in reptilian and mammalian intermediate hosts. A modified form of the single bladder worm is the hydatid cyst, which contains large numbers of attached and free-floating brood capsules, each of which buds many scolices internally or externally. Such hydatid cysts may reach the size of an orange and may be found in various parts of the body. The cyst greatly increases the asexual reproductive power of tapeworms.

Whatever the form of the metacestode, it usually remains quiescent until its intermediate host is eaten by the definitive host. Then the scolex of the cysticercoid or cysticercus emerges, attaches itself to the intestinal wall of the host, and begins to prolif-

erate proglottids as a mature tapeworm. (In cysticercus types the scolex evaginates for attachment.)

The majority of the common tapeworms belong to this extensive order. The most common tapeworm of man, at least in the United States, is the beef tapeworm (*Taenia saginata*, Fig. 7-29, *C*) whose intermediate host is cattle. *Dipylidium* is a common cestode of dogs and cats and may be found occasionally in children. Its intermediate hosts are fleas and biting lice. The dwarf tapeworm (*Hymenolepis*) occurs in children, mice, and rats. Its life cycle is noted for having no intermediate host. The embryos (hexacanths) from the adult worm bore into the intestinal wall, transform to cysticercoids, and emerge into the intestine as adults. In some cases an invertebrate intermediate host (fleas, beetles) may be involved. The ruminant tapeworm (*Moniezia*, Fig. 7-24) occurs in sheep and other ruminants and has certain mites for its intermediate host. *Taenia solium* (Fig. 7-29, *A*), or the pork tapeworm, is found in man; the pig is the intermediate host. Hydatid tapeworms (*Echinococcus*) occur in dogs and related species with man and other vertebrates as the intermediate hosts.

Annotated references

Ax, R. Relationships and phylogeny of the Turbellaria. In Dougherty, E. C. (editor). 1963. The lower Metazoa; comparative biology and phylogeny. Berkeley, University of California Press. *Although the author believes in a monophyletic origin of the Bilateria, he removes the Turbellaria as direct ancestors of more recent groups except the other two classes of Platyhelminthes. According to his scheme the early ancestor for most protostomes was provided with a coelom.*

Brown, F. A., Jr. (editor). 1950. Selected invertebrate types. New York, John Wiley & Sons, Inc. *Good laboratory directions for flatworm types of all classes are given.*

Bullough, W. S. 1958. Practical invertebrate anatomy. London, The Macmillan Company. *Practical descriptions of the anatomy of representatives of the Platyhelminthes are given in Chapter 5.*

Chandler, A. C. 1952. Introduction to parasitology. New York, John Wiley & Sons, Inc. *A good account is given of trematodes and tapeworms in Chapters 12 and 13. Well illustrated with schematic life histories.*

Cheng, T. C. 1964. The biology of animal parasites. Philadelphia, W. B. Saunders Co. *A comprehensive treatise with special emphasis on the natural history and ecology of flatworms and other parasites.*

Goodrich, E. S. 1945. The study of nephridia and genital ducts since 1895. Quart. J. Micr. Sci. **86**:113-392. *An important article that summarizes the problems of the gonocoel theory of coelom formation, genital ducts, and nephridia.*

Graff, L. von. Acoela and Rhabdocoela. In Bronn, H. G. (editor). 1904-1908. Klassen und Ordnungen des Tierreichs, vol. 4, part 1. Leipzig, Akademische Verlagsgesellschaft. *A definitive account of these two orders by a great specialist.*

Grasse, P. P. (editor). 1961. Traite de zoologie, anatomie, systematique, biologie, Tome IV: Platyhelminthes, Mesozaires, Acanthocephales, Nemertiens. (Premier Fascicule). Paris, Masson et Cie. *The most recent account of these four groups in one of the most authoritative treatises in the field of zoologic scholarship.*

Hanson, E. D. 1958. On the origin of the Eumetazoa. Syst. Zool. **7**:16-47.

Hyman, L. H. 1951. The invertebrates: Platyhelminthes and Rhynchocoela; the acoelomate Bilateria, vol. 2. New York, McGraw-Hill Book Company. *The best general up-to-date account that is available at present. In volume 5 (1959) of this treatise a section is devoted to summarizing the more recent work on the flatworms.*

Hyman, L. H., and E. R. Jones. Turbellaria. In Edmondson, W. T. (editor). 1959. Ward and Whipple's fresh-water biology, ed. 2. *Methods of collecting and preparation of specimens as well as keys and figures of the freshwater forms.*

Isseroff, W. J. 1964. Fine structure of the eyespot in the miracidium of *Philophthalmus megalurels* (Cort, 1914). J. Parasitol. **50**:548-554.

Jennings, J. B. 1957. Studies on feeding, digestion, and food storage in free-living flatworms. Biol. Bull. **12**(3):571-581. *This paper describes in detail how certain turbellarians ingest and digest their food. Digestion is both extracellular and intracellular, although the size of ingested particles is often the determining factor.*

Karling, T. G. Some evolutionary trends in turbellarian morphology. In Dougherty, E. C. (editor). 1963. The lower Metazoa; comparative biology and phylogeny. Berkeley, University of California Press. *The author shows how the evolution of the group is limited by the specific structure and organization of turbellarian tissue. Ecologic and functional principles indicate how evolution had to follow certain lines.*

Kimmel, G. 1958. Das Terminolorgan der Protonephridien, Feinstrukter und Dentung der Funktion. Z. Naturforsch [B] **136**:677-679. *A description of the fine structure of flame cells.*

Martin, W. E. 1944. Studies on trematodes of Woods Hole IV; additional observations upon *Cercaria looss* Stunkard developing in an annelid. Trans. Am. Micr. Soc. **63**:237-243.

Martin, W. E. 1952. Another annelid first intermediate host of a digenetic trematode. J. Parasitol. **38**:1-4. *These two reports by Martin indicate the rare exceptions in which a group other than mollusks acts as the first intermediate host.*

Olsen, O. W. 1962. Animal parasites; their biology and life cycles. Minneapolis, Burgess Publishing Co. *The author emphasizes illustrated schemes of parasitic life cycles. Concise descriptions are also given. An excellent treatise.*

Rothman, A. H. 1963. Electron microscopic studies of tapeworms; the surface structures of *Hymenolepis diminuta* (Rudolphi, 1819) (Blanchard, 1891). Trans. Am. Micr. Soc. **82**:22-30.

Threadgold, L. T. 1962. An electron microscope study of the tegument and associated structures of *Dipylidium caninum*. Quart. J. Micr. Sci. **103**:135-140. *This study shows that the cuticle of cestodes is made up of living cells and must be considered an epidermis.*

Threadgold, L. T. 1963. The tegument and associated structures of *Fasciola hepatica*. Quart. J. Micr. Sci. **104**:505-512. *The cuticle is considered to be a surface layer of protoplasm that is an extension of flasklike, nucleated cells of the interior.*

Wardle, R. A., and J. A. McLeod. 1952. The zoology of tapeworms. Minneapolis, University of Minnesota Press. *A pretentious and comprehensive treatise on these highly specialized parasites.*

Phylum Rhynchocoela (Nemertina)

This group of worms, along with the Platyhelminthes, belongs to the acoelomate Bilateria. The Rhynchocoela are commonly known as ribbon worms or nemertine worms. They are elongated, thread-shaped or ribbon-shaped worms that are often cylindric in cross section. They are nonsegmented and are without external appendages. Their epidermis is ciliated, and they are provided with an eversible proboscis in a sheath just above the enteron. With one or two exceptions, all are marine forms that live mostly in muddy or sandy bottoms beneath shells and stones. They are common in coral habitats and often secrete gelatinous tubes in which they live. Many are brightly colored. About 570 species are classified so far. Most species are only a few inches long, but some may reach a length of several meters. Their general organization bears many resemblances to the Platyhelminthes, in which they have often been included as a separate class. They resemble the flatworms in having the space between enteron, epithelium, and epidermis filled with parenchyma and muscle. They have also, like the flatworms, developed the creeping habit of locomotion and have a ciliated epidermis; but, in general organization, nemertines are more highly developed than Platyhelminthes. They have a complete digestive system (mouth and anus), a circulatory system, and a mouth at the anterior end instead of midventrally. They also possess the eversible tubular proboscis altogether lacking in the flatworms. Nemertines, however, have a much simpler reproductive system than Platyhelminthes, and the sexes are usually separate. In contrast to the parasitic habits of most flatworms, ribbon worms are all free living with the exception of a few commensal species.

CLASSIFICATION

The 500 or so species are divided into two classes (or subclasses by some authorities), each of which is subdivided into two orders. The class distinction is based mainly upon the structure of the proboscis and the location of the longitudinal nerves with respect to the muscular layers.

Phylum Rhynchocoela. Body bilaterally symmetric, dorsoventrally flattened or cylindric, and acoelomate; nonsegmented, vermiform shape; body covered by ciliated epidermis; body soft, slimy, and very elastic; eversible proboscis in sheath dorsal to enteron; complete digestive system; excretory system with flame cells; blood vascular system; nervous system of brain and lateral nerves; brain with cerebral organs; body wall musculature of two or three layers; separate sexes usually; gonads of simple sacs; spiral determinate cleavage; pilidium larva in some.

Class Anopla. Mouth posterior to brain; central nervous system just below epidermis or in muscle layers of body wall; proboscis unarmed.

Order Palaeonemertini (Protonemertini). Body wall musculature of two dermal layers—external circular and internal longitudinal—or sometimes with a third innermost circular layer; nervous system external to circular muscles; no cecum to intestine; dermis gelatinous. *Tubulanus* (Fig. 8-8), *Cephalothrix.*

Order Heteronemertini. Body wall musculature of three layers—outer longitudinal, middle circular, and inner longitudinal; lateral nerve cords lie in dermal muscles; enteron with diverticula; no cecum; dermis fibrous. *Cerebratulus, Lineus.*

Class Enopla. Mouth anterior to brain; nervous system inside dermal muscles in parenchyma; proboscis usually with stylet.

Order Hoplonemertini. Proboscis has stylet apparatus with single or many stylets; enteron with diverticula and cecum. *Nemertopsis, Amphiporus* (Fig. 8-3), *Prostoma.*

Order Bdellonemertini. Proboscis unarmed; sinuous intestine without diverticula; esophagus and proboscis open into anterior common chamber; ectocommensal; no intestinal cecum; adhesive disk at posterior end. *Malacobdella.*

BASIC ADAPTIVE FEATURES

The most characteristic organ of the nemertines is the proboscis that is present in some form throughout the group. A separate terminal opening for the proboscis is usually found. This organ, more than any other characteristic, is probably responsible for the lack of parasitism in a group that shares many of the features of its near relatives, the Platyhelminthes, which have so largely adopted the parasitic life. The proboscis is well suited for capturing prey, for defense, and for burrowing habits. The elaborate innervation of the proboscis may indicate that one of its principal functions, at first, was that of a highly sensitive organ for detecting environmental relations. As evidence for this view, it has been observed that many nemertines continually shoot the proboscis backward and forward at the anterior end very much like a snake flipping its tongue in and out. In its later evolution, when it became a strongly muscular organ, additional uses were made of the proboscis. The extensive and forceful use the worm makes of this organ often causes the proboscis to be partly or wholly detached and expelled from the body. In such cases the proboscis is usually regenerated without delay.

Since nemertines are free living and fairly active, their evolution shows greatly stressed advancements in organization over the flatworm plan. Although the enteron is attached to the body wall by the cellular parenchyma that fills the space between body wall and intestine, the different arrangments of the muscle layers in its subdivisions may indicate a tendency to overcome the handicap imposed by the continuity of intestine and body wall. This tendency has resulted in a general organizational plan similar to that of higher forms, having a body wall of epidermis, dermis, and musculature; a complete digestive system for one-way traffic of food; a circulatory system for efficient distribution of food and gases; and a more centralized nervous system of brain, lateral nerve cords, and sense organs for effective nervous coordination.

PHYLOGENETIC RELATIONSHIPS

Zoologists are agreed that the Rhynchocoela resemble the Platyhelminthes more than any other group. As long ago as 1890, O. Bürger, a great student of the group, had suggested that the nemertines were closer in their affinities to the turbellarians than they were to the Annelida, a phylum from which the Rhynchocoela may have been derived. Evidence of flatworm affinities is indicated by the acoelomate condition, the abundant parenchyma between body wall and enteron, the nature of the epidermis, the general musculature, the plan of the nervous system, the structure of sense organs (ocelli, sensory pits, etc.), similarity of serologic tests between the two phyla, and other similarities. Bürger also emphasized the possibility that the nemertine proboscis is homologous with the turbellarian pharynx. L. H. Hyman has advanced the more specific view that the proboscis is derived from such a structure as the anterior protrusible proboscis of certain rhabdocoels (Kalyptorhynchia). The rhabdocoel structure is employed in seizing and manipulating prey in much the same way as the nemertine uses its proboscis. As additional evidence, the pilidium larva of Rhynchocoela is without an anus—a flatworm characteristic—and rhabdites are present in some (Fig. 8-1). As for any annelid characteristics possessed by nemertines, it is possible that the ribbon worms have copied, by convergent evolution, those annelid features that have fitted into their evolutionary development. In brief, the higher organizational features of the nemertean worm over the flatworm have been evolutionary variations of an acoelomate bilateral body pattern first given to the animal kingdom by the Platyhelminthes.

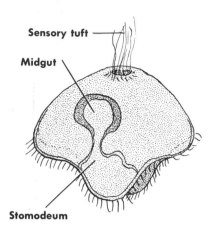

Fig. 8-1

Pilidium larva of Rhynchocoela (early stage). This larva has mouth but no anus, a flatworm characteristic.

GENERAL MORPHOLOGIC FEATURES

Nemertines in their general appearance resemble the Platyhelminthes. They have soft, slender bodies that are highly elastic. The anterior part, which may be lancet shaped or heart shaped, is usually broader than the rest of the body but is really not a head because it lacks the brain. In the forepart of the body the worm is somewhat cylindric and becomes flattened posteriorly, but many variations exist. The outer investment in all species consists of an epidermis of ciliated cells. The epidermis is provided with many unicellular glands, which are principal sources of the mucus with which nemertines are all liberally supplied. Sometimes a cluster of glands is located in the subepidermis and has a common opening to the exterior. Pigments that produce the various colors of orange, red, brown, etc. are principally located in the epidermis, but in some cases the pigments may lie deeper. In some species these pigments may produce stripes or transverse bars. A basement membrane of connective tissue (dermis or cutis) is usually present between the epidermis and the body musculature. In the heteronemerteans this cutis is divided into an outer layer of glands and an inner layer of connective tissue.

The muscular layers that form most of the body wall are not arranged the same way in all orders or even in lower taxa. In those worms that belong to the orders Pa-

laeonemertini, Hoplonemertini, and Bdellonemertini, the musculature consists chiefly of outer circular and inner longitudinal muscle layers; in the order Heteronemertini an outer longitudinal layer, a middle circular layer, and an inner longitudinal layer exist (Fig. 8-2). Some slight variations from this plan also occur.

The region between the enteron and body wall musculature is usually filled with parenchyma or mesenchyme. This mesenchyme is directly continuous with that in which the muscle layers are embedded. Dorsoventral muscle bands course through the mesenchyme and connect ventral and dorsal walls as well as surround the digestive tube. Mesenchyme is made up of an intracellular gelatinous substance in which nuclei are everywhere present. In some cases it is fibrous and consists of branched cells. Mesenchyme may be scanty in forms where the musculature largely replaces it.

Clusters of cephalic, or frontal, glands that open by a common pore above the proboscis pore are found in most Rhynchocoela. These glands may be homologous to the frontal glands of flatworms and may have the same function.

The characteristic proboscis apparatus is made up of a long, eversible, tubular proboscis, a short, anterior canal, or rhynchodeum, that opens anteriorly, and a long cavity, or rhynchocoel, in which the proboscis lies (Fig. 8-3). The tubular proboscis is blind at its inner end and is usually much longer than the body. It opens anteriorly into the rhynchodeum, which, in turn, usually opens by a pore to the outside just above the mouth. The muscular wall surrounding the rhynchocoel constitutes the proboscis sheath. The anterior, or open, end of the proboscis is fastened to the inner end of the rhynchodeum, and the posterior, or blind, end is attached by a retractor muscle to the posterior end of the proboscis sheath. The rhynchocoel, which is a completely closed cavity, is filled with a corpuscular fluid, and when the muscles of the proboscis sheath contract, the pressure on the fluid causes the proboscis to be everted and shot out of the proboscis pore (Fig. 8-4). The retractor muscle at the end of the proboscis then pulls back rapidly the extruded proboscis, aided somewhat by the musculature of the head. The proboscis is

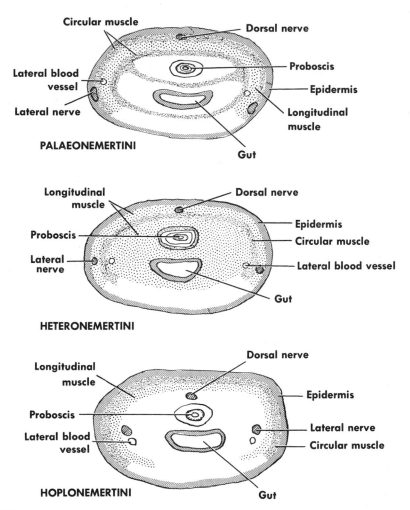

Fig. 8-2

Diagrammatic transverse sections of three orders of nemertines to show different arrangement of muscular layers and other structures. Cilia not shown.

never completely everted because of the retractor muscle, and in the armed specimens or those with stylets there is a muscular diaphragm or bulb that closes off the anterior proboscis at the point of projection. This diaphragm is provided with a stylet and pouches of reserve stylets. When the proboscis is shot forward, or everted, it seizes the prey by coiling around it, by glandular secretions of the proboscis wall, or by the stabbing action of the stylet. In some species, nematocysts and rhabdites appear on the everted surface of the proboscis for overcoming the prey. Some differences exist in the structure of the pro-

boscis in the different groups. In *Malacobdella* and a few others, for instance, there is a single opening for both the proboscis and the mouth (Fig. 8-5). The structure of the proboscis apparatus is similar to the body wall with the layers in reverse (in the resting state), because it has originated as an ectodermal invagination. Since the rhynchocoel is formed by a split in the musculature, which is separated into proboscis muscles and proboscis sheath muscles, the rhynchocoel is considered a true schizocoel coelom.

The digestive system is complete in nemertines with both mouth and anus (Fig.

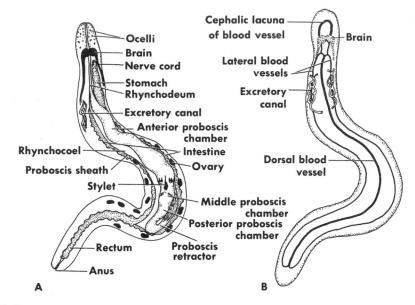

Fig. 8-3

A, Dorsal view of female *Amphiporus* (order Hoplonemertini) (from life). **B,** Diagram of circulatory and excretory system of *Amphiporus*.

Fig. 8-4

Proboscis of nemertine extended in seizing prey.

8-6). The round or slitlike mouth is ventrally located near the tip of the head and in front of or behind the brain in most; in a few species, however, it has a more posterior location. The alimentary canal is a straight tube that is divided into foregut and intestine. The foregut consists of the buccal cavity, esophagus, and stomach, divisions not apparent in some. The lining epithelium of this portion is similar to the epidermis with many gland cells. The intestine (richly supplied with glands) usually lacks its own musculature and may be provided with diverticula and a caecum. Movement of the food is accomplished mainly by cilia. At the posterior end of the

body is the rectum and anus. Digestion appears to be both extracellular and intracellular. Most nemertines are highly voracious, living on annelids, other worms, crustaceans, etc. Food seems to be digested, absorbed, and excreted very rapidly. Many nemertines can undergo starvation for months and still survive. In such cases the body may be reduced to one-twentieth of its original size.

The nemertines are the simplest animals that possess a circulatory system. The system is a closed type, and the blood is restricted to vessels and spaces (lacunae). The chief vessels are three longitudinal trunks—a median and two lateral ones—connected at both the anterior and posterior ends (Figs. 8-3, *B*, 8-7). Various modifications of this plan exist. The lateral vessels often give off a network of lacunae to the wall of the foregut. The middorsal trunk, when present, runs anteriorly in the floor of the rhynchocoel and posteriorly beneath the proboscis sheath. It unites at the posterior end with the lateral vessels by means of anal lacunae. The blood fluid does not flow in any definite direction because its movements are influenced by the muscular

Fig. 8-5

Longitudinal section through anterior region of hoplonemertine, a type in which esophagus enters rhynchodeum and separate mouth is lacking.

body wall and, to some extent, by the muscular walls of the larger blood vessels. In most cases the blood fluid is colorless and contains definite nucleated corpuscles (oval or round) and amebocytes. Some nemertines have blood colored by pigments of orange, green, and red, which are carried in the corpuscles. In some species the red color is due to hemoglobin.

The excretory system is composed of a single pair of protonephridial tubules that are closely associated with the lateral blood vessels (Fig. 8-7). Usually the tubules are restricted to the anterior region, which may mark a tendency to bring the products of excretion to a definite spot of the vascular system. On each side of the foregut region there is a nephridiopore from which a tubule extends anteriorly. On its inner surface each tubule gives rise to terminal flame bulbs that push in and indent the blood vessels, forming small blind caeca reminiscent of the glomeruli of higher forms. In some cases the blood vessel wall may disappear in that region so that the flame bulbs are directly bathed by blood. Many modifications of the system exist among different nemertines. In certain palaeonemertines a ridge of protonephridial capillaries forms a nephridial gland that lacks flame bulbs and whose capillaries open into the blood. In some species the protonephridia give rise to many capillaries and flame bulbs applied to the lateral blood vessels and foregut la-

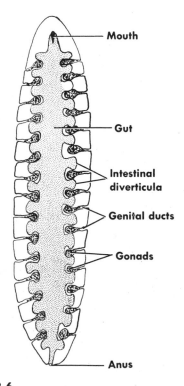

Fig. 8-6

Diagram of digestive and reproductive systems of nemertine. (Modied from Lang.)

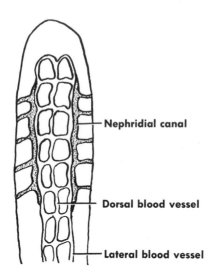

— Nephridial canal

— Dorsal blood vessel

— Lateral blood vessel

Fig. 8-7

Diagram of excretory and circulatory systems of anterior region of a nemertine worm.

cunae; in a few the excretory tubules extend into the alimentary canal. In the fresh-water *Prostoma* and some others, an extensive branching of the excretory system into capillaries and flame bulbs throughout the tissues occurs. A single protonephridium in these species may be broken up into smaller tubules, each with its nephridiopore to the exterior. The flame bulbs of nemertines may be a single cell or a cluster of cells. Large mesenchymal cells known as athrocytes may surround the flame bulbs and tubules and may be excretory in function.

With few exceptions, nemertines are dioecious. A notable exception is the hermaphroditic *Prostoma* that is also viviparous. In contrast with the complicated arrangement of Platyhelminthes the nemertean reproductive system is quite simple. In the usual plan the gonads are a series of sacs lined with epithelium that alternate with the diverticula of the intestine (Fig. 8-6). When mature, each sac forms a genital duct to the exterior for the discharge of the gametes. These genital openings usually form a line dorsal to the lateral nerve. The whole sac, or gonad, with its epithelial wall and genital cells arises from cells of the parenchyma. Sexual dimorphism is not evident, although the males of some species are provided with cirri or copulatory

projections of the male pores. Also, at sexual maturity, each sex may have a different color because of the ripe sex cells seen through the transparent walls. Each ovary may produce only one egg (hoplonemertines) or as many as fifty (palaeonemertines and heteronemertines). The eggs are usually discharged by body contractions. In spawning there may be external fertilization without contact of the sexes, or the male may discharge its sperm as it crawls over the female. Several worms may be enclosed in a mucous sheath where fertilization occurs. Self-fertilization often occurs in hermaphroditic species. The eggs are often laid in gelatinous strings produced by secretions of glands from the body walls.

The nervous system consists of a brain made up of lobes or ganglia, two longitudinal lateral cords, and many smaller nerves (Figs. 8-2, 8-3). The ganglia are generally four in number consisting of a dorsal and a ventral pair (Fig. 8-5). The dorsal ganglia are connected by a dorsal commissure above the rhynchodeum; the ventral pair are connected by a ventral commissure below the rhynchodeum. Through this ring of nervous tissue the proboscis apparatus passes. The ventral ganglia of the brain connect to the two main longitudinal nerve trunks, which are united by the anal commissure above or below the intestine. These longitudinal nerve trunks are made up of one continuous, unsegmented mass of fibrous and cellular nervous tissue and usually do not possess ganglionic swellings anywhere along their course. From the cerebral ganglia, nerves are given off anteriorly to the eyes and other sense organs, and from the lateral trunks small branches pass to the body wall; commissures connect the lateral nerves with each other. The nervous system of nemertines may be considered as local longitudinal accumulations of the less differentiated nerve plexus of primitive ancestors such as coelenterates. Various degrees of sinking of the nervous system from the epidermis to regions internal to the body wall musculature are found in the different orders with the more primitive epidermal position found among the palaeonemertines. In addition to the main lateral cords there also exist, in some forms, minor nerves such as a middorsal nerve, midventral nerve, paired esophageal nerves, and others. The proboscis is especially well supplied with nervous tissue of a primitive nerve plexus type.

A respiratory system is lacking, and exchange of gases occurs by direct diffusion.

Sense organs of a tactile function are widely scattered in the epidermis. These are slender cells with projecting bristles. Chemotactile organs in cephalic slits or grooves or in protrusible frontal organs are found. Eyes are of constant occurrence, although many heteronemertines and some others appear to be blind. Eyes are restricted to the anterior region in front of the brain and are located in the dermis, musculature, or parenchyma (Fig. 8-3). The eyes are mostly of the inverted type of pigment cell ocelli such as are found in flatworms. Simpler and more primitive types of eyes, some only of pigment specks without refracting apparatus, are present in some species. Eyes may number from two to many hundreds. Most nemertines also have a pair of cerebral organs forming two blind, invaginated canals from the epidermis. The inner ends of these canals are surrounded by glands and nerve cells near the dorsal brain ganglia. Their external openings are by way of cephalic grooves or on the body surface. Their function is probably chemotactile as they are richly supplied with nerves from the brain.

Nemertines have spiral and determinate cleavage so that the potentialities of future development are fixed in the zygote before cleavage begins. In some cases the micromeres of the quartets are larger than the macromeres. Development involves the formation of a typical ciliated coeloblastula, and the endoderm is formed by either embolic or epibolic invagination of the macromeres with the fourth quartet of micromeres. In some nemertines, however, a stereoblastula is formed first and later acquires a cavity. In certain nemertines, after early cleavage, development is direct without a larval stage, and the embryo emerges from the egg membranes as a small, ciliated worm. In others, including the familiar *Cerebratulus*, the gastrula develops into a free-swimming, ciliated larva, the pilidium (Fig. 8-1). This helmet-shaped larva is formed by the downward growth of a pair of ciliated oral lobes at the sides of the mouth and bears an apical spike of long cilia. The larval enteron with ectodermal foregut and endodermal midgut has a mouth but no anus (a flatworm characteristic). The blastocoel is filled with a gelatinous fluid and ameboid mesenchymal cells. A similar larva, but without the apical spike and oral lobes, occurs in some other nemertines and is called a Desor larva. Both the pilidium and the Desor larva undergo metamorphosis by ectodermal invaginations called disks, which grow around the enteron, fuse together, and form the epidermis, nervous system, muscular body wall, and other structures of the future nemertine. The young nemertine becomes ciliated, frees itself from the surrounding pilidium investment, and develops into the adult worm.

Regeneration is usually quite common; nemertines have many enemies (annelids, crustaceans, etc.), and loss of body parts is frequent. Some worms may be broken into fragments, each of which may then give rise to a new worm (asexual reproduction). In others more restricted regeneration occurs. Posterior regions are usually easily regenerated, anterior or head regions rarely. The proboscis is often lost and is always regenerated.

CLASS ANOPLA
Order Palaeonemertini

The body wall of the Palaeonemertini is either two-layered or three-layered. If two-layered, the musculature is composed of outer circular and inner longitudinal muscles; if three-layered, the inner and outer muscle layers are circular with the longitudinal layer between. The nervous system usually lies external to the outer circular layer, although it may lie deeper. A middorsal blood vessel and connections between the lateral vessels are usually lacking, and the intestine has a smooth contour. Eyes and cerebral organs are mostly absent. The dermis is gelatinous. In general this order is the most primitively organized of all the nemertines.

Cephalothrix, a common nemertine along the New England coast, is a slender worm about 3 inches long with a long, pointed anterior end. The mouth is on the ventral side of the yellowish or flesh-colored body behind the brain. Other genera of this order are *Tubulanus* (Fig. 8-8) with a

203

Fig. 8-8

Ribbon worm, *Tubulanus annulatus* (order Palaeonemertini). May be several feet long; common along European shores. (Courtesy Encyclopaedia Britannica Films, Inc.)

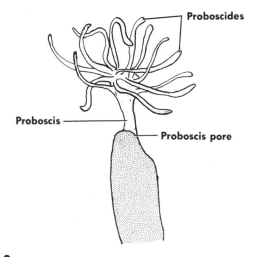

Fig. 8-9

Diagram of head region of *Gorgonorhynchus* (order Heteronemertini). Proboscis may be divided into 30 or more proboscides. Some zoologists think this genus arose suddenly by evolutionary saltation (Wheeler).

broad, rounded cephalic lobe at the anterior end; *Carinina* with the cerebral organs in the form of canals; and *Procephalothrix*, similar to *Cephalothrix*.

Order Heteronemertini

The Heteronemertini have a body wall composed of three muscular layers: an outer longitudinal layer, a middle circular layer, and an inner longitudinal layer. The nervous system lies between the first two muscular layers. A middorsal blood vessel including transverse connections with the lateral blood vessels is present. Cerebral organs usually occur, and the intestine is provided with diverticula but with no cecum.

The most common genus along the Atlantic coast is the large form *Cerebratulus*, which may reach a length of 20 feet and a width of an inch. The body of this familiar flesh-colored nemertine is adapted for swimming by having a thick, narrow anterior end and an expanded, flattened posterior region with very thin margins. It is often found in burrows. Through the terminal proboscis pore the slender proboscis may be extended for more than 3 feet in the larger specimens. In the strange *Gorgonorhynchus* the proboscis is divided into many proboscides (Fig. 8-9). *Lineus* is another well-known genus with a slender, rounded, highly contractile body. Six pairs of eyes are found in the head region of *L. socialis*, which grows to almost a foot in length with a width of ¼ inch. The members of this species are often found together in tangled masses. This species and some others can reproduce by fragmentation and their regenerative powers are especially good. *Micrura* is similar to *Cerebratulus*, and some of its species are considered transitional between the two genera. Some are bright red or orange in color.

CLASS ENOPLA
Order Hoplonemertini

The members of this order are the only nemertines that possess a proboscis armed with a stylet apparatus (Fig. 8-3, *A*). Some have a single stylet and others have many stylets, a condition that causes the order to be divided into two suborders, Monostylifera and Polystylifera. The stylet, or stylets, are situated at the boundary between the eversible and noneversible portions of the proboscis. By this arrangement, when the proboscis reaches its maximum eversion, the stylet apparatus is terminally situated for puncturing the prey. Members of the order possess an intestine with lateral diverticula and a cecum. They have a middorsal blood vessel connected to the lateral vessels. Freshwater, terrestrial, marine, and commensal forms are found in this order.

Amphiporus (Fig. 8-3) is a common marine genus that is much studied. The members of this genus are usually short bodied; most are within the range of ½ to 5 inches in length. They have numerous eyes on the sides and back of the head, and shallow cerebral grooves are present. Their intestinal diverticula and long cecum are branched.

Prostoma (Stichostemma) is the only genus of nemertines that lives in fresh water. Some species of this genus are strictly hermaphroditic with saclike ovotestis, although others are dioecious. *P. rubrum,* the most widely distributed species, is about 20 mm. long and is somewhat reddish in color, although other shades are found. It has a proboscis two or three times the length of the body; in the quiescent stage it is coiled within the rhynchocoel. The single stylet, when lost, is replaced by accessory stylets from lateral pockets in the bulb region of the proboscis. This species appears to be most common in the autumn, when it may be found in masses of filamentous algae and other aquatics. Under harsh weather conditions the worm forms a cyst of hardened mucus where it may live for several weeks, although the cyst cannot withstand dessication. Development of the eggs, which are laid in a mucous sheath, is direct, and the young emerge as juveniles. Several European species of similar habits belong to this genus.

Other hoplonemertines include *Geonemertes,* a terrestrial genus widely distributed in tropical and subtropical regions; *Carcinonemertes,* an ectocommensal on the gills of crabs and provided with a common sperm duct into which all the testes discharge; and *Tetrastemma,* common along seashores and endocommensal in tunicates.

Order Bdellonemertini

This order of a single genus *(Malacobdella)* consists of three species, all of which are commensals that feed on plankton in the mantle chamber or pulmonary sac of mollusks. The poorly developed proboscis does not bear a stylet, and the worms are devoid of cerebral organs, eyes, and other special sense structures. The proboscis pore and mouth form a common opening to the outside. At their posterior end, members bear an adhesive disk for attachment. Their vascular system contains a middorsal vessel and lateral vessels that are freely branched. The worm is usually 1 to 2 inches long, although it may be smaller.

Annotated references

Bohmig, L. Nemertini. In Kukenthal, W., and T. Krumbach (editors). 1929. Handbuch der Zoologie, vol. 2, part 1, section 3. Berlin, Walter de Gruyter & Co. *An excellent technical account.*

Bürger, O. 1890. Anatomie und Histologie der Nemertinen. Z. Wiss. Zool. **50:**1-279. *This and other monographs are classic studies of the nemertines.*

Coe, W. R. 1943. Biology of the nemerteans of the Atlantic coast of North America. Hartford, Transactions of Connecticut Academy of Arts and Science **35:**129-328. *One of many valuable papers on the Rhynchocoela by this author.*

Grasse, P. P. (editor). 1961. Traite de zoologie, anatomie, systematique, biologie, Tome IV: Platyhelminthes, Mesozaires, Acanthocephales, Nemertiens. (Premier Fascicule.) Paris, Masson et Cie.

Hyman, L. H. 1951. The invertebrates: Platyhelminthes and Rhynchocoela; the acoelomate Bilateria. New York, McGraw-Hill Book Company. *The best general treatment in English of the Rhynchocoela.*

Jennings. J. B. Some aspects of nutrition in the Turbellaria, Trematoda, and Rhynchocoela. In Dougherty, E. C. (editor). 1963. The lower Metazoa; comparative biology and phylogeny. Berkeley, University of California Press. *A concise description of the methods by which nemertines capture and digest their prey. Their extracellular and intracellular methods of digestion are appropriate to either a predatory or parasitic mode of life, although the former method is mostly employed.*

Pennak, R. W. 1953. Fresh-water invertebrates of the United States. New York, The Ronald Press Company. *An excellent description of the structure and life history of the freshwater nemertine* Prostoma rubrum.

Phylum Aschelminthes

The bilateral animals include the acoelomates (phyla Platyhelminthes and Rhynchocoela), pseudocoelomates (phyla Aschelminthes, Acanthocephala, and Entoprocta), and eucoelomates (other bilateral phyla). It will be noted that this convenient division of the major groups of bilateral animals is based upon the presence or absence of some form of body cavity (Fig. 9-1). In the acoelomates the space between the enteron and the body wall is filled with mesenchyme or parenchyma (mesoderm). In the pseudocoelomates the original blastocoel of the blastula makes up a space, or pseudocoel, between enteron and body wall without a peritoneal lining. The eucoelomates, or animals with a true body cavity, have a space formed in the endomesoderm or embryonic mesoderm that completely obliterates the blastocoel. Most phyla possess a true coelom and thus belong to the coelomate group.

A true coelom is, therefore, the space between the body wall and digestive system, surrounded on all sides by endomesoderm with a lining of peritoneum. Embryology teaches us that the mesoderm found on the inner surface of the body wall is the somatic or parietal mesoderm, and that part which is reflected over the viscera is the splanchnic mesoderm. The peritoneum is an epithelial specialization of the mesoderm that lines both the inside of the body wall (parietal peritoneum) and covers the exposed surfaces of protruding visceral organs (visceral peritoneum). The mesenteries that provide support for visceral organs are composed mostly of peritoneum.

The development of a coelomic cavity has been of the utmost importance in the evolutionary patterns of animals. The lack of such a cavity greatly restricts the differentiation of organs for special purposes. In a form such as hydra, for instance, transient gonads must lie on the outside surface of the body because there is no other place for them. When the space between body wall and enteron is filled with mesenchyme, the digestive system must increase absorptive surface by branching instead of by elongated coils. A coelom provides spaces for waste products and also for the development of sex cells.

The formation of the coelom is correlated with the formation of endomesoderm. In this respect animals follow one or the other of two methods, the schizocoelous and the enterocoelous. In the schizocoelous method, which may be the primitive one, the coelom arises by a split in a solid mesodermal band which may or may not segment into somites, depending upon whether or not the animal belongs to the segmented group. In whatever way formed, the split expands, pushing the mesoderm against the body wall and the wall of the enteron. The cavity produced between these two mesodermal regions is the coelom. In the enterocoelous method the coelom originates from mesodermal outpocketings of the primitive gut, or archenteron. These pockets are pinched off, fuse together, and expand until they touch the body wall and enteron, thus producing a space (coelom) enclosed within mesoderm. The schizocoelous method is

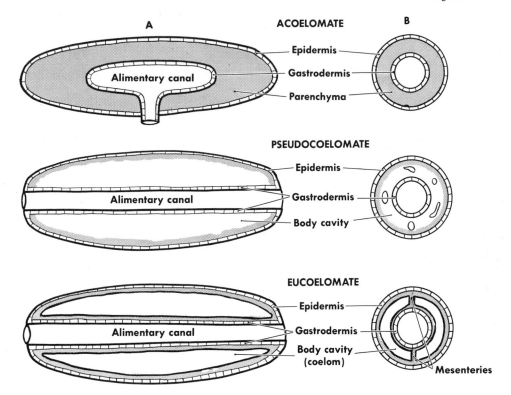

Fig. 9-1

Types of body cavity organization in Bilateria. In pseudocoelomate type, mesoderm may form lining around inner surface of body wall but not around enteron. (From Hickman: Integrated principles of zoology, The C. V. Mosby Co.)

characteristic of Protostomia, and the enterocoelous method characterizes the Deuterostomia.

The phylum Aschelminthes (cavity worms) is a heterogeneous group of vermiform animals and includes most of the pseudocoelomate members of the animal kingdom. Most members of the group are unsegmented or superficially segmented and are often cylindric in body form. Most are small, even microscopic, but some attain a considerable length. The phylum in general is made up of an odd assortment of classes that do, however, share enough common characteristics to be placed together.

The body is covered with a scleroprotein cuticle that often bears spines, scales, and other skeletal structures. In many members the cuticle undergoes regular molting during the growth period of the life cycle. The epidermis may be cellular but is often syncytial. Underneath the epidermis the muscular layers are usually not well defined. Adhesive glands are common throughout the group. Members possess a complete digestive system that is usually straight and without a muscular wall. The pharynx is very highly specialized in some. An excretory system of protonephridia occurs in most classes. The circulatory and respiratory systems are absent. The phylum as a whole is characterized by cell or nuclear constancy for a particular species, and cilia are either absent or greatly reduced. Most members are dioecious, and the reproductive systems are simple. Cleavage is mostly of the spiral determinate type, but in some cases it does not fit into either the spiral or radial types. Both aquatic and terrestrial members are present in the group. Parasitism is fairly common.

At the present time the phylum Aschelminthes consists of five classes. The Priapulida, formerly included as a class under this phylum, is now placed in a phylum of its own. Work of W. L. Shapeero and others

207

plainly shows that the priapulids have a true coelom (eucoelomate) and that their cleavage is of the radial type. Zoologists have long been in doubt about the taxonomic status of this group. With the exception of the classes Rotifera and Nematoda, the known species in each class are few in number. Although only a few thousand nematode species have been classified, it is the opinion of students of the group that this number represents only a small fraction of the actual species.

CLASSIFICATION

Phylum Aschelminthes. Body bilaterally symmetric, vermiform, mostly cylindric or sometimes flattened, and pseudocoelomate; nonsegmented; well-developed cuticle with cellular or syncytial epidermis; digestive tract complete without definite muscular walls; pharynx often specialized; no respiratory or circulatory systems; excretory system mostly of the protonephridial type; reproduction mostly dioecious with simple reproductive system; life cycle simple or involved; cleavage mostly of a modified spiral determinate type; cell or nuclear constancy common; freshwater, marine, or terrestrial; free living, commensal, parasitic; 12,-000 to 15,000 named species.

Class Rotifera. Body somewhat cylindric with anterior ciliated disk (corona) and posterior forked tail or foot; body covered by a cuticle sometimes modified into hardened lorica; size microscopic to 3 mm. but most are not over 0.5 mm.; pharynx with movable jaws (mastax and trophi); trunk often with sensory antennae or palps; epidermis a syncytium; muscles mostly single and not forming layers; digestive tract mostly complete; excretory system of protonephridial tubes and flame bulbs; nervous system of ganglia and nerves; sense organs of membranelles, pits, and ocelli; reproduction dioecious with minute males (sometimes absent); parthenogenesis common; often oviparous; juvenile young; mostly freshwater; 1,500 species.

Order Seisonacea. Body elongated with small head and long neck; corona reduced; body with joined cuticle; foot stalklike with adhesive disk; pharynx with jaws; sexes similar; paired ovaries without vitellaria; no parthenogenesis; epizoic or parasitic; size to 3 mm. *Seison* (Fig. 9-8, *G*).

Order Bdelloidea. Body elongated with retractile head and foot; 15 to 18 cuticular joints or false segments; corona usually of a cingulum and two trochal disks on pedicles; mastax present; lorica absent; paired germovitellaria; males unknown; parthenogenesis of egg; oviparous or viviparous. *Philodina* (Fig. 9-8, *I*), *Rotaria*.

Order Monogononta. Body highly variable; lorica present or absent; foot of not more than two toes; mastax trophi of many types; males usually small or degenerate; one germovitellarium; eggs of three types (amictic, mictic, dormant); sessile or free swimming; parasitic (some). *Collotheca, Asplanchna* (Fig. 9-9), *Epiphanes* (Fig. 9-5).

Class Gastrotricha. Pseudocoelomate body somewhat vermiform and unsegmented with differentiated cuticle and restricted tracts of cilia; microscopic (minute to 1.5 mm.); ventrally flattened; syncytial epidermis with adhesive tube glands; no corona; pharynx without trophi but with bulbous enlargements; muscles mostly longitudinal and not in definite layers; enteron a straight tube with circular muscle fibers; protonephridia (in some); nervous system of a brain and a pair of lateral nerves; parthenogenetic females with two types of eggs in some, hermaphroditic individuals in others; development direct with total cleavage; short life cycle (3 to 21 days); marine and freshwater; 500 species.

Order Macrodasyoidea. Body elongated and cylindric with cuticular projections; adhesive tubes numerous; protonephridia absent; tail pointed or forked; hermaphroditic; marine. *Macrodasys, Cephalodasys*.

Order Chaetonotoidea. Body fusiform with head lobes and forked tail; head lobes with ciliary tufts and tail with one or two pairs of adhesive tubes; one pair of protonephridia; parthogenetic females; freshwater mostly. *Chaetonotus* (Fig. 9-12), *Ichthydium*.

Class Kinorhyncha. Body vermiform with superficial, nonciliated segments (13 to 14 zonites); head with circles of spines or scalids, completely retractable; neck with plates (placids); cuticle covered with bristles; epidermis mostly syncytial forming longitudinal cords; one pair of ventral adhesive tubes on third or fourth zonite; musculature segmentally arranged with a pair each of dorsolateral and ventrolateral longitudinal bands; muscles mostly cross-striated; muscular pharynx lined with syncytial epithelium; enteron straight with muscle layer; pseudocoel with fluid and amebocytes; one pair of protonephridia with flame bulbs; nervous system of a brain encircling the pharynx, a ventral ganglionated cord with a ganglion in each trunk zonite, and ganglia in the lateral and dorsal epidermal cords; reproduction dioecious, each sex with one pair of gonads; male with penial spicules; development largely unknown, but larval stages with molts occur. *Echinoderella* (Fig. 9-13, *A*), *Centroderes*.

Class Nematoda (Nemata). Body vermiform, cylindric, unsegmented, and pseudocoelomate; pointed at both ends; complex cuticle of many layers with various surface differentiations; no cilia; epidermis cellular or syncytial with four longitudinal cords; subepidermal musculature of a single layer of longitudinal fibers arranged in four quadrants between the epidermal cords; a pair of amphids (chemoreceptors) at anterior end; enteron complete with triradiate pharynx and esophagus adapted for suction; excretory system of gland cells (renette) or of intracellular canals without flame bulbs in lateral cords; nervous system of circumenteric ring (brain) with anterior and posterior longitudinal nerves; mostly dioecious with paired or single tubular gonads continuous with ducts; female genital opening (vulva) separate, male opening into cloaca; development direct with determinate and modified spiral cleavage; molts of cuticle and parts of enteron; young juvenile. [Classification of nematodes varies greatly. The most recent schemes are those of B. G. Chitwood and L. H. Hyman. The following scheme is emphasized by some zoologists.]

Subclass or superorder Secernentea (Phasmidia). Body usually with a pair of phasmids near posterior end; caudal glands absent; amphids reduced or porelike on lips; excretory system of lateral canals in cords; accessory copulatory organs mostly absent; mostly parasitic.

Order Rhabditida. Pharynx with two bulbs; pitlike amphids; free living or parasitic. *Rhabditis* (Fig. 9-21).

Order Tylenchida. Buccal stylet; lateral excretory canal on one side only; parasitic. *Tylenchus* (Fig. 9-18).

Order Strongylida. Mouth with small lips; pharynx without bulb; caudal bursa with rays; parasitic. *Ancylostoma, Necator.*

Order Ascaridida. Mouth usually with three large lips; intestine often with ceca; male with two penial spicules; parasitic. *Ascaris.*

Order Oxyuroidea (sometimes included with Ascaridida). Esophagus with posterior bulb; females with long pointed tail; sexual dimorphism usually pronounced; males may have one to two spicules or none; cuticular bursa usually present. *Enterobius* (Fig. 9-25), *Oxyuris.*

Order Spirurida. Mouth usually with two lateral lips; no bursa; spicules unequal; parasitic. *Gnathostoma* (Fig. 9-15, *A, B*), *Thelazia.*

Order Filarioidea (sometimes included under Spirurida). Body filiform; without lips; buccal capsule small or rudimentary; esophagus with anterior muscular and posterior glandular portions; vulva anteriorly; parasitic in blood and tissues of vertebrates. *Wuchereria, Filaria.*

Order Camallanida. Filiform body without definite lips; six large labial papillae; larval phasmids large; no bursa; equal filiform spicules; parasitic. *Camallanus* (Fig. 9-15, *E*).

Order Dracunculoidea (sometimes included with Camallanida). Body filiform; no definite lips or cuticularized buccal capsule; esophagus with anterior muscular portion and posterior glandular portion; vulva near middle of body but reduced in mature worm; bursa lacking; male with equal spicules; parasitic. *Dracunculus, Micropleura.*

Subclass or superorder Adenophorea (Aphasmidia). Body without phasmids; caudal glands present; amphids spiral or disk types; excretory system not of lateral canals but glandular of one or more cells (renette); accessory copulatory structures present; mostly free living.

Order Chromadorida. Body usually with ringed cuticle marked with ornamentations; pharynx with posterior bulb; mostly marine and free living. *Desmodora* (Fig. 9-15, *D*), *Spirina, Plectus* (Fig. 9-14).

Order Monhysterida. Body with smooth or slightly ringed cuticle; circular amphids; outstretched ovaries; terrestrial and aquatic. *Monhystera* (Fig. 9-2), *Cylindrolaimus.*

Order Enoplida. Body with cuticle not ringed but usually with bristles; six labial papillae usually; pocketlike amphids; chiefly marine. *Enoplus* (Fig. 9-15, *C*), *Mononchus.*

Order Dorylaimida. Body with smooth cuticle; dorylaimid type of pharynx; buccal cavity with spear; soil and fresh water. *Dorylaimus* (Fig. 9-17).

Order Dioctophymatida. Mouth without lips and surrounded by papillae; elongated pharynx without bulb; males have muscular, belllike bursa without rays; endoparasitic. *Dioctophyme* (Fig. 9-26), *Hystrichis.*

Order Trichuroidea (Sometimes included with Dorylaimida). Body usually filiform anteriorly; pharynx slender with a stichosome; males without copulatory apparatus or with a cirrus; endoparasitic. *Trichuris* (Fig. 9-27), *Trichinella* (Fig. 9-28), *Capillaria.*

Class Nematomorpha (Gordiacea). Body long, filiform, and cylindric with rounded ends; cuticles may bear thickenings (areoles); lateral epidermal cords usually absent; anterior tip (calotte) bounded posteriorly by dark ring; epidermis of a single layer of cells; pseudocoel mostly filled with mesenchyme; excretory canal absent; enteron mostly degenerate; muscles of longitudinal fibers; nervous system of ventral cerebral mass and nerve cord in or near epidermal layer; dioecious; genital ducts open into intestine; gonads usually of paired cylindric bodies; parasitic as juveniles, free living as adults; holoblastic cleavage with coeloblastula.

Order Gordioidea. Body usually with smooth cuticle; one ventral epidermal cord; pseudocoel with mesenchyme; gonads with lateral diverticula; freshwater with parasitic stage in

209

aquatic or terrestrial arthropod. *Gordius, Paragordius* (Fig. 9-29).

Order Nectonematoidea. Body cuticle with double row of bristles; dorsal and ventral cords present; ventral nerve cord in epidermis; pseudocoel open; gonad single; parasitic phase in crabs; marine. *Nectonema.*

BASIC ADAPTIVE FEATURES

In such a varied assemblage as the Aschelminthes each group probably has its own unique basic adaptive pattern that has determined its evolutionary history. However, of all the classes of Aschelminthes the nematodes are by far the most numerous and have had the greatest biologic success. From a physiologic and ecologic standpoint, they are among the most highly adaptable groups to be found in the animal kingdom. The free-living forms are found in almost any location where other types of life abound (although they are largely absent from microplankton): in fresh and marine water, in damp earth and moss, in decaying organic matter, in the muck of ocean bottoms, in warm springs (Fig. 9-2) and cold alpine lakes, in plants and around the roots of plants. They form all degrees of association with plants and animals. In food habits they range through the whole gamut of nutrition—saprophagous, herbivorous, carnivorous, or parasitic. Some species have an amazing ability to adapt to a wide variety of habitats and ecologic conditions. Many are cosmopolitan and can fit into almost any conditions that support life; others are restricted to a specific habitat of special and unique conditions. Wherever found, their populations often reach fantastic numbers. Many can retain their vitality under the most harsh environmental conditions such as desiccation, extremes of temperature, acid and basic surroundings, lack of oxygen, etc. Both the larvae and adults of some species are still viable after being in a dried-up, shriveled condition (anabiosis) for years. Perhaps this wide range of adaptability explains the unsatisfactory results of their responses to the controlled conditions of isolated factors. Few of them give definite responses to such factors as light, temperature, and chemicals.

A study of nematode morphology reveals no particular adaptation to their wide variety of ecologic niches. Some retain many primitive characters that others have lost, but such modifications cannot, in general, be linked up with special adaptive features. As a group, nematodes represent the tube-within-a-tube plan in its basic simplicity. Most of them show a striking similarity in form and organization with minor, occasional modifications depending upon food and other habits. Predaceous forms, for instance, are often provided with a spear in the mouth for puncturing prey. Locomotion with only longitudinal muscles is very restricted. Serpentine undulations in a dorsoventral plane, with the assistance of cuticular specializations and adhesive structures for purchase, are utilized; many modifications of this plan also exist. Some authorities, such as Chitwood, regard the method of nematodes' serpentine locomotion as one of the primary reasons for their success in the invasion of such a wide variety of habitats and the origin of many evolutionary lines. The lack of ciliary locomotion is thus considered an improvement in their mobility. The simplicity of their morphology and their small size, together with the wide range of their physiologic responses, have

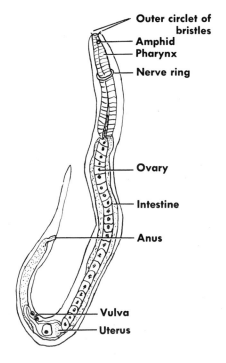

Fig. 9-2

Monhystera, an aphasmid nematode often found in hot springs (order Monhysterida).

also made possible their ability to live in so many environmental niches and helped set the pattern of their evolution.

PHYLOGENETIC RELATIONSHIPS

Students of the Aschelminthes, such as L. H. Hyman and G. Steiner, have presented an array of convincing evidence for the logical grouping of the various classes into the one phylum. All members of the phylum are pseudocoelomate, with a generally radial symmetry at the anterior end. The epidermis (mostly syncytial) in all classes tends to secrete a hard cover (cuticle) that undergoes specializations such as spines, bristles, and scales. Longitudinal thickenings or epidermal cords serve as supporting elements of the exoskeleton. Molting of the cuticle is common in two or three classes. Longitudinal muscles are emphasized throughout the phylum; circular muscles are almost completely absent. The protonephridial system of excretion, characteristic of the flatworms, is greatly reduced and is entirely absent in some. Caudal adhesive glands are present in nearly all classes. The pharynx possesses many similar characters in nematodes, gastrotrichs, and kinorhynchs (Fig. 9-3). Cell or nuclear constancy of somatic tissues is common in Aschelminthes. Most aschelminths have juveniles and no larval stages.

It is the belief of many students of Aschelminthes, or Nemathelminthes, that the various classes of this phylum originated from a ciliated form such as that of a turbellarian, which had a protonephridial excretory system. The only two classes with cilia—rotifers and gastrotrichs—supposedly represent the most primitive members of the phylum, and each of these also possesses protonephridia with flame bulbs. Some authorities think that the resemblance of the trochophore larva to certain rotifers may indicate that rotifers belong to the annelid-mollusk stem.

Authorities do not agree on the place of origin of the largest group (nematodes) of the Aschelminthes. Steiner thinks that nematodes arose in fresh water and later colonized terrestrial and salt water habitats; Hyman maintains that freshwater and terrestrial species came from marine ancestors.

CLASS ROTIFERA

The rotifers, or wheel animalcules, are microscopic animals that range in length from 40 microns to 3 mm. Most are under 500 microns. They derive their name from a ciliated corona that gives the appearance of a revolving wheel. Most species are freshwater forms, although a few are marine. Most are solitary, and some are sessile. They are found in a great variety of habitats from purely aquatic environments to damp soils, sand, and mosses. They are cosmopolitan in their distribution.

External features

In their morphology the body is usually made up of the head, trunk, and foot. The head consists of the corona, the mouth, the mastax, and the brain (Fig. 9-4, *A*). In the trunk are found most of the organs—stomach, intestine, cloaca, excretory system, and reproductive organs. The terminal foot is tapering and consists of two or more superficial segmentlike parts that are usually highly retractile. The foot is absent in some species, but when present, it may consist of

Fig. 9-3

Comparison of pharynx as seen in cross sections of, **A**, Gastrotricha; **B**, Kinorhyncha; **C**, Nematoda. Similarity of pharynx in three groups may have phyletic significance.

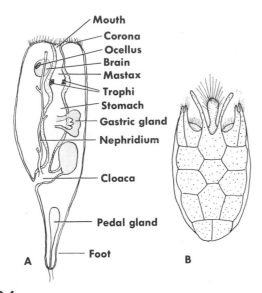

Fig. 9-4

A, Basic organization of rotifer, side view. **B,** *Keratella,* dorsal view, showing cuticle modified into sculptured, spiny lorica. (**A** modified from Lang.)

one to four toes. There are many morphologic variations within the group. The body is usually elongated and cylindric, but some are short, stout, and even spherical. In cross section the body may be round or flattened dorsally or ventrally. The body is covered with a cuticle secreted by the syncytial epidermis and consists of scleroproteins. When the cuticle is much thickened, it is called a lorica and may bear characteristic patterns of plates and ornamentation (Fig. 9-4, *B*). In the bdelloid rotifers, superficial annuli may give the appearance of segmentation (Fig. 9-8, *G, I*), but true segmentation is lacking.

The corona, the most characteristic organ of rotifers, is of many types. The primitive form of the corona is primarily a ventral or anterior ciliated surface, or buccal field around the mouth, derived from a creeping, ventrally ciliated ancestor. From the buccal field a circumapical band, or ring, encircles the anterior margins of the head. The apical field is the unciliated region within the center of the ring and may bear outlets for the retrocerebral organ and sensory hairs. From such a ground plan the patterns characteristic of different groups of rotifers seem to have evolved. Structural modifica-

tions may involve either the buccal field or the circumapical ring or both. Parts of these regions may be lost altogether, cirri may replace short cilia, the circumapical ring may enlarge at the expense of the buccal field as in *Epiphanes* (*Hydatina,* Fig. 9-5), and there may be an absence or reduction of cilia on the coronal surface (*Eosphora*). Ciliary tufts may be found on lateral processes, or auricles (*Notommata*). In *Collotheca* (Fig. 9-8, *B*) the corona forms a sort of funnel with its upper edges folded into lobes bearing stiff setae. In the familiar bdelloid rotifers (Fig. 9-8, *H, I*) the corona is made up of two trochal disks and the cingulum. This arrangement is a modification of two circles of cilia, anterior and posterior. The anterior circle (the trochus) is elevated on pedicels and divided into two trochal disks, each bearing on the edge a single row of membranelles. The posterior circle (cingulum) of small cilia encircles the bases of the pedicels and continues ventrally behind the mouth, which thus lies between the two rings in a ciliated groove. When such a corona is retracted, a projec-

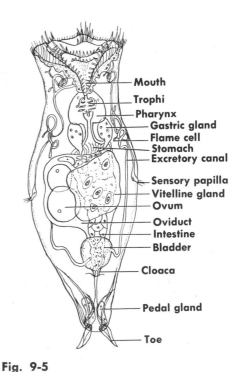

Fig. 9-5

Epiphanes (*Hydatina*) *senta,* ventral view of female (order Monogononta).

tion (rostrum) covered with cilia and bristles is seen, which may be used in locomotion. This structure is retracted also when the corona is extended. In sessile types the corona may be scalloped into lobes that may be radially arranged (Figs. 9-6, 9-8, *B*). Pigmented ocelli (eyes) may appear on various parts of the corona and are involved in reactions to light.

Among the characteristic structures of the trunk of rotifers are the sensory antennae, or palps. These are movable papillae usually with tufts of sensory hairs at the tip. The dorsal antennae (single or paired) are found in the middorsal line near the anterior end of the trunk (Fig. 9-6); the paired lateral antennae (present only in the order Monogononta) vary in position on the trunk and may even be found dorsally or ventrally. A caudal antenna near the base of the toes is found in some rotifers. Long movable spines or skipping blades are present on the trunk of certain Monogononta.

The foot, or tail, is the terminal part of the rotifer. It may be a gradual extension of the body or it may be sharply marked off from the trunk. Often its cuticle is ringed into joints that can telescope together when it shortens. The foot may be modified into a long stalk in sessile forms and may be absent altogether in others. It may bear an adhesive disk but is usually provided with one to four toes. Pedal glands (Figs. 9-4, 9-5) open on some parts of the toes or foot in most rotifers. They secrete a sticky substance for attachment and construction of tubes or cases (Fig. 9-6). In swimming the foot acts as a rudder, and in creeping and looping methods it can anchor the animal temporarily to the substratum.

Internal features

The body wall of rotifers is made up of the cuticle, epidermis, and muscles. The epidermis is a syncytium of scattered nuclei constant in number for each species, although cell or nuclear constancy in some aschelminths has been questioned by some authorities. *Epiphanes* (Fig. 9-5), for example, is supposed to have 960 cells or nuclei. The body cavity is not lined by a peritoneum, and mesenteries are lacking; it is thus a pseudocoel. It is filled with a fluid and a network of branched, ameboid cells.

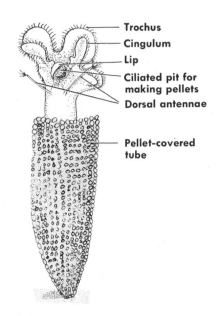

Fig. 9-6

Floscularia, a sessile rotifer that lives in beautiful tube. Particles are pressed into pellets in its specialized pit and attached to tube in rows, or tube may be decorated with sand grains or fecal balls (order Monogononta).

The musculature contains bands of circular muscles especially well developed in the head region; beneath the circular muscles are longitudinal muscles that act principally as retractors of the head and foot. In addition, visceral muscles extend from the body wall to the viscera for moving and holding the viscera in place. Single muscles, rather than layers, seem to be the rule. Group variations of muscular patterns are common in the different groups. Both smooth and striated muscle fibers occur in rotifers; striated muscle is well adapted for rapid movement of spines and appendages.

The nervous system consists of a bilobed cerebral ganglion, or brain, lying on the dorsal surface of the mastax, two main lateral nerves, and fine sensory and motor fibers from the brain to various sensory organs and to the muscles. A ganglion and plexus are found on or in the mastax wall and send nerves to the enteron. Sensory organs in the form of ocelli, antennae, bristles, ciliated pits, and membranelles are common. The controversial retrocerebral organ lying near the brain and opening on the corona is thought by some authorities to be

213

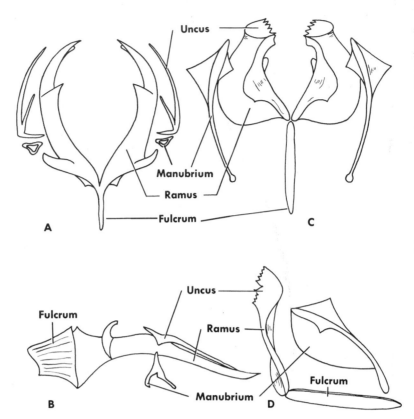

Fig. 9-7

Two types of mastax trophi. **A** and **B**, Anterior and lateral views of forcepslike incudate trophi of *Asplanchna* used to grasp food organisms. **C** and **D**, Ventral and lateral views of virgate trophi of *Synchaeta*. This type is found in pelagic raptorial rotifers which grasp prey by unci and suck in its contents. (**A** and **B** after de Beauchamp, 1907; redrawn from Pennak: Freshwater invertebrates of the United States, The Ronald Press Company; **C** and **D** redrawn from Hyman: The invertebrates: Acanthocephala, Aschelminthes and Entoprocta; the pseudocoelomate Bilateria, McGraw-Hill Book Company.)

a sense organ, but no conclusive evidence about its function has been determined.

A complete digestive system is present in most rotifers. The mouth, which is usually ventrally placed, may have a lower lip formed from the cingulum previously mentioned and usually opens into the pharynx by way of a ciliated tube. The pharynx is modified into a muscular mastax or gizzard lined with cuticle. A variable number of salivary glands open by ducts into the anterior end of the mastax.

The mastax is peculiar to rotifers and contains on its inner wall the masticatory apparatus, the trophi. The trophi are of many types, important in taxonomic diagnosis, and they are made up of hard, cu-

ticularized pieces. The trophi consist of seven parts, three paired lateral and one median (Fig. 9-7). All of these may be modified morphologically for specialized purposes in the different types. The unpaired piece is called the fulcrum, and the paired ones are rami, unci, and manubria. The fulcrum and two rami collectively make up the uncus; an uncus and its associated manubrium collectively form a malleus. Thus a typical trophi is made up of one uncus and two mallei. Eight basic, variable types of mastax, according to development and specialization, are found. The eight basic types are called malleate, fulcrate, ramate, uncinate, virgate (Fig. 9-7, *C, D*), incudate, (Fig. 9-

7, *A*, *B*), forcipate, and cardate. These types are correlated with different methods of feeding, and each type may be characteristic of a particular group of rotifers. For example, the ramate mastax is present in the Bdelloidea and is specialized for grinding plankton and detritus.

In sessile and nonpredatory species the coronal cilia create currents of water that sweep the food particles to the region of the mouth. If there are two trochal disks, such as are found in the Bdelloidea, the membranelles of each disk create a circular current opposite to that of the other disk. These two currents direct the food, by way of a groove between the trochus and cingulum, into the mouth. Most members that feed in this manner are omnivorous and will ingest most particles of the right size. The predatory species feed on protozoans, rotifers, and other small metazoan organisms and detect their prey by chemical stimuli or by touch. They seize their prey by grasping with forceplike trophi (Fig. 9-7, *A*) that can be protruded from the mouth. Some species can literally suck out the contents of their prey, either outside the rotifer or within the mastax. Another method of ingesting food is found in those with widespreading coronal funnels (Fig. 9-8, *B*), which act as traps for small organisms that accidentally wander into the funnels.

After leaving the mastax, the food passes into the tubular esophagus, ciliated or cuticle lined, and thence to the large, thick-walled stomach where most digestion and absorption take place. The stomach bears at its anterior margin a pair of bean-shaped gastric glands that probably furnish enzymes. The stomach wall usually is composed of large ciliated cells, but it may be syncytial in some members. It is provided with both circular and longitudinal muscles. The stomach may be separated from the narrow, ciliated intestine by a sphincter, or it may be indistinctly set off from that part of the enteron. The posterior end of the intestine may also receive the excretory tubules and the oviduct and is thus a cloaca. The cloaca opens to the outside dorsally at the base of the foot. In some rotifers, including *Asplanchna* (Fig. 9-9) and other sucking forms, an anus or cloacal opening is absent. Digestion is primarily ex-

tracellular but is intracellular in those that possess large gastric ceca and lack an anus, such as *Chromogaster*.

There are no special organs of respiration and circulation. Respiration is by direct body surface, but rotifers vary in the amount of oxygen required. Some are found in oxygen-deficient mud in aquatic situations, but most obtain a sufficient supply of oxygen carried by currents of water.

For maintaining a constant internal osmotic pressure and getting rid of metabolic waste, the rotifer is provided with an excretory system of two protonephridial tubules with flame bulbs (Figs. 9-4, 9-5). The number of flame bulbs varies with the group, but usually 4 to 50 of them are scattered through the body. The two collective tubules are much convoluted and often empty into an excretory bladder, which opens by a short duct into the ventral side of the cloaca. A separate bladder is absent in those rotifers which have the posterior part of the cloaca modified into a bladder. The contents of the bladder are emptied through the cloacal opening four or five times per minute.

Reproduction and embryology

Rotifers are dioecious, and the sexes are dimorphic. In some groups males have never been found and in others they are produced sporadically. In only a few groups are the males as large as the females, and most of them have degenerate structures. Parthenogenesis is the only reproductive method in the order Bdelloidea; males are unknown in this group. In the order Monogononta, which has the most complex reproductive methods, males have been described for most species, although parthenogenesis is the usual method of reproduction. When males occur, they are usually found only during a few weeks of the year.

In most species the female has a single, bulky complex consisting of the ovary proper (germarium) with its developing oocytes, and the larger syncytial vitellarium that furnishes yolk to the egg (Figs. 9-5, 9-9). When mature, the egg passes down the short oviduct into the cloaca whence it is expelled to the outside. The bdelloids, however, have two ovaries, two vitellaria, and two oviducts. In males a single, saclike **215**

Fig. 9-8

Some rotifers showing many types of form. **A,** *Noteus.* **B,** *Collotheca.* **C,** *Furcularia (Cephalodeila).* **D,** *Floscularia.* **E,** *Stephanoceros.* **F,** *Trochosphaera.* (**A** to **F** order Monogononta.) **G,** *Seison* (order Seisonacea). **H,** *Rotaria.* **I,** *Philodina.* (**H** and **I** order Bdelloidea.)

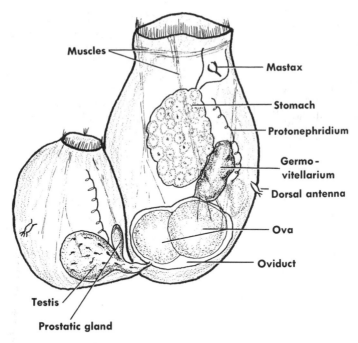

Muscles

Mastax

Stomach

Protonephridium

Germo-
vitellarium

Dorsal antenna

Ova

Oviduct

Testis

Prostatic gland

Fig. 9-9

Asplanchna in copulation (order Monogononta). (Modified from Wesenburg-Lund.)

testis exists, and a ciliated sperm duct usually opens into a gonopore because a cloaca is often absent. A copulatory organ and prostate glands are also present. Males commonly produce two kinds of sperm: a typical kind to fertilize the egg and a smaller, rod-shaped kind to aid the others in penetrating the female body wall. Hypodermic insemination, by which the male penis penetrates the female body wall and deposits sperm in the pseudocoel, is the common method of copulation (Fig. 9-9). The number of eggs produced by a female is restricted to the number of nuclei in her ovary at birth, usually 10 to 20. The egg is constricted into an oval shape as it passes down the oviduct, and it may be laid on a substratum or attached to the body of the female.

In the Monogononta two types of females, which are usually morphologically indistinguishable, occur. One of these types is called amictic, and the females reproduce by parthenogenesis. Their amictic eggs undergo only one nonreductional division in the ovary, have the diploid number of chromosomes, and cannot be fertilized. They give rise only to females. The second type of female is called mictic and appears only at certain times of the year. Their eggs (mictic) are haploid because they are produced by the double meiotic division. If these mictic eggs are not fertilized, they develop by parthenogenesis into haploid males. If fertilized, they develop a thick-walled, resistant shell with more nutritive material and become winter, or dormant, eggs. Upon hatching, these dormant eggs always give rise to amictic females. A mictic female may give rise to both fertilized eggs and male eggs, but an amictic female produces only amictic eggs. Usually there are only two or three mictic generations per year, while there may be 30 to 40 amictic generations. In Seisonacea the eggs are all mictic and hatch into either sex. The Bdelloidea lack males entirely. Parthenogenetic females have a life span of one to two weeks as a general rule. Ecologic factors responsible for bisexual periods as well as abundance in number in the life cycle of rotifer populations are not well known, and many conflicting theories have been advanced.

In their embryology, rotifers have a modified spiral determinate type of cleavage. **217**

Their bilateral cleavage pattern is supposedly similar to that of the Acanthocephala. A gastrula of an outer ectodermal layer of cells enclosing an inner cell mass of endoderm and mesoderm is formed. Cell division ceases when each organ receives its complement of cells. In free-moving species the young hatch as juveniles that attain sexual maturity in a few days; males are sexually mature when they hatch. Sessile species undergo a free-swimming larval stage before assuming the sessile adult condition.

CLASS GASTROTRICHA
General morphology

The 500 species of the microscopic Gastrotricha are about equally divided between those that live in fresh water and those that are marine. The order Macrodasyoidea is mostly marine; the order Chaetonotoidea is all freshwater with few exceptions. Both kinds are found in similar habitats, being especially common in littoral zones where they crawl over the bottom or on masses

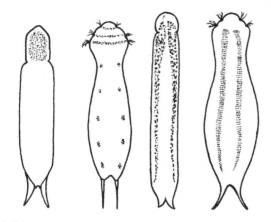

Fig. 9-10

Some patterns of ciliation found in gastrotrichs, ventral views.

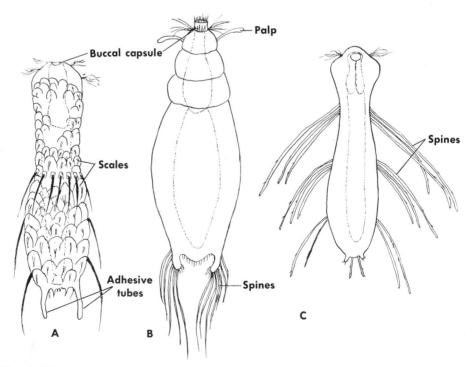

Fig. 9-11

Some gastrotrichs. **A,** *Chaetonotus* sp. is covered with spines and scales of various sizes. **B,** *Neogossea* has clusters of long bristles at posterior end. **C,** *Dasydytes* has bunches of long bristles at posterior end. (**B** modified from Daday; **C** modified from Brunson; both redrawn from Pennak: Freshwater invertebrates of the United States, The Ronald Press Company.)

of vegetation. They are usually less than 1 mm. in length (most are around 500 microns) and are about the same size as rotifers. The body is usually elongated with a convex dorsal surface and a flattened ventral surface. The anterior end may be modified as a lobelike head set off by a constricted neck from the trunk, while the posterior end may be forked, pointed, or of other shapes.

Ciliation is mostly restricted to certain tracts such as the ventral region and the head lobe. The cilia may be arranged in longitudinal bands, in patches, in transverse rows, or in tufts (Fig. 9-10). Very long cilia or bristles are common and may function as sensory organs. The ventral cilia are used for gliding over a substratum. The animals can also swim by ciliary movement.

The body surface is covered with a thin cuticle that may be smooth but is usually provided with a pattern of scales, plates, and spines (Fig. 9-11). The scales or plates may overlap on the head lobe and ventral surface, or they may cover the entire body. Their color is variable but is usually light green to reddish brown: some are transparent and colorless. Some may have pigment spots (ocelli) and a few are provided with palps (Fig. 9-11, *B*). Adhesive tubes, similar to those of rotifers, are found in both orders and are used for attachment to objects (Fig. 9-11, *A*). Each is a cuticular tube supplied by a gland and movable by muscles. The tubes may be very numerous and are often arranged in rows along the lateral margin or on the ventral side of the head; the tail in some species may also bear them.

Beneath the cuticle the body wall is made up of a syncytial epidermis and muscle bands of both circular and longitudinal muscles (usually about six pairs). Some of these muscles operate the adhesive tubes and others are used for shortening and curving the body. The muscular system is similar to the rotifer type.

Gastrotrichs are pseudocoelomate animals, but the pseudocoel is mostly in the form of spaces and is devoid of ameboid cells.

Excretion and osmoregulation are accomplished by two flame bulbs that are fastened to two protonephridial tubules (Fig. 9-12). This system, which is restricted to the freshwater species (Chaetonotidae),

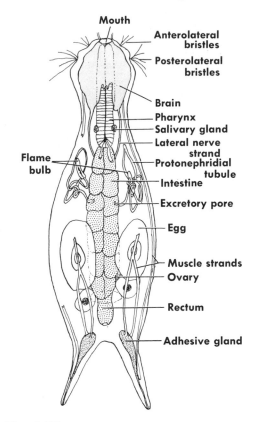

Fig. 9-12

Dorsal view of female *Chaetonotus,* a common gastrotrich showing internal structures (order Chaetonotoidea).

has no bladder. The protonephridia lie coiled in the pseudocoel and open near the midventral line.

The digestive system consists of a terminal mouth, often with small hooks, a short buccal cavity (sometimes with projecting teeth), a nematode-like pharynx (Figs. 9-3, *A*, 9-12) with bulbous enlargements and glands, a straight intestine or midgut, a rectum, and an anus with a sphincter muscle at the posterior end of the trunk. Most of the enteron, with the exception of the midgut, is lined with cuticle. Circular muscle is also found in the wall of parts of the alimentary canal.

Gastrotrichs live upon small organisms such as bacteria, protozoans, algae, and organic detritus. They make use of their head cilia in the ingestion of food. They are most common in standing fresh water where there is decaying vegetation, and they may be found at all seasons of the year. It is thought that they can withstand low oxygen concentrations. Their chief enemies are aquatic insects, ameboid protozoa, annelid worms, and hydras.

The nervous system contains two lateral nerve strands connected to a large, dorsal, saddle-shaped brain covering the anterior part of the pharynx (Fig. 9-12). Fine nerve branches extend to the body wall and viscera. Sensory receptors are represented by tufts of cilia and scattered tactile bristles.

Reproduction and embryology

Most marine species (Macrodasyoidea) are hermaphroditic, and a few are protandrous. Only parthenogenetic females are known in freshwater species. The one or two ovaries consist of cell masses without a capsule and lie lateral to the intestine. They connect to a tiny oviduct that opens to the outside by a gonopore near or in common with the anus. The male system when present is made up of two testes, from each of which a sperm duct carries the sperm to a single or double male gonopore. A vestigial copulatory bursa may also be found. Most females produce one to five eggs, which are of two types according to whether or not they have immediate or delayed cleavage. The tachyblastic eggs begin cleavage as soon as deposited and hatch usually within 12 to 20 hours; opsiblastic eggs are larger and are found in older cultures where they may survive harsh environmental conditions of temperature.

Gastrotrichs have direct development. Their total cleavage pattern in early stages is similar to that of nematodes (Fig. 9-22), producing equal blastomeres. Members of Macrodasyoidea have more cells than those of Chaetonotoidea, and cell constancy is found in the group. Their life span is apparently short; in cultures it is about 3 to 21 days, depending upon ecologic conditions. Like rotifers they do not shed their cuticle.

Chaetonotus (Fig. 9-11, A, 9-12), which also occurs in marine waters, is one of the most familiar gastrotrichs as well as one of the most cosmopolitan. *Macrodasys* is a common marine genus.

CLASS KINORHYNCHA (ECHINODERA)

These small marine aschelminths are superficially segmented and lack external ciliation. They are found mostly in the littoral zone of shallow waters where they dwell in muddy bottoms. The body is divided into three regions—head, neck, and trunk. The head is rounded with a terminal mouth, bears five to seven circles of spines (scalids), and is completely retractile (Fig. 9-13). The neck is enclosed by a number of plates (placids) that may close over the head when the latter is withdrawn. The trunk makes up the remainder of the body. Throughout the body the cuticle is divided into apparent segments called zonites. Head and neck each consist of one zonite, while the trunk usually has 11 zonites (12 in *Campyloderes*). Each zonite is usually flattened ventrally with a midventral groove and is covered with a dorsal or tergal plate and two ventral or sternal plates. Between the zonites the cuticle is thin to allow flexibility. A pair of ventral adhesive tubes is present in the third or fourth zonite. Each of the remaining trunk zonites bears a recurved dorsal spine and a pair of lateral spines. The terminal zonite may also bear a pair of large, movable, lateral spines. Spines are hollow and filled with epidermis and, together with the zonites, are among the features characteristic of the class.

The body wall is made up of the cuticle and a syncytial epidermis, which forms middorsal and lateral longitudinal thickenings or cords that bulge into the pseudocoel. In each zonite each cord is slightly enlarged. There is no subepidermal sheath, but the musculature is segmentally arranged. Two pairs of longitudinal muscle bands run along the dorsolateral and ventrolateral regions of the body. By means of these bands and ring muscles in the first two zonites, the body is compressed and the head is protruded. Locomotion is produced by protruding the head and attaching it to the substratum by the scalids; then, by means of the longitudinal muscles, the head is retracted and the trunk is pulled forward. Repetition of this process produces a characteristic creeping movement. Kinorhynchs cannot swim.

The nervous system is in close contact with the epidermis and consists of a brain encircling the anterior end of the pharynx, a ventral ganglionated nerve cord, and ganglion cells in the dorsal and lateral epidermal cords of each zonite.

The digestive system is a straight tube

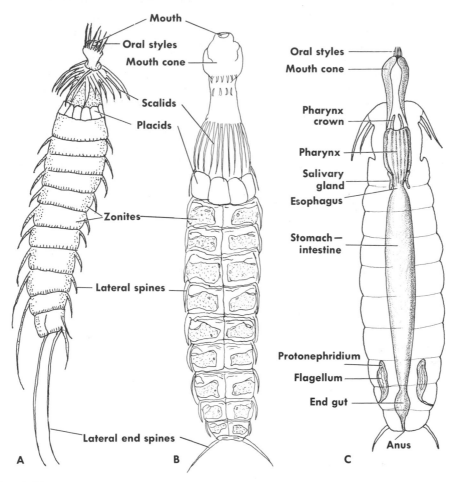

Fig. 9-13

Class Kinorhyncha. **A,** *Echinoderella,* dorsolateral view, with head projected. **B,** *Pycnophyes,* ventral view, with head and neck extended showing sternal plates. **C,** Digestive system and protonephridia of *Pycnophyes.*

that is differentiated into certain specialized regions. The mouth is placed terminally on the protrusible mouth cone that encloses a buccal cavity. Posterior to the buccal cavity is the muscular pharynx (Fig. 9-13, *C*) lined with cuticle and syncytial epithelium. On its exterior the pharynx is covered by several bands of protractor muscles. Following the pharynx is a short, slender esophagus, which has lining continuous with that of the pharynx. To the esophagus are attached two dorsolateral and two ventrolateral salivary glands. The pharynx and esophagus are considered a stomodeum because their lining is cuticular. The stomach-intestine is covered by a network of muscles and lacks cuticular lining and gland cells. Pancreatic glands, however, are present at the junction of the esophagus and stomach. A sphincter separates the intestine from the short hindgut, and another, more posterior sphincter is also present. The posterior end of the hindgut is lined with cuticle and is a proctodeum. The terminal anus is found in the last zonite.

The pseudocoel is fluid-filled and lies between the body wall and enteron. Numerous amebocytes are present in the cavity. The excretory system consists of a single pair of protonephridia, one on each side of the intestine in the tenth zonite. The flame bulb in each protonephridium is mul-

221

tinucleated and usually contains a single flagellum. The protonephridia open by separate nephridiopores on the tergal plate of the eleventh zonite.

The kinorhynchs are dioecious, and the two sexes are similar externally. Each sex contains one pair of saclike gonads that open separately on the thirteenth zonite. The ovary contains ova and nutritive cells and is provided with a short oviduct. The genital pore, or gonopore, of the male is armed with two or three pineal spicules that are useful in copulation.

Not much is known about the embryology of the kinorhynchs. In some the eggs hatch into small larvae that lack external segmentation, spines, head, and other structures. By successive molts the larva acquires zonites and adult morphology.

American genera are best represented by *Echinoderella* (Fig. 9-13, *A*) and *Pycnophyes* (Fig. 9-13, *B*), which, so far, are known only from the northern New England coast.

CLASS NEMATODA (NEMATA)

This extensive group of aschelminths is worldwide in its distribution; they are found in nearly every place where animals (free-living or parasitic) can exist. Details of their varied ecologic habitats have been given in the section on Basic Adaptive Features. Nematodes are vermiform, unsegmented roundworms of a circular or cylindric cross section (Fig. 9-14). The length of adult worms ranges from 100 to 200 microns to more than 7 meters, but the majority of free-living species are only about 1 mm. long. Marine species may reach a length several times this. Free-living nematodes are a homogeneous group, and usually few obvious morphologic distinctions are found among them. The more specialized members are commonly found among the marine species. As a group the ecologic and taxonomic status of roundworms is poorly worked out. Species identification is very difficult, and multitudes of species are undescribed.

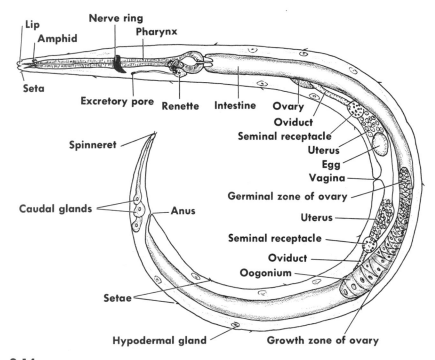

Fig. 9-14

Plectus parietinus, a chromadorid nematode (female), generalized. (After Hirschmann; modified from Sasser and Jenkins.)

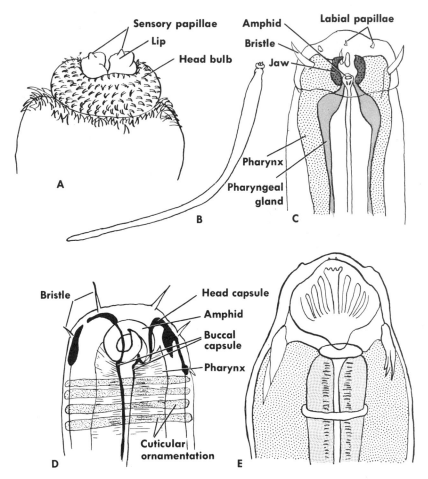

Fig. 9-15

Class Nematoda. **A,** *Gnathostoma,* anterior end with large protruding lips. **B,** *Gnathostoma,* whole specimen (order Spirurida). **C,** *Enoplus,* anterior end showing two of three large, movable jaws (order Enoplida). **D,** *Desmodora,* anterior end showing amphid characteristic of aphasmids (order Chromadorida). **E,** *Camallanus,* lateral view showing shell-shaped half of buccal capsule; has no lips (order Camallanida).

External features

The body of nematodes is covered with a cuticle consisting mainly of scleroproteins but no chitin and is not divided into regions. The cuticle may bear protuberances (Fig. 9-15, *A*), pits, ridges, and striations (Fig. 9-15, *D*), or it may be smooth. The body usually tapers at both ends. Structures around the mouth at the anterior end have a definite radial or biradial arrangement, which may indicate a sessile ancestor. The mouth is surrounded by liplike lobes (three on each side in primitive forms; three fused pairs in terrestrial and parasitic species), each bearing an inner and outer labial papilla or bristle (Fig. 9-15). Thus there are two circles, each of six papillae or bristles. Outside the lips a third circle of four cephalic papillae may also be present. Many familiar nematodes have one dorsal and two ventrolateral lips. Many modifications of the lip structures exist in the various worms by loss, fusion, etc. The lips may also bear cuticular projections such as head shields and toothlike structures. In some animal and plant parasitic nematodes the mouth cavity is provided with a hollow hypodermic needle for penetrating and extracting tissue contents. It will be noted that none of the lips or

223

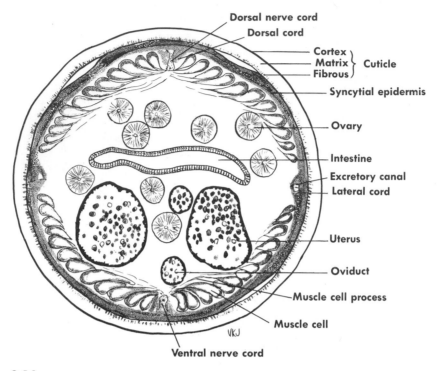

Fig. 9-16

Cross section of *Ascaris* showing cuticle and internal structure. (From Hickman: Integrated principles of zoology, The C. V. Mosby Co.)

sense organs is found in strict medial position. Free-living marine nematodes usually have caudal glands (Fig. 9-14) in their tail region, which secrete an adhesive cement of sticky threads for attachment.

Internal features

In nematodes the body wall consists of cuticle, epidermis or hypodermis, and a muscular tube (Fig. 9-16). The cuticle may be very complex in such nematodes as *Ascaris*. Nine layers have been identified in this form by some investigators. Many substances have been found in it such as lipoids, proteins, and carbohydrates, but keratin appears to be absent. The outermost protein layer is thought to undergo tanning. The cuticle usually undergoes four molts in its development. Beneath the cuticle the epidermis, which may be cellular or syncytial, forms two median and two lateral enlargements that project into the pseudocoel as longitudinal cords. Four subsidiary cords without nuclei may be present in some members. The cords run the body length but

are usually better developed anteriorly. In rows within the cords are the epidermal nuclei that are absent from the epidermis between the cords. Unicellular hypodermal glands (Fig. 9-14) may be present in the lateral cords of free-living nematodes.

The musculature of the body wall is made up entirely of longitudinal fibers arranged in bands, each of which is found in the space between two longitudinal cords. The muscle cells are unicellular, nonstriated, spindle shaped, and interlocking. Each muscle cell has an outer fibrillar zone and an inner protoplasmic zone containing a nucleus, and each cell is innervated by a protoplasmic process from a medial nerve. There are no circular muscles in nematodes. Muscles with special functions include male copulatory muscles, female vulvar muscles, somatointestinal muscles, and rectal muscles.

The pseudocoel is filled with fluid and fixed cells or nuclei, and is usually lined with a pseudocoelomic membrane that is formed from the growing together of proto-plasmic processes of mesenchyme cells during embryology. Visceral organs are also supported in the pseudocoel by these mes-enchymal processes.

Nematode movements are restricted because of the lack of circular muscles and the presence of a generally inflexible cuticle. When observed, they are frequently under-going thrashing movements produced by the alternate bending and straightening of the body. Some can swim by undulations in a dorsoventral plane, movements which also may enable them to glide through thick vegetation. Much of their thrashing seems to be without definite purpose unless it is to explore the environment. Crawling is made possible by throwing the body into sinuous curves or by gripping the substra-tum with cuticular specializations (stilt bristles and their secretions) and pulling the body forward.

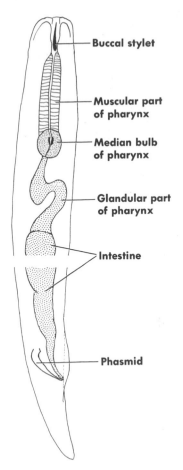

Fig. 9-18

Tylenchus, a phasmid nematode, anterior and posterior ends. Pharynx elongated and muscular (order Tylenchida).

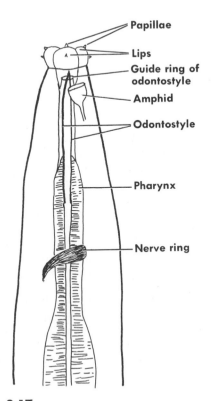

Fig. 9-17

Dorylaimus, an aphasmid nematode. Pharynx wall provided with enlarged tooth (odontostyle) serves as stylet; amphid of cyathiform (cup-shaped) type.

The digestive tract is generally straight with the mouth at the anterior end and the anus or cloaca at the other (Fig. 9-14). The mouth, already described, opens into the tubelike buccal capsule (stoma, Fig. 9-15, *D*) lined with cuticle, which may be specialized into ridges, plates, or teeth. Carnivorous nematodes are especially well provided with teeth, which are often referred to as jaws (Fig. 9-15, *C*). The buccal cavity leads into the esophagus or pharynx (foregut), which is a syncytial muscular tube with a triradiate lumen in which one angle or ray is directed toward the midventral line. It is also lined with cuticle, and its walls usually contain one dorsal and two subventral esophageal glands that may open into the buccal cavity or into the

225

esophagus. The esophagus is provided with a small, complex esophagosympathetic nervous system that coordinates the sucking or pumping action of this highly muscular organ. To aid in the ingestion of food the esophagus may also have bulbs (Fig. 9-18) and valves. It may also be provided with a spear or stylet for puncturing prey (Figs. 9-17, 9-18). An esophago-intestinal valve usually separates the esophagus from the long, straight intestine (midgut) formed of a one-layered cellular epithelium. The intestine is not lined with cuticle, but it may bear ceca and its cells may be multinucleated. Sometimes its cells have stored food inclusions and waste materials. Its posterior end may also be provided with a thin muscle net. The rectum (cloaca in male), or hindgut, is a short, dorsoventrally flattened tube that is set off from the intestine by an intestinorectal valve. Unicellular rectal glands in parasitic nematodes open into the rectum anteriorly. The rectum is lined with cuticle (being a proctodeum) and its wall contains a few large, flat epithelial cells covered externally by muscle tissue. Dilator muscles may run from the rectum to the body wall. The slit-like anus may be terminal or posteriorly ventral in position. The sperm duct in the male usually enters the cloaca ventrally.

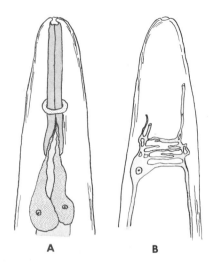

Fig. 9-19

Two types of excretory systems in nematodes. **A**, Glandular type with two large renette cells *(Rhabdias)*. **B**, Tubular or H-type showing network of canals *(Ascaris)*.

Digestion of food is probably extracellular because many nematodes live on food that has been simplified by bacterial action or by enzymes of the host.

The plan of the excretory system in nematodes is not shared with the other aschelminths. Flame bulbs have never been discovered in them. Two types of excretory systems, glandular and tubular, are recognized in the class. The glandular type is characteristic of the free-living marine nematodes and is made up of one or two large cells (renette gland) located at the ventral side of the junction between the esophagus (pharynx) and midgut (Figs. 9-19, *A*, 9-21). The duct from this gland runs forward and opens by an excretory pore in the midventral region of the body. The more specialized tubular type of excretory system is often called the H-type because of the arrangement of the canals of which it consists (Fig. 9-19, *B*). This H-type consists of three canals: a lateral excretory canal in each lateral cord and a single transverse canal that connects the two lateral canals. A short, common excretory canal leads from the transverse canal to the excretory pore located in the midventral line of the body behind the mouth. The renette system is considered to be the primitive plan from which the H-type has evolved by intracellular outgrowths.

The nervous system consists of a circumenteric nerve ring around the esophagus with paired lateral ganglia, dorsal ganglion, and ventral ganglion; other ganglia directly or indirectly associated with the rings; and various nerves that run anteriorly and posteriorly from the nerve ring (Fig. 9-20). Six sensory papillary nerves run anteriorly from the ring to the oral papillae or bristles; a pair of dorsolateral nerves run to the amphidial glands; and four major longitudinal nerves (dorsal, two lateral, ventral) run posteriorly from the circumenteric ring in the corresponding longitudinal cord. The most important of these four nerves is the ventral nerve, which is a partly paired and partly ganglionated nerve chain that gives off branches to the enteron, copulatory organs, etc., and terminates in the anal ganglion or ganglia. The ventral nerve has both sensory and motor functions, while the dorsal nerve is motor with few or

Sensory papillae
Nerve ring
Amphidial ganglion
Lateral ganglia
Ventral ganglion
Lateral nerves
Dorsal nerve
Ventral ganglion
Ventral nerve
Bursal nerve
Lateral nerve
Dorsal nerve
Genital papillae
Ventrolateral connective
Anal ganglion

Fig. 9-20

Nervous system of *Ascaris* as found in head and tail regions.

no ganglia along its course. A sympathetic nervous system is present in both the esophagus and rectum and connects with the nerve ring and anal ganglia respectively.

Free-living nematodes have many sense organs; parasitic forms have lost many of theirs. Most sense organs are in the form of papillae and bristles. Cuticular structures such as the labial and cephalic bristles are each supplied with a nerve fiber from the nearest papillary nerve. Tactile receptors, mostly in the form of bristles, are also scattered on the body surface. Some bristles are supplied with gland cells. Males, especially, have cuticular sensory papillae around their copulatory mechanism.

Unique nematode structures are the amphids, which are best developed in aquatic nematodes but are greatly reduced in terrestrial and parasitic forms. An amphid (Figs. 9-14, 9-15, *D*, 9-17) is a cuticular excavation having a pocket, spiral, or other

shape and provided with a slitlike aperture to the outside. One is present on each side of the body at the anterior end in or near the circlet of cephalic bristles. They are probably chemoreceptors; each has a gland and nerve ending.

A pair of unicellular glands, the phasmids (Fig. 9-21), open by a pore on each side of the tail in one group of nematodes (Phasmidia or Secernentea). Unlike the amphids they possess nearby neurones whose axons run through the lateral caudal nerves to the large ventral nerve. These organs are suposed to be chemoreceptors. A few aquatic nematodes have ocelli on the sides of the anterior region. Free nerve endings are also found in nematodes.

Reproduction and embryology

Sexes are chiefly separate in nematodes, and the females are usually larger than the males, which may have curved ends, spicules, etc. The tubular gonads may be paired or single and are often long and coiled. The germ cells arise either at the blind distal end from a terminal cell in the germinal zone or along the sides of the gonads (Figs. 9-14, 9-21). In hermaphroditic nematodes both sperm cells and oocytes are formed from the same primordial germ cells at different times.

In the male the gonad, or testis, is usually single and extends anteriorly (Fig. 9-21). Its free end is often much coiled. The sperm duct is a continuation of the testis and toward its posterior end it widens to form the muscularized seminal vesicle. Posterior to the sperm duct is a heavier, muscularized ejaculatory duct that opens posteriorly into the ventral side of the rectum or cloaca and bears prostatic glands that furnish secretions in copulation. Most male nematodes are provided with one or two cuticular nonhollow spicules of varying forms that originate from dorsal cloacal pockets. These spicules have special muscles and are pushed into the female vagina during copulation; they aid in the transfer of sperm by spreading the female gonopore. To direct the spicules in the right direction an accessory cuticular piece, the gubernaculum, is sometimes found in the dorsal wall of the spicule pouch.

In the females there are usually two tubular ovaries (Figs. 9-14, 9-21), but re-

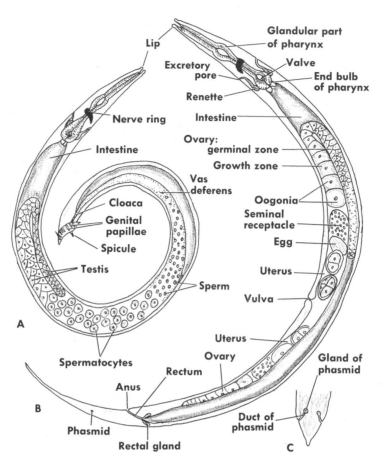

Fig. 9-21

Rhabditis (subclass Secernentea or Phasmidia of order Rhabditida). **A**, Male. **B**, Female. **C**, Posterior end showing phasmids. (**A** and **B** after Hirschmann; modified from Sasser and Jenkins.)

duction from two to one ovary is not rare. An ovary may be straight or coiled. It continues at first as the oviducts with tall epithelium and then widens into the uterus with flat or cuboidal epithelium and muscular walls. A portion of the uterus, the seminal receptacle, functions as a storage place for sperm and a place for the fertilization of the eggs. The seminal receptacle may be in the form of a lateral pouch in some nematodes. As the eggs pass distally along the uterus they are fertilized by the sperm stored there. A shell is formed partly from the fertilization membrane and partly by secretions from the uterine wall. The two uteri unite to form the cuticle-lined single vagina that opens to the outside by the female gonopore, or vulva, found in the midventral line, usually near

the middle third of the body but sometimes elsewhere.

In copulation the male may orient himself at right angles to the female body and partially coil around her body in the region of her gonopore. By extending the copulatory spicules through his cloacal opening (anus) into the female gonopore, both male and female apertures are kept apposed and open. Then, by contracting his cloacal muscles, sperm are discharged into the female vagina. The sperm, which are of various types from flagellate to ameboid, then migrate to the upper end of the uterus. In some nematodes there may be a copulatory bursa that is formed by the union of the lateral cuticular flanges from each side of the cloacal aperture. This structure is used in holding the two sexes together dur-

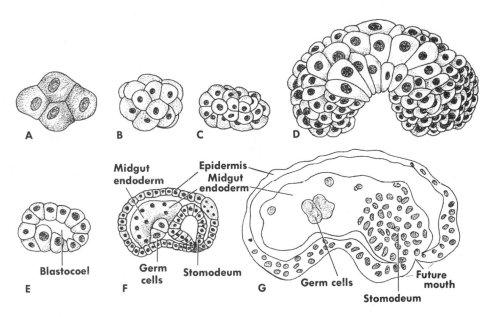

Fig. 9-22

Development in nematodes *(Parascaris equorum)*. **A**, 4-cell stage. **B**, 18-cell stage. **C**, About 30-cell stage. **D**, Later embryo. **E**, Sagittal section through blastula. **F**, Sagittal section through gastrula showing formation of stomodeum. **G**, Sagittal section through later embryo, **D**, showing digestive tract forming. (**A** to **C**, **E**, **F** after T. Boveri, 1899; **D** and **G** after H. Müller, 1903; all modified from Hyman.)

ing copulation. Most females are oviparous, but sometimes the eggs are retained in the uterus until they hatch (ovoviviparous).

Cleavage is bilateral, highly determinate, and is a modified spiral type. The stage of development at which the egg leaves the body varies from the unsegmented egg of *Ascaris* to the fully developed embryos in the eggs of *Wuchereria*. Gastrulation is by epiboly, and a coeloblastula is formed (Fig. 9-22). The embryonic blastocoel is retained as the pseudocoel. Future germ cells are early separated from somatic cells. During late embryonic development multiplication of cells ceases in all but the reproductive organs, and the number of cells or nuclei present at that time remains constant for life. The embryo soon takes a form similar to that of the adult. Stages of growth are marked by four molts, of which one or two may occur within the egg. Regeneration is not found in nematodes.

No animal group has more patterns of sexual reproduction than have nematodes. Almost all types known in the animal kingdom are found among them. Two or three types may be combined in the same species. Perhaps one of the most curious types of reproduction is found in a certain species of *Rhabditis* where, after normal copulation occurs between the two sexes, the sperm merely initiate the cleavage of those eggs that develop into females and do not fuse with the egg nucleus to form a zygote.

Résumé of orders

Nematodes are divided into two great groups, the Phasmidia, or Secernentea, and the Aphasmidia, or Adenophorea. These groups are designated as classes, subclasses, or superorders by various authorities. Only some of the more important orders are described in the following.

Order Rhabditida

These nematodes are small to moderate size and are characterized by having an esophagus with usually two bulbs; the amphids are reduced to small pitlike pockets. There are no caudal glands. Most members are terrestrial and live in rich, decayed organic matter for which their saprophagous

229

habits are best suited. Some are partial or complete parasites. Their life cycle may be direct, or it may include an infective larval stage in an insect or other invertebrate.

The earthworm nematode *Rhabditis maupasi* undergoes part of its development as a parasite in the nephridia or in the coelomic cavity of the earthworm and completes its development by feeding on the carcass of the dead earthworm. The familiar vinegar eel, *Turbatrix aceti,* is found in old vinegar. A similar form occurs in beer mats in certain parts of Germany. *Heterodera rostochiensis,* or the golden potato eelworm, has done much damage to potatoes in recent years.

Order Strongylida

The male worms of this order are distinguished by a caudal cuticular bursa supported by rays. The esophagus is without a spherical bulb and valvular apparatus, and the digestive tract lacks ceca. Members are endoparasites of the digestive system, and some of them are the most harmful parasites that infest man and domestic animals. Their life cycle is direct and usually includes two free-living juvenile stages that are passed in the soil. In size the length of the adult worm may be as short as 1 mm. or as long as 100 mm. in the various species. They are mostly oviparous, although some are ovoviviparous.

Infection of the host occurs by larval penetration of the skin, by ingestion of larvae by mouth, or by the ingestion of an intermediate host. After entering the host, the larvae pass to their definitive habitats by way of the blood or directly through the tissues. Damage to the host is produced by their migratory habits and by blood sucking and tissue damage (Figs. 9-23, 9-24). The host usually shows the effect of this damage by emaciation, loss of weight, anemia, and general lassitude. The amount of damage depends upon the host, number of worms, age of host, etc.

Among the common parasites of this economically important group are the hookworms *Ancylostoma*, found chiefly in the Old World and South America, *Necator*, common in the United States and the West Indies, and *Uncinaria* (Fig. 9-23), which is generally cosmopolitan. Most of these worms infect both man and domestic mammals, producing severe hookworm anemia. *Syngamus*, or gapeworm, is another common strongylid nematode that causes gapes in domestic poultry by blocking the

Fig. 9-23

Anterior end of hookworm *Uncinaria americana.* Note cutting plates pinching off mucosa and thick muscular pharynx that sucks up blood; parasitizes dogs, cats, foxes, and swine; about 8 mm. long. (AFIP No. 33810.)

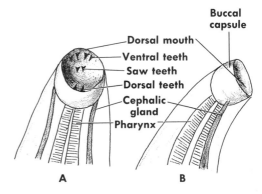

Fig. 9-24

Anterior end of hookworm showing buccal capsule with dorsal mouth and cutting plates. **A,** Dorsal view. **B,** View from left side.

trachea. Many other members of this order are responsible for severe damage to internal tissues, such as ulcerations, pulmonary irritations, and inflammation of various organs in both mammals and other vertebrates.

Order Ascaridida

This group includes roundworms that may reach a considerable size and have a cosmopolitan distribution as endoparasites of vertebrate intestines. They arc characterized by having three large lips, often with interlobia and other cephalic specializations, eight submedian cephalic papillae and two lateral papillae, a muscular cylindric esophagus or pharynx but no buccal capsule, and an intestine, sometimes with an anterior cecum or ceca. Males are nearly always provided with two equal genital spicules. Females are oviparous, may have more than two uteri, and lay unsegmented eggs. The worms may have a direct life history, or some may require an intermediate host as well as a definitive host to complete their development. They produce the disease ascariasis.

Common ascarids are the familiar *Ascaris lumbricoides,* the intestinal roundworm of man, which may reach a length of 40 cm.; *A. suum,* the pig ascarid, which is similar to *A. lumbricoides* but is considered a separate species; *Toxocara cati,* the cat ascarid, which may also infect man; and *T. canis,* common in dogs especially puppies.

Infection with *A. lumbricoides* occurs when the eggs are ingested. The eggs hatch in the intestine; then the larvae burrow into the blood vessels, make their way to the lungs by way of the heart, are coughed up and swallowed, and finally become adults in the intestine. Damage occurs mostly in the lungs as a result of this peculiar migration.

Order Oxyuroidea

These nematode parasites are usually small with a life cycle involving one host. They are found in all classes of vertebrates and in some invertebrates. Their head papillae are usually in a circle and their lips, when present, are three or six in number. The esophagus is commonly divided into a corpus, isthmus, and posterior bulb. The reproductive system may be single or double, and the males may or may not have genital spicules. Females are sometimes viviparous but are usually oviparous. A precloacal sucker is found in some species. The life cycle and method of infection in some species are similar in many ways to that of *Ascaris.*

The common pinworm or seatworm, *En-*

Fig. 9-25

Enterobius vermicularis, female above and smaller male below (order Oxyuroidea). (Courtesy Indiana University School of Medicine, Bloomington.)

terobius vermicularis (Fig. 9-25), is very common in children and produces enterobiasis, characterized chiefly by restlessness and insomnia. The female worm (10 mm. long) deposits eggs around the anal region of the host. These may be carried to the mouth by the hands. Although it is easy to rid the child of the worms, reinfection is also easy because infective ova contaminate surroundings.

Order Dracunculoidea

Dracunculoids are parasitic nematodes without definite lips and with an esophagus divided into a thin anterior muscular portion and a wider posterior glandular part. The vulva is near the middle of the body but is reduced in the mature worm. They are characterized also by their habitat in the deeper subcutaneous tissues and by the way the larvae, which are produced by viviparous females, pass from the body through lesions in the skin.

The classic example of this order is the guinea worm *(Dracunculus medinensis),* or the fiery serpent of Biblical times. The female, which may be a meter or more in length, is found in the subcutaneous tissues of man in Africa and Asia. When mature, she produces with a toxic substance a small lesion in the region over the worm's head. When this part of the host's body comes in contact with water, the worm contracts and expels a large number of juvenile worms through the lesion into the water. These may be swallowed by a *Cyclops* water flea, the intermediate host, and there undergo development to the infective stage. Man is infected by drinking water containing *Cyclops.* It takes 8 to 12 months for the females to mature in the body cavities before migrating to the adult habitat. Rolling the worm out little by little on a stick is the ancient method for getting rid of it, but getting rid of *Cyclops* by chemical treatment is a more modern method.

Order Filarioidea

Filarial worms have no lips or buccal cavity, and the esophagus is similar to that in Dracunculoidea. Their cuticle is chiefly devoid of superficial ornamentation, and the male spicules are unequal and dissimilar. The cephalic papillae are reduced in size and number. The worms are parasites of the vascular system, lymphatic system, coelomic spaces, and some other places in vertebrates. The life cycles of all are similar and require a bloodsucking insect for transmission.

Wuchereria bancrofti, which produces elephantiasis in man, is one of the best-known members of the order. The adults, which may be 4 to 5 inches long, live in the lymphatic system and, if present in large numbers, may block the flow of lymph, producing enormous swellings (elephantiasis) of the legs, scrotum, or other parts of the body. The females are ovoviviparous and release their microfilaria into the lymphatics whence they make their way to the blood. At night the immature worms (150 to 400 microns long) reside mainly in the peripheral vessels where they may be ingested by a bloodsucking mosquito. In the mosquito's stomach the larvae lose their sheath and migrate to the thoracic muscles where they undergo further development and complete two molts. They then pass to the proboscis of the mosquito and into the definitive host (man) through the wound made when a mosquito bites a person.

The life history of the eye worm *(Loa loa)* is similar in many ways to that of *Wuchereria* except that the eye worm is found sometimes in the eye; transmission is made through the deerfly *(Chrysops),* and the microfilariae appear in peripheral blood vessels during the day.

Order Dioctophymatida

In this order the male members are characterized by the peculiar copulatory bursa without rays at their caudal end. They have no lips, but the mouth region is provided with 6 to 18 papillae. Males have only one genital spicule. Some have a sucker around the mouth. The various species are parasites of fish, aquatic birds, and mammals.

Perhaps the largest nematode, free living or parasitic, belongs to this order. This is the giant kidney worm, *Dioctophyme renale* (Fig. 9-26), which is bright scarlet in color and up to 40 inches long (females). It is a parasite of mammals, especially dogs and minks, where it may be found in the kidney, abdominal cavity, and other organs. It is thought that the worm does not become fully mature until it parasitizes the kidney. The complete life cycle, although much investigated, was first worked out by A. Woodhead. The eggs are discharged in the urine of the definitive host and become infective several months later when they are swallowed by branchiobdellid worms (epizoic oligochaetes on crayfish), the first intermediate host. After a period of develop-

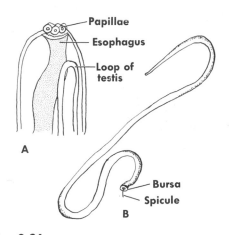

Fig. 9-26

Dioctophyme renale, the giant kidney worm, is largest nematode (up to 40 inches long). Parasitic in kidney and elsewhere (order Dioctophymatida). **A,** Anterior end of male. **B,** Adult male.

ment, the worm encysts in the annelid, which may be eaten by certain fish, the second intermediate host. After further development within the fish, the kidney worm encysts in the mesenteries and becomes infective to the definitive host (mammal) that devours the fish. The complete life cycle is about two years. The giant kidney worm eats away the interior tissue of the kidney where it may remain for two to three years. Another member of this order is *Hystrichis;* it lives in the proventriculus of aquatic birds, which become infected by eating fish.

Order Trichuroidea

The members of this order are endoparasites of the digestive tract of birds, mammals, and other vertebrates. Their chief characteristic is the unique structure of the anterior part of the body, in which the pharynx or esophagus is located. This part of the body is usually very slender and in some members is very much longer than the thicker posterior part. It is known as the stichosome and is made up of a longitudinal row of large esophageal cells (stichocytes) that represent pharyngeal gland cells.

Two very common genera are parasites of man—*Trichuris* and *Trichinella*. The

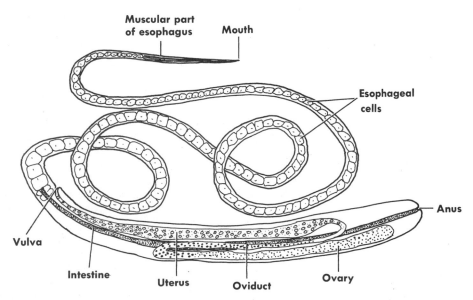

Fig. 9-27

Trichuris trichiura, the whipworm (order Trichuroidea). (Modified from Olsen, 1962.)

Fig. 9-28

Trichinella spiralis, larvae encysted in pig muscle. Larvae may live 10 to 20 years in these cysts; if eaten by another host, larvae are liberated in intestine of host where they mature and release many more larvae into host's blood (order Trichuroidea).

whipworm (*Trichuris trichiura,* Fig. 9-27) has a very long anterior portion (whip) and is a common parasite of man in warm climates. Its eggs develop in the soil, but do not hatch unless they are ingested by the host, usually on contaminated vegetables. The trichina worm (*Trichinella spiralis,* Fig. 9-28) is one of the most common nematode parasites of Americans. Infection occurs when man eats poorly cooked pork, in which the worms are encysted. In either man or pig the female worms burrow into the intestinal wall and give birth to larvae that are carried by the blood and lymph to muscles where they encyst. The symptoms of trichinosis infection occur mainly at the time of migration of the larvae. Pigs become infected by eating uncooked garbage containing contaminated meat scraps, or by eating infected rats.

CLASS NEMATOMORPHA

The members of the class Nematomorpha are usually long, slender worms that are closely allied to the nematodes. The adults are free living, whereas the juvenile worms are all parasitic in arthropods such as insects and crustaceans. Nematomorphs dif-

fer from nematodes in a number of ways such as in having an absence of lateral cords and excretory canal, a more or less degenerate enteron, and the presence of a cloaca in both sexes. They may reach a maximum length of 1.5 meters with a diameter of 3 mm., but the majority are smaller than this, with diameters not exceeding 0.5 mm. They are cosmopolitan and are found in almost every kind of aquatic habitat. Adults do not feed and require only wet or moist surroundings and sufficient oxygen.

The two orders, Gordioidea and Nectonematoidea, total about 225 species. Of the two orders, all the genera with the exception of one belong to the order Gordioidea. The Nectonematoidea has only the single genus *Nectonema,* which are planktonic worms anywhere from 10 to 800 mm. long.

Nematomorphs (Fig. 9-29, *A*) are mostly dark brown or of some darkish shade except for the anterior tip (calotte), which is white with a dark pigmented ring and terminal mouth. The posterior end may be rounded or forked, having two or three lobes with terminal or subterminal cloaca.

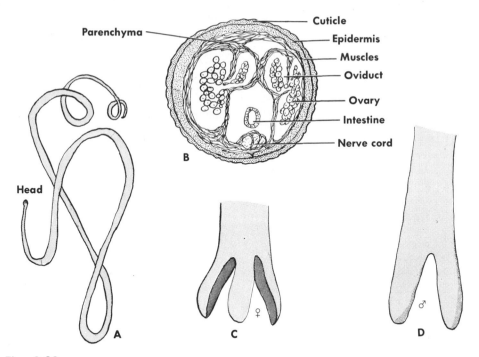

Parenchyma

Cuticle
Epidermis
Muscles
Oviduct
Ovary
Intestine
Nerve cord

B

Head

A   C   D

Fig. 9-29

Class Nematomorpha. **A,** Gordian worm. **B,** Cross section of female nematomorph. Posterior end of *Paragordius* female, **C,** and of male, **D.**

The male is shorter than the female in the Gordioidea, but the reverse is true with the Nectonematoidea. The body is made up of three layers: (1) a thin cuticle of homogeneous, fibrous layers, often provided with prominences (areolae), papillae, and hairs; (2) an epidermis of a single layer of cells or a syncytium; and (3) an inner muscle layer of longitudinal fibers only (Fig. 9-29, *B*). In Gordioidea the pseudocoel is filled with mesenchyme and other cells, so only certain longitudinal spaces are found; in *Nectonema* the pseudocoel is more evident.

The digestive system in the adult is relatively degenerate, and the anterior part may consist of a row of cells. Ingestion of food is absent in the adults. No specific circulatory, respiratory, or excretory organs exist.

The nervous system consists of a circumenteric cerebral mass lying ventrally in the head calotte and a midventral nerve cord that originates in the epidermis. Sensory functions may be restricted to the bristles and areoles of the cuticle. A rudimentary

eye in the form of a large sac is found in *Paragordius.*

Nematomorphs are all dioecious, and the paired gonads are cylindric strings that extend the length of the body. Each gonad of the male enters the cloaca by a sperm duct. There are no genital spicules. In the female the ovaries contain lateral diverticula in which the eggs mature. The eggs pass from the diverticula into the ovarian tubes or uteri and enter the cuticle-lined cloaca separately. A saclike seminal receptacle extends anteriorly from the cloaca.

In copulation the male coils around the female and places a drop (spermatophore) of sperm near the cloacal opening of the female. The sperm then actively enter the seminal receptacle. Sometimes a number of worms of both sexes may be found in a tangled skein together while copulating. Eggs are laid in stringy masses in the water, after which the adults die. When the eggs hatch, the larvae swim to an arthropod, which they enter by means of their proboscis armed with hooks and stylets. In some cases the larvae may secrete mucus

235

in which they encyst until the proper terrestrial host ingests them. In the hemocoel of the host the juvenile worms undergo gradual development without metamorphosis, a process which may last several months. Only one host is involved in the parasitic stage. This host may be a cockroach, cricket, grasshopper, or other arthropod. The hosts of *Nectonema* are various decapod crustacea. Within the host, nematomorphs take all their nutrition by absorption through the body surface because no food enters the enteron during their life cycle. It is possible that their epidermis secretes enzymes for digesting the host's tissues.

When the worms are mature, they molt, discard unnecessary larval characters, and leave the host, usually when the latter is near the water. In the past this often took place in water troughs, which gave rise to the popular superstition that horse hairs turned into worms.

The best known genera of the order Gordioidea are *Paragordius* and *Gordius*. *Paragordius* grows to a length of about 300 mm.; the female is distinguished by a trilobed posterior end and the male by a deeply bilobed one (Fig. 9-29, *C, D*). *Gordius* may reach a length of 900 mm. with a diameter of 1 mm. The posterior end in this genus is unlobed in the female and bilobed in the male.

Annotated references

Baer, J. G. 1952. Ecology of animal parasites. Urbana, University of Illinois Press. *This work stresses the biology of certain parasites and shows how they adapt themselves to the host. A treatise with a well-deserved reputation.*

Beauchamp, P. de. 1907. Morphologie et variations de l'appareil rotateur. Arch. Zool. Exp. Gen. 6:1-29. *In this and other papers Beauchamp was the first to point out that the ground plan of the corona of rotifers consisted of a large buccal field of short cilia around the mouth and a circumapical band encircling the head and that the animal was adapted for a creeping existence.*

Chandler, A. C. 1949. Introduction to parasitology, ed. 8. New York, John Wiley & Sons, Inc. *A standard text on parasitology with good treatment of the nematodes.*

Chitwood, B. G., et al. 1950. An introduction to nematology. Baltimore, Monumental Press. *The best general treatment of the nematodes yet published.*

Edmondson, W. T. (editor). 1959. Ward and Whipple's fresh-water biology, ed. 2. New York, John Wiley & Sons, Inc. *Many groups of pseudocoelomates are treated in this excellent handbook. Keys and figures are emphasized.*

Goodey, T. 1951. Soil and freshwater nematodes. New York, John Wiley & Sons, Inc.

Hyman, L. H. 1951. The invertebrates: Acanthocephala, Aschelminthes and Entoprocta; the pseudocoelomate Bilateria, vol. 3. New York, McGraw-Hill Book Company. *An authoritative treatise of the first rank, and one of the best treatments of these groups yet published.*

Lee, D. L. 1965. The physiology of nematodes. San Francisco, W. H. Freeman & Co., Publishers. *An up-to-date work on a difficult and much neglected field of study.*

Maggenti, A. R. Comparative morphology in nemic phylogeny. In Dougherty, E. C. (editor). 1963. The lower Metazoa; comparative biology and phylogeny. Berkeley, University of California Press. *This chapter attempts to trace the affinities between the different nemic taxa.*

Pennak, R. W. 1953. Fresh-water invertebrates of the United States. New York, The Ronald Press Company. *Good sections with keys are devoted to gastrotrichs, rotifers, and nematodes.*

Remane, A. 1963. The systematic position and phylogeny of the pseudocoelomates. In Dougherty, E. C. (editor). 1963. The lower Metazoa; comparative biology and phylogeny. Berkeley, Univeristy of California Press. *The author regards the pseudocoelomates as playing minor roles in the production and evolution of higher forms. No phyletic relationships of the different members with each other or with other phyla have been established.*

Remane, A. Rotatoria. In Bronn, H. G. (editor). 1933. Klassen und Ordnungen des Tierreichs, vol. 4, pp. 1-4. Leipzig, Akademische Verlagsgesellschaft. *One of the best general accounts of rotifers.*

Sasser, J. N., and W. R. Jenkins (editors). 1960. Nematology. Chapel Hill, University of North Carolina Press. *Many specialists have contributed to this important treatise on nearly every aspect of nematodes.*

Steiner, G. 1921. Untersuchungen über den allgemeinen Bauplan des Nematodenkorpers. Zool. Jahrb. Abt. Anat. 43:1-96.

Swellengrebel, N. H., and M. M. Sterman. 1961. Animal parasites in man. Princeton, D. Van Nostrand Co., Inc. *An English edition of a standard Dutch work. Part 4 is devoted to nematodes.*

Woodhead, A. 1945. The life history cycle of *Dioctophyme renale*. J. Parasitol. 31(suppl.):12-30. *The complicated life history of this large nematode so long investigated was finally solved by this author.*

Phylum Acanthocephala

The second phylum of pseudocoelomate animals is the Acanthocephala, or spiny-headed worms. The adults of this phylum are all endoparasites in the digestive tract of vertebrates, while the juvenile stages are found in arthropods (the intermediate host). Over 500 species have been described to date, and they have been found in all classes of vertebrates. More species have been found in fishes than in any other class of vertebrates; only a few occur in amphibians and reptiles. Most of the small species are found in fishes; the largest are found in mammals. Host specificity is found in some but not in others. However, their host tolerance never extends to both cold-blooded and warm-blooded animals for the same species of acanthocephalan. The distribution of acanthocephs is worldwide, but not all species are cosmopolitan because some are restricted to rather small areas.

CLASSIFICATION

Phylum Acanthocephala. Body cylindric or laterally flattened in form and divided into proboscis, neck, and trunk; spiny proboscis retractile into sheath; epidermis syncytial, covered with cuticle; fluid-filled canal system (lacunae); muscles of both longitudinal and circular types; body cavity a pseudocoel; digestive tract absent; excretory system of branched, ciliated protonephridia; circulatory and respiratory systems absent; nervous system of a brain on the proboscis sheath and two lateral cords; sensory papillae on body surface; separate sexes; male organs of paired testes on ligament, ducts, cement glands, and penis apparatus; female organs of paired ovaries, uterine bell, uterine tube, and uterus; endoparasitic; life cycle involves two hosts, a vertebrate and an invertebrate; develop-

ment of the spiral determinate type; cell or nuclear constancy.

Order Archiacanthocephala. Proboscis spines concentrically arranged; median lacunar channels; excretory system with protonephridia; ligament sacs persistent in females; terrestrial hosts. *Macracanthorhynchus* (Fig. 10-1), *Moniliformis, Gigantorhynchus.*

Order Palaeacanthocephala. Excretory system absent; proboscis spines in alternating radial rows; main lateral lacunar canals; ligament sacs transitory in female; six cement glands in male (usually); aquatic hosts (chiefly). *Leptorhynchoides, Gorgorhynchus, Polymorphus, Centrorhynchus.*

Order Eocanthocephala. Excretory system absent; median lacunar canals; proboscis spines radially arranged; ligament sacs persistent in female; cement glands syncytial with reservoir; aquatic hosts. *Neoechinorhynchus, Pallisentis.*

BASIC ADAPTIVE FEATURES

The group is wholly parasitic, and this method of existence has directed the evolutionary diversity found among them. The parasitic habit has had perhaps a greater influence on the structure of the acanthocephalan body than is the case with any other parasitic group. None has an alimentary canal, and absorption of the host's food is entirely through the skin, similar to the method of tapeworms. While certain structures may have been lost or modified by degeneration, in many respects the worms are highly specialized and have many unique features such as the lacunae of the skin and the lemnisci. The most gen-

237

eralized or primitive structural arrangement seems to be among those worms that are parasitic in fish, where they may have arisen. However, in morphologic features the group is a closely knit one. The size range of the worms represents their greatest diversity in evolutionary development, sizes ranging anywhere from 1.5 mm. to almost 2 feet in length.

Their chief adaptive feature is the invaginable proboscis with its rows of recurved hooks. This holdfast organ represents one of the most efficient in the whole range of parasitic existence and also one of the most injurious to the tissues of the host. This organ differs in minor details among the different orders, but such differences probably have little significance.

PHYLOGENETIC RELATIONSHIPS

The relationship of the spiny-headed worms to other phyla is very obscure, and divergent views have been held by authorities. It is now almost generally agreed that these worms should be considered a phylum in their own right. At the present time their nearest relationships seem to fluctuate between the Platyhelminthes on the one hand and the Aschelminthes on the other. As a matter of fact, acanthocephalans have features that are shared with both the flatworms and the aschelminths. Some of their characteristics, which are also found in some Aschelminthes, are superficial segmentation, a large pseudocoel and its divisions, and cell or nuclear constancy. Flatworm characteristics found in spiny-headed worms are the flattened shape of the acanthocephalan body while in the host; the lack of a digestive system, as in cestodes; the presence of an armed proboscis, also in cestodes; a body wall musculature of both longitudinal and circular muscles; a corresponding reproductive system; similar serologic tests; and, in the embryologic development, a stage similar to the cestode hexacanth. Certain features are found in all the three phyla such as the syncytial epidermis and the flame bulb protonephridia. Our greatest American investigator (H. J. Van Cleve) of the Acanthocephala favors the platyhelminthic affinity, as do others.

Fig. 10-1
Macracanthorhynchus hirudinaceus, the spiny-headed worm of pigs (preserved specimen). Inset is enlarged view of anterior end with proboscis. (From Hickman: Integrated principles of zoology, The C. V. Mosby Co.)

GENERAL MORPHOLOGIC FEATURES

Most species are about an inch long; some may be smaller, and others may be as long as 2 feet. Females are nearly always longer than the males of the same species. In the host the body is often flattened, but after removal it becomes turgid and cylindric (Fig. 10-1). Many different shapes may be found, such as curved or spirally coiled. The surface may be smooth or wrinkled, suggestive of pseudometamerism. The color is mostly translucent or white, but the body often assumes the color of the intestinal contents. The body is divided into the presoma (proboscis and neck) and trunk. Trunk spines are found on the body surface of some species.

The body wall is composed of cuticle, a hypodermis, and an inner muscular layer. The syncytial epidermis is provided with a branching and anastomosing lacunar system of channels without walls, which are arranged in definite patterns (Fig. 10-2). The system may be in the form of a network of lacunal channels, but usually it consists of a pair of longitudinal channels that are connected by a series of smaller vessels, the lacunae. The longitudinal channels may lie in dorsal and ventral median positions, or they may occupy lateral positions. In some species only the dorsal channel is present. The lacunar system does not communicate with the outside or the inside except in the case of the lemnisci, which are supplied by lacunar vessels. The presoma contains lacunae but no longitudinal vessels. The lacunae contain a nutritive fluid and are a means of distributing food absorbed from the host because of the absence of digestive organs. Round or oval giant nuclei are also found in the hypodermis, which rests upon a thin basement membrane or dermis. The muscle part of the body wall is made up of outer circular and inner longitudinal fibers syncytial in nature.

The characteristic proboscis is the main organ of attachment. It may be globular, elongated, or cylindric in shape and is always armed with sharp, recurved hooks, spines, or both. These hooks are arranged in patterns of taxonomic importance. In most species the hollow proboscis can be retracted or everted into a muscular, saclike structure, the proboscis receptacle, that is

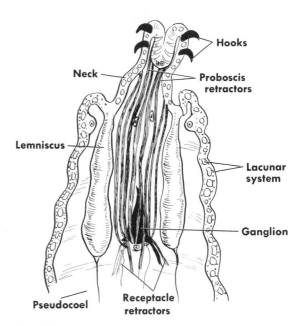

Fig. 10-2

Diagram of longitudinal section through anterior end of acanthoceph with proboscis partially everted. Recurved hooks or spines are numerous; their arrangement has taxonomic significance. (After Hamann; modified from Hyman.)

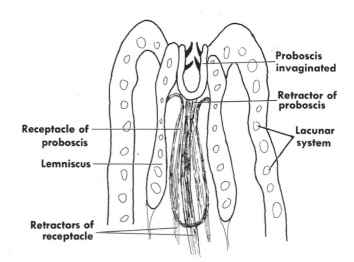

Fig. 10-3

Diagram of longitudinal section through anterior end of acanthoceph showing relations of invaginated proboscis and other structures. Note spines or hooks pointed forward in this position.

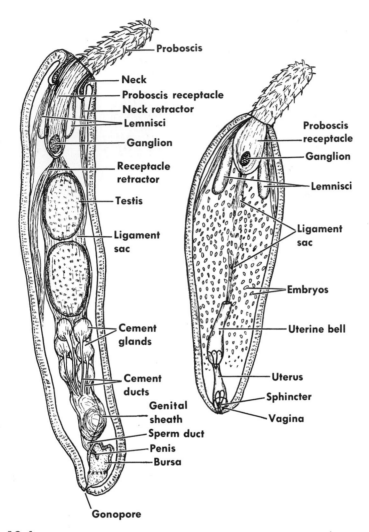

Fig. 10-4

Acanthocephalus, a palaeacanthocephalan. Left, male. Right, ripe female; ligament sac has ruptured; body cavity filled with shelled embryos. (After Yamaguti; modified from Hyman.)

attached to the inner surface of the proboscis wall and hangs suspended in the pseudocoel. When the proboscis is introverted into the receptacle, the hooks are on the inside of the proboscis with their tips directed anteriorly (Fig. 10-3); when everted, the tips of the hooks point posteriorly and fasten into the host's intestinal wall like a thorn (Fig. 10-2). The neck and proboscis receptacle can also be retracted into the pseudocoel, but they cannot be everted. Special muscles (retractor or in-

vertor) operate the proboscis and its receptacle. These muscles are attached to the inside tip of the proboscis and are inserted on the receptacle wall; also, passing through the wall, they are fastened to the inside of the body wall to become the receptacle retractors. The neck is retracted by special muscles that run from the posterior edge of the neck to the inside of the trunk. From the posterior end of the neck region are two lateral diverticula, or lemnisci, which hang down in the pseudocoel and may act as reservoirs for the lacunar fluid when the proboscis is retracted. They communicate with the lacunar system by special channels.

The pseudocoel, or body cavity, extends

also into the presoma and contains the internal organs (Fig. 10-4). The chief organs are the hollow connective tissue ligament sacs that enclose the reproductive organs and run the length of the body. The ligament sac may be single or double and may represent separate parts of the body cavity. Alongside the ligament sacs lies an endodermal ligament strand to which the gonads are attached. A digestive system is entirely lacking in this phylum.

The nervous system consists of a cerebral ganglion (Figs. 10-2, 10-4) located within the proboscis receptacle; two lateral longitudinal nerve branches, the retinacula, pass posteriorly to innervate the trunk wall. The cerebral ganglion also gives off small nerves to such structures as the musculature of the proboscis and sensory papillae. Sense organs are scanty in this phylum. Some are located in the proboscis and in the male copulatory apparatus. Perhaps all the sense organs are tactile.

Only in one order (Archiacanthocephala) is there a definite excretory system consisting of a pair of small protonephridial organs each made up of flame bulbs attached to a common canal. The two canals form a common canal that joins either the sperm duct or the uterus.

Sexes in the Acanthocephala are always separate. The male reproductive system consists of a pair of testes arranged tandem fashion in the ligament sac and fastened to the ligament strand (Fig. 10-4). A sperm duct from each testis runs posteriorly through the ligament sac. These two ducts finally unite to form a common sperm duct that is provided with a saclike seminal vesicle. A cluster of cement glands may also send ducts to the common sperm duct. The complex of sperm ducts, cement gland ducts, and protonephridia (in one order) are all enclosed in a genital sheath that is continuous with the ligament sac. The genital sheath terminates posteriorly on the bell-shaped copulatory bursa, which is eversible and holds the posterior end of the female in copulation. The sperm and secretions of the cement glands are discharged through a penis that projects into the bursa. The secretions of the cement glands hold the bursa firmly in place while the penis enters the female vagina and discharges its sperm in copulation.

Fig. 10-5

Diagram of genital selective apparatus of female acanthoceph. See text for functional description. (From Hickman: Integrated principles of zoology, The C. V. Mosby Co.)

The female reproductive system consists of an ovary (single or double) that is present in larval stages but later dissociates into egg balls. These egg balls float free in the ligament sac and, as the eggs are released from the egg balls, they are fertilized. The ligament sac may rupture and the pseudocoel may be filled with ovarian balls and eggs. Only one quota of eggs can, therefore, be produced in the life cycle of one female. From the ligament sacs the eggs pass into the uterine bell, a funnel-shaped structure which opens into the ligament sac or the pseudocoel (Fig. 10-5). During embyronic development in the pseudocoel, the eggs acquire membranes and a hard shell. From the uterine bell the ripe or mature eggs pass into the narrow uterine tube; the immature ones are detoured back into the body cavity by openings in the selector apparatus. The uterine tube enters the muscular uterus, which opens to the

241

outside by a short vagina. The eggs are thus discharged through the vaginal or genital orifice into the intestine of the host.

The eggs, which are discharged in the feces of the host, can withstand severe environmental conditions for months. At this stage the egg contains a mature embryo, the acanthor, that is surrounded by three membranes. No further development occurs until the acanthors are ingested by a suitable intermediate host, usually an arthropod. Within the intermediate host (grubs, roaches, or crustaceans) the eggs hatch and release the spindle-shaped acanthor with a spiny body and retractor hooks. The acanthor has an inner nuclear mass of undifferentiated nuclei, the endoblast, that gives rise to the structures of following stages. The acanthor is found at first in the intestine of the intermediate host but eventually makes its way into the hemocoel where its further transformation occurs. Its next stage is called the acanthella, in which occur the beginnings of certain adult structures such as the proboscis, reproductive organs, lemnisci, etc. When the larva becomes infective, it is called the cystacanth, which contains all the adult structures in an immature form (a juvenile worm). From the acanthor to the cystacanth may require two to three months. The juvenile usually remains quiescent in the intermediate host until ingested by the definitive vertebrate host, although sometimes encysted juveniles may be found in a vertebrate as a second intermediate host or transport host before reaching the final host.

The cleavage pattern in the embryology of acanthocephalans seems to be a modified spiral determinate type. Cell or nuclear constancy (eutely) seems to be fixed for each tissue. In their development, changes in the form of the nuclei are correlated with a favorable ratio between the nuclear surface and cytoplasm.

The most familar member of the phylum is *Macracanthorhynchus hirudinaceus* (Fig. 10-1), which is cosmopolitan in pigs and some other mammals. A common parasite of fish is *Leptorhynchoides thecatus* whose larval forms are passed in the familiar amphipod *Hyalella knickerbockeri*. *Moniliformis dubius* is a common parasite of rats, and cockroaches serve as intermediate hosts.

Annotated references

Brown, F. A., Jr. (editor). 1950. Selected invertebrate types. New York, John Wiley & Sons, Inc. Neoechinorhynchus emydis, *a parasite of freshwater turtles, is used as a type of an acanthocephalan.*

Bullough, W. S. 1950. Practical invertebrate anatomy. London, The Macmillan Company. *This practical manual gives a concise account of the dissection of* Macranthorhynchus hirudinaceus, *the common acanthocephalan parasite of pigs.*

Chandler, A. C. 1949. Introduction to parasitology, ed. 8. New York, John Wiley & Sons, Inc. A *short section is devoted to the Acanthocephala. The author considers the group as a class without attachment to any phylum.*

Hyman, L. H. 1951. The invertebrates; the pseudocoelomate Bilateria, vol. 3. New York, McGraw-Hill Book Company. *The best English account of the spiny-headed worms.*

Kaiser, J. E. 1893. Die Acanthocephalen und ihre Entwickelung. Bibl. Zool. **2**:1.

Meyer, A. Acanthocephala. In Bronn, H. G. (editor). 1933. Klassen und Ordnungen des Tierreichs, vol. 4, part 2, section 2. Leipzig, Akademische Verlagsgesellschaft. *The definitive German account of* Acanthocephala.

Olsen, O. W. 1962. Animal parasites; their biology and life cycles. Minneapolis, Burgess Publishing Co. *Good schemes of the acanthocephalan parasites found in the pig, rat, and fish.*

Van Cleve, H. J. 1941. Relationships of the Acanthocephala. Am. Natur. **75**:31-45. *This and other papers on this phylum are by a lifelong student of the group. He strongly favors a platyhelminthic affinity of these parasitic worms.*

Phylum Entoprocta

These sessile pseudocoelomates were formerly included in the moss animals Bryozoa or Polyzoa, which also include the coelomate Ectoprocta. They are solitary, colonial, stalked animals, which are always sessile and which have the anus within the circle of tentacles, not outside as in Ectoprocta. The Entoprocta are all small animals and most live in marine waters with only one or two freshwater representatives. The phylum comprises three families and about 90 species. Within the phylum itself the Entoprocta have not been classed in higher taxa than families. The three families are Loxosomatidae, with the calyx pseudocoel not separated from that of the stalk by a septum and with buds arising from the sides of the calyx; Pedicellinidae, with the pseudocoel separated by a septum from that of the stalk and with buds arising from stolons; and the Urnatellidae (freshwater), with small colonies formed by a few chitinized stalks from a basal plate and with deciduous calyces. Only one genus, *Urnatella* (Fig. 11-2), with two species is found in the last family.

BASIC ADAPTIVE FEATURES

The Entoprocta are ciliary feeders and sessile in form; these characteristics have largely guided evolutionary tendencies within the group. Sessile forms are nearly always provided with food-catching devices on their distal end. In the case of Entoprocta the tentacles are ciliated on their inner surfaces and can be turned in different directions by the calyx. Variations in the evolutionary pattern of the group have involved methods of budding, the structure of the stalk, deciduous or nondeciduous tendencies among the calyces, etc. The tentacular arrangement of Entoprocta in their evolution has been kept within a circular outgrowth of the body margin and does not acquire the lophophore ridge of the Ectoprocta.

PHYLOGENETIC RELATIONSHIPS

Although the Entoprocta are often included with the Ectoprocta in the moss animals Bryozoa or Polyzoa (English), there is little or no evidence to show that the two phyla are closely related. The Entoprocta shares with the Aschelminthes and Acanthocephala the presence of a pseudocoel, whereas the Ectoprocta are coelomate animals. However, it is very difficult to find proof of affinity between the Entoprocta and the other pseudocoelomates. The position once taken by L. H. Hyman that a relationship of the Entoprocta to certain rotifers exists is no longer considered tenable. The present view is that the entoprocts probably arose as an early offshoot of the same line that led to the Ectoprocta. E. Marcus thinks that the Entoprocta may have arisen as the attached or sessile larvae of the Ectoprocta.

MORPHOLOGIC FEATURES

Most Entoprocta live in marine waters and are found attached to some hard substratum or to other animals (epizoic habitat). An individual entoproct shows four chief divisions: the crown of tentacles, the calyx, the stalk, and the substratum to which the stalk is attached. Most entoprocts are not more than 5 mm. in length. The internal organs are contained within

243

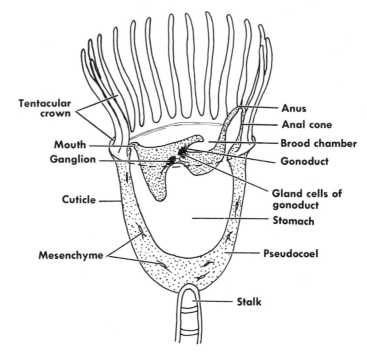

Fig. 11-1

Typical entoproct calyx (partly cut away in front) showing internal structures.

Fig. 11-2

Urnatella, the only freshwater entoproct. (After Cori; modified from Hyman.)

the calyx, a bulbous-shaped structure that bears a circle of 8 to 36 ciliated tentacles around the upper margin (Fig. 11-1). Tentacles are outgrowths of the body wall and can move individually or together. The depression surrounded by the circle of tentacles is the vestibule and contains the mouth at one end and the anus at the other. The crown of tentacles can be rolled inward over the mouth and anus but cannot be retracted into the calyx. Ciliated grooves in the sides of the vestibule run to the corners of the mouth. The calyx is slightly compressed laterally and may be at right angles to the stalk or oriented obliquely to it. The stalk is an elongation of the calyx, but in most species the two parts are partially separated by an incomplete septum. The stalk may have a beaded appearance because of the regular constrictions on it (Fig. 11-2), but many other variations are also found in the stalks of the different species. Smooth muscle fibers are found in the stalks of all species. Although they are sessile forms, entoprocts can move their stalks, curl their tentacles, bend their calyces, etc. In some the basal plate of the stalk sends out slender stolons that run over a substratum and, by branching, give rise to many stalks.

The body wall consists of a cuticle, epidermis, and smooth muscle fibers. The wall is of about the same structure in all parts of the animal. The epidermis is cellular, of cuboidal cells, and is thicker in the more heavily ciliated regions such as the tentacles.

The body wall musculature consists of mostly longitudinal fibers and is thinnest in the wall of the calyx. Muscle fibers are common along the inner wall of the tentacles, and their contraction makes it possible for the tentacles to be pulled toward the vestibule. A sphincter composed of a muscle band contracts the tentacular membrane over the tentacles when the latter curl into the vestibule. The jerky movements of the stalks of some species is brought about by the muscular swellings which can contract independently of each other.

The pseudocoel, or body cavity, is found in the tentacles, stalks, stolons, and calyx between the body wall and viscera. It is filled with a gelatinous mesenchymal tissue. It also contains both free ameboid and fixed cells. The calyx of most species has its pseudocoel separated from that of the stalk by a septum.

The U-shaped alimentary tract is composed of a mouth, a short buccal cavity, a tubular esophagus, a large saclike stomach, a narrow intestine, and a rectum that opens to the outside by the anus within the circle of tentacles. An anal cone is present in some species. Parts of the digestive system are lined with cilia. Glandular regions in the stomach may produce enzymes for extracellular digestion. Absorption may occur in both the stomach and intestine. The Entoprocta are filter feeders. Food particles are directed toward the mouth by the beating of the cilia on the tentacles. Water currents are carried down on the inner ciliated surfaces of the tentacles into the vestibule where a certain amount of rejection or straining may occur by the closure of the esophageal sphincter, so that rejected items are sent back in the outgoing current of water. The food is carried through the alimentary canal by ciliary movement because the walls of the digestive tract lack muscles.

Most of the food consists of protozoans, diatoms, and other small organisms. When feeding, the tentacles of the calyx are well extended and turn about in different directions for the location of food.

The excretory system consists of a pair of flame bulbs in the calyx placed ventral to the stomach near the esophagus. Each bulb is drained by a nephridial tube that unites with its corresponding mate to form a common tubule before opening by a single median nephridiopore in the vestibule between the mouth and anus.

The nervous system is made up of a large, bilobed ganglion in the pseudocoel between the stomach and vestibule, and nerve fibers that radiate through the body to the tentacles, stalk, and parts of the calyx. Tactile sense organs of one or more bristles are found on the margin of the calyx and on the tentacles. The tentacular crown is especially sensitive to touch and retracts inward when disturbed. No special respiratory or circulatory organs are present.

Entoprocts reproduce both sexually and asexually. Sexual reproduction produces new colonies, and asexual budding adds new members to existing colonies. Sexually, some entoprocts are dioecious, some are hermaphroditic, and some are protandrous. An entire colony may be of one sex. The gonads consist of a pair of testes and a pair of ovaries. In the hermaphroditic forms the paired testes lie posterior to the paired ovaries. In dioecious species each gonad has a short gonoduct that unites with the other before opening by a common gonopore on the vestibule near the nephridiopore; in hermaphrodites the sperm duct joins the oviduct of that side before the formation of the common gonoduct. Fertilization occurs in the ovaries, and the developing egg is released through the gonopore. By means of a secreted membrane the egg is attached in the female brood pouch, which lies in a depression of the vestibule between the gonopore and the anus. Here the egg is retained during the period of embryonic development. Cleavage is of the spiral determinate type, and a coeloblastula is formed by the 67-cell stage; a blastula is formed by the 90-cell stage. A free-swimming, ciliated larva of a modified trochophore type is hatched **245**

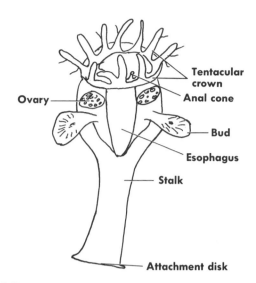

Fig. 11-3

Loxosoma with two buds. This common marine genus is considered to be most primitive of Entoprocta. (Modified from Nickerson.)

Fig. 11-4

Gonypodaria, a pedicellinid entoproct, has slender stalks set in muscular sockets.

and is incubated for a time in the brood pouch. After its release, the larva swims about for a short time before its permanent attachment to a substratum and its metamorphosis into the initial individual of a colony. The colony then is formed by asexual budding from the calyx or from the stalk.

Entoprocts have a wide distribution in marine waters from the poles to the tropics. Some have been found to a depth of 150 fathoms. Of the marine species, the solitary *Loxosoma* is fairly common, usually attached to worm tubes in shallow water (Fig. 11-3). It is not colonial in habit because the asexual buds separate from the parent after maturing and attach their pedal gland independently to a substratum where they lead a solitary existence. The animals vary from $\frac{1}{12}$ to $\frac{1}{50}$ inch in height. Some authorities consider this genus to be one of the most primitive in the phylum. *Pedicellina* is another familiar entoproct of our eastern seashore. Its colonies are attached to the substratum by slender branching stolons from which the stalked individuals are budded. The calyx is separated from the stalk by a septum. Its buds arise from the stolons. This genus is often found on the piles of old wharfs. *Barentsia* is another genus that is found along both eastern and western sea coasts; it is characterized by muscular enlargements which may give rise to branches along the stalk. *Gonypodaria* (Fig. 11-4) has a similar arrangement of muscular swellings along the stalk. The freshwater species *Urnatella gracilis* (Fig. 11-2) seems to have a limited distribution in the streams of the eastern half of the United States. It is found in small colonies, the one to six members of a colony all arising from one basal plate. The stalks, branched or unbranched, are beaded by cuticular constrictions. Individuals do not exceed 5 mm. in length.

Annotated references

Cori, C. Kamptozoa. In Bronn, H. G. (editor). 1936. Klassen und Ordnungen des Tierreichs, vol. 4, part 2. Leipzig, Akademische Verlagsgesellschaft. *An authoritative and technical treatise of the entoprocts.*

Davenport, C. 1893. On *Urnatella gracilis.* Bull. Mus. Comp. Zool. Harvard University **24**:1-44.

Hyman, L. H. 1951. The invertebrates; the pseudocoelomate Bilateria, vol. 3, New York, Mc-

Graw-Hill Book Company. *The most up-to-date account of the Entoprocta. The author does not consider the entoproct as a lophophore animal.*

Nickerson, W. 1901. On *Loxosoma davenporti.* J. Morphol. **17**:357-376.

Pennak, R. W. 1953. Fresh-water invertebrates of the United States. New York, The Ronald Press Company. *The single freshwater species (Urnatella gracilis Leidy) is placed in the key with the Bryozoa (Ectoprocta).*

Rogick, M. D. 1948. Studies on marine Bryozoa. Part II. *Barentsia laxa.* Biol. Bull. **94**:128-142. *A good account of the larva is included in this study. Miss Rogick considers the Entoprocta as a class under the Bryozoa, not a separate phylum (Hyman).*

Phylum Phoronida

This small phylum of wormlike animals is placed with two other phyla—Ectoprocta and Brachiopoda—in a group called the lophophorate coelomates. All three phyla possess in common a lophophore, which is a variously-shaped distal fold of the body surrounding the mouth, specialized as a food-collecting mechanism. L. H. Hyman (1959) has given a recent evaluation of the lophophorates in her valuable and extensive treatise on the invertebrates. The members of this group have many other characteristics in common besides the lophophore. First of all, their body reveals certain indications of the three regional body divisions of the deuterostomes: protosome, mesosome, and metasome, with their corresponding coelomic cavities, protocoel, mesocoel, and metacoel. This regional feature is not always clear cut; it is often obscure because of evolutionary modifications. The three phyla supposedly came from a common ancestral type whose body was composed of head, lophophore, and trunk; but owing to the degeneration or reduction of the head associated with a sessile, sedentary existence, the protocoel has disappeared, leaving only the mesocoel and metacoel divisions of the coelomic cavity. Most lophophorates have a septum separating the mesocoel from the metacoel. Other common features lophophorates usually possess are a U-shaped digestive tract, protective coverings, and an embryology of both protostome and deuterostome characteristics.

Hyman has emphasized the definition of a lophophore and excludes those animals that have clusters of tentacles in similar positions but lack other features of a true lophophore. Her definition of a lophophore involves a tentaculated extension of the mesosome with a coelomic lumen surrounding the mouth but not the anus. The primitive shape of the lophophore is considered to be horseshoelike, but it is circular in some forms. Generally the lophophore is flexible and bears muscles and nerves. In some species it can be retracted into the body cavity; in others it can be pulled back for protection into the secreted tube in which the animal lives.

The tube-dwelling phoronids are benthonic and live just below the surface in the upper littoral zone in intertidal or subtidal mud flats (Fig. 12-1). They are strictly marine and are rare in brackish water. They often form masses of intertwined tubes attached to rocks and other substrata in fairly shallow water (Fig. 12-2). Some have the habit of burrowing in calcareous shells and rocks in which the worms are also enclosed by their secreted tubes. Phoronids are restricted to the tropical and temperate zones where, in favorable environmental conditions, they may be abundant. They occur both along the Atlantic coast south of Chesapeake Bay and along parts of the Pacific coast. In Europe most species have been found from Norway to the Mediterranean region. Certain species live on the coasts of Japan, Australia, and elsewhere. So far, no records of phoronids have been reported from the polar regions.

The major activity of a phoronid consists in protruding the anterior end of the body, erecting and expanding the tentacular crown, and moving the cilia vigorously

Fig. 12-1

Diagram of phoronid in its tube showing some distinctive characteristics. (From Hickman: Integrated principles of zoology, The C. V. Mosby Co.)

to create water currents. At the same time the mouth is kept open to catch the food brought to it. When danger threatens, the body is withdrawn into the tube by contraction of the trunk longitudinal muscles. Protrusion and expansion are brought about by contraction of trunk circular muscles, which force the coelomic fluid forward to the lophophore. The giant fiber or fibers may be responsible for rapid retraction into the tube.

CLASSIFICATION

Phylum Phoronida. Body vermiform and cylindric with lophophore; housed in chitinous case; lophophore a double spiral of horseshoe shape; coelomic cavity of mesocoel and metacoel divisions; digestive system U-shaped; no respiratory organs; circulatory system closed but no heart present; excretory system of two metanephridia; nervous system of an epidermal nerve net and ring with nerves including giant fibers; monoecious with nephridia as gonoducts; asexual reproduction by fission; larva (actinotroch) a modified trochophore; marine. Two genera are represented: *Pho-*

ronis, with lophophore marked off from the trunk by a slight groove (Fig. 12-2); *Phoronopsis,* with a high collarlike fold between lophophore and trunk. The two genera have a total of 16 species.

BASIC ADAPTIVE FEATURES

Evolutionary divergence has been modest in a phylum of so few species. Since phoronids are filter feeders, some of their morphologic differences involve changes in the lophophore and its tentacles. The number of tentacles varies from 18 to 300, with the larger number in the bigger species. Another adaptive feature that has guided their evolutionary divergence is their tube, which varies with the nature of the habitat. In sandy bottoms the tube is erect and cylindric; on hard substrata the tube may be twisted or form tangled masses (Fig. 12-2). **249**

Fig. 12-2

Part of colony of *Phoronis*.

PHYLOGENETIC RELATIONSHIPS

The phoronids belong to the coelomate Protostomia, although they do not fit into the protostomian pattern in all respects, especially with regard to their embryology. Their trochophore type of larva and the origin of the mouth from the blastopore place the phylum among the protostomes. The phoronids bear a remarkable resemblance to certain ectoprocts, especially the phylactolaemates. Some of the English zoologists of the last century regarded the phoronid as a solitary polyzoon (bryozoan). Both bryozoans and phoronids have the same coelomic cavity pattern of mesocoel and metacoel, the same horseshoe arrangement of the lophophore, the same pattern of body wall musculature, and the same type of main nervous center. But there are obvious differences such as the well-developed vascular system and the metanephridia of phoronids; there is a total absence of these structures in the ectoprocts.

The nearest relatives of the phoronids must be the other members of the lophophorates, which share so many things in common despite certain differences found among the three phyla. The Lophophorata as a group seem to stand somewhere between the Protostomia and the Deuterostomia and include some characteristics of both those divisions (Hyman).

GENERAL MORPHOLOGIC FEATURES
External features

The body of the phoronid is cylindric and ranges in length from about ¼ inch to 8 inches with an average of about 4 inches. The chief features of the body are the tentacular crown (lophophore) at the anterior end and the long slender trunk without appendages but with a slightly enlarged posterior end (the end bulb). Each worm is always found in a chitinous tube, which it secretes. The tube is somewhat longer than the worm and is open at the anterior end, from which the forepart of the body with its lophophore can be protruded. The parchmentlike tube with sandy encrustations may be erect and buried in sand or mud, or it may, with others, form masses of intertwining tubes attached to rocks and shells (Figs. 12-1, 12-2).

The most conspicuous part of the worm is the anterior lophophore. This characteristic organ consists of two body wall ridges curved in the shape of a horseshoe whose limbs may each be rolled up into a spiral. The convex part of the horseshoe is located ventrally and the concave side is dorsal. The outer, or external, ridge of the horseshoe runs ventral to the mouth while the inner, or internal, ridge is dorsal to it. Each ridge of the lophophore bears a variable number of flattened tentacles, which are hollow, ciliated extensions of the body wall. The lumen in the tentacles is a continuation of the coelomic cavity and is lined with peritoneum. The tentacles are rather stiff and are supported by a thick basement membrane that acts as a skeleton. The number of tentacles varies in the different species from 18 to more than 300.

Internal features

The body wall consists of an outer epidermis, which may bear a cuticle in certain regions; a musculature of circular and longitudinal layers; and a peritoneal lining (Fig. 12-3). Cilia are restricted to the tentacles and anterior part of the trunk. The epidermis contains many gland cells, especially on the tentacular crown and anterior part of the trunk. The coelomic cavity is made up of the mesocoel, which forms the coelom of the tentacular crown, and the metacoel, which is found in the trunk. The mesocoel and metacoel are separated by a septum. Mesenteries supporting the intestine occur in the metacoel.

The digestive tract is U-shaped with the mouth and anus opening close together at the anterior end of the animal (Fig. 12-4). The mouth between the two ridges of the lophophore is overhung dorsally by a cres-

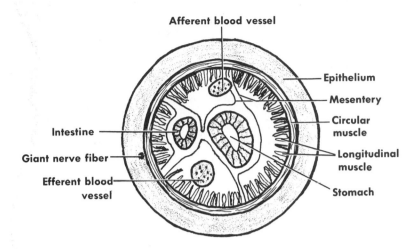

Fig. 12-3

Diagram of cross section through muscular part of trunk of phoronid.

cent-shaped fold, the epistome, which has a cavity that communicates with the lophophoral coelom. The mouth, which can be closed by the epistome, opens into a sort of buccal cavity and then into the long gullet, or esophagus. The latter passes into the globular stomach, which extends into the end bulb of the trunk region. Here the stomach constricts and joins the intestine, which turns sharply, ascends along the dorsal side of the trunk, and terminates in the rectum of the anal papilla on the concave side of the horseshoe lophophore. The digestive tract is lined with mostly ciliated epithelium, and its walls have muscular investments in certain regions. Gland cells are found in the esophagus and prestomach. Digestion is probably intracellular.

Phoronids are filter feeders, and the tentacular cilia create water currents that are directed toward the groove between the two ridges of the lophophore. This groove enters the angles of the mouth on each side. Food particles of plankton are entangled by the mucus of the tentacles and groove and are carried by the cilia to the mouth, while the water current passes dorsally over the anus to the exterior.

Two U-shaped metanephridia open on each side of the anal papillae. Each metanephridium consists of a coiled duct with a funnellike, ciliated opening at each end. They get rid of excess water and excreta and serve as gonoducts for the gametes.

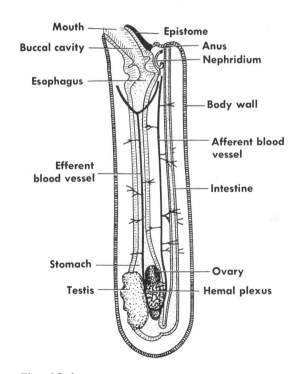

Fig. 12-4

Diagram of phoronid showing principal internal structures. Lophophore has been omitted.

The closed circulatory system is well developed. Basically it consists of two longitudinal blood vessels—an afferent vessel that runs dorsally, and an efferent vessel that is ventral. The vessels are connected **251** with each other anteriorly by a pair of semicircular vessels. From one member of this pair a single blood vessel supplies each tentacle. Blood ascends and descends from the tentacle by the same vessel and is carried away posteriorly by the efferent, or ventral, vessel. The dorsal and ventral vessels are connected by a hemal plexus on the stomach wall. No heart is present, and the blood is driven by pulsation of the muscular walls of the vessels. The blood contains nucleated corpuscles with hemoglobin, which imparts a red color to the blood.

The nervous system consists of a general nerve layer of fibers in the base of the epidermis that thickens into a nerve ring at the outer base of the lophophore. This ring sends nerves to the tentacles, motor nerves to the longitudinal muscles of the body wall, and a lateral or giant fiber through the epidermis on the left side (Fig. 12-3). A smaller lateral nerve may occur in some forms on the right side. The lateral nerves give off branches to the trunk musculature and produce rapid contraction of those muscles. The sensory system is restricted to the neurosensory cells that occur on the tentacles and muscular part of the trunk. A lophophoral sense organ or a cluster of neurosensory cells is found on a flap in some phoronids.

REPRODUCTION AND EMBRYOLOGY

Most phoronids are hermaphroditic, but some are dioecious (e.g., *Phoronis architecta*). The sex cells originate from cells of the thin peritoneum of the blood capillary ceca. The gonads consist of indefinite masses of these cells closely applied to the efferent vessel and capillary ceca. In some hermaphrodites the ovary is on the dorsal side of the efferent vessel and the testis is on its ventral side. The gametes are shed into the body cavity and pass through the metanephridia (which act as gonoducts) to the outside. In *Phoronis hippocrepia* the fertilized eggs are retained on the tentacles until the larval stage. Fertilization is usually external. Some worms brood the eggs in a brood chamber formed by the inner tentacles and the concavity of the lophophore, which holds the eggs in place by mucus secretions. Asexual reproduction by transverse fission occurs in *Phoronis ovalis* in the nonmuscular part of the trunk.

Cleavage in phoronids is holoblastic, but there is no regular radial or spiral pattern. Indications of spiral cleavage exist in *Phoronopsis viridis*. Cleavage produces a coeloblastula with cilia at its apical pole. The gastrula formation is embolic with a very large blastopore that becomes small, ventral, and displaced inward by an overhanging preoral lobe of ectoderm. In this way a mouth is formed at this position with the blastopore still connected to the archenteron. An anus is established by the fusion of the elongated archenteron with the ectoderm. Protonephridia are later established with openings near the anus. When the larva (actinotroch) hatches, it is completely covered with cilia and assumes a planktonic existence (Fig. 12-5). The larva is somewhat oval in shape with a large preoral hood over the mouth, behind which an oblique ridge of hollow tentacles that vary in number with the different species exists. At the posterior end of the larva a ciliated telotroch is formed for locomotion. After its planktonic existence of some weeks, the larva undergoes metamorphosis. The rapid metamorphosis, which occurs after the larva settles to the bottom, first involves eversion of a metasome pouch or future body wall of the trunk, to which a fold of intestine is attached, thus producing the characteristic adult digestive tract loop. The ciliated tentacles are also cast off, but new ones regenerate from their stumps. The preoral lobe and its nervous ganglion are shed along with the tentacles.

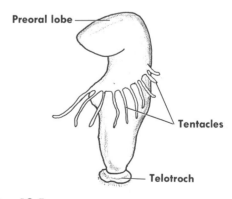

Fig. 12-5

Actinotroch larva of phoronid.

After several internal changes and the completion of metamorphosis, the worm secretes a tube where it will spend the rest of its existence.

Annotated references

Benham, W. B. 1889. The anatomy of *Phoronis australis*. Quart. J. Micr. Sci. **30**:125-158. *One of the early detailed studies of a phoronid.*

Bronn, H. G. (editor). 1939. Phoronidea. Klassen und Ordungen des Tierreichs, vol. 4, part 4. Leipzig, Akademische Verlagsgesellschaft. *An authoritative monograph.*

Cori, C. J. Phoronidea. In Kukenthal, W., and T. Krumbach (editors). 1937. Handbuch der Zoologie, vol. 3, part 2, section 5, pp. 5-138. Berlin, Walter de Gruyter & Co.

Hilton, W. A. 1930. A new *Phoronopsis* from California. Trans. Amer. Micr. Soc. **49**:154-159. *Several species of this genus are found along the Pacific coast.*

Hyman, L. H. 1959. The invertebrates; smaller coelomate groups, vol. 5. New York, McGraw-Hill Book Company. *One of the best treatises yet published on phoronids.*

MacGinitie, G. E., and N. MacGinitie. 1949. Natural history of marine animals. New York, McGraw-Hill Book Company. *This book describes the two species.* Phoronopsis californica *and* P. viridis, *which are common in spots along the California coast.*

Smith, R. I., et al. (editors). 1954. Intertidal invertebrates of the central California coast. Berkeley, University of California Press. *Keys are given for the two genera* (Phoronopsis *and* Phoronis) *found on the California coast. Only one species is listed, although a number are known to occur along the Pacific coast.*

Phylum Priapulida

The Priapulida consist of a small group of vermiform marine animals that are found in the colder waters of both northern and southern hemispheres. They occur from Massachusetts to Greenland on the Atlantic coast and from California to Point Barrow, Alaska, on the Pacific coast of North America, and from the coast of Uruguay in South America to certain islands of the Antarctic region in the southern hemisphere. They are also found in similar regions of Europe and Asia. Some species have been found in deeper, colder waters of tropical and subtropical regions. They live buried in mud and sand on the sea floor and range from intertidal zones to depths of thousands of meters. Although they have the power to plow through the bottom muck in seeking their prey, they usually remain quietly buried in a vertical position, the mouth on a level with the bottom surface. They are predaceous in their eating habits.

Taxonomically the Priapulida have been linked in the past with various other groups such as the Echiuroidea and the Sipunculoidea. Since they were supposed to have a pseudocoel and for various other reasons, some zoologists have considered them a class of the Aschelminthes. However, it has been found in recent years (W. L. Shapeero, 1961) that they are true eucoelomate animals because their body cavity is lined with a thin peritoneum (Fig. 13-1). Because of this and other structural features, the group is now assigned the rank of phylum.

The phylum Priapulida is made up of two genera, *Priapulus* and *Halicryptus*, and eight species, seven of which belong to *Priapulus*. The eight species are *Priapulus caudatus, P. tuberculato-spinosus, P. bicaudatus, P. australis, P. horridus, P. atlantisi, P. profundus,* and *Halicryptus spinulosus. Priapulus* has a caudal appendage that is lacking in *Halicryptus*. In a particular habitat the animals may be fairly common, but usually they are solitary and uncommon. Shapeero collected 13 specimens of *P. caudatus* in one locality along the coast of Washington. However, more spectacular finds have been recorded. For example, a subspecies of *P. tuberculato-spinosus* has been reported to occur at densities of up to 250 individuals per meter.

BASIC ADAPTIVE FEATURES

The Priapulida have undergone little evolutionary divergence as evidenced by the few species in the group. They are bottom muck residents, predaceous, and are not filter feeders. The eversible proboscis with its numerous recurved teeth surrounding the mouth and lining the pharynx is well adapted for predaceous habits. Restricted movements make it possible for the worms to capture only slow-moving prey. Because of their feeding habits and generally stable ecologic niche, perhaps little opportunity has existed for evolutionary diversification within the group. Also the development of oxygen-transporting hemerythrin cells in the coelomic cavity has been of survival value in their special mode of living.

PHYLOGENETIC RELATIONSHIPS

It was pointed out long ago by A. E. Shipley that the Priapulida is an isolated group with no close affinities to any other group. However, some recent students of the group (Hyman, K. Lang) have emphasized its close relationship to the class Kinorhyncha of the Aschelminthes and to the phylum Acanthocephala. This view was based principally upon the supposed pseudocoelomate nature of the three groups in question, the resemblance of their larvae, the syncytial histologic structure of their dermomuscular tubes, the presence of protonephridiae in all three groups, and the resemblance of the proboscis of the Priapulida to that of the Acanthocephala. Because of these and other reasons, Hyman has placed the Priapulida as a class within the phylum Aschelminthes.

This taxonomic status of the Priapulida has recently been challenged by Shapeero, as already mentioned. This investigator has demonstrated that the dermomuscular tube is not made up of syncytial tissues but of discrete cells inconstant in number, that the lining membrane of the body cavity is a peritoneum with distinct nuclei, and that structural or functional differences in the larval stages and proboscis exist between the Priapulida and the aforementioned groups. So far as the solenocytic protonephridia are concerned, this type of excretory organ is also present in many eucoelomate animals such as annelids and cephalochordates. Priapulida are also unique in having a cuticle that contains chitin and is molted throughout their adult life. For these reasons the Priapulida should be placed among the vermiform coelomates as a distinct phylum but with uncertain systematic position.

Perhaps the greatest gap in determining their true affinities lies in the lack of complete knowledge about their embryology.

MORPHOLOGIC FEATURES

The Priapulida are mostly medium-sized animals, the largest being 5 to 6 inches long (Fig. 13-2). The warty body is cylindric, and the trunk is annulated into several unsegmented rings (30 to 40, *Priapulus;* 100 or more, *Halicryptus*). There are three divisions of the body: the proboscis, trunk, and caudal appendage (lacking in *Halicryptus*). The proboscis, which is separated from the trunk by a constriction, is as large in diameter as the trunk and sometimes may be larger. It bears 25 longitudinal ridges (ribs) each made up of rows of papillae or spines which lead toward the mouth. The proboscis is eversible and is used both in capturing prey and in sam-

Pharyngeal wall

Radial and circular muscles attached to thick band of connective tissue

Coelom

Peritoneum covering pharynx

Longitudinal muscle

Fig. 13-1

Cross section of portion of pharynx of *Priapulus* showing peritoneum. (Courtesy W. L. Shapeero, University of Washington, Seattle.)

Fig. 13-2

Preserved specimen of *Priapulus caudatus* Lamarck.
(From Hickman: Integrated principles of zoology, The
C. V. Mosby Co.; photograph by W. L. Shapeero.)

pling the surroundings. At the terminal end
of the proboscis is the mouth, which is surrounded with concentric rows of teeth
(Figs. 13-4; 13-6, *A*). This circumoral region is usually invaginated into the interior,
but when this region is everted in capturing
the prey, the teeth point forward.

Scattered over the trunk region are many
tubercles and spines that give a distinctly
warty appearance to the animal. At the posterior end of the trunk are two urogenital
pores and the anus.

In *Priapulus* one or two caudal appendages (Fig. 13-2) that are hollow stems
containing many oval vesicles communicate
with the coelomic cavity. The function of
these appendages, according to R. Fange
and A. Mattison (1961), is respiratory as
formerly supposed because their thin walls
facilitate the rapid uptake of oxygen and
their rhythmic movements force coelomic
fluid into the coelom. Another view considers them acting as chemoreceptors (K.
Lang). No respiratory or circulatory organs
are found.

The thick, muscular body wall (Fig. 13-
3) consists of a two-layered cuticle, an epidermis, both circular and longitudinal
muscle layers, and the thin peritoneal
lining. The epidermis is made up of a single layer of definite cuboidal or columnar
cells and is not a syncytium (Shapeero).
The cuticle and epidermis are modified in
certain regions to form such integumentary
specializations as the papillae of the proboscis and trunk, the pharyngeal teeth,
the caudal appendage vesicles, and others.
Molting occurs at intervals throughout life.
Before the molting process the epidermis
secretes a new cuticle under the old one,
which is then shed. The cuticle is partly
composed of chitin during the intermolting
periods but only of protein in the newly
molted individual (D. B. Carlisle).

Next to the epidermis is the circular muscle layer arranged in separate rings; inside
the circular muscles are found the longitudinal muscles (in part striated) either in
separate bundles or forming a continuous
layer. In the proboscis only one pair of longitudinal muscles is found in the space
between each rib, so that the circular
muscle layer is attached to the epidermis
only between the ribs. These spaces of the
proboscis are anterior continuations of the
body cavity. The true coelom is lined internally with a thin, nucleated membrane
(peritoneum, Fig. 13-1), which also forms
the outermost layer of the intestine and
mesenteries for the visceral organs and covers the retractor muscles. The body cavity,
the cavity of the caudal appendages, and
the spaces of the musculature are filled with

Fig. 13-3

Cross section through ventral nerve cord of *Priapulus*. Note double-layered cuticle of body wall and relation of nerve cord to epidermal layer. (Courtesy W. L. Shapeero, University of Washington, Seattle.)

a fluid containing cells (coelomocytes). These coelomocytes have a respiratory pigment (hemerythrin).

The digestive system consists of mouth, pharynx, intestine, and rectum (Fig. 13-4). The invaginable pharynx is composed of circular and radial fibers and is lined with an epidermis and cuticle. The cuticle bears teeth (spines) continuous with those around the mouth (Fig. 13-6, *B*). A circle of short and long retractor muscles is attached around the anterior end of the pharynx and originates on the body wall. These retractors are used in the invagination of the proboscis and the inversion of the pharynx into the midgut. The intestine is mostly a straight tube in the center of the trunk with much of its columnar epithelium thrown into folds. The lining epithelium is provided with a brush border (Fig. 13-5). Circular and longitudinal muscle layers are found in its walls. The short rectum is lined with cuticle and opens to the outside by the anus. The Priapulida live on polychaetes, small crustaceans, and even other priapulids, which they swallow whole.

The nervous system consists of a circumenteric nerve ring around the pharynx and a midventral cord (Fig. 13-3) that can be seen as a longitudinal band in the undis-

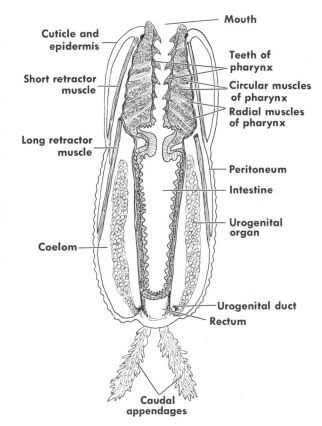

Fig. 13-4

Diagram of major internal structures of *Priapulus*.

257

Fig. 13-5

Portion of lining epithelium of *Priapulus* gut showing brush border of epithelial cells. (Courtesy W. L. Shapeero, University of Washington, Seattle.)

sected specimen. Several pairs of nerves from the nerve ring run to the proboscis ribs and to the pharynx. The nervous system is in very close association with the epidermis, of which it seems to be a thickening. Little is known about the sensory system, but the papillae and spines may be sense organs.

The paired urogenital organs are each made up of a gonad on one side and clusters of solenocytes on the other (Fig. 13-4). A central urogenital or protonephridial tubule serves to carry both excretory and genital products. This common duct is really an excretory duct that picks up the genital duct and then branches into a number of smaller ducts. These smaller ducts expand into nephridial sacs, into which the solenocytes open (A. Norrevang, Shapeero). The two urogenital canals open by separate pores at the posterior end of the trunk. Sex cells are shed into the sea, where fertilization occurs.

Little is known about the embryology of

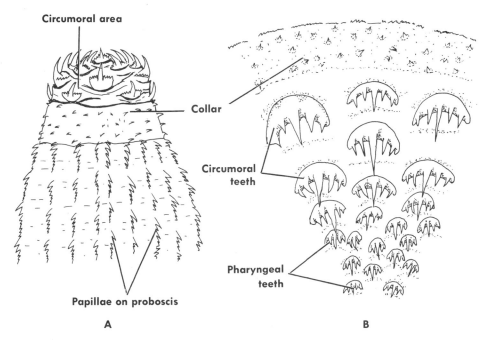

A   B

Fig. 13-6

A, Anterior end of proboscis of *Priapulus tuberculato-spinosus* showing recurved teeth around mouth region. **B,** Small portion from upper part of pharynx of *Priapulus caudatus* showing pharyngeal teeth, large in circumoral area but becoming gradually smaller toward gut. (Modified from H. Theel, 1906.)

this phylum. The egg hatches into a small postgastrula, the larval trunk of which is later encased in a cuticularized lorica similar to that of the rotifers. The lorica is made up of plates that vary in the two genera. The spiny anterior end of the larva is invaginable into the interior. A foot with toes and caudal glands may also be present. Larval internal structures are similar to those of the adult. The larvae live in the same habitat along with the adults and feed on detritus. They molt in about two years and emerge as juveniles without the lorica and with the same structures as adults. As already mentioned, priapulids molt throughout both juvenile and adult life.

The most common species of the Priapulida is *Priapulus caudatus,* which has a wide but spotty distribution in northern waters; a closely related species, *P. tuberculato-spinosus,* is found in antarctic regions. These species have only one caudal appendage, whereas *P. bicaudatus* has two. *Halicryptus spinulosus,* also found in northern regions, has no caudal appendage.

Annotated references

Carlisle, D. B. 1958. On the exuvia of *Priapulus caudatus.* Arkiv. Zool. series 2, **12**(5):79-81.

Fange, R., and A. Mattisson. 1961. Function of the caudal appendage of *Priapulus caudatus.* Nature (London) **190**:1216-1217. *This paper presents evidence to show that the appendages have respiratory functions.*

Hyman, L. H. 1951. The invertebrates: Acanthocephala, Aschelminthes, and Entoprocta; the pseudocoelomate Bilateria, vol. 3. New York, McGraw-Hill Book Company. *The author places the Priapulida as a class under the pseudocoelomate Aschelminthes, but more recent investigation shows the priapulids to be true coelomate animals. Dr. Hyman recognizes three species, but others have since been found.*

Lang, K. 1951. *Priapulus caudatus* Lamarck and *Priapulus caudatus forma tuberculato-spinosus* Baird represent two different species. Arkiv. Zool. series 2, **2**:565-568.

Lang, K. 1953. Die Entwicklung des Eies von *Priapulus caudatus* Lamarck unddie systematische Stellung der Priapuliden. Arkiv. Zool. series 2, **5**:321-347.

Norrevang, A. 1963. Fine structure of the solenocyte tree in *Priapulus caudatus* Lamarck. Nature (London) **198**:700-701.

Shapeero, W. L. 1962. The epidermis and cuticle of *Priapulus caudatus* Lamarck. Trans. Amer. Micro. Soc. **81**(4):352-355.

Shapeero, W. L. 1961. Phylogeny of Priapulida. Science **133**(3456):879-880. *The author presents evidence why the Priapulida should be placed among the true coelomates and why they should be considered a separate phylum.*

Shapeero, W. L. 1962. The distribution of *Priapulus caudatus* Lamarck on the Pacific coast of North America. Amer. Midland Natur. **68**:237-241.

Phylum Ectoprocta (Bryozoa)

The ectoprocts are small marine or freshwater animals that are chiefly colonial (a few are solitary), sessile, and usually live in some form of case of their own secretion. The colony (zoarium) is nearly always attached to a solid substratum such as rock, vegetation, debris, or the body of another animal. Most zoaria are immobile, but some colonies can move slightly over a substratum. The individuals are called zooids, each of which usually lives in its own case, often maintaining organic continuity with the other zooids of the colony. The case in which the zooid lives is called a zooecium; its walls may be in contact or in common with those of others. The opening of the case to the exterior for the protrusion of the lophophore is termed the orifice, which may have a closing device.

The ectoprocts have a worldwide distribution in fresh water and the sea. Freshwater species are found in all altitudes from sea level to high mountain lakes except in the north and south polar regions. The North Temperate Zone contains about the same species everywhere. Marine ectoprocts, which are far more common than freshwater ones, are most abundant in the littoral zone of the continental shelf but have been found in the deep abyssal regions of the ocean at depths of several thousand meters. They occur in the polar regions as well as in tropical waters. They are scarce in brackish water such as the Baltic Sea. Many of their species are cosmopolitan, and others are localized in their distribution. Their general adaptability is very great, and many factors account for their methods of dispersal such as ocean currents, attachment to floating seaweeds, the bodies of other animals, and (in fresh water) by statoblasts. Their fossil record (Fig. 14-3) is impressive, beginning with the Ordovician period. Those with calcified skeletons have left the best record, but those with a membranous zooecium are also found. Their fossils are most abundant in impure calcareous limestone rocks alternating with shale or shell marl. Their paleoecology indicates that they were most abundant in neritic littoral zones. Most bryozoan fossils are fragmentary because of the fragile nature of the colonies.

CLASSIFICATION

The Ectoprocta and Entoprocta are two groups which make up a larger group, the Bryozoa, or moss animals. There is considerable disagreement among authorities as to the exact taxonomic status of these three groups. One classification still held by many students considers the phylum Bryozoa (or Polyzoa of British students) to consist of two subphyla, the Ectoprocta and the Entoprocta. An alternative classification assigns phylum rank to both the Ectoprocta and Entoprocta. The term "Bryozoa" is now often restricted to the phylum Ectoprocta. L. H. Hyman, in her outstanding work on the invertebrates, has accepted the second classification and has advanced cogent reasons for separating the ectoprocts and entoprocts into different phyla. Among her arguments for such a separation are the coelomate nature of ectoprocts against the pseudocoelomate entoprocts, the differ-

Fig. 14-1

Zooid of *Plumatella*, a phylactolaemate ectoproct. (From Hickman: Integrated principles of zoology, The C. V. Mosby Co.)

ences in embryologic development of the two groups, and the presence of a true lophophore in ectoprocts but not in entoprocts.

The present work is based on Hyman's classification. The phylum Ectoprocta has about 4,000 species, of which only about 50 are phylactolaemates.

Phylum Ectoprocta. A protostomial group of coelomate and unsegmented animals; mostly sessile and colonial; animals minute and each in a separate case (zooecium); digestive system U-shaped with anus outside the circumoral ring (lophophore) of tentacles; lophophore retractile into a sheath; coelom with peritoneum; no excretory, circulatory, or respiratory organs; usually hermaphroditic; asexual reproduction by budding; statoblasts in freshwater species; larva a trochophore type; marine and freshwater.

    Class Gymnolaemata. Zooid with circular lophophore; no epistome (upper lip); no body wall musculature; no direct coelomic communications between zooids; three existing orders; mostly marine.

        Order Ctenostomata. Zooids usually with uncalcified zooecia of chitinous cuticle; orifice with pleated collar for a closing apparatus; without brood chambers; zooids may or may not bud from each other; two suborders. *Victorella, Clavopora, Pherusella*.

        Order Cheilostomata. Boxlike zooids with zooecia calcified wholly or in part; ventral orifice usually with operculum; brood chambers present (ovicells); vibracula; two suborders. *Bugula* (Figs. 14-5 to 14-7), *Microporella, Membranipora*.

        Order Cyclostomata (Stenostomata). Zooids tubular with fully calcified zooecia; circular terminal orifice without operculum; brood chambers in form of gonozooids or modified zooids; membranous sac from tentacular sheath to posterior end of zooid; five suborders. *Tubulipora, Crisia*.

    Class Phylactolaemata. Zooids usually with horseshoe-shaped lophophores; epistome present; body wall with musculature; zooecia gelatinous or chitinous (not calcified); zooids with continuous coeloms; no polymorphism; freshwater. *Cristatella, Pectinatella* (Fig. 14-4), *Lophopus, Plumatella* (Fig. 14-1).

BASIC ADAPTIVE FEATURES

The ectoprocts have emphasized a colonial and sessile pattern of organization, **261** and their evolutionary trends have involved changes in certain basic structures characteristic of such a pattern. Two of these basic features are the zooecium and the relationship of the zooids in a colony to each other. A zooid, or the single individual of a colony, is composed of two parts, the body wall and the visceral mass. The nonliving outer covering, or zooecium, varies in composition. In the phylactolaemates, a tendency toward an evolutionary development of a gelatinous zooecium from a chitinous one has occurred, perhaps in the interests of more flexibility (Fig. 14-2). In most of the gymnolaemates the chitinous layer is overlaid with calcium carbonate to form a rigid skeleton. Consequently such forms have fossilized well. Paleontologic study of the bryozoans is wholly devoted to this class (Fig. 14-3). It is generally agreed that the class Phylactolaemata is more primitive than the class Gymnolaemata. In correlation with the rigid skeleton of the Gymnolaemata, there are changes in their body walls. Muscular layers are always absent in the wall, and the epithelial layer is reduced so that the body wall is much simplified. Calcareous forms may overcome the handicap of rigidity by having in the zoaria flexible, chitinous joints. Evolutionary trends are well shown in the dominant order (Cheilostomata) of existing ectoprocts. These members are

Fig. 14-2

Small colony of *Lophopus crystallinus,* a phylactolaemate. (Modified from Kraepelin.)

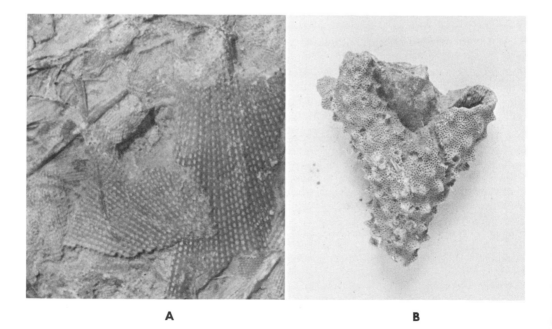

A

B

Fig. 14-3

Fossil bryozoans common from Ordovician to Devonian times. **A,** *Fenestrellina,* a cryptostome found in Indiana limestone, dating from middle Mississippian. (×2.) **B,** *Hallopora,* a treptostome, from Middle Devonian (class Gymnolaemata).

characterized by calcified zooecia, presence of an operculum, polymorphism, a compensating sac for lophophore movement, and branching colonies.

PHYLOGENETIC RELATIONSHIPS

The presence of a form of trochophore larva in bryozoans might indicate a relationship to all the other groups that possess such a larva, but many differences in the embryologic development of ectoprocts as compared with the others makes such a conclusion difficult. Most evidences, therefore, for ectoproct relationships must be deduced from their anatomic structures. On this basis, the resemblance of the phoronids to the ectoprocts, especially the phylactolaemates, is very striking. Both groups have a similar body plan, a septal separation of mesocoel and metacoel, a horseshoe-shaped lophophore, a muscular body wall, and the presence of the chief nervous center in the region between mouth and anus. But they also differ from each other in such features as the presence of a circulatory system and metanephridia in phoronids and their absence in ectoprocts.

Within the phylum Ectoprocta the phylactolaemates are considered the more primitive class because they have the primitive cylindric type of zooid, the trimeric division of the body coelom, the horseshoe shape of the lophophore, and a muscular wall. Of the gymnolaemates, the cyclostomes seem to be the most closely related to the phylactolaemates because of embryologic resemblances, cylindric body, and scanty polymorphism. The cheilostomes are considered to be the dominant existing ectoprocts, primarily because they have exploited the possibilities of the basic adaptive structures possessed by the group.

GENERAL MORPHOLOGIC FEATURES

As described under the section on classification, two major groups or classes of ectoprocts exist, the gymnolaemates and the phylactolaemates. Many striking morphologic differences occur between the two classes, and what applies to one may not apply to the other, although a basic, uniform type of structure is present in the two classes. Evolutionary divergence has greatly modified basic patterns, because one class has evolved in fresh water and the other has evolved chiefly in the sea.

The bryozoan colony

Most ectoprocts live in colonies (zoaria) that vary greatly in shape, size, and organization. The taxonomy of many ectoprocts, especially marine species, depends upon these features. Some colonies are small microscopic patches, and others are huge masses of zooids. The colony is nearly always attached to a great variety of substrata where it remains and grows, but a few colonies can creep about on their substrata. Some colonies are stoloniferous; the zooids are borne on creeping or erect stolons composed of modified zooids, which are divided by nodes or septa into internodes, giving a jointed appearance to the colony. Most colonies are formed by a succession of adjacent zooids fused to each other by their outer parts, or zooecia. Some colonies form a meshwork of regular pattern. Many of the calcified ectoprocts form encrusting masses in the form of flat sheets (laminar) that may be unilaminar or multilaminar when formed by continued superposition of new layers. The most common type is the unilaminar, in which the dorsal surface of the zooids is attached to the substrate with their orifices facing away from the substrate. The freshwater *Pectinatella* consists of a slimy, gelatinous mass with the zooids in the surface. The colonies are in the form of a rosette (Fig. 14-4). The common marine *Bugula* forms branching colonies by a biserial attachment of zooids and has a plantlike appearance (Figs. 14-5, 14-6). When colonies are highly calcified, they often assume compact structures like corals. The arrangement of the zooids in the colonies is also highly variable. A common organization is the attachment of the dorsal surfaces of the zooids to the substratum with the lateral surfaces attached to adjacent zooids and the ventral surface (with orifices) exposed.

The class Gymnolaemata usually illustrates polymorphism, in which several types of zooids or zooid modifications exist. The typical zooid is the autozooid, or feeding individual. The others, or modified zooids, are called heterozooids. Heterozooids are represented by stolons, rhizoids, (rootlike attachments), avicularia, vibracula, or

263

Fig. 14-4

A, *Pectinatella* colony on stem showing rosette arrangement. Zooids form single-layered patches (rosettes) over gelatinous base which may reach size of football or larger. **B,** Part of rosette greatly enlarged showing zooids of colony (class Phylactolaemata).

— Lophophore
— Zooecium

— Autozooid

Fig. 14-5

Arrangement of zooids in colony of *Bugula* (order Cheilostomata of class Gymnolaemata).

any cavity enclosed by walls other than the autozooids. Of these heterozooids, the avicularia and vibracula are of especial interest. The avicularia resemble bird heads and are characteristic of some of the cheilostomes (Fig. 14-7). These modified zooids may occupy a place in the colony normally taken by an autozooid (vicarious), or they may be found anywhere (adventitious). They may be sessile or stalked. The operculum in this modified zooid forms a mandible

that can close and open by muscles. The avicularia help keep the colony free from debris as well as entrap small organisms. In vibracula the opercula are modified into long bristles or setae (in cheilostomes only), which may keep the colony clean by sweeping back and forth.

Communication between adjacent zooids takes place by interzooidal pores often located in pore plates. The pores are not open holes but are filled with epidermal cells. These pores may be located in the transverse end walls or in the lateral walls. A slow diffusion of fluid between the zooids occurs through these pores.

Morphology of the zooid

The zooids or individuals of a particular colony have a uniform structure. Each zooid is very small (0.25 to 2 mm. in length) with an average length of less than 1 mm. The shape of the zooid may be boxlike, tubular, vaselike, or oval. It is made up of a body wall that encloses the lophophore and the polypide (visceral mass). The body wall varies in the two classes of ectoprocts. In the phylactolaemata and a few marine forms the body wall consists of an outer covering, the zooecium, which may be gelatinous, membranous, or chitinous, and an inner layer of epidermis with an underlying musculature of circular and longitudinal muscles. In the calcareous gymnolaemates the zooecium has a calcareous layer between the chitinous cuticle and the epidermis, thus forming a rigid exoskele-

Fig. 14-6

Photomicrograph of portion of *Bugula* colony.

ton. No muscles are present in the wall, and the only other part of the body wall is the peritoneal lining. The frontal wall may remain uncalcified and may be membranous to permit expansion when the lophophore is retracted. If the frontal membrane is calcified, a compensation sac opening by a pore to the outside permits internal expansion. An oral aperture, the orifice, in the zooecium allows the lophophore to protrude. This orifice is often provided with a lid (operculum) that can be closed when the animal withdraws into the zooecium. The body wall is often turned in at the orifice as far as a constriction (diaphragm) provided with a sphincter muscle. The region between the orifice and diaphragm is called the vestibule. At the bottom of the vestibule is a circular collar through which the lophophore can be projected or retracted. A tentacle sheath covers the necklike region of the protruded animal and extends from the base of the lophophore to the diaphragm. The sheath consists of a thin cuticle, an epidermis, a muscular layer, and a peritoneal lining in that order outside in. The sheath contains the anterior portion of the digestive tract and the anus. When the lophophore is retracted, the sheath encloses the tentacles bunched together.

Within the body cavity, or the coelom

Tentacles

Zooecium

Pharynx

Avicularium

Stomach

Fig. 14-7

Small portion of *Bugula* colony showing autozooid and avicularium (Gymnolaemata).

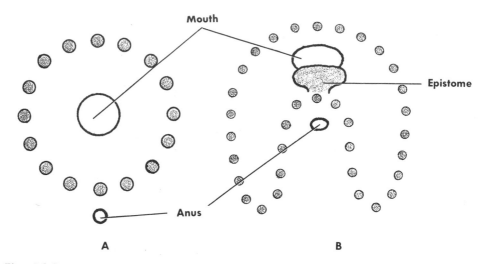

Fig. 14-8

Comparison of lophophore arrangement. **A**, Gymnolaemata. **B**, Phylactolaemata. (Modified from Harmer.)

enclosed by the body wall, are the lophophore and the polypide (visceral mass). The lophophore may be circular (gymnolaemates) or horseshoe shaped (phylactolaemates) and surrounds the oral aperture (Fig. 14-8). It bears a series of hollow tentacles on one ridge (marine species) or two ridges (freshwater species). The number of tentacles varies from 16 to 106 in the freshwater forms and from 8 to 34 in marine forms. The tentacles are ciliated on the median and lateral surfaces. The cavities of the hollow tentacles open into a circular canal at the base of the lophophore. The circular canal may open into the coelomic or body cavity, or it may become separated from it. The lophophore can be retracted into the tentacle sheath or introvert, or it may be extended through the diaphragm, vestibule, and orifice when the animal is feeding. Protrusion is mostly a matter of the evagination of the tentacle sheath, which, being attached to the lophophore base, pushes out the tentacular crown as the sheath everts. The eversion of the tentacle sheath may be brought about by coelomic fluid pressure due to muscular contraction of several types. Retraction is brought about by the retractor muscles of the lophophore, the most powerful muscles in the zooid. The tentacles create water movements and bring food to the mouth.

Internal anatomy of the zooid

The digestive tract has the U shape commonly found in sessile animals, with the mouth and anus both on the dorsal side (Fig. 14-9). The mouth is located in the center of the lophophore and opens into a ciliated pharynx, which may be followed by an esophagus, although pharynx and esophagus are often not delimited. The esophagus opens into the stomach, which is divided into a tubular cardia, a posteriorly elongated cecum, and a narrow pylorus. The cardia and cecum are lined with glandular, nonciliated epithelium, and the pylorus is lined with ciliated epithelium. Circular and longitudinal muscles occur in the stomach walls and in the walls of the entire digestive tract, but not uniformly. The stomach empties into the intestine or rectum, which opens at the anus just outside the circle of tentacles. Attaching the cecum of the stomach to the posterior zooidal wall is a cord called the funiculus, which anchors the digestive tract in position. Food particles may be carried down the digestive tract singly or in mucus cords. Both intracellular and extracellular digestion may occur in the marine species, but only extracellular digestion occurs in the freshwater forms. Food in ectoprocts is often stored in the epithelial lining of the digestive tract.

The excretory, vascular, and respiratory organs are absent in ectoprocts. Gaseous exchange occurs through the body surface, and the coelomic fluid in the spaceous coelom and its divisions circulate the products of digestion. Waste materials are picked up by coelomocytes and other cells and are discharged to the outside.

The nervous center is a ganglion of small nerve cells and fibers and is located on the dorsal side of the pharynx. The ganglion forms part of a nerve ring around the pharynx. From the ganglion and nerve ring a network of nerves runs to the tentacles and the tentacle sheath, the digestive tract, and the muscles. A subepithelial nerve network may extend throughout the wall of the zooid except in that part cemented to a substratum. Nervous connections between zooids are uncertain. No special sense organs exist, but neurosensory cells with projecting bristles are known to occur.

REPRODUCTION AND EMBRYOLOGY

Most ectoprocts are hermaphroditic. Asexual reproduction also occurs, chiefly budding. Perhaps no group exhibits a greater variety of reproductive methods than do the bryozoans. Not only hermaphroditism, but dioecism, polyembryony, protandry, and the curious brown body regeneration are found in the group. The gonads show a wide range of locations, but the ovaries are usually found in the upper or distal end of the zooid and the testes are found in the lower or basal end. In freshwater species the funiculus may bear the testes, although they may be found on the body wall where the ovaries also occur (Fig. 14-9). A gonad of either sex is simply a mass of developing gametes enclosed by peritoneum from which the sex cells differentiate. Gonoducts are entirely absent, and the gametes are shed into the spacious coelom. The male cells may be shed in balls of sperm. Protandry, or protogyny, in which sperm and eggs ripen at different times, may also occur. Many cheilostomes have separate sexes.

Fertilization is mostly internal, and most ectoprocts brood their eggs in some manner. The ova usually develop into embryos in special brood chambers, the ooecia or ovicells. In most cheilostomes, including *Bugula,* the body wall at the distal end

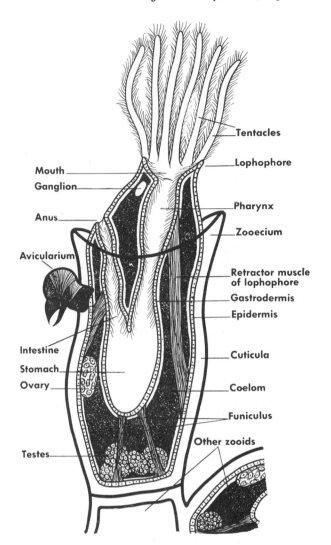

Fig. 14-9

Diagram of zooid of *Bugula,* a gymnolaemate ectoproct, showing principal internal structures. (From Hickman: Integrated principles of zoology, The C. V. Mosby Co.)

of the autozooid forms an outgrowth or hood called the ovicell, which consists of two evaginations, one inside the other. The cavity of the inner evagination is continuous with the coelom of the zooid. In the space between the inner and outer evaginations the egg develops and is supplied with nutrition from the inner evagination. Many species brood their eggs in the coelomic cavity in special evaginations of the body wall, the embryo sacs. Generally, when the embryo in the sac increases in size, the polypide of that zooid degenerates

267

into a dark reddish mass, the brown body, and a new polypide is regenerated. The fate of the brown bodies varies. They may accumulate in the coelomic cavity by successive degenerations, or they may be taken into the digestive tract of the regenerated polypide and voided through the anus. The same body wall and its zooecium (which do not degenerate in the process) can thus house several successive polypides as embryos are formed. Polyembryony, in which several embryos are produced from one zygote by the separation of the cells in early cleavage, is known to occur in some cyclostomes.

Self-fertilization is common in hermaphroditic species that produce sperm and eggs in the same individual, but in dioecious species sperm in some way not yet known must enter the coelom of another individual to fertilize the eggs.

Cleavage is of the holoblastic, radial, or biradial type, and results in a coeloblastula. Gastrulation is by primary delamination at the vegetal pole. The larva is a form of trochophore provided with a ciliated girdle for swimming and an anterior tuft of cilia or flagella. An apical nervous organ and an adhesive sac or sucker are also present in the larva. After escaping from the brood chamber or embryo sac, the larva swims around, and if hatched from a nonbrooding species it may feed during its larval existence. When it is ready for attachment, the larva everts the adhesive sac, which becomes fastened to a substratum. It then undergoes metamorphosis, resulting in the first zooid of the colony called an ancestrula. Then, by budding, the ancestrula gives rise to many other zooids. Repeated asexual reproduction of these zooids results in the formation of a new colony. The budding pattern of a colony varies with the species. The budding process usually involves the constriction of a part of the parent zooid, which includes an evagination of the parent body wall.

The development of freshwater species differs in certain particulars from the foregoing account, which applies to the gymnolaemates. In the freshwater forms development leads to a larva that is really a juvenile colony of primary and secondary polypides; these initiate a new colony after the attachment and degeneration of the larva.

The Phylactolaemata, or freshwater ectoprocts, also have a form of asexual reproduction other than that of budding. This method of propagation is the formation of statoblasts (Fig. 14-10). These resistant bodies are masses of epidermal and peritoneal cells that have come from basal epidermal cells forming the funiculus. The peritoneal cells store reserve food. The germinal mass forms a hollow ball or disk protected by a chitinous shell, the outer part of which is modified into a pneumatic ring (annulus) of air that keeps the statoblast afloat. Statoblasts vary with different species and have taxonomic diagnostic value. Some of them bear hooks around their margins (spinoblasts). Statoblast formation is correlated with favorable conditions of temperature and medium. All must remain dormant for some time before they germinate; they are able to withstand harsh conditions. They generally accumulate in the zooids during the summer and are released when the colony disintegrates before winter begins. In the spring, if conditions are favorable, the statoblast germinates into a zooid and starts a new colony.

Fig. 14-10

Statoblast of *Pectinatella* (about 1 mm. in diameter). (From Hickman: Integrated principles of zoology, The C. V. Mosby Co.)

Annotated references

Cori, C. Bryozoa. In Kukenthal, W., and T. Krumbach (editors). 1941. Handbuch der Zoologie. vol. 3, part 2, section 15. Berlin, Walter De

Gruyter & Co. *The best general account of the phylum.*

Edmondson, W. T. (editor). 1959. Ward and Whipple's fresh-water biology, ed. 2. New York, John Wiley & Sons, Inc. *The section on fresh-water Bryozoa (which includes both entoprocts and ectoprocts) is by the late M. D. Rogick, foremost authority on the group.*

Harmer, S. 1910. Polyzoa. In Cambridge Natural History, vol. 2, London, The Macmillan Company. *One of the many accounts of this group by Harmer.*

Hyman, L. H. 1959. The invertebrates; smaller coelomate groups, vol. 5. New York, McGraw-Hill Book Company. *The best treatise on the ectoprocts so far published.*

Kerkut, G. A. (editor). 1958. The Invertebrata, ed. 3. Cambridge, Cambridge University Press.

Kraepelin, K. 1887. Die Deutschen Susswasser-Bryozoen. Abhandl. Naturw. Verein. Hamburg, 10:1-168. *A classic account of the Bryozoa.*

Moore, R. C., C. G. Lalicker, and A. G. Fischer. 1952. Invertebrate fossils. New York, McGraw-Hill Book Company. *Section 5 of this excellent work is devoted to a good general description of the bryozoans and a detailed account of their fossil record dating back to the Middle Ordovician.*

Pennak, R. W. 1953. Fresh-water invertebrates of the United States. New York, The Ronald Press Company. *One of the best general accounts of the freshwater species, with keys.*

Phylum Brachiopoda

This group of lophophorate animals consists of the lamp shells, which reached their greatest abundance during the Paleozoic era. The present number of 250 or so species is quite modest in view of the more than 25,000 species that existed during that remote geologic time. They were perhaps one of the most abundant forms to be found in the ancient seas. At present they are only locally abundant in such places as the Sea of Japan and Australian waters, although they are found in all seas and at all latitudes.

The brachiopods are exclusively benthonic, marine forms that live from the lowest tide levels to abyssal depths, although most are restricted to the continental shelf regions. None is found in the great abyssal trenches. They are almost entirely sessile forms, being attached by a pedicle to some object. When a pedicle is absent, they attach themselves by the ventral valve. They are commonly found on well-oxygenated and relatively firm sea bottoms. However, the lingulid genera, *Lingula* and *Glottidia*, live in vertical burrows in sandy shores or in mudflats and are the most active of all brachiopods. Some forms are restricted to very specific habitats, and others, such as *Lingula*, are cosmopolitan.

CLASSIFICATION

Phylum Brachiopoda. Coelomate Bilateria with Protostomia and Deuterostomia characteristics; unsegmented, with shells of dorsal and ventral valves somewhat dissimilar; valves may be hinged by articulation or unhinged; valves with mantle originate from body wall; lophophore present; heart present; excretory system of metanephridia; mostly dioecious; free-swimming larva.

    Class Inarticulata. Valves held together by muscles only; lophophore without internal skeleton; anus present.

        Order Atremata. Shell of calcium phosphate; pedicle attached to ventral valve through notch of both valves. *Lingula* (Fig. 15-4), *Glottidia*.

        Order Neotremata. Pedicle attached through notch of ventral valve only; shell of calcium phosphate or calcium carbonate. *Crania, Discina*.

    Class Articulata. Valves hinged together by interlocking device; lophophore with internal skeleton; pedicle emitted through ventral valve; no anus; order status unsettled; many superfamilies recognized. *Orthis, Terebratula, Terebratulina, Terebratella* (Fig. 15-1).

BASIC ADAPTIVE FEATURES

The shell and lophophore have been chiefly responsible for guiding the evolutionary trends of a group which has been slowly declining and is perhaps dying out altogether. The evidence indicates that the articulates have come from the inarticulates, thus producing a more efficient connection between the two valves. The lophophore, an efficient food-catching mechanism, presents many patterns of variations among the brachiopods. The primitive form of the lophophore has a short tentacle-bearing edge that has gradually increased in length in its subsequent evolution. This increased length may take the form of lobulations, arm formations, or spiral coils. An internal skeletal support of the lophophore is another evolutionary trend. On the other hand, the classic genus *Lingula*, which has undergone little change in its 400 million years of existence (al-

Fig. 15-1

External view of articulate brachiopod, *Terebratella*. Left, specimen with dorsal valve up; right, ventral valve up.

though none of its dozen or more present species goes back that far), supposedly illustrates the lack of evolutionary change in an environment that has remained fairly constant during that long period of time. This does not, however, explain the evolutionary divergence of brachiopods during the prime period of their abundance.

PHYLOGENETIC RELATIONSHIPS

Brachiopods arose in Precambrian time, but it has been impossible to trace any fossil record of their early existence. The articulates supposedly developed from the inarticulates along many different lines. Some existing forms have fossil records that can be traced back to the Ordovician period. Since brachiopods are members of the lophophorate group, it is evident that they must be related to the Ectoprocta and the Phoronida. The members of these three phyla share certain features in common such as two body regions (mesosome and metasome) and two coelomic subdivisions; a lophophore of similar structure but of different methods of development; a pair of metanephridia that act as coelomoducts of the metacoel and gonoducts (phoronids and brachiopods); and an epidermal nerve plexus.

Certain distinctive differences do exist between the three phyla. The exoskeleton is different in all three lophophorate phyla. Phoronids possess both a larval as well as an adult set of tentacles; the other two phyla have only the adult set. Certain differences exist in the patterns of the circulatory system such as a closed blood system in phoronids, an open one in brachiopods, and none at all in ectoprocta.

GENERAL MORPHOLOGIC FEATURES
External anatomy

The ventral valve is usually larger than the dorsal valve and is provided with a fleshy stalk, the pedicle or peduncle, by which it attaches itself to a substratum. The pedicle may extend through an opening (foramen) between both valves (*Lingula*, Fig. 15-4), or only through the ventral valve (*Laqueus*, Fig. 15-2). In *Crania* the ventral valve is cemented directly to the substratum. The valves may be oval, circular, or triangular in general contour and may be elongated with rounded anterior margins. Both valves are usually convex externally, although the dorsal one may be flat or concave. Most existing shells fall within the range of 5 to 80 mm. along the long axis, but extinct ones were often much larger. The external surface of the valves may be smooth or variously ornamented with folds, growth lines, ribs, or spines. Some bright colors as well as dull ones

271

Fig. 15-2

Two fossil brachiopods. Bottom, *Kingena* of lower Cretaceous period. Top, *Laqueus* of Recent times.

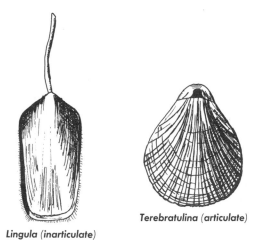

Lingula (inarticulate)

Terebratulina (articulate)

Fig. 15-3

Examples of an inarticulate, *Lingula,* and an articulate, *Terebratulina.*

may be present. The shell consists of calcium carbonate, calcium phosphate, and chitin in various combinations. The shell is composed of three layers: the outermost periostracum of chitin; the middle laminated layer of calcite; and the inner prismatic layer of fibers. Both internal and external shell characters are of taxonomic importance.

The two valves articulate with each other along the hinge line. The nature of the articulation forms the basis for the two classes, the Inarticulata and the Articulata. In the inarticulates (the more primitive forms) the two valves are held together at the hinge line by muscles; in the articulates the valves are bound together by an interlocking device of teeth-and-socket arrangement (Fig. 15-3). The movement of the valves is controlled by two to five pairs of internal muscles between the valves. The inarticulates can open their valves much wider than can the articulates.

The posterior end of the ventral valve in most brachiopods is tapered to form a peak, which is perforated for the passage of the pedicle. The dorsal valve may send out projections that form an internal skeleton in the lophophore.

The body occupies only the posterior part of the space between the shells. From the body wall two double folds extend anteriorly as the dorsal and ventral mantle lobes, which secrete the valves and line their underlying surfaces. The lobes give off fine papillae that penetrate the shell surface.

The pedicle differs in the various groups. In the lingulids (e.g., *Lingula*) it is long and flexible, arises from the ventral mantle lobe, and includes a coelomic evagination continuous with the main body coelom (Fig. 15-4). The wall of the pedicle consists of a cuticle, an epidermis, a connective tissue layer, a muscle layer, and a peritoneal lining. When the animal is in its burrow, the pedicle is stuck in the bottom sand with the anterior end of the valves directed toward the surface opening. Retraction of the pedicle can pull the animal back into its burrow. In the articulates the pedicle is rather short, is made up mostly of connective tissue with no coelom, and is very restricted in its movements.

Fig. 15-4

Lingula, inarticulate brachiopods with long pedicles. One valve has been removed from lower specimen exposing soft parts.

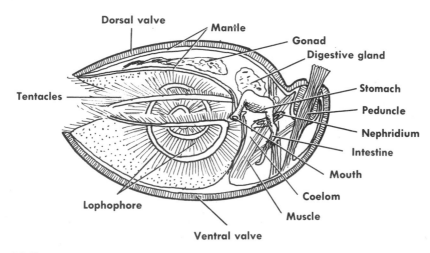

Fig. 15-5

Internal structure of articulate brachiopod shown in longitudinal section.

Internal anatomy

The body of the animal is attached to the undersurface of the two valves by its dorsal and ventral walls (Fig. 15-5). The other parts of its walls are largely free. Since the animal occupies only the posterior region of the chamber between the valves, the anterior body wall sends extensions dorsally and ventrally to cover those parts of the valves not occupied by the animal's body.

The body wall is covered with a one-layered epidermis. Beneath the epidermis is connective tissue and, in those parts of the **273**

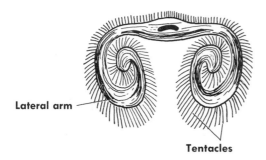

Lateral arm

Tentacles

Fig. 15-6

Pattern of lophophore in *Lingula.* Many other types of lophophores are also found in brachiopods.

body wall not adherent to the valves, a muscle layer is found beneath the connective tissue. Ciliated peritoneum lines the body wall. The mantle lobes are extensions of the anterior body wall and thus consist of a double wall with a coelom between. The coelomic cavity consists of the embryonic mesocoel and metacoel, the protocoel being absent, as already mentioned.

The lophophore is an anterior outgrowth of the body wall and lies in the space between the mantle lobes, filling the greater part of that cavity. The lophophore is supported by a calcareous loop from the dorsal valve. The lophophore is fringed with long, ciliated tentacles that occur in a row along the entire edge of the lophophore (Fig. 15-6). Extensions from the mesocoel extend into the tentacles, which are covered with a tall epidermis of ciliated cells.

The lophophorates are ciliary feeders. Water with food particles entering the gaping valves flows over the lophophore. Water enters the anterior gape by two currents, one on each side, produced by the lateral tracts of tentacular cilia that beat at right angles to the long axis of the tentacles. The two currents converge posteriorly to form a median outgoing current. The inner surfaces of the tentacles toward the brachial groove at the base of the lophophore have mucus glands and cilia that beat toward the groove. Food is caught by the mucus and is carried by the cilia to the brachial groove, whose cilia transport the food to the mouth. Heavy particles are dropped on the ventral mantle lobe and are carried away by outgoing ciliary currents.

From the mouth the food is conveyed into a ciliated alimentary canal made up of an esophagus, a dilated stomach provided with a digestive gland that opens into it, and an intestine that ends blindly in articulates (Fig. 15-5) but in the inarticulates, ends with an anus. Digestion may be intracellular within the digestive glands.

The circulatory system is an open one, consisting of a longitudinal vessel in the dorsal mesentery over the stomach. One part of this longitudinal vessel is enlarged into a contractile vesicle, or heart, from which extends an anterior channel to the sinuses of the intestine and lophophore and a posterior channel to the mantle, nephridia, and gonads. The colorless, coagulable blood may contain coelomocytes.

A respiratory system is absent in brachiopods, and gaseous exchange may occur principally in the mantle and lophophore.

All brachiopods have one or two pairs of metanephridia located on each side of the digestive tract. Each metanephridium has a fringed nephrostome that opens into the coelomic cavity, a tubule that extends anteriorly to the mantle cavity, and a nephridiopore that opens on each side of the mouth. Waste is picked up by coelomocytes from the coelomic cavity and carried into the nephrostomes. The ciliated tubules carry the waste to the mantle cavity for expulsion.

The nervous system consists of an esophageal nerve ring with a small ganglion on its dorsal side and an larger one ventrally, and a number of nerves from these centers to the lophophore, mantle lobes, and valve muscles. The nervous system is located mainly in the base of the epidermis. Nerve plexuses have been found in the lining of the digestive tract of inarticulates. Specialized sense organs have not been identified, except for a pair of statocysts near the anterior adductor muscle in a species of *Lingula.*

REPRODUCTION AND EMBRYOLOGY

Brachiopods are mostly dioecious, and their gonads are localized in regions of the coelomic peritoneum. Usually four gonads, which are quite large when filled with mature gametes, are present. In inarticulates the gonads are found in the free ends of the peritoneal bands among the viscera in the metacoel spaces. In the articulates the gonads occur in the coelomic canals of the mantle. The ripe gametes are discharged into the metacoel and are carried to the outside by the metanephridia, which act as gonoducts. A few brachiopods may brood their young in modified parts of the metanephridia or in a special pouch of the ventral valve. Fertilization is external in those that discharge their gametes to the outside or internal in those that have brood pouches.

Although classed as Protostomia, the development of brachiopods is similar in many ways to that of the Deuterostomia. Their cleavage is radial, mostly equal, and holoblastic with some variations in the early blastomeres. The coeloblastula undergoes gastrulation chiefly by the embolic method. Mesoderm formation occurs by the enterocoelous method, another deuterostome characteristic. In inarticulates the free-swimming larva, which may last several weeks, bears a pair of mantle lobes and valves that enclose the body. The pedicle develops from the ventral mantle lobe. Locomotion of the larva is by the U-shaped ciliated lophophore. Details of development either vary or are lacking in the different groups. In the familar *Lingula* no metamorphosis occurs; the larva develops directly into the adult. In articulates, after the formation of the coelomic sacs, the embryo shows three regions: an anterior lobe that will form most of the body, a median lobe (the mantle), and a posterior lobe (the pedicle). The larva swims around for a few hours by means of the ciliated anterior lobe. After it becomes attached by the pedicle, metamorphosis occurs, in which the mantle, formerly directed backward, now shifts its position forward around the body where it secretes the valves. In most instances, the final stages of embryonic development and metamorphosis in brachiopods have not been clearly worked out.

Annotated references

Chuang, S. 1959. Structure and function of the alimentary canal in *Lingula unguis*. Proc. Zool. Soc. London, **132**:293-311. *An account of the digestive system in the "oldest living fossil in the world."*

Harmer, S. F., and A. E. Shipley (editors). 1900. Cambridge natural history, vol. 3. London, The Macmillan Company. *A small section is devoted to recent Brachiopoda by A. E. Shipley. A good general description.*

Helmcke, J. G. Brachiopoda. In Kukenthal, W., and T. Krumbach (editors). 1939. Handbuch der Zoologie, vol. 3, part 2, section 5, pp. 139-158. Berlin, Walter De Gruyter & Co.

Hyman, L. H. 1959. The invertebrates; smaller coelomate groups, vol. 5. New York, McGraw-Hill Book Company. *The best and most up-to-date treatment of the brachiopods at present.*

MacGinitie, G. E., and N. MacGinitie. 1949. Natural history of marine animals. New York, McGraw-Hill Book Company. *The most common genera of brachiopods of the Pacific coast are* Glottidia, Laqueus, *and* Terebratalia; *the latter are especially common in intertidal zones.*

Moore, R. C., C. G. Lalicker, and A. G. Fischer. 1952. Invertebrate fossils. New York, McGraw-Hill Book Company. *An excellent description of recent and fossil Brachiopoda.*

Phylum Echiurida

The members of this marine phylum are vermiform, protostome animals that live on ocean bottoms in habitats similar to those of the sipunculoids. They are commonly found in U-shaped tubes on sandy or mucky areas, although their habitats may also include crevices in rocks, empty shells, and others. They are found from intertidal zones to very great depths in the ocean and are more common in tropical and subtropical water. Most members live in rather shallow water. Some are called spoonworms from the shape of their prostomium or proboscis. The smallest vary in length from 15 to 25 mm., and the largest from 400 to 500 mm.

Some authorities classify Echiurida into three orders: Echiuroidea, Xenopneusta, and Heteromyota. Another classification places most members in three families: Echiuridae, Thalassematidae, and Bonnelliidae. The classification within this phylum is very uncertain at present.

BASIC ADAPTIVE FEATURES

Echiurid ecologic conditions have stressed an existence typical of a bottom-dwelling detritus feeder. In feeding, the proboscis or prostomium, which is ciliated on its ventral surface, is spread out over the substratum, and the detritus is carried by ciliary channels into the mouth. Modifications of this method are found, however, in some members where a temporary slime tube or feeding net is secreted by a glandular girdle and used to trap and filter the food. The Echiurida spend most of their time in burrows or crevices, but they are capable of gliding movements produced by rhythmic contractions (peristalsis) of their body wall musculature. They can also swim in a sort of corkscrew movement using the proboscis as a steering organ, but no echiurids are adapted for a pelagic existence. In burrowing, the proboscis takes no direct part. The animal lies on its back, ventral side up; the anterior part of the body contracts into a wedge shape and is stiffened by hydrostatic pressure of the coelomic fluid; and the anterior ventral setae are turned down and shoved into the mud, while the posterior setae (when present) are used to anchor the body in the thrust. The body is then drawn forward by muscle contraction as the end plows into the substratum. By repetition of this process, the burrow is slowly dug in the characteristic direction and shape.

PHYLOGENETIC RELATIONSHIPS

The Echiurida show a closer affinity to the Annelida than to any other group. Although they apparently lack segmentation, the presence of setae, the proboscislike prostomium, and the terminal position of the anus indicate annelidlike characteristics. The appearance of transitory ganglia in the nerve cord during development, as well as the arrangement of the storage organs or gonoducts and the metanephridia, may also indicate suppressed metamerism. Some molluscan features, such as the development of the mouth from the blastopore, are also shown. The primitive nature of the phylum is displayed in the retention of the larval anterior end, where the prostomial cavity is derived from the embryonic blastocoel and is secondarily connected to the true body cavity. Perhaps A. E. Shipley's suggestion that the Echiurida arose from the Chaetopoda branch of annelid worms best fits the relationship of this phylum at the present time.

MORPHOLOGIC FEATURES

The body of echiurids consists of a cylindric, saclike, or sausage-shaped trunk and a preoral lobe, (prostomium or proboscis) that is flattened and of varying length, depending upon the species. Although the proboscis cannot be retracted into the body, it is capable of great extension. Its edges are flared so that a ventral ciliated groove is formed along its surface, and its basal edges are so fused as to form a funnel around the mouth. In the common spoonworm (*Echiurus*, Fig. 16-1), the proboscis, when extended, is not half as long as the trunk; but in *Bonellia* (Fig. 16-2) the ribbonlike, bifurcated proboscis may extend to the length of a meter, although the trunk is usually about 2 inches long. The proboscis is solid and consists of connective tissue and muscles covered with a columnar epithelium, which secretes a cuticle (except in the ciliated grooves). It also bears the nerve ring, or brain, and the vascular ring.

The surface of the trunk may be relatively smooth, or it may bear rings of papillae that secrete slime to line the walls of the burrows. Just behind the mouth on the ventral surface are two large, curved, chitinous setae that are used in the burrowing process. Some species also possess one or two rows of small setae at the posterior end of the trunk. These may be used in cleaning out the burrow and in anchoring the body when burrowing, as already described. As in annelids, each seta is produced by a single basal cell and is moved by muscles. Replacements for worn-out setae are kept in reserve sacs.

The body wall consists of: a simple columnar epithelium that secretes a thin cuticle and is modified into glandular cells, papillae, and pits; a subepidermal connective tissue containing pigment cells, which give the characteristic brown, green, or red color to the worm; and a muscular coat of circular, longitudinal, and oblique fiber layers. The longitudinal fibers are very pronounced, and the muscles may be arranged

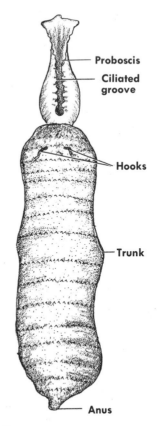

Fig. 16-1

Echiurus, an echiurid common on both Atlantic and Pacific coasts.

in sheets or in bundles. The body cavity is spacious, is without segmentation, and is lined with peritoneum. In the proboscis are found some canals and lacunae that are separated from the true body cavity by a diaphragm. However, coelomic fluid can move between the proboscis cavities and the coelom. Embryologically, the cavities of the proboscis are derived from the embryonic blastocoel, while the coelom is a schizocoel. The coelomic fluid, which circulates freely in the body cavities, has respiratory, nutritive, and excretory functions. It consists of spherical erythrocytes that, in some species, contain hemoglobin; ameboid leukocytes with pigment granules; and a fluid part that contains no plasma proteins and is isotonic with sea water.

The digestive system (Figs. 16-2, 16-3) is a thin-walled tube with many convolutions and irregular loops that are supported

277

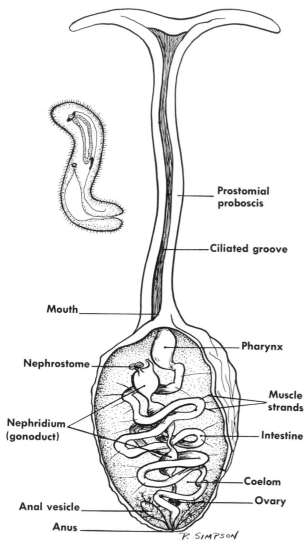

Prostomial proboscis

Ciliated groove

Mouth

Pharynx

Nephrostome

Muscle strands

Nephridium (gonoduct)

Intestine

Anal vesicle

Coelom

Anus

Ovary

P. SIMPSON

Fig. 16-2

Bonellia, internal structure. Left, male. Right, female.

by fine muscular strands running from the body wall. It consists of an ectodermal foregut of mouth, pharynx, and esophagus, and an endodermal midgut and hindgut comprising the intestine. A sphincter separates the foregut and midgut. The mouth at the base of the proboscis opens into a muscular pharynx that is followed by a thick-walled esophagus. The posterior part of the esophagus is dilated into a bulbous crop, which molds the food bolus. A ciliated groove runs along one side of the long, much-coiled intestine. A collateral

tube known as the siphon, of unknown function, arises from the ciliated groove near the anterior end of the intestine and reenters the groove further down the intestine. The intestine is terminated by a short rectum that opens through the anus at the posterior end of the body. The intestine secretes an alkaline digestive juice that contains proteolytic and lipase enzymes.

The excretory system is made up of metanephridia (Figs. 16-2, 16-3), varying in number in the different species. *Bonellia* has only one. A metanephridium contains one or more openings (nephrostomes) into the body cavity and a nephridiopore to the outside. In some species the metanephridia are located anteriorly. Highly characteristic of the phylum is a pair of anal sacs, or vesicles, which open into the intestine close to the anus. They may be much branched; the free ends may be provided with ciliated tunnels, or nephrostomes, that open into the coelom. These anal vesicles are considered to be modified metanephridia and have both excretory and respiratory functions.

The closed vascular system (Fig. 16-3) consists of a ventral vessel that runs along the trunk above the nerve cord and below the digestive tract and bifurcates to form a dilated ring around the margin of the proboscis. A short dorsal vessel receives blood from the ventral vessel by way of periintestinal vessels or sinuses surrounding the intestine and propels the blood forward through a median vessel, which communicates anteriorly with the proboscis marginal loop of the ventral vessel. The circulating blood is colorless and contains only phagocytic amebocytes, but not the same kind of corpuscles as those found in the coelomic fluid.

The nervous system consists of a ventral nerve cord that separates anteriorly into circumpharyngeal connectives. These latter form a loop at the margin of the proboscis and are united at the tip (Fig. 16-4). No separate ganglia can be recognized in the ventral nerve cord and there are no cerebral ganglia. Lateral nerve fibers are given off along the ventral cord and unite dorsally to form rings in the skin of some species. Tactile or chemoreceptor sensory cells are found in the epidermis, especially in the proboscis; but special sense organs are lacking in the adult.

REPRODUCTION AND DEVELOPMENT

Echiurids are dioecious, and sexual dimorphism is conspicuous in some, such as *Bonellia*. The gonad of each sex is attached to the ventral vessel, and the gametes are shed into the coelomic cavity while still immature. When mature, the gametes pass from the body through the nephridia. Fertilization occurs in the seawater, except in *Bonellia* and one or two other species where it occurs in the nephridium of the female. In the common *Echiurus* two pairs of modified metanephridia, known as gonoducts or storage organs, open to the outside behind the ventral setae. These serve as storage chambers for the mature gametes.

Bonellia is noteworthy in two particulars —its extreme sexual dimorphism and its unique sex determination. The males are only about 1 mm. long and live as parasites upon or within the bodies of the females, which may reach a length of 1 meter. Mature males (Fig. 16-2, left) are usually found in the single metanephridium of the female; most are equipped with functional reproductive organs, a few degenerative or larval structures, and a ciliated surface. According to the work of F. Baltzer and some others, all larvae are potentially bisexual. Those that develop independently become females; those that become attached to the female proboscis undergo a transformation into a male. Various degrees of intersexuality are correlated with different periods of attachment to the female. It may be that the male absorbs from the female proboscis secretions that serve as masculinizing agents by causing genes for maleness to be expressed while repressing those of femaleness, although the active principle of such a secretion has not been identified as yet.

In their early embryology, spiral cleavage, so characteristic of annelids and others, is the echiurid type. In later stages of development certain molluscan features appear. A transitory segmentation of the mesoderm is shown in some species by the development of several pairs of rudimentary coelomic pouches. The larva is a free-swimming trochophore, and in the adult

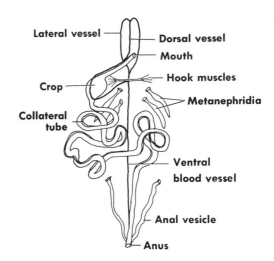

Fig. 16-3

Diagram of digestive, vascular, and excretory systems of *Echiurus*.

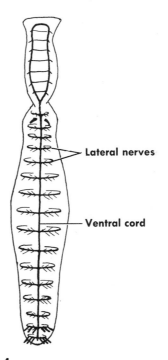

Fig. 16-4

Nervous system of *Echiurus* (diagrammatic).

— Entrance to burrow

— Slime tube

— Attachment of slime tube to body

— Echiuroid worm

Portion of burrow

"Guests"

Fig. 16-5

Urechis, a burrowing echiurid common to California mud-flats. Spins slime tube in U-shaped burrow. Food is collected in slime tube from currents pumped through it; tube and food are ingested. Often called "innkeeper" because of characteristic "guests" safely harbored in its tube. (Modified from Fisher and MacGinitie.)

the anterior part of the animal is of a persistent larval type.

The Echiurida are best represented by the genera *Echiurus, Urechis, Thalessema,* and *Bonellia. Echiurus* is found on both the Atlantic and Pacific coasts as well as elsewhere and is characterized by a relatively short, spoon-shaped proboscis and a trunk bearing spiney rings. *Urechis* (Fig. 16-5) lives along the California coast in U-shaped burrows and has a short proboscis and an anterior band of mucus

glands that secrete a mucus net for entrapping food particles swept into the net by peristaltic contractions of the worm. Some of them may be 15 to 20 inches long. In *Thalessema,* found along the Atlantic coast and tropical regions, the body is small with no anal setae, and the proboscis may be very long. Some of them may be found in the shells of sea urchins and sand dollars.

Annotated references

Baltzer, F. Echiurida. In Kukenthal, W., and T. Krumbach. (editors). 1931. Handbuch der Zoologie, vol. 2, part 2, section 9, pp. 63-168. Berlin, Walter De Gruyter & Co. *An excellent authoritative account.*

Dawydoff, C. In Grasse, P. P. (editor). 1959. Traite de zoologie, vol. 5, part 1, pp. 855-907. Paris, Masson et Cie. *One of the best general treatments of the echiurids. Extensive bibliography.*

Fisher, W. K., and G. E. MacGinitie. 1928. The natural history of an echiuroid worm. Ann. Magaz. Natur. Hist., series 10, 1:204-213. *A good presentation of echiurid habits and behavior.*

MacGinitie, G. E., and N. MacGinitie. 1949. Natural history of marine animals. New York, McGraw-Hill Book Company. *A fine section on the Echiurida with descriptions of the physiology and behavior of* Echiurus *and* Urechis.

Newby, W. W. 1940. The embryology of the echiuroid worm *Urechis caupo.* Mem. Amer. Phil. Soc. **16:**1-219. *An important embryologic study with evidences for considering the Echiurida as a separate phylum.*

Ricketts, E. F., and J. Calvin. 1952. Between Pacific tides, ed. 3. Stanford, Stanford University Press. *Summarizes the movements of* Urechis caupo *in its burrow and its use of the slime net in capturing its prey.*

Shipley, A. E. Echiuroidea. In Harmer, S. F., and A. E. Shipley (editors). 1896. Cambridge natural history, vol. 2, pp. 434-444. *A short description, chiefly of* Bonellia.

Smith, R. I., et al. (editors). 1957. Intertidal invertebrates of the central California coast. Berkeley, University of California Press. *A brief section on the phylum Echiurida with a key to two species.*

Phylum Sipunculida

This phylum of unsegmented worms belongs to the protostomatous coelomates. The worms vary in length from a few millimeters to 2 or more feet; most are less than a foot long. There are 275 species of them (L. Rothschild), and they have been found in all seas from intertidal zones to depths of several thousand meters. They live on the ocean floor (benthonic) where they make mucus-lined burrows or mucus-sand tubes in the sand or mud. Sometimes they are found in empty mollusk shells and in various kinds of crevices. Some have developed special devices at their posterior end for anchoring their position. In some of their localities a spadeful of intertidal mud may yield several specimens.

These worms, together with the priapulids and the echiurids, have long been included under a hodgepodge phylum called Gephyrea. Since there are no close affinities between these three groups, many zoologists (but not all) have assigned each of them to phylum status. Sipunculids are often called peanut worms because of their shape. Only genera, at present, are recognized in the phylum; none has been assembled into higher taxa.

BASIC ADAPTIVE FEATURES

The sipunculids are primarily adapted for burrowing through sandy, mucky bottoms and for a sedentary existence in burrows or in any protective crevice. Habitat preferences are generally characteristic of the various species. Some, for instance, prefer substrates of sand or gravel in which to burrow or hide; others prefer matted vegetation. Although spending most of their time in a burrow or crevice, they also have the power to crawl and even to swim from one position to another. The introvert, or proboscis, with its accessory structures is the chief adaptive structure for burrowing. This eversible organ can be projected by hydrostatic pressure generated by the contraction of the strongly muscular wall on the coelomic fluid in the body cavity. It can be invaginated, or contracted, by special retractor muscles that originate on the body wall and run to the tip of the introvert. Whenever it burrows, the tip of the introvert is applied to the desired substratum and pushed into it by the hydrostatic force. The longitudinal muscles of the trunk contract and bring the body forward to an erect position while the swollen introvert is fastened in the muck. Then the introvert is retracted and everted again in the substratum. By repetition of this process the burrow is deepened until the animal is buried. Burrowing through the sand is performed in the same way. The forward displacement of the anus near the proboscis is also well adapted for a burrowing position and does not require a U-shaped tube.

The introvert with its tentacles is also used for exploring the surroundings and for feeding. Food, mostly microscopic, is collected by mucus and ciliary action and is then ingested by the invagination of the introvert.

PHYLOGENETIC RELATIONSHIPS

The sipunculids show many annelid affinities, although they are not segmented. It has been suggested that the lack of segmentation is a suppression correlated with the forward position of the anus. Sipunculids have a trochophore larva, and their development has much in common with annelids, such as typical spiral cleavage, method of endomesodermal formation, and schizocoel body cavity. The two groups also show many similar anatomic features, such as the structure of the body wall and the central nervous system. Biochemically, sipunculids have both creatine phosphate and arginine phosphate, which is also true of certain annelids, but both these phosphagens have a wide distribution throughout the invertebrates and have little phylogenetic significance.

L. H. Hyman considers the Sipunculida as an intermediate stage in the evolutionary development of segmented forms belonging to the coelomate protostomes. They would thus be placed near the ancestral line leading to the great annelid-mollusk-arthropod division of the animal kingdom.

MORPHOLOGIC FEATURES

The body of the sipunculid is cylindric in shape and is divided into a posterior trunk and an anterior eversible introvert, or proboscis, which bears the terminal mouth. The introvert may be shorter or longer than the trunk in the different species. The mouth may be entirely or partly surrounded by ciliated tentacles or folds, which may be in single or multiple circlets. In *Phascolosoma,* the crescentic series of tentacles are dorsal to the mouth. Retractor muscles from the body wall of the trunk to the base of the tentacles are used to withdraw or invaginate the proboscis into the body. Evagination of the introvert is performed by the hydraulic pressure of the coelomic fluid when the circular muscles of the body wall contract. This pressure may be equal to almost one atmosphere. The introvert may be smooth, but often bears spines, hooks, and papillae or other rough projections. In a few cases the anus may be placed on the introvert. The proboscis base in one or two species is encircled by a collar formed of calcified plates. *Aspidosiphon* (Fig. 17-1, *C*), found in crevices of coral, has a shield-shaped or caplike plate to close the opening into its burrow.

The trunk, which may be dull whitish to grayish brown in color, varies from a short, saclike form to a long cylinder. The shape of the trunk may depend upon the nature of the worm's habitat. Those found in gastropod shells may even have a twisted body to conform to the shape of the shell. The trunk of those that live in shells may also be provided with modified papillae in the form of chitinous holdfast organs at the ventral extremity. The trunk of most sipunculids bears papillae or scalelike thickenings but lacks spines and hooks. The trunk in *Sipunculus* is marked off into a pattern of small squares or rectangles by the circular and longitudinal muscle layers, which produce external grooves in the body wall (Fig. 17-2). Glands are also found in the body wall and open to the outside to furnish secretions for the tube linings. The anus is a middorsal opening on the anterior end of the trunk.

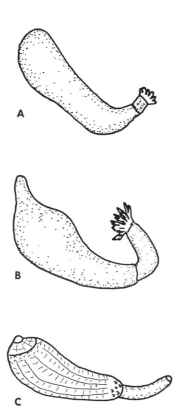

Fig. 17-1

Some types of sipunculids. **A,** *Phascolosoma,* most common genus along Pacific coast. . **B,** *Dendrostomum.* **C,** *Aspidosiphon.*

The body wall consists of a chitinous cuticle secreted by a simple epithelium, a dermis of connective tissue, a circular muscle layer, an oblique muscle layer (in some), a longitudinal muscle layer, and a peritoneum. The longitudinal muscle layer may be in bundles or it may be continuous. The retractor muscles of the introvert come from the longitudinal layer. Smooth muscle fibers are characteristic of sipunculids. Many glands are found in the epidermis; some are unicellular, but others have two or more cells.

The large coelom is a schizocoel filled with coelomic fluid and traversed by muscular fibers and mesenteric supports of the viscera. In some coeloms septal partitions may be present, but true segmentation is absent. Coelomic fluid contains some protein and is isotonic with seawater. The coelomic fluid contains many kinds of cells or corpuscles. The abundant red corpuscle is a biconvex nucleated disk and bears the respiratory pigment, the iron-containing hemerythrin, which is pink when oxidized and colorless when reduced. This kind of pigment is also found in a few polychaetes. Some species may have as many as 100,000 red corpuscles per cubic millimeter. The chief function of the respiratory pigment is to serve as a reservoir for oxygen, which is given up in times of great need or deficiency. Other types of cells in the coelomic fluid are phagocytic amebocytes, chlorogogue cells, and peculiar cells known as urns, which may be fixed or free swimming (Fig. 17-3). The urns are budded off from the peritoneum, from the intestinal wall, or from the surface of compensation sacs. An urn is composed of a vesicle enclosed in flat peritoneal cells and is filled with a fluid and some cytoplasmic strands. It also has an apical ciliated cell and a circlet of cilia. The urns assist in the circulation of the coelomic fluid and help clear the coelomic fluid of foreign substances and degenerating cells collected by the ciliated cell. Such accumulated debris may be carried to the nephridia for disposal.

A kind of vascular system is the lacunar or tentacular system that is found in connection with the tentacles and the anterior part of the esophagus. Around the beginning of the esophagus is a circular ring space which sends canals forward into the

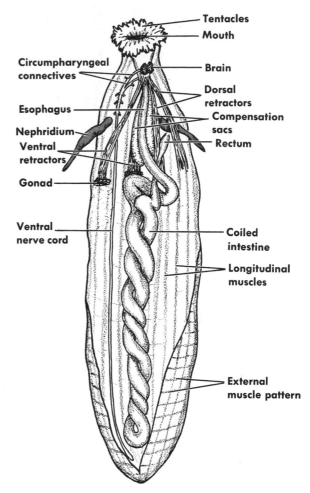

Fig. 17-2

Internal structure of *Sipunculus*.

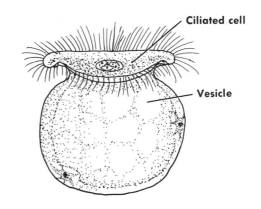

Fig. 17-3

Free urn of *Sipunculus*. These curious bodies originate from peritoneum and are useful for ridding body of waste debris. (Modified from Selensky.)

hollow tentacles, and sends one, two, or several blind tubes called compensation sacs (formerly called polian vesicles) backward alongside the walls of the esophagus. The fluid in this system contains corpuscles similar to those in the body cavity. The system is considered a part of the coelomic cavity, and the hydrostatic pressure initiated on the body cavity in the eversion of the introvert also presses upon the blind sacs. This pressure, together with the contraction of the sacs, forces fluid into the tentacles and causes them to expand; when the tentacles contract, the compensation sacs receive the fluid.

No special organs of circulation are present because the functions of the blood are largely assumed by the coelomic fluid. Respiration occurs through the skin and the tentacles.

The digestive system of the Sipunculida is fitted for the sedentary life of the animal, being somewhat U-shaped (Fig. 17-2). Sipunculids live on organic matter that is collected in the muck and sand by the tentacles and taken to the mouth by ciliary action. From the wide but jawless mouth a ciliated esophagus lies in the introvert and leads to a long, coiled intestine, or midgut. The intestine passes to the end of the trunk and then forward to the anus with the limbs of the loop generally twisted around each other. The intestinal spiral so formed is supported by a spindle or fixing muscle that runs from near the anus to the anterior part of the trunk. The intestine opens into a short rectum, or hindgut, which runs to the anus. A blind diverticulum associated with rectal glands may be attached to the rectum; it may be secretory in nature. The digestive tract is lined throughout its course with ciliated columnar epithelium, but it contains no definite muscular layers. A ciliated groove runs along the digestive tract, usually from the mouth to the rectal diverticulum, and is often distinguished as a reddish line.

The excretory system consists of a pair of metanephria (only one in some) that open on the ventral surface of the body near the anus (Fig. 17-2). A nephridium may be straight or V-shaped and is partly saclike and partly a ciliated tube. These organs remove the waste brought to the nephrostome by the coelomic amebocytes and the urns previously mentioned.

The nervous system consists of paired cerebral ganglia located above the pharynx and connected by circumenteric connectives to a ventral nonsegmented nerve cord that runs to the posterior tip of the animal. The brain receives sensory nerves from the tentacles and various sense organs and sends motor nerves to the retractor muscles of the introvert. The ventral nerve cord gives off many lateral nerves to the muscles of the introvert wall and elsewhere. The structure of the nerve cord is complex, consisting of an outer peritoneal covering, a connective tissue layer with longitudinal muscles, and an inner sheath around the nerve elements.

Numerous sense organs, especially for tactile and chemical stimuli, are present, particularly on the tentacles, introvert, and skin papillae. There are also frontal or cerebral organs and ciliated pits (nuchal organs) whose functions are not well understood. Pigment spots, or ocelli, are also found in various species.

REPRODUCTION AND DEVELOPMENT

Sexes are separate in this phylum, but externally they are similar. The gonads are attached on the coelomic wall at the origin of the retractor muscles. Immature sex cells are shed into the coelomic fluid where they become mature before they pass to the outside through the nephridia, which thus serve as gonoducts. Females are stimulated to shed their gametes when they are touched by the sperm of the males. Fertil-

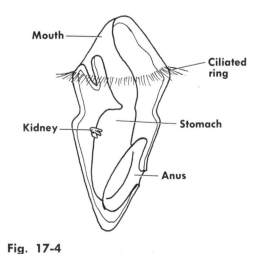

Fig. 17-4

Larva of *Sipunculus*. Cilia omitted, except for metatroch (ciliated ring).

ization occurs in the sea. In some sipunculids, females greatly outnumber the males.

In their development, cleavage is of the spiral type characteristic of annelids, mollusks, and others of the protostome pattern. Gastrulation is partly by epiboly and partly by invagination. The larval form (Fig. 17-4) is a type of free-swimming trochophore provided with a prototroch and a metatroch (bands of cilia). After swimming around in plankton for a number of days, the larva, depending on the species, metamorphoses into a juvenile worm by elongation of the trunk, loss of the ciliary bands, and other changes. In this metamorphosis the anus is shifted to an anterior position, and the intestine becomes spirally twisted as it elongates. Throughout its development no visible evidence of segmentation occurs.

Although they have no asexual method of reproduction, these worms can regenerate parts such as tentacles, parts of the introvert, posterior ends, etc. Ameboid coelomocytes supposedly play an important part in the regeneration processes.

The most familiar sipunculid is, without doubt, *Sipunculus nudus*, which has a very wide distribution. The most characteristic feature of this genus is the rectangular pattern of the trunk surface produced by raised areas of the circular and longitudinal muscles (Fig. 17-2). *Phascolosoma*, with horseshoe-shaped arrangement of tentacles, is common along certain parts of the At-

lantic coast and also in European waters. Certain species of this genus are also common along the Pacific coast, and some species may be 6 to 7 inches long. The genus *Dendrostomum* has many-branched tentacles. *Golfingia* is another genus on which much work has been done. *Aspidosiphon* has shields of plates in front of the anus and also at the end of the body.

Annotated references

Baltzer, F. Sipunculida. In Kukenthal, W., and T. Krumbach. (editors). 1931. Handbuch der Zoologie, vol. 2, part 2, section 9, pp. 15-61. Berlin, Walter De Gruyter & Co. *One of the best technical discussions.*

Gerould, J. 1913. The sipunculids of the eastern coast of North America. Proc. U. S. Nat. Mus. 44:373-437. *A useful work for American students of the sipunculids.*

Hyman, L. H. 1959. The invertebrates; smaller coelomate groups, vol. 5. New York, McGraw-Hill Book Company. *The most up-to-date account. Excellent illustrations and bibliography.*

Peebles, F., and D. L. Fox. 1933. The structure, functions, and general reactions of the marine sipunculid worm *Dendrostomum*. Bull. Tech. Series 3:201-224. *The burrowing habits and general reactions of the animal to experimental stimuli are described.*

Pickford, G. 1947. Sipunculida. Encyclopaedia Britannica, vol. 20. *A concise, well-written account.*

Smith, R. I., et al. (editors). 1957. Intertidal invertebrates of the central California coast. Berkley, University of California Press. *A short section with a key is devoted to the sipunculids of the Pacific coast.*

Chapter 18

Phylum Annelida

The great phylum Annelida has reached the peak of vermiform construction as we know it today, and it is the best example in the animal kingdom of animals that have used serial repetition of similar parts, or metamerism. Metamerism, or segmentation, is merely a biologic extension or application of a basic organization principle found throughout the world of matter, viz. polyisomerism, or the repetition of like units in the formation of an individual unit. In three great phyla of animals—Annelida, Arthropoda, and Chordata—the bodies are serially divided into units (metameres or segments) that are generally similar. Two of these phyla, Annelida and Arthropoda, are definitely related as revealed by morphologic and embryologic evidence. The annelidan ancestry of the arthropods seems to be well established. However, metamerism in chordates must be considered as having an independent origin, an example of convergent evolution. Thus metamerism has arisen at least twice, in annelids and in chordates, and probably has a different adaptation in each case. In annelids, it is an adaptation for burrowing; in chordates, for swimming. These three phyla have been very successful by whatever criteria one may use to measure success in the animal world. Perhaps three-fourths of all named animal species belong to these metameric groups. It is, however, a difficult matter to assess the degree in which they owe their success to metameric organization. One may speculate on this or that advantage accruing from metamerism, but the evolutionary pattern of animals is too complex, from our present knowledge, to assign their differential survival and success to any one contributory factor.

In the three groups a considerable degree of variation exists in the intensity or degree of metamerism. Annelids possess the generalized type of metamerism, and it is in them that one can best see the basic plan of a metamere. In the annelid the metameres are marked off from each other by external grooves and by internal partitions (septa). The inner longitudinal muscles form a continuous sheath throughout the worm, but the fibers of a metamere run only between intersegmental junctions. The outer circular muscles are arranged in segmental groups. Many internal organs such as nephridia, certain blood vessels, ganglionic enlargements, and lateral nerves are serially arranged according to segments. On the other hand, the alimentary canal and parts of the reproductive system show little or no metameric organization. Each metamere thus functions individually to some extent.

The chief advantage of metamerism, especially of the primitive plan, is that it allows controlled movement. Such a metameric arrangement largely restricts the coelomic fluid to separate septal compartments. By muscular action the coelomic fluid of a compartment can be compressed transversely to lengthen a metamere, or it may be compressed longitudinally to thicken and shorten the metamere. Compression of the fluid on one side of a metamere will cause the other side of the segment to lengthen and thus produce a curve. The septa are therefore of paramount importance in that they allow each segment to move separately from the other, and directional changes are easily effected.

It may be stated that the concept of segmentation is not so simple as the foregoing description of conditions, such as those in an earthworm, might indicate. As will be seen later, this generalized pattern is often greatly altered and modified. If the repeated segments are generally alike, as they are in the earthworm, the metamerism is called homonomous; when they are unlike, as in most arthropods, it is termed heteronomous. Fusion and specialization have made many alterations in the primitive basic plan. An additional fact is that many groups other than the three mentioned have some tendencies toward a segmental arrangement. Some authorities think that in the cestodes the proglottids may represent true segmentation, although in these flatworms new units are added just behind the anterior scolex, whereas in true metamerism new segments are formed just in front of the terminal segment. However, there may be many types of metamerism for different adaptive reasons—swimming, reproduction, and repetition of organs in elongated animals for effective control.

The origin of metamerism has been speculative among zoologists ever since the process has been studied. The fission theory explains its origin as the result of an incompletely divided chain of zooids, a common method of asexual reproduction. Another theory is that of pseudometamerism found in some forms where organs were repeated and scattered through the body before segmentation occurred. The muscular theory of segmentation stresses the idea that metamerism first arose as a locomotory device in the somite arrangement of muscles for undulating movements, such as are found in certain larvae and in the freshwater origin of the vertebrates. It is possible that segmentation could have arisen first from the repeated arrangement of certain body units with the later development of interseptal partitions separating these units from each other.

The phylum Annelida consists of bilateral animals that belong to the Protostomia, which have spiral cleavage and a schizocoelic coelom. They are commonly divided into three main groups—Polychaeta, Oligochaeta, and Hirudinea. Of these, the poly-

chaetes are mainly marine; the oligochaetes are chiefly terrestrial and freshwater; and the leeches (Hirudinea) are wholly or partly parasitic, chiefly in freshwater or on land.

CLASSIFICATION

Phylum Annelida. Body vermiform and metamerically segmented externally and internally; cuticle thin and secreted by an epidermis or hypodermis; chitinous setae paired, few or many in number; fleshy parapodia in some; body wall of circular and longitudinal muscles; coelom may be divided by septa; blood system closed, with respiratory pigments; digestive system complete and not metamerically arranged; nephridia paired; respiration by skin or gills; nervous system of brain and midventral nerve cord with ganglia and nerves; sensory system of tactile, photoreceptor, and equilibrial organs; hermaphroditic or dioecious sexes; larva, when present, a trochophore; terrestrial, freshwater, and marine.

  Class Polychaeta. Body has numerous metameres with lateral parapodia that bear many setae; head distinct with eyes and tentacles; clitellum absent; sexes usually separate; gonads transitory; asexual budding in some; trochophore larva usually; mostly marine.

  Subclass Errantia. Body of many segments, usually similar except in head and anal region; parapodia alike and with acicula; pharynx usually protrusible; head appendages usually present; free living, tube dwelling, pelagic, mostly marine. *Neanthes (Nereis), Aphrodite, Manayunkia, Glycera* (Fig. 18-9).

  Subclass Sedentaria. Body with unlike segments and parapodia, and with regional differentiation; prostomium small or indistinct; head appendages modified or absent; pharynx without jaws and mostly nonprotrusible; parapodia reduced and without acicula; gills anterior or absent; tube dwelling or in burrows. *Arenicola* (Fig. 18-10) *Chaetopterus* (Fig. 18-13), *Amphitrite* (Fig. 18-11).

  Class Clitellata. Body with clitellum; segmentation conspicuous; segments with or without annuli; segments definite or indefinite in number; parapodia absent; hermaphroditic; eggs usually in cocoons; mostly freshwater and terrestrial.

    Order Oligochaeta.* Body with conspicuous segmentation; setae few per metamere; head absent; coelom spacious and usually divided by intersegmental septa; development direct, no larva; chiefly terrestrial and freshwater.

---

*There is much discussion at present as to the classification of Oligochaeta and Hirudinea. Some authorities consider them as classes coordinate in rank with Polychaeta; others place them as orders under the class Clitellata.

Suborder Plesiopora. Male pores or gonopores in segment following the testes; seminal receptacles in region of, or in front of, genital segments; mostly aquatic, *Aeolosoma, Nais, Tubifex* (Fig. 18-27), *Enchytraeus.*

Suborder Prosopora. Male gonopores in same segment with last pair of testes (if more than one pair); gonads and seminal receptacles variable in position and in number; aquatic. *Branchiobdella.*

Suborder Opisthopora. Male gonopores at least one segment or more behind last pair of testes. *Lumbricus* (Fig. 18-37), *Eisenia, Allolobophora.*

Order Hirudinea.[*] Body has definite number of segments (33) with many annuli; body with anterior and posterior suckers usually; setae usually absent; coelom closely packed with connective tissue and muscle; terrestrial, freshwater, and marine.

Suborder Acanthobdellida. Body with posterior sucker only; no proboscis or jaws; segments 30 in number; setae present; body cavity spacious with segmental septa; primitive and intermediate between Oligochaeta and Hirudinea. *Acanthobdella.*

Suborder Rhynchobdellida. Body with or without anterior sucker; protrusible proboscis without jaws; blood colorless; marine and freshwater. *Placobdella* (Fig. 18-41), *Glossiphonia.*

Suborder Gnathobdellida. Body with both anterior and posterior suckers; proboscis lacking; three pairs of jaws; blood red; land and freshwater. *Hirudo* (Fig. 18-41), *Macrobdella, Haemopis.*

Suborder Pharyngobdellida. Without proboscis and jaws; teeth lacking; land and aquatic. *Erpobdella, Dina.*

BASIC ADAPTIVE FEATURES

The evolutionary diversity among the annelids has centered primarily around the metameric arrangements of the fluid-filled compartments and parapodia. This plan has made possible controlled movement, whether that of free-swimming forms or that involving tube-dwelling or burrowing types. The typical parapodia are provided with setae, but in some groups the parapodia and setae have been reduced or are absent altogether. The typical parapodia are well adapted for swimming, crawling, and respiration. In tube-dwelling forms the undulations of the body plus the modified parapodia serve to draw currents of water through the tube. Among other locomotor adaptations of great significance are the powerful circular and longitudinal muscles of the body wall. By means of these the body can be flexed up and down and can be shortened or elongated by the alternate use of longitudinal and circular muscle bands. In addition, certain oblique muscles are so arranged on the parapodia that they can give varied thrusts in burrowing or digging in sandy substrata. The advantages of septal arrangement and coelomic fluid compartments, where fluid turgor can be shifted in producing bending or undulatory movements, have been pointed out in the introduction. The oligochaetes must depend upon this method of locomotion to a very great extent.

The paddlelike parapodium serves as an organ of many functions. Besides having the functions of locomotion, respiration, and crawling, it is also sensory and is used for exploring the environment, for facilitating the discharge of waste and gametes, and for anchoring the worm in burrows or other parts of the substrate.

The highly specialized leeches, while retaining many annelid features, have evolved an ecologic relationship different from most others of the segmented worms. Basic adaptive features have stressed a bloodsucking habit mostly of an ectoparasitic nature. Most leeches are adapted for moist, primarily aquatic environments, and their cosmopolitan nature is shown by the fact that few leeches are restricted to one kind of host.

PHYLOGENETIC RELATIONSHIP

It is believed by most zoologists that polychaetes represent the ancestral stem of all the annelid groups. Various theories have been proposed to account for the origin of the Polychaeta, but none of them has been generally accepted. The trochophore larva (Fig. 18-1), which is characteristic of many groups such as mollusks, bryozoans, nemertines, phoronids, and others, also occurs in polychaetes and presumably indicates a close evolutionary relationship among these groups. The recent

---

[*]There is much discussion at present as to the classification of Oligochaeta and Hirudinea. Some authorities consider them as classes coordinate in rank with Polychaeta; others place them as orders under the class Clitellata.

discovery of a segmented mollusk (Monoplacophora) may not have much significance, because metamerism has arisen independently at least twice in the animal kingdom. In certain flatworms pseudometamerism or even true metamerism exists, according to some interpretations. At the present time the origin of the polychaetes from another group cannot be supported with any convincing evidence.

Within the phylum Annelida it is thought that the Clitellata have arisen from a polychaete stem, but definite evidence is lacking here also. It is impossible from present knowledge to indicate the polychaete group from which the oligochaetes have come, although some oligochaete families, such as the Aeolosomatidae, possess certain primitive characters of prostomium, ciliated pits, nervous system, the double function of nephridia for excretion and reproduction, etc. that fit them, to some extent, as transition types between polychaetes and oligochaetes. More than one line of ancestral polychaetes leading to the oligochaetes may also have existed. Many authorities think that the more strictly terrestrial oligochaetes are degenerate or have lost many polychaete characters in their adjustment to a different environment. Leeches differ mainly from oligochaetes in having adaptations fitted for their specialized existence.

CLASS POLYCHAETA

The polychaetes are the largest and oldest group of the Annelida. More than 10,000 species and 1,600 genera of these worms exist, and most of them are marine. They display an enormous size range, varying from less than a millimeter to about 3 meters in length, although the majority are around 50 to 100 mm. long. Many are highly colored (red, green, etc.), and some are very beautiful. An ecologic classification divides them into two subclasses, the errant, or free-moving, Errantia and the sedentary tube dwellers, or Sedentaria. The Errantia include active burrowers, pelagic forms, crawlers, and tube dwellers (Fig. 18-2) that may leave their tubes for food or for breeding or may even carry their tubes about with them. The Sedentaria live in tubes and rarely expose more than the head from the end of the tube (Figs. 18-3, 18-4).

Fig. 18-1

Diagram of trochophore larva. Trochophore of some form is found in several phyla and may indicate relationship.

Tube structure and building

The tubes constructed by the polychaetes vary a great deal. Mucus secreted by special gland shields may simply harden to form a protective covering around most of the body, or in other cases the mucus secretions may be used to stick mud and sand particles together to construct a more or less cylindric tube. The tube itself may be smooth and regular, or it may be jagged and rough in appearance. Sometimes it is branched and very extensive. It may be fixed in position (*Sabella*), or it may be carried around with the worm (*Pectinaria*).

Materials used by the worms in making their tubes also show considerable variation. Some worms are very selective in their choice of materials, and others simply make use of whatever material is at hand. *Sabella*, for instance, chooses only sand particles of a very fine size, while *Terebella* often makes its irregular tube of sand and fragments of detritus. The serpulids secrete carbonate of lime from glands located under their collars and construct a tube of this mineral. Some species of *Eunice* form a parchmentlike tube that is translucent. Various substances of both an organic and an inorganic nature from tubes have been chemically analyzed.

In constructing their tubes certain worms make use of a collar that is formed by the folding back of the peristomium (*Sabella, Serpula*). In *Sabella* the collar is employed in molding the additions of particles that are first stored in ventral sacs below the mouth and mixed with mucus. **289**

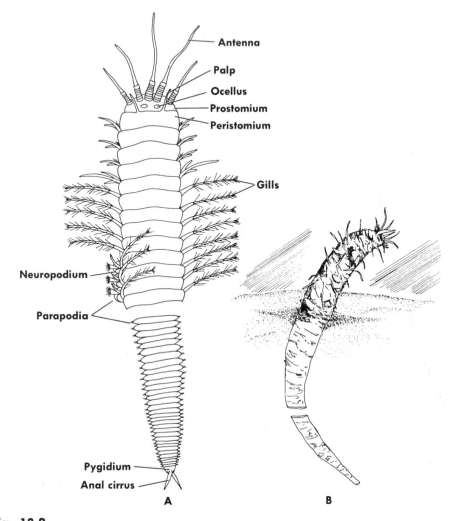

Fig. 18-2

A, *Diopatra cuprea,* an errant tubeworm, dorsal view (midportion omitted). **B,** Long membranous tube of *Diopatra* is fixed in sandy bottom camouflaged with sand, bits of shell, and seaweed. (Both sketched from life.)

These sacs then deliver strings of mucus and sand to the collar folds that are located below the sacs. The collar is provided with lappets that mold the mucus-sand strings to the end of the tube as the worm rotates in the tube. In this way the tube is slowly built up. *Serpula,* which forms its tube entirely from calcium carbonate secretitions, secretes the material into the space between the body wall and collar where it hardens in the space as a ring, so that the tube is elongated by the fusion of rings on top of each other. As the worm rotates, a mucus coating is laid down on the inner surface of the tube.

In nearly all tube-building worms part of the tube projects above the surface as a chimney. *Chaetopterus* with its U-shaped parchment tube has two chimneys, one at each end, that project above the sand surface. Many worms have tubes located vertically in the bottom of the sea or in intertidal zones, but some have tubes placed at different angles to the surface. Usually only the head emerges from the tube opening in order to procure food. A

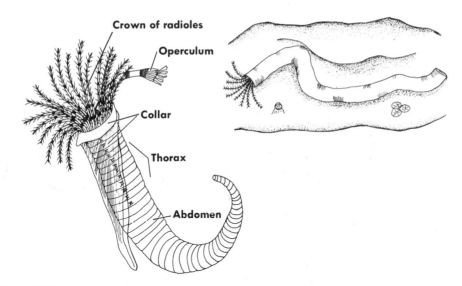

Fig. 18-3

Eupomatus dianthus, a serpulid fanworm (Sedentaria). Glands beneath collar produce calcium carbonate secretions, which collar molds into place at end of tube. Operculum serves as plug in tube when head is withdrawn. Its calcareous tube (right) is usually cemented to rock or shell. (Sketched from life.)

number of tube-dwelling forms entrap their food in various ways by the use of mucus.

Morphologic features

Polychaetes as a class show great diversity. They may be classified morphologically as scale-bearing, jaw-bearing, or crown-bearing forms.

Typically, the polychaete worm consists of an anterior head or prostomium, which may be a simple lobe above or in front of the mouth; or it may be pushed far back on the body; or it may be retractile into one of the first segments. The head may bear eyes, antennae, and a pair of palps (Fig. 18-5). The first segment, the peristomium, surrounds the mouth forming the lower lip and may bear setae and other complex structures such as the tentacular crown of the sabellid group. In some cases the peristomium may fuse with more posterior segments to form a food-gathering structure. It also often bears a pair of palps.

The trunk consists of a definite or indefinite number of segments that may be quite similar or may be modified into specialized regions such as thorax, abdomen, and tail. The Sedentaria are usually the

Fig. 18-4

Some fanworms in their tubes. (From Encyclopaedia Britannica film, "Worms—the Annelida.")

most modified worms. Most body segments have a pair of lateral, fleshy expansions of the body called parapodia (Fig. 18-6, *E*). Each parapodium may be single (uniramous) or double (biramous), consisting of a dorsal notopodium and a ventral neuropodium. Each may also have lobes or processes such as tentacles, cirri, folds,

291

etc. Each parapodium may also have embedded rodlike acicula and emergent setae, which are secreted by special cells within their bases. When lost or worn away, the setae are replaced by these cells. The type of setae and their arrangement has taxonomic value. Setae (Fig. 18-6) function in swimming, in gripping surfaces, in reproduction, in respiration, as organs of defense or offense, and as sensory organs. In many pelagic polychaetes the setae may

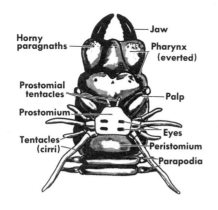

Fig. 18-5

Dorsal view of head and anterior segments of *Neanthes* with pharynx and jaws protruding. (From Hickman: Integrated principles of zoology, The C. V. Mosby Co.)

be entirely absent, and the parapodia function as paddles in swimming (Fig. 18-7). The dorsal setae in some scaleworms form a dorsal mat or feltwork over most of the body.

The body wall of polychaetes consists of a dermomuscular tube that is separated from the gut by the coelom and the peritoneum (Fig. 18-8). The outer layer of the tube is formed of a single layer of columnar epithelium, which is covered by a thin cuticle. Some of the epithelial cells are modified into glands that secrete mucus. Sometimes restricted areas of the epidermis are ciliated. Below the epithelium is a basement membrane of connective tissue followed by the smooth muscle layer of circular and longitudinal muscles, the latter of which is usually in the form of two dorsolateral and two ventrolateral bundles. Oblique muscles often extend from the midventral to the midlateral line on each side, usually at the level of the parapodia.

The coelom of polychaetes is spacious and is usually divided into compartments in accordance with the metamerism of the body. The successive compartments are separated by the intersegmental septa, each of a double layer of peritoneum,

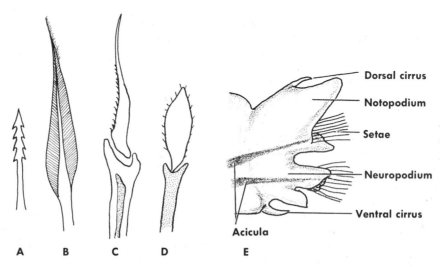

Fig. 18-6

A to D, Some types of polychaete setae. **A,** *Hermoine,* a scale worm. **B,** *Amphitrite.* **C,** *Neanthes.* **D,** Oar-shaped swimming seta of *Heteronereis.* **E,** Diagram of polychaete parapodium.

which extend from the gut to the body wall. The gut thus runs through the septa and is suspended dorsally and ventrally by longitudinal mesenteries. In this way each coelomic compartment is divided into left and right halves. However, the successive cavities are not completely closed off from each other, because the septa may be deficient or may be entirely lacking. The coelomic fluid contains excretory granules as well as many kinds of cells and gametes. Communication between the coelomic cavity and the outside takes place through the nephridia, the coelomoducts, and the dorsal or head pores (in some).

The alimentary canal is usually a straight tube running from the anterior mouth to the anus in the terminal segment (pygidium). In a few worms the gut is coiled and may also bear branched ceca for increasing the surface. Regional specializations of the alimentary tube vary, but a buccal cavity or pharynx is usually present as well as a short esophagus (sometimes with glandular ceca), a stomach, and a rectum. A sort of gizzard is present in a few worms. The cuticle-lined pharynx or buccal cavity is

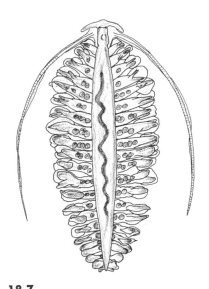

Fig. 18-7

Tomopteris sp, a planktonic polychaete; has few or no setae; parapodia are adapted for swimming. (Modified from Davis.)

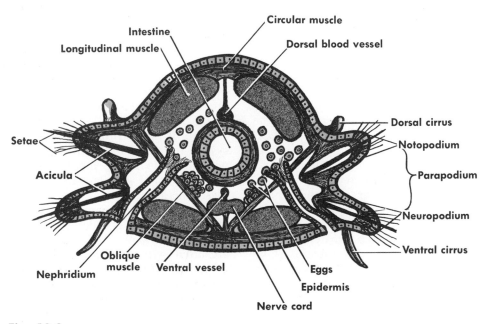

Fig. 18-8

Diagram of transverse section through *Neanthes*. (From Hickman: Integrated principles of zoology, The C. V. Mosby Co.)

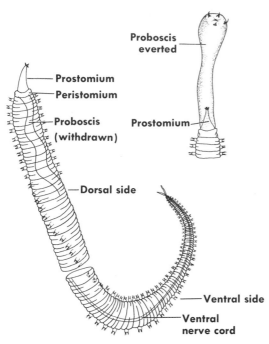

Fig. 18-9

Glycera dibranchiata, the "beak thrower." Pointed head is adapted for burrowing. At right, anterior end with proboscis everted (family Glyceridae of subclass Errantia). (From life.)

armed with characteristic jaws in many errant polychaetes that are raptorial feeders. The pharynx is eversible, and one or more pairs of jaws are usually located on its lateral walls (Figs. 18-5, 18-9). By everting the pharynx, the food is seized by the jaws and drawn into the body when the pharynx is retracted. Eversion of the pharynx is effected principally by the coelomic fluid pressure induced by the contraction of the body wall muscles; the pharynx is withdrawn by special retractor muscles fastened to its posterior end and to the body wall. The pharynx usually occupies the first six body segments, but it may extend posteriorly a much greater distance in those worms with a long proboscis (*Glycera,* Fig. 18-9). Some active forms burrow through the sand and mud by swallowing quantities of soil with organic food by means of an eversible pharynx or proboscis without jaws (*Arenicola,* Fig. 18-10). Others, having a proboscis that is free at the anterior end, merely extend the

proboscis when feeding and suck in food. A circle of teeth instead of jaws is usually found at the tip of the proboscis in such arrangements.

Sedentary, or tube-dwelling, forms are ciliary feeders and collect microscopic food by means of ciliated mucus grooves on numerous extensible and contractile tentacular filaments (*Amphitrite,* Fig. 18-11). Fanworms, such as *Sabella* (Fig. 18-12) and *Serpula,* have an enormous number of head appendages or bipinnate tentacles (radioles) that are stiff branched but can be extended or withdrawn into the tube. Ciliated grooves carry particles down the tentacles to their bases where the small particles are sorted out and passed to the mouth. Large particles are rejected, while medium ones are used in tube construction.

The unique *Chaetopterus* (Fig. 18-13) has a different method of feeding. These worms live in U-shaped parchment tubes with two apertures. Their tentacles are rudimentary and play little part in food collecting. Instead, three pairs of modified notopodia near the middle of the body form fans and, by rhythmic oscillation, produce currents of water that pass through the tube from end to end. Food particles carried by these currents are entangled in a baglike sheet of mucus formed by the specialized winglike (aliform) notopodia of the segment just anterior to the fans. These notopodia are richly supplied with mucus glands for the formation of the mucus bags, which are continually being produced as successive boluses of food and are carried along a cliated middorsal groove to the mouth.

Food is moved through the digestive system by muscular contraction in the gut wall, by cilia lining the lumen, or by a ventral ciliated groove. More than one of these methods may be involved in the same worm. Since many polychaetes take in a large amount of indigestible substances along with organic food, extensive castings are often extruded through the anus. This is especially the case with *Arenicola,* which leaves its castings on the intertidal beaches. Sedentary forms living in tubes with two apertures have their egested waste removed by water currents, but those that live in deeply buried tubes may have to thrust out the anal end during defecation.

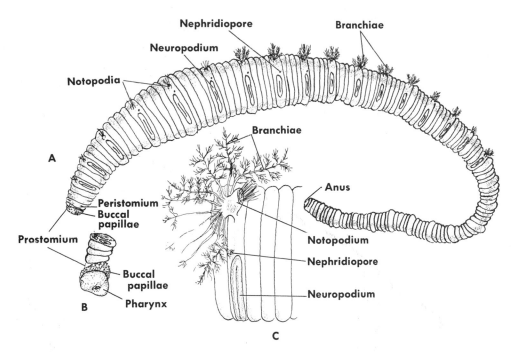

Fig. 18-10

A, *Arenicola cristata.* Lives in U-shaped burrow in sand or mudflat, usually identified by little mound of castings at one end of burrow. **B,** Everted pharynx. It everts and withdraws, carrying sand and organic substances into esophagus. **C,** One segment of *Arenicola* showing annuli, notopodium, and gills. (Subclass Sedentaria.) (Modified from Ashworth.)

Some worms, such as the fanworms, have a ciliated groove (partly ventral and partly dorsal) that extends from the anus to the head region for the expulsion of fecal material released from the anus. Esophageal glands found in many polychaetes, including *Neanthes,* probably produce proteolytic enzymes for digestion.

The nervous system (Fig. 18-14) consists of a brain or dorsal ganglion mass located primarily in the prostomium; a pair of circumesophageal connectives; and paired ventral, ganglionated, or smooth cords that may be separated in primitive forms and fused into a single cord in others. The brain sends nerves to supply eyes, palpi, antennae, and nuchal organs. Lateral branches from the ventral cord supply parapodia and other segmental structures. In some forms the ventral cord is embedded in the epidermis; in others it lies in the coelomic cavity. Many variations of the nervous plan exist among the polychaetes. Ganglionic swellings may be single or double per seg-

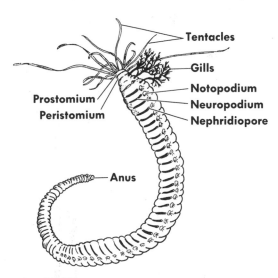

Fig. 18-11

Amphitrite, lateral view. Lives in mucus-lined burrow from which it extends tentacles. Each tentacle has long ciliated groove that directs mucus-trapped detritus to base, where it can be wiped off on ciliated lip and carried into mouth (subclass Sedentaria). (Drawn from life.)

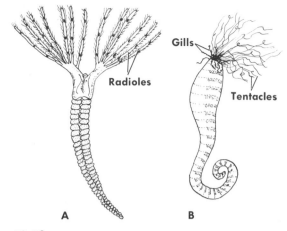

Fig. 18-12

A, *Sabella,* a fanworm. B, *Terebella*. Both are tubicolous polychaetes. Sabellids have no gills. They have stiff food-gathering tentacles which can be withdrawn and curled up in tube. They are often beautifully pigmented and sometimes bear eyes. Terebellids have extensible, independently movable food-gathering tentacles and two or three pairs of branchiae.

ment; lateral nerves vary from two to five pairs per ganglion; pedal ganglia separate from the ventral cord may innervate the parapodia; and giant fibers in the cord may vary from the characteristic number of three. The giant fiber system is especially characteristic of the Sedentaria. In some pelagic polychaetes the sense organs are well developed; the eye is complex enough to form an image (Fig. 18-15). Simpler eyes are of the retinal-cup type (Fig. 18-16, *A*), in which rodlike photoreceptors, pigment, and refractile bodies are used for light detection in many errant polychaetes. They are usually located on the prostomium and may consist of several pairs. Eyespots may be present in forms such as fanworms. Statocysts (Fig. 18-16, *B, C*) occur in *Arenicola* and some others. Other sense organs include the head nuchal organs, tactile

Fig. 18-13

Chaetopterus lives in mudflats in leathery, open-ended, U-shaped tube. Has complicated food-gathering device involving mucus bag secreted by aliform twelfth notopodia to trap detritus and plankton from water that is kept flowing by means of beating fans. Food and mucus are rolled into ball by ciliated cup below aliform notopodia, then carried up ciliated groove to mouth (subclass Sedentaria). (From Hickman: Integrated principles of zoology, The C. V. Mosby Co.)

cells scattered over the body, and others. The nuchal organs are glandular sensory pits located on the first segment of certain polychaetes, and are comprised of chemoreceptors.

Respiration in polychaetes may occur through the body surface (scale worms and some others) or by epithelial outgrowths (gills or branchiae). Gills are lobes or simple filaments, sometimes much divided for increase of surface, and are supplied with vascular loops. Gills may be found in various localities but they are chiefly associated with the parapodia. The neuropodium or, more commonly, the dorsal cirrus may be modified into a kind of gill. Forms such as *Arenicola* (Fig. 18-10) have gills on several segments in the middle of the body, whereas *Amphitrite* (Fig. 18-11) has gills only on the first three segments. Forms with less regional differentiation are more likely to have gills on most of the segments. In the crown of fanworms the numerous radioles serve for gas exchange. Water currents over the gills are chiefly produced by bands of cilia on the gills or on the body surface. Water currents may also be produced by undulatory movements of the worms and by the devices employed for keeping the water circulating through the tubes of tubicolous worms.

Polychaetes in general have a closed vascular system (Fig. 18-17). The circulatory plan consists of median longitudinal dorsal and ventral vessels with transverse connections segmentally arranged. The blood flows forward in the dorsal vessel, which lies over the digestive tract. At its anterior end the dorsal vessel is connected to the ventral vessel by means of one or more vessels. The ventral blood vessel carries the blood backward beneath the digestive tract. The propulsive power of blood flow is produced by the contractile walls of the dorsal vessel and to some extent by that of other vessels as well. The ventral vessel, however, seems to have little or no peristaltic contraction. A part of the dorsal vessel may be modified as a bulbous, muscular heart in some worms, especially in the Sedentaria. Blood passes from the ventral vessel to the dorsal vessel by indirect routes. In each segment the ventral vessel gives rise to vessels which supply the parapodia, the body wall, the nephridia, and

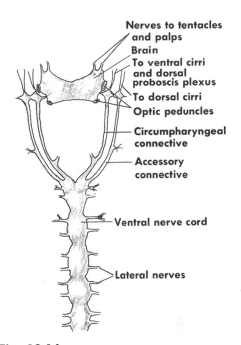

Fig. 18-14

Anterior end of nervous system of *Neanthes*. (After Turnbull; modified from Brown.)

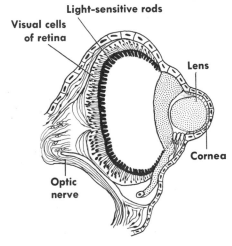

Fig. 18-15

Diagram of section through eye of polychaete *(Alciope).*

the digestive system. The dorsal vessel receives vessels from the parapodia and from the alimentary canal. The branches of these ventral and dorsal systems are interconnected by a meshwork of smaller vessels. Many variations of this plan are found, and

297

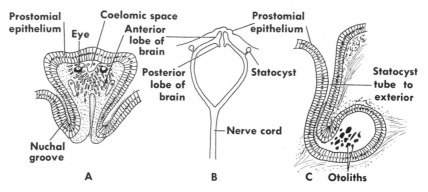

Fig. 18-16

A, Diagrammatic horizontal section of prostomium of *Arenicola* showing relationship of brain, eyes, and coelomic spaces. (×35.) **B,** Anterior end of nervous system of *Arenicola;* nerves to statocysts arise from esophageal connectives. (×3.) **C,** Section of statocyst and tube to exterior *(Arenicola);* irregular otoliths are chiefly quartz grains. (×100.) (Modified from Ashworth.)

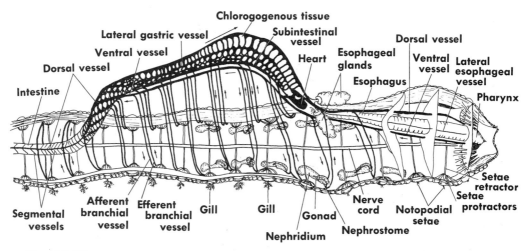

Fig. 18-17

Internal structure of *Arenicola,* dorsal view, with portion of digestive tract lifted out to show arrangement of circulatory system. (Modified from Ashworth.)

in some Errantia the vascular system is an open one instead of closed.

The blood, in its course from the ventral to the dorsal vessel, undergoes many changes in its composition. In the body wall the blood loses carbon dioxide and picks up oxygen; in the nephridia it loses waste and picks up nutrients from the intestine. The blood also varies greatly in color. In some forms it is colorless (scale worms, syllids, phyllodocids), but it may also be greenish, reddish, or other hues. Most polychaetes have some kind of re-

spiratory pigments dissolved in the plasma of their blood. These pigments aid in the transport of molecular oxygen. One respiratory pigment is chlorocruorin, which shows up as red in high concentrations or bright green in more dilute solutions. This pigment is common in the blood of the serpulid and sabellid fanworms. Red hemoglobin is one of the most common pigments, and some polychaetes such as *Serpula* have both chlorocruorin and hemoglobin. Hemoglobin molecules may be large or small. In *Arenicola* the molecular

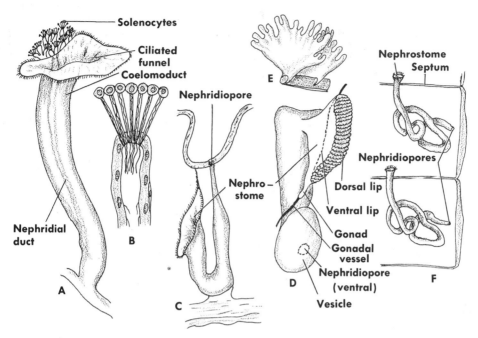

Fig. 18-18

Nephridia. **A,** Protonephridia and coelomoduct of *Phyllodoce*. **B,** Group of solenocytes and branch of protonephridium of same. **C,** Metanephridium of *Nerine*. **D,** Metanephridium of *Arenicola;* dorsal lip bears many highly vascular, lobed, ciliated processes; vesicle is shown distended with sperm. **E,** Two lobed processes from dorsal lip of nephridium of same. **F,** Metanephridia of *Neanthes*. (**A** to **C** modified from Goodrich; **D** and **E** modified from Ashworth.)

weight of the molecule is 3,000,000. Some polychaetes contain amebocytes in their blood, and in *Glycera,* which has no blood vessels, erythrocytes with hemoglobin are present in the coelomic fluid.

A pair of nephridia is typically found in every segment that bears parapodia (Fig. 18-17). A nephridium is usually an invaginated ectodermal tube, although some may be mesodermal in origin. Two kinds occur—protonephridia and metanephridia (Fig. 18-18). In some polychaetes only one pair of nephridia may be present in the entire animal; in others a pair is found in each segment. The typical metanephridium extends into two segments. The nephridial tubule and its external opening, the nephridiopore, lie in one segment, while the other end of the tubule is a ciliated funnel (nephrostome) opening into the coelom of the next anterior segment (Fig. 18-18, *F*). The primitive protonephridial tubule does not open directly into the coe-

lom but has at the preseptal end a slender solenocyte tubule provided with a long flagellum (Fig. 18-18 *A, B*). Fluid passing from the coelom through the walls of the solenocyte tubule is driven by the flagellum into the chief lumen of the nephridium. There may be several of these solenocytes to a single nephridium. Nephridial tubules are ciliated for driving the fluid and for discharging it through the nephridiopore. Metanephridia are generally coiled and are chiefly found in Sedentaria but also occur in Errantia. All types of nephridia collect and transport waste from the coelom to the exterior through the nephridiopores. In some polychaetes the nephridia are surrounded by a network of blood vessels that furnish some of the waste to the tubules. Chlorogogen tissue on the wall of the intestine (Fig. 18-17) and coelomocytes may also play a part in excretion.

Polychaetes have both asexual and sexual methods of reproduction. Asexual repro-

299

duction occurs by budding and transverse fission; sometimes it may happen by accidental fragmentation. In a few worms a chain of sexual individuals is formed by an asexual stolon (blastogamy or budding). This is most common among the fanworms, serpulids, and syllids. In sexual reproduction most polychaetes are dioecious, but occasional cases of hermaphroditism, parthenogenesis, and protandry also exist. Gonads or masses of sex cells are usually widely scattered in the coelomic cavity. They usually appear first as swellings of the peritoneum on the septa of certain segments. In some forms the gonads may have a generally segmental arrangement (*Aphrodite*); in the familiar *Neanthes* the ventral septal peritoneum is the region of gonad formation. There is no differentiation of special sex ducts or receptacles such as uteri, seminal vesicles, gonoducts, etc. in *Neanthes*. Unripe sex cells are shed into the coelom where maturation occurs in the coelomic fluid. Special nurse cells may nourish the ova as the latter develop. Gametes are released from the body cavity through special gonoducts, through modified nephridia, or through a breakdown of the body wall. When the body wall ruptures, the adults die. Perhaps the majority of polychaetes shed their sex cells to the exterior through the metanephridia.

It is thought by some authorities that in the primitive plan of polychaetes each segment bore a pair of protonephridia with solenocytes for excretion and a pair of gonoducts for carrying the gametes. The union of the ciliated opening of a gonoduct with the protonephridial tubule produced the metanephridium (the nephromixium of E. S. Goodrich). The degeneration of the solenocytes in this combination would result in the typical metanephridium with both genital and excretory functions. Other investigations, however, have shown that in some polychaetes the metanephridia may arise as new developments from the mesoderm and are not homologous to the protonephridia as the Goodrich theory implies. Moreover, such metanephridia may have both excretory and genital functions the same as the nephromixium, or they may have only an excretory function.

Fertilization occurs in the sea outside of the worms. During the breeding season, worms of both sexes swim together near the surface of the water, and the proximity of the worms insures contact of sperm and eggs.

The external form of the body of a sexual worm may involve radical changes in color, body texture, setae morphology, and parapodia. This phenomenon is called epitoky and is characteristic of the Nereidae, the Syllidae, and the Eunicidae. The

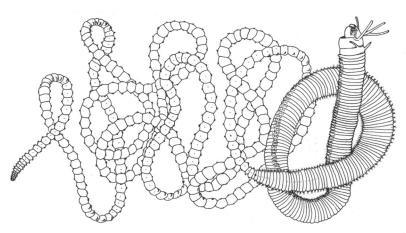

Fig. 18-19

Eunice viridis, the palolo worm of Samoa and Fiji. Epitokal region is long chain of posterior segments, each with eyespot on ventral side. (Modified from Woodworth.)

reproductive individual, which is usually pelagic, is called an epitoke; the nonsexual and nonpelagic form is an atoke. The most striking modifications in epitokal forms are found chiefly in the gamete-forming segments, which are much distended with gametes. Their parapodial lobes are greatly enlarged with long swimming setae. The palolo worm (*Eunice viridis,* Fig. 18-19) is a classic example of epitoky. Once a year during the full moon in October and November the posterior segments, full of eggs or sperm, are cast off by the adult worms, which live in burrows of coral reefs. These segments rise and swarm at the surface, making the water milky with the discharged gametes. Similar behavior is found in the West Indian palolo, *Eunice schemacephala* (L. B. Clark and W. N. Hess,

1940). In these worms, swarming occurs in July during the first or last quarter of the moon. The physiologic reasons for swarming apparently involve environmental factors that are poorly understood.

Another striking case of epitoky is found in *Autolytus* (Syllidae), which has marked dimorphic phases of male and female sexes. In the male epitoke of this form the body is divided into three distinct regions, the pre-epitokal, the epitokal, and the post-epitokal. The female epitoke is more slender with the prostomial antennae simple instead of forked, as in the male.

Polychaetes usually have marked regenerative powers. Most lost organs such as parapodia, tentacular crowns, and tails are replaced. In a few species an entire worm may regenerate from a single segment. Au-

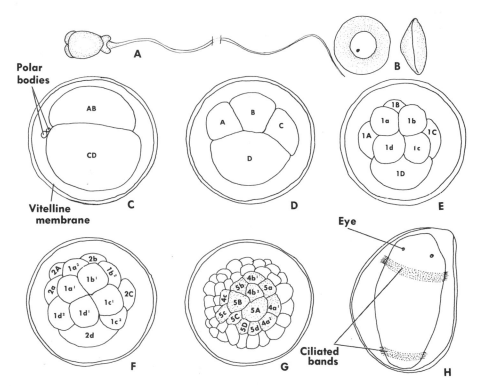

Fig. 18-20

Early development of *Arenicola*. **A,** Spermatozoa. (×3,000.) **B,** Two views of flat ovum. (×100.) **C,** Two-cell stage about 4½ hours after fertilization. **D,** Four-cell stage, from anterior pole. **E,** Eight-cell stage, with first quartet of micromeres. **F,** Sixteen-cell stage about 2 hours after first cleavage; second quartet has formed. **G,** Blastula at end of 24 hours, seen from posterior pole; fourth quartet has formed; 4d, mesoblast cell, has sunk into segmentation cavity; 4a, 4b, and 4c, along with 4A, 4B, 4C, and 4D, are endoderm cells at posterior pole. **H,** Larva 72 hours after fertilization; has eyes and two ciliated bands and is ready to hatch. (**C** to **H** ×210.) (Redrawn from Ashworth.)

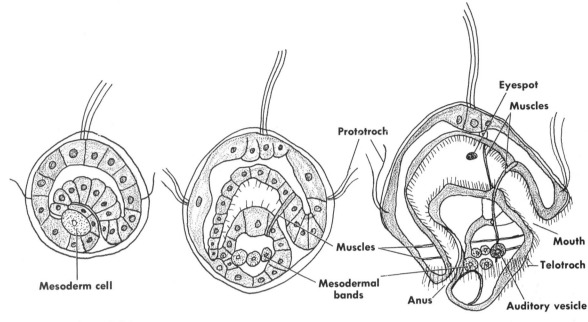

Fig. 18-21

Gastrula and two trochophore stages of *Eupomatus uncinatus*. (Modified from Hatschek.)

totomy, or the voluntary discarding of damaged parts, is also a frequent occurrence.

Development

In development the polychaete egg has typical spiral cleavage with mosaic development (Fig. 18-20). Although the egg is telolecithal, the amount of yolk is variable and determines the type of gastrulation. In some polychaetes the egg has little yolk, and the macromeres and micromeres are about the same size. In such cases gastrulation takes place by invagination. Most polychaetes, however, have micromeres much smaller than macromeres in their spiral cleavage. Gastrulation in these forms occurs by epiboly. In some polychaetes gastrulation may involve a combination of both invagination and epiboly. A solid blastula or stereoblastula, instead of a coeloblastula, is chiefly characteristic of those forms with unequal cleavage. In *Neanthes,* for instance, the first two divisions are equal, producing four similar blastomeres or macromeres. Each of these macromeres in its further cleavage gives rise to one of the quadrants of the embryos. The third, fourth, and fifth divisions are unequal and

at right angles to the first two cleavage stages and produce from the macromeres three quartets of small micromeres. These three quartets of cells give rise to the ectoderm and its derivatives. The sixth division involves a fourth quartet and results in the separation from the macromeres of cells that produce the mesoderm and aid in the formation of the endoderm.

Characteristic of many polychaetes, but not of *Neanthes,* is the formation during development of a pelagic, ciliated larva called a trochophore (Fig. 18-21). In some forms this stage is found in the egg, and the larva has no opportunity for a free-swimming existence because the egg hatches into a post trochophore form. In the typical free-swimming trochophore the chief band of cilia is the prototroch, which is preoral in position. Later, another band of cilia, the telotroch, rings the larva near the anus followed by a third girdle, the metatroch, located just below the mouth. Both the mouth and the anus may arise from the elongated blastopore, or the anus may arise as a new opening. The alimentary tract, in addition to the mouth and anus, consists of an ectodermal esophagus (stomodeum), an

Fig. 18-22

Three larval stages of *Polygordius*. **A,** Trochophore. **B,** Polytroch with early segmentation. **C,** Free-swimming, segmented larva. (Modified from Hatschek.)

endodermal stomach, and an ectodermal rectum. The body cavity is the old blastocoel and is the space between the gut and ectoderm. The cavity contains larval muscle bands, processes of mesenchymal cells, and two larval protonephridia. A group of ganglionic cells near the apical plate, together with several nerves that encircle the trochophore, may make up a nervous system in the fully-developed larva. An apical organ of a tuft of cilia and other sensory structures may also be present.

The trochophore varies in certain details among the different polychaetes that have such a larva. The most typical ones are perhaps found in *Polygordius* (Fig. 18-22), *Eupomatus* (Fig. 18-21), and some others, where the larva has a free-swimming, planktonic existence. In their metamorphosis the trochophore larvae pass through stages in which larval structures are replaced by those characteristic of the adult. A polytroch stage with a few segments (Fig. 18-22, *B*) follows the trochophore

stage, and in turn, the polytroch is succeeded by various free-swimming larval forms (Figs. 18-22, *C*, 18-23). Some of the most characteristic changes during metamorphosis are the transformation of the apical organ into the adult prostomium with brain, eyes, and tentacles; the development of trunk segments between mouth and anal regions that results in a gradual lengthening of the body; and the arrangement of the metameric segmentation into a pair of mesodermal hollow somites for each segment. From each hollow somite there develops half a coelomic compartment, the splanchnic mesoderm of the gut musculature, the somatic mesoderm that forms the body wall under the ectoderm, and the adult nephridia and blood vessels. In addition, mesenteries and septa are also laid down by the somites. This development results in the elimination of the old blastocoel, and its place is taken now by the peritoneum-lined cavities of the segments.

303

Fig. 18-23

Nectochaete larva of polychaete. (From Encyclopaedia Britannica Films, Inc.)

Fig. 18-24

Ventral view of anterior end of earthworm *Lumbricus*.

CLASS CLITELLATA
Order Oligochaeta

The members of the order Oligochaeta were probably derived from some branch of the polychaetes, but they differ from the latter in several important particulars. They have both external and internal segmentation, but with the exception of one family (Branchiobdellidae) they have no parapodia, and their setae are comparatively few in number. External regionalization of the body is mostly nonexistent, and the pharynx is not eversible. They are hermaphroditic instead of dioecious, and mutual insemination is the rule. Gonads are usually one or two pairs in number, and special genital ducts (coelomoducts) exist for discharge of the gametes. A clitellum is found at sexual maturity, and the eggs are laid in a cocoon. Eggs develop directly into juvenile worms without larval stages. Ecologically, these worms are divided into two main types: burrowing terrestrial forms and aquatic dwellers (mostly freshwater). Some are marine, and several species are intertidal. They range in size from small aquatic species less than a millimeter in length to the large terrestrial earthworms, which may reach a length of 7 to 9 feet with a diameter of 1 inch. About 3,100 species have been named at the present time.

MORPHOLOGIC FEATURES. The body of oligochaetes is generally cylindric, although it is sometimes slightly flattened, with the anterior mouth usually overhung by a rather small prostomium that does not bear tentacles. The anus is terminal, although in a few forms it is displaced dorsally. The external segmentation is well marked by furrows, but the segments are not distinctive of species and are not fixed in numbers. In some aquatic species the segments may number only six or seven; in giant earthworms they may number 600 or more.

The setae are not as numerous as in the polychaetes; they display a variety of lengths from very short to very long, and they may be straight or curved, simple or branched. A characteristic arrangement of setae is a pair of ventrolateral bundles and a pair of ventral bundles on each segment (Figs. 18-24, 18-27). The number of setae in a bundle varies from one to many. In the genus *Achaeta*, setae are entirely

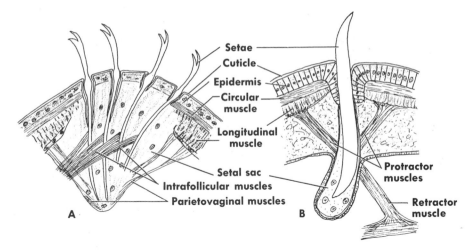

Fig. 18-25

Sections through setal sacs. **A,** *Tubifex.* Parietovaginal muscles regulate movement of whole follicle; intrafollicular muscles direct movement of individual setae. (×510.) **B,** *Lumbricus.* (**A** modified from Dixon; **B** modified from Stephenson.)

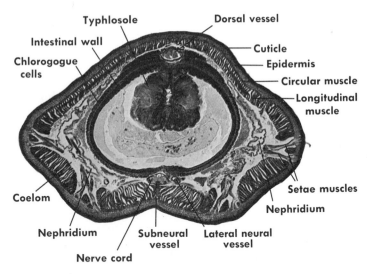

Fig. 18-26

Cross section through intestinal region of *Lumbricus.*

absent. The setae are produced in setal sacs in the body wall (Figs. 18-25, 18-26); in some species a separate setal sac occurs for each seta. A cell in the base of each sac secretes the seta and replaces lost ones, either in a new sac or in the old one. Setae are manipulated by protractor and retractor muscles and can be set at different angles for effective use. Projecting gills are found in the body of some species. Besides the mouth and anal openings, reproductive pores on some segments, openings of the nephridia, and in many terrestrial forms, dorsal pores that open externally from the coelom occur. At sexual maturity the oligochaete has a clitellum. This glandular structure may consist of only a few cells restricted to one or two segments in aquatic forms, or it may consist of many cells that cover many segments, as in earthworms.

305

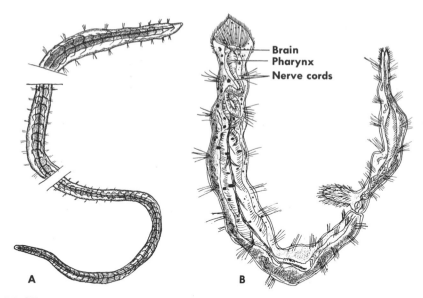

Brain
Pharynx
Nerve cords

Fig. 18-27

A, *Tubifex,* with portions of body omitted. *T. rivulorum* is 30 to 50 mm. long; lives in tube in mud of pond or lake. **B,** *Aeolosoma* dividing by transverse fission; single zooids are usually less than 5 mm. long, but some species up to 10 mm. (**B** modified from Lankester.)

The body wall consists of a simple columnar epithelium interspersed with glandular and sensory cells, a delicate cuticle secreted by the epithelium, a muscular coat of outer circular and inner longitudinal layers, and a lining peritoneum (Fig. 18-26). A connective tissue dermis or basement membrane is found beneath the epidermis in some forms. The cuticle is ciliated in *Aeolosoma* (Fig. 18-27). The longitudinal muscle layer is very thin in aquatic forms and is a muscular syncytium in others.

Locomotion of terrestrial forms involves alternate contraction of the circular and longitudinal muscle layers with the resulting extension and contraction of the body. This peristaltic progressive motion is aided by the gripping and anchoring action of the setae on the substratum. Undulatory movements, so characteristic of polychaetes, are absent in terrestrial oligochaetes.

The coelom is well developed and is segmentally partitioned by septa. It communicates with the exterior by dorsal pores regulated by sphincter muscles. In some aquatic forms a single pore, usually on the prostomium, is found. Coelomic fluid, which fills the septal compartments, may be discharged through the dorsal pores of the intersegmental furrows or through special openings in the floor of the pharynx. The fluid, which may be highly malodorous, plays an important role in the differential turgor of the septal compartments and in regional movement of the body for burrowing, as mentioned regarding the polychaetes. In composition the coelomic fluid may contain protein, coelomocytes, pigment, bacteria, and sarcolytes (fragments of muscle). Some of the formed elements—lymphocytes, leukocytes, and monocytes—resemble types found in vertebrates and are phagocytic. Eleocytes with oil droplets are also present. In some coelomic fluids phosphorescent discharges from special granules occur.

The digestive tract consists of a buccal cavity, pharynx, esophagus, and intestine. The pharynx is highly muscular and is used to suck in the food by pumping contractions; in aquatic worms the pharynx may be protrusible and eversible, and food adhering by mucus contact is pulled in when the pharynx retracts. To assist in the action of the pharynx, muscle strands are present between the pharynx and body wall. Jaws are absent except in the family Branchiobdellidae. Pharyngeal glands secrete a saliva containing mucus and a proteolytic enzyme. A narrow, tubular esophagus follows the pharynx and may be modified (usually at its posterior end) to form a crop and muscular gizzard (Fig. 18-28). A dilated pouch or stomach may be present in some oligochaetes. In terrestrial forms such as earthworms one or more pairs of diverticula or evaginations of the esophageal wall, known as calciferous glands, are present. These glands may be separate but communicate with the lumen of the esophagus by a duct. The glands are well supplied with blood vessels and secrete calcium carbonate into the esophagus in the form of calcite crystals. The glands thus play a part in the pH regulation of the blood by controlling the level of calcium and carbonate ions in the blood. These glands are mostly absent in primitive and aquatic forms. The thin-walled crop stores food, and the cuticle-lined muscular gizzard grinds the food with the aid of soil particles.

The intestine is a straight tube lined with cilia, secretory cells, and absorptive epithelial cells. To increase the absorptive surface, a longitudinal dorsal fold (the typhlosole) (Fig. 18-26) projects downward into the lumen of the esophagus. Digestive secretions contain enzymes for breaking down proteins, fats, and carbohydrates. The intestine has thin muscular layers and is invested by a modified peritoneum of yellowish cells, the chloragogen tissue, which serves for fat and glycogen synthesis and storage. It may also play a part in excretion, such as the formation of ammonia and urea. The intestine in earthworms may have an osmoregulatory function of assisting the nephridia in eliminating excess water when the worm becomes water soaked.

Excretion in oligochaetes occurs by segmentally arranged, paired metanephridia (Fig. 18-29). The primitive plan seems to have been a pair of nephridia per segment, but this arrangement is slightly modified in some worms. A typical metanephridium (Fig. 18-30) consists of the funnellike preseptal nephrostome that opens into the

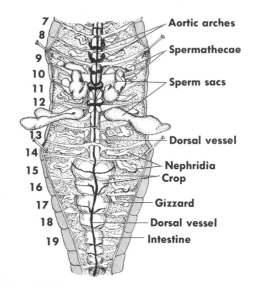

Fig. 18-28
Dissection of *Lumbricus*.

coelom, a duct through the septum, and a coiled tube that discharges ventrolaterally to the exterior by an opening (the nephridiopore). The coiled tube has various differentiations such as a ciliated region, variations in the tubular bore, and a terminal dilated vesicle. Nephridia are variously modified in the different species. Instead of the typical paired nephridia per segment (holonephridia), the nephridia may be multiple (meronephridia). In some giant earthworms many nephrostomes exist for each nephridium. The cells composing the lips of the nephrostomes are of diagnostic value in taxonomic determinations. The nephridia may open to the exterior (exonephric), into the pharynx (pharyngeal), or into the intestine (enteronephric). More than one type of nephridia may be found in the same worm.

In addition to the waste fluid that is drawn from the coelom into the nephrostome by ciliary action, each nephridium is also richly supplied with blood from branches of the chief ventral artery; this blood is involved in active reabsorption of fluid from the nephridial tubule as well as excretion of waste into the tubule. As the coelomic fluid passes down the tubule, much of the water is reabsorbed back into the blood, thus concentrating the waste. **307**

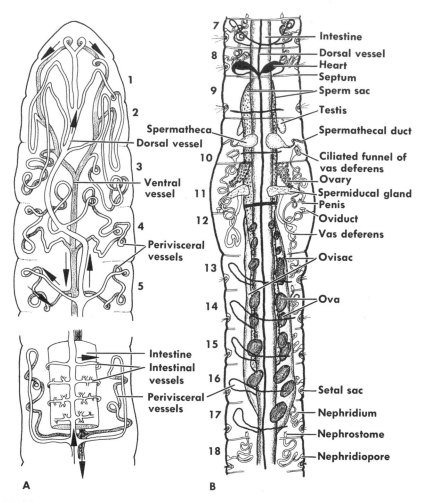

Fig. 18-29

Tubifex. **A,** Circulation in anterior portion and in one of segments of intestinal region. **B,** Reproductive system. (Modified from Dixon.)

Some salts are also reabsorbed back into the blood. Among the chief wastes excreted are ammonia (mostly in aquatic forms) and urea (chiefly in terrestrial species). The nephridium in oligochaetes is thus seen to have about the same functions as has the nephron unit of the vertebrate kidney, viz. filtration, secretion, and reabsorption.

Respiration is chiefly a function of the body surface in oligochaetes. The skin is usually well vascularized, and when moist, the exchange of gases can readily occur through it. In some aquatic species (Naididae) anal respiration by the circulation of

water in and out of a rectal chamber takes place. *Dero* and some other aquatic genera have a circle of anal gills (Fig. 18-31). A few oligochaetes have tuftlike gills on certain segments, usually in the posterior part of the body. Many oligochaetes, including earthworms, can do without oxygen for some time and can build up an oxygen debt by the accumulation of lactic acid.

In oligochaetes the circulatory system is a closed system which includes a pulsating region for driving the blood, arteries to carry the blood away from this region, fine capillaries for the exchange of foods and wastes between blood and tissues, and

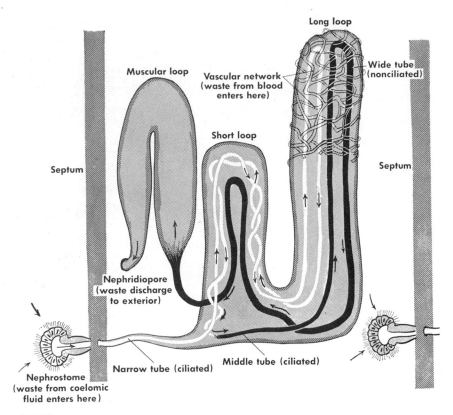

Fig. 18-30

Diagram of earthworm nephridium. (Modified from Moment.)

veins for returning the blood to the propulsive structures, or heart. The primitive plan of the circulatory systems seems to be a contractile dorsal vessel arising posteriorly from a periintestinal blood sinus. a ventral vessel for blood distribution, and a few pairs of segmental, commissural connectives at the anterior end between the dorsal and ventral vessels. Such a plan is found in *Aeolosoma* at the present time.

In more advanced oligochaetes the dorsal vessel has become separated from the intestinal sinus and extends to the posterior end (Figs. 18-29, 18-32). In addition, a subneural vessel and two lateroneural vessels are present. Dorsal and ventral blood vessels are also connected by lateral vessels in every segment. The functional heart, or pumping organ, is really the contractile dorsal blood vessel, although the five or more pairs of aortic arches or "hearts" (in segments 7 to 11 in the earthworm) have been assigned this function in

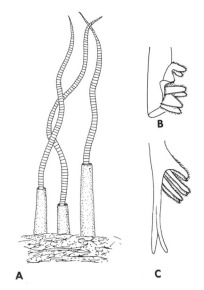

Fig. 18-31

A, *Tubifex*, a small red oligochaete, is tube builder in bottom mud of ponds or lakes. (×2½.) Exposed posterior end waves vigorously, possibly to increase oxygen supply to its thin-walled surface. Anal gills (lateral view) of *Dero limosa*, **B**, and *Aullophorus*, **C**. (Modified from Pennak.)

Fig. 18-32

Scheme of circulatory system of earthworm *Lumbricus*. **A,** Circulation in any segment posterior to esophagus. **B,** Circulation in segments 7 to 11 showing aortic arches around esophagus. Septa not shown. (From Hickman: Integrated principles of zoology, The C. V. Mosby Co.)

the past because of their vigorous contractions. They may assist the flow of blood and also regulate the pressure. The blood is propelled forward and downward by rhythmic contractions which begin near the posterior end of the dorsal blood vessel. The main distributing artery is the ventral vessel, which is found below the gut and above the nerve cord. This vessel receives blood from the paired aortic arches and carries the blood toward the tail. From the ventral vessel a pair of segmental arteries is given off in each segment and delivers blood to the body wall musculature. Small branches in each segment from the main ventral artery also send blood to the nephridia, to the lateral neural artery, and to the underside of the intestine. In the regions supplied by these branches from the ventral vessel the arteries break up into capillaries where food and waste exchanges are made. The principal vein for the return of blood is the subneural blood vessel. It receives blood from the nerve cord and delivers it posteriorly toward the tail and up-

ward through segmentally paired parietal vessels. The parietals also receive blood from the body wall before discharging into the dorsal vessel. Also, in each segment the dorsal blood vessel gives off a branch to the typhlosole and receives a pair of veins from the intestine.

The blood is colorless in some oligochaetes but usually carries hemoglobin or erythrocruorin in solution in the plasma, producing a red color. The formed elements, or amebocytes, are colorless but are phagocytic.

The typical central nervous system in oligochaetes consists of a bilobed cerebral ganglion (brain), circumpharyngeal connectives, and a ventral nerve cord. In some simple or primitive oligochaetes (Aeolosomatidae), two ventral nerve cords as well as the brain are united to the epidermis. In more advanced oligochaetes the two ventral cords are fused into one; and the brain lies just above the pharynx in the third segment (Fig. 18-33), instead of at the base of the prostomium, as in *Aeolosoma* (Fig, 18-

310

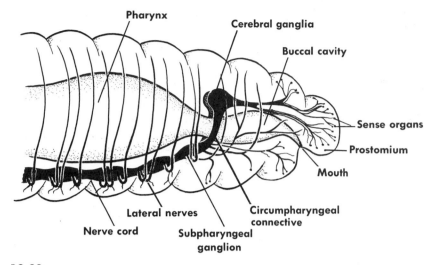

Fig. 18-33

Nervous system of anterior end of earthworm. (From Hickman: Integrated principles of zoology, The C. V. Mosby Co.)

Fig. 18-34

Escape mechanism of earthworm. Three giant fibers in nerve cord permit rapid transmission; median fiber conducts posteriorly, lateral fibers anteriorly. Arrangement of simple reflex arc shown in right foreground. (From Hickman: Integrated principles of zoology, The C. V. Mosby Co.)

27, *B*). In the nerve cord, segmentally arranged ganglia give off lateral nerves to the body wall and intestine. Some aquatic oligochaetes have four pairs of lateral nerves per segment, but terrestrial forms usually have only three pairs per segment. These lateral or segmental nerves contain both sensory and motor fibers. The brain supplies a pair of prostomial nerves to the prostomium and first segment. The subpharyngeal ganglion, at the union of the circumpharyngeal connectives with the ventral nerve cord, also gives off nerves to the first as well as the second trunk segment. The subpharyngeal ganglion exerts a control over the motor activities and reflexes of the worm. The worm is unable to adapt to environmental conditions when

311

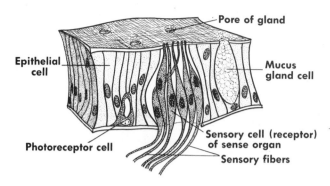

Epithelial cell
Pore of gland
Mucus gland cell
Photoreceptor cell
Sensory cell (receptor) of sense organ
Sensory fibers

Fig. 18-35

Diagram of portion of epidermis of earthworm showing various sensory specializations. (From Hickman: Integrated principles of zoology, The C. V. Mosby Co.)

the brain is removed; when the subpharyngeal ganglion is destroyed, all movements cease.

The nerve cord contains nerve fibers of all three types of neurons: motor neurons with their cell bodies in the segmental ganglion, association neurons for carrying impulses from one cell to another, and sensory neurons with their cell bodies in the body wall. In locomotion the ordinary rhythmic peristaltic movements are produced by a succession of tactile reflexes involving reflex arcs of sensory and motor neurons. Whenever a segment is stretched, receptors are stimulated, and sensory nerves carry impulses to the motor neurons of the cord. The motor neurons produce contractions of the longitudinal muscles, which cause the adjacent segment to stretch. The stretch receptors in this adjacent (second) segment are stimulated, causing this segment to contract; this stimulates the third segment, and so on. Thus a wave of muscular contraction passes over the worm.

For rapid movements to avoid danger, nearly all oligochaetes have an escape mechanism in the giant fibers (Fig. 18-34). Of the five giant fibers, the three large ones on the dorsal side of the ventral nerve cord are primarily concerned with the rapid movement of escape. In these large giant fibers the rate of nerve conduction is five times faster than in the regular neurons. The median giant fiber conducts impulses toward the tail; the two lateral ones conduct impulses toward the head. When-

ever a worm is overstimulated at one end, the rapid impulses in the giant fibers produce a simultaneous contraction of all the body segments that jerks the worm into its burrow and out of danger. Giant fibers differ from other neurons in being multicellular and in having the two lateral fibers connected with each other at regular intervals so that they react as a unit.

Nerve plexuses found in the epidermis and muscle layers are connected with the central nervous system through the segmental nerves. Some neurons apparently are independent and initiate local responses of muscles. An enteric nervous system attached to the circumpharyngeal connectives innervates the muscle fibers of the digestive tract in earthworms.

The sensory system consists of sense organs of several types located primarily in the epidermis (Fig. 18-35). Most oligochaetes show a wide range of reactions to stimuli, but they generally lack eyes, although a few aquatic forms have eyespots. Free nerve endings among the epithelial cells may respond to tactile, heat, and pain stimuli. The photosensitive cells in the anterior end of the worm are oval with a lens-like body. The work of W. N. Hess and others indicates that the prostomium bears many sense organs. Chemoreceptors are common, especially in the anterior end (C. L. Prossor). Earthworms are very sensitive to vibrations but do not respond to sound waves.

All oligochaetes are hermaphroditic, with distinct gonads that are derived from the septal peritoneum. The gonads are usually restricted to a relatively few segments. Members of the primitive family Aeolosomatidae resemble the polychaetes in lacking distinct gonads and in having masses of reproductive cells scattered through many segments. The testes in oligochaetes are located anterior to the ovaries. In some aquatic species one pair of testes and one pair of ovaries are located in successive segments (Fig. 18-29), but the typical plan in terrestrial species is two pairs of testes and two pairs of ovaries with each pair in a different segment (Fig. 18-36). Most earthworms retain only the posterior pair of ovaries. The location of the reproductive segments is not the same in all genera. Gametes are released into the coelom or special coelomic pouches where maturation is completed, and they reach the outside through the differentiated gonoducts. The coelomic pouches (seminal vesicles and ovisacs) are produced by septal outpocketings in the reproductive segments. Many variations exist in the number and position of the pouches. In the common earthworm *Lumbricus* (Fig. 18-36) one pair of the testes is located in the tenth and the other is in the eleventh segment. The testes are very small and usually lobed. Each is enclosed in a sperm sac or seminal vesicle. Of the three pairs of seminal vesicles, one pair projects forward from the septum anterior to the first pair of testes; the other two pairs project from the septa posterior to the two pairs of testes. Each segment containing a pair of testes is provided with a pair of sperm ducts, or vasa deferentia, one on each side. The internal opening of each duct is a ciliated funnel located on the posterior septum of each testicular segment. From the funnel the vas deferens extends backward through the septa of several segments. Before opening on the ventral side of the body, the two pairs of vasa deferentia on each side join, so there is only one pair of openings on the fifteenth segment. This outer opening may be enlarged in some oligochaetes (aquatic) to form a muscular antrum with an eversible penis (Fig. 18-29, *B*). The vasa deferentia are straight in the earthworm but may be coiled in other worms. A prostate gland of glandular tissue may be attached to the posterior end of the vasa deferentia in some aquatic species, or it may be a separate structure.

A single pair of pear-shaped ovaries in *Lumbricus* is located on the anterior septum of the thirteenth segment. Ovisacs are small or entirely absent. The narrow end of the ovary projects into the coelomic cavity, into which the eggs are discharged in ovulation.

Each of the paired oviducts is provided with a funnel that is located on the posterior septum of the ovarian segment. The oviducts penetrate the septum to which the funnels are attached, and each opens by an oviducal pore on the ventral surface of the segment following the ovarian segment. The female system also includes the seminal receptacles (spermathecae) that

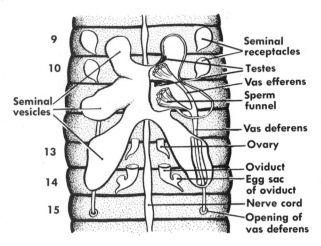

Fig. 18-36

Dorsal view of reproductive organs of earthworm, with seminal vesicles partly removed on right side to reveal testes. (From Hickman: Integrated principles of zoology, The C. V. Mosby Co.)

receive sperm from another worm. They are small, round structures that usually open on the ventral surface of the segments in which they are found. Two pairs of these receptacles are found in *Lumbricus,* but there may be more in some oligochaetes. Each pair is located in a separate segment, and in *Lumbricus* the openings are in the intersegmental furrows between segments 9 and 10, and 10 and 11.

Reciprocal copulation is the rule in oligochaetes, with heads in opposite directions and the anterior ventral surfaces of the mating pair in contact (Fig. 18-37). In some species (but not in *Lumbricus*) the male pores of one mate are directly opposite the seminal receptacles of the other, and the sperm from the male pores are transmitted directly into the seminal receptacles of the partner. In others, including *Lumbricus,* the male pores and those of the seminal receptacles are not in apposition, and the sperm must be carried externally along the ventral seminal grooves from the male pores to the clitellar region where the openings of the seminal receptacles of the partner are found (Fig. 18-38). Each worm is also enclosed in a slime tube. Sperm are propelled through the ventral grooves by muscular contractions. The mating pairs are held together in two zones

313

Fig. 18-37

Earthworms in copulation. (Photograph by Guy Carter.)

Fig. 18-38

Reciprocal copulation in *Lumbricus;* sperm from male gonopores of each partner travel along seminal grooves to seminal receptacles of mate, where they are stored until used to fertilize eggs in cocoons formed after copulation. (From Encyclopaedia Britannica film, "Segmentation—The Annelid Worms.")

by a common mucus coat secreted by the clitellum and by special ventral setae which penetrate the body of the other. After the mutual exchange of sperm, the two worms separate. Copulation may last for more than two hours. After separation, each worm produces a series of cocoons for the eggs. For each cocoon a slime tube is first secreted around the anterior segments and the clitellum. Within this slime tube, the clitellum secretes around itself another tougher band which will form the cocoon. Eggs and albumen enter the cocoon before it slides off the clitellum. As the slime tube with the cocoon slides forward over the anterior end of the worm, sperm from the seminal receptacles enter the cocoon and fertilize the eggs. When the worm has backed completely out of the slime tube and cocoon and freed itself, the mucus tube disintegrates, and the ends of the cocoon constrict to form a yellowish, lemon-shaped case. Cocoons of *Lum-*

bricus (Fig. 18-39) are about 7 mm. long, but those of the giant earthworm of Australia *(Megascolides)* are over 3 inches long. From each cocoon will hatch from 1 to 20 juvenile worms, depending on the species. Cocoons are formed every few days, and mating may occur frequently during the spring and fall.

Copulation in some oligochaetes is impossible, and eggs are self-fertilized. Parthenogenesis may also occur in a few. Asexual reproduction is common in the aquatic families Aeolosomatidae and Naididae. The members of these families reproduce asexually by transverse fission (Fig. 18-27, *B*). Sexual reproduction is unknown in some of these species. Chains of zooids are often found in *Aeolosoma* (Fig. 18-27, *B*) and *Chaetogaster,* where a new fission occurs before the old division is completed.

Considerable regeneration occurs in oligochaetes. In earthworms, if the worm is bisected anterior to segment 18, a new anterior end of one to five segments will form. If the tail is cut off posterior to segment 18 a tail may grow forward from the cut, forming a worm with two tails. An anterior piece of 35 or more segments forms a new tail, but the number of segments regenerated will depend upon the level of the cut. A cut at segment 50 will regenerate 10 fewer segments than one made at the level of segment 40. Grafting is also possible with earthworms.

DEVELOPMENT. The entire development of the egg into the juvenile worm takes place in the cocoon. There are no larval stages, for development is direct. The eggs of lower oligochaetes, especially aquatic species, are provided with a great deal of yolk. Eggs of terrestrial forms usually have less yolk, but sufficient albumen for growth is supplied to the cocoons by the clitellum before the cocoon is discharged from the body. The segmentation is a modified form of spiral determinate cleavage. There are, however, many divergent opinions about the origin of various structural features. For instance, some views hold that the nephridia are derived from ectoderm; others consider these organs to have originated from mesoderm. A few opinions maintain that nephridia are derived from both germ layers.

The holoblastic cleavage in earthworms

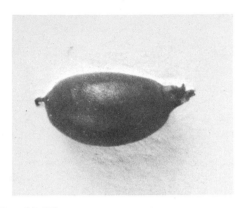

Fig. 18-39

Earthworm cocoon *(Lumbricus).* (From Hickman: Integrated principles of zoology, The C. V. Mosby Co.)

is unequal (Fig. 18-40), producing a rather small blastocoel enclosed by small ectodermal cells above and larger endodermal cells below. At first spherical, the blastula elongates with the endodermal cells becoming distinctly columnar (Fig. 18-40, *D*). During gastrulation the endoderm is invaginated as the future enteron with the blastopore at the anterior end becoming the future mouth (Fig. 18-40, *E, F*). The somites and muscles are formed from two cords of mesoblastic cells that arise between the ectoderm and the enteron (Fig. 18-40, *G*). The anus is a new formation. The juvenile worms of *Lumbricus* hatch from cocoons in a few weeks, although the length of time depends upon environmental conditions.

Order Hirudinea

The Hirudinea are commonly known as the leeches, of which more than 300 species have been classified at the present time. Although derived from the oligochaetes and included with them in the same class (Clitellata), leeches have evolved beyond the level of organization of all other annelids. With the oligochaetes they share certain common features of embryologic development; both groups have a clitellum for secreting a cocoon; both are hermaphroditic with well-defined gonads; and both have separate nephridia and coelomoducts. However, leeches differ from oligochaetes in the lack of setae (with one

315

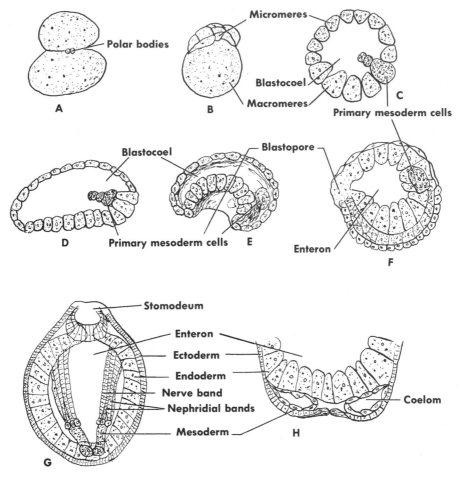

Fig. 18-40

Early development of *Lumbricus*. **A,** Two-cell stage. **B,** Eight-cell stage. **C,** Blastula. **D,** Blastula elongating; macromeres forming flat ventral plate. **E,** Early gastrula, formed by invaginating macromeres. **F,** Later gastrula, after formation of mesoblastic cords, obliteration of blastocoel, and closure of blastopore. **G,** Ventral view of embryo after formation of stomodeum and germ bands. **H,** Ventral part of embryo, in transverse section, showing origin of coelom. (Modified from Wilson.)

or two exceptions), in having a reduced coelom mostly filled with mesenchyme, in having ventral suckers at the ends of their bodies, and in having a fixed number of segments with secondary external annulation. Many of their unique features are associated with their bloodsucking habits, such as the suckers for clinging to their host and the modifications of the enteron for storage of blood. Most are found in inland waters or in damp places on land. A few are marine. Although most of them are bloodsuckers on other animals, some of them are not parasitic. A few have even become predators and feed on earthworms and insects, which they swallow whole. Leeches show a considerable diversity in size. Some are less than ½ inch long, and the larger ones may exceed a foot in length when fully extended. All have great powers of extension and contraction.

MORPHOLOGIC FEATURES. The body of the leech is vermiform, subcylindric, and flattened ventrally (Fig. 18-41). The shape of the body, however, varies greatly with the amount of blood in its digestive tract and

Fig. 18-41

Common leeches. **A,** *Placobdella,* commonly found on turtles; living specimen about 1 inch long. **B,** *Hirudo medicinalis,* a form once used in bloodletting; preserved specimen, about 3 inches long. (**A** suborder Rhynchobdellida; **B** suborder Gnathobdellida.)

the state of its contraction. Leeches are usually not highly colored. Many have a greenish background of color with a diversified pattern of spots and stripes. Their ventral surface is often black interspersed with grayish markings. Because they lack parapodia and setae and have secondary rings (annuli), the 33 (or 34 according to some authorities) segments are not always clearly defined. Each segment usually bears a variable number of annuli. Leeches have no caudal growth zone similar to that of oligochaetes, and growth in length occurs by subdivision and growth of the annuli, especially in the middle of the body where the number of annuli is usually constant for a species. A clitellum is usually present in segments 9, 10, and 11. Of the characteristic suckers, the anterior is usually smaller than the posterior and generally surrounds the mouth.

The body is commonly divided into five regions: (1) a head region of four segments bearing the ventral oral sucker, mouth, eyes, and jaws (in some), (2) a preclitellum of four segments (5,6,7,8), (3) a clitellum of three segments (9,10,11), (4) a middle region of 15 segments (12 to 26), and (5) the terminal region of seven segments modified to form the posterior sucker. The number of annuli varies usually from one to five per segment with the larger number in the middle of the body, but there are many variations in the dif-

ferent species. The pygidium, or terminal segment, is a part of the posterior sucker, and the anus opens dorsally in front of the posterior sucker. Segmental analysis is based mainly upon the distributional pattern of the paired ganglia of the ventral nerve cord.

The body wall consists of a skin made up of a single layer of epidermal cells and unicellular glands, a dermis of connective tissue, pigment cells, and blood vessels, and a musculature of outer circular and inner longitudinal layers between which are crossed oblique muscles (Fig. 18-42). Muscle strands pass from one side of the body to the other. Muscle fibers are striated in the outer margins, but their centers consist of unmodified protoplasm.

With the exception of the Acanthobdellida, the body cavity is much reduced by the invasion of connective tissue (botryoidal tissue). The characteristic septa and coelomic compartments of the oligochaetes have entirely disappeared. Instead, the coelom in leeches consists of spaces or sinuses connected by capillary branches, forming a sort of lymphatic system. The coelomic fluid of the spaces contains coe-

317

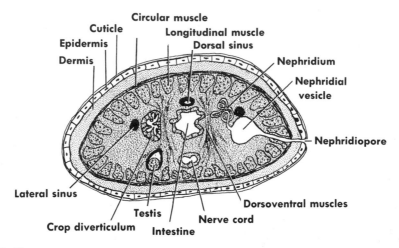

Fig. 18-42

Diagrammatic cross section of *Hirudo*. Nephridium, crop diverticulum, and testis shown in one side only.

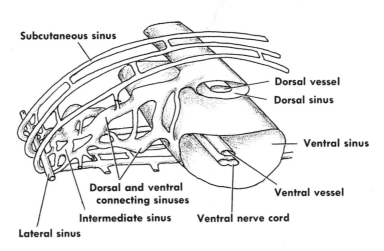

Fig. 18-43

Portion of coelomic sinus system of *Glossiphonia*, a rhynchobdellid. Dorsal sinus contains contractile dorsal blood vessel; ventral sinus contains nerve cord, ventral vessel, female organs, and funnels of nephridia. Blood is carried forward in dorsal vessel and backward in ventral vessel. (After Oka; redrawn from Mann: Leeches (Hirudinea), their structure, physiology, ecology, and embryology, Pergamon Press, Inc.)

lomocytes; in some forms the fluid is kept in circulation by special pulsatile vesicles. In some suborders the coelomic spaces are a part of the vascular system and contain red blood. The botryoidal tissue also contains yellow cells, similar to chloragogue cells, which are excretory in function. In some of the Rhynchobdellida, longitudinal canals are generally connected with nu-

merous transverse canals (Fig. 18-43). A network of sinuses between the epidermis and muscular layers in the wall connects with the longitudinal canals.

The blood-vascular system in leeches is of two main types: (1) a system of definite blood vessels and (2) a system of coelomic sinuses that serve to circulate the blood. The first type is characteristic of the suborder Rhynchobdellida (Fig. 18-43) in which dorsal and ventral longitudinal vessels (above and below the gut) are connected at their extremities with paired loops. These vessels lie in coelomic sinuses. One median and four pairs of lateral blind pouches extend from the posterior part of the dorsal vessel for increased absorptive areas. The contractile nature of the blood vessels, especially the anterior part of the dorsal vessel, serves as a heart in the propulsion of the blood. The other type of vascular system is characteristic of most leeches. It consists of sinuses that have become modified to form circulatory channels. The ventral sinus vessel is the principal channel, although a dorsal vessel is sometimes present. Lateral coelomic sinus vessels, one on each side, are also present and connect by transverse vessels to the ventral vessel. Paired contractile vesicles, or ampullae, are found on these transverse vessels in the posterior region of the body. These vesicles may have little to do with pumping the blood, which is carried on principally by contraction of the lateral longitudinal sinus vessels. A capillary network, formed chiefly from the botryoidal tissue and communicating with the sinus vessels, occurs in some leeches. Respiratory pigments are absent in the blood of some leeches (rhynchobdellids), but plasma pigments are found in others and produce a red color. The blood of leeches is really the same as the coelomic fluid.

Respiration in leeches occurs primarily through the general body surface, but a few have leaflike gills *(Branchellion);* others have vesicles that may serve for the exchange of gases. Investigation with leeches on the rate of oxygen uptake at different oxygen concentrations has yielded variable results. Some leeches maintain a constant rate of oxygen uptake independent of oxygen concentration, but in others uptake is proportional to the concentration. Many leeches are known to exist in fresh water with low amounts of oxygen.

The digestive system consists of a mouth, buccal chamber and sinus, pharynx, esophagus, stomach, intestine, rectum, and anus (Fig. 18-44). The mouth opens within the anterior sucker. In the rhynchobdellid leeches an eversible proboscis (muscular and lined with cuticle) is

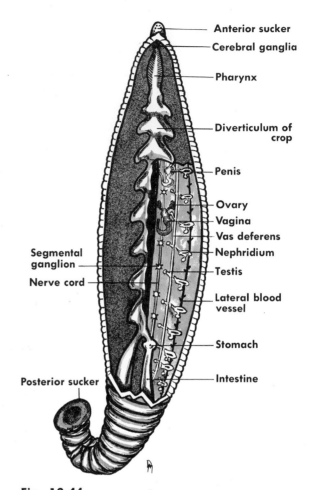

Fig. 18-44

Internal structures of leech *(Hirudo medicinalis).* Dorsal view with part of crop cut away to show underlying structures. (From Hickman: Integrated principles of zoology, The C. V. Mosby Co.)

forced out of the mouth into the tissue of the host when the anterior sucker is attached. In those that lack a proboscis (most leeches) toothed jaws occur inside the mouth (Fig. 18-45). The muscular action of these three jaws produces a Y-shaped incision on the skin of the host when a leech attacks. The secretions of the salivary glands (in the walls of the pharynx) containing an anticoagulant (hirudin) are poured into the wound and prevent the clotting of blood. V. F. Lindemann, however, believes that the free flow of blood is due to the enlargement of blood vessels by histamine from the leech. The anticoagulant, in such cases, may prevent blood

319

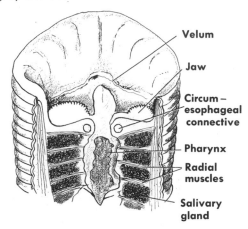

Fig. 18-45

Ventral view of dissected anterior region of leech showing toothed jaws. (Modified from Mann.)

clotting in the leech's stomach. In those leeches that are not bloodsuckers, the jaws are reduced to muscular ridges for seizing the prey, which is then swallowed whole. Some bloodsucking leeches can store up to ten times their weight in blood, which may furnish them nutrition for many months before they need to feed again. The buccal chamber empties into the muscular pharynx, which exerts a powerful suction in drawing blood from the host. A short esophagus connects the pharynx to the stomach, which, in bloodsucking leeches, becomes a crop with paired lateral ceca or diverticula for the storage of the solid parts of the blood. In predaceous leeches the stomach is usually a simple chamber. A sphincter valve separates the stomach from the intestine, which may also bear some paired ceca. Most digestion and absorption probably occurs in the intestine, although the stomach may be involved. The digestive process is not well understood because it has been difficult to identify proteolytic enzymes (most of the leech's food is protein) in the gut wall. Bacterial decomposition of the food has been described in some leeches. The globin part of the hemoglobin seems to be the chief source of nutriment in the leech. From the intestine a short rectum leads to the dorsal anus in front of the posterior sucker.

The excretory system of leeches consists of paired metanephridia that are more specialized than those found in oligochaetes.

Their typical arrangement is one pair to each segment in the middle region of the body. The number varies with different species, but 17 pairs occur in *Hirudo* (Fig. 18-46). A nephridium typically consists of a ciliated nephrostome that projects into a coelomic channel at one end and into a nonciliated capsule at the other, and a tubular structure composed of cells through which runs a canal that may drain a network of finer canals. The canal may or may not open into the capsule. Externally, the nephridium opens by a vesicle or bladder and a nephridiopore on the ventral or lateral surface. The unique capsule is supposed to receive and store excretory phagocytes and to manufacture coelomic amebocytes. This plan of the nephridium has many variations among the different species. From the coelomic fluid or blood the nephrostome receives excretory particles that are taken up by the capsular phagocytes. These phagocytes may carry the waste particles to the intestine or to the epidermis. The fluid urine is obtained by filtration through the walls of the tubule and eventually is discharged through the nephridiopore. Most of the urine is made up of ammonia, although small amounts of such constituents as purines, urea, creatinine, etc. also occur. The excretory system is also concerned in maintaining the water balance of the body. Since the osmotic pressure of the body fluids is higher in most cases than that of the water in which they live, an excess of water must enter the leech's body at all times and must be eliminated by the nephridia. Experiments by A. Krogh indicate that leeches have special mechanisms in the epidermis for taking up sodium and chloride ions to replace those lost in metabolism, and thus are able to maintain a constancy in the osmotic pressure of body fluids.

The nervous system of leeches follows the general annelid plan of a paired ventral nerve cord made up of paired ganglia. Of the 34 paired ganglia, 6 are in the head, 21 are along the trunk region, and 7 are fused in the posterior sucker. Each ganglion is composed of 6 groups (capsules or follicles) of nerve cells, which innervate that particular segment. The brain in segment 6 consists of a paired suprapharyngeal ganglion connected to a paired subpharyngeal

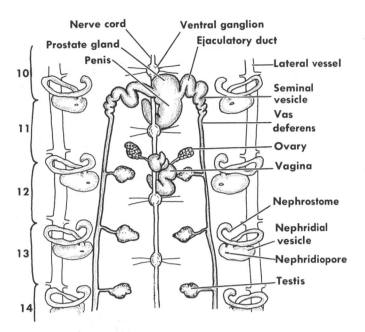

Fig. 18-46

Diagram of segments 10 to 14 of *Hirudo* showing reproductive organs and nephridia. This form has 10 pairs of testes in segments 12 to 21. (Modified from Brown.)

ganglion by circumpharyngeal connectives. The number of ganglia fused in the subpharyngeal ganglion can be determined by the number of capsules present in it. The capsules of the brain may be generally scattered and do not form a compact mass. From these various ganglia, peripheral nerves run to the prostomium and other regions of the head. From each trunk ganglion two pairs of mixed nerves innervate the wall and structures of the corresponding segment, the anterior pair going to the dorsal part of the segment and the posterior pair going to the ventral part. Sense organs are similar to those in oligochaetes and are grouped into three categories: (1) free nerve endings in the epidermis for temperature and touch, (2) epidermal sense organs (sensillae) of tall spindle-shaped cells with terminal hairs, probably tactile or chemoreceptor in function, and (3) photoreceptor cells (eyes). The eyes contain a pigment cup and are found on the dorsal surface of the anterior end.

Like oligochaetes, leeches are hermaphroditic with a single pair of ovaries and many pairs of testes (Fig. 18-46). They are also provided with ducts for carrying the gametes. The 4 to 10 pairs of spherical testes (usually 10 pairs in *Hirudo*) are arranged on each side of the enteron, one pair to a segment, in the body region where they are found. They are enclosed in coelomic sacs, and those on each side join a vas deferens running anteriorly to a single midventral opening (the male gonopore), which is located about one-third of the distance back of the anterior sucker. The vas deferens is greatly coiled and forms a seminal vesicle followed by a muscular ejaculatory duct that opens into the single antrum. The antrum is surrounded by glands and may form an eversible penis by which sperm are transferred directly to the female gonopore of another leech. When a penis is lacking, the sperm are formed into spermatophores, which are attached to the body of another worm. Here the sperm migrate (hypodermic impregnation) through the skin and tissue to fertilize the eggs in the ovisacs. The paired ovaries are located between the anterior pair of testes and the antrum. Each ovary is enclosed in an ovisac, which is derived from the coelom. From each ovisac a short oviduct extends forward and joins its mate to form a common vagina that opens by a single female gonopore just behind the male gonopore. When the eggs are laid, a glandular clitellum enlarges and secretes a cocoon over the genital pores. Albumen and fertilized eggs are placed in the cocoon, which is then worked over the head much as in the earthworm. The cocoons are deposited in various places—on stones, in damp places, on aquatic vegetation, and even on the ventral surfaces of their own bodies where the leeches, on hatching, are carried about by the parent for some time. Cocoons may have few or many eggs and may be deposited soon after the eggs are fertilized, or there may be a considerable delay between fertilization and cocoon formation. Self-fertilization probably does not occur.

DEVELOPMENT. Leeches have spiral determinate cleavage, but the pattern of cleavage depends to a great extent upon the amount of yolk. In the development of leeches the eggs of some may have so much yolk that absorption of albumen from the cocoon is unnecessary; in others the eggs with little yolk absorb much of the fluid albumen. Young leeches are juveniles and are provided with both anterior and posterior suckers when hatched from the egg.

Annotated references

Ashworth, J. H. 1904. Annelids. Liverpool Marine Biology Committee Memoirs XI. London, Williams & Norgate, Ltd.

Beddard, F. E. 1901. Earthworms and their allies. Cambridge, Cambridge University Press. *This book is out of date but still useful.*

Bell, A. W. 1947. The earthworm circulatory system. Turtox News **25**:89-94. *Perhaps the best and most accurate description of the blood system in this worm.*

Brown, F. A. 1950. Selected invertebrate types. New York, John Wiley & Sons, Inc.

Buchsbaum, R., and L. J. Milne, 1960. The lower animals. Garden City, Doubleday & Company, Inc. *Superb illustrations of many marine worms.*

Bullock, T. H. 1945. Functional organization of the giant fiber system of *Lumbricus*. J. Neurophysiol. **8**:55-71.

Clark, L. B., and W. N. Hess. 1940. Swarming of the Atlantic palolo worm, *Eunice schemacephala*. Tortugas Lab. Papers, 33(2):21-70. *A study of the swarming behavior that occurs in July during the first or last quarter of the lunar cycle.*

Dales, R. P. 1963. Annelida. New York, Hillary House Publishers, Ltd. *An up-to-date treatise on this group.*

Davis, C. C. 1955. The marine and freshwater plankton. East Lansing, Michigan State University Press.

Dixon, G. C. 1915. *Tubifex.* Liverpool Marine Biology Committee Memoirs XXIII. London, Williams & Norgate, Ltd.

Edmondson, W. T. (editor). 1959. Ward and Whipple's fresh-water biology, ed. 2. New York, John Wiley & Sons, Inc. *Sections devoted to Oligochaeta (C. J. Goodnight), Polychaeta (O. Hartman), and Hirudinea (J. P. Moore) are given in this important work. Keys are emphasized.*

Goodrich, E. S. 1945. The study of nephridia and genital ducts since 1895. Quart. J. Micr. Sci. **86**:113-392.

Grasse, P. P. (editor). 1959. Traite de zoologie, vol. 5, part 1. Paris, Masson et Cie. *An authoritative and comprehensive treatise of the annelids.*

Hanson, J. 1949. The histology of the blood system in Oligochaeta and Polychaeta. Biol. Rev. **24**:127-173.

Hess, W. N. 1925. Nervous system of the earthworm, *Lumbricus terrestris*. J. Morphol. Physiol. **40**:235-259. *One of the best accounts of the nervous system in annelids.*

Krivanek, J. O. 1956. Habit formation in the earthworm, *Lumbricus terrestris*. Physiol. Zool. **29**:241-250. *A study in animal behavior.*

Laverack, M. S. 1963. The physiology of earthworms. New York, Pergamon Press, Inc. *An excellent monograph on the physiologic aspects of the earthworm. A fine addition to the many treatises on this common animal.*

MacGinitie, G. E. 1939. The method of feeding of *Chaetopterus*. Biol. Bull. **77**:115-118. *This work describes how* Chaetopterus *in its tube gathers the food into mucous bags and forms pellets that are carried to the mouth.*

Mann, K. H. 1962. Leeches (Hirudinea), their structure, physiology, ecology and embryology. New York, Pergamon Press, Inc. *A useful, up-to-date monograph on leeches.*

Nicol. J. A. C. 1948. The giant axons of annelids. Quart. Rev. Biol. **23**:291-323. *The morphology and functional significance of these fibers.*

Moment, G. B. 1953. On the way a common earthworm, *Eisenia foetida*, grows in length. J. Morphol. **93**:489-503.

Pennak, R. W. 1953. Fresh-water invertebrates of the United States. New York, The Ronald Press Company. *A good general account and useful keys to the freshwater annelids of all three classes.*

Stephenson, J. 1930. The Oligochaeta. New York, Oxford University Press, Inc. *One of the best known treatises on this group and still very useful, although out of date in some particulars.*

Phylum Tardigrada

Water bears, or tardigrades (Fig. 19-1), are minute forms, usually less than 1 mm. in length, and are found in both fresh water and salt water, wet moss, sand, damp soils, pond debris, liverworts, and lichens. Not more than 10 percent of the known species have been reported from the sea. Marine species are usually found in the sandy beaches of shallow water where they may occur several inches under the surface. Tardigrades are found in all latitudes from the tropics to the arctic. Only 40 to 50 species of tardigrades have been found in North America, but 300 to 400 species occur in other parts of the world.

The affinities of tardigrades are among the most puzzling of all animal groups. They are coelomate animals, and their mesoderm is enterocoelous like deuterostomes, although they may be highly modified protostomes. Various authorities have placed them near the arthropods, annelids, nematodes, or chaetognaths.

The body is elongated, cylindric, or a long oval and is unsegmented. The head is merely the anterior part of the trunk. The body bears four pairs of short, stubby, unjointed legs armed with four single or two double claws that may be unequal in size and are used for clinging to the substrate. Tardigrades cannot swim. The last pair of appendages lies at the posterior end of the body. The body is covered by a nonchitinous cuticle that may be smooth or ornamented with spines or plates, and which is secreted by the hypodermis. Cilia are absent. The cuticle is shed (ecdysis) four or more times in its life history. The body consists of a prostomium and five indefinite segments. Cell constancy is characteristic of the group, and the number of epidermal cells is the same for all members of a genus.

The mouth (surrounded by cuticular rings) is at the anterior end of the prostomium and opens into a tubular and oval pharynx (Fig. 19-2, A), which is adapted for sucking by radial muscle fibers. The oval pharynx contains six sclerotized macroplacoids for support. The tubular pharynx is supplied with two needlelike stylets that can be protruded through the mouth or withdrawn by muscular action. These stylets are used for piercing the cellulose walls of the plants that tardigrades live upon, and the liquid contents are sucked in by the pharynx. A pair of glands, which secrete the stylets at each molt, open into the tubular pharynx. The pharynx has a triradial lumen. The rest of the digestive tube consists of a short esophagus, a large stomach, a short rectum, and a cloacal aperture or anus that opens between the posterior pair of legs. Glands empty into both the pharynx and the intestinal tract. At the junction of the stomach and rectum two paired, ventral Malpighian tubes and a single dorsal gland empty into the digestive system and may be excretory in function (Fig. 19-2, B). Although they live primarily on plant juices, which they suck out with their pharyngeal pumping action, some tardigrades may suck out the body fluids of nematodes, rotifers, and other small animals. Most of the body cavity is a hemocoel with the true coelom restricted to the gonadal cavity. No circulatory or respiratory systems are present, as fluids

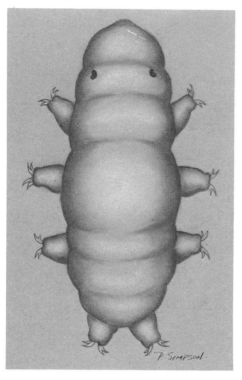

Fig. 19-1

Dorsal view of tardigrade. (From Hickman: Integrated principles of zoology, The C. V. Mosby Co.)

freely circulate through the body spaces, and gaseous exchange can occur through the body surface.

The muscular system consists of a number of long muscle bands, each of which is composed of a single fibrillar cell that may be a syncytium. These muscles have most of their origins and insertions on the body wall, and they manipulate body movements and the legs. Circular muscles are absent, but the hydrostatic pressure of the body fluid may act as a sort of skeleton. The legs are manipulated by a set of muscles fastened to the body wall and inserted near the tip of the leg.

The lobed brain is large and covers most of the dorsal surface of the pharynx (Fig. 19-3). It connects, by way of circumpharyngeal connectives around the pharynx, to the subpharyngeal ganglion, from which the double ventral nerve cord extends posteriorly as a chain of four ganglia. Sense organs usually consist of a pair of pigmented eyespots and various tactile organs such as bristles and spines.

Tardigrades are dioecious, but females are usually more common than males and may make up an entire population. Parthenogenesis is common. The ovary or testis (Fig. 19-2, *B*) lies dorsal to the intestine and opens by a single oviduct or two sperm ducts that open into the cloaca or

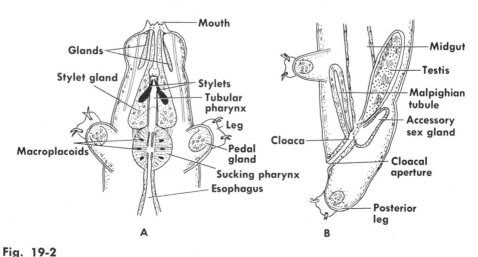

Fig. 19-2

Structural features of tardigrade. **A,** Buccal apparatus and pharynx. **B,** Internal anatomy of posterior region of male.

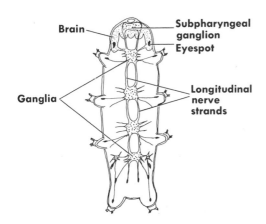

Fig. 19-3

Nervous system of tardigrade (ventral view). (Redrawn from Pennak: Freshwater invertebrates of the United States, The Ronald Press Company.)

through a separate gonopore near it. Both thin-shelled and thick-shelled eggs similar to the summer and winter eggs of rotifers occur. Eggs are often found in the shed cuticle. Up to 30 eggs may be deposited by the female at one time. Eggs may be up to 200 microns in diameter. Fertilization may occur in the ovary or in eggs deposited in the old cuticle. The young are juveniles.

Development is direct and may last for a month or less, depending upon the species and temperature. Cleavage is holoblastic but is irregular because of the asynchronous division of the blastomeres. The endomesoderm has an enterocoelous origin, and five pairs of coelomic sacs are formed, of which the four anterior pairs form mus-

cles and storage cells, while the posterior pair merge to form the gonad. When the young juveniles hatch, they are rarely more than 50 microns long. They grow by water intake and increase in cell size, rather than by increase in cell number.

Like rotifers, tardigrades have great ability to withstand harsh environmental conditions (desiccation, freezing, etc.). Under such conditions the tardigrade loses water, shrivels, and contracts into a generally rounded condition with low metabolism (anabiosis). When placed in water, it becomes normal again even after being in the anabiotic state for years. By such a method the life span of these little animals may be extended several years.

Common American genera of tardigrades are *Macrobiotus*, *Echiniscus*, *Milnesium*, and *Hypsibius*.

Annotated references

Cuenot, L. 1932. Tardigrades. Faune de France **24**:1-96. *An excellent French account of the tardigrades.*

Marcus, E. Tardigrada. In Bronn, H. G. (editor). 1929. Klassen und Ordnungen des Tierreichs, vol. 5, part 4, pp. 1-608. Leipzig, Akademische Verlagsgesellschaft. *The most important monograph on the tardigrades.*

Marcus, E. Tardigrada. In Edmondson, W. T. (editor). 1959. Ward and Whipple's freshwater biology, ed. 2, pp. 508-521. New York, John Wiley & Sons, Inc.

Mathews, G. B. 1938. Tardigrades from North America. Amer. Midland Natur. **19**:619-626.

Pennak, R. W. 1953. Fresh-water invertebrates of the United States. New York, The Ronald Press Company. *The best American account of the group is given on pages 240 to 255. A good general description and keys to the common species.*

Phylum Onychophora

This group of wormlike animals was formerly placed in the Arthropoda as a class or subphylum but is now often classified as a phylum in its own right. The group has been of special interest because it has characteristics of both the Annelida and the Arthropoda and therefore has been considered as the "missing link" between these two great phyla, which have an unmistakable relationship. However, onychophorans are neither worms nor arthropods but have distinctive characteristics of their own. Although they comprise a small group of few species which are so much alike that the description of one applies to all, the unique organization and characters of both a primitive and specialized nature have given the little animal an unusual evolutionary significance.

Onychophorans are often cited as a classic example of discontinuous distribution. They are found in tropic and subtropic regions but only in certain restricted parts of those regions. The various species are found in Mexico, Central America, northern South America, South Africa, the West Indies, Malay Archipelago, India, Australia, and New Zealand. This discontinuity of occurrence indicates that they were once very widespread. It may also suggest that they are on the verge of extinction, because they have very poor powers of distribution.

In regions where they are found their habitats are in moist situations, although under dry conditions they have ways of protecting themselves and surviving. They live under logs, stones, tangled vegetation, bark, crevices in rotting stumps, or near stream banks. They are nocturnal in their habits and are not seen out in the open during daylight.

They have a fossil record as far back as the Cambrian period. In the famous Burgess Shale deposit found in British Columbia (1911) one of the soft-bodied forms found in this unique collection was *Aysheaia*, a marine form that had a general body form and other characteristics very much like the modern onychophoran. This fossil history plus studies on their comparative anatomy and embryology suggest that the Onychophora represent a persistent specialized relic of an ancestral line that gave rise to many of the various groups of arthropods.

CLASSIFICATION

Phylum Onychophora. Body vermiform and somewhat cylindric; body of adult not segmented; head not distinct; skin with soft cuticle and transverse rows of fine papillae; anterior end (head) with a pair of antennae, a pair of oral papillae, and a pair of single eyes; ventral mouth with jaws; double row of short, thick legs segmentally arranged; spiracles numerous and tracheal system of unbranched tracheae; one pair of nephridia per each pair of legs; body cavity a hemocoel; nervous system of dorsal brain and a pair of ventral nerve cords; dioecious; oviparous, ovoviviparous, or viviparous; juvenile young; terrestrial.

1. Two families: Peripatidae (equatorial regions) and Peripatopsidae (subtropic or south temperate regions).
2. Seven genera: *Peripatus, Peripatoides, Eoperipatus, Opisthopatus, Paraperipatus, Peripatopsis, Oöperipatus.*
3. Seventy-three species.

In popular usage the term *Peripatus* is often used as the generic name for all species.

BASIC ADAPTIVE FEATURES

So little is known about the past history or fossil record of onychophorans that almost nothing is known about their adaptive radiation if any occurred. Their discontinuous distribution indicates that they were far more numerous in the past and probably were represented by many species. In the widespread regions where they are found the habitats of present species are very similar, and they have never adapted themselves to a wide environmental range. This may account for the striking uniformity of characters in the different species. The greatest diversity among the several species is the number of legs, which vary from 14 to 44 pairs. The short, conical, stumpy legs define a great landmark in the locomotory evolution of invertebrates. The body is elevated above the substratum by the upright position of the legs directly under the body instead of a lateral position, as in annelids, which forces the belly to be dragged over the substratum.

Onychophoran morphology has also stressed the power to distort the body as an adaptation to squeezing through small spaces. The nature of the muscular body wall of unstriated circular, diagonal, and longitudinal muscles, together with the flexible cuticle, has been a primary factor in their ability to work the body through crevices only a fraction of its width. Their whole structure, including their connective tissue support, permits maximum deformability of their bodies.

PHYLOGENETIC RELATIONSHIPS

Onychophorans have both annelid and arthropod characteristics, although they resemble arthropods more than annelids. Annelid characteristics are their simple ocellus eyes, segmented nephridia, ciliated reproductive ducts, flexible cuticle, musculature of the body wall, and nonjointed appendages. In contrast, their chief arthropod characters are the hemocoel as the chief body cavity, modified appendages as jaws, dorsal tubular heart with ostia and open blood system, and a tracheal system of breathing. As their own unique features, they possess scanty metamerism, only one pair of jaws, a peculiar structure of appendages, scattered spiracles, and nerve cords without ganglia. Three phyla often placed together in the artificial grouping Pararthropoda all show some characteristics of both the annelids and the arthropods. These phyla are the Onychophora, Pentastomida, and Tardigrada. E. Marcus (1958) thinks the Onychophora have descended from the annelids. He reasons that there is a general homology between the polychaete parapodium and the arthropodan limb. He regards the fossil *Aysheaia,* a marine form with terminal mouth of the Middle Cambrian period, as coming long after the origin of arthropods from the annelids in Precambrian time. He unites into one group the onychophorans and the tardigrades because of similar legs and other likenesses.

Onychophorans have the same basic pattern of development as arthropods and are probably an offshoot from an ancestral arthropodan line. The theory that they form a "missing link" between annelids and arthropods is not stressed as much as formerly.

GENERAL MORPHOLOGIC FEATURES
External anatomy

Onychophorans are vermiform with a generally cylindric body that is from 15 to 100 mm. or more in length (Fig. 20-1). The head is not distinct from the body,

Fig. 20-1

Peripatus in natural habitat. (Courtesy Ward's Natural Science Establishment, Inc., Rochester, N. Y.)

Fig. 20-2

Ventral view of anterior end of *Peripatus*. (Courtesy Ward's Natural Science Establishment, Inc., Rochester, N. Y.)

and the only external evidence of segmentation is the paired arrangement of the legs. The head, or anterior end, bears a pair of very extensible preoral antennae and a simple eye on each side. Below and slightly behind each antenna is a blunt oral papilla, between which is the buccal cavity. The mouth is located at the posterior end of the buccal cavity, which is ventral and surrounded by a circumoral fold. The buccal cavity contains a pair of horny jaws, each of which terminates in a two-hooked structure. The jaws are modified appendages. The surface of the body bears transverse ringlike ridges or bands of small spine-bearing tubercles (Fig. 20-2). The legs (14 to 44 pairs) are conical, tapering lateroventral outgrowths of the body wall, and each leg terminates in a pair of sickle-shaped claws. Like the trunk, the surface of the legs bears rings of tubercles. The anus is located at the extreme posterior end, and a genital pore is present on the ventral surface between the last pair of legs. The skin is somewhat

dry and velvety in texture. The color of the different species may be gray, olive green, reddish above and light below, uniform in color, or of variegated pattern.

Locomotion in onychophorans is slow. A few segments, with their attached legs, are used at one time for movement. The legs are shortened by intrinsic muscles, swung forward, and then given a propulsive backward stroke by extrinsic muscles. Successive waves of contraction and extension pass posteriorly, involving both the legs and body.

Internal anatomy

The body wall from outside to inside consists of a thin, chitinous cuticle that is not made up of movable plates; a single layer of epidermis; a thin basement membrane (dermis) of connective tissue; a musculature of circular, diagonal, and longitudinal layers; and a lining membrane. Like the arthropods, the major body cavity is a hemocoel, and the coelom is restricted to cavities associated with the gonads and nephridia (Fig. 20-3). The hemocoel is divided by longitudinal partitions of tissue sheets into a dorsal pericardial sinus containing the heart; a central sinus containing the intestinal tract, slime glands, and reproductive organs; and two ventrolateral sinuses, each with a nerve cord, nephridia, and salivary glands.

The alimentary canal is usually a straight tube from mouth to anus (Fig. 20-4). A mouth, located at the back of the buccal cavity, is provided with a pair of jaws or mandibles, already referred to. The jaws, which are really cutting plates, move backward and forward instead of sideways and thus are an adaptation for narrow passageways. The mouth passes into a short, muscular pharynx from which an esophagus opens into an enlarged intestine, or stomach, according to some authors. The pharynx and esophagus make up the foregut, which is lined with chitin. The intestine passes back to a short, narrow rectum that opens at the anus on the ventral posterior end of the body. A pair of salivary glands, which open by a common duct into the buccal cavity, represent the only glands known with certainty to be in the alimentary canal. The large intestine is the site of digestion and absorption.

Fig. 20-3

Cross section of female *Peripatus*. (Modified from Lang.)

Onychophorans are mostly carnivorous and feed upon small insects, worms, and other small forms, which they capture directly. From their oral papillae they discharge a milky fluid that hardens on contact with the air. Enemies are immobilized when this fluid is thrown on them, but onychophorans do not use this method to capture prey. The fluid is produced by a pair of slime glands that open at the ends of the papillae and extend posteriorly in the body (Fig. 20-4). The animals will also eat decomposing vegetation when hard pressed for food. They are capable of enduring a long fast.

They breathe by means of a tracheal system so characteristic of many arthropods. However, the tracheal system in onychophorans is different from that in arthropods and probably has evolved independently. The spiracles are small pits, or epidermal pockets, which are numerous all over the surface of the body between the bands of tubercles. These spiracles are too small to be seen externally with the unaided eye. From the inside of each spiracle a bunch of fine, unbranched tracheae run parallel with each other to the tissues they supply. The tracheal tubes are supplied with tiny spiral thickenings, the same as those found in insects and other arthropods. In some species of onychophorans the spiracles are arranged in definite rows. In the legs of some a small vesicle, which opens near the nephridiopore of the nephridium, is pres-

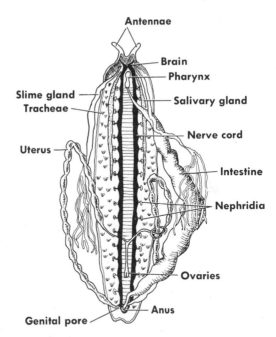

Fig. 20-4

Internal anatomy of female *Peripatus*.

ent and may serve as a sort of gill under humid conditions.

The excertory system consists of a pair of nephridia for each segment or each pair of legs (Fig. 20-4). Each nephridium is made up of a tube that opens into a reduced coelomic vesicle at one end and at a nephridiopore at the other end. Near the nephridiopore, or external aperture, the tubule enlarges into a bladderlike collecting vesicle, which is contractile. The nephridiopore is located on the inner base of each leg except the fourth and fifth pairs, where it opens on a papilla more distally. Cilia are present in the excretory tube near the coelomic vesicle, thus sharing with the reproductive female ducts the only place where cilia are present in onychophorans. Cilia are characteristically absent in the great arthropod group.

The vascular system has about the same pattern as that of arthropods. A tubular heart in the form of a long, pulsating dorsal blood vessel is open at both ends and is provided with a pair of lateral ostia for each segment (Fig. 20-3). The heart lies in the pericardial sinus, and its contraction keeps the blood from the vast hemocoel moving forward and in circulation. Partitions between the four or five major sinuses have openings through which the blood passes as it circulates. The blood carries no respiratory pigments and is colorless. Some formed elements, such as amebocytes, occur in it.

The nervous system includes a well-developed bilobed brain located over the pharynx and a subesophageal ganglion from which extend two widely separated ventral nerve cords connected with commissures. From the brain, nerves are given off to the antennae, the eyes, and the jaws, and circumesophageal commissures run to the subesophageal ganglion. The ventral nerve cords in each segment form ganglionic swellings from which paired nerves are given off to the legs and body wall. Paired eyes of the direct type are located near the base of the antennae, and each has a chitinous lens and simple retina. Sensory taste spines are found on the circumoral ridges of the mouth, and sensory receptors on the large tubercles respond to vibrations and tactile stimuli. Some onychophorans, such as *Peripatus*, are very sensitive to chemical stimuli.

REPRODUCTION AND EMBRYOLOGY

Onychophorans are all dioecious, the males being somewhat smaller than the females; they may also have fewer legs. A

saclike crural gland found near the nephridium of most legs in the male may play a part in reproduction. The gonads in each sex are paired and lie in the posterior part of the body above the intestine. The paired, elongated ovaries are partially fused, and each is connected to a nephridium that has been modified to form a genital tract consisting of a seminal receptacle and a uterus. The two tracts, or uteri, merge together and open to the exterior by a common genital pore on the ventral posterior end of the body. The paired male testes remain separated, and each is connected to a modified nephridium that becomes an ejaculatory tube in its lower part. Both ducts join to form a common median opening in front of the anus. In the common median tube the sperm are packaged into elongated spermatophores. Fertilization is internal, and sperm is deposited in the seminal receptacles of the female. In one or two species the female has no seminal receptacle, and the spermatophores are injected through the body wall into the hemocoel, where the sperm make their way to the ovaries. Most species produce living young, except a few in Australia, which lay large yolk-laden eggs in sculptured shells. The oviducts of those females that produce living young are usually enlarged into a number of uterine

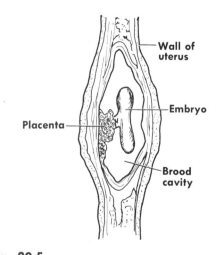

Fig. 20-5

Uterus of *Peripatus* with young and placenta. (Modified from Lang.)

chambers in which the embryos develop. The young may simply develop in the uteri without maternal connection, ovoviviparous, or they may have a placental attachment, viviparous (Fig. 20-5).

The basic pattern of embryonic development in onychophorans is similar to that in arthropods, especially to those of the lesser groups (Pauropoda, Chilopoda, and Symphyla). The coelomic cavity is well developed in the embryo. After the gastrula stage the blastopore elongates and gives rise to the mouth at its anterior end and the anus at its posterior end, while the median margins fuse together. The paired mesoblastic somites arise behind the blastopore. The first pair becomes the preoral somites and form the mesoderm of the segment bearing the antennae. All the somites acquire a coelomic cavity and divide into ventral and dorsal parts. The ventral part migrates to the region of the appendage and becomes a part of the nephridium, while the dorsal portion approaches its partner from the opposite side at the mid-dorsal line to form the tubular heart between them. In the posterior region of the body the fusion of the dorsal coelomic cavities of the somites form the paired gonads. The remaining parts between the organs are filled with blood and become partitioned into sinuses as the hemocoel. In this way the coelom is restricted to the segmented excretory organs and the cavities of the gonads.

Annotated references

Grasse, P. P. (editor). 1949. Traite de zoologie, vol. 4. Paris, Masson et Cie. *An authoritative account of the onychophorans.*

Gregory, W. K. 1951. Evolution emerging, vol. 1. New York, The Macmillan Company. *This work compares the structure of* Peripatus *with that of insects.*

Kukenthal, W., and T. Krumbach (editors). 1926. Handbuch der Zoologie; Onychophora, vol. 3, part 2. Berlin, Walter De Gruyter & Co. *A comprehensive account of the group.*

Lang, A. 1891. Textbook of comparative anatomy; Onychophora, pp. 427-437. (English translation.) *A concise account of the group.*

Manton, S. M. Onychophora. In Gray, P. (editor). 1961. Encyclopedia of the biological sciences, pp. 705-706. New York, Reinhold Publishing Corp. *This author considers their basic pattern as definitely that of an arthropod.*

Phylum
Pentastomida

These wormlike animals are bloodsucking internal parasites of carnivorous vertebrates. They live in the lungs or nasal passageways. Another name for the phylum is Linguatulida, and they are often placed in a class or subphylum under the Arthropoda. Their common name is tongue worm. Adults resemble small worms, but the larval forms are mitelike with stumpy legs, which may indicate their relationship to the arachnids.

They are found chiefly in tropic regions where they may parasitize a large variety of vertebrates such as snakes, crocodiles, amphibians, and sometimes birds and mammals. Most adults are found in reptiles, especially snakes and lizards. Their life history usually includes an intermediate host for the larval stages, although they complete their life history in the same animal. Among those that have mammals as the definite host, the most common intermediate hosts are fishes, reptiles, and amphibians. Some have a host preference. Human infection is known in Africa and Northern Europe, where man may act as an intermediate host for one stage in the life history of pentastomids.

A typical life history is illustrated by *Linguatula taenioides*, which lives in the nasal passageways of carnivorous mammals. When the eggs of the adult worm leave the host in the feces or mucus secretions and hatch, the larvae climb on vegetation where they are eaten by rabbits. In the rabbit the larvae encyst in the liver. After larval development involving several molts, the rabbit may be eaten, whereupon the parasite takes up residence in the nasal passages of the definite host.

CLASSIFICATION

Phylum Pentastomida. Vermiform and unsegmented; body cylindric or flattened; chitinous cuticle undergoes molting; mouth with two pairs of retractile hooks; legless; no antennae; no respiratory or excretory system; some with complex life histories; dioecious; parasitic in respiratory passages of vertebrates.

    Order Cephalobaenida. With six-legged larvae; adults live in mammals, birds, and reptiles. *Reighardia, Cephalobaena.*

    Order Porocephalida. With four-legged larvae; adults in snakes, larvae in mammals. *Porocephalus, Armillifer.* 50 to 60 species.

ADAPTATIONS AND PHYLOGENY

Most pentastomidan adaptations are about the same as those of many other metazoan parasites, such as hooks in both adults and larvae for attachment to the host. As in most internal parasites, the reproductive system is stressed above other systems, which may be omitted. They are bloodsuckers, and the anterior part of the digestive tract is adapted as a pump.

The three phyla—Pentastomida, Onychophora, and Tardigrada—are often placed together as a group called Pararthropoda because they have unjointed limbs with claws (at some stage), a cuticle that molts, and some other common features. They may bridge the gap between annelids and arthropods, although this theory is disputed. The pentastomids show several arthropodan characters such as jointed appendages in the larva, skin with breathing pores (stigmata), molting cuticle, striated muscle, lobular gonads, and lack of ciliated epithelium. R. Heymons thinks the pentastomids have evolved from polychaetes because they show some features of the Myzostomidae, an aberrant group of polychaetes usually commensal or parasitic on echinoderms. *Myzostoma* has a rounded body with a fringe of limblike appendages and a protrusible proboscis for sucking food from ambulacral grooves.

GENERAL MORPHOLOGIC FEATURES
External anatomy

The adults of pentastomids vary from 20 to 130 mm. in length. They are elongated with cylindric or flattened bodies. There is no differentiation of head, thorax, or abdomen. The body has a thick, chitinous cuticle which is molted during development; it is transversely ringed to give the appearance of superficial segmentation (Fig. 21-1). The anterior end bears on each side of the mouth region four retractile hooks, each of which is located on a short protuberance and provided with strong muscles. The type of hook and the number of body rings are important in the diagnosis of species. Body wall muscles are striated and arranged in layers very much like those of annelids. The genital pore and the anus are on the ventral side of the body. Tiny pores (stigmata) are found in the skin.

Internal anatomy and life history

The digestive tract is a straight, undifferentiated tube with the mouth end adapted for sucking the host's blood, on which these worms live (Fig. 21-1, *A*). They have no respiratory, excretory, or circulatory organs. The simple nervous system is similar to that of annelids and arthropods with three pairs of ganglia located along the ventral nerve cord.

The sexes are separate, and the females are much larger than the males (Fig. 21-1, *A*). The genital pore in each sex may be located ventrally near the anterior end, especially in the primitive species, or sometimes it is found posteriorly. Fertilization is internal, and the ripe eggs of the female are discharged through the mouth of the host in the mucus secretions. In some life cycles the eggs may pass with the feces. The intermediate host is commonly infected by ingesting eggs in contaminated water or food. The larvae are released from the eggs

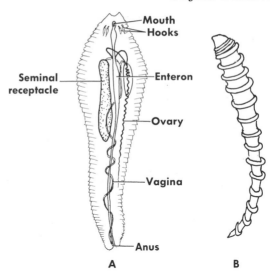

Fig. 21-1

A, Pentastomum, a common pentastomid in lungs and nasal cavities of snakes and other vertebrates. Female specimen is shown with certain internal structures. *B,* Female *Armillifer,* a pentastomid with pronounced body rings. In Africa, man is frequently parasitized by immature stages of this pentastomid, adults of which are usually found in lungs of snakes. Human infection may occur from eating snakes or from contaminated food or water. Adult of this genus grows to be 4 inches or more in length.

during digestion and encyst in some visceral organ such as the liver. By eating the intermediate host, the definite host becomes infected, and the larval worms migrate to the lungs where they mature. The immature stages have four or six legs and include larval and nymphal stages.

Annotated references

Chandler, A. C. 1952. Introduction to parasitology, ed. 8. New York, John Wiley & Sons, Inc. *A short section with several illustrations is given to the Pentastomida in this well-known textbook.*

Heymons, R. Pentastomida. In Bronn, H. G. (editor). 1935. Klassen und Ordnungen des Tierreichs, vol. 5, part 4, pp. 1-268. Leipzig, Akademische Verlagsgesellschaft. *Perhaps the best account of the pentastomids is given in this monograph.*

Hill, H. R., 1960. Pentastomida. In McGraw-Hill encyclopedia of science and technology, vol. 9, pp. 623-624. New York, McGraw Hill Book Company. *A concise account of the group.*

Swellengrebel, N. H., and M. M. Sterman. 1961. Animal parasites in man, pp. 435-441. Princeton, D. Van Nostrand Co., Inc. *An account of Linguatula and* Armillifer *as pentastomid parasites of man.*

Chapter 22

Phylum Arthropoda:
Introduction

GENERAL DESCRIPTION

The great phylum Arthropoda includes about 80 percent of all known species in the animal kingdom. About 1,000,000 species have already been described and some authorities think the number in time will exceed 5,000,000. Arthropods occupy about every conceivable ecologic niche from low ocean depths to very high altitudes, and from the tropics far into both north and south polar regions. Different species are adapted for life in the media of air, land, fresh water, brackish water, marine water, and the bodies of other animals. Some species are known from only a few individuals, but most species are represented by thousands of individuals wherever found. In size, they range from microscopic mites to the giant Japanese spider crab, which in its overall dimension may exceed 10 to 12 feet. The phylum includes insects, spiders, mites, crustaceans, ticks, centipedes, millipedes, and some smaller groups.

Both morphologic and embryologic evidences indicate that the arthropods have evolved from annelidan ancestors. Some of these lines of evidence will be described later. Their evolutionary divergence no doubt has depended upon many factors, but one of the most significant is their mechanism of locomotion. A successful invasion of land and air environments, to a great extent, stresses methods for getting around. Arthropods succeed in these meth-

ods to a remarkable degree; their dynamic nature is shown in their rapid locomotion when avoiding enemies and pursuing prey. Their most extensive subdivision, the insects, have evolved flight, thus sharing with some vertebrates this most efficient method for wide distribution.

External anatomy

The typical arthropod body plan is a series of segments that have muscular movement, and each segment is provided with a pair of jointed appendages. This basic plan is greatly modified in their adaptive radiation because, unlike the annelids, the arthropods have their segments and appendages specialized for many varied functions. This trait has contributed to their evolutionary divergence into various ecologic niches.

One of the most unique features of arthropods is their integument, which has been an important factor in the transition from water to land. The armorlike exoskeleton of arthropods has been the subject of much investigation (A. G. Richards and V. B. Wigglesworth). The general plan of the integument consists of a single layer of cells (hypodermis), an internal basement membrane, and an external cuticle secreted by the hypodermis. This external cuticle is made up of two basic layers: an outer thin epicuticle without chitin and an inner, thicker endocuticle, or procuticle, with chitin as its chief constituent. The epicuticle usually varies in thickness from 0.1 to 1 micron and is a waxlike substance in many arthropods. It is this wax that confers most of the impermeability of the cuticle to water. Two layers are usually found in the epicuticle: the outer lipoid (waxy) layer and an inner layer of proteins and lipoids. Other substances, especially in insects, have been identified in the epicuticle, which is very complex. The much thicker endocuticle (often in two layers) consists primarily of a chitin-protein complex that varies greatly in the different arthropods. The characteristic chitin is a polymer (polysaccharide) of a high molecular weight and similar to cellulose. It is not found in nature in a pure condition but is always associated with proteins. Its metabolic source may be glycogen. It is often sclerotized into hard plates by the addition of other substances such as calcium salts (e.g., calcium carbonate and calcium phosphate). Flexible portions of the cuticle are called membranes and are found wherever movable articulations occur. Cuticle is also found in the ectodermal derivatives of the foregut and hindgut, tracheae, and parts of the reproductive ducts.

Arthropods often display a range of color patterns in the different groups, especially in insects and crustaceans. Both true pigments (biochromes) and structural colors (schemochromes) are represented. The biochromes are mostly carotenoids, although the darker melanin shades also occur as well as some of the rarer pigments. The brilliant yellow, orange, and red colors are due to carotenoids, while shades of blue, green, and some other colors are primarily produced by the effects of light interference. Combinations of the two kinds of colors yield many shades. Pigment may be deposited directly in the cuticle or in chromatophores, which are multicellular and may or may not bear more than one kind of pigment.

The thick and generally inflexible cuticle or exoskeleton imposed upon arthropods problems of locomotion and growth. Jointed limbs, however, made possible a wide variety of adaptations for specialized living. With the exception of the highly specialized flying insects, arthropods have evolved a segmented limb especially adapted for rapid movement on a substratum. For flexibility the appendages are provided with articular membranes, articular sockets, and systems of separate muscles. The propulsive force for exerting thrusts against the body is thus produced by extrinsic limb muscles. The division of the exoskeleton into separate sclerites, which are also connected by flexible articular membranes, also allows a movement of the body as well as of the jointed legs. Typically, each body segment is made up of a dorsal tergum, a ventral sternum, and two lateral pleura. Many modifications of this plan by fusion, elimination, or otherwise are found in the varied assortment of arthropods. Sclerotization of the integument also makes possible a greatly lengthened and stiffened limb for locomotor efficiency.

During the growth of the arthropod the hard exoskeleton allows little room for expansion and must be shed periodically (molting or ecdysis) to permit additional growth. A new cuticle then must be secreted to replace the one discarded. This process is under hormonal control and involves also the shedding of the ectodermal derivatives such as foregut and hindgut, tracheae, and some other parts. Just before molting most of the endocuticle is digested away by enzymes in the molting fluid secreted by the hypodermis. In this way the cuticle is freed from the hypodermis. Some constituents (limy salts) of the cuticle are also salvaged and stored temporarily in the liver or stomach gastroliths. While this is taking place, a new cuticle is secreted beneath the old by the hypodermis. The actual molting or shedding of the old cuticle now occurs, the cuticle being split typically along the middorsal line and other strategic places. This rupturing is aided by swelling induced by an absorption of water and air. The animal pulls out of the old cuticle and absorbs more water to increase its body size. In this enlarged state the new cuticle is hardened by the resorbed chitin and by the reserve of limy salts temporarily stored as well as by the addition of new salts from the water. During the growth period between molts the animal is called an instar, the number of instar periods varying with different species. Molting, or ecdysis, usually occurs frequently in the larval stages when growth is rapid, less often as the animal becomes older. In the postmolt period before the new cuticle has hardened the animal has little protection from enemies and usually seeks a hiding place. The many problems connected with ecdysis have no doubt restricted the size of many land arthropods.

The sclerotization of the cuticle and the formation of sclerites have resulted in the formation of distinct striated muscle groups. The muscles are supplied with few nerve fibers, of which usually at least one is inhibitory in its action. Each muscle fiber is also supplied with many motor endplates. Most of the body and limb muscles are attached directly on the inner surface of the integumental sclerites. Apodemes or endoskeletal ingrowths of the exoskeleton also serve for muscle attachments. Appendages are moved with a lever system the same as in vertebrates, except that in arthropods the muscles are attached to the inner surface of the exoskeleton and work across joints from the inside. Since the skeleton occupies the outside of the body and is heavy and bulky, this is another factor that has limited the size of arthropods.

Internal anatomy

The arthropods are all provided with the organ systems characteristic of higher forms. The coelomic cavity, however, is much reduced, being restricted to the gonocoel, where the gonads lie, and the space around the excretory coelomoducts. Most of the spaces form the hemocoel (blood sinuses) or swollen parts of the vascular system, which have generally obliterated the coelom proper.

The blood system is an open one, and the internal organs are contained in perivisceral cavities filled with blood. From these sinuses, blood is collected in a pericardial sinus (a part of the hemocoel) that surrounds the heart. The heart is an elongated dorsal structure and corresponds to the dorsal blood vessel of annelids. This heart is provided with lateral slits, or ostia, typically one pair to a segment. By pulsation the blood is forced forward into smaller vessels (arteries), which empty into the tissue sinuses. In Pauropoda and some other arthropods no heart is present, and the blood is circulated by the movements of the body or body organs. There are many modifications of the circulatory system within the phylum. The arthropodan

blood bears some resemblance to that of annelids. The blood pigments, hemoglobin and hemocyanin, are represented in the plasma of many arthropods, hemoglobin being restricted mostly to the lower crustaceans. Several types of formed elements (leukocytes, amebocytes, and thigmocytes) are also found. The blood of some arthropods clots rapidly as a defense mechanism against wounds.

The digestive system may be straight or coiled with the mouth in the head and the anus on the terminal segment. Embryologically, it consists of three divisions: an anterior stomodeum, a posterior proctodeum (both of ectodermal origin and lined with chitin), and the mesenteron (midgut) of endodermal origin. The stomodeum, or foregut, is variously modified in many arthropods into a pharynx, esophagus, and storing or grinding organs. Lateral diverticula (blind pouches) may be found on the mesenteron, especially in the Arachnida and Pycnogonida, where they often extend into the legs. The proctodeum, or hindgut, may be divided into anterior intestine and posterior rectum. At the junction of the midgut and hindgut, the Malpighian tubules (excretory) are present in some forms, including insects.

In some of the simpler arthropods (e.g., Pycnogonida) respiration takes place through the body wall; in most arthropods, however, the exchange of gases is effected by gills or tracheae. Some special breathing mechanisms such as book lungs are found in Arachnida. Gills are formed as branching outgrowths of the body wall or its appendages, while tracheae have arisen as tubular invaginations of the ectoderm and cuticle. Tracheae may be unbranched in primitive forms, but usually they are branched and open to the outside by spiracles. Tracheae are lined with cuticle that is thickened in places, forming spiral staves to keep the tubes open. A tracheal system represents one of the most efficient breathing systems in the animal kingdom because it delivers oxygen directly to the tissues. Blood plays a very restricted role in the transportation of oxygen in arthropods.

Many kinds of excretory organs exist in arthropods. Some simple forms may have no organs at all, and excretory products are discarded at molting. Nephridia appear to be absent, but segmented excretory organs such as antennal, coxal, and maxillary glands, which are remnants of coelomic sacs, communicate with the exterior by coelomoducts. The coelomoducts in some forms open at the base of the legs. In arachnids, insects, centipedes, and millipedes, Malpighian tubules of endodermal or ectodermal origin carry on the work of excretion. The chief excretory products include ammonia, amines, urates, and guanine.

The nervous system reaches a high degree of complexity in higher arthropods. The basic plan, however, is similar to that of annelids. Typically, it consists of two ventral nerve cords (far apart in some primitive forms), a dorsal brain, and a pair of ganglia for each somite. Many of the ganglia may be fused together in accordance with the merging of the head segments. In the mandibulate arthropods the first three ganglia (protocerebrum, deutocerebrum, tritocerebrum) are fused to form the brain. In insects especially, the ganglia of the thorax and abdomen undergo merging. From the ganglia, nerves run to the body wall and to the visceral organs. Sense organs include internal proprioceptors and many surface receptors such as olfactory, tactile, visual, and chemical.

Most arthropods are dioecious, but a few are hermaphroditic. Parthenogenesis is common in some groups. The gonads are nearly always in direct contact with the coelomoducts, and the genital openings are not constant in position. They may open near the posterior end of the body, near the middle of the body, and often toward the head end. Fertilization is internal in terrestrial forms but is often external in aquatic species.

EMBRYOLOGY

Eggs of arthropods usually contain a great deal of yolk and are of the type known as centrolecithal or some modification thereof. The nucleus is centrally located, and after fertilization it undergoes mitotic division without formation of cell membranes or cleavage of the yolk materials. In time the products of nuclear division migrate to the periphery, where cell membranes are formed around the nuclei in the layer of protopla on the surface of the yolk. This is the stage of the stereoblastula. Gastrulation may occur by invagination toward the yolk mass, by other methods involving migration of cells, or by delamination. From a germinal band along one side of the embryo, cells form a cell mass of mesoderm and endoderm by overgrowth or proliferation. A plate outside this mass forms the ectoderm. Numerous variations of this pattern exist. Immature stages of the arthropods vary from juvenile-like forms to larval forms wholly unlike the adults, such as the larval stages of insects.

CLASSIFICATION

Phylum Arthropoda. Bilateral symmetry with body segmented and jointed externally; head somites fused with thorax, and abdomen distinct or fused; appendages usually one pair per somite with hinge joints and variously differentiated; exoskeleton of a chitinous cuticle secreted by the epidermis and molted periodically; muscles striated and arranged in units; coelom much reduced and largely replaced by a hemocoel; mouthparts adapted for chewing or sucking; digestive system complete with terminal anus; excretory system of coelomoducts or tubules; circulatory system open, dorsal heart with vessels and tissue spaces; respiration direct or by gills, tracheae, or book lungs; nervous system of brain, paired ventral cords, ganglia, and connectives; sensory system of tactile, chemical, and visual receptors (simple or compound); parthenogenesis and dioecious sexes; eggs with much yolk (centrolecithal); cleavage superficial with gradual or abrupt metamorphosis; usually one or many larval stages; terrestrial, freshwater, and marine.

Subphylum Trilobita. Body divided by two longitudinal furrows into three lobes; head distinct with abdomen of varying number of somites and fused caudal plate; somites with jointed biramous appendages fringed by setae and present on most segments; one pair of uniramous antennae; development with larval stages; wholly extinct; Cambrian to Permian periods; marine. *Triarthrus, Isotelus.*

Subphylum Chelicerata. Body usually divided into a cephalothorax (prosoma) and an abdomen (opisthosoma); cephalothorax unsegmented with paired preoral chelicerae bearing chelae or claws and paired postanal pedipalpi variously modified; antennae absent; four pairs of legs (usually); abdomen has varying number of segments, usually without appendages; respiration by gills, book lungs, or tracheae; excretion by coxal glands or Malpighian tubules; sexes separate with single genital opening located anteriorly on the abdomen; chiefly terrestrial and predaceous.

Class Xiphosura. Cephalothorax a horseshoe-shaped carapace convex above and concave below; abdomen (opisthosoma) unsegmented or of fused segments with spikelike terminal segment (telson); cephalothorax appendages a pair of typical chelicerae and five pairs of walking legs, usually chelate; opisthosoma with six pairs of biramous appendages, the first forming an operculum on which the paired genital pores are located; other abdominal appendages carry book gills; marine. King crabs—*Xiphosura (Limulus), Tachypleus*.

Class Eurypterida. Body elongated and lanceolate in shape; cephalothorax cuboid; abdomen of 12 freely articulated segments and a terminal telson; preabdomen (mesosoma) of seven segments and bearing ventral appendages; postabdomen (metasoma) narrow, of five segments without appendages; cephalothorax appendages six in number, made up of a pair of pincerlike chelicerae, four pairs of walking legs, and one pair of paddlelike swimming legs; abdominal appendages six in number, of which the first pair form the operculum and the others bear gills; bottom crawlers usually in brackish water; Cambrian to Permian periods; wholly extinct. *Pterygotus, Eurypterus*.

Class Pycnogonida (Pantopoda). Body reduced to a series of cylindric segments (four to six) with vestigial opisthosoma; head or cephalon fused to first trunk segment; appendages of one pair of chelicerae, a pair of palps, a pair of ovigers, and usually four to six pairs of long walking legs; first four pairs of appendages usually on first (cephalic) segment; marine. Sea spiders—*Nymphon, Pycnogonum*.

Class Arachnida. Body divided into a prosoma and abdomen; prosoma (cephalothorax) usually covered dorsally with carapace and consisting of six fused segments; prosoma appendages of one pair of chelicerae, one pair of pedipalps, and four pairs of legs; opisthosoma (abdomen) of 13 segments generally fused and divided into a preabdomen and postabdomen; prosoma and opisthosoma fused in some; mostly terrestrial.

    Order Scorpionida. Body divided into a prosoma (cephalothorax) and opisthosoma (abdomen); prosoma covered by unsegmented carapace; opisthosoma divided into mesosoma (preabdomen) and metasoma (postabdomen); tail of metasoma and terminal sting; opisthosoma of 12 segments; cephalothorax with paired chelicerae and pedipalps, and four pairs of walking legs; terrestrial. Scorpions—*Centruroides*.

    Order Amblypygi. Body crablike; prosoma with unsegmented carapace; opisthosoma of 12 segments without tail and sting; pedipalps large with pincers; first pair of legs modified into long whips for sensory feelers; mostly tropic or warm climates. *Acanthophrynus, Charinus*.

Order Uropygi. Body elongated and flattened; prosoma with single or divided carapace; opisthosoma (abdomen) with terminal many-jointed, whiplike flagellum; pedipalps stout with spines and pincers; first pair of legs modified into feelers; tropical or warm regions. Whip scorpions—*Mastigoproctus*.

Order Palpigradi. Body elongated with terminal, multisegmented flagellum set with setae; size minute; chelicerae stout; abdomen of 11 segments; pedipalps as walking legs; first pair of walking legs sensory; tropic and warm temperate climates. *Prokoenenia*.

Order Araneae. Body of unsegmented cephalothorax and abdomen; cephalothorax separated from abdomen by narrow pedicel; body covered with chitinous plates often with outgrowths; chelicerae with poison glands; pedipalps with enlarged basal joints, modified in male for copulation; legs with seven segments; spinnerets on abdomen for extruding silk; mostly terrestrial. Spiders—*Miranda, Latrodectus, Lycosa*.

Order Solpugida. Cephalothorax and abdomen not divided by pedicel; abdomen visibly segmented (10); chelicerae long and stout, joined to carapace; pedipalps and first pair of walking legs tactile in function; tropic and warm temperate or arid regions. False spiders, sun spiders, wind scorpions—*Eremobates*.

Order Pseudoscorpionida. Body small (scorpionlike) with cephalothorax broadly joined to abdomen of 12 segments; no sting; chelicerae with comblike serrula and often connected with silk glands; pedipalps unusually large with poison glands and chelae; four pairs of walking legs; terrestrial and cosmopolitan. False scorpions—*Chelifer*.

Order Ricinulei. Body ticklike with a pedicel connecting cephalothorax and abdomen; abdomen of 12 fused segments with terminal anus on a tubercle; carapace with anterior hood; chelicerae and palps with chelae; third legs of male modified as copulatory structures; tropic and warm climates. *Ricinoides*.

Order Phalangida (Opiliones). Body short with cephalothorax broadly joined to segmented abdomen; carapace simple with tubercle; chelicerae small; pedipalps not chelated; legs very long and delicate; scent glands with openings along the cephalothorax often present; cosmopolitan. Phalangids, harvest spiders, harvestmen—*Phalangium*.

Order Acarina. Body compact, rounded, and

(*Classes Xiphosura and Eurypterida are sometimes assigned the rank of subclasses under class Merostomata.)

divided into anterior gnathosoma of mouth and mouthparts and a posterior idiosoma; segmentation absent; chelicerae and pedipalps highly variable; legs usually widely separated and variously adapted; free living or parasitic; cosmopolitan. Ticks, mites—*Dermacentor, Trombicula.*

Subphylum Mandibulata. Body of two or three divisions (cephalothorax-abdomen, head and trunk, or head-thorax-abdomen); antennae of one or two pairs, mandible or jaws paired; maxillae one or two pairs; walking legs three or more pairs; respiration by gills or tracheae; excretion by glands or Malpighian tubules; sexes usually separate; development usually with larval stages; terrestrial, freshwater, or marine.

Class Crustacea. Body segmented with chitinous and limy exoskeleton and usually with carapace and telson; head usually with five pairs of appendages (antennules, antennae, mandibles, first and second maxillae); eyes compound; appendages typically biramous; segments of varying regional specializations and number; excretion by antennal glands; respiration by gills or body surface; usually dioecious; larval stages in development; cosmopolitan and mostly aquatic; free living or parasitic.

Subclass Cephalocarida. Body shrimplike with primitive organization; head horseshoe shaped with short, paired antennae; trunk of 19 or 20 segments, of which the first 9 bear similar biramous appendages; eyes absent; hermaphroditic with larval stages; marine. *Hutchinsoniella.*

Subclass Branchiopoda. Body with variable number of segments (usually more than 15 postcephalic); carapace usually present; antennae may be adapted for swimming or reduced; trunk appendages of four pairs or more and broad or leaflike in structure; abdomen usually without appendages; parthenogenesis common; mostly freshwater.

Order Anostraca. Body elongated with no carapace; trunk usually of 19 segments, of which the first 11 (or more) bear foliaceous swimming legs; antennae in male stout for clasping; first paired legless segments bear ovisac or penes; telson with paired flattened cercopods; compound eyes stalked; cosmopolitan, freshwater, and marine. *Branchinecta, Artemia.*

Order Notostraca. Trunk of 25 to 44 segments, usually partially covered with a broad carapace; first 11 segments with one pair of legs each; others with more than one pair; many legless segments; antennae reduced; telson with long, paired cercopods; cosmopolitan and freshwater. *Lepidurus, Apus.*

Order Conchostraca. Body laterally compressed and covered with bivalve shell or carapace; trunk segments 10 to 27 (or more), each with a pair of foliaceous appendages; antennae modified for swimming; telson with clawlike cercopods; freshwater. *Limnadia, Lynceus.*

Order Cladocera. Body, but not head, covered with bivalve shell; second pair of antennae large and two branched; trunk appendages (four to six pairs) are leaf shaped with setae and enclosed in shell; apical spine usually at terminal part of carapace or shell; sexes separate, but two kinds of eggs, one of which develops by parthenogenesis; freshwater and cosmopolitan. Water fleas—*Leptodora, Daphnia.*

Subclass Ostracoda. Body covered with bivalved shell or carapace made up of chitin and calcium; body segments not distinct; head large in proportion to body; antennae well developed; usually only two pairs of trunk appendages; cosmopolitan, both freshwater and marine.

Order Myodocopa. Shell, when closed, with notch for extension of second pair of antennae; second antennae only organs of locomotion; three pairs of thoracic legs; cosmopolitan and marine. *Philomedes.*

Order Cladocopa. Carapace without a notch; antennae adapted for swimming (second pair is biramous); two pairs of postoral appendages; body terminates in process with clawlike spines; marine. *Polycope.*

Order Podocopa. Carapace without a notch; antennae for locomotion; mandible with palp and setae; four pairs of postoral appendages; freshwater and marine. *Darwinula, Cypris.*

Order Platycopa. Carapace without a notch; antennae not used for locomotion, second pair with broad, flattened appendage segments; three pairs of postoral appendages; marine. *Cytherella.*

Subclass Mystacocarida. Body wormlike; microscopic; antennae long with bristles; labrum large; maxillipeds on thoracic segment separate from head; four thoracic segments with platelike appendages; abdominal segments (six) without appendages; caudal rami large; restricted intertidal sandy beaches; recent. *Derocheilocaris.*

Subclass Copepoda. Body variable but usually short and cylindric, divided into head, thorax, and abdomen; antennae for swimming and grasping; first antennae usually long; median eye of fused ocelli; thorax usually of six segments with swimming limbs; abdomen of four or five segments without appendages except caudal rami; appendages mostly biramous; ovisacs as brood chambers; free living and parasitic; freshwater and marine.

Order Calanoida. Body elongated and cylindric, often with plumose setae; first antennae usually long, the second pair biramous; movable articulation between sixth and seventh thoracic segments; often brightly pigmented; bioluminescence common; planktonic at variable depths; freshwater and marine. *Diaptomus, Calanus.*

Order Harpacticoida. Body linear and cylindric; last thoracic segment with abdomen; antennae biramous; antennules prehensile in male; first pair of swimming legs for grasping; last pair of legs usually reduced; ovisac single or double; nauplius eye; freshwater and marine. *Harpacticus, Epactophanes.*

Order Cyclopoida. Body oval and sharply separated from posterior end; 9 to 10 body segments; antennae mostly uniramous, first pair long with many segments; male antennae fitted for grasping; five pairs of swimming legs with a sixth rudimentary leg in male; ovisacs present; cosmopolitan; freshwater and marine. *Cyclops.*

Order Notodelphyoida. Body mostly with uniform segmentation; thorax humped or swollen in female for brood chamber; trunk appendages small; articulation between fourth and fifth thoracic segments in male and between first and second abdominal segments in female; often commensal in tunicates; marine. *Notodelphys, Doropygus.*

Order Monstrilloida. Second antennae and mouthparts lacking; cephalic segment fused with first thoracic; legs usually long with spines; larval stages in marine invertebrates; marine. *Monstrilla.*

Order Caligoida. Body with distinct carapace and mostly fused segments; sucking mouth; second antennae and second maxillipeds prehensile; swimmerets modified; articulation between third and fourth thoracic segments; adults parasitic on fish; freshwater and marine. *Caligus.*

Order Lernaeopodoida. Body segmentation reduced or absent; thoracic appendages usually lacking in female; male with modified head appendages for clinging to female; ectoparasites on fish; freshwater and marine. *Salmincola, Lernaea.*

Subclass Branchiura. Body flattened dorsoventrally; carapace shieldlike, covering head and thorax; compound eyes; abdomen bilobed, small, limbless, and not segmented; antennae small; four pairs of swimming legs on underside of body; sucking mouth; some appendages with claws for clinging; suction cups; ectoparasites on skin or gill cavities of freshwater and marine fish.

Order Arguloida. *Argulus.*

Subclass Cirripedia. Body indistinctly segmented; usually carapace of a fleshy mantle;

calcareous plates present or absent; sessile forms attached by cement glands at base of first antennae; stalked forms with peduncle for attachment; second antennae absent; usually six pairs of biramous appendages (cirri) adapted for feeding; abdomen vestigial; usually hermaphroditic; two larval stages (nauplius and cypris); marine.

Order Thoracica. Mantle usually with calcareous plates; six pairs of biramous thoracic appendages; abdomen absent or represented by caudal furca; sessile or stalked with body in soft mantle (capitulum). Barnacles— *Lepas, Balanus.*

Order Acrothoracica. Mantle without calcareous plates; thoracic appendages fewer than six pairs and often reduced; posterior cirri widely separated from the first cirri; abdomen usually absent and represented by caudal furca; first antennae absent; sexes usually separate. *Trypetesa.*

Order Ascothoracica. Body bivalved or saclike and mantle without calcareous plates; thoracic appendages six or less and often reduced; abdomen present; piercing or sucking mouthparts; first antennae usually modified for grasping; separate sexes usually; sexual dimorphism with males smaller than females; parasites of coelenterates or echinoderms. *Baccalaureus.*

Order Apoda. Mantle lacking; body segmented; thoracic appendages lacking; mouth suctorial; first antennae and cement glands present; digestive system degenerate or lacking; hermaphroditic; parasitic and marine. Only one genus described by Darwin. *Proteolepas.*

Order Rhizocephala. Mantle present but shell lacking; body saclike with absorptive roots; no appendages or digestive system; mostly parasitic on decapod crustaceans; males may be hyperparasitic on females in some species, although sexes are often considered hermaphroditic. *Sacculina, Loxothylacus.*

Subclass Malacostraca. Body usually of 19 segments, of which five make up the head, eight the thorax, and six (rarely seven or eight) the abdomen; carapace or shell present or absent; abdomen long or short; appendages on all 19 segments; antennules usually biramous, antennae biramous; typical biramous appendages of exopodite and endopodite; thoracic appendages with well-developed endopodite; abdominal appendages biramous; the first five abdominal pairs (pleopods) for swimming; last pair of abdominal appendages (uropods) forming with telson a tail fan for backward movement; freshwater and marine; cosmopolitan.

Series Leptostraca. Abdomen with seven segments; last segment with no appendages;

adductor muscle connecting the two halves of the carapace; telson with articulated furcal rami; primitive.

Order Nebaliacea. Thorax and part of abdomen covered by bivalved shell; adductor muscle joining the two valves; head appendages well developed; thoracic limbs foliaceous; last abdominal segment without appendages; first four pairs of abdominal appendages biramous, others uniramous. *Nebalia.*

Series Eumalacostraca. Abdomen with six segments; adductor muscle and furcal rami lacking.

Superorder Syncarida. Body lacks carapace and calcareous plates; thoracic appendages biramous; chelae absent.

Order Anaspidacea. Body with only slight differentiation from abdomen; pleopods with long fringed exopodites, but endopodites reduced or absent; tail fan well developed; primitive; freshwater in Tasmania and South Australia. *Anaspides.*

Order Bathynellacea. Body with first thoracic segment free; thoracic limbs with epipodites as gills; some abdominal appendages reduced or absent; eyeless; caves. *Bathynella.*

Superorder Pancarida. Body mostly cylindric with no division between thorax and abdomen; head and first thoracic segment fused; carapace with brood pouch, covering only first three thoracic segments; eyeless.

Order Thermosbaenacea. Found in transitional zone between fresh and marine water of Italy and central Europe. *Thermosbaena.*

Superorder Peracarida. Body with or without carapace; carapace never united with more than four segments; thoracic brood pouch; thoracic appendages flexed between fifth and sixth segments; epipodites modified for vibratory movements or gas exchange; abdominal pleopods five pairs or less.

Order Spelaeogriphacea. Body shrimplike with short carapace united to first thoracic segment; second antennae with very long flagella; three pairs of oval gills attached to five to seven thoracic appendages; first pair of thoracic limbs modified as maxillipeds; freshwater lake of South Africa. *Spelaeogriphus.*

Order Mysidacea. Body with carapace over thorax but last four or five thoracic segments free; typical number (19) of body segments; one pair of biramous appendages on each segment; tail fan of uropods and telson; eyes pedunculate; mostly marine. Opossum shrimps—*Neomysis, Mysis.*

Order Cumacea. Body with carapace fused to first three or four segments; carapace with lateral extensions often joined over head anteriorly; first three pairs of thoracic appen-dages modified as maxillipeds; antennae long in male; uropods not forming a tail fan; pleopods only in males; marine. *Diastylis.*

Order Tanaidacea. Body with first two pairs of thoracic segments fused to head and covered by small carapace; respiratory chamber on each side enclosed by carapace; first pair of the eight thoracic appendages forming the maxillipeds; second thoracic pair with chelae; exopodites absent in all thoracic appendages except second and third; last abdominal segment fused with telson; pleopods present or absent; mostly marine and cosmopolitan. *Tanais, Apseudes.*

Order Isopoda. Body dorsoventrally flattened; no carapace; one or two thoracic segments fused to head; abdomen wholly or partly fused and short; first antennae short and uniramous; abdominal appendages foliaceous except last pair (uropods) and fitted for respiration; last abdominal segment fused to telson; parasitic, terrestrial, freshwater, or marine. *Asellus, Porcellio, Hemioniscus.*

Order Amphipoda. Body usually laterally compressed; carapace absent; one to two thoracic segments fused to head; antennae without exopodites; first pair of thoracic appendages modified as maxillipeds; second and third thoracic appendages prehensile; abdomen flexed ventrally between third and fourth segments; pleopods usually in two groups, the first three pairs for swimming and the other two pairs similar to uropods; freshwater and marine. *Hyalella, Gammarus, Cyamus.*

Superorder Eucarida. Body with large carapace fused to all the thoracic segments; eyes on movable stalks; thoracic gills; brood chamber absent.

Order Euphausiacea. Body shrimplike; thoracic appendages not forming maxillipeds, and all biramous; gills at bases of second to eighth thoracic appendages; pleopods with long setae for swimming; telson with pair of spines; planktonic and marine. Krill, whalefeed—*Euphausia.*

Order Decapoda. Body with 20 pairs of appendages; first three pairs of thoracic appendages modified as maxillipeds; eyestalks of two to three segments; five pairs of walking legs (pereiopods) with the first pair often stout and chelated (cheliped); head and thoracic segments fused together; usually more than one series of gills; first five pairs of abdominal appendages modified for swimming but one to two pairs in male modified as copulatory gonopods; last abdominal appendages (uropods) with telson forming tail fan; terrestrial, freshwater, and marine. *Cambarus, Palaemonetes, Homarus, Callinectes.*

Superorder Hoplocarida. Body elongated and

dorsoventrally flattened; carapace shield shaped and fused to the first two thoracic segments; last four thoracic segments uncovered by carapace; carapace with movable rostrum; second thoracic leg greatly enlarged (raptorial); first pair of antennae with three flagella and larger than second pair; the first five pairs of abdominal appendages (pleopods) biramous with first two pairs in the male forming a copulatory organ; pleopods with gills; sixth abdominal pair of appendages (uropods) large and forked; marine and burrowing in sand.

Order Stomatopoda. Mantis shrimps—*Squilla, Pseudosquilla.*

Class Chilopoda. Body long, flattened dorsoventrally, and of many similar segments; head distinct with single pair of antennae; one pair of jaws and two pairs of maxillae; most segments with a pair of appendages; first pair of legs behind the head modified into poison claws; segments vary, up to 190; ocelli present or absent; dioecious; genital opening on midventral next to last segment; terrestrial; cosmopolitan. Centipedes.

Order Scutigeromorpha. Trunk with 15 pairs of long legs; seven tergal plates; unpaired spiracles on middorsal tergal plates; young hatch with seven pairs of legs (anamorphic). *Scutigera.*

Order Lithobiomorpha. Trunk with 15 pairs of short legs; spiracles lateral but variable; anamorphic; temperate, subtropic, and tropic; cosmopolitan. *Lithobius.*

Order Scolopendromorpha. Trunk with 21 or 23 pairs of legs; epimorphic; cosmopolitan but chiefly tropic. *Scolopendra.*

Order Geophilomorpha. Body slender and specialized for burrowing; pair of lateral spiracles on each segment except first and last; mouthparts variable; intraspecific variability of trunk segments; segments up to 183; epimorphic; cosmopolitan. *Geophilus.*

Class Diplopoda. Body long and cylindric or hemicylindric with distinct head and trunk; segments double with single dorsal plate and two pairs of appendages per couple, except certain single anterior and posterior segments; one pair of antennae; mandibles and maxillae (gnathochilarium); tracheae two pairs per double segment and not anastomosing; genital opening on midventral line of third segment; dioecious; cosmopolitan. Millipedes.

Subclass Pselaphognatha. Body soft with usually 11 segments; integumental bristles forming long tufts; maxillae leglike; no gnathochilarium; cosmopolitan. *Polyxenus.*

Subclass Chilognatha. Body with chitinized and calcareous integument; body bristles simple or absent; head with gnathochilarium.

Order Limacomorpha. Body usually of 22 segments; male gonopods present on last segment; 36 pairs of legs; not ball-rolling. *Glomeridesmus.*

Order Oniscomorpha. Body of 12 or 13 segments; 17 to 21 pairs of legs; male gonopods present; ball-rolling. *Glomeris.*

Order Colobognatha. Body with 30 to 70 segments; head conical with reduced mandibles; male gonopods on seventh and eighth segments. *Platydesmus.*

Order Nematomorpha. Body of 26 or more segments; tergum with bristles; anal segment with two or three pairs of spinning glands. *Striaria.*

Order Polydesmoidea. Body with 19 to 22 depressed segments; male gonopores on seventh segment; stink glands present; spinning glands absent. *Polydesmus.*

Order Juliformia. Body of 40 or more cylindric segments; gonopores on seventh segment; stink glands present; *Julus, Spirobolus.*

Class Pauropoda. Body small, soft, elongated, and generally cylindric; trunk of 12 segments with six tergal plates; 9 to 10 pairs of legs; antennae two branched with flagella; mouthparts of one pair of mandibles and one pair of maxillae; no respiratory organs or eyes; dioecious; anamorphic; cosmopolitan. *Pauropus.*

Class Symphyla. Body small and elongated; 15 to 22 similar segments, 12 of which usually bear legs; mouthparts of one pair of mandibles and two pairs of maxillae; moniliform antennae of many joints; cerci stout; no pigment; eyes absent; dioecious and anamorphic; cosmopolitan. *Scutigerella.*

Class Insecta (Hexapoda). Body divided into three distinct divisions: head, thorax, abdomen; head of six segments and one pair of antennae; mouthparts modified for chewing, sucking, or lapping; thorax of three segments with three pairs of legs and two pairs of wings (reduced or absent); wings dorsolateral outgrowths with characteristic venation; abdomen typically of 11 segments without ambulatory appendages; respiration chiefly by a tracheal system of tubes and spiracles; body cavity a hemocoel; excretion by Malpighian tubules of the gut; nervous system of brain, ventral nerve cord, and segmental ganglia variously fused; eyes simple and compound; sexes separate with genital apertures near anus; development direct, gradual or complete metamorphosis; mostly terrestrial or freshwater. (A resume of insect orders and other taxonomic arrangements is given under the section on class Insecta, pp. 464-477.)

BASIC ADAPTIVE FEATURES

A group as extensive and as diverse as the Arthropoda presents many morphologic patterns. Their structural features and physiologic habits have enabled them to move into most ecologic niches available to animals. By whatever criteria they are appraised—number of species, variety of habitats, behavior patterns, general adaptability, etc.—this group ranks first among the invertebrates. They are the most highly specialized of all the invertebrates. An analysis of arthropods, however diversified they may be, reveals distinctive structures which have guided them in their great evolutionary development. There are excellent reasons, therefore, for considering them as monophyletic in origin and not polyphyletic, because certain common adaptive features have been modified and exploited in their amazing diversification.

Although authorities are generally agreed that arthropods have come from annelid ancestors, it is impossible at present to find convincing fossil records to demonstrate the evolutionary transition between the two groups. On more logical grounds it may be stated with conviction that the arthropods have characteristics that are an outcome of their annelid ancestors and others that are their own. In their segmentation and early embryologic development, arthropods share a basic plan with annelids. Segmentation in general tends to be suppressed in part or in whole by many arthropods, but most of them retain definite segmentation in some part of the body such as the abdomen, tail, or even most of the body. Fusion of segments, however, is characteristic of their specialized tendencies. Segmentation has also been modified in arthropods in connection with their lack of compartments and septa. The hydrostatic skeleton of annelids is not needed by a group that has such a hard exoskeleton. Fusion of segments for special structures, such as the thorax and firm attachments for muscles, has been common for adaptive reasons. Wherever segmentation has been retained, it is mainly for mobility and dexterity.

Arthropods have retained much of the nervous system plan of the annelids. Their appendages are segmentally arranged and some parts, such as the abdomen, retain a segmental pattern of muscles. Such morphologic units are best served by a nerve cord with properly spaced ganglia.

Ganglion consolidation occurs to a much greater degree with them than with annelids, especially in the head region, where advancement in cephalization demands such changes. Leg muscles in arthropods largely correspond to the annelid circular body musculature, while the longitudinal muscles of the annelid are retained for mobility of those arthropodian segments that are still present. As already mentioned, muscles in arthropods differ from the muscle layers of annelids in being broken up into units for more precise movements.

The morphologic pattern of the arthropods involves a large blood cavity (hemocoel)—an open blood system with few blood vessels and no capillaries. Such an arrangement has been the outcome of the loss of internal partitions or septa along with loss of segmentation, because such a blood cavity allows the free circulation of blood materials throughout most of the body. Although a hemocoel is best developed in those arthropods with tracheal systems, it is found, with modifications, in all members of the phylum.

It cannot be ignored that the segmentation arthropods inherited from their annelid ancestors has been a great factor for the high degree of structural complexity and diversity found in this group. Whole segments specialized for functional advantage are found throughout the group. Perhaps no single morphologic feature has been more fruitful in their evolution than the way in which arthropods have fused together and changed adaptively the primitive plan of their segments. The two features that arthropods do not share with annelids are the exoskeleton and jointed appendages. These structures, together with the modifications of the segments, have guided the arthropod throughout its evolutionary range of diversity. How appendages originated is not known, but speculation suggests that they arose from lobelike limb rudiments. As the integument became hardened (sclerotization), limbs could increase in length and become jointed for greater efficiency. In the trilobites, the most primitive of arthropods, the paired appendages, except the antennae, are all biramous and mostly uniform. Some doubt exists, however, about the exact homology of the trilobite limb with that

343

of certain other arthropods such as the crustaceans. The monopodial or phyllopodial origins of arthropod appendages has never been satisfactorily settled. Whatever their origin, the arthropod appendages have undergone extensive specializations such as jaws and other feeding mechanisms, grasping organs, sense organs, walking legs, swimming appendages, accessory sex organs, weapons of offense and defense, silk spinning, and egg laying. Perhaps more than any other factor the enormous diversity of the phylum can be attributed to the many ways in which arthropods have made use of their appendages. Not the least of these limb modifications is the distinctive use of the appendages behind the mouth for the formation of jaws, so that some authorities (e.g., E. R. Lankester) have thought the group should be called "gnathopoda." After all, locomotion and feeding methods have played an enormous role in the development of their morphologic patterns.

PHYLOGENETIC RELATIONSHIPS

As stated in a former section, arthropods are generally believed to have originated from annelids or annelidlike ancestors. This view is supported by both morphologic and embryologic evidence, but direct transition forms between the two phyla are not known. The Precambrian fossil worm *Spriggina*, found in South Australia, had similarities to early trilobites, such as parapodia that could well be the forerunners of arthropod appendages. The nature of the arthropod ancestor must be largely speculative from present knowledge, but it may have been a form with an unsegmented head (acron) and a segmented trunk with paired appendages on each segment except the telson. Little differentiation was found in both segment and appendage. Whether the primitive appendage was biramous or uniramous is an unsettled controversy. Terrestrial arthropods have uniramous appendages, and their embryology supports this plan. Arthropods such as primitive crustaceans usually have biramous or phyllopod appendages, but this pattern may be specialized instead of primitive. However, there is no embryologic evidence to support an ancestral phyllopodial appendage in any arthropod.

Three major lines of evolution seem to have occurred in the phylum: the Trilobita, Chelicerata, and Mandibulata. Each of these is usually assigned a subphylum rank. The oldest known arthropods are the extinct trilobites. They were the dominant forms in the Lower Cambrian, Ordovician, and Silurian periods. They survived to the Permian period. Adapted for crawling and swimming, they supposedly descended from a Precambrian stock (Protoarthropods) that was ancestral to all the arthropods. According to some authorities, the Protoarthropoda gave rise to three branches—the Prototrilobita, the Protocrustacea, and the Protomyriapoda. The Prototrilobita is considered the oldest branch of the three. From the trilobites came the Xiphosura (extant) and the extinct Eurypterida, which are the first of the Chelicerata. The Xiphosura date from the middle Paleozoic era or Ordovician period. The Eurypterida existed from the Cambrian to the Permian periods. The oldest known Arachnida are the scorpions, which are often considered the "land-living cousins" of the eurypterids. They date from the Silurian period. The major changes in the evolution of the Chelicerata were the transformation of gills to book lungs and to tracheae, the loss of compound eyes, reduction of the abdominal legs, and fusion and differentiation of segments. There is also a tendency for the anterior segments to fuse with the acron to form a composite head.

Spiders date as fossils back to the Late Palaeozoic era. Their origin is very obscure, but some authorities think that they too may have come from scorpion stock. Their intense specialization of certain abdominal appendages as spinnerets may have originated from the habit of laying their eggs in silky threads. Some Arachnida, such as the Pycnogonida, depart so radically from the chelicerate body (the lack of cephalothorax, the nature of their long walking legs, vestigial opisthosoma, etc.) that they cannot be related directly to other groups of arthropods.

The Mandibulata, or Antennata, differ from the chelicerates mainly by having antennae as the most anterior appendages and mandibles as biting and chewing jaws. The mandibles may be variously modified, such as piercing stylets or cutting blades.

The Mandibulata are represented by crustacean fossils from as early as the Cambrian period. This extensive group probably arose in Precambrian time from a stock that had both trilobite and crustacean characteristics. Crustaceans are by far the most extensive group of the Mandibulata. It is very difficult to appraise the origin and evolution of the protocrustaceans, which, by adaptive radiation, gave rise to one of the more successful groups in the animal kingdom. Crustaceans demonstrate such a diversity of the basic pattern of the class that it is not always possible to distinguish between what is primitive and what is specialized. The strong possibility exists that divergence within the group began quite early in their evolution. There seems to be no question, however, that some of them are far more primitive than others, such as the cephalocaridans and anostracans. Many show closer interrelationship with some than with others. Of the important subclass Malacostraca, evolution indicates two important trends, one toward a differentiation of the integument into carapace and abdomen, and the other toward the more primitive uniform segmentation.

Of the other mandibulates, the insects probably represent more different species than all other animals combined. Their closest affinities seem to be with the Symphyla. Fossil insects have been found in many rock formations, the earliest being rocks of the upper Carboniferous age. Many wonderful insect fossils have been found in the Baltic amber, a fossil resin of a coniferous tree. Their evolution presents a very diversified fauna, from wingless forms similar to the present order Thysanura to the more specialized winged orders. The most distinctive feature of the class as a whole is the usual presence of two pairs of wings, which arose from lateral outgrows of the dorsal plates in the thoracic region. They represent true "creative evolution," because insect wings are not homologous with any appendages of other arthropods.

Phylum Arthropoda: the trilobites and chelicerates

Subphylum Trilobita (Trilobitomorpha)

Trilobites are considered the most primitive of all arthropods. They had a wide distribution in the Cambrian and later periods but are now wholly extinct, having died out by the end of the Paleozoic era. Their fossils are common in limestone and sandstone deposits, and they apparently inhabited the shallow Paleozoic seas. There were several kinds of trilobites, ranging in size from a fraction of an inch to 27 inches, although most were between 1 and 3 inches.

The body was oval, flattened, and three lobed because of two lengthwise dorsal furrows (Figs. 23-1, 23-2, *B*). The dorsal surface was covered by a chitinous and mineral exoskeleton that also extended over the side. This exoskeleton was molted at intervals to allow the trilobite to increase in size. For a long time only this dorsal surface was discovered, and little was known about the ventral surface and appendages. Specimens were eventually found with the ventral surface exposed, and the structure of the limbs has been ascertained (Fig. 23-2, *A*).

The body was divided into a head region, or cephalon, composed of four or five fused segments, with a head shield somewhat semicircular in shape; a thorax, or trunk region, of a varying number of free segments, each of which was made up of a convex tergal piece and a pair of lateral plates (pleura); and a terminal region or tail (pygidium) of fused segments, also variable in number (Fig. 23-1).

The mouth was located on the midventral region of the cephalon (Fig. 23-3, *A*), which also usually bore a pair of compound eyes on the pleural region or cheeks. A pair of many-jointed antennae was placed on the sides of the forelip (hypostoma). The other appendages were all similar in structure. Four pairs of these were placed in the head region and one pair each on the segments of both the trunk and pygidium. Each appendage was two branched (biramous) and was made up of an inner seven-jointed branch or telopodite (walking leg) and an outer epipodite bearing a fringe of bristles (Fig. 23-3, *B*). Both branches of an appendage arose from a single coxal segment that bore a lobe (gnathobase). The gnathobases are thought by some authorities to have been used to seize and grind the food. In the region of the pygidium the appendages were smaller. The appendages lacked specializations, although the epipodites may have functioned as gills. The anus was situated at the posterior end of the pygidium. Many structural differences are found in trilobites.

Trilobites appear to have been bottom dwellers, although some were adapted for swimming. Some trilobites may have been planktonic. They fed upon small organisms they could seize and master. When disturbed, they could bury themselves in the mud or they could roll themselves into a ball. They have never been found in Mesozoic or more recent geologic deposits.

Trilobites have had a varied evolution, with their greatest development in the late Cambrian and early Ordovician periods. Only one family survived to the end of the Paleozoic era. Theories of their relationships fluctuate between the crustaceans on the one hand and the Arachnida on the other. The recent discovery of *Hutchinsoniella* (order Cephalocarida) in 1954, with its trilobite characteristics of primitive, unspecialized appendages, may indicate a link between the crustaceans and the trilobites. As additional evidence, *Hutchinsoniella* is the only crustacean with a seven-jointed endopodite—a trilobite characteristic.

The early development of some trilobites is fairly well known. The early larval form

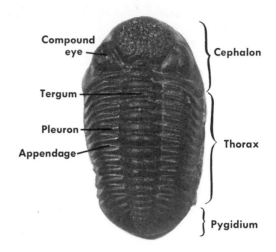

Fig. 23-1

Fossil cast of *Phacops* (middle Devonian period). These arthropods have been found in Silurian to Devonian rock in both North America and Europe.

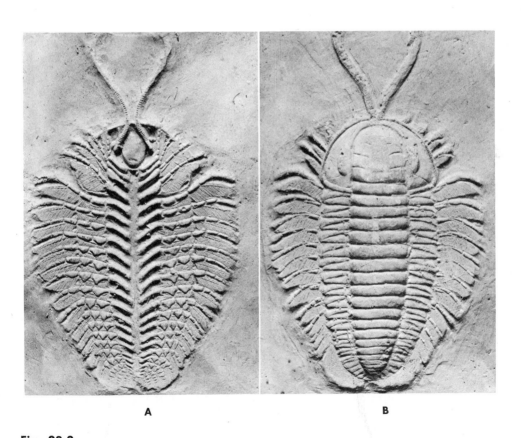

A

B

Fig. 23-2

Cast of *Triarthrus,* an Ordovician trilobite. **A,** Ventral view. **B,** Dorsal view.

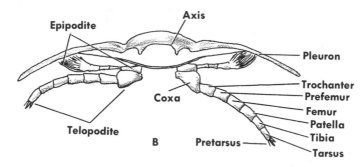

Fig. 23-3

A, Diagrammatic longitudinal midsection through axis of trilobite. **B,** Diagrammatic transverse section through trilobite showing attachment and segmentation of legs.

has only indications of a head and pygidium (Fig. 23-4, *A, B*). Between these two regions new segments are developed from the front end of the pygidium in succession (Fig. 23-4, *C* to *F*). Several molts occur during this development. The evidence indicates that the pygidium is older than the thorax or trunk region.

Subphylum Chelicerata
CLASS XIPHOSURA

Fossils of horseshoe crabs have been found as early as the Devonian period, although some relatives of the group date as far back as the Cambrian period.

These ancient relics have the body divided into three divisions—the horseshoe-shaped prosoma (fused head and thorax), the segmented opisthosoma, and the spike-like tail (telson). The members of this group were characteristically found in shallow, brackish water, and their fossil record extends back to the Cambrian period. Four or five species and three genera are found living today. Their distribution is restricted to the Atlantic coast and to certain Indo-Pacific regions. The three genera are *Xiphosura (Limulus)* (Figs. 23-5 to 23-9), *Carcinoscorpius,* and *Tachypleus.*

Xiphosura (Limulus) polyphemus, the horseshoe crab, is the most familiar member of the group. Its distribution is along the Atlantic coast and the Gulf of Mexico. It reaches a length of 2 feet or more and its body is covered by a dark brown carapace, horseshoe shaped and dorsally convex. The posterior lateral angles of the carapace extend backward on each side of the abdomen. Joined to the cephalothorax is the broad abdomen (opisthosoma), with six spines on each side (Fig. 23-6, *A*). The sharp, triangular telson consists of fused tergites, or dorsal plates, of certain abdominal segments. The dorsal surface of the carapace has a median and two longitudinal ridges. Two lateral compound eyes and two median simple eyes are present on the carapace. Altogether there are 15 segments more or less fused together in the body.

The prosoma bears five pairs of walking legs in addition to the chelicerae on the underside of the cephalothorax (Fig. 23-6, *B*). Each walking leg (except the last) consists of a coxa, a prefemur, a femur, a tibia fused with a patella, and two tarsal segments, which form chelae (Fig. 23-7).

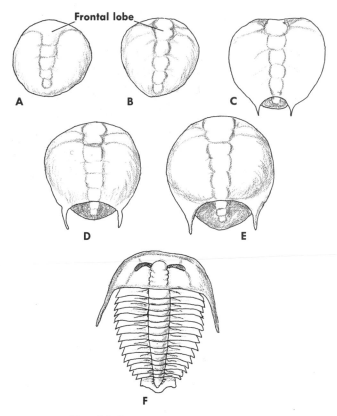

Fig. 23-4

Developmental stages of trilobite *Olenus,* an upper Cambrian trilobite. **A** and **B,** Protaspis stages, representing only head, or cephalon, of adult. Four divisions of glabella correspond to four pairs of head legs. **B,** Frontal lobe divides to form frontal lobe and free cheeks of adult. **C** to **E,** Small region behind cephalon generates new somatic segments, each new somite being added between last one and pygidium. **F,** Mature *Olenus.* (**A** to **E** after Störmer; redrawn from Snodgrass: Arthropod anatomy, Comstock Publishing Associates.)

The coxae of the first four pairs of walking legs are provided on the median side with spines that act as gnathobases for macerating the food. The coxae of the last pair of legs have flat processes (flabella) for cleaning the gills and for clearing away debris during burrowing.

The abdomen, or opisthosoma, bears seven pairs of appendages. The first pair, called chilaria and often considered to be the last pair of cephalothoracic appendages, is found between the coxae of the fifth pair of walking legs (Fig. 23-6, *B*). The second pair is fused medially to form a genital operculum, a membranous flap, on the underside of which are the two sexual apertures (Fig. 23-6, *C*). The last five pairs of appendages are modified as book gills. They also are flaplike and membranous, and on the underside each bears more than a hundred leaflike folds, or lamellae (Fig. 23-6, *C*). Movement of the gills circulates the water over the respiratory surfaces and also provides propulsive power for the animal, the gills serving as paddles.

The endoskeleton is made up of a connective tissue plate (endosternite) in the cephalothorax between the esophagus and the midgut, a number of endochondrites on the floor of the opisthosoma, and ectodermal invaginations (apodemes). Attached to these processes and to the carapace are paired and single muscles that move the cephalothoracic appendages. In addition, other muscles move the book gills and the telson.

The digestive system consists of a ventral mouth just behind the labrum or upper lip, an esophagus, a muscular gizzard, a

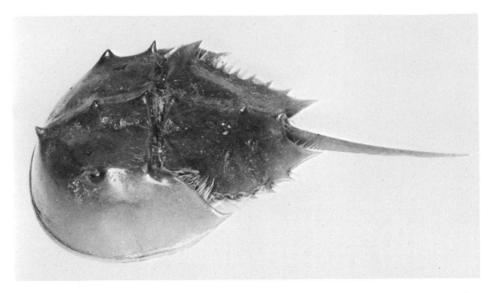

Fig. 23-5

Xiphosura, commonly called horseshoe crab or king crab.

midgut separated from the gizzard by a valve, and a short rectum that opens with an anus at the end of the abdomen (Fig. 23-8). A pair of large digestive glands (hepatic ceca) in the cephalothorax open by two pairs of ducts into the enlarged anterior part of the midgut. Horseshoe crabs live on mollusks and other organisms. Food is seized by the chelae of the appendages, macerated by the gnathobases, and passed to the mouth. Large indigestible particles are regurgitated through the esophagus and mouth. Ingested food is ground up in the gizzard, and the fine food particles are passed into the midgut where they undergo enzymatic action. The food is then passed into the digestive glands where further digestion and absorption occur. Digestion may be partly intracellular as well as extracellular. Indigestible particles are returned to the midgut and egested through the short rectum and anus.

Excretion occurs through two pairs of coxal glands or modified nephridia that are found in the cephalothorax near the gizzard. The glands open to the outside at the base of the coxae of the last pair of walking legs. Coxal glands can be distinguished by their red color.

Horseshoe crabs have a heart, arteries,

and veins (Fig. 23-8). The dorsal tubular heart is situated in both the cephalothorax and abdomen. It has eight pairs of dorsoventral slits, or ostia, which serve as valves. The posterior end of the heart ends blindly. Blood is sent from the heart through a short aorta, which branches into three large arteries that carry blood to the carapace and to the sides of the gut where they open into the ventral arterial sinus. From the ventral sinus, blood is supplied to the book gills where it is oxygenated. Four pairs of lateral arteries also lead from the heart and supply blood to organs in the cephalothorax and abdomen. A median dorsal abdominal artery runs along the entire length of the telson. A number of paired veins carry the blood from the gills to the pericardium that surrounds the heart. From the pericardium the blood passes into the heart through ostia. Although provided with arteries and veins, the blood system is an open one.

Respiration occurs in the book gills through hundreds of thin, leaflike lamellae (Fig. 23-6, *C*). Here gaseous exchange occurs between the blood in the lamellae and the surrounding water. The blood contains the pigment hemocyanin, which imparts a blue color to it.

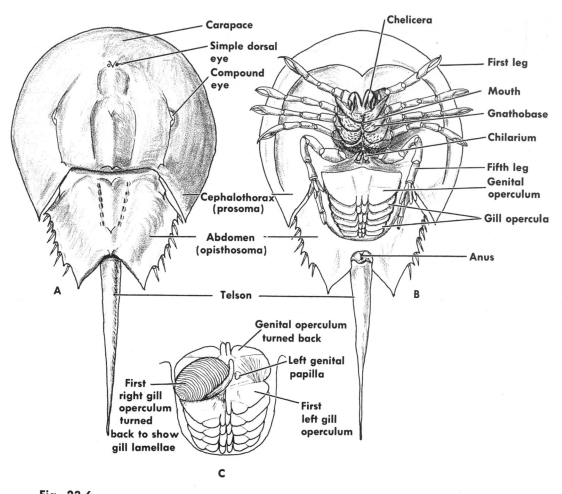

Fig. 23-6

Xiphosura. **A,** Dorsal view. **B,** Ventral view. **C,** Abdominal appendages, with genital operculum and one of gill opercula turned back to show gill lamellae.

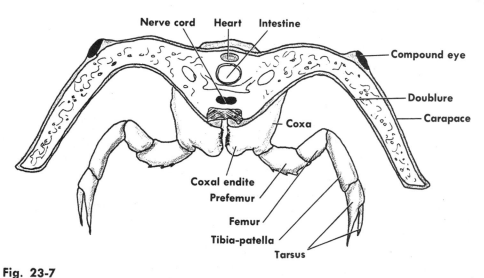

Fig. 23-7

Diagrammatic transverse section through prosoma of *Xiphosura.*

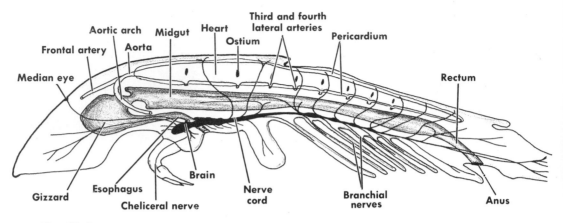

Third and fourth lateral arteries · Pericardium · Rectum · Heart · Ostium · Midgut · Aortic arch · Aorta · Frontal artery · Median eye · Gizzard · Esophagus · Cheliceral nerve · Brain · Nerve cord · Branchial nerves · Anus

Fig. 23-8

Diagram of sagittal section through *Xiphosura*.

The entire nervous system of horseshoe crabs is enclosed within the ventral sinus (Fig. 23-8). The brain forms a compact ring around the esophagus. Only the protocerebrum forms the brain. Part of the nerve ring is composed of fused ganglionic masses that give off nerves to the thoracic appendages. From the nerve ring a ventral nerve cord, with paired ganglia enclosed in the longitudinal sinus, runs posteriorly. Each ganglion gives off an anterior motor and a posterior sensory nerve. Sense organs are represented by a pair of median ocelli and a pair of compound eyes. Rudimentary ocelli and compound eyes are also found. The compound eyes are uniquely constructed in that the ommatidia are made up of clusters of retinal cells with no intervening pigment. Taste buds may also be found in the gnathobases.

The sexes are separate, and the plan of the reproductive system is the same in both male and female. The reproductive glands form a sort of network of tissues—a pair of vasa deferentia in the male and a pair of oviducts in the female. These ducts open to the outside at the base of the genital operculum. No copulatory organs are present, but the males can be distinguished by the enlarged basitarsus of the first pair of legs. Mating occurs by a sort of amplexus, with the male holding on to the female carapace by the aid of hooks from his first pair of feet. As the eggs are discharged by the female into a scooped out depression in the sand, the male discharges his sperm over them. The eggs, which are about 3 mm. in diameter, are laid in batches of 200 to 300. In some places (e.g., Delaware Bay) spawning coincides with the new or full moon.

Eggs are centrolecithal and cleavage is total. Hatching usually occurs within two weeks, although it may be delayed. The newly hatched larva resembles a trilobite (Fig. 23-9) and is mostly incomplete in

Fig. 23-9

Trilobite larva of *Xiphosura*, so called because of superficial resemblance to trilobites.

the development of its systems. Molting occurs many times during the first years of its life. Three years are required for the crabs to reach sexual maturity, although full maturity is not reached until much later. Like the adults, the young at all stages swim on their backs.

The body cavity of *Xiphosura* is a hemocoel and is derived from the fusion of several coelomic pouches. The cavity extends into all appendages.

CLASS EURYPTERIDA

These primitive arthropods are wholly extinct, but they flourished from the Cambrian period to the end of the Paleozoic era. They are commonly known as giant water scorpions. Their elongated and lanceolate body, encased in a chitinous exoskeleton, was divided into a prosoma (cephalothorax) and opisthosoma (abdomen) (Fig. 23-10). The cephalothorax had a pair of marginal compound eyes and a pair of centrally located ocelli. They share many similar characteristics with the horseshoe crabs. Usually, the appendages of the cephalothorax consisted of one pair of chelicerae, four pairs of walking legs, and one pair of paddlelike swimming legs. There were many variations among the different species. The bases of the appendages around the centrally located mouth were provided with masticatory organs.

Unlike that of the horseshoe crabs, the abdomen of eurypterids consisted of twelve separate segments, seven of these forming the mesosoma (preabdomen), which bore appendages, and five forming the metasoma (postabdomen) without appendages. The terminal telson probably had a poisonous sting. There were six pairs of abdominal appendages. The first pair formed the operculum and the other five pairs made up the gills.

Many eurypterids were less than 1 foot long, but some reached a length of 9 feet. Although much of their evolution occurred in marine and brackish water, they also invaded fresh water. Mostly they were bottom crawlers, but some could probably swim. They seemingly had a close affinity to the trilobites, from which both the xiphosurids and eurypterids apparently descended. Eurypterids may have left no direct descendants, but one theory holds that

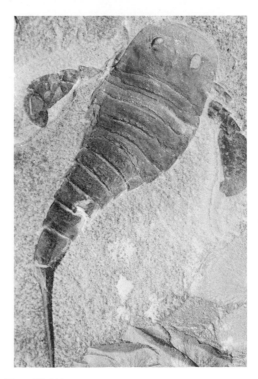

Fig. 23-10

Eurypterus. Eurypterids flourished in Europe and North America from Ordovician to Permian periods. (From Hickman: Integrated principles of zoology, The C. V. Mosby Co.)

they were the ancestors of the great class Arachnida (Fig. 23-11).

Among the common fossil genera are *Pterygotus, Carcinosoma,* and *Eurypterus* (Fig. 23-10).

CLASS PYCNOGONIDA (PANTOPODA)

Pycnogonids are commonly known as sea spiders because of their long legs and spiderlike form (Fig. 23-12). About 600 species are known. They are mostly small forms not over 10 mm. long, although some of the deep-sea forms may reach a length of 2 feet. Their body is greatly reduced, consisting of cylindric trunk and segments that support the appendages. They are also provided with a proboscis on the head (cephalon), with gonopores on the second joints of the legs, and a much reduced abdomen. The posterior part, or neck, of the

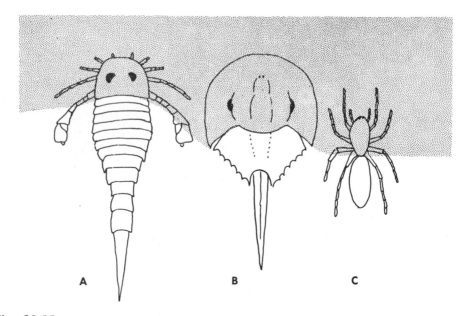

Fig. 23-11

Body divisions of chelicerates. **A,** Eurypterid. **B,** Xiphosurid. **C,** Spider. Shaded area denotes prosoma; white area shows opisthosoma.

Fig. 23-12

Anoplodactylus lentus, a pycnogonid (preserved specimen).

cephalon has on its dorsal surface four eyes on a tubercle. The trunk usually consists of four to six segments, of which the first is fused to the cephalon (Fig. 23-13, *A*). In some pycnogonids there are seven pairs of legs, of which the first four—chelifores (chelicerae), palps, ovigers, and first pair of walking legs—are on the ce-

phalic segment. Each of the other trunk segments bears a single pair of legs. Some species are known to have 12 legs. Some genera may lack chelifores, palps, and other structures. The palps are located just behind the chelicerae and bear sensory hairs. The ovigerous legs are used by the male to carry the eggs and are reduced or absent in the female.

Each of the walking legs has eight segments. The legs are longer in those forms that have reduced bodies. The proboscis bears a three-cornered mouth at its end (Fig. 23-13, *B*).

Pycnogonids are carnivorous animals that suck out the juices of their prey, such as corals, bryozoans, and sponges. The chelicerae are used for seizing and carrying their prey to the mouth. The digestive and reproductive systems extend into the legs. Digestion is intracellular in the walls of the intestine, which opens into a short rectum with the anus at the end of the abdomen. The nervous system is made up of a dorsal brain, circumesophageal ring, paired ventral ganglia, and ventral nerve cords. The circulatory system is open and consists of a dorsal tubular heart with

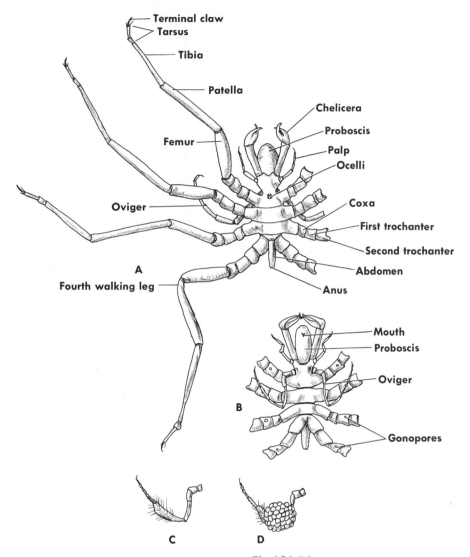

Terminal claw
Tarsus
Tibia
Patella
Chelicera
Proboscis
Palp
Ocelli
Femur
Oviger
Coxa
First trochanter
Second trochanter
A
Abdomen
Fourth walking leg
Anus

Mouth
Proboscis
B
Oviger
Gonopores

C   D

Fig. 23-13

Nymphon, a pycnogonid. **A,** Female, dorsal view. **B,** Female, ventral view. **C,** Ovigerous leg of male pycnogonid. **D,** Ovigerous leg of male, carrying eggs. (Modified from Snodgrass.)

a hemocoel which is divided into dorsal and ventral parts. Blood flows from the hemocoel into the legs and is returned to the heart by the dorsal hemocoel. Excretory and respiratory organs are absent.

In reproduction the male fertilizes the eggs as they pass from the female and collects the eggs into masses on his ovigerous legs (Fig. 23-13, *C, D*). Glands on the femurs of these appendages form a secretion for attaching the egg masses.

Sea spiders are more common in the cold waters of the Arctic and Antarctic seas than they are elsewhere, although they are found in all seas. They may be found from littoral or intertidal zones down to depths of several thousand meters. Some are ectoparasites on hydroids and other forms. Their exact relationships are very obscure, although their structures indicate that they are chelicerates.

Common genera of Pycnogonida include *Nymphon* (Fig. 23-13), *Pycnogonum,* and *Anoplodactylus* (Fig. 23-12). A Devonian fossil species, *Palaeopantopus,* is known.

CLASS ARACHNIDA

The arachnids are the most important of all the chelicerates. They are the spiders, scorpions, ticks and mites, harvestmen, and some lesser known types. Most are terrestrial forms, although a few mites are aquatic. Their general distinguishing characters are four pairs of thoracic legs, tracheae or book lungs for breathing (but no gills), simple eyes (ocelli), the first pair of appendages (chelicerae), and the second pair (pedipalps), which are variously modified. They have a chitinous exoskeleton and a body that is divided into two portions—an unsegmented cephalothorax (prosoma) and an abdomen. The prosoma is covered dorsally by a carapace, and on its ventral side there are sternal plates and coxae of the appendages. In its primitive condition the abdomen is divided into a preabdomen and a postabdomen, but this distinction is lost in most forms. The abdomen is composed of 12 segments which may be modified in various ways. A telson is found in some. In many arachnids, segmentation is more or less lost by fusion of segments. The segmentation of the cephalothorax is hard to determine but probably consists of 9 segments, thus making a total of 21 segments the typical number in Arachnida. The sternites, which cover the ventral surface of the abdomen, may also be fused so that they may be fewer in number than the dorsal tergites. There are many variations among the different groups. In some arachnids the tergites may be fused to form a single dorsal plate with the carapace. The cephalothorax may be broadly joined to the abdomen, or the two divisions may be joined by a narrow pedicel.

Of the six pairs of cephalothoracic appendages, the chelicerae are either two or three jointed. They may bear pincers (chelate) for holding and crushing prey, but they may also bear other structures, such as poison fangs, intromittent organs for transferring sperm, spinnerets, etc. The second pair (pedipalps) is built on the same plan as the legs but usually has only six joints. They may also vary and have different functions, serving as intromittent organs, for crushing food, as pincers, as sensory organs, and other functions. The four pairs of walking legs are typically seven jointed; and each is composed of a coxa, trochanter, femur, patella, tibia, metatarsus, and tarsus. In some arachnids the coxae are provided with gnathobases.

The endoskeleton consists of an endosternite (mesodermal in origin) and apodemes (ectodermal invaginations), variously modified. The complex muscular system is made up of many muscles for moving the numerous body parts, such as the cephalothoracic appendages, digestive specializations, abdomen, and spinnerets.

Although most arachnids are carnivorous, they possess no mandibles. They commonly predigest their food in the mouth and then suck the juices into the stomach. Their digestive system is made up of foregut, midgut, and hindgut (Figs. 23-16, 23-22). The foregut and hindgut (ectodermal) are lined with chitin, which is shed at each molt. Digestion is completed in the midgut. The three digestive parts are modified in the different groups. In some forms the foregut consists of a pharynx, which may serve as a pump and a sieve; an esophagus; and a gizzard, which may also serve as a pump. The midgut, or mesenteron, has cells for absorption and for producing enzymes; it is provided with lateral diverticula, which become filled with partially digested food. Some food is stored in the interstitial tissue. The hindgut has a short rectum, which opens by an anus at the end of the abdomen.

Excretion in arachnids chiefly occurs through a pair (or sometimes two pairs) of coxal glands in the cephalothorax and also through Malpighian tubules in the abdomen. Coxal glands are modified nephridia or saclike structures, which open at the coxae of the appendages. The position of the outlet varies. The waste is absorbed into the gland from the blood. Many arachnids have one or two pairs of long Malpighian tubules that arise at the junction of the hindgut and the midgut. These tubules pick up guanin crystals (one of the end products of nitrogenous metabolism) and discharge them into the alimentary canal, or the crystals may be stored in special cells. Some arachnids may have one or the other or both types of excretory organs. Some excretory substances may be picked up by special cells (nephrocytes). Most arachnids have a dorsal tubular heart within a pericardium (mostly in the abdomen) and arteries to various parts of the body (Figs. 23-16, 23-22). The heart may be segmented to coincide with the segmentation of the abdomen. Ostia, or funnel-shaped openings with valves, allow blood to enter the heart from the pericardium. True capillaries and veins are absent. From the heart the anterior aorta follows the gut in the cephalothorax, bifurcates, and sends a branch on each side of the gut under the endosternite. Here they open into a sinus that feeds arteries to the appendages. In the abdomen the heart gives off lateral arteries and a posterior artery to the abdominal region. Blood collected in the ventral sinus bathes the book lungs and is conducted back to the heart by tissue sinuses. Hemocyanin, a copper-bearing compound, is the respiratory pigment in the blood plasma of some arachnids.

Arachnids have book lungs or tracheae (sometimes both) for breathing (Figs. 23-15, 23-23). The number of book lungs varies from one to four pairs. The book lungs may be invaginations of the ventral abdominal wall and are actually groups of leaf tracheae, as compared with ordinary tubular tracheae. A book lung is made up of leaflike lamellar folds of one side of the wall through which air circulates and oxygenates the blood in the lamellae. One part of the book lung is in the form of an air chamber, which contracts and dilates by muscular action, thus sucking in and expelling air. The book lung opens to the outside by a spiracle. The tracheae are homologous to and may be derived from book lungs. Their spiracles are usually paired and may open directly into the main tracheal tubes, or they may open first into chambers. The main tracheal trunks divide and subdivide into smaller and smaller tubes, which eventually deliver the air to fluid-filled and branching tracheoles that pass the oxygen directly to the tissue cells. The tracheal tubes are lined with cuticle, usually in the form of spirals (Fig. 23-23, *C*).

The central nervous system is typically made up of a dorsal brain and a ventral chain of paired ganglia, usually one pair to each segment. The forebrain, or protocerebrum, furnishes nerves to the chelic-

erae. In many arachnids the abdominal ganglia of the ventral nerve cord migrate anteriorly and fuse with the subesophageal ganglia, forming a ganglionic mass or ring-like structure. Often some of the posterior ganglia are lost completely. In some arachnids with primitive nervous systems each fused ganglion of the ventral chain sends two pairs of nerves to each of its original segments, but such a pattern has been greatly modified in the various groups.

Sense organs in arachnids are represented by simple eyes, the corneal lens of which is lost or shed with the rest of the cuticle at each molt. The shape of the lens may be spherical, oval, or even triangular. The photoreceptors of the retina may be oriented toward the source of the light (direct eyes) or toward the postretinal membrane or reflector (indirect eyes) (Fig. 23-24). Photoreceptors may or may not be separated by pigment. The number of eyes varies greatly in the different orders. Many arachnids are totally blind. The sense of touch is well developed and is mediated by sensory hairs all over the body, especially on the appendages. One type of sensory hair (trichobothrium) can detect air currents and thus presumably may function in audition. Slit organs, or special pits in the cuticle, may have a function in olfaction, as mechanoreceptors, or vibration receptors. Some arachnids stridulate, thus producing sounds.

Arachnids nearly always have separate sexes, although there are rare exceptions in the order Acari. The genital opening in both sexes is located on the second abdominal sternite. The gonads are found in the abdomen and may be single or paired. Copulatory organs exist in a great variety of forms. The males of some arachnids have a tubular penis, and others make use of pedipalps or other appendages as copulatory organs (Fig. 23-19). Long, retractile ovipositors also occur. With the exception of the scorpions and some Acari, all arachnids are oviparous.

Order Scorpionida

The distinguishing characteristics of this arachnid order are the large chelate pedipalps, which are always kept in a forward position; the abdomen, which is divided into a broad portion and a slender,

357

Fig. 23-14

Centruroides, a scorpion.

segmented portion; and the terminal caudal sting (Fig. 23-14). Although they vary
in size from less than 1 inch up to 7 inches,
they all have these basic characteristics.

Scorpions are tropical or semitropical
forms, which in general prefer arid or
desert regions, although they may be found
in some humid areas. They are found on
all continents but are absent from such islands as New Zealand. There are about
650 species, 40 of which are found over a
large portion of the United States. Arizona
and California appear to have the largest
number of species.

Scorpions in their natural habitat live
under stones, in crevices, under bark of
trees, under rubbish, in open fields and
woods, and almost anywhere that provides
hiding places for them. In tropical countries they enter houses and often become a
nuisance. As they are sensitive to moisture,
they stay underground in dry seasons but
emerge during a wet period and live under
rocks and other hiding places. They are
solitary in their habits and are never
found in associations.

The body is made up of a prosoma, or
cephalothorax, of a single piece and an
abdomen, or opisthosoma. The abdomen
consists of two divisions—an anterior preabdomen (mesosoma) of seven segments
and a postabdomen (metasoma) of five
segments. The preabdomen is as wide as
the cephalothorax, while the postabdomen
is slender with a curved sting at its end.
The prosoma is relatively short and four
sided. It is covered by an unsegmented
carapace on which are located a median
pair and two to five lateral pairs of eyes.
The cephalothorax bears a pair of small
chelicerae in front of the mouth, a pair of
large pedipalps, and four pairs of walking
legs. Each of the walking legs has seven
segments and two pairs of claws. The segments of a leg are a coxa, trochanter, prefemur, femur, tibia, basitarsus, and tarsus
complex with the claws. The first two pairs
of walking legs have their coxae provided
with plates and glands that secrete digestive enzymes.

On the ventral surface of the second abdominal segment behind the last pair of
legs are the paired pectines, each of which
consists of three rows of chitinous plates
and a series of toothlike projections (Fig.
23-15). The teeth of the pectines bear
sense cells that may be used by the male
to touch the ground and select a suitable
mating site, or they may be used to explore the surface over which he crawls.

A single, slender sternite covers the ventral surface of the cephalothorax between
the coxae of the walking legs. Each of
the seven preabdominal segments is covered by a tergal plate, and the ventral
surface is covered by a sternal plate. The
genital aperture, covered by the genital
plate (Fig. 23-15), is located on the ventral side of the first abdominal segment.
On the second segment a small basal
piece articulates laterally with each of the
pectines. On the undersurface of the preabdomen and along the lateral regions of
the third to sixth sternites are four pairs of
slits (spiracles), which serve as openings
to the book lungs.

The sternite, pleurites, and tergites of
each segment of the postabdomen are
fused together in a ring. The anus is placed
on the ventral side of the last segment. The
base of the sting is enlarged and contains
a pair of poison glands that open near
the tip of the sharp, curved spine. The

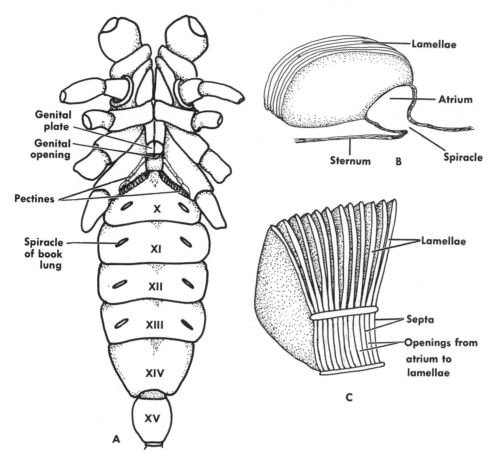

Fig. 23-15

A, Ventral view of scorpion *Pandinus* (appendages and most of postabdomen not shown). B, Vertical section of book lung of scorpion. C, Ventral view of book lung showing openings into lamellae from atrium. (Modified from Snodgrass.)

scorpion thrusts forward the tail over its back to inject the venom from the sting into its victim. The most dangerous scorpions in North America are members of the genus *Centruroides* (Fig. 23-14) found in Arizona, New Mexico, and Mexico, where they have been responsible for some deaths, especially among children. Other scorpions are poisonous enough to kill prey but are not harmful to man. Their poison is mostly neurotoxic.

Scorpions live mainly on small arthropods, especially insects. They seize their prey with the pincers of their pedipalps, sting it, and macerate it with their chelicerae. They then discharge digestive fluids with enzymes over the soft parts and suck the predigested food into the mouth by the pharynx, which acts both as a pump and a strainer. After passing through the esophagus, the food enters the midgut and the large digestive glands (Fig. 23-16), where it is subjected to further digestion and absorbed by special cells. The indigestible part is discharged through the anus. Scorpions can exist many months without food or water.

The circulatory system (Fig. 23-16) is made up of a seven-segmented heart in the preabdomen, several pairs of ventrolateral arteries to regions of the preabdomen, and various venous channels. The book lungs (four pairs) are placed in the ventral blood sinus, where the gaseous exchange between oxygen and carbon dioxide takes place. The oxygenated blood then

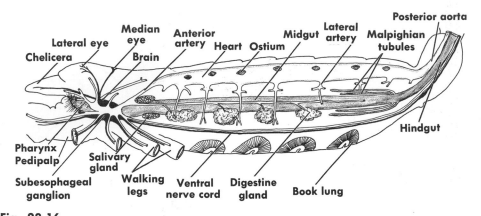

Fig. 23-16

Internal structure of scorpion. Diagrammatic sagittal section of cephalothorax and preabdomen. (Modified from Leuckart.)

passes to the pericardium of the heart. Excretion occurs through the paired coxal glands, which open on the coxae of the third pair of legs, and through the Malpighian tubules which discharge into the gut.

The nervous system of scorpions (Fig. 23-16) consists of a brain, a ventral nerve cord with seven ganglia, and nerves that innervate various regions of the body. In addition to the eyes and the pectines already mentioned, scorpions have other sense organs, such as the special tactile hairs (trichobothria) on the femur, tibia, and pedipalps.

Although there are only slight differences between the male and female, the male is usually more slender and has a longer tail region. His copulatory organs (hooklike structures) are found on the opercular plates on the ventral side. The reproductive organs of each sex open by a ventral aperture on the second abdominal segment. The gonads are similar in both sexes and are located between the midgut diverticula in the preabdomen. From each group of ovarian tubules a short oviduct leads to a single genital atrium. Each oviduct may have a dilated seminal receptacle. The testes are also made up of tubules, and the paired vasa deferentia also empty into a common genital atrium. There is a complicated courtship pattern in which the male seizes the female pedipalps with his

own pedipalps and undergoes a sort of dance made famous first by Fabre, and later by Walt Disney in one of his nature films. The male then deposits a spermatophore on the ground, which is picked up by the female vulva. In some scorpions the two sexes may actually copulate by bringing their ventral surfaces together. As in spiders, the female has been known to devour the male after copulation.

The fertilized eggs develop inside the lumen of the ovarian tubules, and the young are born alive (ovoviviparous). The eggs are telolecithal with meroblastic cleavage. In some scorpions the young are nourished internally by maternal secretions from a tube attached to the diverticulum (viviparous). The eggs of viviparous forms have little yolk and show equal, or holoblastic, cleavage. As soon as they are born, the tiny young climb on the back of the mother, often completely covering her since they may number several dozen. While on her back they get their nourishment from embryonic yolk. The period of gestation may be from 6 to 15 months. Growth occurs by molting, the first molt occurring while the scorpion is still on its mother. Adulthood is attained in about a year.

Order Amblypygi

These arachnids are commonly known as the tailless whip scorpions. They are flattened, crablike animals that are found in tropical and the warmer temperate regions. They occur in the United States in some of the southern states and in the Southwest as well as in California. Altogether there are some 50 to 60 species. They are reddish brown in color and have a body divided into a prosoma covered with an undivided carapace and an abdomen of 12 segments. Their pedipalps are heavy and adapted for grasping and crushing prey (mostly insects). The first pair of legs is long and sensory in function. Their whiplike appearance is the basis for the common name for these animals. The other three pairs of legs (each of seven segments) are used for locomotion. The chelicerae have a movable claw. No tail is present. The carapace bears a pair of median eyes and three small eyes on each side. Other sense organs are represented by lyriform organs or chemoreceptors for taste and smell found on the chelicerae. No poison glands or repellent organs are present. They have two pairs of book lungs which lie in the second and third abdominal segments. Excretory organs are coxal glands and Malpighian tubules. So far as is known, they have no elaborate courtship pattern. The 50 to 60 eggs are carried by the mother attached to the underside of her abdomen, where they hatch and where the young undergo a first molt.

The Amblypygi prefer semidesert and somewhat humid regions. They live under stones, logs, and leaves during the day. Some are found in caves. They vary in length from 4 to 45 mm. *Acanthophrynus* and *Charinus* are common genera.

Order Uropygi

The uropygids are known as the tailed whip scorpions and have about 70 species. They are found mostly in tropical and semitropical regions of Asia and the Americas. In the United States and Mexico a common species is *Mastigoproctus giganteus*. Some species do not exceed 2 to 3 mm. in length, and some, such as *Mastigoproctus* (Fig. 23-17, A), may reach 65 mm.

The prosoma of their flattened bodies may be single or divided. The chelicerae are small, two jointed, and provided with a hooklike fang. The six-jointed pedipalps are thickened, with strong spines, and adapted for grasping prey, while the first

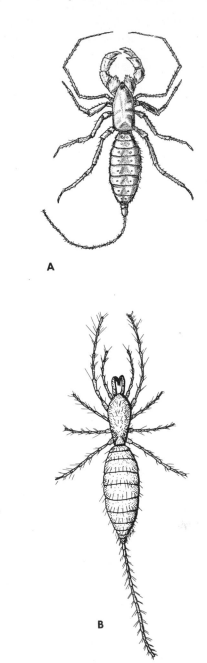

Fig. 23-17

A, American whip scorpion, *Mastigoproctus giganteus,* a uropygid. B, *Koenenia,* a palpigrade. (B after Hansen and Sörensen; redrawn from Snodgrass: Arthropod anatomy, Comstock Publishing Associates.)

pair of legs is very long, secondarily segmented, and modified as feelers. Their long whiplike shape give the common name to the group. The other three pairs of legs are unmodified.

The abdomen is made up of 12 segments, of which the first and the last three are not as wide as the others. At the terminal end of the abdomen is the many-jointed flagellum. In the smaller species the flagellum is short and composed of few segments. They have two pairs of book lungs on the ventral side of the second and third abdominal segments. At the base of the tail there is a pair of large anal glands which expel a liquid with the strong odor of acetic or formic acid when the animal is disturbed. This fluid acts as a repellent against potential enemies and serves also in catching insect prey. They do not have poisonous glands. Excretion is by coxal glands and Malpighian tubules. Some have one pair of median and three pairs of lateral eyes; in others, median eyes are absent and lateral eyes may or may not be present. The heart has five to nine pairs of ostia in the different species. A ganglionic mass is usually found in both the thoracic and abdominal regions.

Uropygids display an elaborate courtship pattern like that of scorpions. They are oviparous, and the female lays about 35 eggs in a subterranean brood chamber. The young remain with the mother until after the second molt.

They feed mostly on insects and are nocturnal in their habits. They prefer dark places and burrow in the ground, especially in damp humus soil. *Schizomus,* and *Thelyphonus,* in addition to *Mastigoproctus,* are well-known genera.

Order Palpigradi

Palpigrades are small, whitish, eyeless forms which never exceed 3 mm. in length (Fig. 23-17, *B*). They all belong to one family of about 20 species. They have been found in tropical and hot temperate regions in all the continents. A few species are present in Texas and California.

The body is made up of three divisions—prosoma, abdomen (opisthosoma), and flagellum. The carapace is divide into three plates (propeltidium, mesopeltidium, and metapeltidium). The chelicerae are three

jointed and prominent. The pedipalps are used as walking legs, while the first pair of legs serves as sensory appendages and are vibrated to test the substratum since these forms are eyeless.

The abdomen contains 11 segments with transparent tergites and sternites. The last three segments are small, annular, and progressively reduced in size. The 15-jointed flagellum is provided with lateral setae. There are no book lungs. Some of the sternites bear eversible ventral sacs, which may serve in respiration. Excretion occurs by a pair of coxal glands. The nervous system contains an abdominal ganglionic mass in the second abdominal segment.

Palpigrades live mostly under stones, but in extreme drought they burrow deeply within the soil. Practically nothing is known about their feeding habits or their reproduction. Egg laying seems to occur at all seasons. *Koenenia* (Fig. 23-17, *B*) and *Prokoenenia* are two of the known genera.

Order Araneae

This order, which is made up of spiders, is one of the most extensive groups of arachnids. Spiders are found in most regions of the world and in almost every kind of habitat and represent one of the oldest of all groups. Their fossils, or evidences of their existence, date back to Devonian and Carboniferous times. Wherever found, their populations may reach enormous sizes in small areas. Because of their interesting habits and natural history, spiders have attracted the interest of biologists since man began to study animals. The number of species known to science is estimated between 28,000 and 50,000. In size they may be as small as 0.4 mm. or as large as 4 inches in length. They differ from other arachnids by having one or more of the following characteristics: chelicerae, usually with poison fangs; book lungs, tracheae, or both; spinnerets in all; pedipalps in male as copulatory organs; and unsegmented abdomen in most.

GENERAL STRUCTURE. The body of a spider is divided into a cephalothorax and an abdomen, which are connected by a slender pedicel. The head and thorax may be slightly separated by the cervical groove.

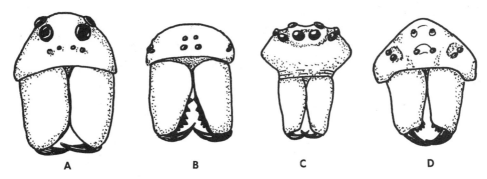

Fig. 23-18

Front view of several spider carapaces showing chelicerae and eye arrangement. **A**, *Lycosa carolinensis*. **B**, *Araneus*. **C**, *Theridion*. **D**, *Argiope trifasciata*.

The hard integument that forms the dorsal wall of the cephalothorax is called the carapace. The body is covered with chitinous plates, which often bear accessory structures such as spines and tubercles.

The eyes, located near the front end of the head region, are all of the simple type, or ocelli. They are usually arranged in two rows of four each, although there may be fewer or none at all (Fig. 23-18).

Spiders have six pairs of cephalothoracic appendages. The first pair is called the chelicerae, or jaws, each of which consists of a basal piece and a slender distal fang. The duct of the poison gland opens at the tip of the fang. A few spiders have lost their poison glands. The second pair of appendages is the six-segmented pedipalps. The pedipalps differ from the legs in having no metatarsus. The male pedipalps are modified in various ways as copulatory organs (Fig. 23-19). In male spiders the tarsus of the pedipalps contains a coiled tube, which is often found in a bulblike enlargement of the tarsus. In the female the pedipalp is used only as an organ of touch and manipulation. Each leg consists of seven segments, and each of the four pairs of legs undergoes some variations in the different families. These differences of relative lengths, related sense organs, kinds and number of claws, etc. are of adaptive significance as well as of taxonomic importance.

The large saclike abdomen is usually without a trace of external segmentation, except in a few forms that have up to 12 segments. Many variations are found in the shape as well as size of the abdomen. The narrow pedicel that connects the abdomen to the thorax is usually concealed when viewed from above. On the ventral side of the abdomen the anterior, often densely chitinized, portion is called the epigastrum, and the crescent-shaped furrow that separates the epigastrum from the caudal part of the abdomen is known as the epigastric furrow. Openings of the reproductive organs are situated in the middle of this furrow, and a spiracle at each end of the furrow opens to a book lung.

The spinnerets are modified appendages of the fourth and fifth abdominal embryonic segments (Figs. 23-22, 23-23, A, B). They are found on the ventral surface anterior to the anus. There are usually six spinnerets, but the number varies from four to eight; eight is the primitive number. Each spinneret is a conical projection, enclosing many duct openings at the ends of the spinning tubes. Different kinds of silk are spun out of different types of glands within the abdomen. The silk of spiders is a scleroprotein of a fine, elastic, and strong character. Spiders spin several kinds of silk, each with special qualities. No one spider spins all the kinds recognized, but most species spin at least four or five types. The silk is produced as a fluid, but hardens under the pressure of being drawn out as well as exposed to the air. The complex web of the orb-weaving spiders (Fig. 23-20) is made up first of a rectangular or irregular framework of silk within which radial threads are spaced like spokes in a wheel from the center of the net. These

363

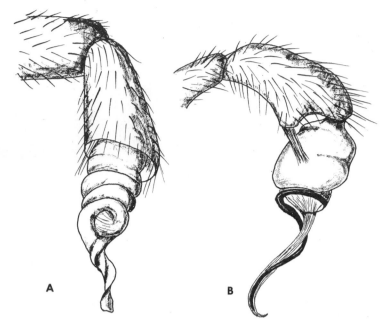

Fig. 23-19

Male pedipalps. **A,** *Filistata hibernalis.* **B,** *Hypochilus thorellii.* (Modified from Comstock.)

Fig. 23-20

Web of orb-weaving spider. Starting with "bridge thread," framework of boundary threads is made of dry silk, usually an irregular four- or five-sided figure. Radii of dry silk are spun next, then functional spiral of sticky viscid silk. Spider working inward from rim to hub is careful to walk only on nonsticky radii. (From Hickman: Integrated principles of zoology. The C. V. Mosby Co.)

threads are nonviscid. The spiral viscid threads are fastened in concentric patterns to these radiating threads (Fig. 23-21). The spider carefully does its traveling on the nonviscid threads. In certain spiders a sieveplate, the cribellum, lies anterior to the spinnerets; from this plate a banded silk is extruded.

Spiders use silk in many ways. Although all spiders have spinnerets, not all of them make webs for ensnaring prey. Most of them use silk for other purposes, such as draglines for marking their course, sperm webs by the male before copulation, gossamer threads for ballooning, lining for burrows, hinges for trap doors, cocoons or egg sacs, attachment disks, swathing bands for binding prey, and many others. All spiders form draglines as they run about.

The alimentary canal (Fig. 23-22) exhibits the typical arthropod plan of foregut, midgut, and hindgut. The foregut is a stomodeum consisting of the pharynx, esophagus, and sucking stomach. The mouth cavity is between the bases of the pedipalps, the coxae of which form the sides of the cavity. A liplike structure, the so-called rostrum, lies at the top of the mouth region; and a lower lip, the labium, is at the bottom. The wall of the sucking stomach is strengthened by chitin as a firm support for the attachment of the powerful muscles that extend to the inner surface of the carapace and to the endosternite.

Fig. 23-21

Enlarged view of small portion of a nonviscid, inelastic radius and two viscid spiral threads of spider web.

Sphincter muscles are also found close to the stomach. The midgut (mesenteron), with its diverticula, or ceca, constitutes a large part of the abdomen and thorax. A bladderlike diverticulum, the stercoral pocket, is found on the dorsal side of the hindgut and serves as a reservoir for fecal material.

Spiders are carnivorous. Their food consists mostly of insects and other arthropods. Some of the larger members are also known to feed on birds, small fishes, and other vertebrates. The mouth lacks mandibles. When the prey is caught (by web or otherwise), it is bitten and in some spiders is macerated by the chelicerae. Hairs of the labium and endites of the pedipalps act as strainers for coarse particles. After some predigestion of food in the mouth, the pharynx and sucking stomach draw the liquefied food into the gut. Although voracious, many spiders can endure long fasts.

A much-branched Malpighian tubule opening into the midgut on each side and a pair of reduced coxal glands serve for excretion (Fig. 23-22). Some primitive spi-

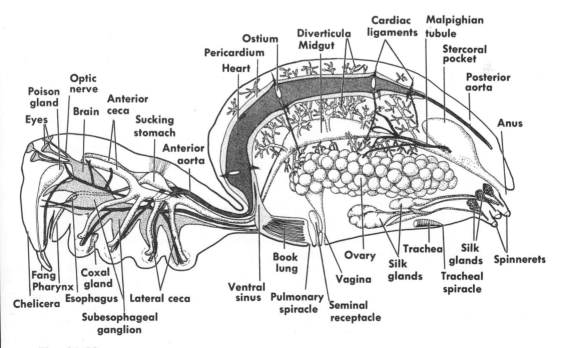

Fig. 23-22

Diagram of internal structure of female two-lunged spider. (Modified from Comstock.)

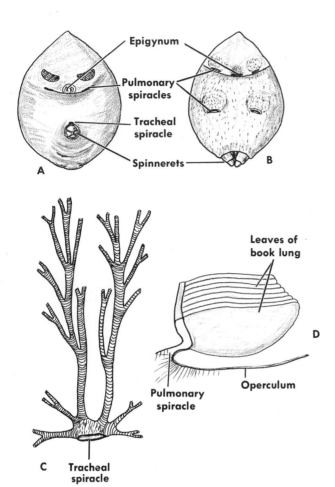

Fig. 23-23

Respiration in spiders. **A,** Abdomen of *Argiope,* with one pair of book lungs and one pair of tubular tracheae. **B,** Abdomen of tarantula, with two pairs of book lungs. **C,** Pair of tubular tracheae, with single spiracle. **D,** Vertical section of book lung.

ders have two pairs of coxal glands. The wall of the gut may also be involved in excretion.

Respiration takes place by book lungs and tracheal tubules (Figs. 23-22, 23-23). Some spiders have only one of these types, but most have both. Usually there is only one pair of book lungs, but there are two pairs in tarantulas. The openings of the book lungs are slitlike clefts on the ventral side of the abdomen. In some spiders the anterior book lungs also may be transformed into tracheae. There is usually only a single tracheal spiracle which is placed,

in most cases, just in front of the spinnerets. There are two pairs of tracheal tubules which are highly variable in their distribution and branching in the different species.

The circulatory system of spiders (Fig. 23-22) is an open one, for the blood courses partly in the hemocoel. The heart is in the dorsal part of the abdomen above the gut and has two to five pairs of ostia. The primitive condition appears to be five pairs, but tracheate spiders have two pairs exclusively. The heart is a simple tube which is not divided into chambers. Anterior and posterior aortae, as well as lateral abdominal arteries, extend from the heart. The heart is surrounded by a thin-walled sac, the pericardium. Cardiac ligaments hold the heart in position. Blood is carried from the book lungs to the pericardium by "pulmonary veins," or ventral sinuses, which are really hollow ligaments.

In most spiders the central nervous system is concentrated in the cephalothorax (Fig. 23-22). The ganglia in general are consolidated into a mass around the esophagus. The brain is the dorsal part of this mass, and the subesophageal ganglion is the part below. A visceral nervous system of scattered ganglia is connected with a median single nerve to the pharynx or paired nerves to the brain. Of the eight eyes most spiders possess, the anterior median eyes are of the direct type, while the others have an indirect retina (Fig. 23-24). Indirect eyes have a tapetum for reflecting the light rays. The direct eyes may be provided with muscles. The eyes of hunting and jumping spiders are better developed for the formation of sharp images than those of most spiders.

Spiders differ sexually from most other animals in having a male copulatory apparatus separate from the reproductive system. The reproductive system of each sex is located in the abdomen (Fig. 23-22). The female has two elongated ovaries, a pair of oviducts, a uterus, and a vagina (Fig. 23-25). In addition there are usually two pouches (seminal receptacles) that are associated with the vagina. In most spiders the seminal receptacles open by little tubes into the vagina and also to the outside by external openings, so that the female has three external openings—the opening of the

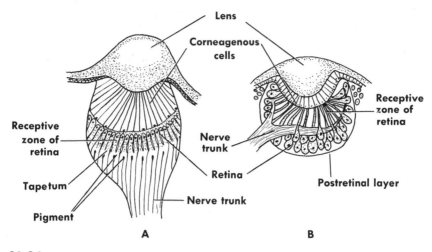

Fig. 23-24

A, Structure of indirect eye *(Lycosa agricola)*. B, Structure of direct eye *(Tegenaria derhami)*. (Modified from Widmann, 1908.)

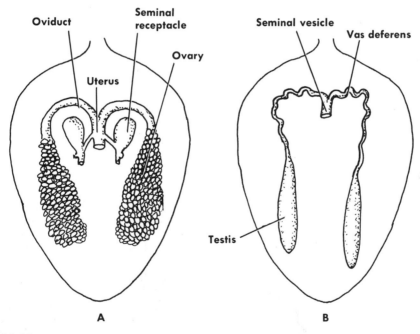

Fig. 23-25

Reproductive organs of spider. **A,** Female. **B,** Male.

vagina and the two openings of the seminal receptacles. The ovaries are tubelike and bear ovarian follicles like bunches of grapes, especially during the breeding season when the ovaries are greatly distended. Ripe eggs rupture into the lumina of the ovaries and are carried by the oviducts to the common uterus and vagina. The external openings of the vagina and two seminal receptacles open on a chitinized plate, the epigynum, which is found in front of the epigastric furrow on the mid-

367

ventral line of the body. Sperm from the male is stored in the seminal receptacles until the time of egg laying, at which time the eggs are fertilized.

In the male the reproductive organs consist of a pair of testes, a pair of sperm ducts (vasa deferentia), and a common ejaculatory duct, or seminal vesicle, which opens to the exterior at the same place on the body as the genital openings of the female (Fig. 23-25). The male copulatory organ, as mentioned, is not connected with the reproductive system; the seminal fluid is transferred to the female by means of the specialized male pedipalps (Fig. 23-19). The tarsus of each pedipalp is modified in various ways in different spiders. One of the simplest types of copulatory organ is a bulb with a curved spout or embolus. Inside the bulb there is a reservoir for the sperm, with a tube that opens at the end of the embolus. To fill its reservoir, the male first ejects a drop of its semen into a silk web, and then transfers it into the opening of the embolus. During the mating process the copulatory apparatus is distended by blood engorgement, and the male inserts the embolus into one of the seminal receptacles. That the male copulatory organ is fitted only for the epigynum of its species—the "lock-and-key" theory—is held by some authorities. Since the smaller male is often eaten by the female, the process of mating may be quite dangerous to the male, so that elaborate courtship patterns have evolved. Courtship patterns between the male and female vary with different spiders.

Some species lay relatively few eggs and others large numbers. Some females deposit all their eggs at one time, and others lay their eggs in several batches, each enclosed in an egg sac. The egg sac, or coccoon, is more or less peculiar to each species and may in some even serve to identify the species. Some females guard the cocoons in their retreats or burrows; others carry the sacs along with them; while others have nothing to do with the cocoon after it is formed. The young spiders hatch in the sac, where they stay until after the first molt. Various types of maternal care are found among spiders, from those that take no care to those that stay with the young for a long time and some who even carry their young on their backs.

There is no metamorphosis during growth, and the young differ from the parents mainly in size. Growth occurs by a series of molts, highly variable in number among the various species. At the final molt the sex organs are mature. In a few of the larger, long-lived species the females may even molt after sexual maturity. Regeneration of lost parts is possible only if there are still molts to undergo. Some spiders live for only a single season, but others (some of those kept in captivity) live for many years.

With a few exceptions, the poison glands of all spiders are constructed on the same plan (Fig. 23-22). The gland is located either in the basal segment of the chelicera or else in the cephalothorax proper, with its duct opening at or near the tip of the fang. The flow of poison is voluntarily controlled by the spider. All spiders may use their poison in defense or when trying to escape. Only a few spiders are very dangerous to man. The black widow (*Latrodectus mactans*) is perhaps our most dangerous one. The poison seems to be neurotoxic in its action, bringing on severe pain, high pressure of the cerebrospinal fluid, muscular spasms, and finally respiratory paralysis. The venom of *Lycosa raptoria,* a Brazilian wolf spider, and of *Loxosceles reclusa* in our own southern states is hemolytic rather than neurotoxic, producing a necrosis of tissue around the bite. The large tarantulas are mainly inoffensive.

SOME CHARACTERISTIC FAMILIES OF SPIDERS

Authorities are far from agreeing on the way spiders should be classified. Each revision of the order Araneae usually shows a marked tendency to increase the number of families. Most of the 60 odd families are found in two suborders—Mygalomorphae and Araneomorphae.

Suborder Mygalomorphae

This suborder includes about eight families to which the trap-door spiders, tarantulas, and purse-web spiders belong. The members of this suborder have paraxial chelicerae, i.e., with the fang movable in the anterior-posterior plane of the body (Fig. 23-26, *B*), two pairs of book lungs

(Fig. 23-23, *B*), and usually four spinnerets.

Family Ctenizidae—Trap-door spiders. These spiders make burrows in the ground, line the burrow with silk, and close the entrance with a hinge lid (Fig. 23-27). Lid and entrance are artfully concealed by vegetation. Their chelicerae are adapted for digging. They are found in the southern and western United States. *Bothriocyrtum californicum* (Fig. 23-28) is a common species in California.

Family Theraphosidae (Aviculariidae)—Tarantulas. These hairy spiders of large size are common in the western and southwestern states. Although venomous, their bites are relatively harmless to man. The tarantulas in America (Fig. 23-29) should not be mistaken for what is called a tarantula, actually a wolf spider, in southern Europe. Tarantulas have been known to live more than 20 years. Some species live in shallow holes, which they dig with their fangs and pedipalps. They are often associated in groups of a dozen or more. About 30 species are found in the United States.

Suborder Araneomorphae

Most of the common spiders in the United States belong to this suborder. About 49 families are included in this group. These spiders have diaxial chelicerae, i.e., articulating at right angles to the long axis of the body (Fig. 23-26, *A*); one pair of book lungs; usually one pair of tracheal spiracles; and six spinnerets (some with cribellum).

Family Argiopidae (Araneidae)—Orbweavers. Most members of this family form circular or orb webs, often of beautiful geometric design (Fig. 23-20). The plane of the web may be vertical, horizontal, or at any angle. The frame and radii are constructed of nonviscid threads, whereas the main spiral threads are viscid (Fig. 23-21). Many of the species have bright patterns, such as the common garden spider, *Argiope aurantia*, which has yellow, reddish, and black colors (Fig. 23-30).

Family Agelenidae—Funnel-web or grass spiders. These spiders form a web that has a tube or funnel with a platform on which the insect is seized. When the prey is caught, the spider retreats with it into the

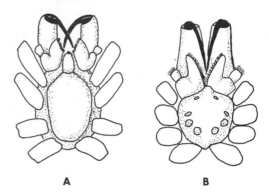

A **B**

Fig. 23-26

Types of chelicerae. **A,** Diaxial, *Dysdera crocata.* **B,** Paraxial, *Atypus milberti.* (Modified from Kaston.)

Fig. 23 -27

Entrance to burrow of trap-door spider. (From Hickman: Integrated principles of zoology, The C. V. Mosby Co.)

Fig. 23-28

Bothriocyrtum californicum, the common trap-door spider of California. (Redrawn from McCook: American spiders and their spinning work, Academy of Natural Science.)

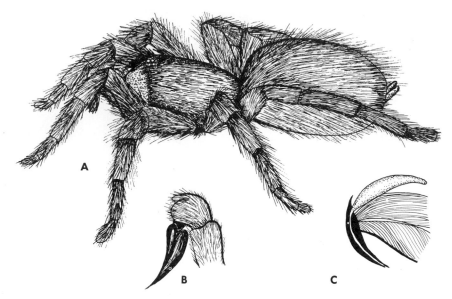

Fig. 23-29

A, *Dugesiella hentzi,* the tarantula common in our western and southwestern states. **B,** Male pedipalp of tarantula. **C,** Fang of tarantula with poison gland and muscles. (**A** redrawn from Kaston and Kaston: How to know the spiders, William C. Brown Company, Publishers; **B** and **C** modified from Baerg.)

Fig. 23-30

Argiope aurantia, the black and yellow garden spider.

funnel. The common genus *Agelenopsis* (Fig. 23-31) can be recognized by the long hind spinnerets that extend posteriorly. In addition to the horizontal sheet or platform the spider spins a sort of labyrinth or stopping maze above the funnel for hindering the flight of insects and causing them to fall upon the platform. The spider apparently catches the insect by its own rapid and deft movements, since the web is not composed of viscid shreads.

Family Salticidae (Attidae)—Jumping spiders. Jumping spiders (Fig. 23-32) build no snare, but by their keen eyesight they stalk their prey and suddenly spring upon it. They also spin retreats for molting, hiding, and other purposes. Their front legs are often unusually heavy and are used in pinning down the prey. There are many species in the family, especially in the southern climates. In the tropics many of them are brightly colored.

Family Pisauridae—Fishing spiders. These spiders do not spin webs for ensnaring but catch their prey by hunting. The genus *Dolomedes* (Fig. 23-33) lives near the water and is known to catch small minnows

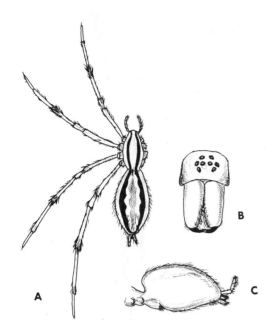

Fig. 23-31

Agelenopsis, the grass spider. **A,** Dorsal view. **B,** Front view of carapace. **C,** Abdomen, side view, showing spinnerets.

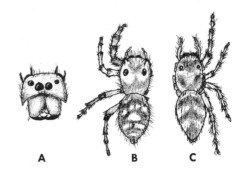

Fig. 23-32

Jumping spiders (family Salticidae). **A,** Front view of carapace of *Phidippus.* **B,** Dorsal view of *Phidippus.* **C,** Dorsal view of *Salticus*

Fig. 23-33

Dolomedes tenebrosus (family Pisauridae).

as well as aquatic insects. The members of this family can usually be seen around ponds or else running over aquatic vegetation.

Family Lycosidae—Wolf spiders. These common spiders are often found running through the grass of pastures or among the leaves of the forest floor. Wolf spiders (Fig. 23-34) are usually stoutly built, with eyes that are unequal in size (Fig. 23-18, *A*). They can be spotted at night with a flashlight because their light-colored eye tapetum reflects some of the light to the observer. The female carries her globular egg sac attached to the spinnerets. Some species (burrowing wolf spiders) build burrows. Three common genera are *Lycosa, Pirata,* and *Pardosa.*

Family Theridiidae. These spiders build irregular snares and suspend themselves upside down while awaiting their prey. The family includes one of the most poisonous members of the spider group—the black widow (*Lactrodectus,* Fig. 23-35). The black widow has a globose, shiny black abdomen, with an hourglass-shaped reddish mark on the underside. Variations of abdominal markings are common. Although far more prevalent in the southern sections of the United States, this species has been found in every state and in most Canadian provinces as well.

Order Solpugida (Solifugae)

These arachnids are often called sun spiders and occur mostly in dry tropical and

371

Fig. 23-34

Huntsman spider (family Lycosidae).

Fig. 23-35

Black widow, *Latrodectus* (family Theridiidae). Note "hourglass" on her abdomen. (From Hickman: Integrated principles of zoology, The C. V. Mosby Co.)

warm temperate regions. Most solpugids are from 10 to 50 mm. in size, although some may be larger. About 60 of the 200 known species are found in the southwestern states.

The most striking feature of these arachnids is the enormous chelicerae, which do not possess poison glands (Figs. 23-36, 23-37, *C*). The chelicerae are two jointed, with the pincers articulating vertically. The pedipalps are simple, leglike, nonchelate, and terminate in an adhesive organ (Fig. 23-36). These appendages seize the prey and pass it to the chelicerae which hold and crush the prey.

The carapace of the prosoma is made up of three plates which represent the terga of the first six somites; the anterior of the three plates is the largest. The carapace bears anteriorly one pair of median eyes and obsolete lateral eyes. The first pair of legs is tactile, and the other three pairs

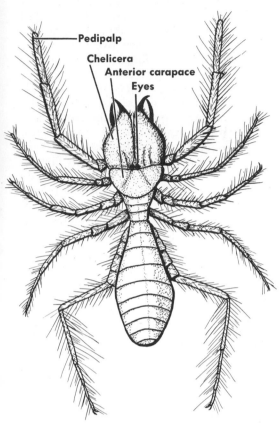

Fig. 23-36

Eremobates cinerea, a solpugid. (After Putnam; redrawn from Comstock: The spider book, Doubleday & Company, Inc.)

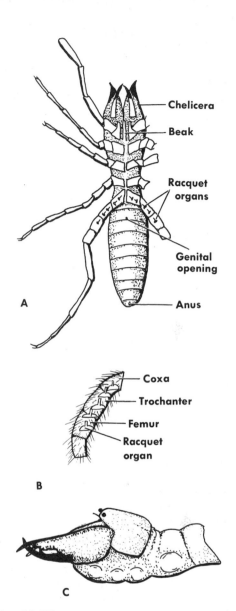

Fig. 23-37

A, Ventral view of *Eremobates formicaria* (order Solpugida). **B,** Portion of fourth leg of *Eremobates* showing racquet organs. **C,** Cephalothorax of *Galeodes,* side view, showing massive chelicerae. (**A** modified from Petrunkevitch.)

are ambulatory. The abdomen is made up of 10 or 11 segments, which are plainly visible. The animal has no book lungs; but there are seven ventral, slitlike spiracles, which open into a well-developed tracheal system. The paired spiracles are located between the second and third coxae and on the third and fourth abdominal segments. A single median spiracle may occur on the fifth segment. Excretion takes place by a pair of coxal glands in the prosoma and by a pair of Malpighian tubules. A heart with eight pairs of ostia is placed partly in the cephalothorax and partly in the abdomen. The nervous system consists of both a thoracic and an abdominal ganglionic mass. On the last pair of legs are the characteristic racquet organs. These are T-shaped sense organs, of which there are

five on the ventral side of each leg (Fig. 23-37, *A, B*).

After a courtship ritual, in which the female is thrown into a trancelike condition, the male transfers his sperm into her genital orifice. The female lays her eggs in bur-

Fig. 23-38

Pseudoscorpion. (From Hickman: Integrated principles of zoology. The C. V. Mosby Co.)

rows, where she remains until after they are hatched. The solpugids are among the most agile of all arachnids and are mostly nocturnal in their habits.

Eremobates (Fig. 23-36) in the southwestern states and *Galeodes* (Fig. 23-37, *C*), an Old World form, are common genera.

Order Pseudoscorpionida

These arachnids derive their name from their resemblance to scorpions; however, they have no postabdomen or sting (Fig. 23-38). Most of them are between 4 and 10 mm. in length. They live in forest debris, leaf mold, nests of birds, mammals and insects, beneath bark, under stones, in barns, and among books. One genus occurs on marine algae. Their food is chiefly small arthropods, such as mites and small insects. Fossil pseudoscorpions similar to present-day forms have been found in Baltic amber. The form of their appendages may indicate a relationship to true scorpions, but the presence of a pregenital segment (which scorpions lack) indicates an ancestor common to both groups. About 800 to 1000 species have been described.

The prosoma is covered by a single dor-

sal shield or carapace and contains six fused segments. One or two pairs of eyes are present, although some species are blind. The chelicerae are two jointed and chelated, and each finger of the pincers bears a serrula of plates. Near the end of the movable finger, ducts of silk glands lead to a spinneret, or galea, located in the prosoma. The pedipalps are the largest and most conspicuous of all the appendages. They are chelated, with a poison gland opening by a duct on one or both fingers. All the coxae meet in the median line. The four pairs of walking legs are all similar; each leg has two claws, between which there is an adhesive pad. The legs have an additional joint (trochantia) between the trochanter and femur.

The abdomen is composed of 11 or 12 visible segments and is rounded at the terminal end. There are two pairs of tracheal spiracles on the ventral side of the third and fourth abdominal segments. Book lungs are lacking. Excretion takes place by a pair of coxal glands that open on the coxae of the third pair of walking legs. The heart has two or three pairs of ostia. The nervous system is concentrated in the cephalothorax.

The opening of the reproductive organs is between the second and third abdominal sterna. The gonads are single in both sexes. In the males, near the genital aperture, are genital sacs, which in some forms can be extended (the "ram's horn organs") and may be used to excite the female. In mating, the male deposits a spermatophore on the ground after an elaborate courtship display. The female is induced by the male to pick up the sperm with her genital orifice. The eggs and larval forms are carried on the underside of the female abdomen. Maturity is reached in about a year, after several molts.

The silk that is spun by the chelicerae is used to make a sort of cocoon in which the pseudoscorpion molts and hibernates. The serrulae of the chelicerae are used in forming the cocoon.

Pseudoscorpions eat their prey as most arthropods do—by sucking the juices and predigested tissues into the mouth and esophagus after the chelicerae have torn open the exoskeleton and macerated the tissues. Among the typical genera are

Chthonius (in caves) and *Chelifer* (in books and households).

Order Ricinulei (Podogona)

This small group of arachnids of some 20 species has been found in tropical Africa and in the New World from Texas to the Amazon River. Their fossil records indicate that they were more common and more widespread formerly than now. Their size range is around 4 to 10 mm. in length, and they resemble ticks in general appearance (Fig. 23-39).

The prosoma is covered by a shieldlike carapace in two divisions of different sizes, the smaller one in front. The anterior part articulates with the posterior one and can be raised and folded over the mouth and chelicerae like a hood. Both the chelicerae and pedipalps are chelate. The basal segments of the pedipalps are united in the middle line below the mouth. There are no eyes. There is no visible segmentation in the cephalothorax. The walking legs of the female are similar, except that the first pair is shorter and the second pair is longer than the others. The number of joints is variable, and their tarsi have two claws. In the male the third pair of legs is modified into peculiar copulatory organs that may be used in the transfer of spermatophores to the female. The cephalothorax at the posterior end also bears the tracheal

Fig. 23-39

Cryptocellus, male (Ricinulei). (After Hansen and Sörensen; modified from Cambridge Natural History.)

tubes which open by spiracles above the third coxae. There are no book lungs.

The abdomen is connected by a movable, membranous joint to the prosoma, although the narrow pedicel, which connects the two divisions, is not apparent; only a shallow groove appears to separate the two, as seen dorsally. The segments of the abdomen are fused.

The reproductive organs open between the first and second abdominal segments, but little is known about the copulation and development of ricinuleids except that they are oviparous and have a six-legged larva at one stage. Their natural habitat is not known to any extent. Some have been collected from leaf molds and such places.

Order Phalangida (Opiliones)

The members of this order include the daddy long-legs, or harvestmen (Fig. 23-40). They range in length from about 1 to 15 mm. This order has a worldwide distribution but is most abundant in moist tropical regions. There are more than 3,000 species. The cephalothorax and abdomen are joined together without a furrow between them. The carapace is a single shield with a median tubercle, on each side of which there is an eye. The stout chelicerae have three joints and are chelated, and in some forms they are comparatively long. The pedipalps are leglike but shorter and are also provided in some species with pincers. The legs are long and slender, which is their most distinctive feature. In walking, the body appears to be suspended from the long arched legs. The legs are made up of seven segments, but the tarsus in some forms is subdivided. The coxae of the pedipalps and first and second pairs of legs, each bear an anterior process (endite). The abdomen appears to consist of about 10 segments, only some of which are visible. A single pair of tracheal tubes opens on the second abdominal sternite. Secondary spiracles are found on the legs of certain species. Book lungs are lacking.

Near the anterior margin of the cephalothorax close to the attachment of the first pair of legs are the openings to a pair of scent glands. They produce a material with a strong, pungent odor. Excretion is by means of a pair of coxal glands that open

375

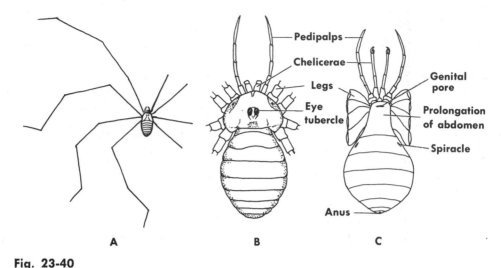

Fig. 23-40

Phalangida, commonly called harvestmen, or daddy longlegs. **A** and **B**, Dorsal views. **C**, Ventral view.

on each side between the third and fourth coxae. The heart is provided with two pairs of ostia, and the nervous system is highly concentrated in the cephalothorax.

The reproductive organs open in the region between the cephalothorax and the abdomen. The genital openings are on a plate (operculum), which in some cases covers the genital orifices. In the female there is an ovipositor, a tubular organ that is retracted into a sheath or sac when not in use. The ovipositor can be extended a long distance when laying eggs. The male is provided with a large penis, which can be injected into the genital orifice at copulation. Eggs are laid in the ground or in crevices of wood by the ovipositor. Eggs laid in the fall do not hatch until the following spring. After the first molt the young are white, but they gradually acquire the color of the adult.

The phalangids have a varied diet of soft-bodied insects, both living and dead, and will also eat vegetable matter. Plant lice seem to be one of their favorite foods. Food is seized by the pedipalps and passed to the chelicerae which macerate it. In addition to fluid the phalangids eat some coarse particles.

In temperate climates most harvestmen die in the autumn, although in warmer regions they undergo hibernation. They often get into human habitations and are common in barns and outbuildings. They are most active at twilight and usually remain in hiding during the day. Familiar genera include *Phalangium* and *Leiobunum*.

Order Acarina

This diverse order includes ticks and mites; mites are the largest in number. There are so many species of them, of which only a fraction (about 20,000 species) has been described, that it is impossible to estimate the number even approximately. They exist in many morphologic patterns. In some ways they are the most important economic group of arachnids because of their parasitic habits, their destruction of crops useful to man, and their role as vectors of disease germs. They have a worldwide distribution. Several hundred species of Acarina have been described in the United States, but their taxonomy is a difficult one. Acarina vary in size from less than 1 to 30 mm. in length with ticks as the largest members of the group.

Since the body divisions do not correspond to those of the other arachnids, different names have been assigned to them. The body is commonly divided into an anterior gnathosoma and a posterior idiosoma. The gnathosoma is made up of the

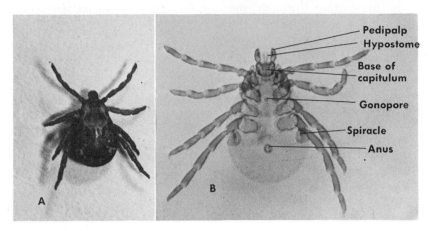

Fig. 23-41

Wood tick *Dermacentor* (order Acarina). **A,** Dorsal view. **B,** Ventral view.

first two segments, which include the mouth region and its parts, while the idiosoma includes the rest of the body. The so-called abdomen of mites includes the typical arachnid abdomen plus the last two thoracic segments. These two divisions are often imperceptibly fused together, producing a more or less saclike globular body. Many mites have transverse, fine lines that give a false impression of segmentation.

The head region with the mouthparts is called the capitulum. A dorsal projection of the body wall forms a rostrum (tectum), or beak. The basal segments of the pedipalps may be fused together to form a lip or labium (hypostome), with a labrum above (Fig. 23-41). With other structures, these processes may form an oral tube, through which the chelicerae are projected. The chelicerae usually consist of two segments and may be chelate. However, these organs are variable. Many are needlelike for piercing. The pedipalps consist of five segments. They vary according to function. They may be simply tactile organs, or they may be large and chelate for predation. The four pairs of walking legs are each made up of six segments, with the tarsus bearing a pair of claws. The legs may be modified in various ways, depending upon the kind of mites and their habits.

Most mites breathe by tracheal tubes, but some lack tracheae and breathe through the general body surface. The spiracles

(one to four pairs) are located near the base of the appendages in the anterior half of the body. The excretory organs consist of coxal glands or Malpighian tubules or both. Parts of the gut also serve for excretion. The circulation is much simplified, usually consisting of a network of sinuses without a definite heart. Most organs found on the cephalothorax of other arachnids are found in the idiosoma of mites. Many mites are blind, but when eyes occur, they are usually present in the idiosoma. Pits and slit sense organs are also present.

The male reproductive system consists of a pair of testes, a pair of vasa deferentia, and a chitinous penis. The penis can project through the genital orifice, which is variable in position. The female system usually has only one ovary that is connected to the genital orifice by an oviduct. The genital orifice is usually ventral but may be dorsal in some. Seminal receptacles are also present for the reception of sperm. The male usually deposits his sperm in a spermatophore which is picked up by the female, or the sperm may be transferred by the male chelicerae or by the third pair of legs. In other species the male injects his penis into the female genital orifice.

Most species are oviparous but some are ovoviviparous. The female of some groups has an ovipositor. A six-legged larva hatches from the egg; the fourth pair of legs is absent. After a molt all appendages are present. There may be a number of nymphal molts in passing through the nymph stage. After a resting period the nymph is gradually transformed into an adult. There are many variations in their metamorphosis.

Because of their small size and habitat preferences, mites and ticks are rarely considered important parts of faunal populations. However, they are abundant in the soil, humus, decaying vegetation, and other places. One group, often red in color, lives in water (mostly fresh water), but some groups are marine. Such forms may be parasitic on the gills of mollusks, or they may live on small aquatic organisms. Ticks are the largest members of the order and are parasitic on the higher vertebrates. Some ticks are responsible for transmitting serious diseases, such as Texas tick fever and Rocky Mountain spotted fever. The itch mites burrow into the skin of man and other animals, causing mange or scabies. Predaceous mites usually have typical arachnid digestive systems and ingest the juices of their prey, such as other small arthropods. Many live on plant juices. One group, the gall mites, with only four legs, produces galls on leaves of plants. The six-legged larvae of the family Trombidiidae, commonly called red legs or chiggers, cause severe dermatitis in man by burrowing under the skin.

Annotated references

Arthur, D. R. 1962. Ticks and disease. New York, Harper & Row, Publishers. *The role of ticks as vectors of disease.*

Baerg, W. J. 1958. The tarantula. Lawrence, University of Kansas Press. *A monograph on the habits and natural history of the tarantula.*

Baker, E. W., and G. W. Wharton. 1952. An introduction to acarology. New York, The Macmillan Company. *Stresses taxonomy of the group with keys to the families.*

Brady, A. R. 1964. The lynx spiders of North America, north of Mexico (Araneae:Oxyopidae). Bull. Mus. Comp. Zool. 131(13):432-518. *A systematic study of this active family of hunting spiders that fasten their egg sacs to shrubbery or other objects.*

Bristowe, W. S. 1958. The world of spiders. New York, The Macmillan Company. *A comprehensive treatise on this extensive group.*

Bullock, T. H., and G. A. Horridge. 1965. Structure and function in the nervous system of invertebrates. San Francisco, W. H. Freeman & Co., Publishers. *Certain aspects of the nervous system of arachnids are given in this comprehensive summary.*

Carthy, J. D. 1965. The behavior of arthropods. San Francisco, W. H. Freeman & Co., Publishers.

Cloudsley-Thompson, J. L. 1958. Spiders, scorpions, centipedes, and mites. New York, Pergamon Press, Inc. *The natural history and ecology of the group.*

Edmondson, W. T. (editor). 1959. Ward and Whipple's fresh-water biology, ed. 2. New York, John Wiley & Sons, Inc. *A section is devoted to the aquatic mites (Acari) by I. M. Newell. Keys are given of this extensive group.*

Gertsch, W. J. 1949. American spiders. Princeton, D. Van Nostrand Co., Inc. *One of the best general works on spiders; excellent illustrations.*

Grasse, P. P. (editor). 1949. Traite de zoologie, vol. 6, pp. 219-262. Paris, Masson et Cie. *Good accounts of the Merostomata and the Pycnogonida by L. Fage. A definitive work with extensive bibliographies.*

Hedgpeth, J. W. 1948. The Pycnogonida of the Western United States, North Atlantic and the Carribean. Proc. U. S. Nat. Mus. 97:157-342. *An excellent treatment of the sea spiders by the foremost American student of the group.*

Hedgpeth, J. W. 1954. On the phylogeny of the Pycnogonida. Acta. Zool. (Stockholm) 35:193-213. *Sea spiders have some characteristics that suggest affinities to the Chelicerata, and some superficial resemblances to crustaceans.*

Hoff, C. C. 1949. The pseudoscorpions of Illinois. Bull. Ill. Natur. Hist. Surv. 24:407-498. *This paper and the one by the same author on the pseudoscorpions north of Mexico afford an excellent taxonomic approach to the group.*

Hughes, A. M. 1961. The mites of stored food. Tech. Bull. No. 9. London, British Information Service. *A treatise on the economic importance of mites.*

Kaston, B. J. 1948. Spiders of Connecticut. Hartford, State Geol. Natur. Hist. Surv. Bull. 70:1-874.

Kaston, B. J., and E. Kaston, 1953. How to know the spiders. Dubuque, William C. Brown Company, Publishers. *An excellent field manual for ready identification. Line drawings and keys.*

McCook, H. C. 1889-1893. American spiders and their spinning work. Philadelphia, Academy of Natural Science. *The three volumes of this classic work may be outdated in some respects, but the beautiful plates and informal descriptions will never cease to interest all students of spiders.*

Pennak, R. W. 1953. Fresh-water invertebrates of the United States. New York, The Ronald Press Company. *A section is devoted to the water mites (Hydracarina). A good introduction* is included as well as keys, figures, and bibliography.

Petrunkevitch, A. 1939. Catalogue of American spiders. Trans. Connecticut Academy of Arts and Sciences, part 1, vol. 33, pp. 133-338. *A valuable work for all students of spiders.*

Savory, T. 1964. Arachnida. New York, Academic Press, Inc.

Snodgrass, R. E. 1952. A textbook of arthropod anatomy. Ithaca, Cornell University Press. *A detailed account of the morphology of this group. A work of established reputation and usefulness; well illustrated.*

Phylum Arthropoda: the crustaceans

The Mandibulata

The mandibulate arthropods are characterized by jaws, maxillae, and antennae as head appendages. The body is made up of two or three divisions. In its simplest form it consists of a head and trunk, but it may be divided into a head, thorax, and abdomen. The head and thorax are often fused into a cephalothorax division. Within this extensive group there are many variations in accordance with specializations for different purposes. This subphylum represents one of the two major lines of evolution of arthropods, the other being the Chelicerata. Evolutionary trends involve the composite head of fused segments and shifting positions and the modifications or specializations of appendages by fusion and differentiation or otherwise. In general the mouth has passed backward, and the segments have pushed forward.

The antennae, which are absent in chelicerates, may be represented by two pairs in the mandibulates. The first pair of these is called the antennules in the crustaceans that have two pairs and simply antennae in those that have only one pair (insects, chilopods, diplopods). The antennule is homologous to the prostomial palps of polychaete worms. The second pair of antennae, when present, represents derivatives of trunk appendages borne by the first of the four trunk segments that have fused with the head region. This appendage may be vestigial or entirely lacking. The mandibles are the second postoral appendages and are modified appendages of the second fused trunk segment. Their evolution from primitive trunk appendages is evidenced by the small palpi they bear, since the major part of the mandible has evolved into its masticatory specialization from the original basal segments of the appendage. Some variations are found in the fate of the appendages of the third and fourth segments. In crustaceans they are the maxillae—two pairs of accessory feeding structures. In insects they become the maxillae and labium. In diplopods and chilopods they form the maxillae. The outer trunk appendages are used mainly for walking or swimming but vary in the different groups. In a simple form the head of the mandibulate may consist of only the eyes, antennae, and a preoral lobe (labrum), with the segments of the mandibles and maxillae united to the thorax. Usually these two latter structures are included in the head.

The mandibulates include the crustaceans, the centipedes, the millipedes, the pauropods, the symphylans, and the insects (hexapods).

CLASS CRUSTACEA

This important class of arthropods comprises a group of such diversity of structure, function, and development that it is difficult to define them in characters that apply to all members of the group, because the characters that apply to one subdivision of crustaceans may be highly modified or nonexistent in another subdivision. In general a crustacean is an arthropod of aquatic habits with two pairs of antennae, three pairs of masticating and feeding appendages, and typical biramous appendages. However, this definition must be applied only with reservation.

Some members of this extensive group are familiar to everyone. They include crayfish, shrimps, crabs, lobsters, prawns, sow bugs, sandhoppers, wood lice, barnacles, water fleas, copepods, and others. Although typically aquatic, there are some members that are terrestrial or semiterrestrial. Crustaceans generally have avoided strictly terrestrial habitations.

A broad classification divides crustaceans into the smaller forms called entomostracans and the larger members called malacostracans. Entomostraca is not considered a valid taxonomic division because the members differ from each other in such diverse ways. Malacostraca is more clearly defined because all members of this group have abdominal appendages, an eight-segmented thorax, a gastric mill, and an abdomen of six (sometimes seven or eight) segments. About eight subclasses of crustaceans are recognized at present, although there is less agreement among carcinologists about lesser taxa, such as orders and families. There are more than 30,000 known species in the class.

EXTERNAL MORPHOLOGY

All parts of the external anatomy of crustaceans are covered with a chitinous exoskeleton, which may be thick with limy salts or may be delicate and transparent. The exoskeleton is divided into segments (somites, or metameres) that may be more or less fused together, or in the more primitive forms they may be more or less distinct. No crustacean, however, has all of the somites distinct. Body segmentation may be absent altogether (Cladocera, Ostracoda). The three parts of the body—head, thorax, and abdomen—may be distinct, but often one or more thoracic segments are fused with the head to form a cephalothorax. The cephalothorax is often wholly or partly covered by a carapace that arises as a fold of the head and fuses with certain tergites behind it. However, in some forms the carapace may be an integumental fold that remains free of the thoracic segments, or it may coalesce with the thoracic terga in the middle but remain free at the sides, forming gill chambers. In other crustaceans

the carapace is in the form of a bivalve, and in barnacles it is modified into a mantle bearing calcareous plates. Branchiopods have no carapace at all.

Typical segments are usually not as regular as circular rings but are somewhat compressed. Each is separated from the one in front and the one behind by a region of softer integument that forms a joint. The dorsal arched part of the segment is called the tergum; the lower narrow ventral part, the sternum; and each lateral part, the pleuron. The pleuron may extend over the attachment of the appendages to form a free plate, the epimeron.

The part of the body that bears the anus is usually called the telson. In nonmalacostracon forms the telson may be referred to as a true segment, although it never bears typical limbs. Various interpretations have been made about its nature. Some regard it as a median appendage or the fusion of a pair of appendages. In larval forms of primitive crustaceans the number of segments increases by addition of new segments between the last formed segment and the terminal unsegmented region that forms the telson.

The nauplius larva (Fig. 24-1), charac-

Fig. 24-1

Nauplius larva (From Encyclopaedia Britannica film, "Life in a Drop of Water.")

teristic of crustaceans, has in its head three pairs of appendages—the antennules, antennae, and mandibles—which represent the appendages of three fused segments. To this primary head (protocephalon) are added two additional segments bearing the first and second maxillae to form the cephalon of later stages. The typical adult crustacean head thus has five pairs of appendages. In addition to these five pairs of appendages are the upper lip (labrum) from the body wall and the lower lip (labium) from the foregut. The compound eyes are not true segmental appendages but are simply specialized structures at the anterior ends of the nerve cord. Embryologically they do not develop in the regular segmental pattern.

The paired appendages of crustaceans are typically biramous, consisting of two branches, endopodite and exopodite (Fig. 24-2). These are attached to a basal proto-

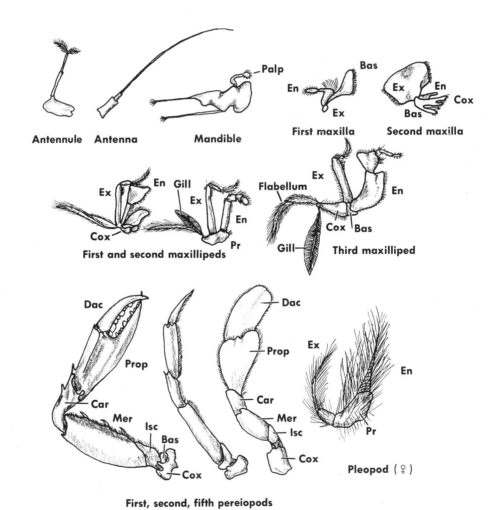

Fig. 24-2

Crustacean appendages (*Callinectes sapidus*). Key to labels is as follows:

Bas	Basipod	**Ex**	Exopodite
Car	Carpopod	**Isc**	Ischiopod
Cox	Coxopod	**Mer**	Meropod
Dac	Dactylopod	**Prop**	Propod
En	Endopodite	**Pr**	Protopodite

podite composed of two segments, the coxopodite (coxa) articulated to the body and the basipodite (basis). The two branches exhibit many modifications in the different groups. Either the endopodite or the exopodite may be reduced or entirely absent, or they may coalesce into a foliaceous limb. The protopodite may bear on its outer margin a process called an exite or on its inner margin an endite. Exites in some crustaceans function as gills, while endites of appendages near the mouth function as gnathobases. The subdivisions of foliaceous limbs are usually considered as endites and exites. The appendages are all more or less similar in their primitive pattern, but the evolutionary trend has been toward reduction in number and specialization for different functions. In the more advanced crustacean the endopodite is segmented. The segments, named outward, are the ischiopodite, meropodite, carpopodite, propodite, and dactylopodite (Fig. 24-2). The endopodites in the different groups assume a variety of functions—perception, crawling, respiration, defense, offense, sperm transmission, and food handling. When present, the exopodite may be paddlelike for swimming or for respiration.

In a more specific way the functions of the various paired appendages may be summarized in the following manner. The antennules are mainly sensory in most crustaceans but may be used as clasping organs by some. In the higher crustaceans the antennae are chiefly sensory but may be used as swimming organs in some or as attachment organs in others. The mandibles are often heavy and short for grinding and biting but may also be used for swimming and other functions in the more primitive forms. The first and second maxillae are used mainly as accessory feeding appendages. They are often flattened and leaflike with gnathobasic lobes. The thoracic series of appendages (eight pairs in number) in malacostracans are modified into maxillipeds for accessory food handling and into walking legs. Usually only the endopodite is present in these, while the exopodite (if present) may be used as a swimming organ. The abdominal limbs (six pairs) are usually biramous and are used mainly for swimming, although they are often sexually differentiated for the attachment of eggs and for copulatory organs.

The integument of the crustaceans consists of an inner, single-layered, cellular hypodermis or epidermis and an outer noncellular cuticle (Fig. 24-3). The cuticle shows many variations. In its typical form it is divided into two or more horizontal layers. The two chief cuticular layers are an outer, thin epicuticle and a thicker

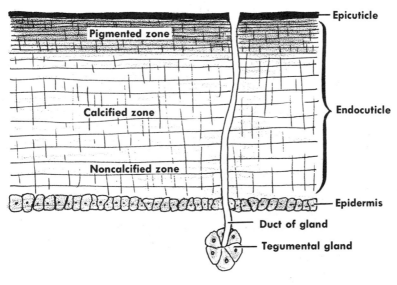

Fig. 24-3
Diagram of crustacean cuticle.

endocuticle (procuticle). The epicuticle is usually a waxy layer to shed water. The endocuticle has a chitin-protein complex, calcium salts, and scleroproteins. Pigmentation may occur in the inner part of the epicuticle and the outer part of the endocuticle. The innermost layer of the endocuticle does not contain minerals. The epidermis contains blood cells and cells for molting and is largely glandular. Certain large glands (tegumental) just beneath the epidermis may be involved in the secretion of the epicuticle. They are provided with ducts that open on the surface of the epicuticle.

INTERNAL MORPHOLOGY
Digestive system

The food canal is a relatively straight tube, except for the dorsal curve of the part that runs down anteriorly to the mouth. In some cases it is coiled upon itself. The mouth lies between the mandibles on the underside of the head. The fleshy upper lip of the mouth is called the labrum; the lower lip, the metastoma or labium. The metastoma is sometimes bilobed, each lobe being called a paragnatha. The anterior part of the foregut is the esophagus (stomodeum), whereas the posterior foregut is modified into some form of stomach. In malacostracans the stomach is modified

into the gastric mill, which is provided with chitinous ridges or teeth and setae for churning and straining the food (Fig. 24-4). The teeth are manipulated by muscles to triturate the food as it passes into the stomach proper. The midgut or mesenteron is provided with pouchlike diverticula that serve as glands for secretion and for absorption of food. In the decapods the glands are massive and are called the hepatopancreas, or liver. The midgut may be very short and is the only division of the gut not lined with chitin. The hindgut (proctodeum) terminates at the anal opening. In filter-feeding crustaceans, fine setae on the appendages around the mouth collect food particles. Crustaceans vary in their food habits. Besides the filter feeders, many are scavengers, predators, or herbivores. Raptorial habits are characteristic mostly of the larger forms whose appendages are modified for seizing prey. Several crustaceans have multiple feeding methods. Parasitic forms are represented by both ectoparasites and endoparasites. In the highly modified parasites the alimentary canal is vestigial or absent.

Circulatory system

Circulation in crustaceans is similar to that in most arthropods. It is an open system consisting of heart, arteries, and si-

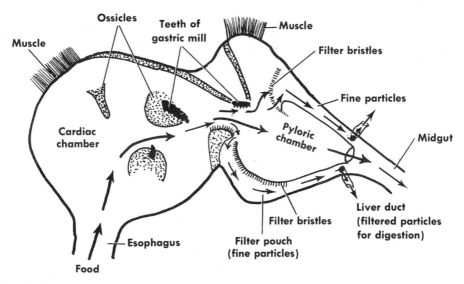

Fig. 24-4
Diagram of malacostracan stomach showing gastric mill and direction of food movements. (Modified from Yonge, 1924.)

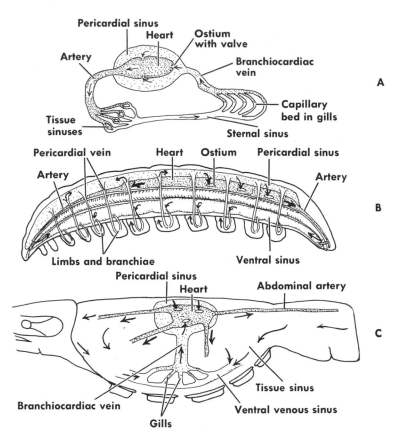

Fig. 24-5

Circulation in crustaceans. **A,** Generalized plan in crustaceans. **B,** Circulation in amphipod. **C,** Circulation in decapod.

nuses (Fig. 24-5). The heart is often tubular and may extend the greater length of the body but it may also be a compact organ. It lies in a pericardial blood sinus from which the blood passes by valvular ostia into the heart. In the more advanced crustaceans the blood is pumped by certain arteries through the connecting sinuses of the tissues. A heart may be absent in lower crustaceans, and the blood is then driven by body movements.

Most crustaceans have blue blood because of the respiratory pigment hemocyanin, but a few have the respiratory pigment erythrocruorin. Crustaceans are usually represented by hemocyanins of smaller molecular weight. The blood has a variety of leukocytes and amebocytes, which may represent variations of a single basic type. Blood corpuscles may range from a few hundred to several thousand per cubic centimeter of plasma, depending upon species, age, and physiologic states. Some of their corpuscles have phagocytic

power. Blood coagulation in crustaceans appears to take place by several methods. Certain amebocytes may release substances that convert fibrinogen into fibrin, thus trapping blood cells. Spastic contraction of muscles at the place of a lost appendage may produce the same effect as clotting.

Respiration

Crustaceans use gills, general body surface, or some modification of such structures for breathing. Most gills are associated with the appendages (Fig. 24-6). In some cases, the exites of the basal segment have the functional aspects of respiratory surfaces, being flat or branched. Among the malacostracans, with few exceptions, gills are present on one or more pairs of thoracic

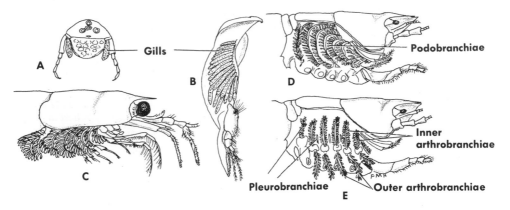

Fig. 24-6

Malacostracan gills. **A,** *Corophium,* an amphipod (transverse section), has pouchlike gills on protopodites of thoracic legs. **B,** *Diastylis,* a cumacean, has epipodites forming branchial tubes on first thoracic appendages. **C,** *Euphausia* has gills on protopodites of seven pairs of thoracic legs. **D,** *Astacus,* a decapod (branchiostegite removed), has podobranchiae arising from basal joints of thoracic limbs. **E,** *Astacus* (podobranchiae removed), also has two rows of arthrobranchiae attached to membranes between joints and body and pleurobranchiae attached to body itself.

appendages. Many different patterns of gill arrangement are found. They may be vascular sacs or lamellae or more complicated structures in which the lamellae are arranged with a central axis containing blood vessels. Such plans may be highly foliaceous or filamentous. In the decapods, gills are arranged in three series near the bases of the thoracic limbs and are enclosed in a pair of branchial chambers covered over by the carapace (Fig. 24-6, *D, E*). Water currents are facilitated by the beating of appendages, some of which are specialized for this purpose.

Terrestrial crustaceans may have the vascularized branchial chambers enlarged to serve as lungs. Isopods may have tufts of branching tubules filled with air similar to tracheae. Some small crustaceans have no gills but breathe through the body surface or through restricted regions of the body surface.

Excretion

The paired excretory organs of crustaceans lie at the base of the antennae or maxillae. Early in development there may be two pairs, one called the antennal and the other the maxillary glands. Usually only one or the other of the two pairs persists, but both may be found in the adults of some forms. The structure of both glands is similar, and they may represent survivors of a segmentally arranged pattern of nephridia. Each type is made up of a thin-walled end sac and an excretory tubule (Fig. 24-7). Some modifications may be found in this arrangement, such as a labyrinth and a bladder. The end sac is a vestigial part of the coelom, and the tubule represents a persistent coelomoduct. In malacostracans the antennal glands are more typical and open externally on the underside of the bases of the antennae. The maxillary glands, when present, open at the bases of the second maxillae.

The waste product of crustaceans is mostly ammonia with some urea and a little uric acid, but much of this waste may diffuse through the gills. Uric acid is sometimes stored in special cells (nephrocytes); it may form a part of the white chromatophores; or it may be deposited in the integument and cast off with the molt. The excretory products may be secreted by active transport, or they may be separated from the blood by filtration. Experimental evidence is divided on this point (N. S. R. Maluf, J. A. Riegel, and L. B. Kirschner). Crustacean urine is mostly isotonic with the

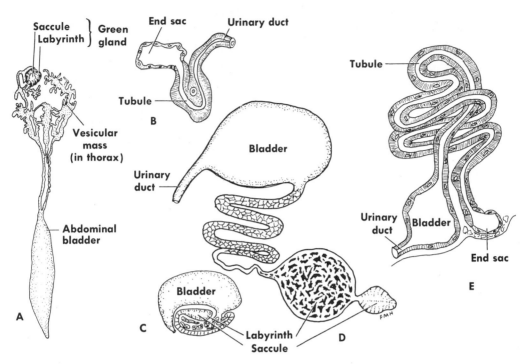

Fig. 24-7

Crustacean excretory systems. **A,** In pagurid hermit crabs, bladder ramifies throughout much of thorax with single or paired extensions the length of abdomen. **B,** Maxillary gland in larva of branchiopod *Estheria.* **C** and **D,** Antennal gland of decapod *Astacus.* **C,** Parts of gland in natural relation. **D,** Parts of gland unraveled. **E,** Section through antennal gland of *Mysis.* (**B** and **E** modified from Grobben.)

blood but may be hypotonic. *Artemia,* a salt-water form, produces a hypertonic urine. Water resorption may occur after filtration into the end sac in some cases, which could account for a more concentrated urine. The gills may be responsible for regulating the ionic balance of salts in the crustacean body by either expelling or absorbing salt.

Nervous system

The nervous system is typical of arthropods, consisting of a large supraesophageal ganglion, or brain, connected by circumesophageal commissures with a double ventral nerve cord of segmentally arranged ganglia (Fig. 24-8). The primitive arrangement of the nervous system is best seen in the branchiopods where the ventral nerve cord has a ladderlike pattern of two widely separated chains of ganglia (Fig. 24-8, *A*). The paired ganglia, one in each chain, are connected by double transverse commissures. This primitive arrangement of two chains is more or less coalesced in most groups.

In general the nervous systems of the different groups show a marked tendency toward concentration and fusion of the ganglia (Fig. 24-8, *B, C*). The chain ganglia may be drawn into a single mass representing the ventral chains, as in the true crabs. The brain also has many variations. In higher crustaceans, ganglionic masses, which in lower forms are found on the esophageal commissures, are incorporated in the brain. More centers are found in the brain of decapods than in that of other crustacean groups.

Each pair of ganglia in the ventral nerve cord usually gives off three pairs of lateral nerves for the innervation of the various organs and tissues. The posterior pair of each group of three pairs is mostly motor

387

Fig. 24-8

Three types of crustacean nervous systems. **A,** *Branchinecta* (subclass Branchiopoda). **B,** *Astacus* (subclass Malacostraca, order Decapoda). **C,** *Argulus* (subclass Branchiura).

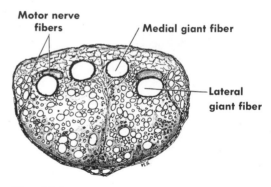

Fig. 24-9

Cross section of nerve cord of crustacean showing giant fibers. (From stained slide.)

and runs to the flexor muscles of the body wall. The other two pairs of nerves are larger and are mixed motor and sensory in function. They innervate the appendages and the segments. The brain supplies pairs of nerves to the antennules, to the antennae, to the compound eyes, and to the ventral nerve cord (the circumesophageal commissures). Other nerves may also run from the brain to various parts of the body, depending upon the group.

Many crustaceans have giant fibers in the central nervous system that are adapted for rapid transmission of impulses and resultant quick reactions, such as those in the escape mechanism. Decapods, especially, are provided with these fibers, which may reach a diameter of 200 microns. There are usually two dorsomedial giant fibers and two dorsolateral ones (Fig. 24-9). Each of the medial fibers has a large nerve cell in the anterior brain, but the axon it gives off crosses to the opposite side of the posterior brain. These giant fibers extend the entire length of the ventral cord and make synaptic junction with motor nerves from the ganglia. The dorsolateral giant fibers are made up of a series of neurons, each of which has its cell body in a ganglion of the nerve cord. Thus impulses for the dorsolateral giant nerves can arise from any of the ventral ganglia of the cord, whereas impulses for the dorsomedial giant fibers originate in the brain. A single impulse in either of the two types of giant fibers will produce muscular contractions for the rapid escape mechanism.

Crustacean reflexes are numerous, such as claw closing, autotomy, escape, feeding, sex behavior, etc. Some of these reflexes will occur even in the complete absence of the brain, which may exert a regulative control but is not necessary for the initiation of the process.

Sense organs

The sensory system of crustaceans is among the most extensive in the arthropods and has been much studied during the past two or three decades. In general the various senses are grouped into visual receptors,

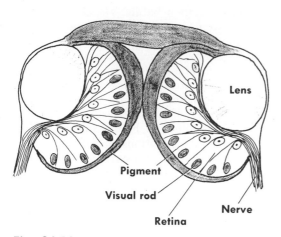

Fig. 24-10

Diagram of section through median eye of *Cypris,* an ostracod.

chemoreceptors, proprioceptors, tactile receptors, statocysts, and myochordotonal receptors. Some of these are special sense organs that are primarily specialized for a definite sensory impression, and others have a more general function. In any integrative reaction there is, of course, an overlapping and functional correlation of the different groups.

The eyes are of two types, the unpaired median or nauplius eye and the paired compound eyes. The median eye is characteristic of the common nauplius larval form and may be the only eye, as in the copepods. It may exist along with the compound eyes, or it may be vestigial or disappear altogether, as in most of the malacostracans. The median eye (Fig. 24-10) usually consists of three pigmentary cups, or ocelli. Each pigmentary cup contains columnar retinal cells or photoreceptors which are connected by nerves to the brain. Lenslike structures may or may not be present. The functions of these eyes may vary with the groups in which they are found. Some may function in movement perception, orientation by polarized skylight, and visual recognition; but present knowledge does not justify definite conclusions about such matters. Some may be concerned only with distinguishing between light and dark for orientation.

A pair of compound eyes is characteristic of most crustaceans. They are similar to

those of insects. Usually they are separated, each being placed on a movable peduncle or eyestalk; but they may be fused into a single organ in such forms as cladocerans and amphipods. Compound eyes may also be sessile or without a peduncle. In blind crustaceans of caves or other regions the peduncles may persist and become modified into spines for defense.

The compound eye (Fig. 24-11) is made up of a varying number of elongated, cone-shaped bodies, called ommatidia (Fig. 25-11). They are covered by a transparent membrane of the cuticle to form the cornea, which is divided into facets corresponding to the underlying ommatidia. The facets may be hexagonal or square in shape. The cornea is secreted by two corneagenous cells (modified epidermal cells) in each ommatidium. Lying behind the cornea is the long, cylindric, crystalline cone, functioning as a second lens and formed of four cone cells. Below this is a core of crystalline translucent material called the rhabdome surrounded by seven or eight photo-

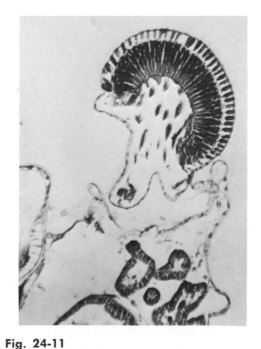

Fig. 24-11

Cross section through compound eye of fairy shrimp *Eubranchipus* (order Anostraca).

sensitive cells, the retinular cells, which are stimulated by the light rays scattered and diverted by the rhabdome (Fig. 25-11). Retinular cells give off axons, or nerve fibers, which issue from the ommatidium and run to an optic ganglion that may be located in the eyestalk. The rhabdome itself may have a photoreceptive role and become the center of the first photochemical response. In turn, it would stimulate the retinular cells.

Each ommatidium is surrounded by a distal collar of black or brown pigmented cells around the crystalline cone and by a proximal collar of retinal pigment around the retinular cells at the base of the ommatidium. The manipulation of these two pigment collars makes possible two different forms of vision. In daylight the two collars can migrate centrally and distally and merge to form a collar completely surrounding each ommatidium. In such a condition each ommatidium will pick up those light rays that come in parallel to its long axis. Such an image is a mosaic (appositional) image; each unit sees only what is directly opposite it. For suffused light at night the collars are separated, leaving the middle of the ommatidium free of pigment. Thus each ommatidium can be stimulated by light rays entering from adjacent ommatidia (superposition image) as well as through the cornea; and thus the intensity of the light stimulation at night can be stepped up to compensate for the fewer light rays present at such times. Night vision, however, is far less precise than day vision.

Compound eyes are adapted for detecting slight movements. Any shift of light rays would be detected by a few or many ommatidia, according to the degree of movement. Several ommatidia could also be stimulated by the same beam of light by overlapping stimulation. The outer convex surface of the corneal facets ensures a fairly large field of vision, so that in some stalked eyes the corneal surface can cover an arc of 180 degrees. Compound eyes show many grades of structural and functional components in a group as vast as the crustaceans. Some have only day- or night-adapted eyes. Superposition eyes are characteristic of deep-sea crustaceans and those that are strictly nocturnal in their habits. Visual acuity is to some extent correlated with the number of ommatidia in the compound eye. Some small terrestrial forms may have as few as two dozen ommatidia in a compound eye; the large lobsters may have 12,000 to 15,000. In no case can it be stated that the visual acuity of a crustacean is comparable to that found in higher forms such as mammals. Investigations reveal that a certain amount of color discrimination is present in certain crustaceans, especially in the malacostracans, in which chromatophore mediation occurs through the eye. Shades of yellow, red, and blue, for example, can be disinguished by *Crangon.*

One of the most common types of sense organs in crustaceans is the hairs or setae on the surface of the exoskeleton, which are variously modified for special functions. Some hairs are for touch reception, detection of water currents, or orientation. Such receptors are especially common on the appendages that are in most direct contact with the environment. Since the exoskeleton is a hard, insensitive armor that shields the underlying sensitive tissue from external stimuli, hairs and such receptors must communicate with the interior by channels similar to the prototrichs found in lizards and snakes, and for the same reason. Tactile hairs or setae have chitinous shafts that articulate by ampullae to the exoskeleton.

Statocysts or ectodermal sacs are found at the base of the antennules, telson, and other parts in most decapods. They are open or closed sacs; their interiors are lined with sensory hairs and contain a statolith or statoliths, which may be grains of sand or secreted substances (Fig. 24-12). They are concerned with the maintenance of equilibrium.

Muscle or tendon receptor organs (or proprioceptors) have been described in all advanced crustaceans and may be found in varying degrees in the lower members. Each organ is made up of a modified muscle cell, a pair of which is found on both sides of the dorsal musculature of each abdominal segment as well as in the extensor muscles of the seventh and eighth thoracic segments. Each proprioceptive organ has dendritic (sensory) connections with a multipolar neuron.

The dendritic terminals are stretched either by the flexion of the abdominal muscles or by contraction of the receptor muscles that are supplied by motor fibers. There is also a differential rate of contraction in the two members of a pair of receptor muscles, one fast and the other slow. Much is yet to be learned about the complicated nature of the muscle receptor organs.

Whether or not crustaceans can hear, or have definite auditory organs, has never been resolved. In some way the statocysts seem to be involved in reactions to sound. Delicate hairs on certain appendages are apparently sensitive to vibrations of high and low intensity.

A special type of sensory receptor, called a myochordotonal organ, occurs in the lumen of the meropodite or fourth segment of the walking leg. It consists of a thin membrane containing sensory cell bodies of bipolar neurons. The organ probably has a proprioceptive function.

A number of chemoreceptors are present in such places as the antennules, antennae, and other appendages around the mouth. These include aesthetascs (Fig. 24-13) (sensory hairs or plates), which occur in rows on the outer flagellum of the antennules and are innervated by the dendrites of certain bipolar neurons. Other possible chemoreceptors are represented by canals, pores, etc. Little is known about thermoreception in crustaceans. The two kinds of antennae are supposed to be sensitive to thermal stimuli. Thermal responses vary greatly in the different groups, especially to temperature gradients.

REPRODUCTION

Most crustaceans are dioecious, but in the Cirripedia, a few parasitic isopods, and scattered instances in other groups they are hermaphroditic. Parthogenesis occurs in some branchiopods, ostracods, and a few others. There may be alternation of generations in lower crustaceans. The gonads of crustaceans are usually elongated, paired organs in the dorsal region of the thorax or abdomen or sometimes in both. The gonoducts (sperm ducts or oviducts) are chiefly tubules that open either on a sternite or at the base of a pair of trunk appendages. There are some variations in the

Fig. 24-12

Head end of lobster showing brain and nerve connection to statocyst in basal segment of right antennule. Below, diagrammatic section through statocyst with rows of sensory hairs cushioning statolith.

Fig. 24-13

Diagram of tip of antennule of brachyuran crab with aesthetascs, or long sensory hairs, each connected to cluster of sense cells. Nerve fibers from each cluster make up "olfactory nerve" component of antennular nerve. (After Hanström; modified from Waterman.)

place of opening from one group to another.

Sexual dimorphism may be pronounced. Either sex may be larger than the other. The males are often provided with clasping organs modified from almost any of the appendages (thoracic limbs, antennae, mouthparts, etc.). In the decapods the first and second pairs of abdominal appendages are used by the males for transmitting sperm. A penis is present in some crustaceans. In copulation (Fig. 24-14) the male may clasp the female and deposit sperm or

Fig. 24-14

Mating behavior in *Gammarus*, a freshwater amphipod. **A,** Precopulation. **B,** Copulation. (Modified from Kinne.)

spermatophores in or near the female seminal receptacles. The seminal receptacles may be located near the openings of the oviducts or in ectodermal, invaginated pouches of an adjacent segment.

DEVELOPMENT

The eggs are usually carried on female appendages until hatched. They may also be contained in special brood chambers located on the female body, or they may be placed in a saclike structure, from which the eggs are expelled. In brood chambers a nutrient may be secreted for the young until they are released. Some shrimp attach the eggs to aquatic vegetation.

The nauplius larva is characteristic of many crustaceans (Figs. 24-1, 24-15). It has an oval, unsegmented body and three pairs of appendages (antennules, antennae, and mandibles). Of these appendages the antennules are uniramous and the other two pairs are biramous. These appendages carry on the functions of sensory reception, feeding, and locomotion. A single median eye is found on the front of the head and represents a simple compound eye.

The nauplius may be found only in the egg of the higher forms and may be absent altogether in some crustaceans. Life histories may be simple or complex. The young of some crustaceans resemble the parents in general structure as soon as hatched. Following the nauplius stage in some groups the postlarva becomes a characteristic larva, such as the cypris larva of barnacles, the phyllosoma larva of spiny lobsters, the zoea and megalops of crabs, and the mysis of lobsters.

In the Malacostraca the nauplius larva is found only in some primitive decapods and a few others. In its further development the body of the nauplius larva elongates and, by successive molts, becomes segmented and acquires additional appendages (Fig. 24-15, *B*). New segments are added from a formative zone in front of the telson. A carapace is formed, and paired eyes appear at the sides of the head but not on stalks until later. This scheme of development appears to be the primitive one and is characteristic of the Branchiopoda and Copepoda. This primitive plan, however, is modified in most of the other crustaceans. Early stages are often passed through within the egg so that the hatched larva is more advanced than the nauplius. More advances are made at a single molt, and the regular order of succession of segments and appendages may be disturbed. This results, especially in the Malacostraca, in a larval form known as the zoea (Fig. 24-15, *C*), the most typical form of which is found in the Brachyura (true crabs). In the true crabs the posterior five or six segments are delayed in development, while the abdominal segments (often with appendages) are fully formed. After additional molts the adult features, except for size and sexual maturity, are attained. The various groups of crustaceans show many modifications of this basic plan of development. The nauplius and zoea stages may be entirely suppressed, the young hatching as a postlarva. In the crayfish the young are juveniles, and larval development is suppressed.

MOLTING (ECDYSIS)

Because of its tough exoskeleton a crustacean must shed its outer cuticle in order to grow. This process is under hormonal

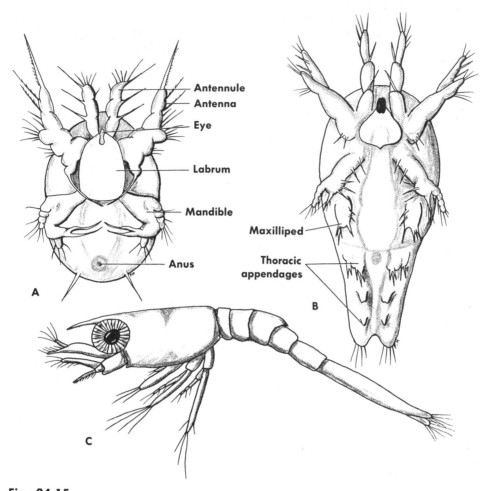

Fig. 24-15

A, Nauplius larva of *Cyclops.* **B,** Metanauplius larvae of *Cyclops* (order Cyclopoida). **C,** Zoea stage of *Crangon* (order Decapoda). (**A** and **B** modified from Claus; **C** modified from Sars.)

control and involves shedding not only the external cuticle but also the ectodermal linings of the foregut and hindgut, the tracheae, external parts of the eye, reproductive ducts, etc. The process of molting, which refers to all the processes involved in the shedding of the exoskeleton, may cease as soon as the crustacean attains sexual maturity; in others it may continue throughout life but at a decreasing tempo. Several steps are involved in this rather drastic procedure. There is first the preparatory stage (proecdysis), in which a new epicuticle is secreted beneath the old. During this time there is some resorption or dissolution of the old cuticle and the accumulation and storage of limy salts such

as calcium in the hepatopancreas or in the gastroliths for use in the new endocuticle. The new cuticle is secreted to some extent while most of the old endocuticle is being digested by the enzymes of the molting fluid, and it is finished after ecdysis. Calcium, especially, is withdrawn from those strategic places where the old skeleton must be broken. The actual molting takes place by a swelling process in which blood is forced into certain parts of the body, water is absorbed from the gut, and excess air is taken in. This causes the old cuticle to split usually along the middorsal line, and the animal emerges. Because of its helpless condition in the postmolt period the animal seeks a safe shelter for the pro-

393

cess. The periods between molts are called the intermolts. Much of the intermolt, however, is taken up with either the terminal process of the last molt or the beginning of the next molt.

The molt control mechanism involves mainly the interaction of a molting hormone of the Y-organs or glands, located ventral and lateral to the eye socket, and a molt-inhibiting hormone of the X-organs, a group of neurosecretory cells of the eyestalk. The molting hormone initiates and integrates the metabolism of ecdysis, growth of tissue, and increase of size, while the molt-inhibiting hormone controls the molting gland activities by the degree of its own activity.

REGENERATION AND AUTOTOMY

Crustaceans have great power to regenerate lost parts, although many molts may be required before a new part attains the size of the lost part. There may also be some irregularities in the replaced parts, as compared with the originals.

Autotomy is the voluntary parting with an injured appendage by muscular contraction. The limb is broken at a fracture plane especially provided. In many crustaceans this plane runs through the basipodite of the limb. At the fracture plane the integument is folded in to form a double-walled diaphragm with a small opening for the nerves and blood vessels. When the limb is broken off at this point, the proximal wall of the diaphragm prevents loss of blood and promotes the clotting of blood for closing the ruptured opening.

Subclass Cephalocarida

Cephalocarids were first discovered in Long Island Sound in 1954. This small, shrimplike form is transparent and about one-tenth of an inch long. The head is horseshoe-shaped and covered by a head shield or carapace. The head bears two pairs of short antennae and a median (naupliar) eye on the ventral side. There are two pairs of maxillae. The trunk is made up of 19 segments, of which the first 9 bear paired appendages. The similar appendages are biramous (endopodite and exopodite) with a pseudoepipodite or plate as a sort of third division. The terminal end (telson) of the abdomen bears two

Fig. 24-16

Hutchinsoniella (subclass Cephalocarida), the most primitive crustacean. (Modified from Waterman.)

long spinelike structures. The ventral nerve cord is composed of two separate cords connected by commissures. Cephalocarids are hermaphroditic and carry two egg sacs, each with an egg, suspended from the abdomen.

These tiny crustaceans are of primary interest because of their primitive characters, which place them among the most primitive crustaceans yet known. They share many characteristics of the ancient, extinct trilobites. In both groups all appendages, except the first, are used for locomotion and obtaining food. No appendage is specialized for a particular function. Both trilobites and cephalocarids have a seven-jointed endopodite, not found in other crustaceans. In cephalocarids a head limb (the second maxillae) is similar to the trunk appendages. This small group seems to represent an early stage in the evolution of crustaceans because its limb pattern is intermediate between the primitive arthropod limb plan and the pattern found in other crustaceans.

The original species found in Long Island Sound has been named *Hutchinsoniella macracantha* (Fig. 24-16). A similar species has been found in San Francisco Bay.

Subclass Branchiopoda

Most branchiopods live in fresh water, and some of them are the characteristic forms to be found in temporary pools during the spring and early summer. They are mostly absent from running water. One genus of them, the brine shrimp (*Artemia*), lives in salt lakes. Within the subclass the

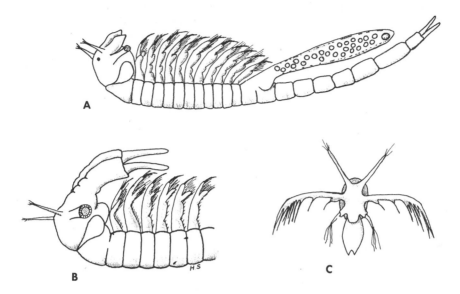

Fig. 24-17

Branchinecta, a fairy shrimp common in western regions of United States (order Anostraca). **A,** Adult female with brood sac. **B,** Anterior end of male showing enlarged antennae adapted as clasping organs. C, Nauplius larva. (Modified from Sars.)

various groups show many diverse characters (some of them primitive). The number of trunk segments ranges from 5 to 44 and may vary in the same species. The appendages are mostly restricted to the anterior part of the trunk. They are mostly foliaceous, being of a flat, leaflike form. A carapace is common to most members. It is a dorsal shield or in the form of a bivalved shell. These crustaceans have compound eyes and reduced mouthparts. The coxae of the appendages are provided with a flattened epipodite, which serves as a gill, so that most appendages are fitted for both respiration and locomotion. Most branchiopods are detritus and filter feeders, and their trunk appendages are adapted for such feeding.

The subclass Branchiopoda is commonly divided into four orders: Anostraca, Notostraca, Conchostraca, and Cladocera. The first three orders are sometimes grouped together in the divison Eubranchiopoda, with body distinctly segmented and many thoracic appendages; and the order Cladocera is classified in the subdivision Oligobranchiopoda, with no external body segmentation, body enclosed by a folded carapace, and only five or six pairs of trunk appendages. The members of the division Eubranchiopoda are often called phyllopods because of their flat, leaflike appen-

Fig. 24-18

Eubranchipus vernalis, a fairy shrimp common to northern part of United States (order Anostraca). Top, female; bottom, male.

dages. The term "Phyllopoda" is sometimes used in place of Branchiopoda for the entire subclass. Their occurrence is very sporadic. A species may be abundant for several years in particular pools and then disappear entirely. A pond rarely contains more than one genus at a time.

Order Anostraca

The members of Anostraca include the fairy shrimps (Figs. 24-17, 24-18) and brine shrimps. They vary in size from 5 to 180 mm. in length. There are about 175 species of them, of which less than 30 are known in America. Their body is elongated, consisting usually of 19 segments, the first 11 segments of which (sometimes more) bear appendages. The first legless segments have the penes or the egg sac. There is no carapace. The eyes are compound and stalked (Fig. 24-11).

Anostracans have small antennules, generally; but the antennae in the male are strong, two-jointed, clasping organs. Fairy shrimp swim upside down. Two flattened cercopods are present on the telson. Their legs are foliaceous and, with exites, form filter chambers, into which water is sucked by leg movements and filtered through setae. In this way, planktonic forms are collected and moved forward to the mouth in a ventral groove bordered with setules between the legs. Food particles in the grooves are formed into mucus chains, which are directed into the mouth mostly by the first maxillae.

The digestive system consists of a short esophagus and a midgut that is modified into a stomach. A dorsal tubular heart with ostia extends most of the length of all the body segments and forces blood to the tissues. Blood from the hemocoel is brought back to the heart. Blood contains colorless amebocytes and blood pigments such as erythrocruorin or some form of hemoglobin. The chief excretory organs are the coiled maxillary glands which empty at the base of the second maxillae. *Artemia,* the brine shrimp, produces a hypertonic urine, although other crustaceans have a hypotonic or isotonic urine. Respiration takes place through the body surface and by means of the lamellar epipodites of the appendages. The nervous system is ladderlike, with a pair of ganglia

and a pair of transverse commissures per segment as a rule. In copulation the male uses his large clasping organs to clasp the dorsal abdomen of the female and inserts the paired eversible penes into the female gonopore. The female develops a conspicuous ovisac at the junction of the thorax and abdomen when the eggs are extended from the uterus. Since fairy shrimp live in temporary spring pools the clutch of eggs often must withstand desiccation when the pools dry up. Eggs will hatch in some species without undergoing drying or freezing. The young hatch as nauplii. Some Anostraca have as many as 17 instars in their life history.

Some common genera of fairy shrimp are *Branchinecta* (Fig. 24-17), *Eubranchipus* (Fig. 24-18), and *Chirocephalopsis.*

Order Notostraca

Notostracans are commonly known as tadpole shrimp. They range in size from 20 to 90 mm. in length. There are 12 to 15 species of them divided between two genera. Six species have been found west of the Mississippi River in North America. The number of their segments varies from 25 to 44, and each of the first 11 segments bears a pair of appendages and may be called a thorax. Behind these the segments may each have as many as 10 or more pairs of legs, which serve for both locomotion and respiration. Some of the segments are legless, and the posterior appendages taper off to a small size. Altogether the pairs of legs number 35 to 71. The telson bears two caudal filaments. The dorsal shieldlike carapace is rounded and flattened dorsoventrally and covers much of the anterior part of the body. The paired eyes are sessile, and the second pair of antennae are reduced or absent. The females carry their ovisacs on the eleventh pair of appendages. Their food is detritus. It is collected and transferred into the ventral groove by special setae (endites) or gnathobases, which are located on the basal part of the appendages, and then carried to the mouth. Tadpoles live in the mud where they burrow. Their dorsal tubular heart is short. Sperm is discharged through short vasa deferentia, which open separately by genital pores and not through

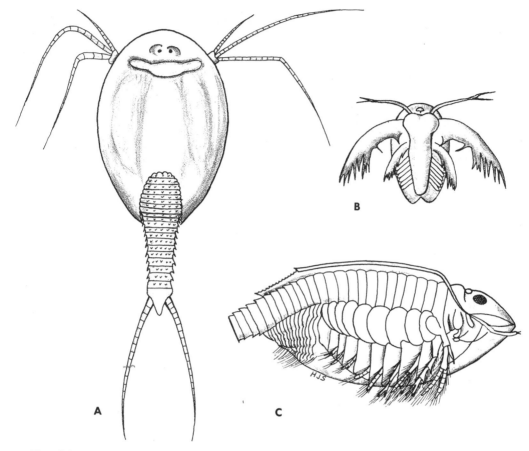

Fig. 24-19

Apus, freshwater tadpole shrimp (order Notostraca). **A,** Dorsal view. **B,** Nauplius larva. **C,** Side view. (Modified from Sars.)

penes. Some species are parthenogenetic. In copulation the male clasps the female at right angles to his own body. The eggs are carried by the female in a receptacle made by the fan-shaped flabellum and branchia on the eleventh paired trunk appendages. The eggs hatch into a nauplius larval form. The more familiar genus is *Apus* (Fig. 24-19). The only other genus is *Lepidurus.*

Order Conchostraca

Clam shrimps or claw shrimps are mussel-like crustaceans. About 26 species are known from North America. The body is enclosed in a bivalve shell that closes by a transverse adductor muscle (Fig. 24-20). The paired eyes are sessile. The trunk append-

ages number 10 to 28 pairs. The telson is provided with two clawlike cercopods. The legs are foliaceous, and there is a pair for each segment. Filter chambers for the food are similar to those in Anostraca. The second pair of antennae is used for swimming as well as the trunk appendages. The clasping organs of the male are the first two pairs of trunk appendages. In the female, elongated flabella of two pairs of posterior legs form a receptacle for holding a mucus mass of developing eggs. Usually only one generation is produced each year. The eggs in some are brooded in a brood chamber beneath the carapace.

Ecologically, clam shrimps frequently occur in muddy, alkaline waters. They crawl around on the muddy substratum. **397**

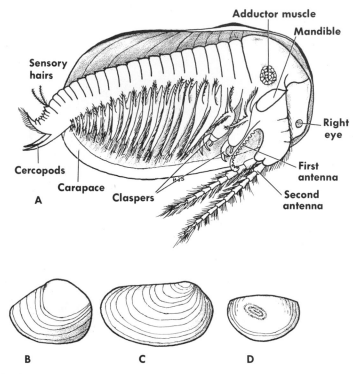

Fig. 24-20

A, *Leptestheria* (order Conchostraca), right valve removed. B, *Limnadia,* right valve. C, *Cyzicus,* right valve.
D, *Eulimnadia,* male shell.

They prefer warmer waters for hatching
and developing and are common later in
the season than other phyllopods.

Of the many genera, the more common
ones are *Lynceus, Leptestheria* (Fig. 24-
20, A), and *Eulimnadia* (Fig. 24-20, D).

Order Cladocera

These small, familiar organisms are from
0.15 to 3 mm. in length. They number
between 425 and 450 species. Cladocerans
are commonly known as water fleas and
are closely related to the conchostracans,
with which they are sometimes placed as
suborders under the order Diplostraca. An
unhinged valve shell, or carapace, encloses
the trunk and trunk appendages but leaves
the head and antennae free (Fig. 24-21).
The first antennae are small, but the second
are very large, biramous, and branched.
The head projects ventrally as a beaklike
rostrum, and the body is compact with no
external segmentation. The head bears a

sessile, median compound eye and a nauplius eye, or ocellus. The five or six pairs of
trunk appendages are flattened, leaf shaped,
and fringed with setae. Their movement
creates currents of water for oxygen and
food particles. The true abdomen is reduced, but there is a large postabdomen at
the posterior end of the body. It is bent
downward and forward and bears two terminal claws as well as two abdominal setae.
In general the antennae are the chief organs of locomotion. Movement is jerky and
by spurts.

The mouth is located near the junction
of the head and body and has as mouthparts a labrum, a labium, a pair of stout
mandibles, and a pair of pointed maxillae.
The transparent body reveals most of the
visceral organs. Food is collected and filtered by the setose appendages into the
ventral median groove between the base
of the legs. The mouth opens into an
esophagus, which leads to the stomach and
intestine. Digestive ceca may open into
the anterior part of the intestine, which
may be straight or convoluted. The anus
is usually placed on the lower or dorsal
part of the postabdomen.

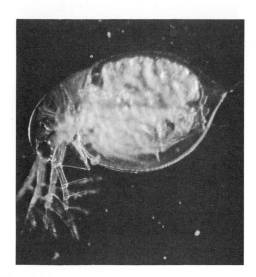

Fig. 24-21

Daphnia, the water flea, a common cladoceran. (From Encyclopaedia Britannica film, "Microscopic Life: The World of the Invisible.")

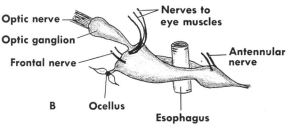

Fig. 24-22

Some internal structures of cladocerans. **A,** Circulation in heart and adjacent sinuses of *Simocephalus.* **B,** Central nervous system of *Daphnia.* (Modified from Herrick.)

The oval heart is on the dorsal side behind the head and has two ostia (Fig. 24-23, *A*). Blood vessels are absent, and blood is circulated in the hemocoel among the many thin mesenteries (Fig. 24-22, *A*). The beat of the heart can easily be seen in the living animal. The rate of beat is influenced by temperature, time of day, and condition of the adult. The blood contains many colorless corpuscles. The blood is colorless in well-oxygenated water but pink in stagnant water. The respiratory pigment is erythrocruorin. Looped shell or maxillary glands function as excretory organs in the anterior part of the trunk. The nervous system is a double ganglionic chain, except that it may be concentrated in a few species. The brain lies dorsal to the esophagus (Fig. 24-22, *B*). In addition to the eyes, there are sensory abdominal setae and sensory hairs on the basal segment of the antennae.

Parthenogenesis is common among cladocerans. Several generations of female young are produced. After undergoing a single maturation in the ovary the eggs are released through the oviducts into the brood chamber. The number of eggs per clutch is usually between 10 and 20. After further development in the brood chamber the eggs hatch. Under certain conditions of temperature, scarcity of food, congestion, and waste accumulation, a generation arises with both males and females. Syngamic eggs with thick shells are then possible and are the winter eggs. The winter or dormant eggs give rise to females when they hatch. In some forms, such as *Daphnia* (Fig. 24-23), the large fertilized eggs are carried in special dorsal pouches (ephippia) that are cast off with the eggs when the animal molts. The ephippia serve as protective cases for the discharged eggs, protecting against drying and freezing, and can be dispersed on the mud, picked up by aquatic birds or by other agents. Some males also appear in the spring, but the factors controlling their appearance are still unknown. Populations of cladocerans may consist entirely of parthenogenic females, or they may consist of males, unfertilized sexual females, and fertilized sex-

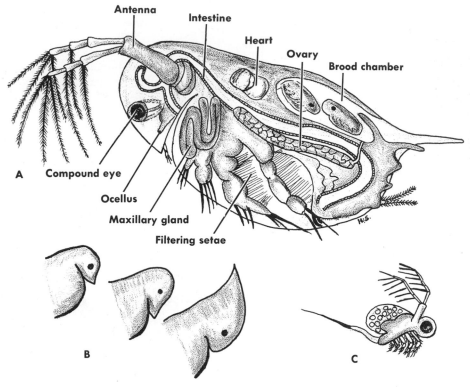

Fig. 24-23

A, Water flea *Daphnia pulex,* female (order Cladocera). **B,** Some seasonal head variations (cyclomorphosis) of *Daphnia.* Temperature seems to be controlling factor. **C,** *Polyphemus,* a predaceous cladoceran. (**A** and **B** modified from Pennak.)

ual females. Population cycles are common in cladocerans. Some may have one seasonal rise in numbers during the warmer months (monocyclic), and others may have two pronounced maxima in spring and fall (dicyclic). The mode of reproduction is influenced by environmental factors, according to experimental work.

Length of life is also highly variable under different environmental conditions. In general it is only 30 to 60 days but may be longer. The first molt produces the juvenile; three to five instars as a rule produce a sexually mature animal. Some cladocerans may undergo 25 instars during the adult stage.

Cyclomorphosis, or the changes in gross morphology occurring in successive seasonal variations, is striking in some cladocerans (Fig. 24-23, *B*). Females of *Daphnia pulex* and *Daphnia longispina* undergo a change from the round-headed condition, which they have in late fall to early spring, to a helmet-shaped one during the warm summer months. Later, in the fall, the head gradually reverts back to its original shape. Cyclomorphosis varies greatly with different kinds of aquatic habitats and is less pronounced in shallow water.

Although cladocerans are mostly freshwater forms, there are some marine forms. They are especially common in aquatic vegetation along pond, lake, and river margins. They may occur in both temporary and permanent pools. They have a wide temperature range, although some are restricted to warmer waters. They live on a great variety of foods such as protozoans, bacteria, algae, and organic detritus. The genera *Polyphemus* (Fig. 24-23, *C*) and *Leptodora* are predaceous and have appendages modified for seizing such prey as rotifers. *Anchistropus* is parasitic on hydra, whose favorite food is cladocerans such as *Daphnia*.

Subclass Ostracoda

The common name of the members of this subclass is seed shrimps or mussel shrimps. Ostracods have a worldwide distribution and comprise about 2,000 named species. They inhabit both fresh water and the sea. One or two species are terrestrial. Most are free living, but some such as *Entocythere* and *Sphaeromicola* live as commensals on the gills of crayfish and on amphipods and isopods. *Cypridopsis* preys upon certain aquatic snails. Ostracods have some resemblance to conchostracans, for both have bivalved carapaces; but ostracods have fewer appendages. They vary in size from about 0.25 to 8 mm., although one marine species is more than 20 mm. long.

EXTERNAL MORPHOLOGY

The body and appendages are enclosed in a calcium-impregnated bivalve shell which is oval shaped. Dorsally a noncalcareous hinge of cuticle holds the valves together. The shell has three layers: a waxy outer layer, a middle layer of organic substances and minerals, and an inner layer of chitin and protein. The shell may be pigmented (light and dark colors) and bear spines, tubercles, and setae. Adductor muscles close the valves. When the animal is active, the valves gape open and the locomotor appendages protrude. Ostracods lack concentric lines of growth on the valves.

The body has lost all traces of segmentation, and the trunk is much reduced. The head makes up about one half of the body. A single or double eye is usually present. The head region bears four pairs of appendages: antennules, antennae, mandibles and maxillae (Fig. 24-24). Both the first and second pairs of antennae are well developed. The first pair (antennules) have clawlike bristles for digging. The antennae are adapted for locomotion and (in the male) for clasping the female during copulation. The mandibles are strongly toothed and bear three-segmented palps. Each maxilla consists of a branchial plate and four basal processes, the outmost of

which is palplike. The thoracic region usually has three pairs of appendages, but there may be fewer among the different species. They are commonly referred to as walking legs, but some are not used for that purpose. They may or may not be similar. The first thoracic legs may be modified in the males of some to form prehensile structures for grasping the female during copulation; the second thoracic legs have tapering claws; and the third thoracic legs are dorsally bent and specialized for keeping the inside of the shell cavity free from debris. The remainder of the trunk (sometimes referred to as the abdomen) has two unsegmented caudal or furcal rami, which are variable and may be mere spines.

Most ostracods live near or on the botton substratum, often in the ooze. They burrow for food by means of beating movements, especially by the two pairs of antennae that are specialized for locomotion. Well-developed muscles are attached to both pairs of antennae as well as to the other appendages and to the mouthparts. The antennae may be modified in other ways for climbing vegetation or for swimming. Some ostracods can bounce or hop around. Some species are found on sandy bottoms and others on soft mud.

INTERNAL MORPHOLOGY

The digestive system consists of the mouth, the foregut variously modified, the midgut, and the hindgut. The food consists of bacteria, algae, organic detritus, and dead animals. In general they are considered scavengers. Beating movements of the mandibular palps, the maxillae, and the branchial plates of the first legs create currents of water between the valves. Fine particles are strained out by the setae on the appendages and directed to the mouth. Inedible materials are mostly removed by the respiratory plates of the maxillae. Mucus strings of food may be employed by some species to convey food into the mouth. Large particles are broken up by the mandibles. The foregut may be modified into a short esophagus and a region where in some (order Podocopa) a sort of gastric mill is found. The midgut is fitted for absorption, and in some a digestive gland on each side empties into it. **401**

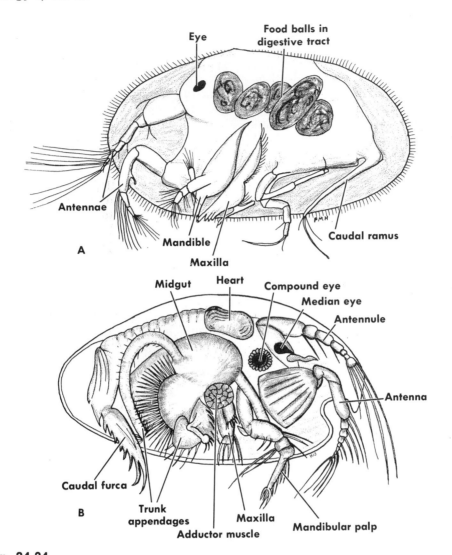

Fig. 24-24

Ostracods. **A,** *Cypricercus* (order Podocopa). **B,** *Cypridina* (order Myodocopa). (**A** modified from Hoff; **B** modified from Claus.)

Following the intestine is the hindgut and the anus, which lie at the base of the caudal rami.

Ostracods have both antennal and maxillary glands, presumably excretory in function. A pair of large shell glands of unknown function opens near the base of the second antennae.

Most ostracods have no special respiratory organs such as gills. Respiration takes place through the inner epithelium of the shell lamellae, branchial plates of the ap-

pendages, and antennae setae. Heart and blood vessels are restricted to the order Myodocopa, in which the heart has two ostia and is provided with anterior and ventrolateral arteries.

The central nervous system is made up of a brain (supraesophageal ganglion), a pair of circumesophageal connectives, a subesophageal ganglion, and a ventral chain of fused ganglia. In some species all the ganglia are fused in one mass. Nerves include the optic, those to the two pairs of antennae, the mandibles, and the maxillae, and those to the appendages. The sense organs include a nauplius eye (Fig. 24-10) and sessile compound eyes in the order Myodocopa. Other sense organs are auditory structures at the base of the antennules, an olfactory organ on one of the segments of the antennae, and setae or sensory hairs on various appendages.

Parthenogenesis is found among some members, but in general they are dioecious. Sex ratios may vary greatly in some species, with the males in a minority. The female system consists of a pair of tubular ovaries in the posteroventral region of the shell, paired oviducts with seminal receptacles, and genital openings between the bases of the third thoracic legs and caudal rami. Male organs include the testes (each of four coiled tubes placed between the valve lamellae), two sperm ducts (vasa deferentia), a pair of ejaculatory ducts, and a pair of penes just in front of the caudal rami. The ejaculatory ducts may not open through the penes in a few. In copulation the male becomes attached to the female shell dorsally and inserts the penes between the valves into female genital pores. The sperm are unusually long for a crustacean. Fertilization occurs in the seminal receptacle, and the eggs are brooded in the dorsal part of the shell cavity in some (*Darwinula*). In most forms the eggs are dropped into the water where they may be attached to vegetation. Eggs are viable for long periods of time under harsh conditions. Normally the eggs hatch within a few days to weeks after they are shed. The egg hatches into a bivalved nauplius. Sexual maturity is not attained until the ninth or last instar.

Order Myodocopa

The members of this order are worldwide in distribution and are entirely marine. They include the two families Cypridinidae and Conchoeciidae. The shell is provided with a notch through which the second antennae are extended when the shell is tightly closed. They have a heart, blood vessels, and compound eyes. No digestive glands empty into the intestine. The exopodites of the antennae, with well-developed muscles, are fitted for locomotion; the endopodites in the male are adapted for grasping. There are seven pairs of appendages and the caudal rami. A frontal organ on the head is also present. The Asteropinae are the only ostracods with true gills.

Cypridina (Fig. 24-24, *B*), *Pyrocypris*, and a few others are luminescent. The bluish light they produce is from secretions of a gland in the labrum. The light is under reflex control. The genus *Gigantocypris*, a deep-sea form, is the largest ostracod.

Order Cladocopa

These ostracods have no permanent aperture in their shell for the antennae. The shell can close tightly all around. They are marine and consist of one family, Polycopidae. Their biramous antennae are much flattened for locomotion. They have no heart or eyes. The body terminates in a process bearing clawlike spines. There are no trunk appendages.

The common genus *Polycope* has a smooth, circular shell. This is the smallest order of ostracods; they have been collected mainly in Atlantic water.

Order Podocopa

This order includes mostly freshwater forms, but there are marine representatives also. It is a large order and is made up of four families based upon the thoracic legs and caudal rami. The families are Cypridae, Darwinulidae, Cytheridae, and Bairdiidae. The second antennae are uniramous, and two pairs of trunk appendages are present. The valves of the shell have no aperture and are usually flattened on the ventral side. In the family Cypridae (Fig. 24-24, *A*) all the thoracic legs are different. The first pair of thoracic legs is modified for mastication, and the endopodites form a prehensile palp in the male. The third pair of legs is adapted for keeping the shell clean. This family has marked seasonal population cycles and has both marine and freshwater species. The family Darwinulidae also has the first pair of thoracic legs modified for mastication, but the second and third pair are adapted for crawling. This family lacks caudal rami, and the female bears living young. One genus, *Darwinula*, with two species is known. One of the two species lives in fresh water. In the family Cytheridae the three similar pairs of thoracic legs are adapted for crawling, and there is no ejaculatory tube. Most members of this family are marine. In the family Bairdiidae only marine forms are found. The valves of

403

their shells are unequal in size, the left being the larger. Their antennae are not adapted for swimming, but three similar pairs of thoracic legs are all adapted for locomotion. No ejaculatory ducts are present. Two common genera are *Bairdia* and *Bythocypris*. The fossil record of the Podocopa is better known than that of most other groups of ostracods, dating back to the Ordovician period.

Order Platycopa

This order consists of a single family of ostracods, the Cytherellidae. The biramous second antennae are large and have flattened segments. Neither pair of the antennae is used for locomotion. Heart and visual organs are absent. The three pairs of thoracic legs are nonleglike. All platycopids are marine. The only genus is *Cytherella*.

Subclass Mystacocarida

These small crustaceans share with the Cephalocarida the distinction of being among the most primitive of living crustaceans. They were first discovered off the coast of New England in 1939. They are less than 5 mm. long and live in the intertidal sand. The body is elongated and wormlike. Head and thorax are separate. The paired maxillipeds are on a separate segment that is not fused with the head. The thorax proper has four segments, each with a pair of platelike appendages. The six abdominal segments have no appen-

dages but bear a pair of caudal rami. A nauplius eye is present. The labrum is very large, and the mouth appendages bear setae that may be used in filter feeding. Sexes are separate, and the genital pore is on the thorax.

All three species belong to the genus *Derocheilocaris* (Fig. 24-25).

Subclass Copepoda

The copepods are strictly aquatic forms that are found in all kinds of water except that which is very salty. They represent the largest group of all the small crustaceans, the so-called Entomostraca. There may be as many as 6,000 named species. Most are free living, but some are parasitic or commensal on other animals. Their abundance and wide distribution have made them an important food item for fishes and other animals. Most of them are less than 2 mm. long, but some are as small as 1 mm. or less, while others may reach a length of 3 to 4 mm. Parasitic forms may be even larger. Most species are grayish and transparent, but freshwater forms in high altitudes may be orange, red, or other colors. There may also be seasonal variations in color.

EXTERNAL MORPHOLOGY

Copepods have a similar basic pattern, but there are many variations among them. In general the body is cylindric and definitely segmented. It is composed of head, thorax, and abdomen. The head is com-

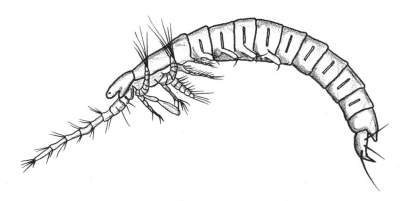

Fig. 24-25

Copepod *Derocheilocaris* (order Mystacocarida). This group shares with cephalocarids distinction of being among most primitive of crustaceans. (Redrawn from Pennak: McGraw-Hill encyclopedia of science and technology, vol. 8, McGraw-Hill Book Company.)

posed of one segment, rounded anteriorly, and sometimes bears a rostrum. At its posterior end the head is fused with the first (and sometimes second) thoracic segment. The head and the fused segments of the thorax are often referred to as the cephalothorax, forming as they do a more or less fused compact structure. Compound eyes are absent, but there is a single, median (naupliar) eye. The true head region consists of five pairs of appendages: the antennules, the antennae, the mandibles, the first maxillae, and the second maxillae (Fig. 24-26). The first thoracic segment, which is fused to the head, bears a pair of maxillipeds. The two pairs of antennae are adapted for swimming, balancing, or grasping. The other anterior appendages are for feeding. Counting both fused and unfused segments, the thorax is composed usually of six segments. Each of the unfused thoracic segments bears a pair of swimming legs.

The abdomen consists of 1 to 5 segments and bears no appendages except a pair of caudal rami. In some species the seventh or genital segment has a pair of vestigial swimming legs. A common way of dividing the copepod body is to separate it into an anterior metasome consisting of the head, the cephalothorax, and the first two pairs of unfused thoracic segments; and a posterior urosome composed of the last thoracic segments and the abdomen. There are many variations of fusion conditions among the different groups of copepods.

Basically the head and thoracic appendages are biramous, but there are many modifications of this plan. The antennules are uniramous and may contain as many as 25 segments. The antennae are usually biramous, much smaller than the antennules, and may have nine segments in the endopodite. In some the exopodite is missing. The biramous mandibles may have four segments in both branches. The two pairs of maxillae and the maxillipeds may be biramous or uniramous. The biramous swimming legs (usually with three segments in each branch) are generally similar, but the last two pairs may be highly modified. They bear many setae. The sixth pair is lacking in the female and may be vestigial in the male. Locomotion in co-

pepods is mostly by jerky movements produced by the action of the swimming legs. While the animal is swimming the antennules are carried alongside the body. Some make use of the two pairs of antennae in swimming. A few swim upside down.

INTERNAL MORPHOLOGY

Copepods have a variety of feeding habits depending upon whether they are planktonic or benthonic in their distribution. Some have their mouthparts adapted for filter feeding, and others for seizing and biting. In filter feeders the antennae, mandibular palps, and the first antennae are provided with setae, which by rapid vibrations create a current of water alongside the body. This swirl of water is partially directed into a median filter chamber by the maxillipeds. From this current, particles of food are filtered, collected, and passed to the mouth by the action of the setae and endites of the maxillae and maxillipeds. The members of the order Cyclopoida have the mouthparts adapted for capturing their prey of unicellular plant and animal organisms. Some copepods are filter feeders as well as predaceous and have their mouthparts modified accordingly.

In transparent copepods the digestive system can be seen clearly because the food outlines its contour. The system is a more or less straight tube with few regional specializations. The anus is placed on the last abdominal segment between the bases of the caudal rami. A simple heart (Fig. 24-26) is present only in the order Calanoida *(Diaptomus)* and some parasitic forms; in others the blood is moved through the hemocoel by muscular movements of the body, appendages, and digestive tract. No gills are present, and gas exchange occurs through the body surface. Maxillary glands provide the means of excretion. The nervous system is mostly concentrated into a mass by coalescence of the ganglia. Distinct ventral ganglia are restricted to a few groups. Besides the nauplius eye, which shows up as a clear median pigmented spot near the anterior end, tactile sensory organs are scattered over the body, especially on the appendages. Light organs, which make use of luminescent secretion of glands in the in-

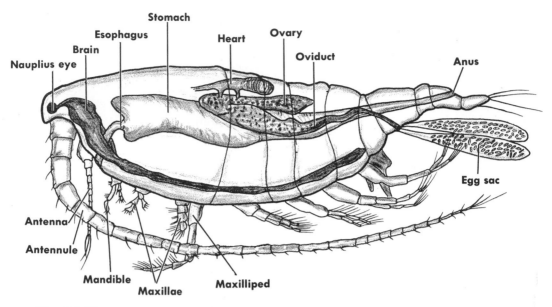

Fig. 24-26

Female *Diaptomus*, a calanoid copepod. (Modified from Herrick.)

tegument, are found in some species and may be used for sex recognition.

REPRODUCTION

The female reproductive system consists of an ovary (single or paired) and two glandular oviducts with diverticula. The genital opening is on the ventral surface of the first abdominal segment (Fig. 24-26). Near it are the separate openings of a pair of seminal receptacles. There may be connections between the seminal receptacles and the oviducts. The male system usually comprises a single testis and paired or single sperm ducts. The male genital opening is also on the first abdominal segment. The antennae, and sometimes the fifth pair of thoracic appendages, are modified for clasping the female's abdomen in copulation. Sperm are transferred to the female genital segment in spermatophores, which are stored in the seminal receptacles. Usually only one mating is necessary for the fertilization of all subsequent eggs laid by the female. Fertilized eggs are extruded into two ovisacs secreted by the oviducts. Some have only one sac and others have no sac at all. Each ovisac may contain 5 to 40 eggs. The female may shed the entire ovisac or shed the eggs singly into the water. The number of generations varies with the species. Some freshwater forms produce a generation at least every two weeks; others have three or four broods a year, and even fewer. In many the largest number of eggs is produced in the spring. In the familiar *Cyclops* (Fig. 24-27) the incubation period in the ovisac is from 12 hours to 5 days, and as soon as the newly hatched ones are shed a new brood is produced in new ovisacs. Only one or two species are known to be parthenogenetic.

DEVELOPMENT AND LIFE HISTORY

The copepod egg hatches into a nauplius larva with its characteristic three pairs of appendages (antennules, antennae, and mandibles). There may be as many as six naupliar instars, but some have fewer, especially in the parasitic forms. In each successive instar, new appendages are added until there are seven or eight pairs. When the fifth and sixth nauplius stage molts, the instar resembles the adult and is called a copepodid. In six copepodid instars the adult finally emerges. In parasitic forms there may be fewer copepodid instars. The time for complete development may be only a few days, or it may last several months.

Most of the parasitic crustaceans are found among the copepods. Some orders are exclusively parasitic. Certain aspects of parasitic forms will be described under the appropriate orders.

HABITATS AND ECOLOGY

Most copepods live in the sea. They form an important part of plankton populations. Most of them live in the upper 200 to 300 meters of water. However, there are others that are abyssal or bathypelagic. Some are bottom dwellers and many are found clinging to aquatic vegetation. Some species are adapted for living in the sand. Diurnal migrations are common among those that live near the surface waters.

Populations of copepods may reach tremendous numbers. Up to 600,000 or 700,-000 have been found in each cubic meter of fresh water. They play important roles in converting plant into animal substance. They make up as much as 70 percent of the animal populations of plankton and serve as food for innumerable animals such as fishes and baleen whales.

Temperature may play an important role in their worldwide aquatic distribution. Some are definitely cold-water forms, and others prefer southern waters. Some are known to form cysts under harsh environments. Such encystments usually occur in some of the copepodid stages rather than in adult stages.

Order Calanoida

Most calanoids are planktonic forms and probably represent the most abundant and economically important of all marine animals. They occupy a unique position as the base of the animal food chain. The number of their species may be in excess of 1,200, which are divided into 120 genera. They are found in all depths of the ocean from the surface to abyssal depths. Many of them live in fresh water. They generally migrate toward the surface at night and return to deeper levels at day. Many of them bear very long antennae and plumose setae which aid them in flotation. These free-living copepods have the metasome-urosome articulation between the fifth and

sixth thoracic segments. Many of them are brightly colored, and some have brilliant displays of bioluminescence. They are mostly filter feeders and have certain mouth appendages specialized as passive filters. They possess a saccular or tubular heart provided with a single, unbranched aorta. The sperm duct is single. Usually the antennae are not specialized for grasping the female, and the spermatophores are transferred to the female by the male thoracic appendages.

Common genera are *Calanus* (Fig. 24-28, *A*), *Diaptomus* (Fig. 24-26), *Metridia*, and *Calocalanus*.

Order Cyclopoida

These copepods are found in both salt and fresh water. Some are planktonic and others are benthonic. The order includes a number of parasitic forms as well as free-living forms. Some are intermediate hosts for human parasites. The body in general is oval shaped, with the abdominal part rather sharply set off from the anterior region. There are usually ten segments in the male and nine in the female, in which two segments are fused at the genital region. The metasome-urosome articulation is placed between the fourth and fifth thoracic segments. Two caudal rami with un-

Fig. 24-27

Cyclops, a cyclopoid copepod. Note paired ovisacs. (Photograph of stained preparation.)

equal setae are present. The antennae are uniramous, but most appendages are biramous. The antennules of the male are adapted for grasping the female. No heart is present, and the colorless blood is circulated by general body movements. The anus is found on the dorsal side of the last abdominal segment. The large ovisacs are paired. A dorsal brain is connected by circumesophageal connectives to a ventral chain of ganglia. Cyclopoids are not filter feeders; food is seized and eaten by the biting mouthparts.

Cyclops (Fig. 24-27) of which there are many species, is the most common genus.

Order Harpacticoida

These copepods have a worldwide distribution, both in fresh water and in the sea. They are mostly free living and benthonic but are found at all levels. Some species are pelagic, commensal, or parasitic. There are about 1,400 species of them. They vary in length from 0.3 to 4 mm. In general the first thoracic segment is fused to the cephalothorax, and the last thoracic segment is a part of the abdomen. The male biramous antennules are specialized for grasping. The maxilliped and first part of the swimming legs may also be prehensile. The metasome-urosome articulation is between the fourth and fifth thoracic segments. The ventral ovisac may be single or double. The abdomen is unusually wide for copepods. The nervous system consists of a brain, subesophageal ganglion, circumesophageal ring, and a ventral chain of ganglia. Frontal organs are present in some. An aesthete, or long sensory process, may be present on the antennules and other appendages. The two oviducts open into a seminal receptacle. The species

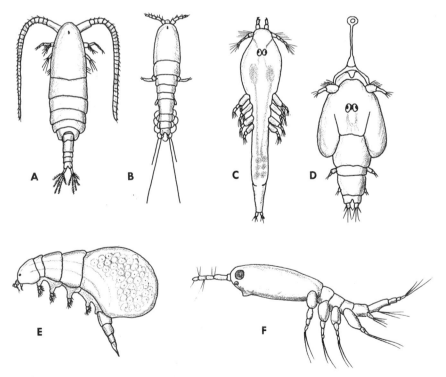

Fig. 24-28

Some copepods. **A,** *Calanus,* a planktonic form (order Calanoida). **B,** *Harpacticus* (order Harpacticoida) is found in marine, brackish, and fresh water. **C,** *Lernaea* female taken from gills of flounder (order Lernaeopodoida). **D,** *Lepeophtheirus* young attaches by filament to gills of fish (order Caligoida). **E,** *Doropygus* female commensal or parasitic in ascidians (order Notodelphyoida). **F,** *Monstrilla,* from marine plankton (order Monstrilloida). (Modified from: **A,** Miner; **B,** Lang; **C** and **D,** Scott; **F,** Davis.)

Elaphoidella bideris is parthenogenetic. Two other well-known genera are *Harpacticus* (Fig. 24-28, *B*), found in marine, brackish, and fresh water, and *Epactophanes,* a freshwater form often found in damp moss and on sandy beaches.

Order Monstrilloida

These copepods belong to a small order of about 35 species, most of which are rarely encountered. The adults lack antennae and mouthparts. In their life history the nauplius is free swimming, but other immature stages are parasitic upon marine invertebrates, especially polychaetes. After emerging from the host the adults become free swimming in plankton populations. The digestive tract is vestigial, and food is absorbed directly from the host. Dorsolateral eyes may be present as well as the single median eye.

Monstrilla, a marine form (Fig. 24-28, *F*), is the best known genus.

Order Notodelphyoida

These, like the preceding order, are parasitic or commensal copepods. There are about 300 known species, all marine. Few can be called parasitic in a strict sense, but they live in the cavity or pharynx of tunicates, whose food they share. The metasome-urosome articulation is located between the fourth and fifth thoracic segments in males and between the first and second abdominal segments in females. Their size is similar to that of planktonic copepods. Because of their commensal habits, notodelphyoids are only slightly modified from free-living copepods. The exopodites of the thoracic limbs often bear claws for attachment to the host. The trunk and head appendages are usually small. Eggs are normally incubated in a large brood pouch in the dorsal region of the thorax. Larval development includes several naupliar instars. Infective stages are usually early copepodid stages.

Among the many genera are *Ascidicola, Notodelphys,* and *Doropygus* (Fig. 24-28, *E*).

Order Caligoida

Caligoida are chiefly ectoparasites on freshwater and marine fishes. They live on the host's blood by becoming attached to the gills, fins, integument, and other parts of the body. They usually have a distinct carapace and fused segments. The antennae and maxillipeds are prehensile, and the sucking mouth is provided with pointed mandibles for piercing the host's skin. Swimming legs are much modified, with loss of setae, reduction of joints, and fewer numbers. There are about 400 species. The metasome-urosome articulation is between the third and fourth thoracic segments. They vary in size from a few millimeters to the largest copepod *Penella,* which may reach a length of several inches. There are many morphologic variations in the order. Many of these modifications are clinging adaptions. Copulation may occur in the last larval stage, with the male dying soon after.

Penella has been found in great numbers on whales as well as on other forms. *Caligus* on the skin and gills of fishes and *Lepeophtheirus* (Fig. 24-28, *D*) on the skin of freshwater fishes are other common genera.

Order Lernaeopodoida

These copepods are commonly known as fish maggots. They are ectoparasitic on freshwater and marine fishes. The body has little or no segmentation, especially in the female, which appears wormlike. Males are very small but are distinctly segmented. Thoracic appendages may be reduced or absent. The second maxillae are strongly modified for attachment after they are buried in the host's tissue. Postembryonic development is reduced to two or three stages. The free-swimming larvae emerge from the ovisac in the first copepodid stage. Some are provided with a preformed, coiled frontal organ, which can be everted and embedded in the host's tissue. This tube finally degenerates when the larva emerges into the vermiform stage.

These ectoparasites feed on blood or body fluids of the host. They number about 300 species.

Salmincola, Lernaea (Fig. 24-28, *C*), and *Brachiella* are common genera.

Subclass Branchiura

These crustaceans are known as fish lice, of which there are fewer than 100 **409** species all included in the order Arguloida. Their morphology shows fewer variations than found in most other groups of small crustaceans. The body is made up of a flattened, disk-shaped cephalothorax and a small, unsegmented, bilobed abdomen. They have a pair of antennules, a pair of antennae, a pair of mandibles, two pairs of maxillae, and four pairs of swimming legs. The appendages are set along the longitudinal axis on the underside of the body and are covered by the thin cephalothorax. This adaptation fits them for their role of ectoparasites against the skin of a fish host. They have compound eyes. They are adapted for attachment by having hooks and suction cups on the underside of the body. The second to fourth pairs of swimming legs, which have a reduced number of segments, are used for copulation. There are usually no larval stages or nauplius, and development into a juvenile is direct. Sexual maturity requires about seven molts. They feed on blood and other tissue fluids by making rasping wounds with their mandibles. *Argulus* (Fig. 24-29) often leaves its host to attach its eggs to some object.

Argulus is the most common genus.

Subclass Cirripedia

The cirripedes in the adult stage are a group of attached crustaceans. They consist of the barnacles, acorn shells, and some related forms of different habits, including some parasitic forms of highly modified structure. They are exclusively marine. There are more than 800 species divided among five orders. Barnacles make up more than half of all the cirripedes.

Since there are few common characteristics that apply to all the orders, each will be considered separately. Their relationships are indicated by their larval development.

Order Thoracica

Barnacles can be divided into the stalked and sessile types. Stalked forms have a long peduncle which comprises the preoral part of the animal. Most Thoracica are free living and some are commensal, but it is doubtful that any of them are truly parasitic. Barnacles will attach themselves to almost any object of the sea, dead or alive, to which they can fasten themselves (Figs. 24-30, 24-31). Their fouling of ships and pilings is known in all seas.

The body of the stalked barnacle is enclosed in a soft mantle (capitulum), which is commonly protected by calcareous plates (Fig. 24-32). The capitulum includes all the body except the preoral part. The calcareous plates usually include the anterior keellike carina, two lateral terga, and two posterior scuta. By means of adductor muscles the margins of the terga and scuta can be pulled close together for protection or opened for extrusion of the appendages or cirri. In some barnacles there is a tendency for the number of calcareous plates to be reduced. In *Conchoderma*, often found on ships, nearly all the plates are greatly reduced or lost.

In sessile barnacles the body is enclosed within an immovable wall formed by the overlapping of four to eight plates. The movable operculum of two to four plates

Fig. 24-29

Argulus, a common ectoparasite on fish (subclass Branchiura). Adult fish lice range from 5 to 25 mm. in length.

Fig. 24-30

Large cluster of *Lepas* (gooseneck barnacles, suborder Lepadomorpha) attached to fishing-net glass float. Collected near Vancouver, British Columbia, in August, 1958. (From Hickman: Integrated principles of zoology, The C. V. Mosby Co.)

is provided with muscles for opening and closing (Figs. 24-33, 24-34). Sessile barnacles usually have wide attachment bases which are calcareous or membranous. This corresponds to the preoral region of stalked barnacles and bears cement glands. In the sessile forms the plates are modified and adapted for different purposes from those in the stalked forms. The lateral plates become the mural plates in sessile barnacles. The mural plates in partial or complete fusion with the carina and rostrum form a complete vertical wall around the body of the animal. The other stalked-barnacle plates, terga and scuta, cover the top of the animal. Acorn shells (Fig. 24-33) have a conical shell and are cemented directly to the rocks. Their orifice is opened or

Fig. 24-31

Closeup of few of *Lepas* shown in Fig. 24-30. Note cirri extending between valves (order Thoracica of subclass Cirripedia).

Fig. 24-32

Mitella, a stalked barnacle (order Thoracica of subclass Cirripedia) showing long peduncle and plates covering capitulum. Compare plate arrangement with that of *Lepas.*

Fig. 24-33

Group of acorn barnacles *Balanus* (order Thoracica of subclass Cirripedia).

closed by four movable plates. The largest barnacle is perhaps *Balanus psittacus,* which grows to a length of 8 to 10 inches with a diameter of 3 inches. There are many variations in the arrangement of the plates in sessile barnacles. Plates may be reduced, or they may be fused together in a continuous or compact wall. The terga and scuta may be lost altogether, or the wall surrounding the animal may consist of one tergum and scutum, with the other tergum and scutum making up the lid. Some forms are completely naked.

The arrangement of the body is such that the long axis of the mantle is at right angles to that of the body. This organization makes it possible for the cirri to be directed toward the mantle opening. The body is composed chiefly of a head and a thoracic region; the abdomen is lacking or represented only by the caudal rami or furca. The remains of the antennules are usually found in the cement glands, which serve for the attachment of the larva (Fig. 24-36). The antennae are lacking in the adult but are present in the larva.

The mouthparts consist of a labrum, paired mandibles bearing palps, maxillulae, and maxillae (Fig. 24-35). There are usually six pairs of long, curled, biramous thoracic appendages or cirri. These are fringed with hairs and can be protruded from the slitlike opening of the mantle to sweep in small particles of animal or plant food. The six cirri on each side form a sort of net, and the two nets come together to enclose the food, which is scraped off and passed to the mouth by the maxillulae.

The digestive system includes a foregut, an enlarged midgut with glands, a hindgut, and an anus that opens near the base of the cirri. Paired maxillary glands (excretory) open on the maxillae. Respiration occurs chiefly through the body surface and the mantle; circulation takes place through the lacunar spaces without a heart. The brain is located in front of the midgut, while the ganglia of the nerve chain are more or less fused into a few masses (Fig. 24-35).

Most barnacles are hermaphroditic. The reproductive system (Figs. 24-34, 24-35) consists of ovaries that lie in the mantle wall (sessile) or in the peduncle (stalked), with paired oviducts opening on the first thoracic cirri, and of testes with paired

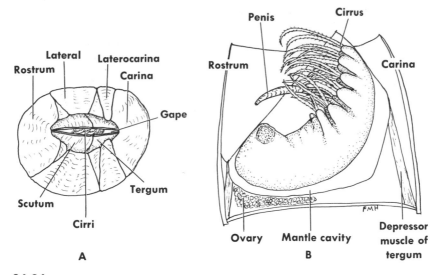

Fig. 24-34

Balanus amphitrite. **A,** Enclosed by valves. **B,** Valves partially removed to expose soft parts. (Drawn largely from life.)

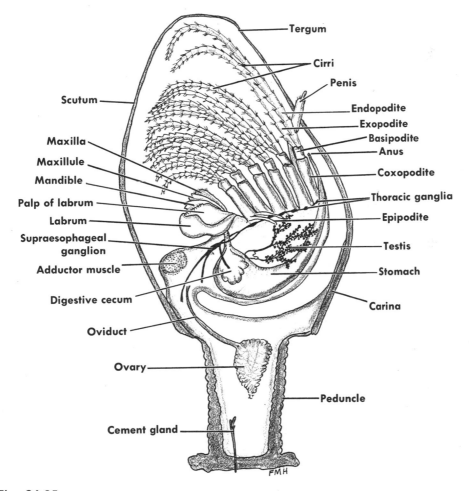

Fig. 24-35

Lepas, drawn with left valves removed, showing only six cirri on left side. (Drawn largely from life.)

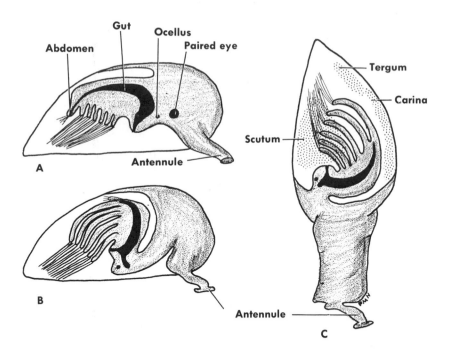

Fig. 24-36

Metamorphosis of *Lepas*. **A,** Cypris stage. **B,** Attached larva. **C,** Young larva with developing valves still surrounded by cypris shell. (Modified from Korschelt and Heider.)

sperm ducts enlarged into seminal vesicles that open into the penis. In copulation the penis can be projected out of the body and sperm deposited near the oviduct openings of an adjacent barnacle. Cross-fertilization is thus the rule, but self-fertilization may also occur. Marked sexual dimorphism is characteristic of many of the stalked barnacles. In some the males are small, dwarflike forms attached inside the mantle cavity of larger, normal individuals. These may be minature complemental males attached within hermaphroditic individuals, for example, *Scalpellum* and *Ibla*. Fertilized eggs are usually brooded in an ovisac or a thin lamella. The egg normally hatches into a free-swimming nauplius (less frequently into the cypris stage) with frontal horns on the carapace. After a number of molts the last nauplius instar gives rise to a cypris larva, in which the body is enclosed in a bivalve carapace with compound eyes

and six pairs of thoracic appendages (Fig. 24-36, *A*). The number of larvae reaching the cypris stage is only a fraction of those released as nauplius larvae. The cypris larva settles down and becomes attached to a substratum by means of the cement glands of the antennules (Fig. 24-36, *B*). Many changes now occur which involve the infolding of the mantle and the formation of the five primary valves—a pair each of scuta and terga, and a carina—(Fig. 24-36, *C*). At the next molt the mantle fold opens, and the barnacle assumes the adult position. The barnacle is attached at its preoral surface, with the ventral surface at right angles to the attached surface and its posterior side directed upward.

The order Thoracica is commonly divided into the suborder Lepadomorpha (pedunculate barnacles), suborder Verrucomorpha (reduced pedunclate barnacles), and suborder Balanomorpha (sessile barnacles).

Order Acrothoracica

These are naked, boring barnacles that are permanent residents of holes in the shells of mollusks, corals, and barnacles. They have no calcareous plates and usually only four pairs of cirri. The last pairs are widely separated from the first pair. An abdomen is lacking or else is represented by the caudal furca. The ovary is present in the thick part of the mantle or disk, which is often the organ of attachment. Sexes are usually separate, with the males minute and usually attached within females. The size of most species rarely exceeds 10 mm. Only about a dozen species are known, of which *Trypetesa* has a wide distribution.

Order Ascothoracica

These cirripedes are mainly parasites of coelenterates or echinoderms. They are naked barnacles but have a bivalve or saccular mantle. They are not attached at the preoral region as are most barnacles. Their mouthparts are mostly modified for piercing and sucking. The antennules, when present, are usually adapted for clinging.

The thoracic appendages, six or less, are reduced, and an abdomen may be present. There are no cement glands. Both the digestive tract and the ovaries have extensive diverticula, which are distributed in the mantle. Sexes are separate, with the males much smaller than the females.

There are some 25 species, the most representative genera of which are *Baccalaureus, Dendrogaster, Ascothorax,* and *Laura* (Fig. 24-37).

Order Apoda

These parasitic cirripedes are of doubtful taxonomic status. They have no mantle or appendages but are segmented and possess an abdomen. The mouth is suctorial. Antennules and cement glands are present. The digestive system is incomplete. They are hermaphroditic, but their development is not known. So far, the order is based (by

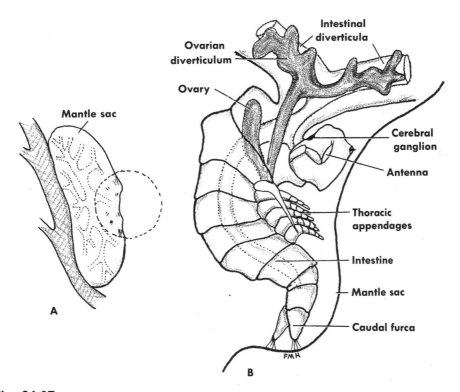

Fig. 24-37

Laura gerardiae, an ascothoracid barnacle attached to piece of coral *(Gerardia).* **A,** Minute animal is enclosed in mantle sac in which are papillae that penetrate into host tissues. Diverticula of digestive tract and ovaries extend through mantle. Circled portion is enlarged in **B. B,** Body of animal exposed and greatly enlarged. (After Lacaze-Duthiers; modified from Lankester.)

Charles Darwin) on one specimen found as a parasite in a stalked barnacle.

Order Rhizocephala

Probably the best known of the parasitic barnacles are the rhizocephalans because of their worldwide distribution and their habit of using other crustaceans, especially the Decapoda, as hosts. They are naked, but a thin bag-shaped mantle encloses the visceral mass, which consists chiefly of gonads. This saclike structure is fastened to the abdomen of the host by a short stalk. They have no appendages, segmentation, sense organs, or digestive system. A rootlike system, modified from the peduncle and composed of fine threadlike structures, penetrates to all parts of the crustacean host and sucks out its body fluids. The fertilized eggs develop in a brood sac, from which the larvae escape by an opening into the sea. The free-swimming nauplius develops into a cypris larva which, if it attaches to a crab, becomes a kentrogon larva. This larva injects into the host's intestine a cell mass that develops into a tumor and root system. In a few weeks the endoparasite emerges as a small sac. Those cypris larvae that settle on immature rhizocephalans become larval males. These males inject into the brood pouch a cell mass that later differentiates into sperm. The saccular animal becomes sexually mature some weeks later. This sex pattern, first discovered in *Peltogasterella*, may be general in rhizocephalans, which are often called hermaphroditic because of the presence of sperm repositories and eggs in the same sac.

Parasitism by members of this order produces a characteristic parasitic castration in the infected host. Some of these striking changes involve secondary sex changes, such as the broadening of the abdomen of a parasitized male so that it resembles that of a normal female; and in parasitized immature female crabs an adult type of abdomen appears precociously. However, the growth of the swimmerets is retarded. Other changes may be the complete atrophy of the gonads in the host. Such changes may be explained by metabolic disturbances or hormonal imbalance.

Sacculina (Fig. 24-38), a common parasite of crabs, is a classic example. Other genera are *Briarsaccus*, the largest member of the order, and *Loxothylacus*, which parasitizes the blue crab (*Callinectes*).

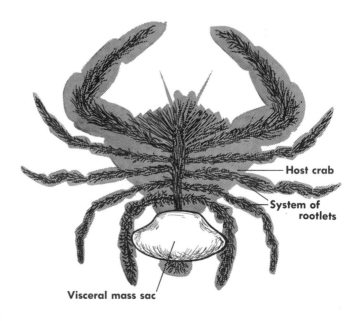

Host crab

System of rootlets

Visceral mass sac

Fig. 24-38

Sacculina, a barnacle parasitic on crabs (order Rhizocephala). (From Hickman: Integrated principles of zoology, The C. V. Mosby Co.)

Subclass Malacostraca

The subclass Malacostraca is the largest taxon of the crustaceans. It includes the shrimps, crabs, lobsters, sow bugs, beach hoppers, wood lice, and a host of others and takes in the largest crustaceans as well as many smaller types. The group is worldwide in its distribution, embracing upward of 18,000 to 20,000 species. These species form a natural taxonomic group because of certain common characteristics, but there is an enormous diversity among the members within the group. The trunk is usually composed of eight thoracic segments and six abdominal ones, each of which bears a pair of appendages. A carapace may be present, vestigial, or absent. For other general characteristics of this subclass see the classification, p. 340.

The malacostracans are usually divided into two arbitrary series: the Leptostraca, with seven abdominal segments and an adductor muscle connecting the two halves of the shell; and the Eumalacostraca, with six abdominal segments and lacking an adductor muscle.

The common primitive type of crustacean (caridoid facies) from which the various members have specialized has a shrimplike body, a carapace enveloping the body, stalked and movable eyes, biramous antennules, antennae, thoracic limbs with swimming exopodites and respiratory epipodites, and one or more pairs of thoracic limbs forming maxillipeds as part of the mouthparts. In addition, the ventrally flexed abdomen is provided with five pairs of biramous swimming appendages (pleopods), a tail fan formed of the flat uropods (sixth abdominal appendages), and the telson. Some present groups of crustaceans that approach this primitive plan are the Mysidacea, Anaspidacea, and Eucardia.

Malacostracans have the female genital duct located on the sixth thoracic segment and that of the male on the eighth segment. Males often have the first two pairs of pleopods modified as copulatory organs.

Series Leptostraca
Order Nebaliacea

Nebaliacea is the only order of the series Leptostraca and represents a marine group of 15 to 20 species and varieties. Its members are relics of a much larger group that were common in the Paleozoic era. They average 4 to 12 mm. in length and live mostly as bottom dwellers in shallow water. The thorax and part of the abdomen are enclosed by a carapace with an adductor muscle in the head region, joining the two valves (Fig. 24-39, A). A small, ringed rostral plate covers the head. The eight thoracic segments are free with clearly indicated suture lines. The thoracic appendages are similar and foliaceous. In some members the whole limb is rather flattened; in others the epipodite is small, while the endopodite and exopodite are long and slender. The thoracic limbs are usually adapted for creating water currents, from which food is collected into a ventral groove and then conveyed to the mouth (Fig. 24-39, B, C). The abdomen has seven segments, the last one of which is without appendages. The telson is provided with two articulated furcal rami. The first four biramous abdominal appendages are used for swimming; the last two uniramous appendages are reduced.

Gills are formed from the flattened thoracic epipodites. The breeding female has a fan of plumose setae that are arranged to form a basketlike brood chamber. The eggs hatch into a postlarval stage.

Most members of the order live in shallow, muddy bottoms or among stones and aquatic vegetation. Some, such as *Nebaliella*, have eyes, antennules, and other head parts adapted for burrowing. *Nebaliopsis* lives at great depths and feeds mostly on the eggs of various animals. Its midgut is provided with a large diverticulum for holding reserves of food.

Series Eumalacostraca
SUPERORDER SYNCARIDA

This superorder includes two orders, the Anaspidacea and the Bathynellacea. Syncarids vary in length from 0.5 mm. to 5 cm. They are found mostly in caves, springs, and mountain lakes where they swim and crawl over the bottoms or on aquatic vegetation. As a group they are characterized by lack of a carapace, calcareous plates, and chelae. There are about 30 species in the superorder, and all are freshwater forms.

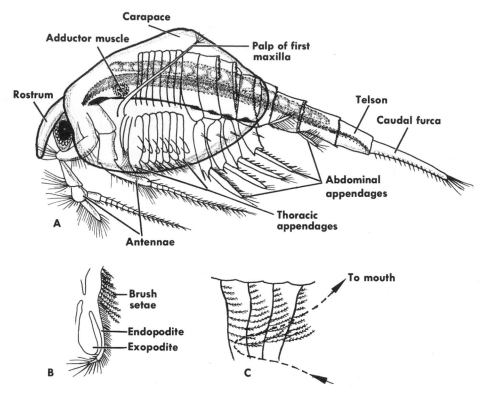

Fig. 24-39

Nebalia, a malacostracan (order Nebaliacea). **A,** Female specimen. **B,** Portion of thoracic appendage showing brush setae. **C,** Diagram of brush setae of several appendages showing how food particles are moved toward mouth. (**A** modified from Claus; **B** and **C** modified from Green.)

Order Anaspidacea

These primitive crustaceans are represented by only a few species, which are found in the fresh waters of Tasmania and South Australia. Anaspidaceans have a slender body that is almost uniformly segmented. Both their antennules and antennae are long. The biramous thoracic appendages are used mainly for swimming. The coxopodite of each thoracic appendage bears a pair of lamellar gills. The abdominal appendages or pleopods have fringed exopodites, but the endopodites are reduced or absent except in the male, where the first two pairs are used as copulatory organs. Each mandible bears a palpus and is fitted for macerating the food. The stalked compound eyes usually project from the dorsal wall above the antennae, but in some the eyes are sessile. The principal food is organic detritus, which covers the rocks of their habitat, and also dead in-

sect larvae and worms. Some of these crustaceans have the second maxillae adapted for filtering. Currents of water are directed into a median channel to the mouth by the beating of the thoracic exopodies and maxillae. A heart and excretory maxillary glands are present. On the underside of the broad, flattened telson is the anus.

Anaspides (Fig. 24-40, *A*) is the best known genus and has been thoroughly studied. It is found in the lakes of Tasmania at high altitudes and may reach a length of 2 inches. It is considered the most generalized of modern malacostracans. *Paranaspides* and *Koonunga* are other genera from Tasmania and South Australia.

Order Bathynellacea

These syncarid crustaceans are found in the subterranean waters of central Europe. They are less than 2 mm. long and are

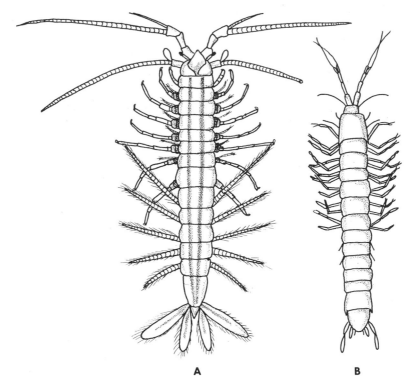

Fig. 24-40

A, *Anaspides,* a syncarid in natural walking position (order Anaspidacea). **B,** Male *Monodella,* a pancarid (order Thermosbaenacea). (**A** modified from Smith; **B** modified from Karaman.)

eyeless. The antennules and antennae bear clusters of setae. The thorax and abdomen are similar in structure, and each of the thoracic appendages has two epipodites that function as gills. Some of the abdominal appendages are reduced or absent. A typical telson is wanting, but the abdomen bears a pair of caudal furcae and a pair of elongated, jointed uropods. The eggs hatch directly into juvenile forms.

Bathynella and *Thermobathynella* are recognized genera.

SUPERORDER PANCARIDA

Pancaridans are small crustaceans of 1 to 4 mm. in length. Only one order, Thermosbaenacea, is represented in the superorder. This group is characterized by a dorsally located brood pouch formed by the carapace. The maxillipeds may have either an exopodite or an endopodite (sometimes both), and a respiratory epipodite. The body is mostly cylindric, with no division between the thorax and abdomen. There are no eyes, and the head and first thoracic segment are fused. The antennules are biramous and the antennae consist of exopodites only. There are five

pairs of biramous thoracic appendages that lack epipodites. The last two thoracic segments lack appendages (except in the genus *Monodella*) (Fig. 24-40, *B*). Two pairs of appendages occur on the abdomen. The uropods are biramous with a one-jointed endopodite and a two-jointed exopodite.

Pancaridans have been found in the transitional zone between fresh water and marine water in Italy and Yugoslavia.

The group is represented by two genera, *Thermosbaena* and *Monodella*. Only four or five species are found in the two genera.

SUPERORDER PERACARIDA

This superorder is made up of six orders, which include aquatic sow bugs, opossum shrimps, and some others. In these orders the young undergo development in a ventral brood pouch (marsupium), which is formed by oostegites or flat plates that extend medially from the coxopodites of the thoracic legs. The roof of the brood pouch is formed by the thoracic sternites. They also differ from other malacostracans by having a three-segmented protopodite in the antenna and a marked flexion of the thoracic legs between the fifth and sixth segments. The first of the thoracic segments is fused with the head.

Order Spelaeogriphacea

This order is represented by a single species found in a freshwater lake in Africa. It is a blind, shrimplike form about 6 to 9 mm. long. It has a short carapace united to the first thoracic segment. The thorax consists of eight segments, the first one of which is fused to the head. The abdomen is made up of six segments. The antenna has a long flagellum. The rostrum is triangular with a small ocular scale on each side. The first pair of thoracic appendages forms the maxillipeds, each of which has a cup-shaped respiratory organ at its base. The other seven pairs of thoracic appendages are adapted for walking. Three pairs of oval gills are attached to the exopodites of the fifth through the seventh thoracic segments. Of the abdominal appendages, the first four pairs are biramous swimming paddles, the fifth pair is vestigial, and the sixth pair, with the telson, forms a tail fan. The incubation of the few large eggs occurs in the ventral brood pouch characteristic of the superorder. The only known species is *Spelaeogriphus lepidops.*

Order Mysidacea

The order is made up of about 550 species, and its members are commonly known as opossum shrimps, so called because of the ventral marsupium at the base of the last two pairs of thoracic legs in the female. Although they are mostly marine some mysidaceans are found in fresh water. The body is composed of the typical malacostracan number of 19 segments, 5 of which form the head, 8 the thorax, and 6 the abdomen, with a tail fan of uropods and telson. Each segment has a pair of biramous appendages. A carapace covers the thorax but is not united with the last four thoracic segments. The eyes are stalked and movable. In cave-dwelling forms, eyes may be vestigial. The first pair of thoracic

appendages (and sometimes the second pair) is modified as maxillipeds. The other thoracic appendages are filamentous, usually with setae, and are used mostly for swimming. The abdominal appendages (pleopods) are generally all similar but may be modified or reduced in some species. Several mysidaceans (especially primitive forms) use pleopods for swimming, whereas others use the thoracic appendages for this purpose. Walking is usually done with the thoracic endopods. Mysids range from 3 to 85 mm. in length; some lophogastrids may reach as much as 200 mm.

Raptorial feeding is characteristic of the members of the suborder Lophogastrida. Living or dead animals are captured by the subchelate thoracic endopods and mandibular palps and are passed to the mandibles where they are masticated. In the other suborder, Mysida, most of the members are filter feeders. Rotatory movements by the thoracic exopods, aided by the beating of the maxillipeds, produce currents that flow forward along the ventral food groove. The food is filtered by maxillary setae and passed into the mouth. Such filter feeders derive much of their food from the organic detritus of the sea floor. Lophogastrids have foliaceous thoracic gills and cause currents of water to flow backward over the gills by beating the lamellar epipod on each of the first thoracic appendages. The current of water flows through the branchial chamber lying between the thorax and carapace on each side and is directed over the gills from the second to the eighth thoracic appendages. In Mysida, which have no gills, the current of water is directed forward by the beating of the thoracic exopods, and the exchange of gases is made through the thin-walled, highly vascular lining of the carapace.

Sense organs include the eyes, usually with movable stalks, and statocysts with statoliths in the uropodal endopod (Fig. 24-41, *B, C*).

Developing eggs are carried in the marsupium one to three months (Fig. 24-41, *A*) and hatch directly into juveniles. The members of this order continue their growth just after each molt throughout life.

Mysids are active forms that dart among

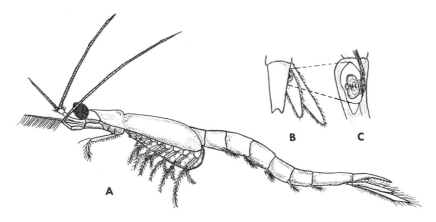

Fig. 24-41

Mysis, a peracaridan (order Mysidacea). **A,** Female with ventral marsupium. **B,** Telson and right uropod of *Mysis* showing statocyst near base of endopodite. **C,** Side view of statocyst of same showing statolith and sensory nerve. (**A** modified from Pennak; **B** and **C** modified from Sars.)

rocks and other shelters in their native habitats. During the day they feed mainly in the bottom waters, but at night they migrate to the surface. They may also migrate shoreward at night and away from the shore during the day.

Examples of mysids are *Neomysis* and *Mysis* (Fig. 24-41), North American freshwater forms. *Gnathophausia* is a deep-sea lophogastrid.

Order Cumacea

Cumaceans occur throughout the world in all the seas including the Caspian sea. They vary in size from 1 to 35 mm. in length. There are 600 to 650 species recorded. All are characterized by an inflated carapace and a slender abdomen. The carapace, with a pair of anterolateral extensions (false rostrum), is fused to the first three or four thoracic segments and overhangs the sides to form branchial chambers. The eyes are sessile and are often fused into a single median eye, or they may be absent. There are eight pairs of thoracic appendages, three pairs of which are modified as maxillipeds. The epipodite of each first maxilliped bears filamentous gills (Fig. 24-6, *B*), which are enclosed in a branchial chamber formed by the epipodites and the carapace. Water is drawn over the mouthparts by the action of the epipodites (Fig. 24-42, *B*),

passed upward through the branchial chamber, and then forced anteriorly by siphonlike structures on the first maxilliped on each side. The antennae are very long in the male (Fig. 24-42, *A*) but vestigial in the female. Some of the thoracic appendages are used mainly for swimming and burrowing. Pleopods are absent in the female, but 1 to 5 pairs occur in the male.

Many cumaceans are filter feeders. Food particles are filtered from the water current that is passed over the mouthparts by setae on the second maxillae. Some species scrape organic detritus from the sand by rotating the sand in cuplike modifications of the first and second maxillipeds and then pass the selected food to the mouth by the exhalant water current.

In their natural habitat, cumaceans live partially buried in the sand and mud of littoral regions (Fig. 24-42, *A*). Some live at considerable depths. The more common genera of Cumacea include *Cumopsis, Leptocuma, Diastylis,* and *Cyclaspis.*

Order Tanaidacea

Most tanaidaceans are marine and have a wide distribution. They are benthonic and are found at various depths. They number about 350 species. Their size rarely exceeds 2 mm., and most are smaller. The body is elongated and is dorsoventrally flattened to some extent (Fig. 24-42, *C, D*).

421

Biology of the invertebrates

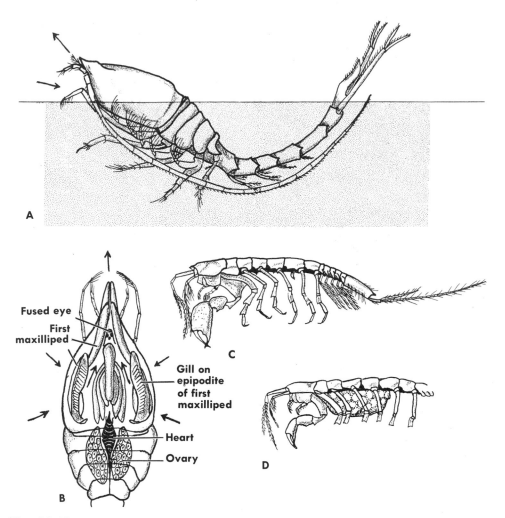

Fig. 24-42

Some peracaridans. **A,** Male *Diastylis,* a cumacean, buried in sand. Arrows show direction of water currents for feeding and respiration. Note long antennae, vestigial in female. **B,** Female *Diastylis,* dorsal view, showing direction of water currents created by epipodites of first maxilliped. **C,** Male *Apseudes* (order Tanaidacea). **D,** Portion of female *Apseudes* with marsupium. (**B** to **D** modified from Sars.)

The first two pairs of thoracic segments are fused to the head to form a carapace that encloses a respiratory chamber on each side. The left mandible may bear a small movable process (lacinia mobilis), which may be absent on the right mandible. When eyes are present, they are usually located on immovable stalks. The thorax has eight pairs of appendages. The first pair is maxillipeds and the second pair, gnathopods, is large and chelate. The other six pairs of thoracic appendages are similar and used for swimming, except the third pair which in some is specialized for burrowing. Exopodites are present only in the second and third pair. The pleopods of the abdomen may be reduced or absent, especially in the female.

The digestive system consists of a ventral mouth, a stomach provided with filtering and masticatory apparatus, a midgut, and the terminal anus. A feeding current produced by the epipodites passes over the mouthparts carrying food particles

422

filtered by the second maxillae. Some raptorial feeding also occurs in the group. Two pairs of hepatopancreas glands usually open into the midgut. Excretion is by a pair of maxillary glands. The nervous system is made up of a brain, a subesophageal ganglion, and a ventral chain of ganglia. Sense organs are represented by special sensory organs (aesthetascs) on the antennules of the male and by tactile sensory hairs or spines on both sexes. The exchange of gases occurs mainly in the inner surface of the carapace when the water current produced by beating of the thoracic appendages passes anteriorly through the branchial chamber. The gonads are paired in each sex. The oviducts open at the base of the fourth pair of pereiopods; and the vasa deferentia, with a common seminal vesicle, open on the last thoracic segment. Sexual dimorphism is most marked in the antennules of the two sexes, but there are other differences. Some forms are hermaphroditic. The eggs are incubated in a brood chamber formed by the flat plates (oostegites) of some of the thoracic appendages, and they hatch as postlarvae. Several broods are produced in succession by the female. Four larval instars may be necessay to produce the adult stage.

Apseudes (Fig. 24-42, *C, D*), *Sphyrapus, Tanais,* and *Heterotanais* are representative genera.

Order Isopoda

This large order of 4,000 species includes the sow bugs, pill bugs, wood lice, and others. They are found in the soil (terrestrial), in fresh water, and in the sea. Most of them are marine. Some are parasitic, but they are chiefly free living. They range in length from 1 mm. to 20 cm. (Figs. 24-43, 24-44).

They have a dorsoventrally flattened body, which may be distinctly segmented or made up of segments more or less fused, especially in the abdominal region. The head region is made up of the true head fused to the first thoracic segment. The head is somewhat flattened; and the similar thoracic segments, as well as the abdominal segments, are expanded laterally to form projections (terga) over the basal parts of the appendages. The uniramous antennules are short or vestigial; the antennae with flagella are usually large, but

may lack the exopodite. The compound eyes are sessile but may be vestigial in cave forms. There is no carapace. The thorax and abdomen are about the same width. Each of the seven distinct thoracic segments bears a pair of pereiopods. The first pair of appendages is modified to form the maxillipeds, and the others are mostly for crawling. The thoracic appendages are uniramous, with the expanded coxal plate usually fused to the sternum. The first five pairs of abdominal appendages are foliaceous and modified for respiration. The last pair of appendages is the uropods, which may be styliform or fan shaped. The last abdominal segment is fused with the telson to form a pleotelson.

Isopods live on a variety of food, both living and dead. Many are scavengers and will eat both green and decaying vegetation. They do not employ filter feeding. The mouthparts are arranged into a ventrally projecting mound that is covered by the labrum and maxillipeds. The mandibles are strong and toothed. Feeding may be assisted by the anterior legs. The digestive system (Fig. 24-43, *C*) contains a short esophagus, a stomach with a gastric mill, and an intestine. One to three pairs of ceca are attached at the junction of the stomach and the intestine. Symbiotic bacteria help digest cellulose in such forms as *Porcellio*.

The large heart is found mostly in the posterior part of the thorax (Fig. 24-43, *C*). The heart discharges blood into the hemocoel by a large number of arteries. Blood is returned from the hemocoel to the pericardial chamber around the heart. Maxillary glands for excretion occur at the base of the second maxillae.

Respiration takes place mainly through the pleopods, the endopodites and exopodites of which are modified into lamella or gills (Fig. 24-43, *A*). Some exchange may take place through the body surface. In some isopods the gills may be protected by a sort of operculum formed by certain pleopods or by elongated, flexed uropods. The ventral surface of the abdomen may be covered by two rows of overlapping opercula.

The nervous system shows various arrangements in the different isopods. In general it consists of a supraesophageal ganglion (brain) with circumesophageal

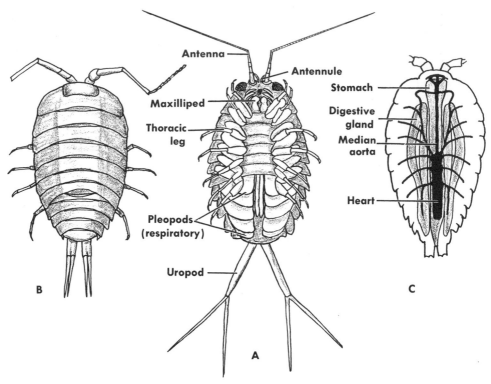

Fig. 24-43

A, *Ligyda exotica,* a marine isopod (suborder Oniscoidea), ventral view. **B,** *L. oceanicus,* dorsal view. **C,** Diagram of *Ligyda* showing digestive and circulatory system. (**A** from life; **B** and **C** modified from Hewitt.)

connectives, subesophageal ganglia, a double ventral cord with segmental ganglia in the thorax, and a group of fused ganglia in the abdomen. In some there is a tendency for the ganglia to be concentrated and fused anteriorly.

The males have their testes in the thorax and dorsal to the intestine. The sperm ducts open on the genital segment or seventh thoracic segment at the tips of two (or one) projections. The two ovaries are long, baglike, and located dorsally. The oviducts have two openings on the ventral surface of the fifth thoracic segment. Each oviduct may also be provided with a seminal receptacle. The endopodites of the first two pairs of pleopods may be modified in the male for transferring sperm into the gonopores during copulation. Fertilization of eggs takes place in the oviducts. Eggs are brooded in a brood pouch that is formed prior to egg deposition by the oo-

stegites. The young hatch as juveniles, lacking only the seventh pair of thoracic appendages.

Freshwater isopods live mostly under rocks and debris in streams and ponds. They are rarely found on the open water. In the sea they have been found from intertidal zones to abyssal depths. Terrestrial forms live in humid regions; their cuticle is not adapted for living in dry, arid conditions, although some families can endure a drier climate than others. One familiar isopod is the sow bug, which rolls up into a ball when disturbed. The marine form *Limnoria* can damage piers by eating the wood. Some isopods such as the suborder Gnathiidea, while still in the larval stage, are parasitic on the skin of fish. *Cymnothoa* and related forms have piercing mouthparts for living on fish. Members of the suborder Epicaridea are bloodsuckers on crustaceans.

The order Isopoda is commonly divided into seven suborders as follows:

Suborder Oniscoidea. Usually with distinct segmentation, vestigial antennules, and expanded coxal plates. Represented by terrestrial sow bugs, pill bugs, and wood lice. *Oniscus, Porcellio, Armadillidium, Ligyda* (Fig. 24-43).

Suborder Asellota. All abdominal segments fused with large telson; coxae never expanded to form plates; pleopods used as gills; commonly freshwater, but also some marine types. *Asellus* (Fig. 24-44, *B*).

Suborder Valvifera. Valvelike uropods inflexed as opercula to cover pleopods; some fusion of abdominal segments; both marine and freshwater. *Idotea, Arcturus.*

Suborder Gnathiidea. Mouthparts adapted for sucking (females) or pinching (males); lateral uropods; ectoparasitic at some stage on marine fishes. *Gnathia* (Fig. 24-44, *A*).

Suborder Flabellifera. Flattened body; uropods expanded laterally with telson to form tail fan; mostly marine, but some are freshwater; free living, predaceous, and parasitic genera. *Cirolana, Limnoria, Cymnothoa, Bathynomus.*

Suborder Epicaridea (Bopyroidea). Suctorial mouthparts and piercing mandibles; parasites on marine crustaceans; body may be greatly modified. *Bopyrus* (Fig. 24-44, *C*), *Ione, Liriopsis.*

Suborder Phreatoicoidea. Laterally compressed bodies; styliform uropods; genus *Phreatoicus* (Fig. 24-44, *D*) found in fresh water in New Zealand and South Africa.

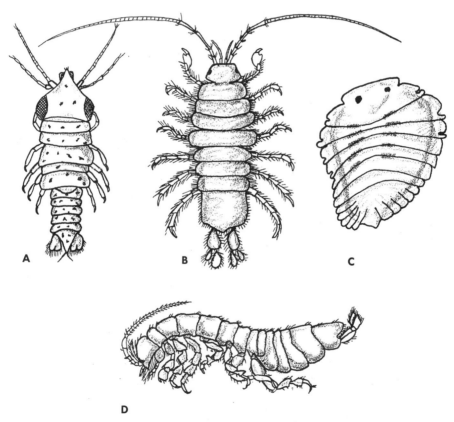

Fig. 24-44

Some isopods of different suborders. **A,** *Gnathia* (suborder Gnathiidea); segmented larva with sucking mouthparts; ectoparasitic on fish (about 4 mm.). **B,** *Asellus* (suborder Asellota), a common freshwater form (up to 20 mm.). **C,** *Bopyrus* (suborder Epicaridea), female from gill chamber of *Palaemon* (8 mm.). Specimens taken from opposite side of host would be bent in opposite direction. **D,** *Phreatoicus* (suborder Phreatoicoidea), female. (**A** and **B** modified from Smith; **C** redrawn from Green: Biology of Crustacea, H. F. and G. Witherby, Ltd.; **D** modified from Chilton.)

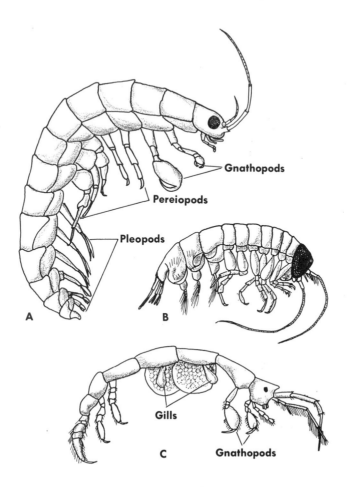

Fig. 24-45

Group of amphipods. **A,** *Orchestia,* the common sand flea, less than ½ inch long, found under damp seaweed at high-water mark along Atlantic coast (suborder Gammaridea). **B,** *Hyperia,* male, about ⅗ inch long, lives in pits on underside of large medusae (suborder Hyperiidea). **C,** *Caprella geometrica,* common in eelgrass of southern New England coast (suborder Caprellidea). (**A** from life; **B** modified from Davis; **C** modified from Miner.)

Order Amphipoda

Next to the Isopoda, this order is the largest in the superorder Peracarida. They number more than 3,800 species, about 50 of which are American freshwater forms. Altogether more than 600 species are found in fresh water in various parts of the world; the others are marine. Some are semiterrestrial. Four suborders are recognized in the group: Gammaridea, Caprellidea, Hyperiidea, and Ingolfiellidea. Most of them are of modest size (3 to 12 mm. in length),

but some may attain a length of more than 120 mm.

In general the order is characterized by having no carapace, sessile or unstalked eyes, first (and sometimes second) thoracic segment fused to the head, and a body flattened laterally. Thoracic exopodites are absent, and gills are located on the thorax. The first pair of thoracic appendages forms maxillipeds with fused coxae but lacks epipodites. Seven pairs of pereiopods are elongated, with coxae modified as plates. The second and third thoracic appendages are prehensile (gnathopods) (Fig. 24-45, A, C). Both antennules and antennae (without exopodites) are usually well represented. The abdomen has its appendages divided into an anterior group of three pairs of biramous swimmerets and a posterior group of three pairs of uropodlike appendages. The telson may or may not be lobed. There are many morphologic variations in such an extensive order. Some of these differences will be indicated in a summary of the suborders.

Some amphipods are pelagic and most of them can swim. However, the great majority are bottom dwellers. The thoracic appendages are used for crawling and walking, being assisted by the pushing of the uropods, which are directed backward. Grasping claws are used by some in climbing among vegetation. Many amphipods move on one side of their body, which undergoes a great deal of flexing and squirming movements in both swimming and crawling. Many species are active burrowers; some can construct mud tubes similar to those of certain crayfish or make unattached tubes of sand-shell fragments *(Siphonectes)* or hollow plant stems *(Cyrtophium)*. Some tubicolous species even carry their tubes along with them *(Cerapus)*.

Amphipods eat a great variety of foods of both plant and animal nature. Organic detritus is a common food of many filter feeders. In general they are scavengers. A few such as *Lafystius* are parasitic. Food is commonly held by the prehensile gnathopods and other thoracic appendages and chewed by the mandibles. Filter feeders often use the antennae as filters in trapping the food, which is then scraped off the gnathopods. The digestive system consists of a short esophagus, a stomach with a gastric mill, an intestine, and an anus below the telson. Two or three pairs of ceca are associated with the midgut.

The tubular heart with ostia has an anterior and posterior artery (Fig. 24-5, *B*). Excretory organs are the antennal glands that open at the base of the second antennae. The coxal gills of the thoracic appendages are the chief organs of respiration (Fig. 24-6, *A*). These gills vary in structure and number among the various suborders and species, but they usually number two to six pairs. Water currents over the gills are created by the beating of the pleopods. The general body surface may play an important role in the respiration of terrestrial forms. Terrestrial amphipods must live in moist or humid conditions for their gills to function properly.

The nervous system consists of a brain, circumesophageal connectives, and two ventral nerve cords connected here and there by segmented ganglia. Some species are eyeless, but most have sessile compound eyes. There are many different arrangements of the eyes. Both antennules and antennae have olfactory and tactile properties. In some there are antennal statocysts. Most amphipods are negatively phototropic and are nocturnal feeders.

The sexes are separate, and the paired gonads in each sex are elongated, tubular structures lying ventral to the heart. The male genital openings are on papillae located on the sternum of the last thoracic segment; the female oviducts open at the base of the fifth coxal plates. The female discharges her eggs into a ventral brood pouch formed by setose lamellae of the medial bases of the legs. In copulation the male transfers his sperm with his uropods to the brood pouch of the female. Development is direct and the young are juveniles. Marine forms may produce more than one brood a year, but freshwater species usually have only one.

The major characteristics of the four suborders are summarized as follows:

Suborder Gammaridea. Distinct head, thorax and abdomen; maxilliped with palp; large coxal plates on thoracic appendages; rather primitive ventral nerve cord with eight pairs of thoracic ganglia and four pairs of abdominal ganglia. Largest suborder of amphipods; includes all freshwater amphipods. *Gammarus, Hyalella, Orchestia* (Fig. 24-45, *A*), *Calliopius, Siphonectes.*

Suborder Hyperiidea. Distinct thoracic segments; maxillipeds without palps; large eyes; elongated appendages; mostly pelagic and exclusively marine. Double eyes in some (upper and lower portions), fused eyes in others; lateral arteries present in heart. *Hyperia* (Fig. 24-45, *B*).

Suborder Caprellidea. Vestigial abdomen; head fused to second thoracic segment; slender body; appendages reduced or absent. Often grotesque compared with members of other suborders. *Caprella* (Fig. 24-45, *C*) is a familiar genus found living on seaweeds and other marine vegetation.

Suborder Ingolfiellidea. Distinct thoracic segments and well-developed abdomen; vestigial abdominal appendages (except fourth and fifth pairs); eyeless (in some); four species. *Ingolfiella.*

SUPERORDER EUCARIDA

This important superorder includes the lobsters, crayfish, shrimp, and crabs. The eucaridans include most of the larger and more specialized malacostracans. The diagnostic features of the group are the large carapace, which is fused to all of the thoracic segments; the movable, stalked, compound eyes; the lack of a brood chamber; and some form of metamorphosis in their development. There are two orders, the Euphausiacea and the Decapoda. Less than a hundred species belong to the euphausiaceans, but the decapods have between 8,000 and 9,000 species and are the largest order of crustaceans.

Order Euphausiacea

The euphausiaceans are a small group of shrimplike crustaceans that are chiefly pelagic. They have many primitive characteristics and in general retain the basic caridoid facies. They are about 1 to 2 inches in length. Many are surface forms and are important planktonic items of food (krill) for certain species of whales. Some, however, are found at great depths. Many undergo extensive diurnal, vertical migrations. They are worldwide in distribution and are strictly marine.

The carapace does not completely en-

close the sides of the body, and the gills (of one series) are exposed. The maxillae have tiny exopodites. None of the thoracic limbs are modified as maxillipeds, but they may be specialized for filter feeding. The pleopods bear long setae and are used in swimming. The elongated telson has a pair of movable spines. The compound eyes are bilobed in some species for seeing upward and downward.

Most euphausiaceans are luminescent. They have on the abdomen photophores that give off a blue-green light (Fig. 24-46, *A*, *B*). The photophores are specialized organs with lens and reflector as well as light-producing cells (Fig. 24-46, *E*). The body is bright red; swarms of euphausiaceans sometimes so redden the water that seamen call it "tomato soup."

Euphausiaceans are mostly filter feeders and have their first six thoracic appendages modified as a filtering apparatus. Each of the endopodites of the appendages bears a fringe of setae, which form a net to capture food from the water current passing through it as the animal swims forward. A few have the third pair of thoracic ap-

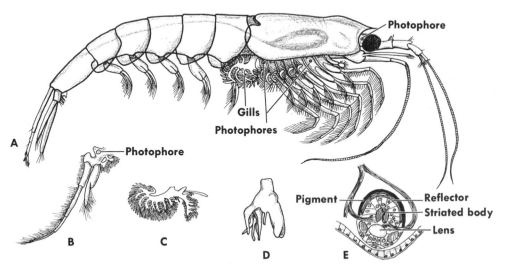

Fig. 24-46

Euphausia pellucida (order Euphausiacea). **A**, Adult female. Paired photophores are located on ocular stalk and thoracic appendages; unpaired photophores on abdomen between bases of first four pairs of pleopods. **B** and **C**, Second and eighth thoracic appendages of euphausiacean with attached gills. **D**, Endopodite of first male pleopod with copulatory apparatus unfolded. **E**, Section through a thoracic photophore. Striated body is apparently source of light. Photophores on ocular peduncle have no lens. (**A** modified from Sars; **B** to **E** modified from Calman.)

pendages chelated for capturing prey and are predaceous. The digestive system is of the typical crustacean pattern.

Respiration is by means of foliose gills at the bases of the second to eighth thoracic appendages (Fig. 24-46, *A* to *C*). A heart with three pairs of ostia is present, and the blood has hemocyanin as its respiratory pigment.

The male transfers his sperm in spermatophores to the spermatheca of the female where the eggs are fertilized. The fertilized eggs may be released into the water, or they may be retained on the undersurface of the female's body. There are many larval stages—the nauplius, metanauplius, calyptopis, furcilia, and postlarval (cyrtopia) stages—through which the larva passes in succession. Each of these, except the nauplius, has a number of substages.

Some of the genera are *Euphausia* (Fig. 24-46), *Meganyctiphanes*, *Nyctiphanes*, and *Bentheuphausia* (a deep-sea form).

Order Decapoda

This largest order of the crustaceans includes the shrimps, crayfish, lobsters, and crabs. Most of them are marine; but the crayfish, certain prawns and shrimps, a few species of Anomura, and a few crabs have invaded fresh water and moist terrestrial habitats. These nonmarine members probably do not number more than 150 to 200 species, whereas there are more than 8,000 marine species. They vary in size from some commensal crabs, which are less than ½ inch in length, to the giant Japanese crab, which may have a span of more than 12 feet between the tips of the chelipeds.

Although this extensive order is diverse, there are some common features that apply to the whole group. In general the diagnostic characteristics of the decapods are as follows: the first three pairs of thoracic appendages are modified as maxillipeds; the other five pairs of thoracic appendages are modified as legs; the first pair of legs are usually chelate and heavy (chelipeds); usually there is more than one series of gills; the head and thorax are fused to form a cephalothorax; and the carapace overhangs the sides to form a branchial chamber on each side. The decapods may be divided into the long-tailed members (shrimps, lobsters, crayfish), and the short-

tailed members (crabs). The long-tailed forms have a cylindric or laterally compressed carapace, usually with a rostrum. In the short-tailed crabs the carapace is broadened and flattened dorsally, usually without a rostrum. The short abdomen or tail in these forms is flexed under the thorax. This division is purely arbitrary and is not based upon a natural relationship of members.

The order Decapoda is usually classified as follows:

Suborder Natantia. Body laterally compressed and well-developed abdomen; cephalothorax with keel-shaped, serrated rostrum; legs mostly slender; shrimps and prawns.

  Section Penaeidea. Body with pleura of first abdominal segment overlapping those of second; first three pairs of legs usually chelate. *Penaeus* (Fig. 24-47), *Lucifer*.

  Section Caridea. Body with pleura of second abdominal segment overlapping those of the first; third pair of legs not chelate. *Crangon* (Fig. 24-48), *Heterocarpus*.

  Section Stenopodidea. Body with pleura of second abdominal segment not overlapping those of first; third thoracic legs very stout, long, and chelate. *Stenopus*.

Suborder Reptantia. Body dorsoventrally flattened, or cylindric; cephalothorax with rostrum depressed or absent; abdomen well developed or reduced; legs usually heavy and lacking exopodites. Lobsters, crayfish, crabs.

  Section Macrura. Body with well-developed abdomen and tail fan; carapace longer than broad and with rostrum. Lobsters (Fig. 24-49) and mud shrimps.

  Section Anomura. Body with abdomen usually bent ventrally without lateral plates; third pair of legs not chelate. Hermit crabs (Figs. 24-50, 24-54) sand crabs (Fig. 24-51). *Polyonyx* (commensal in *Chaetopterus*).

  Section Brachyura. Body with abdomen reduced, without a tail fan, and bent under the thorax; cephalothorax very broad and short; rostrum absent. True crabs. *Callinectes* (Fig. 24-53), *Uca* (Fig. 24-55), *Neopanopeus* (Fig. 24-52).

In general the Natantia are adapted for swimming. They use the pleopods, which are large and setaceous, for this function. On the other hand, the Reptantia are suited more for crawling, although many of them can swim. When they do swim, they do so without their pleopods, which are not adapted for swimming. Many of the Reptantia use their legs for swimming, **429**

Fig. 24-47

Penaeus, an edible swimming shrimp (section Penaeidea, suborder Natantia).

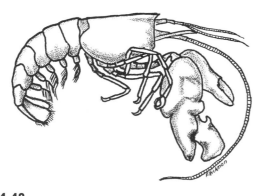

Fig. 24-48

Crangon (Alpheus) heterochaelis, a snapping or pistol shrimp common among oyster reefs along coast from Virginia to Florida (section Caridea, suborder Natantia).

for example, certain crabs. Others use the strong, muscular abdomen for darting backward (crayfish, lobsters).

EXTERNAL MORPHOLOGY. The decapods have 19 pairs of appendages (Fig. 24-2) and a pair of segmented eyestalks. The eyestalks of the compound eyes consist of two to three elongated segments. The eyes may be set in a notch of the carapace, or they may be covered by thin margins of the carapace. The antennules have a three-segmented peduncle and usually two flagella. The antennae consist of five or fewer segments and a single flagellum. They may be very long (Fig. 24-47). They may also have a scalelike exopod. Their coxopodite is a small operculum over the opening of the excretory (antennary) gland.

The mouthparts number six pairs. In the mandibles the incisor process (biting edge) is toothless, and the molar process is usually a moundlike elevation behind the biting edge. There may be modifications of this arrangement. A three-segmented palp, but no lacinia mobilis, is usually present on each mandible. The first maxillae (maxillulae), the second maxillae, and the first pair of maxillipeds are mostly leaflike and subdivided into lobes. Each maxilla usually bears a paddle-shaped scaphognathite ("bailer"), which fits the exhalant end of the branchial chamber. The second maxillipeds have broad, flattened segments, while the third maxillipeds may be elongated, or they may form an operculum over the other mouthparts. The mouthparts have a plate or epistome above them and are enclosed laterally by the carapace. In crabs the buccal frame is more or less square and is formed by the fusion of the

Fig. 24-49

A, Common crayfish *Cambarus*. B, *Cambarus*, female, "in berry," with eggs attached to swim-merets. C, Lobster *Homarus* (section Macrura, suborder Reptantia).

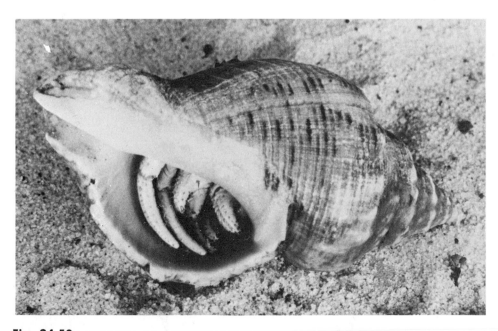

Fig. 24-50

Hermit crab *Clibanarius* in snail shell (section Anomura). See also Fig. 24-54.

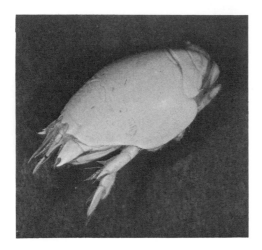

Fig. 24-51

Emerita talpoida, the mole crab, follows tidal waves up and down open ocean beach, burrowing quickly backward into sand as each wave recedes, leaving feathery mouthparts exposed to filter food from water (an anomuran).

Fig. 24-52

Neopanopeus texana, a mud crab common along East coast (section Brachyura, family Xanthidae). (Drawn from life.)

epistome with the carapace. This buccal frame is covered by the two plates, or operculum, of the third maxillipeds.

The five posterior pairs of thoracic appendages are the walking legs, although some of them may be modified. In the long-tailed decapods, one or more pairs may be chelate; in the short-tailed decapods, generally only the first pair is so modified. The legs may be modified into

swimming paddles in swimming crabs (Fig. 24-53). The pereiopods in shrimp usually consist of seven segments. In other decapods the second and third segments are commonly fused. In some, one or two pairs of pereiopods may be reduced or absent. In most long-tailed decapods, the first five pairs of pleopods (abdominal) are modified into swimming organs. The first one or two pairs in the male, however, may be modified into copulatory organs (gonopods); in the female, they are reduced or absent. In the short-tailed decapods, the pleopods are used for sperm transfer in the male and for the attachment of eggs in the female. The pleopods may be reduced in the female. The last pair of abdominal appendages (uropods) in the long-tailed decapods form, with the median telson, a tail fan (Fig. 24-49, *C*). In most short-tailed species, such as crabs, the uropods are absent. However, in the hermit crab they are present and are twisted into a spiral for holding the crab in the snail shell where it normally lives (Fig. 24-54).

INTERNAL MORPHOLOGY. The digestive system is divided into the foregut (stomodeum), the midgut, or mesenteron, and the hindgut (proctodeum). The foregut and hindgut are lined with chitin. In most decapods the foregut is modified into a short esophagus and a dilated stomach. The anterior, or cardiac, part of the stomach bears movably articulated ossicles of calcium, the gastric mill, which is controlled by a complex system of muscles (Fig. 24-4). The posterior, or pyloric, part has hairy or setaceous ridges that form a straining apparatus. A hepatopancreas, or liver, empties by ducts into the midgut. The anus is located at the ventral base of the telson.

The circulatory system (Fig. 24-5, *C*) consists of a short polygonal heart with paired ostia under the posterior carapace, a median anterior artery, paired antennal arteries, paired hepatic arteries, a median posterior artery, and a sternal artery to various organs. It also has a venous sinus system that carries blood to the gills and back to the pericardial sinus around the heart. Modifications of this pattern are found, especially in terrestrial forms. The respiratory pigment of the blood is hemocyanin, which is dissolved in the plasma.

432

Fig. 24-53

Callinectes sapidus, the blue crab, an important seafood product (section Brachyura). Note last pair of legs flattened into paddles for swimming.

Excretion is carried on chiefly by the antennal or green glands (Fig. 24-7, *C, D*), since the maxillary glands of the larva are transitory. The antennal glands are mostly compact and more complex than those in the other crustaceans. Each consists (in sequence) of an end sac, or saccule, which may be partitioned into cavities; a labyrinth of a spongy mass of canals; a nephridial or excretory tubule; and a bladder with a duct to the exterior. The bladder may be a simple vesicle (crayfish) or lobated (shrimp and some crabs). In some cases the bladder sends diverticula throughout a great part of the body. These may unite by lobes to form a single vesicle above the stomach or may anastomose to form complex networks, as in hermit crabs (Fig. 24-7, *A*). Nitrogen excretion (ammonia, urea, uric acid) occurs largely by diffusion through the gills. Uric acid may be collected by migratory cells called nephrocytes, or it may be deposited in the integument and cast off in molting. Crustacean urine is mostly isosmotic with the blood, except in certain freshwater crayfish where the urine is hypo-osmotic. Other freshwater crustaceans produce urine that is isosmotic with the blood. *Artemia,* the saltwater shrimp, may produce a hyperosmotic urine. Regulation of ionic concentration may be maintained by the gills or by the

Fig. 24-54

Clibanarius, a pagurid, or hermit crab, removed from safety of its snail shell. Note vulnerable soft abdomen, which it never exposes except briefly when moving into larger home (section Anomura).

excretory tubule through secretion and reabsorption.

With one or two exceptions, all decapods have gills connected to the lateral walls of some or all of the eight thoracic segments and to the basal segments of the thoracic appendages (Fig. 24-6, *D, E*). On each side of the thoracic segments there is typically a set of four gills. Each set consists of a pleurobranch attached to the lateral wall of the thoracic segment; two arthrobranchs fastened to the articular membrane between the first segment of the appendage and the body wall; and one podobranch attached to the coxa of the appendage. There are thus four series of gills, with omissions and modifications, running on each side of the thoracic segments of all decapods. No decapod has all the possible sets of this arrangement (8 sets or 32 gills on each side). The number of gills varies greatly with different groups. The lobster, for instance, has 20 gills on each side; the freshwater crayfish *(Cambarus)* has 17 on each side. The greatest number is 24 on each side (the primitive *Benthesicymus*). There may be as few as three gills on a side *(Pinnotheres)*.

The gills are enclosed in a gill chamber covered by the lateral part (branchiostegite) of the carapace on each side of the thorax. The gill chamber has restricted access to the outside. The paddlelike scaphognathite, or bailer, of the second maxilla on each side moves back and forth in a channel under the carapace and draws forward currents of water to bathe the gills so that gaseous exchange may take place. The water is expelled anteriorly in front of the head.

The direction of the water current may be reversed in burrowing forms, which may also extend the exhalant channel anteriorly in order to form a tubelike structure with the antennal flagella, antennal scales, and third maxillipeds. In some burrowing forms such tubelike siphons are used as inhalant siphons. Water may enter the gill chamber along the lower margin, which bears setae to prevent access of silt and mud. In the Brachyura, or true crabs, this arrangement is modified by having the free margins of the branchiostegite fitting snugly at the bases of the legs, leaving an opening for the ingress of water around the base of the chelipeds. The epipodites of the third maxillipeds form opercular valves for the inhalant opening. The course of the respiratory water current in brachyurans is through the inhalant opening, then posteriorly in the hypobranchial chamber, next dorsally over the gill lamellae, and finally anteriorly through paired openings in the upper lateral corners of the buccal frame. The fringed epipodites of the maxillipeds are used by crabs for cleaning the gills. The bases of the chelipeds and the coxa of the legs also have setae for filtering the incurrent water.

The basic plan of a gill structure involves an axis with numerous lateral branches. In the axis of the gill there is an afferent and an efferent branchial sinus. Blood passes from the afferent channel to the gill filaments and back to the efferent channel. According to the arrangement of the lateral banches, three types of gills are recognized: the trichobranchiate, with filamentous branches that are arranged in series around the axis; the phyllobranchiate, or lamellar, with flattened platelike branches arranged in two series along the axis; and the dendrobranchiate, with extensive and often complex biserially arranged main branches that are subdivided by secondary branches. The last type is characteristic of the primitive Penaeidea, but the first two types have a wide distribution among the decapods. The Caridea and most of the Brachyura, for instance, have phyllobranchiae, while most of the Macrura have the trichobranchiae.

Terrestrial or semiterrestrial decapods have a different arrangement of gas exchange surfaces from that of typical gills, which are unsuitable for air breathing. Whether in air or water, the respiratory surface must be kept moist. Land decapods must have large moist respiratory surfaces that afford little evaporation of water. Terrestrial forms depend less upon gill breathing or else have gills modified by sclerotized ridges that hold the filaments apart and prevent them from collapsing. Some, such as *Uca*, carry water in the gill chambers and circulate air through the water. In this form there are special respiratory openings between the third and fourth legs through which the air enters. In many land decapods the walls of the gill chamber have been transformed into vascular tufts, villi, and vascularizations so that the chamber functions as a sort of lung. Along with these changes the gill covers may also have highly vascularized lacunar systems *(Ocypode)*. The coconut crab, *Birgus,* which is one of the best adapted of all terrestrial crabs, has an especially well-developed respiratory epithelium with extensive blood lacunae and folds. Although oxygen consumption is greater in terrestrial than in marine decapods, the terrestrial forms can still survive when their gills are removed.

The Decapoda as a group show many variations of the nervous system, especially in the disposition of the ventral chain of ganglia. The maximum number of unfused ganglia posterior to the esophageal ganglion is five thoracic and six abdominal ganglia. This pattern is found in lobsters and crayfish (Fig. 24-8, *B*). In the true crabs (brachyurans) the ventral ganglia, both thoracic and abdominal, are fused together in one rounded mass in the ventral thorax. From this concentrated mass of ganglia, nerves radiate out to various parts of the body. Between these two extreme types there are varying degres of coalescence of the ganglia among the different groups. Decapods have a system of visceral nerves that involves a gastric plexus formed by the anastomosis of a posterior cerebral nerve and a pair from the esophageal commissures. A cardiac ganglion as well as nerves from the central system regulates the heart action.

The Decapoda are perhaps the best equipped with sense organs of all crustaceans. The paired compound eyes are found in all except those species that live deep in the sea and in caves. The facets of the cornea are square or hexagonal in outline. The nauplius eye may persist as a vestigial organ in lower decapods. The stalk or peduncle of the compound eye consists of two or three segments, one of which may be lengthened to produce a very long stalk. In macrurans and some others the carapace above the eye is notched, and in the snapping shrimps the eye is covered with a thin margin of the carapace.

A pair of statocysts, or balancing organs, occurs on the proximal segment of the antennules (Fig. 24-12). They are saclike cavities lined with sensory hairs and open to the outside by large or small slitlike openings. In a few species the statocyst appears to be closed off from the exterior. A mass of sand grains held together by secretions from the sac wall acts as a statolith in each statocyst. Sensory hairs or setae from the walls of the sac are in contact with the statolith. At each molt the chitinous lining of the statocyst with the statolith is cast off. The lining and the grains of sand must be replaced at each molt. Gravitational pull on the statolith produces stimuli through the sensory setae and receptor cells that are attached to a branch of the antennular nerve. Various positions of the body alter the gravitational pull on the statoliths, producing different stimuli to the brain and leading to orientation of the body. Many investigations have been made to explain the complex movements and reflexes of the statocyst functions.

Olfactory setae are present on the outer flagellum of the antennules (Fig. 24-13), and tactile hairs are numerous on the body and appendages. Noise or stridulation involving the rubbing of one part of the body with another is produced in some (e.g., *Ocypode*). The snapping shrimp (Fig. 24-48) produces a loud noise by using a movable finger that can be cocked open in a socket of the immovable finger and then, by a special mechanism, released suddenly. This adaptation may be employed as a warning.

According to E. N. Harvey, at least 17 genera of shrimp luminesce in some form or other. Luminescent organs are chiefly photophores, which are found on various parts of the body. Some shrimp are able to eject a luminous fluid from mandibular glands.

Most decapods are dioecious, but a few shrimps are protandric hermaphrodites. The paired testes lie mostly in the thorax but may extend into the abdomen. In hermit crabs they may lie wholly in the abdomen, and both may lie on the left side. Each testis is usually connected to the other by a diverticulum, or they may be fused together as a single organ. Each of the paired vasa deferentia usually opens on the basal segment or coxa of the last pair of thoracic legs, or they may open on the last thoracic sternum. Parts of the sperm ducts are modified with glands for spermatophore formation. Just before it opens to the outside, each duct becomes a muscular ejaculatory duct. A single tubular penis is characteristic of some hermit

435

Fig. 24-55

Uca minax, male and female. Male (left) has one very large chela that he moves horizontally in front of him, giving rise to common name fiddler crab (section Brachyura, family Ocypodidae).

crabs, and a pair of penes (modified first pair of pleopods) are found in true crabs. The ovaries are similar to the testes in shape and position. The oviducts usually open on the coxa of the third thoracic pereiopods, except in the true crabs (brachyurans), where they open on the sternum. In the brachyurans each oviduct is modified as a seminal receptacle and vagina for the reception of the male penes. In many decapods a single median seminal receptacle, with a separate opening to the outside, may be formed by processes of the thoracic sternites.

Sexual dimorphism may be found in some decapods, such as the fiddler crab *Uca* (Fig. 24-55), where one of the male claws is much larger than the other. Many species have distinct courtship rituals. Copulation of the true crabs involves the insertion of the first pair of male pleopods (with penes) into the female vagina and seminal receptacles. The sperm are discharged as spermatophores, which may break up into sperm as they are driven through the grooves of the first pleopods by the second pleopods. In crayfish and lobsters the tips of the first pleopods are inserted into the seminal receptacle, and sperm is transmitted along grooves in the pleopods. Other copulatory behavior patterns are known among decapods. In those decapods with seminal receptacles, where sperm are stored, fertilization occurs when the eggs are shed.

Some shrimp shed eggs directly into the water, but most decapods carry the eggs attached by a cement to the pleopods (Fig. 24-49, *B*). In some shrimp, all primitive larval stages are represented (Fig. 24-56). A typical nauplius (with three pairs of appendages) is the first stage, followed by the metanauplius with four pairs of appendages. The protozoea, or third stage, with seven pairs of appendages has a carapace, unsegmented abdomen, and paired rudimentary eyes. In the fourth stage (zoea) there is further development of the eyes and carapace, and all thoracic appendages are present. In the last stage (mysis) the thoracic appendages replace the antennae as swimming organs, and an abdomen develops similar to the adult form (Figs. 24-56, *D,* 24-57). There are many differences in the hatching stage among the decapods. In most of them the nauplius stage is completed in the egg, and the animal hatches as a zoea. The mysis stage may be replaced by postlarval forms. The postlarval stage in crabs is called megalops, with a large, unflexed abdomen and a full complement of pleopods for swimming (Fig. 24-58). The larval stages may be reduced or completely absent in freshwater decapods. Crayfish and freshwater crabs hatch as juveniles. Some terrestrial crabs return to the sea where the eggs pass through the larval stages of marine forms.

Molting is of course characteristic of all decapods. Ecdysis is absolutely necessary for an increase in body size. The young molt several times during their development; the adults less often. The process of molting is similar in all of them and has al-

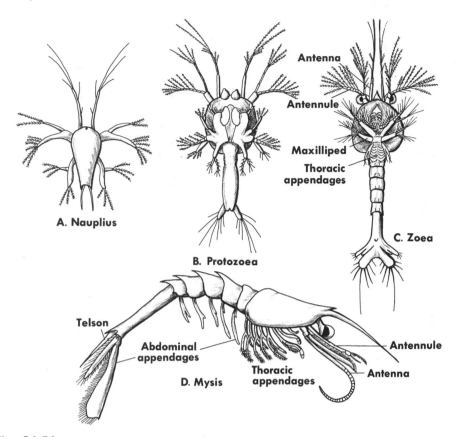

Fig. 24-56

Metamorphosis of *Penaeus* showing different stages. **A,** Dorsal view. **B** and **C,** Ventral view. (**A** to **C** modified from F. Müller; **D** modified from Claus.)

ready been described. This period is a critical one, and the animal must hide away to avoid enemies.

Regeneration among the different members varies to some extent but is greater in young animals than in adults. Lost limbs and some other structures are usually replaced. Sometimes the regenerated structure is different from the original (heteromorphosis). Crayfishes and crabs especially have the power of autotomy or self-amputation, the fracture occurring at a definite breaking plane, such as the basal segment of the endopodite of a cheliped. Special muscles bring about the breaking, and a valve or other adaptations prevent excess loss of blood.

ECOLOGY AND PHYSIOLOGY OF DECAPODA. Such an enormous group of crustaceans as decapods has a great range of ecologic relationships. Their economic importance need not be mentioned here to any great extent. It will suffice to state that members of this group, shrimp, lobsters, crabs, etc., are extensively used as food by people of all parts of the world. All of them serve as important food chains for other animal groups. Their ability to adapt to a wide range of ecologic conditions explain their wide distribution. Many striking ecologic behavior patterns are found among them. One of these is the vertical migration of aquatic forms, in which there is a diurnal movement to considerable depths during the day and a return toward the surface at night time. This migration, characteristic of many groups of crustaceans, is mostly under the control of light conditions. Many prefer dim light intensities. The distance of migration varies with the group. Some larger forms may descend to a depth of several hundred meters; smaller species restrict the vertical movement to shorter distances.

Color changes by chromatophore action are also common in crustaceans. A great variety of pigments is found in their chromatophores, sometimes several in the same chromatophore (polychromatic). Both melanin and carotene derivatives are represented, such as black, brown, red, blue, and yellow pigments. The typical chromatophore is a stellate-shaped cell of many noncontractile processes. A blanching or lightening effect is produced when the pigment granules become concentrated toward the center of the cell; a darkening effect occurs when the pigment granules flow into and are dispersed through the processes. Many color patterns are possible, especially in certain shrimp that have trichromatic chromatophores of yellow, red, and blue pigments.

Much investigation has shown that the control of chromatophore behavior is directed by hormones from a neurosecretory system in the eyestalk or nearby. The sinus gland, which appears to be the center of hormone release, is found between the two basal optic ganglia. This sinus gland receives secretions through nerve fibers from

Fig. 24-57

Mysis stage of lobster.

A

B

Fig. 24-58

Developmental stages of *Sesarma cinereum*. **A,** Fourth zoea. **B,** Megalops. (Modified from Costlow, Bookhout, and Monroe, 1960.)

secretory cells of the eyestalk and central nervous system. The sinus gland may not secrete hormones itself but may serve as a reservoir or releasing point of hormones. The hormones are produced by secretory cells in the nervous system and secretory masses in the eyestalk, such as the X-organ in the medulla terminalis (M.T.X. organ). Investigative methods involve the removal of the eyestalk, injections of eyestalk extracts, and then notation of the results in each case. Retinal pigment migrations for light and dark adaptations are also under the control of eyestalk hormones, although the mechanism is not fully known.

The process of molting involves control by hormones. A molt-inhibiting hormone apparently is found in the sinus gland and may be produced by the brain. On the other hand, a molt-accelerating hormone occurs in the eyestalk but not in the sinus gland. Hormones produced by the X-organ and sinus gland regulate the preparation of proecdysis, accelerate proecdysis, and control the amount of water taken up. The Y-organ, which is located in the head, may produce a hormone that stimulates the onset of proecdysis and also acts as the medium through which the molt-accelerating and mold-inhibiting hormones perform their effects. Cessation of molting may be due to degeneration of the Y-organ or an excess of molt-inhibiting hormone.

In 1954 the discovery of the androgenic gland was made in the amphipod *Orchestia*. It has since been found in many malacostracans. This gland is located between the muscles of the coxopodite of the last walking leg and near the end of the vasa deferentia, except in the Isopoda where it is found within the testis. When the gland is removed, male characteristics are lost; the testes are converted into ovarian tissue. When the gland is transplanted into a female, the ovaries become testes.

Physiologic clock mechanisms of pigment movement have been extensively studied in the fiddler crab (*Uca*) by F. A. Brown, Jr., and others. Normally, the body color of *Uca* is dark during the day and light at night. This rhythm persists even when it is kept in continual darkness. Some phase shifting can be induced by low temperatures so that the rhythm can be stabilized at a new phase. Periodicities of color changes may also be related to the normal fluctuations of such environmental factors as ocean tides. Within their burrows during high tide, the usual nocturnal paleness of color is characteristic, reflecting their minimum metabolic rate. This produces a dispersion of black color through the daylight hours in accordance with the lunar day of 24.8 hours, which is different from the solar day of 24 hours. Two hypotheses have been advanced to account for the mechanism of persistent rhythms. One theory stresses the idea that the organism possesses, independently of its physical environment, periods of oscillation that match all the natural geophysical frequencies and that have been genetically determined by natural selection. An alternative theory holds that the organismic periods depend upon a continuous response of the animal to geophysical rhythms that produce corresponding metabolic cycles in the organism. The adaptive nature of the cyclic mechanisms, such as feeding, migration, and breeding, enable the animal to best meet environmental changes. Whatever their causes and changes, cycles are built around a 24-hour period.

SUPERORDER HOPLOCARIDA

The only order of the hoplocaridans is the Stomatopoda or mantis shrimps (Fig. 24-59). The order is made up of one family (Squillidae), which contains about 200 species. They represent, with the Decapoda, the largest of the crustaceans. They range in size from about 20 mm. to more than 30 cm. in length. They have elongated bodies that are dorsoventrally flattened. Part of the cephalic and thoracic segments are fused and covered by the dorsal carapace. The cephalic segments that carry the antennules and eyes are not covered by the carapace. The third and fourth thoracic segments are reduced, while the last four thoracic segments are unfused and not covered by the carapace. The carapace at its anterior end bears a flattened plate, the rostrum. The abdomen is broader than the thorax and is made up of six distinct segments. The tail fan consists of a median telson and two large uropods. The stalked eyes are large and mov-

439

Fig. 24-59

Squilla, a mantis shrimp (order Stomatopoda).

able. The antennules are much larger than the antennae, and each is made up of three segments and three flagella. The antennae each have two segments, a single flagellum, and a large fringed scale. The mouthparts consist of a pair of strong mandibles (sometimes with palps), a pair of small flattened maxillulae, and a pair of large flattened maxillae. The first pair of the eight pairs of thoracic appendages is slender and hairy for cleaning, while the second pair is very large and adapted as a raptorial claw, with the distal segment folding back into a deep groove in the penultimate segment. By means of this claw the mantis shrimps catch their prey. The third to fifth pairs of thoracic appendages are provided with oval chelae and help bring the food to the mouth. The last three pairs of appendages are slender, without chelae, and are used as walking legs. They are the only biramous thoracic appendages since the others lack an exopodite. In the males a long slender penis is modified from the base of each of the last pair of thoracic legs.

Each of the first five abdominal appendages bears a pair of well-developed biramous pleopods. The exopod of each of the pleopods bears a filamentous gill. The appendages of the last abdominal segment are the uropods.

The digestive system consists of a cardiac stomach provided with a pair of lateral ossicles for trituration, a pyloric stomach with filtering bristles, an intestine enveloped by a large digestive gland, and an anus that opens on the telson. The circulatory system is made up of an elongated, tubular heart extending through most of the body, a single anterior artery, a pair of anterolateral arteries, and a system of sinuses for returning the blood. Excretion occurs through a pair of maxillary organs. The nervous system consists of many fused ganglia in the anterior region followed by a ventral chain of ganglia. The male reproductive system is made up of a pair of convoluted tubules in the abdomen and a pair of sperm ducts, each of which opens into the penis already mentioned. The female system contains a pair of ovaries located in the thorax and abdomen and a pair of oviducts that open on the middle of the sixth thoracic sternite.

When the eggs are discharged the female carries the egg mass between the anterior thoracic legs. The larvae differ from the adults and are pelagic. They undergo many molts before becoming adults.

Stomatopods are marine crustaceans and are sometimes found in brackish water in tropical and subtropical regions. Most species live in littoral zones, but a few have been found at considerable depths. Most adult members are burrowing forms, usually in mud or sand. *Gonodactylus* has been found in coral reefs. Stomatopods are carnivorous and live on other crustaceans, mollusks, and fish, for the catching of which their large raptorial claws are well suited. Some of them can make a snapping noise with their raptorial claws.

Besides *Gonodactylus*, other common genera are *Squilla* (Fig. 24-59), *Pseudosquilla, Coronida,* and *Odontodactylus.*

Annotated references

Barnard, J. L. (editor). 1962. Abyssal Crustacea. New York, Columbia University Press. *Some of the results obtained from the deep-sea explorations of the Columbia University vessel* Vema. *Many new genera and species are described.*

Brown, F. A., Jr. 1961. Physiological rhythms. In Waterman, T. H. (editor). The physiology of crustaceans, vol. 2, pp. 401-430, New York Academic Press Inc. *The author presents evidence that the periodicity of organisms depends upon a continued response of the organism to geophysical rhythms but with the possibility that there is also an endogenous component involved in the mechanism.*

Buchsbaum, R., and L. J. Milne, 1960 The lower animals: living invertebrates of the world. Garden City, Doubleday & Company, Inc. *Several excellent photographs of the crustaceans with concise text descriptions.*

Bullough, W. S. 1950. Practical invertebrate anatomy. London, The Macmillan Company. *This work includes many examples of crustaceans.*

Calman, W. T. Crustacea. In Lankester, E. R. (editor). 1909. Treatise on zoology, vol. 7. London, Adam & Charles Black, Ltd. *A classic account that has proved useful to all students of crustaceans.*

Carlisle, D. B., and F. Knowles. 1959. Endocrine control in crustaceans. New York, Cambridge University Press. *A good summary of what is known about this widely investigated subject.*

Coker, R. E. 1939. The problem of cyclomorphosis in *Daphnia*. Quart. Rev. Biol. 14:137-148. *An account of the seasonal changes in the gross morphology of* Daphnia *and some explanatory theories.*

Costlow, J. D., Jr., and C. B. Bookhout. 1953. Moulting and growth in *Balanus improvisus*. Biol. Bull. 105:420-433. *This paper discusses some of the factors that inhibit and promote molting.*

Edmondson, W. T. (editor). 1959. Ward and Whipple's fresh-water biology, ed. 2. New York, John Wiley & Sons, Inc. *Many keys and figures of North American freshwater crustaceans are included.*

Green, J. 1961. A biology of Crustacea. London, H. F. & G. Witherby, Ltd. *A good concise introduction to the crustaceans, with emphasis on their evolution, physiology, and behavior.*

Herrick, C. L. 1884. Crustacea of Minnesota. Minneapolis, Johnson, Smith & Harrison.

Hesseler, R. R. 1964. The Cephalocarida: comparative skeleton-musculature, vol. 16. Memoirs of the Connecticut Academy of Arts and Sciences. Hartford, Acadamey of Arts and Sciences. *A study of the structures of the most recently found and most primitive group of crustaceans.*

Kaestner, A. 1959. Lehrbuch der Speziellen Zoologie, part 1, pp. 659-979. Stuttgart, Gustav Fischer.

Lockwood, A. P. M. 1962. Osmoregulation in Crustacea. Biol. Rev. 37:257-305.

MacGinitie, G. E., and N. MacGinitie. 1949. Natural history of marine animals. New York, Mc-Graw-Hill Book Company. *A well-known account of Pacific coast animals, including many crustaceans.*

Manton, S. M. 1952. The evolution of arthropodan locomotory mechanisms, part 2. J. Linnean Soc. London (Zoology) 42:93-117. *The significance of locomotory devices in arthropods.*

Passano, L. M. 1961. The regulation of crustacean metamorphosis. Am. Zool. 1:89-95. *Metamorphic adaptive changes of crustaceans are mainly for dispersive purposes instead of for feeding as in insects.*

Pennak, R. W. 1953. Fresh-water invertebrates of the United States. New York, The Ronald Press Company. *Keys and figures for identification.*

Pennak, R. W., and D. J. Zinn. 1943. Mystacocarida, a new order of Crustacea from intertidal beaches in Massachusetts and Connecticut. Smithsonian Misc. Coll. 103:1-11. *Only one genus,* Derocheilocardis, *has been found in this new order.*

Prosser, C. L., and F. A. Brown, Jr. 1961. Comparative animal physiology, ed. 2. Philadelphia, W. B. Saunders Co. *Many physiologic aspects of crustaceans are scattered through this important treatise.*

Sanders, H. L. 1957. The Cephalocarida and crustacean phylogeny. Syst. Zool. 6:112-128.

Snodgrass, R. E. 1952. A textbook of arthropod anatomy. Ithaca, Cornell University Press. *A fine account of crustacean morphology is given in part 6 of this work.*

Tiegs, O. W., and S. M. Manton. 1938. The evolution of the Arthropoda. Biol. Rev. 33:255-337.

Van Name, W. G. 1936. The American land and fresh-water isopod crustaceans. Am. Mus. Bull. 71:1-535. *A taxonomic treatment of wood lice and freshwater Isopoda.*

Waterman, T. H. (editor). 1960-1961. The physiology of Crustacea, vols. 1 and 2. New York, Academic Press, Inc. *One of the most important treatises on the functional aspects of crustaceans.*

Phylum Arthropoda: the myriapods and insects

The Myriapoda

The term "Myriapoda" is often applied to that group of arthropods which includes the classes Chilopoda, Diplopoda, Pauropoda, and Symphyla. These classes will be dealt with separately.

CLASS CHILOPODA

The chilopods are commonly known as centipedes. They have worldwide distribution and are found in both temperate and tropical climates. They number several thousand species. Like all myriapods they are ground dwellers, living in soil, rotten logs, and under stones. They are usually restricted to habitats with a high environmental moisture. Unlike the Diplopoda they are exclusively carnivorous and are very active, agile animals.

Chilopods are slender, elongated, segmented, and flattened dorsoventrally (Figs. 25-1, 25-2). The body in different species varies from 15 to 180 segments. The head has a pair of long, unbranched antennae with a varying number of segments, a pair of mandibles, two pairs of maxillae, and in some, eyes that may be simple ocelli or modified, compound eyes. Many are eyeless. The first pair of flattened maxillae is located underneath the mandibles and forms a sort of labium, which is not comparable to the labium of insects. Second maxillae are long, leglike, and project beyond the first maxillae. The first pair of trunk appendages (maxillipeds) is modified into large, raptorial pincers (prehensors), which are provided with poison glands for injecting venom through the terminal claw into the prey. With the exception of the last two or three segments, each of the other trunk segments bears a pair of small, seven-segmented, walking legs. The arrangement of the sternal and tergal plates varies with the different orders. Most centipedes are adapted for running, which they can do at a rapid rate. Some have unusually long legs, with increasing leg length from anterior to posterior regions of the trunk. The head, body, and limbs are covered with chitin, which is flexible where movement of the parts is necessary, especially at the joints of the appendages.

Centipedes live upon slugs, insect larvae, other arthropods, and even larger prey (small snakes, mice) in certain cases. After capture, the prey is usually killed by the poison claws. The food is broken into pieces and masticated by the mandible. Although the bite of most centipedes may be painful, it is usually harmless to man. Bites by *Scolopendra,* however, may be dangerous to life, especially if the victim is a small child.

The digestive system is a straight tube with one or two pairs of salivary glands in the region of the esophagus and a long hindgut into which open a pair of Malpighian tubules for excretion. The anus is located on the last trunk or anal segment.

The vascular system consists of a tubular heart that runs through most of the body and possesses a pair of ostia and lateral arteries in each segment. Anteriorly the heart ends in a cephalic artery and a pair of arteries that join to form a supraneural vessel. Blood is returned to the heart through hemocoelic spaces.

Breathing takes place through air tubes or trachea that open by spiracles in the pleural region on each side of the body, except in the Scutigeromorpha in which the openings are located in a dorsomedian position along the middle line of the body. Some centipedes have a pair of spiracles in each segment, except for the first and a few of the last trunk segments. The tracheal tubes within the body usually branch and anastomose to the various tissues and possess spiral thickenings to prevent collapsing.

The male reproductive system contains a varying number of testes (1 to 24) that lie above the midgut and a single pair of sperm ducts that pass around the hindgut and open by a median genital opening, the penis, on the genital segment. The female system consists of a single tubular organ above the gut and an oviduct that also opens on the ventral surface of the genital segment. Small gonopods may be found on the genital segment, but they probably play no part in the copulatory process. Many centipedes brood their eggs, after depositing them on a substratum, by curling their bodies around them. Some simply lay their eggs, after a short retention on certain appendages, in the soil without further care. The egg contains much yolk which serves as food for the developing young. Some of the young are hatched with the full complement of segments (epimorphic), while others have fewer segments than the adult (anamorphic).

Résumé of orders

The class Chilopoda may be divided into two subclasses, the Notostigmophora and the Pleurostigmophora. The subclass Notostigmophora contains the single order Scutigeromorpha. The subclass Pleurostigmophora has lateral spiracles along each side of the body. Classification varies but usually includes three chief orders: Scolo-

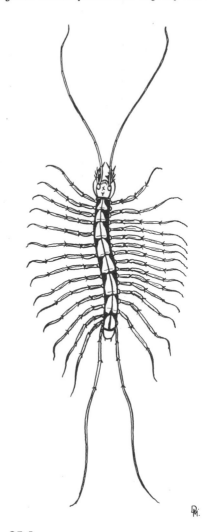

Fig. 25-1

Scutigera (Cermatia) forceps, the common house centipede (order Scutigeromorpha). (From Hickman: Integrated principles of zoology, The C. V. Mosby Co.)

pendromorpha, Geophilomorpha, and Lithobiomorpha.

Order Scutigeromorpha

The members of this order are characterized by both primitive and specialized features. They have a single row of dorsal spiracles, long legs and antennae, compound-type eyes, 15 leg-bearing segments, and 7 terga. Their development is anamorphic. The most familiar example is the common house centipede *Scutigera* (Fig. 25-1).

443

Fig. 25-2

Scolopendra, a large centipede of tropics and American Southwest. All have poisoned claws, and some species may be dangerous to man (order Scolopendromorpha). (From Hickman: Integrated principles of zoology, The C. V. Mosby Co.)

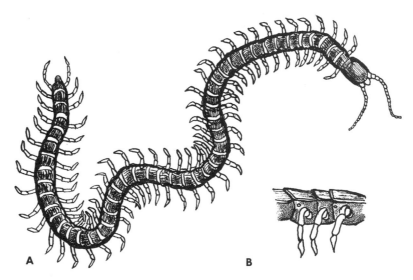

Fig. 25-3

A, Geophilomorph centipede. B, Side view of three segments of *Lithobius,* a lithobiomorph centipede, showing variable length of tergal plates and arrangement of appendages and spiracles. (Modified from Snodgrass.)

Order Scolopendromorpha

This order of centipedes is one of the most abundant, especially in the tropics. It also includes the largest centipedes, some of which are almost a foot long. Some have eyes while others are blind. They have 21 or 23 leg-bearing segments. Their tergal plates are similar in size, and their development is epimorphic. Genera include the well-known *Scolopendra* (Fig. 25-2) and *Otocryptops.*

Order Geophilomorpha

Geophilomorpha are the most specialized of all centipedes. They are adapted for burrowing in the soil and have long, dorsoventrally flattened bodies and short legs (Fig. 25-3, A). They can squeeze through narrow crevices with their pliable bodies. All are blind. They have a pair of lateral spiracles on all leg-bearing segments except the first and last. Their mouthparts show numerous variations. They have from 33 to more than 180 leg-bearing segments. Their development is epimorphic. Common genera are *Geophilus*, the type genus, and *Strigamia*.

Order Lithobiomorpha

These centipedes are characterized by having dissimilar tergal plates; usually a short tergum alternates with a long one. The antennae may have many segments, although they are usually short and thick. Lithobiomorphs possess 15 leg-bearing segments. Most of them have eyes. Their head and body are flattened, and their legs are short. Their development is anamorphic. The most representative genus is *Lithobius* (Fig. 25-3, *B*).

Fig. 25-4

Common millipede. Note rhythmic action of legs. (From Encyclopaedia Britannica film, "Animals—Ways They Move.")

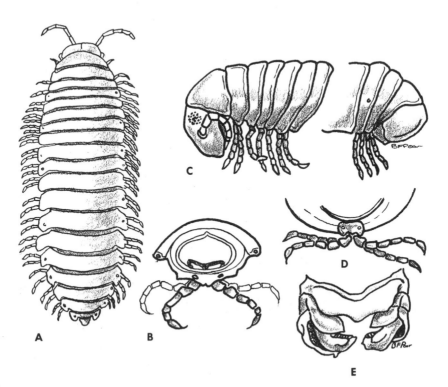

Fig. 25-5

Diplopoda. **A,** Polydesmoid millipede. **B,** Transverse section of fifth segment of polydesmoid millipede, anterior view. **C,** Juliform millipede *Arctobolus,* anterior and posterior ends. **D,** Ventral portion of middle segment of juliform millipede. **E,** Gonopods and sternum of seventh segment, anterior view, of *Arctobolus.* (Modified from Snodgrass.)

CLASS DIPLOPODA

The name "Diplopoda" refers to the most distinguishing feature of millipedes—the presence usually of two pairs of legs on each segment. (Figs. 25-4, 25-5). The double nature of the segment is indicated also by the presence of two pairs of ganglia in the ventral nerve cord and two pairs of heart ostia for each segment. The ontogenetic development indicates that the double nature of the segment has been derived from the fusion of two segments that were originally single. Another common name for diplopods is thousand-legged worms. They have worldwide distribution.

In contrast to the carnivorous centipedes the millipedes are mostly herbivorous or saprophytic. They vary in size from 2 mm. to more than 8 inches in length. The larger members are mostly tropical. More than 8,000 species have been described, but the number may eventually far exceed this number.

The body of the millipede is chiefly cylindric, although some may be dorsoventrally flattened (Fig. 25-5). The chitin of the body wall in most millipedes has calcareous deposits, so that the walls are hard and brittle. There is no differentiation of the body into thorax and abdomen. The trunk is composed of a variable number of similar segments (from 20 to more than 100). A cross section of one segment (Fig. 25-5, B) reveals that it is covered by a convex dorsal tergum, which may extend laterally as a tergal lobe; two small pleural plates extending ventrolaterally; and two small sternal plates on the ventral side. These segmented plates may be more or less fused.

The head of a diplopod is convex above and flattened beneath. It bears a pair of short antennae, usually of seven segments. The antennae are located behind the anterior margin of the epistome and labrum. The mouth appendages are the large mandibles, whose convex sides cover the sides of the head, and the lower lip, or gnathochilarium. The mandibles are segmented, and each consists of a large basal part with a movable gnathal lobe articulated at the basal part. The gnathal lobe bears teeth. The nature of the gnathochilarium is debatable. It may represent the first maxillae, in which case the second maxillae in diplo-

pods are absent. Some diplopods are blind, but when eyes are present they are simple ocelli, which may exist in small aggregates. The roof of the preoral food cavity is the epipharyngeal surface that extends posteriorly from the labrum and epistome; its floor is the gnathochilarium. The posterior floor of the preoral cavity is made up of a group of suboral lobes known as the hypopharynx. Most of the preoral cavity is filled by the gnathal lobes of the mandibles.

The first four trunk segments differ from the other segments or diplosegments, and some authorities call this region a thorax. Of these four segments, the first (collum) is legless, while the others have one pair of appendages apiece. Each of the diplosegments bears two pairs of walking legs arising close together against the midline (Fig. 25-5, B, D). The legs are six or seven jointed and in large millipedes may number more than 200 pairs. The last segment bears no legs and may represent the telson. Millipedes walk with a slow, graceful movement. They do not perform the wriggling movement of the centipedes. As they walk, waves of movement pass along their row of legs and produce a strong pushing force against the debris of the substrata (Fig. 25-4). Some millipedes have special adaptations such as tergal lobes or lateral carinae for squeezing through crevices. When disturbed, millipedes roll themselves into a spiral for protection. Many of them also are provided with a pair of stink glands on each of most segments. The openings of these glands are located on the sides of the tergal plates or on the tergal lobes (Fig. 25-5, A, C). The secretion, which is yellow or red in color, has a pungent, offensive odor and contains among other constituents hydrocyanic acid and iodine. The larger millipedes can squirt this fluid a considerable distance from their bodies.

Internal morphology

The diplopod's food of plant and dead animal matter is moistened and masticated by the mandibles. Some Colobognatha have adaptive suctorial mouthpart arrangements or a beak for sucking juices out of plants. The digestive system is usually a straight tube with the mouth and salivary gland behind the preoral cavity, a narrow esophagus, a long distended midgut, and a narrow hindgut into which open one or two pairs of excretory Malpighian tubules. The anus is in the last segment and is provided with two anal valves. The foregut is lined with cuticle, and the midgut contains a cuticular tube (peritrophic membrane). Little is known about their digestion.

Respiration takes place through a profuse but largely unbranched tracheal system. The two pairs of spiracles in each diplosegment, are located just anterior to the coxae of the two pairs of walking legs. The spiracles open into pits that are hollow, cuticular ingrowths of the body wall (apodemes) where leg muscles are attached. Each pit is protected by branching processes that prevent solid particles from entering with the air. The three pairs of anterior single segments may or may not be supplied with spiracles.

A heart runs along the length of the trunk above the alimentary canal; its anterior end is a short aorta. In the diplosegments the heart is provided with two pairs of ostia, but in the anterior single segments only one pair of ostia is provided.

The nervous system consists of a small, bilobed brain in the head above the esophagus, around which are commissures to the ventral nerve cord that runs the length of the trunk. From the brain, nerves pass to the antennae and to the eyes (when present). In each diplosegment are two pairs of ganglia, from each of which issues a pair of lateral nerves. Sense organs (in some) include eyes or simple ocelli, which vary greatly in number; tactile and chemoreceptors on the antennae; and a pair of sensory pits, or organs of Tömösvary, near the base of the antennae. The sensory pits may be covered by cuticle and may serve as hearing organs. The eyes show a variety of forms among the different millipedes. In general the eye is cup shaped, with photoreceptor cells convergent toward its axis. Each eye usually has a thick convex lens; but in the Julidae, where there are several contiguous eyes in each group, there may be a common flat corneal covering, the inner surface of which projects a thick lens into each retinal cup. Most millipedes, with or without eyes, are negatively phototropic.

The male reproductive system consists of paired tubular testes, joined together and lying between the midgut and ventral nerve cord, and a sperm duct from each testis. The sperm ducts may open through of pair of penes near the coxae of the second pair of legs, a median penis, or a groove behind the coxae. Modified appendages, gonopods (Fig. 25-5, *E*), may be represented by one or both pairs of appendages of the seventh segment. They transfer sperm from the genital openings on the third segment of the male to the seminal receptacles of the female. In some millipedes only the first pair of appendages on the seventh segment is called gonopods. The structure of gonopods varies greatly among millipedes and has taxonomic value. The female system contains a single, long, tubular ovary between the midgut and nerve cord; an oviduct; and a uterus that divides into two vulvae. The vulvae open on the ventral surface of the third or genital segment near the coxae. Each vulva communicates with a seminal receptacle which receives the male sperm. In oniscomorph millipedes, gonopods are absent, and the male transfers his sperm in the form of spermatophores with his mouthparts. Fertilization is internal and probably takes place at the time of egg laying. The eggs, which vary in size and number, may be laid in a cluster in the soil, scattered singly, or placed in a specially constructed dome-shaped, mud or excreta nest formed by the female. In some cases the female may brood the cluster of eggs or lie coiled around the egg nest. The development of the eggs is anamorphic; and when the young hatch they have only the first three pairs of legs and a few segments. Additional appendages and segments are added at each molt until the adult complement is reached.

Classification of Diplopoda

Millipedes are classified chiefly according to the structure of the male gonopods, which are more or less characteristic for each species. Other useful taxonomic criteria are the types of segments, appendages, and mouthparts. Most species are restricted in their distribution and remain fairly close to their centers of origin. Few genera are common to more than one continent.

A brief classification of the subclasses **447**

and orders and the more common genera of diplopods is given on p. 342.

CLASS PAUROPODA

Of the four classes of myriapods the pauropods are the least well known. They are minute, soft-bodied forms that rarely exceed 2 mm. in length. Their normal habitat is in moist soil, leaf litter, under bark and debris, or among decaying vegetation. They are often overlooked in places where they may exist in considerable numbers. Not more than 60 to 70 species have been described so far. They apparently have a wide distribution but are not found in deserts or colder zones.

The body of a pauropod consists of a conical head and a trunk of twelve segments. Each of the nine trunk segments bears a pair of legs. The legless segments are the first (collum), the eleventh, and the twelfth (pygidium). A ten-legged pauropod, *Decapauropus,* has been described. The entire dorsum of the trunk is covered by only six tergal plates, one plate for every two segments (Fig. 25-6, A). This tendency to form diplotergites does not extend to the formation of diplosegments or to the ventral region. Each of the tergal plates, except the first, bears a pair of long, lateral setae which are tactile in function. The collum, or first segment, is small dorsally and expanded ventrally. Each side of the head has an oval area that covers a fluid-filled chamber and gives the appearance of an eye, but is thought to be a sensory organ of unknown function. The head bears a pair of large, branched antennae. Each antenna consists of a four-segmented basal stalk and two branches. The dorsal branch terminates in a single flagellum; the ventral branch bears two short flagella with a club-shaped sensory appendage between them. Each of the paired mandibles is a single piece bearing teeth and deeply buried in the head. The first pair of maxillae may be represented by the lower lips and may be comparable with the gnathochilarium of the diplopods. The pauropod legs are six segmented with a variable pretarsus consisting of a median claw, ventral lobe, and one or two accessory claws.

The ovaries are found between the gut and nerve cord; the oviducts discharge through a single median depression on the genital or third trunk segment. A sperm receptacle is connected to the genital depression. The adult testes lie above the gut, and the sperm ducts open through paired penes near the coxae of the legs. Eyes, trachea, spiracles, and circulatory systems are lacking in the entire group. In their development, pauropods are anamorphic, similar to that of diplopods. They are considered to be more primitive in their organization than the diplopods to which they appear to be closely related. This relationship is most evident in the similarity of their head organization, position of gonads, and the opening of the genital ducts on the third trunk segment. Representative genera are *Pauropus* (Fig. 25-6, A), and *Allopauropus.*

CLASS SYMPHYLA

The symphylans are small myriapods with centipedelike bodies (Fig. 25-6, B). They live in about the same kinds of habitat as the pauropods, i.e., leafy mold, humus, and various kinds of debris. They often become greenhouse pests. Most of them are between 2 and 10 mm. long. Some 60 species are known. Although they resemble diplopods, some of their characteristics are shared with the lower insects. For this and other reasons many authorities consider them to be possible ancestors of

Fig. 25-6

A, *Pauropus silvaticus,* adult (class Pauropoda). B, *Scutigerella immaculata,* adult (Symphyla). (A modified from Tiegs; B modified from Snodgrass.)

the insects, but this theory is questioned by others.

Their bodies are soft and slender and consist of 12 leg-bearing segments and a larger number of tergal plates. Some of the tergal plates are duplicate terga of certain segments (3, 5, 7). A thirteenth, or preanal segment, bears a pair of unjoined appendages that function as spinnerets and have silk-forming glands connected to them. The last segment is the small anal segment, which carries a pair of sensory hairs (the trichobothria) and the anus.

The legs are much alike with six segments; the first pair, however, has only five segments and is usually smaller than the others. The terminal pretarsus of the legs is provided with an accessory lateral claw. Each leg arises from a moundlike structure, the limb base or coxa. Near the base of the leg and attached to the body wall is a short stylus or bristlelike process and an eversible vesicle, the functions of which are not known. These vesicles and styli are absent on the first body segment.

The head resembles that of other myriapods, with the mouthparts lying beneath its surface. The epistome and bilobed labrum project forward, and the head may be flattened on top. The head bears on its dorsal surface a pair of long, many-segmented antennae that are simple and unbranched. Each mandible bears a movable gnathal lobe. The flattened gnathal lobes lie horizontally in the preoral cavity of the head; each is articulated to the basal plates of the mandibles. The mandibles are manipulated by a complex musculature. The first maxillae are long appendages lying against the underside of the head, while the second pair is fused to form the labium or lower lip. The labium is a broad, oval, bilobed plate with six papilla-bearing lobes.

The tracheal system is restricted to the anterior region of the body. It consists of a single pair of spiracles arising in the head and tracheal tubes that ramify through the first three trunk segments. Although eyeless, symphylans have a pair of well-developed organs of Tömösvary near the bases of the antennae.

As in many other myriapods, the genital openings are located on the ventral side of the third trunk segment. Eggs are laid in small clusters and attached by stalks. The

development is anamorphic, with the first instar having six or seven pairs of legs. The symphylans molt throughout their life; and some, such as *Scutigerella immaculata,* live several years.

The most familiar genera are the *Scutigerella* (Fig. 25-6, *B*), which include the garden centipede of the greenhouse, and *Hanseniella.* Both of these genera have been extensively studied, although many details of their life history are still lacking.

CLASS INSECTA (HEXAPODA)

It is not within the scope of this textbook to treat in detail the most extensive group of organisms within the animal kingdom. No group has had a more extensive coverage in texts and monographs than has this arthropodan class. Nevertheless, it would be a serious omission to ignore a group that has reached such a high peak of invertebrate evolution. The plan of the present work is to fit the insects into the morphologic patterns characteristic of the arthropod group.

The present discussion will first emphasize the general morphologic features of insects as a group and will then show how each of the principal orders has modified these features in its adaptive and ecologic relations.

An insect may be defined as a member of the Arthropoda, in which the body is usually divided into head, thorax, and abdomen; with never more than three pairs of jointed legs carried by the thorax; and often with one or two pairs of wings on the second and third segments of the thorax. In addition, it has only one pair of antennae and usually both simple and compound eyes. The second maxillae are fused into a labium, or lower lip, and the mouthparts are variously modified and adapted for different feeding practices. Breathing occurs by means of tracheae. The genital openings are located toward the end of the abdomen, and the female is usually provided with an ovipositor. A technical definition of insects restricts the number of postcephalic somites to 14.

Most insects are strictly terrestrial and are found in almost every kind of habitat. Some are adapted for an aquatic existence, either for all or part of their life history. Only a few species are found in marine

449

waters. There are more species in this class than in all the rest of the animal kingdom. The number of insect species already described has been estimated to be at least 800,000 with many millions yet to be described. In insect populations the number of individuals reaches fantastic proportions in even a small area. The variety of insects is also markedly increased by the occurrence of two or three different forms in most species, such as the metamorphic stages, larva and pupa, in addition to the adult. The genus *Phylloxera,* for example, has as many as 21 different forms. Since each form of a species usually has a different food habit, a great variety of habitats is occupied.

The economic importance of insects need not be mentioned here except to say that they pose some of the great problems confronting man. As a group, insects embrace within their food habits almost every kind of organic material and thus become the greatest pests to man's food supplies. On the credit side there are many beneficial insects, such as those that are essential in cross-fertilization of plants; those that are predaceous and parasitic and are used for biologic control of other insects; and those that are used as food by countless birds and other animals.

Insects show a great range in size. Some are of almost microscopic size. Certain beetles are only 0.25 mm. long. Most fall within the range of 5 to 40 mm. in length. Some tropical moths may have a wingspread of about 30 cm. Fossil records indicate that some early insects were much larger.

Insect evolution is a never-ceasing marvel to students of evolution. The fossil record indicates that they are not so old as many other groups. The earliest known fossil insects date about 300 million years ago to the upper Carboniferous age. Many of these early insects were closely related to the dragonflies and cockroaches of the present time (Fig. 25-7). Early insects were more primitive than any other known insects and may have been close to the ancestors of the winged forms. Amber deposits of the Tertiary period of around 50 million years ago indicate that insects had already undergone an amazing evolutionary development. Many of the genera found in those deposits are still around. Living genera of bees, however, are practically nonexistent in amber deposits. Evidence also indicates that the earliest insects were wingless and similar to the present order Thysanura; they may have arisen from the ancestral stock of the Symphyla.

The rapid evolution of insects in comparison with other major groups may have

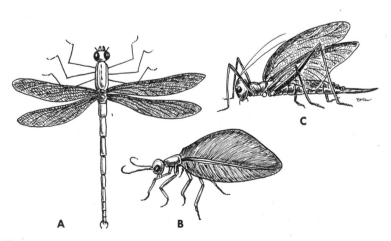

Fig. 25-7

Fossil insects. **A,** *Tarsophlebia,* Jurassic dragonfly, southern Germany. (×1.3.) **B,** *Mesopsychopsis,* Jurassic lacewing, Germany. (×1.) **C,** *Metoedischia,* Permian orthopteran, Russia. (×1.) (Redrawn from Moore, Lalicker, and Fischer: Invertebrate fossils, McGraw-Hill Book Company.)

been due to their short generations, reproductive rate, gene fluctuations in relation to environment, behavior patterns, locomotion, etc. Their actual mutation rate may not be greater than other germ plasm lines. Another factor of primary importance in their rapid evolution is their small size, which enabled them to fit into a great diversity of small ecologic niches that may have been denied to larger forms. Evolution involves not only alteration in the animal but the availability of a suitable environment into which it can fit. On the other hand, their chitinous exoskeleton has been a factor in restricting the evolution of arthropods because of ecdysis. The fossil record further indicates that the number of insect groups now living is only a small percentage of those that existed in the past, although there have been some progressive changes in their morphology and physiology.

External morphology

Adult insects differ from other groups of the Mandibulata in the fusion of certain segments and the division of the body into three marked parts. The head, which is sharply defined from the other two divisions (thorax and abdomen), is made up of the fusion of six segments. The thorax consists of three segments that form a compact, rigid unit with an extensive musculature for the manipulation of the legs and muscles. The abdomen, which is made up basically of 11 segments, contains most of the visceral organs. In some cases the terminal abdominal segments are reduced or vestigial.

The integument of insects is basically the same as that of other arthropods. It consists of a cuticle produced by a single layer of epithelial cells (hypodermis). The basic constituent of the cuticle is chitin of a complex chemical nature, chiefly a nitrogenous polysaccharide with other substances to give color and rigidity. A variety of cuticular outgrowths, such as hairs, spines, and scales, are attached to the integument. In order to grow, the old cuticle must be shed (ecdysis) as in other arthropods.

Head

The head varies greatly in the different groups of insects and contains three basic

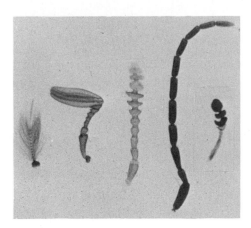

Fig. 25-8

Some types of insect antennae. From left to right: plumose (mosquito), laminate (May beetle), serrate (click beetle), moniliform (tenebrionid beetle), and clavate (water scavenger beetle).

sets of structures—antennae, eyes, and mouthparts. There is only one pair of antennae, which corresponds to the first pair of antennae (antennules) of crustaceans. They arise from socketlike structures on the first postoral segment. The antennae are of several forms and are usually made up of many segments. They may be slender and tapering, clubbed, filamentous, feathered, or serrated; and each type may have developed with respect to specific environments (Fig. 25-8). A typical antenna may consist of three divisions: a basal segment or scape, a small segment or pedicel, and a long, many-segmented flagellum. Antennae usually have chemical and mechanical receptors for olfactory, auditory, and tactile stimuli (Fig. 25-9). The pedicel, or second antennal segment, often bears Johnston's sense organ, which is sensitive to vibrations. Most insects do not have intrinsic muscles beyond the pedicel of their antennae. A few insects have no antennae, while in others they are reduced to one segment.

Insect eyes are of two types, simple and compound. Simple eyes (ocelli) may be numerous in insect larvae, but there are never more than three in the adult. They are often situated in the angles between the compound eyes and the rims of the antennal sockets. Each simple eye consists of **451**

Fig. 25-9

Finer details of insect antennae. **A,** Longitudinal section of two terminal segments of antennae of worker bee. Numerous openings of sensory (olfactory) nature are seen in cuticle. (×83.) **B,** Sense organs (sensilla) on antennae of grasshopper *Romalea.* In this type of olfactory organ, sensory bristle ends in pit overlaid by thin membrane. (×1125.) (From Andrew: Textbook of comparative histology, Oxford University Press, Inc.)

Fig. 25-10

Section through eyes of insect.

a cuticular disk, a lens, a vitreous body, and a group of retinal cells that are connected to nerve fibers running to the brain. Pigment may be absent in the ocelli of most insects. Ocelli probably do not form images.

The insect compound eye (Fig. 25-10) has the same basic structure as that of the crustacean compound eye already described, although certain details are different. The compound eye (paired) is made up of numerous ommatidia, each of which is a pencil-shaped structure that abuts on a facet of the cuticle (Fig. 25-11). Since each ommatidium lies at a slightly different angle from its neighbors, it points in a slightly different direction from that of its neighbors. The compound eyes may be composed of from only a few to several thousand ommatidia (more than 20,000 in dragonflies). Usually, the compound eyes are so large that they comprise a great part of the head. Compound eyes produce a composite erect image made up of a mosaic of images from each ommatidium. They are very well adapted for picking up motion and for precise information about distance. In some insects they are also sensitive to different colors. In bees the compound eyes can analyze polarized light and use skylight as a compass.

The mouth consists of four closely united parts: the labrum or upper lip, the mandibles, the maxillae, and the labium or lower lip (Fig. 25-12). All of these, except the labrum, are homologues of paired appendages found in other arthropods. The mandibles are heavy, triangular structures that are often provided with toothlike projections. They are commonly used for crushing food; but in some insects they are modified into long, sharp stylets that, with other mouth structures, are adapted for sucking sap or blood. Each maxilla usually consists of a coxa with endites and a jointed palpus, but they may be modified to form piercing organs or sucking tubes (proboscis of butterflies and moths) (Fig. 25-13). The typical form of the labium or lower lip consists of an immovable basal part and a distal part, which is movably articulated with the basal part and bears a palpus. The basal part in some insects is known as the postmentum, and the distal part is known as the prementum. The labium is really formed by the fusion of the second pair of maxillae as in many other arthropods. The labrum, or upper lip, is a flat plate hinged to the head anterior to the mandibles. The labrum also is variously modified and, in the suctorial type of mouth, may serve as a sheath for the other mouthparts. The hypopharynx is a tongue-like lobe found behind the labrum. It is in the preoral cavity (cibarium) and furnishes saliva. The preoral surface of the labrum is highly sensitive and is called the epipharynx.

The typical head is divided into three regions (Fig. 25-14): the vertex, which is the top of the head between the eyes; the frons, which is the region below the antennae; and the clypeus, which is below the frons, between the bases of the mandibles, and above the labrum. There are many modifications of this plan.

Thorax

The thorax is usually connected to the head by a membranous neck, or cervical sclerites, and is the center for locomotion in the insect body. It is composed of three closely knit but recognizable segments. Each segment is made up of a dorsal tergum, lateral pleuron, and a ventral sternum;

Fig. 25-11

Several ommatidia of compound eye of grasshopper *Romalea*. (×400.) (From Andrew: Textbook of comparative histology, Oxford University Press, Inc.)

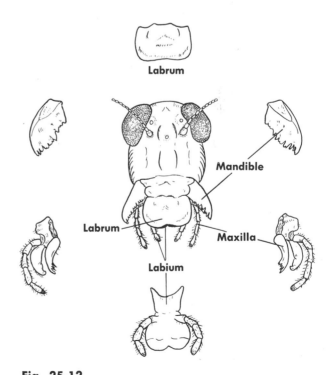

Fig. 25-12

Diagram of mouthparts of grasshopper. (From Hickman: Integrated principles of zoology, The C. V. Mosby Co.)

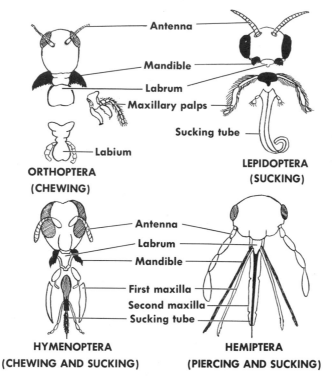

Fig. 25-13

Adaptations of insect mouthparts for various types of feeding. (From Hickman and Hickman: Laboratory studies in integrated zoology, The C. V. Mosby Co.)

and each of these may consist of a number of sclerites, except the sternum which usually has only a single sclerite. Because of its functions the thorax forms a stoutly built, compact box with thick walls. The first segment, or prothorax, is usually the smallest of the three segments and bears the first pair of legs. Each of the next two segments, the mesothorax and metathorax, bears a pair of legs, and in the Pterygota, a pair of wings also (Fig. 25-14). In the Pterygota the walls of the pleural regions of these two segments are strengthened by thicker layers of chitin and by invaginations to form struts. The legs are walking legs and usually consist of six segments. Beginning at the body these segments, in order, are called coxa, trochanter, femur, tibia, tarsus, and pretarsus (Fig. 25-14). The coxa forms a ball-and-socket joint with the subcoxa of the body wall; the trochanter is small (divided into two

parts in dragonflies); the femur is the largest of all; the tibia is slender; the tarsus is divided into five or fewer segments; and the pretarsus bears a pair of lateral claws, between which may be a fleshy lobe, the pulvillus. In different insects these legs may be modified for special functions. The front legs may be adapted for prehension or digging; the hind legs (Fig. 25-15) may be modified for jumping or swimming; or legs may be adapted for clinging, etc.

In their development the wings arise as lateral outgrowths of the body; they are not modified appendages. They are adult structures, and the only immature insects that have them are the mayflies. They are really flat integumental folds strengthened by cuticular thickening that form branching, riblike structures called veins. The pattern of venation is distinctive for taxa as low as families. Blood is circulated through the wings in the hollow veins, the main branches of which are connected by cross veins. Wings have usually been the best fossilized parts of the insect body.

The mechanism of wing movement may be based upon muscles that are also

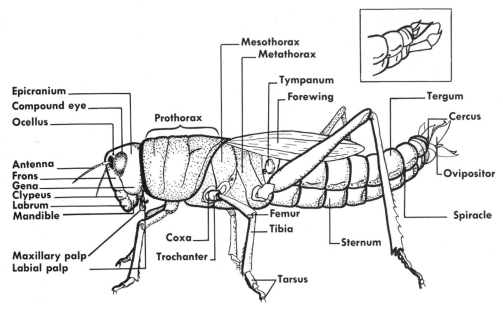

Fig. 25-14

External features of female grasshopper. Inset, above, posterior end of male. (From Hickman: Integrated principles of zoology, The C. V. Mosby Co.)

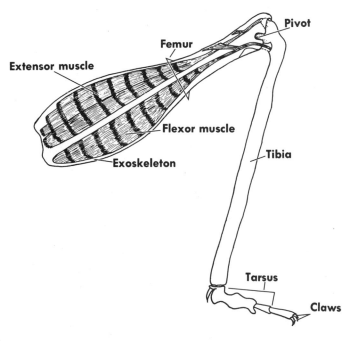

Fig. 25-15

Diagram of hind leg and femur muscles of grasshopper. Muscles operating leg lie within hollow cylinder of exoskeleton, attached to internal wall from which they manipulate segments of limb on principle of lever. Note pivot joint and insertions of extensor and flexor muscles, which act reciprocally to extend and flex tibia. (From Hickman: Integrated principles of zoology, The C. V. Mosby Co.)

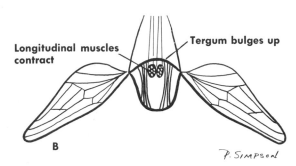

P. SIMPSON

Fig. 25-16

Diagram of flight mechanism of insect. Flight muscles have no direct connection with wings but change shape of body wall to which wings are attached. **A,** When vertical muscles between tergum and sternum contract, tergum flattens and causes wings to rise. **B,** When longitudinal muscles contract, tergum bulges upward and causes wings to be lowered. (From Hickman: Integrated principles of zoology, The C. V. Mosby Co.)

found in the wingless ancestors of present-day winged forms. Each wing arises at the margin of the tergum and pleuron. To produce the up-and-down movement an alternate depression and elevation of the tergum occurs where the wing is hinged with a pleuron support (Fig. 25-16). These tergal movements are caused by dorsoventral tergosternal muscles that depress the tergum and elevate the wings and by longitudinal intertergal muscles that elevate the tergum and cause the downstroke of the wings. In addition, there are special muscles for certain movements of the wings. In moving up and down the wing undergoes a twisting movement or torsion on its long axis. As the wing moves up, the membranous part with fewer veins is bent downward; as the wing moves down, the membranous part is turned upward by the air pressure. Flight forward is caused by the horizontal force thus produced by the twisting of the wings. The faster the wings vibrate the more they are twisted and the greater the pressure from behind.

In the different orders, wings have undergone many modifications that will be mentioned in the discussion of the distinguishing characteristics of each. Perhaps the dragonflies show the greatest divergence from the basic pattern of other insects. In these insects the wings do not flex but are moved by muscles attached directly to the wing bases. These muscles, however, are specializations of muscles that are found in most insects. The thorax of dragonflies, for instance, is highly specialized for this simplest of all wing movements. In most orders of winged insects (Pterygota), certain members have lost their wings; and in some orders, all the species are completely wingless.

Abdomen

The abdomen is made up basically of 11 segments. It is devoid of appendages except the last segment, which may bear a pair of long, segmented sensory cerci. An ovipositor of six slender plates combined to form a tube is found in the females of many insects. This device is used for depositing eggs in the ground or other places. The abdomen of some insects may have fewer segments, especially at the posterior end. External genitalia of the male often occur in a great variety of forms near the posterior abdominal end. The stings of bees and wasps are modified genitalia. A pair of spiracles, or openings of the tracheal system, is usually found on each of the first eight segments as well as on the mesothorax and metathorax.

Internal morphology

The internal anatomy of insects has much in common with that of crustaceans. Most systems in the two groups are similar, with minor differences here and there. A basic unity of internal structures runs throughout the extensive group; it is the diversity of external features that has formed most of the criteria for their classification.

Muscular system

This active group is well supplied with muscles that connect one part of the exoskeleton with another. The locomotor system is similar to that of the vertebrate tetrapods. In the tetrapods the stiffness of limb segments is due to bone; in arthropods the stiffness of each segment is due to the rigid cuticle that forms a hollow cylinder enclosing the muscles. In both tetrapods and insects, joint action is controlled by pairs of muscles acting reciprocally; and the limbs act as levers (Fig. 25-15). Whereas the muscles of the tetrapod limb are fastened to the outside of the bone and act over the joint, the muscles of the insect limb are attached to the inside wall of the cuticle and act over the joints from within. In soft bodies, such as the caterpillar, movement is produced by a combined action of the muscular wall and the hydraulics of body fluids, similar to that of annelids. Insect muscles are segmentally arranged in the abdomen but not in the head and thorax. Muscles are mostly striated and very strong for their size. Their innervation is different from that of tetrapods. Only a few nerve fibers run to each insect muscle. The muscle is usually supplied by a fast axon, which responds only when impulses in excess of 15 per second pass over it and produce relatively slow contractions. Insect axons usually supply several end plates to each muscle fiber and may allow local contractions of the fiber.

In walking, the insect uses an alternate tripod method whereby the anterior and posterior limbs of one side and the middle limb of the other are used for support while bringing the other three limbs forward.

Digestive system

The basic plan of the alimentary canal consists of a foregut, midgut, and hindgut. The foregut (stomodeum) and the hindgut (proctodeum) are ectodermal in origin and are lined with cuticle. The midgut is endodermal in origin and lacks a cuticular lining. The alimentary canal may be straight or convoluted but usually has certain common, specialized regions. The first part is the preoral cavity, or cibarium, which is followed by the pharynx (which may have a pumping device) with a pair of salivary glands, and then by a slender esophagus. The esophagus is commonly provided with a dilated portion, the crop (Fig. 25-17), that often has teeth for grinding food. The last part of the foregut is the proventriculus, or gizzard. The midgut is the stomach, into which eight double gastric pouches pour their digestive juices. Into the posterior end of the midgut or the anterior end of the hindgut 2 to 150 long Malpighian tubules empty and discharge certain wastes. Urates are discharged with the feces. The hindgut consists of a narrow intestine and a wider rectum which opens by an anus on the eleventh segment. Most digestion takes place in the crop and the midgut. Absorption of food occurs largely in the midgut, whereas most of the water is absorbed from the hindgut.

Since insects use different kinds of organic foods, there are many different feeding and digestive mechanisms. Some insects chew their food (ants, beetles); some pierce

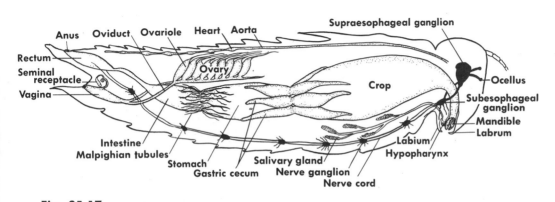

Fig. 25-17

Diagram of internal structure of female grasshopper. (From Hickman: Integrated principles of zoology, The C. V. Mosby Co.)

the skin and suck blood (flies, bugs); and others suck nectar (moths, butterflies). In some cases the midgut is provided with a delicate detached membrane of chitin, the peritrophic membrane. Special kinds of enzymes are found in insects that feed on substances hard to digest (keratin). Termites make use of flagellate protozoans for digesting their woody food. Many insects have rectal glands for recovering water from the feces.

Excretory system

The chief excretory organs are the Malpighian tubules already referred to (Fig. 25-17). They are blind vessels that are coiled in the hemocoel and open into the gut. They are not found in Collembola and are much reduced in some other orders. Other structures (gut wall, hypodermis, cuticle, and nephrocytes) may also assist in waste disposal. The type of excreta varies with the nature of the food. The chief waste is uric acid, which is often found in crystal form. These crystals may be stored in urate cells scattered throughout the body among the fat cells and epidermis. The hollow wing scales of certain butterflies contain uric acid. Part of the Malpighian tubules are modified in some insects to spin silk. The Malpighian tubules in certain aquatic larvae serve as osmoregulative organs by expelling excess water taken in by the anal papillae.

Circulatory system

Insects have an open circulatory system. Their principal body cavity is a hemocoel with sinuses through which blood circulates freely. The dorsally placed heart is really a tube that extends most of the length of the body. It is provided with paired ostia, through which blood enters from the hemocoel and is pumped forward to be discharged through the anterior aorta into the hemocoel. Accessory pumping organs may also occur for pumping blood to the wings and appendages. The blood, which plays little part in respiration, is greenish or yellowish in color. It contains a variety of formed elements called hemocytes, some of which are phagocytic. In the abdomen is an important fat body connected with the circulation, which serves as storage for fats, proteins, and glycogen during hibernation and pupal stages.

Nervous system

Insects have a typical arthropod nervous system consisting of a dorsal brain of three fused ganglia and a pair of closely connected nerve cords (Fig. 25-17). Typically there is a pair of ganglia for each body segment, but this plan is often modified. The two nerve cords separate in the head and pass around the esophagus to form circumesophageal connectives to the brain. Autonomic fibers (both sensory and motor) pass from certain ganglia to the heart, gut, and other organs. Nerve cells are typical neurons with cell bodies and axons. The brain serves for general coordination, but it is not absolutely necessary for vital processes; a decapitated insect can still live, walk, and perform many other bodily processes. This is due perhaps to lack of inhibition from the higher centers. In the brain, neurosecretory cells secrete a hormone that activates other hormones to control molting and the stages of metamorphosis.

Sense organs

The eyes of insects were described in the section on the head. That insects have an amazing sensory system is indicated by a great array of evidence. The variety of stimuli to which they can respond is still not entirely known in spite of much investigation. Insects are sensitive to waves of light and sound, chemical stimuli of taste and smell either directly or indirectly, temperature and humidity, color stimuli, ultraviolet light, ultrasonic sound waves, and gravity, etc.

A common form of receptor organ is the sensillum, which is a cell or group of cells, sometimes in a sensory pit and commonly associated with a chitinous structure. Many of these sensilla are little hairlike processes connected to a nerve beneath and found at various points on the cuticle. Many such sensilla are tactile, but they may also have olfactory, gustatory, and temperature functions. Some are located on the antennae, especially those of smell, taste, and touch (Fig. 25-9). The cerci of some insects as well as the antennae are responsive to sound vibrations. Taste organs are known to be located on the feet of some butterflies, as well as in the mouth and on the palps. Many Orthoptera (grasshoppers and crickets) have sound receptors, which are spindle-shaped bundles of chordo-

Fig. 25-18

Large tracheae of grasshopper *Romalea* showing spiral thickenings of walls. (×142.) (From Andrew: Textbook of comparative histology, Oxford University Press, Inc.)

tonal sensilla attached to the integument and called scolophores. These may be associated with a tympanic membrane, as in grasshoppers and cicadas. The amazing ability of moths to smell odors a long distance away is usually due to thin-walled hairs or small cone-shaped bodies widely distributed over their feathery antennae. Proprioceptor sensilla can detect the degree of joint flexion, and similar ones can pick up gravity stimuli. Where these receptors are located has not been precisely determined in many instances.

Respiratory system

Most insects breathe by a tracheal system, which attains its greatest development in this group. The tracheae are invaginations of the cuticle. They branch and anastomose to form an extensive network that conveys air directly to all tissues (Fig. 25-18). This system communicates with the exterior by means of ten pairs of spiracles or stigmata. Eight of these pairs are located on the abdomen and the other two pairs on the thorax. The main branches of the tracheae lead away from the spiracles and break up into finer and finer tubules before reaching the tissues. The various tubes communicate with each other by lateral trunks and form a network. The walls of the larger branches are stiffened, and spiral threads of the cuticular lining, which is either thinned down or absent in the fine terminations, prevent it from collapsing. The finest tubules, however, are more or less filled with fluid and are called tracheoles. Tracheoles differ from the larger tracheae in not shedding their lining. Tracheoles may envelop or penetrate the tissues, and when needed, they can migrate to regions of oxygen deficiency.

Spiracles usually open at the bottom of an atrial depression. They open and close by a special muscular mechanism which may be somewhat different in the thoracic spiracles from that in the abdomen. These sphincter valves are kept closed most of the time to prevent undue loss of moisture and are opened only at intervals as air is needed. The opening and closing of the spiracles is timed to the muscular respiratory movements of the abdomen so that there is a regular circulation of air in the tubes. Respiratory movements are mainly due to the contractions of the abdomen by tergosternal muscles to expel the air through open spiracles and the alternate recovery to the original form by elastic rebound of the sclerites. When the spiracles

459

are closed, the abdominal contractions force the air in the system to the finer terminations. In small insects, air may be conveyed from spiracle to tissue entirely by diffusion, which also occurs to some extent in those insects that have active respiratory movements. The respiratory movements are regulated by carbon dioxide stimulation of the respiratory center of the brain.

Aquatic insects have several modifications of the tracheal system. The abdominal spiracles in some (often reduced in number) communicate with a supply of air that is held under the thick elytra and renewed when the animal surfaces. In some larval forms the tracheal system is closed, and the tracheae communicate with tracheal gills on the body surface or within the rectum where water is pumped in and out. In some insects, small hairs around the spiracles trap air, and gaseous exchange is made.

Reproductive system

Insects are almost universally bisexual. Some special forms of reproduction, such as parthenogenesis (aphids), polyembryony—where several larvae arise from the same egg (Chalcididae)—and paedogenesis (*Miastor*), are very exceptional. The male organs (Fig. 25-19) include the paired testes, each of which empties into a vas deferens with a seminal vesicle; an ejaculatory tube formed by the union of the vasa deferentia; and accessory glands for secreting fluid to assist in the transfer of sperm. The ejaculatory tube opens on the subgenital plate between the ninth and tenth abdominal sterna. The female system (Fig. 25-19) consists of paired ovaries, each ovary being made up chains of ova (ovarioles); a pair of oviducts that unite to form a vagina; and the genital opening (vulva) on the ventral side of the eighth segment. Special glands and a spermatheca for the reception of sperm empty into the oviduct. Fertilization of the egg occurs as the completed egg in the oviduct passes the opening of the spermatheca where sperm from the male have been stored. Sperm are sometimes transferred to the female in the form of spermatophores. There are many variations of this plan of reproduction in the different groups of insects. An opening (micropyle) in the eggshell makes possible the entrance of the sperm. Most insects are oviparous, but viviparity is found in some flies, such as the tsetse fly (*Glossina*).

The eggs of insects belong to the centrolecithal type (Fig. 25-20). Such eggs are yolky and provided with vitelline membranes and strong chorionic shells. By incomplete cleavage involving mitosis of only the nuclei, the egg becomes a syncytium of yolky cytoplasm containing the cleavage nuclei. These nuclei migrate to the peripheral cytoplasm where they form a cellular blastoderm. A ventral thickening of the blastoderm forms a germ band that will produce the embryo, with the lateral and dorsal cells forming the serosa membrane. End and side folds of the germ band become the amnion that encloses the embryo in an amniotic cavity. From the ventral line along the germ band, certain cells pass by invagination and overgrowth to form a mesoderm above the germ band. The part left outside forms the ectoderm. By cross furrows the mesoderm layer gives rise to a series of segments that become the head and appendages. The endoderm lies against the yolk and will form the midgut. The foregut (stomodeum) will start as a pit at the anterior end, and the hindgut (proctodeum) will arise in a similar manner from the posterior end. The origin of other organs and systems has already been mentioned.

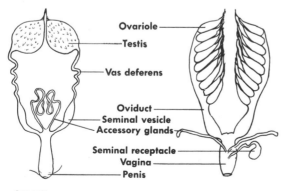

Fig. 25-19

Reproductive organs of grasshopper. Male on left; female on right. (From Hickman: Integrated principles of zoology, The C. V. Mosby Co.)

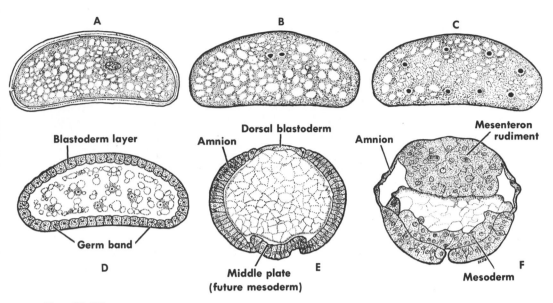

Fig. 25-20

Early development of egg of honeybee *Apis*. **A**, Centrolecithal egg. **B**, First division of nucleus. **C**, Eight-cell stage is really syncytium. **D**, Blastula. (**A** to **D** longitudinal section.) **E**, Gastrula. Ventral thickening will produce embryo; dorsal blastoderm becomes outer serosa layer; end and side folds will form amnion around embryo. **F**, Median ventral plate gives rise to mesoderm and endoderm; lateral plates give rise to ectoderm. (**E** and **F** transverse section.)

Metamorphosis and growth

After hatching, insects change not only in size but, often to a striking extent, in form also (Figs. 25-21, 25-22). Insects attain their maximum size by successive molts (ecdysis). The number of molts varies with the species, some having far more than others. The period between any two molts is called the instar, or growth period. In the life history of most insects there is a succession of instars followed finally by the adult instar. Metamorphosis refers to the abrupt changes in form from one distinctive stage to another in the life history. There are various degrees of metamorphosis from those that have none at all to those in which the adult has no resemblance to the larval stages. Classification of insects is often based on the type of metamorphosis they have. The following represents such a classification:

Ametabola. This group includes orders that have no metamorphosis, such as Collembola, Protura, and Thysanura. Stages in development: egg, growth stages, and adult.
Metabola. This artificial taxon refers to insects that have some distinct changes in form and size from larva to adult. The group is subdivided into three distinct types:

Paurometabola. These orders of insects have simple, gradual metamorphosis in which immature forms (nymphs) resemble adults except in size. They are represented by such orders as Orthoptera (Fig. 25-23), Isoptera, and Hemiptera. Early instars in some are called larvae if succeeding instars are somewhat different. Stages of development: eggs, series of nymphs, and adult.

Hemimetabola. Insects belonging to this group have incomplete metamorphosis represented by series of immature aquatic forms called naiads. Although naiads do have gills they are still similar to adults except for size, body proportions, and lack of wings. Hemimetabolous orders are represented by Odonata, Ephemeroptera (Ephemerida), and Plecoptera. Stages of development: egg, series of naiads, and adult.

Holometabola. These insects have complete or indirect metamorphosis that includes resting stage (pupa) between larva and adult (Fig. 25-22). Larva has a series of instars different from pupa and adult. Majority of insects belong to this group. Stages of development: egg, larva, pupa, and adult (imago).

Ecdysis and metamorphosis are under

A   B

Fig. 25-21

A, Mosquito *Culex* lays her eggs in small packets or rafts on surface of standing or slowly moving water. **B,** Mosquito larvae are familiar wrigglers of ponds and ditches. To breathe they hang head down, with respiratory tubes projecting through surface film of water. Motion of vibratile tufts of fine hairs on head brings constant supply of food. (From Encyclopaedia Britannica film, "Mosquito.")

A   B

Fig. 25-22

Development of honeybee (holometabolous metamorphosis). **A,** After hatching, tiny larvae are fed for several days by young worker bees; then more food is placed in cells and cells are capped. **B,** Larvae feed and grow another day or two and pupate for 13 days. Then young bees gnaw away cell cap and emerge to take over their first duties within hive. (From Encyclopaedia Britannica film, "The Honey Bee.")

A

B

Fig. 25-23

Praying mantid illustrates paurometabola, or gradual metamorphosis. Mantid eggs are laid in fall in large masses, covered with quickly drying, tough mucus and attached to branches and plant stems. **A,** In spring dozens of young mantids emerge from case, each a pale, tiny copy of adult. **B,** After several moltings to develop its wings, adult mantid reaches length of about 2½ inches. Beneficial insect that lives on other insects. (**A** and **B** from Hickman: Integrated principles of zoology, The C. V. Mosby Co.; **B** courtesy Joseph W. Bamberger.)

the control of hormones. In every molt a new skin with changes is laid down underneath the old (Fig. 25-24). The old skin ruptures as the insect takes in water and air and increases in size. The new skin is at first wrinkled and allows the body to expand before hardening. A sequence of ecdyses eventually brings about the adult form. In holometabolous insects the hormone-dependent process is controlled chiefly by ecdysone, a hormone produced in the prothoracic gland, which is activated by a brain hormone from the neurosecretory cells of the brain. Another hormone, the juvenile hormone from the corpora allata glands, prevents the metamorphosis of the insect larva into the pupa under the influence of ecdysone. As long as the juvenile hormone is active, each molt simply results in a larger larva; but when

this hormone declines, the ecdysone is free to bring about the change from larva to pupa and then to the adult.

Metamorphosis has evolved along with the evolution of wings in insects. In many insects, wings are restricted to the reproductive stages, where distribution of the species can be of greatest advantage. In time, however, the evolution of this plan

Fig. 25-24

Ecdysis in cicada. **A,** Having outgrown its cuticle, cicada emerges from cuticle through longitudinal dorsal split and leaves it empty, still attached to leaf. **B,** Last molt; wings are now developed. **C,** Adult cicada. (From Encyclopaedia Britannica film "Insect Life Cycle, The Periodical Cicada.")

has resulted in fitting the wingless larva and winged adult into different ecologic niches and different food habits. In this way the insect could restrict its energy for growth and development to the larval and pupal stages and its energy for locomotion and distribution to the adult stage.

Résumé of insect orders

Insects may be classified in various ways, depending upon what basic plan is em-

phasized. Such classification could be made with reference to the presence or absence of wings, presence or absence of metamorphosis, types of metamorphosis, types of mouthparts, etc. A natural classification would emphasize the fossil record, comparative structures, and relationships; but sufficient details are not always available to make such a classification satisfactory to all students of entomology.

The following brief summary of the major orders gives the student a general idea of the diversity of structure and function in the largest group of invertebrate animals. (There is a considerable divergence of opinion about the number of orders.)

CLASS INSECTA (HEXAPODA)—INSECTS

Body with head, thorax, and abdomen distinct; single pair of antennae; mouthparts modified for chewing, piercing and sucking, or lapping; thorax of three segments, each with a pair of jointed legs, and last two segments with one or two pairs of wings, or none; abdomen typically of 11 segments without ambulatory appendages; respiratory system of branched tracheae; excretory system of Malpighian tubules; nervous system of brain and ventral double nerve cord; eyes of both simple and compound types; sexes separate with genital openings near end of abdomen; development with or without true metamorphosis; chiefly terrestrial or freshwater.

Subclass Apterygota (Ametabola)

Primitively wingless insects; true metamorphosis absent; abdomen with ventral appendages other than sexual appendages and cerci.

Order Protura

Minute size (less than 1.5 mm.); body without eyes or antennae; abdomen of twelve segments; each of first three with one pair of small appendages; have nine abdominal segments on hatching, with an extra segment added to abdomen at each of first three molts; mouthparts of long, slender stylets for piercing; some with spiracles and tracheae; found in moist and decaying vegetation; about 60 to 90 species have been described. *Acerentulus* (Fig. 25-25, *A*) is typical genus.

Order Collembola (springtails)

Body up to 5 mm. long; primitive wingless insects; antennae of four joints; mouthparts chewing or sucking; simple eyes; abdomen of six segments with springing organ (furcula) on fourth abdominal segment (Fig. 25-26); furcula released by catch (hamula) on third abdominal segment; ventral tube (collophore) produces sticky secretion as adhesive organ on first abdominal segment; leg appendages lack tarsi but have pretarsus present with claw; respiration by tracheal system or through integument; no true metamorphosis; live in humid leaf mold; often found on snowbanks in spring of year; some 2,000 species; earliest known insect fossil (*Rhyniella*) belongs to this order. *Entomobrya* and *Achorutes* are common genera.

Order Diplura (japygids)

Body mostly 8 to 10 mm. in length, but some larger; no eyes; antennae many segmented; abdomen of eleven segments with two slender cerci or with pincers (Fig. 25-25, *B*); mandibles and maxillae enclosed in head pouches; thorax of three segments with three pairs of legs; respiration by tracheal system; live in rotting logs and damp humus; about 400 species. Common genera are *Campodea* and *Japyx*.

Order Thysanura (bristletails)

Body up to 30 mm. in length with soft integument, sometimes scaly; mouthparts mandibulate with mandibles and maxillae fully exposed; antennae and maxillae long; eyes may be compound, ocelli, both, or absent; abdomen of eleven segments with two or three many-segmented cerci; live under stones and leaves and around human habitations;

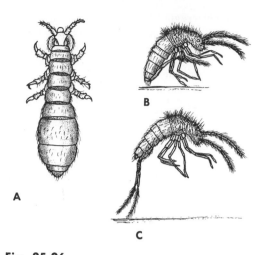

Fig. 25-26

Springtails (Collembola). **A,** *Anurida.* **B** and **C,** *Orchesella* in resting and leaping positions.

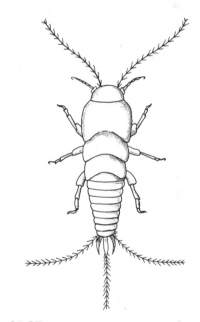

Fig. 25-27

Silverfish *Lepisma* (Thysanura), often found in homes.

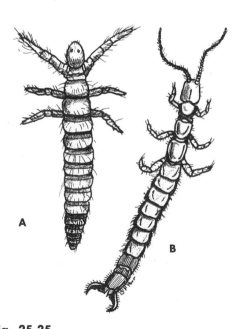

Fig. 25-25

A, *Acerentulus* (order Protura). **B,** *Heterojapyx* (order Diplura) has caudal forceps.

about 150 species; silverfish (*Lepisma*) (Fig. 25-27) eats starch of books, and firebrat (*Thermobia*) is often found in warm places in homes.

[NOTE: Since mouthparts of first three orders of Ametabola are mostly hidden in the head, they are referred to as Entotropha; order Thysanura has visible mouthparts (Ectotropha)].

465

Subclass Pterygota (Metabola)

Wings usually present, but some with vestigial wings or none at all; wingless forms probably arose from winged ancestors; abdominal styli lacking; larva hatched with full complement of adult segments; abdominal appendages restricted to genitalia and cerci; metamorphosis incomplete or complete; includes most insects.

Division Hemimetabola, including Paurometabola (Exopterygota)

Young stages are nymphs with compound eyes; wings develop externally; metamorphosis gradual or incomplete.

Order Orthoptera (grasshoppers, crickets, etc.)

Body with two pairs of wings, first thick and leathery and second membranous and folded beneath first; wings may be absent; mouthparts for chewing; nymph resembles adult; abdomen usually with cerci and ovipositor; well-developed sound-producing and sound-perceiving organs; sound may be produced by rubbing inner faces of femora against outer wings, or by rubbing wings together; eggs frequently laid in clusters (oöthecae); mostly live on plants; an extensive order (25,000 species) of several families. Principal families and genera are Locustidae or Acrididae, true grasshoppers *(Romalea)*; Gryllidae, true crickets *(Gryllus)*; Phasmidae, walking sticks *(Anisomorpha)*; Blattidae, cockroaches *(Periplaneta)*; Mantidae, praying mantids *(Stagmomantis)*; Tetrigidae, grouse locusts *(Tetrix)*; Tettigoniidae, long-horn grasshoppers *(Microcentrum)*; Gryllotalpidae, mole crickets *(Gryllotalpa)* (Fig. 25-28).

Order Dermaptera (earwigs)

Body 60 to 200 mm. in length; chewing mouthparts; tough, shiny bodies with slender antennae; forewings short and leathery, hindwings large and membranous, with radial veins, and folded under forewings at rest; some without wings; abdomen with cerci modified into strong, movable forceps; mostly herbivorous, eating both living and dead vegetation, but may be carnivorous in tropics; about 1,100 species; mostly nocturnal, terrestrial forms, living under stones, refuse, and barks of trees; European earwig *Forficula auricularia* (Fig. 25-29), introduced in this country, has become a garden and household pest; *Labia* is common native genus about 6 to 8 mm. long.

Order Plecoptera (stoneflies)

Body soft with chewing mouthparts; size 15 to 50 mm. in length; primitive in structure; except for wings and tracheal gills, aquatic immature forms resemble adults; long antennae with setae; membranous wings held close to back when resting, with hindwings pleated and hidden; tarsi three jointed, and abdomen usually with two many-segmented cerci; naiad usually with filamentous gill behind each leg; but gills may be attached to the sides of the thorax and abdomen or at the tip of the abdomen; naiad life may extend from one to three years; undergoes many molts before assuming adult condition; adult life relatively short; naiads live under stones in clean, swift streams, and adults found on stream banks around vegetation; eggs laid in large clutches in or near water; in some places, stoneflies emerge each month of year; mostly herbivorous, but some are carnivorous; about 1,500 species. *Perla* (Fig. 25-30) and *Pteronarcys* are common genera.

Order Isoptera (termites)

Body soft with abdomen joined broadly to thorax, biting mouthparts; social insects of many castes and divisions of labor; castes include wing-

Fig. 25-28

Mole cricket *Gryllotalpa* (Orthoptera) showing forelegs adapted for digging.

Fig. 25-29

A, Earwig *Forficula.* **B,** Forcepslike cerci of earwig.

Fig. 25-30

A, Adult stonefly *Perla* (Plecoptera), with one pair of wings outspread. **B,** Naiad of stonefly.

less, sterile workers and soldiers (Fig. 25-31, *B, C*), sexual males and females (Fig. 25-31, *A*) with similar membranous wings that are carried flat on back at rest and are shed at breakage suture after dispersal flight; after reaching favorable place for new colony, males and females mate; since female lacks sperm receptacle, male fertilizes her from time to time; queen may lay 30,000 eggs each day; some queens, by feeding on special diet, may be 4 or 5 inches long and may live many years; in addition to castes already mentioned, there are many intermediate castes among the termites, such as supplementary reproductives, including fertile soldiers, several types of sterile male and female workers, and male and female soldiers; also a nurse caste; castes are far more numerous in termites than in other social insects such as ants and bees; variations in castes include no working caste in primitive species and no soldier castes in others; food mostly cellulose from both living and dead vegetation; cellulose digested in many termites by symbiotic, intestinal protozoan flagellates which supply necessary enzymes; to supplement their cellulose diet, termites eat their own dead and fecal material for protein; young may become infected with necessary symbiotic protozoans by eating dead termites or by licking anus of adults; live in some form of closed

nest, which may be located in tunnels within soil or in wood; in dry tropical regions they build huge mound nests up to 25 feet high (termitaria) with soil and dry fecal material forming hard surfaces; within termitaria, an orderly arrangement of cells and galleries fitted for special purposes is found; usually different castes cannot be distinguished until after third molt; regulation and determination of caste differentiation appear to be under influence of ectohormones that inhibit nymphal development of individuals of same sex or caste, thus tending to keep caste numbers **467**

Fig. 25-31

Some castes of termites (Isoptera). **A,** Winged sexual adult
(left wings not shown). **B,** Worker. **C,** Soldier.

Fig. 25-32

A, Female embiid. **B,** Male embiid (Embioptera).

within bounds; this process of passing inhibiting
substance to nymphs through mutual feeding is
called trophallaxis; some undifferentiated nymphs
may not come under influence of trophallaxis and
become additional members of caste; initial trend
of development is toward reproductives, but if in-
hibited, soldiers or workers result; cause great
economic damage to wooden structures wherever
found, especially in tropics, but also are of benefit
in building up soil by aeration and releasing nutrients; more than 2,100 species in six families
have been described in all regions except Arctic
and Antarctic. Familiar and important genera are
Reticulitermes, Kalotermes, and *Macrotermes.*

Order Embioptera (embiids)

Body soft and straight sided, varying in length
from 3 to 25 mm.; chewing mouthparts; females
wingless, but males usually have subequal, membranous wings that are folded when not in use;
legs short with three-segmented tarsi; forelegs
adapted for spinning with spinning organs; cerci
short and two jointed; spinning organs located in
swollen basal segment of tarsi; construct silk-
lined galleries in grass or under objects; live on
decayed vegetation; about 1,000 species, chiefly
tropical in distribution. Common genera are *Em-
bia* (Fig. 25-32), *Pararhagadochir,* and *Gynembia.*

Order Odonata (dragonflies, damselflies)

Body large and slender, often brightly colored;
compound eyes large (20,000 to 30,000 ommatidia) and antennae vestigial; three ocelli; chewing
mouthparts; paired, transparent, membranous
wings equal in size (up to 7 inches in wingspread), with a complex network of veins; each
wing has a notch (nodus) midway along its leading edge and a distal, pigmented stigma; wings
usually held in horizontal position while at rest
(dragonflies); thorax divisible into prothorax and
fused meso-metathorax; legs crowded forward for
capturing prey in flight and for perching, but not
for walking; tarsi three jointed; cerci small; male
abdomen at end has claspers for grasping female
head or prothorax with female behind male in
tandem fashion while flying; copulation usually occurs at rest with female looping her abdomen
forward to male accessory genital organs to receive
sperm; eggs are dropped in water or inserted in
plants (Fig. 25-33, *C*); immature forms, naiads or
nymphs, are aquatic (Figs. 25-33, *B,* 25-34), with
hinged prehensile labium that can be thrust out
to capture prey; naiads breathe with flattened,
terminal gills or with rectal gills; development into
adult requires many molts and up to five years;
transformation usually above water on vegetation;
newly emerged adults (tenerals) are weak; adults
are mostly active on clear, sunny days, and males
establish territories; some species migrate long
distances; highly predaceous, capturing almost any

flying insects and even fish fry; serve as intermediate hosts for amphibian and avian trematodes; mass migrations occur frequently over long distances; order divided into suborders (sometimes ranked as orders) Anisoptera (dragonflies) and Zygoptera (damselflies); anisopterans have thick thorax and large wings held laterally when resting; zygopterans are slender, with transparent wings held vertically over back when resting. Nymphs have three external, leaflike caudal gills; about 5,000 species with worldwide distribution; dragonflies more numerous than damselflies. *Gomphus, Anax,* and *Libellula* are common genera of dragonflies; *Lestes, Agrion,* and *Argia* are common American damselflies.

Order Ephemeroptera (Ephemerida) (mayflies)

Body soft, grayish, and up to 25 mm. long; mouthparts of adults vestigial; most primitive winged order of insects; may have derived from ancestral Thysanura; prothorax and metathorax reduced in size and may be consolidated with the enlarged mesothorax; wings membranous and held vertically above back at rest, with forewings much larger; wing expanse up to 75 mm.; setiform antennae and small to large eyes; one to five segmented tarsi; slender legs with forelegs of male specialized for grasping female; very long, segmented cerci, two or three in number (Fig. 25-35); eggs are dropped in water in packets or fixed to surface of rocks in currents; naiad stage lasts from a few weeks to two or three years; naiads have paired tracheal gills on back of each of first seven abdominal segments; mouthparts for chewing, usually with segmented maxillary and labial palpi; feed on plant material, although a few are predators; legs adapted for burrowing or clinging; unique subimago stage follows naiad when flies emerge at surface of water (sometimes underneath surface) and shed their skins; subimago has functional wings, but does not feed, and is immature sexually; subimago within minutes or hours molts to adult or imago stage, only instance of an insect molting in its winged form; adult emerges with transparent wings and vestigial mouthparts; adults undergo rhythmic dancing and mating flight, oviposit, and die without feeding; shortest adult life among insects; more than 1,500 species, 500 of which are found in the United States. *Ephemera, Hexagenia, Potamanthus.*

Order Mallophaga (biting lice)

Body flat and up to 5 mm. long; parasitic on birds and mammals, mostly among feathers of birds; body with long, smooth hairs; biting mouthparts with well-developed mandibles; antennae and eyes reduced; wingless; thorax short or fused; legs short, with or without tiny claws; ovipositor very much reduced; eggs are laid singly and attached to hair or feathers of host; young similar

Fig. 25-33

A, Damselfly *Archilestes* (Odonata). **B,** Damselfly naiad. **C,** Female damselfly ovipositing her eggs in plant stem, while male holds her in position.

Fig. 25-34

Dragonfly naiad (Odonata).

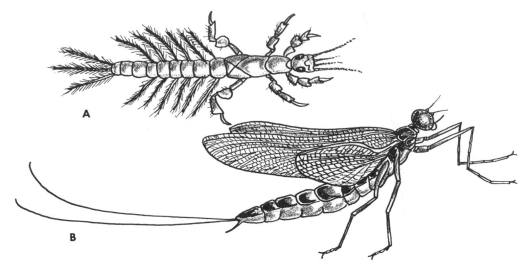

Fig. 25-35
Mayfly (Ephemeroptera). **A**, Naiad. **B**, Adult.

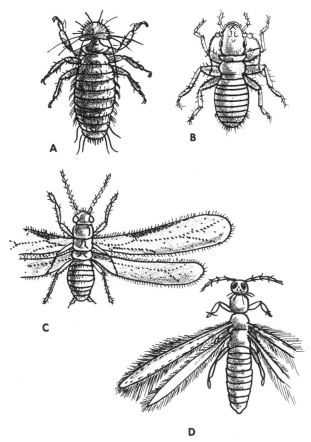

Fig. 25-36
A, Common chicken louse *Menopon* (Mallophaga). **B**, Wingless book louse *Atropos* (Corrodentia). **C**, Winged female *Zorotypus* (Zoraptera). **D**, *Thrips* (Thysanoptera).

to adult, and all stages on host; feed mostly upon feathers, hair or skin scales; most harm to host from irritation when lice population is excessive; about 2,800 species. *Menopon* (Fig. 25-36, *A*), *Goniodes,* and *Trichodectes* are familiar genera.

Order Anoplura (sucking lice)

Body depressed, flat, and up to 6 mm. long; head small; mouthparts (retractile) of three slender stylets adapted for puncturing and sucking; antennae three or five segmented; thorax fused; eyes reduced or absent; tarsi one jointed and enlarged on one or more pairs for grasping a hair; ovipositor reduced; eggs (nits) attached to hairs by glue from ovipositor; young escape from a lid at free end of egg; young resemble adult; exclusively ectoparasitic on mammals; feed on blood of host and transmit typhus fever, trench fever, relapsing fever, and others; about 250 species. *Pediculus humanus* (head and body louse) (Fig. 25-37) and *Phthirius pubis* (crab louse) are common ectoparasites of man.

Order Psocoptera (Corrodentia) (book lice, bark lice)

Body up to 10 mm. long; chewing mouthparts, maxillae with lacinia; antennae long; wings present or absent; tarsi two or three segmented; cerci absent; head and eyes large; gradual metamorphosis; some live under bark or on foliage of trees, others in old books and museums; live on molds, glue, cereals, dead insects, and organic debris; about 1,250 species, 150 of which occur in United States. Common genera are *Psocus, Psocathropos, Trogium,* and *Atropos* (Fig. 25-36, *B*).

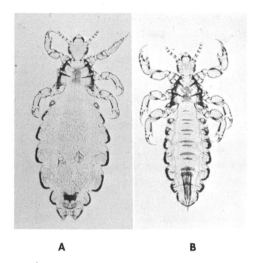

A   B

Fig. 25-37

Head louse *Pediculus humanus* (Anoplura). **A**, Female. **B**, Male.

Order Thysanoptera (thrips)

Body from 0.6 to 14 mm. in length and slender; piercing cone-shaped mouthparts; wingless, or with two pairs of similar, narrow, membranous wings with few or no veins; wings fringed with long hairs; tarsi with one or two joints and terminating with bladderlike organ on tip; antennae with six or nine segments; parthenogenesis common, and males unknown in some species; 1 to 10 generations each year; many species give birth to living young; suck out juices of plants; very destructive to fruit and as vectors of plant diseases; some have wide host range and feed on many kinds of plants; some are carnivorous bloodsuckers; two suborders are recognized, Terebrantia and Tubulifera; members of Terebrantia have sawlike ovipositor for inserting eggs in epidermis of plants; Tubulifera lack this ovipositor and lay eggs on surface; about 3,500 species; common genera are *Hercothrips, Heliothrips,* and *Thrips* (Fig. 25-36, *D*).

Order Zoraptera

Body up to 2.5 mm. long; a rare order related to the termites or book lice; discovered in 1913; wings, when present, may be shed; antennae nine segmented; tarsi two segmented; cerci short; chewing mouthparts; often found in small colonies near termite nests; may have caste social system; may occur in old sawdust piles; about 21 species known, all in genus *Zorotypus* (Fig. 25-36, *C*).

Order Hemiptera (true bugs)

Major order of insects; size range about 2 to 100 mm. in length; wings present or absent; fore-

A

B

Fig. 25-38

A, Box elder bug *Leptocoris,* family Coreidae. **B**, Harlequin cabbage bug *Murgantia,* family Pentatomidae (Hemiptera).

wings with thick basal area, hindwings membranous and fold under forewings; mouthparts elongated into a piercing-sucking mechanism with a sheathlike labium; stylets are grooved and slide up and down during feeding, mandibles adapted for holding substance that is being penetrated; antennae of four or five segments; compound eyes, and often with two ocelli; pronotum of thorax large; triangular mesothoracic scutellum; metathorax partly fused with first abdominal segment; front legs in some predaceous forms may be chelate, while middle and hind legs may be adapted for swimming in some; tarsi usually three segmented; two claws are commonly present; abdomen of 10 to 11 segments, some of which may be

471

hidden; males usually have ninth segment developed as genital capsule with which a pair of claspers may be associated; female usually has ovipositor arising from eighth and ninth segments; spiracles (open or closed) mostly dorsolateral; midgut of stink bugs and squash bugs has specific symbiotic bacteria; about 25,000 species of worldwide distribution except Antarctica; live on sap or animal body fluids; many of great economic importance; about 40 to 50 families represented, the most familiar of which are Corixidae (water boatmen), Nepidae (water scorpions), Belostomatidae (giant water bugs), Gerridae (water striders), Cimicidae (bedbugs), Coreidae (squash bugs), (Fig. 25-38, *A*), Reduviidae (assassin bugs), Lygaeidae (chinch bugs), Pentatomidae (stinkbugs) (Fig. 25-38, *B*), Miridae (plant bugs), and Tingidae (lace bugs).

Order Homoptera (cicadas, aphids, scale insects, treehoppers, leafhoppers)

Often included as a suborder under Hemiptera; large number of diverse species; body mostly small, but cicadas reach length of several centimeters; four membranous wings in winged form, and all wings are of same structure; wings roofed over body at rest; mouthparts of piercing-sucking type, with beak placed well back on ventral side of head; beak of two pairs of stylets (maxillae and mandibles) ensheathed by labium; male scale insects have only two wings; digestive system may

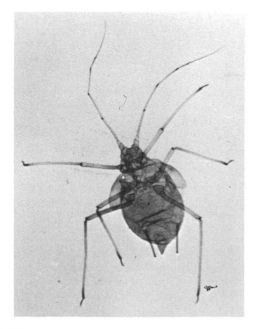

Fig. 25-39
Aphid (Homoptera).

form filter chamber for food, certain unneeded parts of which are shunted around the digestive part of intestine; periodical cicada occurs in many broods in the United States; for different broods in group, nymphs grow 13 to 17 years, feeding on plant juices from tree roots; final instar of cicada emerges from ground and, on tree limb or trunk, molts to form adult; female cicada deposits eggs in woody twigs with sharp ovipositor; male has vibrating organ on ventral part of metathorax with which it sings; number of instars varies greatly with different species; many destructive to plants and some serve as vectors of disease to plants; parthenogenesis common in aphids; more than 30,000 species have been named, but actual number is far in excess of this; two suborders, Auchenorhyncha and Sternorrhyncha, are recognized; between 30 and 40 different families, the common ones of which are Cicadidae (cicadas or locusts) (Fig. 25-24), Cercopidae (spittle bugs and froghoppers), Membracidae (treehoppers), Cicadellidae (leafhoppers), Aphidae (true aphids) (Fig. 25-39), and Coccidae (scale insects and mealybugs).

Division Holometabola (Endopterygota)

Young stages (larvae) without compound eyes; wings develop internally; complete metamorphosis.

Order Mecoptera (scorpion flies)

Body small to medium sized; head prolonged into beak with chewing mouthparts; head held vertically; antennae long; eyes large; four long, slender, membranous wings with many veins; wings at rest held as roof over back; wings absent in some; end of male abdomen (clasping organ) may be recurved over back, scorpionlike; larvae resemble caterpillars; pupae with free appendages; both larvae and adults carnivorous; mostly in moist woodlands; about 250 species. Common genera are *Panorpa* (Fig. 25-40) and *Bittacus,*

Order Trichoptera (caddis flies)

Body size 3 to 25 mm.; soft bodied; feeble mouthparts suitable for lapping liquids; antennae long; two pairs of wings, well veined and hairy, folded tentlike over body (Fig. 25-41, *A*); body hairy, may be in form of scales; adults live up to several months and crawl into fresh water where they lay their eggs under stones or debris; eggs hatch into aquatic larvae, which construct movable cases of leaves, sand, and gravel bound together by silk secreted by larval glands (Fig. 25-41, *B*); cases often funnel shaped to capture food; some do not build cases but live in crevices or other retreats; most larvae are omnivorous, living on algae and small organisms carried to them by water currents; some are entirely predaceous and live on other insect larvae; free-living larvae spin cocoons in which they pupate; case-building larvae pupate within their anchored cases; pupae emerge as adults on vegetation or other objects; about 7,000 species distributed among some 26 families; cosmopolitan. Common genera are *Hydropsyche, Helicopsyche, Rhyacophila,* and *Goera.*

Order Neuroptera (dobson flies, lacewings, ant lions)

Body small to large and soft; chewing mouthparts; all wings are about equal, membranous, with many cross veins; wings roofed over abdomen at rest; long antennae; tarsi have five segments; cerci absent; larvae carnivorous, with mouthparts modified for piercing and sucking; suborder Megaloptera (dobson flies—Fig. 25-42—and alderflies) has cross veins rather than branching veins near anterior margin of wings; aquatic larvae usually with tracheal gills and biting mouthparts; hellgrammites, larvae of dobson fly *Corydalus cornutus* (Fig. 25-43), are prized as bait by fishermen; suborder Planipennia (lacewings and ant lions) has wing veins branching at margin; larvae mostly terrestrial (aphid lions and ant lions) and with sucking mouthparts; eggs of lacewings on stalks; larvae of ant lion (Myrmeleontidae) dig circular pits in sand for trapping ants as prey; larvae of ant lions feed on aphids; pupation occurs in silken cocoon from which adult escapes through hole; about 4,000 species; most primitive insects to have complete metamorphosis. Common genera are *Corydalus* (Fig. 25-42), *Chrysopa,* and *Myrmeleon.*

Order Lepidoptera (moths, skippers, butterflies)

Body with wings spread from 2 to 300 mm.; mandibles usually lacking; adults with hairs or flattened setae (scales) on body, legs, and wings; varicolored; most with two pairs of membranous wings of equal size; antennae long, of many segments; coiled proboscis formed by maxillary galeae; proboscis extended by blood pressure, coiled by diagonal muscles; fluid is sucked up by muscular pump formed by the pharynx and buccal cavity; large compound eyes, but ocelli often absent; mesothorax large and may overlap the metathorax; venation of wings primitive with few cross

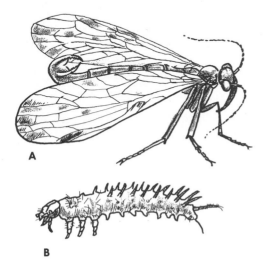

Fig. 25-40

A, Scorpion fly *Panorpa* (Mecoptera), male. Note recurved abdomen with scorpionlike clasping organs. **B,** Larva of scorpion fly.

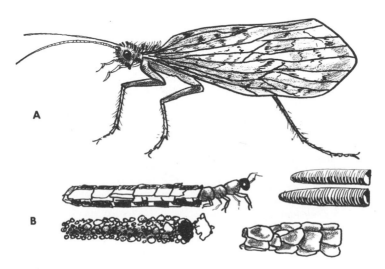

Fig. 25-41

Caddis fly (Trichoptera). **A,** Adult caddis fly. **B,** Several types of larval cases built by caddis fly larvae.

473

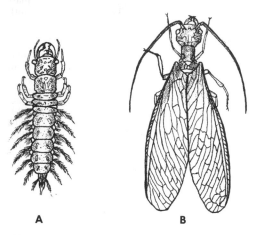

Fig. 25-42

Dobson fly *Corydalus* (Neuroptera). **A,** Naiad (hellgrammite). **B,** Adult.

Fig. 25-44

Swallow-tailed butterfly *Papilio* (Lepidoptera). (From Encyclopaedia Britannica film, "Introducing Insects.")

Fig. 25-43

Hellgrammite larva of dobson fly *Corydalus* (Neuroptera), used by fishermen as bait.

veins; the larvae or caterpillars may be naked or adorned with setae, spines, hair, and tubercles; larvae have three pairs of thoracic legs and a variable number of pairs of forelegs or false legs; larvae usually have six pairs of ocelli but no compound eyes; silk for spinning their cocoons is produced by the labial glands of long simple tubes that unite to form a spinneret opening at the front of the labium; no silk cocoon in butterflies, but chrysalis is suspended by a silken loop. Classification of such an extensive order naturally varies, but the 100,000 to 200,000 species are grouped by many authorities into two suborders of unequal size, Homoneura (Jugatae) and Heteroneura (Frenatae); suborder Homoneura has forewings and hindwings similar in shape and venation, with mandibulate mouthparts and vestigial mandibles;

includes ghost moths and a few others; suborder Heteroneura has hindwing smaller than forewing, of different shape, and with fewer veins; sucking mouthparts; of the more than 150 families, the following heteroneurans deserve notice: Aegeriidae (clearwing moths), Cossidae (carpenter moths), Tineidae (clothes moths), Tortricidae (leaf rollers), Psychidae (bagworms), Eucleidae (slug caterpillar moths), Geometridae (measuring worm moths), Bombycidae (silkworm moths), Saturniidae (giant silkworm moths), Sphingidae (hawk moths), Noctuidae (owlet moths), Arctiidae (tiger moths), Hesperiidae (skippers), Papilionidae (swallow-tailed butterflies) (Fig. 25-44), Pieridae (white and sulphur butterflies), Lycaenidae (blue, copper, hairstreak butterflies), Nymphalidae (four-footed butterflies); the two great groups of Lepidoptera are the moths (by far the greater number) and the butterflies; moths are mostly nocturnal with featherlike or threadlike antennae without knobs; butterflies are diurnal with threadlike antennae bearing knobs at the end.

Order Diptera (true flies, mosquitoes, gnats, midges)

Adults range in size from minute to those that have a wingspread of 100 mm.; only one pair of wings (forewings) with few veins; hindwings represented by a pair of balancers or halteres; some wingless; third largest order; mouthparts for lapping or piercing, often in form of proboscis; labium serves as a guide for the piercing mandibles and maxillae, as well as for the sucking tube of the elongated epipharynx and hypopharynx (many variations); body divisions of head, thorax, and abdomen distinct; antennae usually of two basal segments and a flagellum with one or more segments; compound eyes large, and usually three ocelli; mesothorax large and united to prothorax and metathorax; legs with claws mostly alike, although they may be modified in some for raptorial or other functions; beneath claws a membranous pad, or pulvillus, is usually found; abdomen commonly shows four to nine visible segments; setae and bristles over the head and body are common and are valuable taxonomic characters; metamorphosis complete with egg, larva (maggot), pupa, and imago; eggs may be placed in almost any situation; many, such as mosquitoes, have aquatic larvae with head and chewing mouthparts; other larvae live in mud, damp wood, moist earth, blood, fecal material, and organic refuse; larval skin often serves as cocoon for pupa, or in some pupae, developing adult may be free; economic importance of group very great; some are pollinators of flowers; many destroy other arthropods directly or by laying eggs in their bodies where developing larvae use host as food; diseases transmitted to man by dipteran vectors are malaria, yellow fever, dengue, filariasis, equine encephalitis, kala-azar, sleeping sickness, tularemia, and many virus diseases; flies can spread from infected persons such germs as typhoid fever, dysentery, cholera, etc.; domestic animals much affected by screwworms and botflies that produce direct damage upon tissues and hides; 85,000 species; about 140 families divided between two suborders: Orthorrhapha, in which the adult emerges from the pupa by a straight, longitudinal, dorsal slit; and Cyclorrhapha, in which the adult escapes from its puparium (its transformed last larva skin) by pushing off the anterior end of it. Some of the principal families of Orthorrhapha are Tipulidae (crane flies); Psychodidae (mothflies), Culicidae (mosquitoes) (Fig. 25-21), Simuliidae (blackflies), Tabanidae (deerflies and horseflies), Stratiomyiidae (soldier flies), Asilidae (robber flies), Chironomidae (midges), Muscidae (houseflies); some families of Cyclorrhapha are Drosophilidae (pomace flies), Sarcophagidae (flesh flies), Tachinidae (tachinid flies), Oestridae (botflies), Calliphoridae (blowflies), Hypodermatidae (warble flies), and Conopidae (wasp flies).

Order Siphonaptera (fleas)

Body laterally compressed, compact, and around 3 to 4 mm. in length; no wings; ectoparasites on

Fig. 25-45

Common flea *Pulex irritans* (Siphonaptera), female, ectoparasitic on man and other mammals.

mammals and some birds; legs modified for jumping; mouthparts for piercing and sucking; body armed with spines and setae; coxae enlarged, and tarsi five jointed; antennae short and concealed in grooves; simple eyes only, or none; eggs laid on host pelt or on places where host lies; segmented larvae are legless and eyeless, and feed on host feces, host's blood obtained from adult flea feces, organic debris, and vegetable matter; larva spins a cocoon where molting takes place to form the pupal stage; may remain as nonfeeding pupa up to a year, or much shorter, before emerging as adult; adults live exclusively on blood of host; usually live only part time on host and spend part of the time in debris of the substratum; transmit various diseases, especially bubonic plague, and act as intermediate hosts for cat and dog tapeworms; general pests of irritation on all hosts; about 1,000 species; common species are *Pulex irritans* (man, rat) (Fig. 25-45), *Ctenocephalides canis* (dog), *C. felis* (cat), and *Xenopsylla cheopis* (rat).

Order Coleoptera (beetles and weevils)

Body minute to large size with heavy cuticle; chewing mouthparts with some modifications; mouthparts include labrum, mandibles, maxillae, and labium; forewings modified into horny veinless elytra, and form tight, straight line down back; hindwings membranous with few veins and folded under forewings at rest; elytra usually extend to abdomen, but may be truncate; some wingless; abdomen lacks first sternum; usually seven or eight pairs of abdominal spiracles; antennae usually 11 segmented; prothorax is free with large notum; **475**

Fig. 25-46

Tiger beetle *Cicindela* (Coleoptera). Note sensory hairs on legs. (Courtesy Encyclopaedia Britannica Films, Inc.)

mesothorax and metathorax are fused; head usually with a pair of compound eyes and three small ocelli; number of tarsal segments varies in different groups, but five is a common number; tarsal formulas are useful in taxonomy; larvae grublike with thoracic legs usually present; change from larva to pupa may occur in cocoon but usually in wood cell or debris; mature adult emerges from the pupal skin; many variations in their complete metamorphosis; ecologic diversity surpasses that of all other groups; occupy all animal habitats, except marine; most beetles are plant feeders and will eat almost any form of organic substance; some are parasitic on other insects or animals; others are predators; some are beneficial as scavengers; both larvae and adults of the lower taxa often differ greatly in their niche requirements, so that an enormous range of ecologic relationships is set up; many species have established symbiotic associations with ant and termite colonies; many such beetle inquilines give off exudates that are highly prized by ants and termites; about 275,000 species, or 40 percent of all insects; two to four suborders and some 160 families are recognized; suborder Adephaga have filiform antennae and hindwings with one or two cross veins; suborder Polyphaga have diversified antennae and hindwings lacking cross veins; among the chief families are Cicindelidae (tiger beetles) (Fig. 25-46), Carabidae (ground beetles), Dytiscidae (predaceous diving beetles), Gyrinidae (whirligig beetles), Staphylinidae (rove beetles), Silphidae (carrion beetles),

Lucanidae (stag beetles), Tenebrionidae (darkling beetles), Hydrophilidae (water scavengers), Coccinellidae (ladybird beetles), Lampyridae (glowworms and fireflies), Elateridae (click beetles), Dermestidae (skin beetles), Anobiidae (powderpost beetles), Psephenidae (water penny beetles), Cerambycidae (longhorn beetles), Chrysomelidae (leaf beetles), and Circulionidae (weevils or snout beetles).

Order Strepsiptera (Stylops) (twisted-winged insects)

Size minute; mouthparts for chewing, or vestigial; male hindwings fan shaped, but forewings club shaped (pseudohalteres); female wingless and legless, endoparasitic in other insects; female, as primary larva, bores into host and becomes an egg-producing sac with loss of eyes, antennae, and legs; head and thorax of female fused into a cephalothorax; females and larvae remain parasitic in bees, wasps, and homopterous bugs; absorb nutrition from host; the order is often considered a highly specialized parasitic branch of the Coleoptera, and may be placed as a family under that group; hypermetamorphosis and life history unique in the far-flung patterns of insect life; 200 to 300 species in six families. Two common genera are *Xenos* and *Stylops*.

Order Hymenoptera (ants, bees, wasps)

Body length from 0.5 to 50 mm. and more or less hairy; most species with four membranous

Fig. 25-47

Ichneumon fly, family Ichneumonidae (Hymenoptera). Inset, head of ichneumon fly.

wings, the forewings larger, with reduced venation; hindwings locked to forewings by hooklets; wings absent in some, especially the workers of ants, females of some solitary wasps, and many parasitic forms; mouthparts for chewing or chewing-lapping; compound eyes moderate to very large; usually three ocelli; antennae vary from short (about 12 segments) to long with many segments; legs usually slender, but modified in some for carrying pollen; abdomen constricted at posterior end of first segment, which is fused into hind end of thorax; females have ovipositor modified for piercing, sawing, or stinging; ovipositor very long in ichneumon flies; some have caterpillar-like larvae, but many larvae are legless and maggotlike with well-developed head; pupae usually have free appendage and silk cocoons; most species are dioecious, but parthenogenesis of several types is common; sexual dimorphism, with males usually smaller than females, is common; most species are solitary, but specialization for social life has reached one of its highest peaks in this order; behavior patterns and complicated adaptations for rearing young and general life habits are in line with their high social organizations; employment of sign language for communication among honeybees represents a high level of intelligent behavior; nearly all members of the order are terrestrial, living in or near the earth's surface; most adults feed on plant nectar or honey dew; some are parasitic; larvae may be herbivorous, but many live as parasites on hosts provided for them by the females; several hymenopterans have economic importance both injurious and beneficial to man's interests and animal economy; more than 120,000 species have been described and distributed among scores of families; two suborders, Symphyta and Apocrita, are commonly recognized; the Symphyta have abdomen

Fig. 25-48

Bald-faced hornet *Vespula,* family Vespidae (Hymenoptera).

broadly joined to the thorax, larvae provided with legs, and include more primitive members; Apocrita have abdomen more or less constricted at the base, legless larvae, and include majority of Hymenoptera; some of important families of Hymenoptera are Tenthredinidae (sawflies), Ichneumonidae (ichneumon flies) (Fig. 25-47), Chalcididae (chalcid wasps), Cynipidae (gall wasps), Scelionidae (scelionid wasps), Formicidae (ants), Vespidae (hornets, yellow jackets) (Fig. 25-48), Sphecidae (mud-dauber wasps), Megachilidae (leaf-cutting bees), and Apidae (honeybees, bumblebees).

Annotated references

Borror, D. J., and D. M. De Long. 1964. An introduction to the study of insects. New York, Holt, Rinehart & Winston, Inc. *The best up-to-date treatise on insects.*

Bronn, H. G. (editor). 1926-1934. Klassen und Ordnungen des Tierreichs. Leipzig, Akademische Verlagsgesellschaft. *Volume 5 of this great work is devoted to the Chilopoda, Diplopoda, Symphyla, and Pauropoda.*

Carter, W. 1963. Insects in relation to plant diseases. New York, John Wiley & Sons, Inc. *A comprehensive account of insect vectors and the plant viruses they transmit.*

Cloudsley-Thompson, J. L. 1958. Spiders, scorpions, centipedes, and mites. London, Pergamon Press, Inc.

Corbet, P. S. 1963. A biology of dragonflies. New York, Quadrangle Books, Inc.

Davey, K. G. 1965. Reproduction in the insects. San Francisco, W. H. Freeman & Co., Publishers. *A summary of the different methods insects employ.*

Frost, S. W. 1965. Insects and pollinia. Ecology 46:556-558. *Pollinia are traplike pollen masses in such plants as milkweeds and orchids, which insects frequently carry away attached to their appendages.*

Gilmour, D. 1965. The metabolism of insects. San Francisco, W. H. Freeman & Co., Publishers.

Grasse, P. P. (editor). 1949. Traite de zoologie, vol. 9. Paris, Masson et Cie. *A comprehensive and authoritative account.*

Kennedy, J. S. (editor). 1961. Insect polymorphism.. London, Royal Entomological Society. *Polymorphism results from the simultaneous occurrence of several genetic factors or gene arrangements in a population that produce discontinuous phenotypic effects. Its ecologic significance is not clear in all cases.*

Kukenthal, W., and T. Krumbach (editors). Handbuch der Zoologie. 1926, vol. 4, Progoneata, Chilopoda; 1929, vol. 52, Myriapoda, Geophilomorpha; 1930, vol. 54, Chilopoda, Scolopendromorpha; 1937-1940, vols. 68-70, Diplopoda, Polydesmoidea. Berlin, Walter De Gruyter & Co. *A very extensive account of these groups.*

Manton, S. M. 1954. The evolution of arthropodan locomotory mechanisms. Part 4: The structure, habits and evolution of the Diplopoda. J. Linnean Soc. London (Zoology) 42:299-368.

McKittrick, F. A. 1964. Evolutionary studies of cockroaches; Memoir 389. Ithaca, Cornell University Agricultural Experiment Station.

Smith, R. F. (editor). 1965. Annual review of entomology, vol. 10. Palo Alto, Annual Reviews, Inc. *This annual review is useful in the evaluation of current work in the field of insects.*

Snodgrass, R. E. 1952. A textbook of arthropod anatomy. Ithaca, Cornell University Press. *A good account of the morphology of the groups considered in this chapter.*

Swan, L. A. 1964. Beneficial insects. New York, Harper & Row, Publishers. *The useful side of a group that has been the chief target of the pesticide war.*

Tiegs, O. W. 1947. The development and affinities of the Pauropoda, based on a study of *Pauropus silvaticus.* Quart. J. Micr. Sci. 88:165-267, 275-336.

Walker, E. M. 1953. The Odonata of Canada and Alaska, vol. 1. Toronto, University of Toronto Press. *A systematic study of the dragonflies.*

Chapter 26

Phylum Mollusca

This second largest phylum of the animal kingdom is made up of such forms as clams, mussels, oysters, snails, slugs, octopuses, squids, and some others.

The group has enormous diversity, both in shape and size, ranging all the way from the twisted, wormlike solenogastrids to the baglike octopuses, and from minute snails to the giant squids, which are the largest of all invertebrates.

In number of species described (around 100,000) the mollusks are next to the arthropods. Their fossil record is also impressive, with many thousands of fossil species. The possession of a durable shell by many mollusks has made preservation of their remains easy compared with many other invertebrate groups.

Their ecology is also very diversified, for they have been able to live in nearly all kinds of habitats. Some are found in the greatest depths of the oceans and others are present at about the highest altitudes recorded for animal life. The shell-bearing forms are restricted somewhat by the calcium content of their environments, but the shell-less mollusks can live even in regions that are more or less devoid of lime. As a consequence, mollusks are found in the sea, brackish water, fresh water, and on land. They share with the arthropods the capacity to adapt themselves to terrestrial life better than most groups of invertebrates. Some are strictly aquatic in both fresh and marine water, and others are exclusively terrestrial. In whatever region they are found, they exist in almost every variety of habitat that will support life. For diversity of habits and behavior, they include some of the slowest and most sluggish of animals and some that are among the swiftest of invertebrates. In structural and functional adaptations, mollusks rank with the arthropods because some of the most unique invertebrate behavior patterns are found among them. Nutritionally, they range from primitive filter feeders to highly carnivorous predators.

Most mollusks live in the sea. Three of their classes—Amphineura, Scaphopoda, and Cephalopoda—are not represented at all on land or in fresh water. Both gastropods and bivalves have colonized fresh water; however, they are fewer in number than their representatives in the sea. The chief physiologic requirements for conquest of the land involve air breathing, temperature regulation, and water control. Bivalves have successfully invaded fresh water but have been unable to meet the requirements for terrestrial life. The feeding method of bivalves has been a deterrent to their colonization of land. The class Gastropoda is the only group of mollusks that has successfully invaded terrestrial habitats. Although both prosobranch and pulmonate gastropods are found in fresh water, the larger number belong to the pulmonates.

Mollusks are coelomate, unsegmented animals (except class Monoplacophora) which have modified the invertebrate pattern by stressing features that are either absent in other invertebrates or occur in an entirely different form. These bilaterally symmetric (modified in some) animals exhibit a great range of morphologic varieties, but all are essentially built around certain common features that have been modified for adaptive purposes in their evolutionary radiation. The mollusk typically has a head, a visceral mass, a mantle, a shell, and a

Fig. 26-1

Some of many shell varieties among mollusks. (From Encyclopaedia Britannica film, "Mollusks".)

foot. The head is located at the anterior end; the compact visceral mass is enclosed in a soft integument; the mantle is a modified dorsal part of the integument and hangs down as free folds or flaps around the body to form a mantle cavity; the calcareous shell is secreted by the mantle; and the ventral muscular foot, modified from the integument, is the organ of locomotion. All these structures may be modified in various ways in the different groups of mollusks. A head, shell, or mantle may be lacking altogether in some. The shell may be bivalved, univalved, spiral, or cone shaped (Fig. 26-1). Most mollusks have a rasping organ, the radula, a kind of toothed tongue that bears denticles or teeth.

Students of mollusks have reconstructed a hypothetical primitive mollusk (Fig. 26-2) which is supposed to have existed in Precambrian seas. Such a generalized ancestor was bilaterally symmetric with a dorsally arched body. Its head bore a pair of tentacles that had pigment spots or

ocelli at their bases; and its mouth was provided with a protrusible radula similar in structure and arrangement to that in modern snails. From the dorsal side a mantle (pallium) extended over the body and secreted the arched, shieldlike shell. This shell may not have been calcareous at first, but consisted of a hard, horny substance. Both mantle and shell increased radially, chiefly by marginal growth. On the ventral surface was the flat, muscular creeping foot. The shell was attached to the foot by muscles that could either draw the shell closely against the substratum or draw the foot into the protective shell.

Between the mantle and foot at the posterior end was a mantle cavity containing paired gills, openings to the nephridia (kidney), and the anus. Each gill consisted of a central axis, bearing on each side alternating rows of filaments. The gill was attached to the floor of the mantle cavity by membranes dorsally and ventrally. Such an arrangement divided the mantle chamber into an upper and lower chamber. Within the axis of each gill both afferent and efferent blood vessels were provided for the exchange of respiratory gases. Water currents were drawn into the cavity by the beating of cilia located on the gill filaments. A ciliated, mucus-producing hypobranchial gland between each gill and the rectum helped carry waste particles into the dorsal branchial chamber for rejection. A small sensory patch, the osphradium, at the base of each gill tested the chemical nature of the incoming current.

The digestive system consisted of a tube that was differentiated into a narrow esophagus, a broadened cone-shaped stomach, and a coiled intestine. The canal was lined with cilia and mucus glands. Chitin lined the anterior part of the stomach, into which a pair of digestive glands (liver) opened. The posterior part of the stomach was differentiated into the style sac. A median ciliated groove extended along the stomach floor. The food of this early ancestor was probably algae and other material scraped from rocks over which it crept. Digestion may have been primarily intracellular. The early coelomic cavity was mostly the pericardium, which surrounded the heart and consisted of two auricles and a ventricle. Blood circulation was similar to that of present-day mollusks. Paired

gonads also opened into the pericardial sac. Gametes were carried by the nephridia, which thus served as gonoducts, to the posterior mantle cavity. The kidneys consisted of a pair of metanephridia. Each metanephridium opened at one end by a nephrostome into the coelomic cavity and at the other end by a nephridiopore into the mantle cavity. Waste probably came from both the coelomic cavity and the blood. The nervous system was made up of a central nerve ring around the esophagus, with two pairs of longitudinal nerve cords extending posteriorly under the esophagus. The more dorsal of these nerve cords ran to the mantle and viscera, and the ventral pair innervated the muscles of the foot. Commissures also connected various parts of the cords. Nerve cells were probably diffused and not gathered into ganglia. Sense organs were represented by the tentacles, eyespots, statocysts in the foot, and the osphradia already mentioned.

From such a hypothetical ancestral form the various groups of mollusks could have evolved by adaptive radiation into the diversity demonstrated by both the fossil record (Fig. 26-3) and the existing classes.

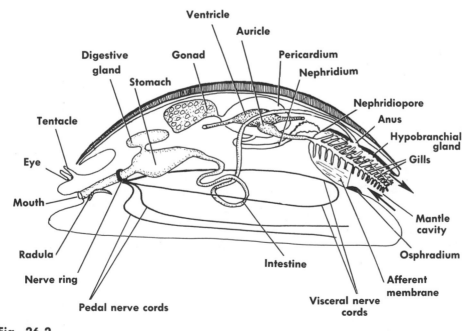

Fig. 26-2

Hypothetical primitive mollusk, longitudinal optical section.

A   B   C

D   E

Fig. 26-3

Some fossil mollusks. **A** to **C**, Gastropods. **A**, *Hormotoma*, middle Ordovician. **B**, *Trepospira* and, **C**, *Worthenia*, both Pennsylvanian. **D**, Pelecypod, *Grammysia*, middle Devonian. **E**, Cephalopod, *Scaphites*, an Upper Cretaceous ammonoid. All shown at approximately natural size.

CLASSIFICATION

Phylum Mollusca. Body bilaterally symmetric with some modifications; chiefly unsegmented; coelomic cavity reduced; body soft and covered by a mantle or extension of the outermost layer of the body wall, which often secretes a calcareous shell of one to several parts; usually provided with a head and ventral muscular foot; mantle cavity, produced by mantle flaps, encloses gills (ctenidia) or lunglike structures; digestive system complete, U-shaped or coiled, and provided with a radula (usually), digestive glands, and an anus opening into the mantle cavity; excretory system of one or two pairs of nephridia (kidney) connecting pericardium and mantle cavity; circulatory system of a heart consisting of a ventricle and paired auricles, a pericardium, an arterial system, and an open venous system expanded into a hemocoel; nervous system of a circumesophageal ring modified usually into three pairs of ganglia (cerebral, pedal, and visceral) with longitudinal and cross connectives; sense organs of statocysts, touch, vision, smell, and variously modified; sexes separate (usually) or monoecious (a few); gonads one or two with ducts; fertilization internal or external; determinate and unequal total cleavage; development with larval stages (veliger, trochophore, or glochidium) or direct; terrestrial, freshwater, or marine.

Class Monoplacophora. Body bilaterally symmetric with ventral foot; internal segmentation; mantle covered with a single dome-shaped shell; shallow mantle cavity containing five or six pairs of branched gills; dorsolateral and ventral coelomic cavities; digestive system with radula, crystalline style, and much-coiled intestine; heart with two pairs of auricles; six pairs of nephridia; nervous system with longitudinal and pedal cords; paired gonads, with the gametes discharged through two pairs of nephridia which act as coelomoducts; sexes separate. *Neopilina* (Fig. 26-5) (two species: *N. galatheae* and *N. ewingi*).

Class Amphineura. Body elongated and bilaterally symmetric; mantle extensive with shell of eight plates or none; head reduced and no tentacles; nerve ring and two pairs of nerve cords (pallial and pedal) with cross connections; sexes separate or hermaphroditic.

Subclass Aplacophora. Body wormlike; no shell; foot absent or reduced; integument with calcareous spicules; mantle completely covers body except for vestigial foot groove (in some); mostly aberrant mollusks; hermaphroditic or dioecious; typical trochophore larva; deep marine water. *Neomenia, Chaetoderma* (Fig. 26-14, *B, C*).

Subclass Polyplacophora. Body elliptic or oval with shell of eight transverse plates; broad ventral foot; shell bordered by scaly girdle or mantle; gills vary from few to many and located in groove around foot; separate sexes; single median gonad; trochophore larva; marine coastal waters. *Chiton* (Fig. 26-13, *B*), *Lepidopleurus*.

Class Scaphopoda. Body in slightly curved, tubular shell and mantle open at both ends; foot conical and pointed; no gills; head with captacula for catching food; no eyes; .sexes separate without genital ducts; one gonad; veliger larva; shallow to deep marine water. *Dentalium* (Fig. 26-48), *Cadulus* (tusk shells).

Class Gastropoda. Body asymmetric, usually with a spiral shell of one piece; shell reduced or absent in some; foot broad and flattened; visceropallium typically with torsion of 180 degrees on head and foot, and coiled in shell; operculum for closing shell present in some; one or two gills or lung modified from mantle cavity; one or two nephridia; radula present; sexes separate or monoecious; mostly oviparous; larva veliger, trochophore, or none; terrestrial, freshwater, or marine.

Subclass Prosobranchia (Streptoneura). Body with visceral torsion, shell, and operculum; visceral loop in form of figure eight (streptoneury); head with single pair of tentacles and bearing eyes at base; mantle cavity opens anteriorly and bears one or two gills (ctenidia); heart posterior to gills; sexes separate with one genital opening; veliger larva usually; terrestrial, freshwater, and mostly marine.

Order Aspidobranchia (Archaeogastropoda). Primitive forms; respiration with one or two ctenidia or none; ctenidia plumelike with two rows of filaments (bipectinate); nervous system not concentrated; heart usually with two auricles; one pair of nephridia; shell mostly coiled or secondarily symmetric in limpet; some with slit or perforated shells; terrestrial, freshwater, and marine. *Patella* (limpet), *Haliotis* (abalone, Fig. 26-23), *Trochus* (top shell).

Order Pectinibranchia (Mesogastropoda, Monotocardia). Snails with organs of the posttorsional right side lost; with only one ctenidium, one auricle, and one nephridium; ctenidium with only one row of filaments (pectinibranch); eversible proboscis in some; nervous system partially concentrated; operculum often present; larva often a veliger; terrestrial, freshwater, and marine. *Littorina* (periwinkle, Fig. 26-22, *G*), *Crepidula* (slipper or boat shell, Fig. 26-22, *B*), *Strombus* (conch, Fig. 26-22, *H*), *Campeloma, Cypraea* (cowrie).

Order Neogastropoda. Snails with highly concentrated nervous system; shell with siphon, eversible proboscis, and large bipectinate osphradium; many species carnivorous, some with poison glands; radula often with a few large teeth in each row; veliger larva mostly suppressed with intracapsular embryos; strictly marine. *Urosalpinx* (oyster drill, Fig. 26-22, *F*), *Busycon* (Fig. 26-21), *Buccinum* (whelks) *Terebra* (auger shell), *Murex* (rock shell, Fig. 26-22, *J*).

Subclass Opisthobranchia (Euthyneura) Shell reduced or none; operculum mostly absent; mantle cavity and opening posterior; viscera with tendency to detorsion; nervous system concentrated around esophagus (no streptoneury); one or no gill; when present, gill posterior to heart; accessory respiratory organ may be present; usually one nephridium and one auricle; two pairs of tentacles (usually); hermaphroditic; marine.

Order Tectibranchia. Body with large head and with or without shell; when present, thin shell usually enclosed in mantle; operculum mostly lacking; one gill. *Aplysia* (sea hare, Fig. 26-26), *Acteon, Bulla* (bubble shell).

Order Pteropoda. Foot modified into fins for swimming (Fig. 26-20); shell present or absent; nervous system secondarily untwisted; pelagic; hermaphroditic; marine. *Clione, Cavolina* (sea butterfly, Fig. 26-19, *B*).

Order Nudibranchia. Shell absent (usually); no mantle cavity or true gill; respiration by skin or by secondary gills (cerata) near anus, around edge of mantle, or in dorsal rows; digestive gland large and branched; nervous system concentrated; hermaphroditic; marine.

483

Polycera, Doris (sea lemon), *Dendronotus, Aeolis* (sea slug, Figs. 26-25, 26-26, *D*).

Subclass Pulmonata. Mostly small; shell a simple spiral or none; respiration by pulmonary sac; no gills; usually no operculum; one or two pairs of tentacles; one pair of eyes; gonad single; monoecious; development direct; terrestrial, freshwater, marine (rarely).

Order Basommatophora. Head with one pair of tentacles; eyes at base of tentacles; some with secondary gills; terrestrial, freshwater, and marine. *Physa* (Fig. 26-22, *D*), *Lymnaea* (Fig. 26-30, *C*) (pond snails), *Planorbis* (ramshorn snail).

Order Stylommatophora. Head with two pairs of tentacles; eyes on tip of posterior pair of tentacles; some without shell; terrestrial. *Helix, Polygyra* (land snails), *Limax* (land slug).

Class Pelecypoda. (Bivalvia or Lamellibranchia). Shell a pair of lateral symmetric valves, sometimes multivalve, usually with dorsal hinge and ligaments; head rudimentary; no radula; labial palps; mantle lobes paired and enclosing laterally compressed body; usually two pairs of gills (ctenidia) in mantle cavity; posterior margin of mantle modified usually into siphons or apertures; foot for burrowing, creeping, other functions, or absent; mostly dioecious; larva a veliger or glochidium; freshwater and marine.

Subclass Protobranchia. Gills with flat, nonreflected filaments; filaments of each gill arranged in two divergent rows (protobranch) on opposite sides of axis; hinge simple or with similar teeth along hinge area (taxodont); extensions from labial palps may be used as deposit-feeding proboscides; foot with flat ventral surface; marine. *Yoldia* (Fig. 26-35, *H*), *Solemya, Nucula.*

Subclass Lamellibranchia. Gill filaments elongated and reflected, forming two-sided lamellae; adjacent filaments may be attached (incompletely fused) by ciliary junctions or fused by tissues; gills chiefly ciliary-feeding organs; foot variously modified for different functions; marine and freshwater.

Order Filibranchia. Gills usually W-shaped in cross section, with vascular interlamellar junctions; incompletely fused filaments with adjacent filaments attached by ciliary connections (filibranch); muscles unequal with reduced (or absent) anterior adductor and enlarged posterior adductor; often attached by byssus or cementing substance. *Mytilus* (Fig. 26-36), *Ostrea, Pecten* (Figs. 26-35, *F*, 26-41), *Arca.*

Order Eulamellibranchia. Gill W-shaped, with reflexed lamellae of each half (demibranch) joined at regular intervals by vascular tissue connections forming enclosed spaces; two ad-

ductor muscles of same size. *Anodonta, Lampsilis* (Fig. 26-35, *E*), *Cardium, Ensis, Teredo, Donax.*

Subclass Septibranchia. Gills absent; adductor muscles about equal; mantle partially open and divided horizontally by muscular partition (modified from gill); respiration through walls of suprabranchial chamber; muscular septum acting as pumping mechanism; marine. *Poromya, Cuspidaria.*

Class Cephalopoda. Well-developed head surrounded by circle of prehensile tentacles, at least partially derived from foot; tentacles mostly provided with suckers; body lengthened along dorsoventral axis to become functional anteroposterior axis; shell external, internal, or absent; mouth with horny jaws and radula; muscular funnel or siphon for "jet propulsion" beneath head; mantle bulky and fleshy with extensive mantle chamber; mantle may be modified into fins; coelom continuous with pericardium; one or two pairs of gills; nervous system centralized in head and contained in a cartilaginous capsule; eyes well developed; dioecious; development direct; marine.

Subclass Nautiloidea (Tetrabranchia). Shell external, coiled in one plane in existing species, and chambered; simple sutures; retractile tentacles suckerless; funnel of two separate folds; two pairs of gills; two pairs of kidneys; eyes without cornea or lens; marine. *Nautilus* (Fig. 26-51).

Subclass Ammonoidea (Tetrabranchia, Fig. 26-53). Wholly extinct.

Subclass Coleoidea (Dibranchia). Mantle naked with reduced internal shell, or none; body more or less cylindric, usually with fins; 8 to 10 arms, some with suckers; some with retractile filaments; one pair of gills and nephridia; siphon a closed tube; eye with crystalline lens, and cornea often closed; ink sac present; includes all existing cephalopods except *Nautilus;* marine.

Order Decapoda. Eight short arms and pair of longer, tentacular, retractile arms; suckers pedunculate with horny rings; internal shell; body with fins; ink sac present. *Sepia* (cuttle fish, Fig. 26-54), *Loligo* (squid, Fig. 26-56), *Architeuthis.*

Order Octopoda. Body globose, usually without fins; eight arms with one to three rows of sessile suckers; mantle forms muscular sac around viscera; internal shell lacking; some with special egg case secreted by dorsal arms; third arm of male may be modified as copulatory organ (hectocotylus); ink sac present. *Octopus* (Figs. 26-58, 26-62), *Argonauta* (paper nautilus).

Order Vampyromorpha. Similar to Octopoda but with eight long arms and two small, retractile, filamentlike arms; no hectocotylus arm; ink sac absent; light organs present. *Vampyroteuthis* (vampire squid).

BASIC ADAPTIVE FEATURES

Although mollusks exhibit a vast range of diversity in both morphology and function, they all possess certain common structural details that have guided their evolutionary pattern (Fig. 26-4). Their adaptations have led them into almost every kind of ecologic habitat. They utilize most types of locomotion, except flying. They have evolved most kinds of feeding habits—from filter feeders on the smallest organisms to predators of the highest efficiency.

They share some of their structural features with other coelomate animals, but the characteristic organs that set them apart from other major groups are the mantle, shell, foot, gills, and radula. In primitive types their major axis was the anteroposterior one laid down by the longitudinal foot. A second axis, the dorsoventral one, appeared early in their evolution as their body took on more bulk. On top of the muscular foot the visceral mass was somewhat dome shaped. This laid the basic mollusk design of two interacting symmetries—a visceropallium, composed of viscera and overhanging mantle, and a head-foot complex. The head-foot part had definite bilateral symmetry; the visceropallium at first had radial symmetry, with a tendency later toward biradial symmetry.

According to the hypothetical ancestor described earlier, other features or modifications have been added to the basic design, such as a shell and gills. The head is best developed in the Gastropoda and in the Cephalopoda (where it is fused with the foot). In Amphineura and Scaphopoda the head is less stressed; and in the Pelecypoda it is absent altogether.

The mantle is one of the most versatile structures in molluscan evolution. It not only secretes the shell in all mollusks but forms the mantle cavity where the digestive system, nephridia, and gonads open. The mantle is also modified into the gills or into lungs in air-breathing forms. Siphons and apertures for inhalant and exhalant water currents are modified from the mantle. The mantle serves an important role in locomotion in some, such as the cephalopods, and in the feeding processes in many. The lack of a head in bivalves may be partly due to the mantle's assumption of food collecting and other functions ordinarily performed by the jaws and radula in other mollusks. Perhaps no molluscan structure has demonstrated more creative adaptive capacity than has the glandular mantle.

Fig. 26-4

Molluscan types. **A,** Amphineura. **B,** Monoplacophora. **C,** Scaphopoda. **D,** Pelecypoda. **E,** Gastropoda. **F,** Cephalopoda. Intestinal tract, gills, heart, shell, and cerebral ganglia are indicated in diagrams.

Two of the greatest modifications of the basic plan of mollusks were made by the gastropods and cephalopods. The gastropods, although retaining much of the ancestral molluscan plan, have undergone an asymmetric growth known as torsion. Torsion and the coiling of the shell result in changes in the location of many basic structures, which will be described later. On the other hand, the cephalopods have no torsion, but the body lengthens along the dorsoventral axis and becomes the functional anteroposterior axis, while the original anteroposterior axis is shortened and becomes dorsoventral in position. As a result, the former ventral surface is now anterior, and the dorsal surface is posterior. The foot has moved forward, surrounding the mouth, and has become transformed into circumoral prehensile tentacles or arms. This change, together with other features, has greatly stressed the head region and added much to the most advanced members of the mollusk group. The foot is no longer the chief organ of locomotion, but has been largely replaced by jet propulsion of water from the mantle cavity through a funnelform foot.

The branchial current in many aquatic mollusks is brought directly into the animal by the cilia which cover the gills. In this way a sluggish organism can receive a constant food supply. In cephalopods, cilia are absent, and the current is induced by muscular action, a method more suitable for a very active group.

Not the least of molluscan adaptive features is the radula, which is the chitinous teeth-bearing band that is manipulated by a cartilage-muscle apparatus. It appears to have been present in the ancestral mollusk (Fig. 26-2) and has been retained in most modern mollusks, except in certain degenerate gastropods and bivalves. Originally used perhaps for rasping off algae and other particulate matter from substrata, it has become specialized for a varied assortment of uses in the evolution of mollusks.

The characteristic molluscan shell has had its full share in the evolutionary adaptation of mollusks. Endless evolutionary trial and error on the part of the shell has evolved structural changes in keeping with the diverse ecologic patterns of the group. Some mollusks have thick, heavy shells for withstanding stress and pressure; some have thin, delicate shells for swift movement; others have boring shells for burrowing into hard objects; still others swim by snapping the shells open and closed. Other shell patterns, such as the spirality of snails, the reduction or absence of the shell altogether, and the varied structural organization of shells, represent marked evolutionary trends in this important organ.

PHYLOGENETIC RELATIONSHIPS

Little can be stated with certainty regarding the relationship of the mollusks to other phyla, although two or three theories have been proposed by students of the group. One theory stresses a possible connection between flatworms (Turbellaria) and mollusks, basing the evidence mainly upon the shell-less Solenogastres (Aplacophora), which have some features of chitons and also certain reproductive tubes similar to primitive flatworms. Another theory, which is more generally accepted, stresses the similar trochophore larva found in mollusks and annelids. Additional evidence for this second theory has been the recent (1952) discovery of certain specimens of Monoplacophora (Fig. 26-5). These show some conditions of primitive segmentation or metamerism, such as six pairs of nephridia, eight pairs of shell muscles, and a pallial groove with

Fig. 26-5

Neopilina, a monoplacophoran, ventral view. Note mouth, anus, and five pairs of gills surrounding foot. (Modified from Lemche.)

five or six pairs of gills, all metamerically arranged.

The exact status of the monoplacophorans is very much in doubt. Their metamerism is slightly superficial, involving only some of the systems and lacking external segmentation of the body wall altogether. At present they cannot be considered a basic mollusk type because of their irregular metamerism and isolated case. If metamerism were a primitive molluscan feature, it would be difficult to account for its total absence in other mollusks. All this may be interpreted to mean that metamerism in the monoplacophorans has been secondarily acquired. More embryologic evidence may shed some light on the problem.

Stronger evidence for the annelid affinity is shown perhaps by the resemblance between the embryology of mollusks and that of polychaetes. A similar spiral cleavage is found in both groups, with the exception of the cephalopods.

The relations between the various molluscan classes are also obscure. Although logical explanations can be made for the modifications of most groups from the hypothetical ancestral type, these throw little light on possible interrelationships. Each class seems to have distinct evolutionary tendencies. The amphineurans have departed least from the primitive plan although their fossil record is not so old as that of more specialized groups. Convergence of characters may well add to the confusion about relationships. The gastropods and the cephalopods share many characters, although there is a wide gulf in basic plan between the two classes. At present there are few logical reasons for grouping the classes according to relationships. The recent discovery (1959) of a bivalved gastropod, *Tamanovalva limax,* off the coast of Japan, and similar ones elsewhere, may pose aspects of relationship of great interest. This type has the characteristic valves of a bivalve and the sluglike head and foot of a gastropod. The evolutionary appraisal of this and related species awaits further study.

Within the phylum two classes, the gastropods and the bivalves, each demonstrate some rather striking phylogenetic relationships and evolutionary differentiations among the members of the class. The most primitive basal gastropods are the Prosobranchia with torsion and a helical shell. Prosobranchs exhibit two grades—those with bipectinate (aspidobranch) gills (two rows of gill leaflets on the branchial axis) and those that have pectinibranch gills (one row of gill filaments). From the pectinibranchs the evolutionary lines lead to two orders—the Opisthobranchia and the Pulmonata. The evolutionary trends in the Opisthobranchia have led to a reduction or loss of the shell, detorsion, loss of streptoneury, and reduction of visceral mass. The pulmonates retain many of the prosobranch characteristics but have lost streptoneury, and some are shell-less. Most evident evolutionary changes in gastropods have been associated with torsion and modifications of the respiratory organs and foot. The fossil record indicates that the prosobranchs date from the Paleozoic era, whereas the Opisthobranchia and the Pulmonata appeared in the Carboniferous period.

The bivalves have been a slowly evolving group of organisms. Many date back as far as the early Paleozoic, while others have arisen in the Recent era. The Protobranchia are considered the most primitive group of existing bivalves, although they have some specialized characters. The most primitive of the living bivalves is the protobranch *Nucula*. *Nucula* has a pair of equal adductors and two pairs each of protractor and retractor muscles. Its gill structure is not unlike that of the gastropod *Haliotis* (Fig. 26-23).

Except in the Septibranchia, there are two gills in all bivalves. The primitive form of the gill consists of a vascular axis carrying a series of filaments on opposite sides. This is the type found in the Protobranchia. From this type of gill has emerged the various modifications found in the different groups (Fig. 26-37). Gills in the protobranchs are small, but in most bivalves the gills have increased in size and length. The filaments bend back to form two arms that are united by ciliary junctions in the Filibranchia (Fig. 26-41, *D*) or by tissue connections in the Eulamellibranchia (Fig. 26-38). Each gill thus consists of two platelike half gills (demibranchs), and each gill has four series (lamellae) of filaments. Of the four lamellae, the two next to the central axis are

487

Biology of the invertebrates

the direct lamellae, while those formed by the upturned filaments are the reflected lamellae. The direct and reflected lamellae are connected by interlamellar junctions, which are interciliary in the Filibranchia and vascular tissue in the Eulamellibranchia. In further changes the free ends of the filaments may fuse with the mantle; and the lamellae may be thrown into folds, thus subdividing the mantle cavity into upper and lower chambers. In the Septibranchia the gills are transformed into a pumping muscular septum (Fig. 26-39, *C*). Vibrations of the cilia in tracts on the gills play an important role in sorting out and directing food particles to the palps and mouth. In the primitive *Nucula,* which are deposit feeders with long proboscides, the gills are chiefly respiratory; but in more advanced forms the gills have largely assumed the function of food collection, so that the organisms are efficient ciliary feeders.

ECOLOGY

The most primitive mollusks are aquatic, and the fossil record shows that they originated in the sea. Most mollusks are still marine, but about a third of all species live on land and in fresh water as a result of their invasion of those regions. This terrestrial invasion began in the Devonian period and has continued ever since. Although evolutionary diversification in those invaders has taken place more rapidly among strictly land forms, there has also been a slow evolution of freshwater types, producing considerable numbers but less variety of form and behavior than among the land dwellers. It is thought that this invasion occurred through littoral zones and estuaries.

Of the two mollusk classes that were able to overcome the handicaps of a radically new type of habitat (land and fresh water), the Pelecypoda must have entered by the estuarine route alone. The estuary is not an easy route by which to gain access to fresh water. Some authorities believe that only a restricted number of animals have succeeded in passing through the estuaries, which support few types but often considerable populations of animals.

Estuaries are characterized by brackish

water of varying salinity and tide cycle fluctuations. There are also many changes in estuarine substrates because of the constant deposition of sediment, silt, mud, etc. by both sea tides and continental streams. Oxygen tensions and acidity ranges are also wider in brackish regions. One of the chief problems of those forms that live in estuaries is osmoregulation. Experimental work (L. C. Beadle and J. B. Cragg) shows that marine animals, in making the transition to fresh water, at first retain blood salts of sea water concentrations and gradually shift to lower blood-salt concentrations as their tissues build up a tolerance and a hypotonic urine regulation. Bivalves are probably less subjected to the fluctuations of an estuary because of their semiburrowing habits in the estuarine substratum. However, it may be stated that no marine species could pass into a land or freshwater habitat without an "internship" in littoral or estuarine existence (C. W. Cooke).

Although the mollusks are one of the most adaptive of all animal groups, as evidenced by their wide distribution in altitudinal ranges and varied habitats, they do have marked limitations in acclimation to rapid environmental changes. Recently, C. M. Yonge has given an account of the changes in molluscan life brought about by the great dyke across the Zuider Zee in Holland. One of the effects of the construction of this dyke was to transform a shallow region of brackish water, considerably lower in salinity than sea water, into fresh water. Brackish water has its own unique physiologic properties, to which animals that live there must adjust themselves. Within two years after the erection of the dyke, all the marine mollusks (periwinkles, mussels, and cockles) were dead in the transformed region. In their place a number of fresh water mollusks from rivers invaded the region formerly occupied by the marine forms. Two bivalves, belonging to the genera *Dreissena* and *Anodonta* were extremely mobile in entering the new region. Freshwater snails have been slower, although some parthenogenetic species have a foothold. Sediment carried down to the freshwater lakes formed by the reclaimed land was actually an advantage to molluscan life, especially to those whose habits are adapted to substrata of a semi-solid medium.*

On the other hand, certain dykes in Holland were destroyed in World War II, and sea water flowed into regions formerly occupied by fresh water. Before the dykes were rebuilt, a number of marine mollusks, such as *Mytilus, Cardium,* and *Mya,* established themselves in the new saline region. Mollusks without pelagic larvae or those that could not swim, such as certain gastropods, had little opportunity to establish themselves. Some mollusks (e.g., *Urosalpinx*) have, however, a wide range of tolerance to different concentrations of salinity (H. Federighi).

Although accounts of ecologic experimentation on mollusks are numerous, they are scattered; and few attempts have been made to integrate them into general summaries.

Temperature ranges of various mollusks have been determined by many investigators. R. G. Evans (1948) found that British littoral species could withstand temperature ranges well beyond those they would encounter under natural conditions. Lethal temperature effects show many variations in the different mollusks. There seems to be a correlation between the normal living temperatures of bivalves and the temperatures that are lethal to them upon heating, although some experiments are not in agreement with this. A freshwater mollusk often can withstand the same temperature range as that of general metazoan metabolism. Ordinarily, temperatures beyond 45° C. are lethal to many mollusks. The time factor of exposure is also important in thermal determinations. Some species will react much more quickly than others.

Size and growth ranges also depend upon many factors. C. R. Boettger (1950) found that molluscan populations had smaller-sized individuals in lower salinities, and J. S. Gutsell (1931) showed that *Pecten* grew much faster in swifter currents than in slower ones. P. A. Dehnel (1955) demonstrated that rates of gastropod growth were correlated with the latitudes in which the populations were normally found. Embryos

and larvae of certain prosobranchs from northern latitudes (Alaska) grew two to nine times as great as those from southern populations (California) at a comparable temperature. W. R. Coe (1942) showed that dwarf forms of *Crepidula* will grow into much larger ones when placed in suitable environments.

Land snails perhaps show the greatest range of physiologic factors that determine their existence and survival. The chief factors that restrict their lives are temperature, humidity, and physiochemical aspects of their substrata. Those with shells require calcium, but many without shells (e.g., slugs) may be found where the soil is deficient in this mineral. Poikilothermous slugs and snails often maintain an internal temperature below that of their surroundings by water loss from their surfaces. E. Segal (1959) finds that the slug is able to adapt to different levels of environmental temperatures (2° to 30° C.) by increasing or decreasing oxygen consumption. This investigator, working on the pulmonate gastropod *Limax flavus,* maintained animals at 2°, 5°, 10°, 20°, and 30° C.; and after they were given time to acclimate at each temperature, their oxygen consumptions were measured at the same temperatures. He found that the animals that were acclimated to temperatures of 2° and 5° C. consumed more oxygen than those kept at 20° and 30° C., but that those at 10° C. had the highest rate of oxygen consumption. He therefore concluded that 10° C. represented the optimal acclimation temperature for this species. He also established the limits of acclimation for this pulmonate at 2° and 30° C. He has also summarized many of the problems of acclimation in other mollusks when subjected to specific tests.

The wide range of physiologic variations that have been reported may be due not only to phenotypic differences but to genetic differences as well (C. L. Prosser).

GENERAL MORPHOLOGIC FEATURES

Although each class of mollusks has its own distinctive features of morphology, the basic molluscan plan makes it possible to present certain generalized descriptions of their characteristic organs. More details of

---

*C. M. Yonge: Zuider Zee to Ijsselmeer, Times Sci. Rev., Winter, 1965, p. 9.

Fig. 26-6

Integument of mollusks. **A,** *Anodonta* (Pelecypoda). Note abundant, long cilia of epidermis and mucus-secreting cells. (×810.) **B,** *Limax* (Gastropoda). Note large mucus glands beneath epidermis. (×480.) (From Andrew: Textbook of comparative histology, Oxford University Press, Inc.)

group modifications will be presented in the discussion of the different classes.

External anatomy

The epidermis of mollusks is chiefly cellular and ciliated. Much of it, especially outside the mantle, contains mucigenous cells or mucus-secreting glands (Fig. 26-6).

These cells and glands produce slime for locomotion and food-collecting strings. Some mollusks, like the cephalopods, have many chromatophores, whereby they can produce the fastest color changes in the animal kingdom. Each chromatophore consists of a thin elastic membrane that surrounds the fluid-filled space containing the pigment. Radially disposed muscle fibers are attached to the elastic membrane, and by contracting and relaxing, the sac of pigment is dilated or contracted, thus dispersing the pigment or concentrating it. There are many variations in the epidermis among the different molluscan groups.

The shell is one of the most characteristic structures of mollusks, although it may be reduced or absent altogether in some. Its formation has been the subject of many investigations because the process of its origin and development involves many problems of crystal formation and deposition, calcification, and synthesis of components. In its structural organization there are many variations among the different taxa. Although the shell is secreted by the mantle in all mollusks, there are variations in the way the components are put together. The formation of the shell involves three major processes: the synthesis of the organic matrix of conchiolin (an albuminoid material) and calcium carbonate formation; the secretory activity of the mantle in forming the shell components; and the arrangement of the crystalline layers and the deposition of crystals. According to K. M. Wilbur, the organic matrix is first secreted in soluble form before being deposited as a sheet layer on the inner shell surface. Calcium carbonate is laid down in layers, alternating with the organic matrix. First laid down as small crystals, these grow and unite to form a crystalline layer that eventually assumes the character of columns —the so-called middle prismatic layer (Fig. 26-7). The crystalline columns are laid down at right angles to the inner laminated layer. The calcium carbonate may occur as calcite or aragonite. The forward edge of the mantle, which secretes both organic and inorganic components, forms the growing edge of the shell. The thickness of the shell is formed by the epithelial cells on the outer side of the mantle (Fig. 26-7). The innermost or nacreous layer (mostly in the form of aragonite of calcium carbonate) may be laid down as plates forming prisms that reflect light. If a foreign substance gets between the mantle and shell, concentric layers of nacreous shell may be formed around it, producing a pearl. The outer layer, the periostracum, is composed of horny conchiolin and protects

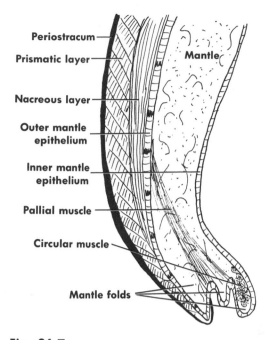

Fig. 26-7

Vertical section of shell and mantle of bivalve (semidiagrammatic).

the shell from the corroding action of acid. The shell reaches its greatest development in the gastropods and the bivalves, both groups showing a similarity of plan.

The molluscan foot is adapted for attachment to a substratum or for locomotion, or for both of these functions. The foot has been exploited in various ways and is found in diverse forms and shapes among mollusks. Its primitive form has been generally an elongated, broad, solelike structure with successive waves of contraction for creeping locomotion. Among its modifications are the attachment disk of the limpets, the compressed hatchet foot of the bivalves, and the many divisions of the anterior foot of the cephalopods. Besides these types there are many other adaptive forms of the foot. In most mollusks the foot is the only organ of locomotion. It corresponds to the ventral body wall of most other animals. The foot in most mollusks has great powers of expansion and contraction, using the hemoskeleton of blood turgidity together with an extensive system of muscles to change the shape of the foot for adaptive purposes. For attachment and locomotion

Fig. 26-8

Locomotion in mollusks. **A,** Creeping *(Helix aspersa).* **B,** Leaping *(Laevicardium).* **C,** "Galloping" *(Helix dupetithouarsi).* **D,** Burrowing *(Terebra).* **E,** Burrowing *(Ensis).* **F,** Swimming by means of muscular waves of notal margin and flexion of body in sagittal plane *(Hexabranchus).* **G,** Swimming by means of parapodia, using upward recovery stroke and downward effective stroke *(Limacina,* a pelagic pteropod). (Modified from Morton.)

of many of the mollusks, the action of the foot is aided by the abundant mucus, which can act either as an adhesive or as a mucus sheet over which the foot can glide by ciliary action.

Methods of locomotion are as diverse as the form of the foot (Fig. 26-8). In some snails, instead of a creeping movement brought about by waves of contraction and relaxation, there may be a type of bipedal locomotion involving an alternate extension and contraction of first one half of the foot and then the other. Many are able to make leaping movements by vigorous muscle contractions. Swimming is performed in many by means of lobes or parapodia of the foot, by the whole body, by mantle appendages such as fins, or by the highly efficient jet propulsion of cephalopods with lateral fins acting as keels or gliding surfaces.

Internal anatomy

The alimentary canal varies in the different mollusks, depending upon nutritional habits. In general, it is composed of an anterior buccal mass and esophagus (of ectodermal origin) in which are the radula and jaws (Fig. 26-9), the midgut (endodermal) of stomach and liver, and the hindgut or intestine. Mollusks have different feeding habits. Those living on coarser food use the radula as a rasp. Carnivorous mollusks, such as the cephalopods, have powerful jaws for seizing and tearing their prey and a radula to aid in the process. There are many modifications of the feeding habits, especially in bivalves which have no mandibles, radula, or pharyngeal musculature but have efficient ciliary-feeding devices.

In many bivalves and some gastropods that depend upon filtering organic materials from suspensions or deposits, there is a special rodlike crystalline style that protrudes into the stomach (Fig. 26-10). This rod may lie free in the first part of the intestine or in a special pouch or sac. The rod is composed of a gelatinous substance containing a digestive enzyme. The

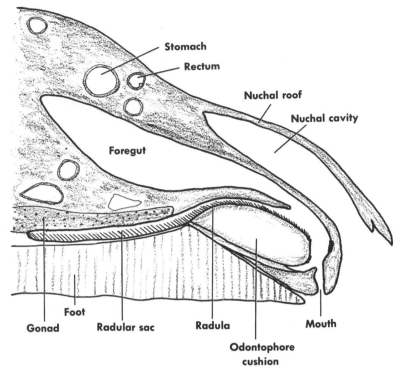

Fig. 26-9

Sagittal section of anterior end of *Patella* showing relationship of radula and other buccal organs. (Modified from Davis and Fleure.)

crystalline style is kept rotating by means of cilia in the style sac or pouch. Its free end is attached to a string of mucus, which extends into the esophagus and in which entering particles of food become embedded. Turning of the style causes a twisting of the mucus-food cord into spiral coils and keeps it under tension, thus regulating the gradual and orderly entry of food into the stomach. At the same time the surface of the style head becomes softened and dissolves in the stomach fluid, setting free an amylase that is active in preliminary extracellular digestion. Since most of the fine food of these filter feeders is later phagocytosed for intracellular digestion, ciliary sorting areas are provided in the stomach, in which the particles freed from the food cord are graded by size and weight. Cilia in grooves direct larger particles to the intestine. Other cilia beating at right angles to those in the grooves keep fine particles circulating till they find their way to the cells of the digestive diverticula.

Part of the stomach is lined with cuticle, thickened at one point into a heavy flange or gastric shield against which the projecting crystalline style rotates. The shield may also serve as a protection against coarse or sharp particles in the whirling food cord.

In ciliary-feeding gastropods and in most bivalves the finest particles released from the food chain are diverted into the apertures of the digestive diverticula in the anterior part of the stomach (Fig. 26-10, *A*). These apertures (usually two in number) open into ciliated ducts that branch into the digestive gland. The digestive gland is an organ of absorption and intracellular digestion. Some preliminary extracellular digestion may occur in the stomach, but digestion is chiefly intracellular. The digestive gland consists of many blindly ending tubules, each made up of one or more cell types. Many of the cells may bear several long cilia. Food particles in mucoid suspensions are carried by the incurrent ducts into the lumen of the tubules where

493

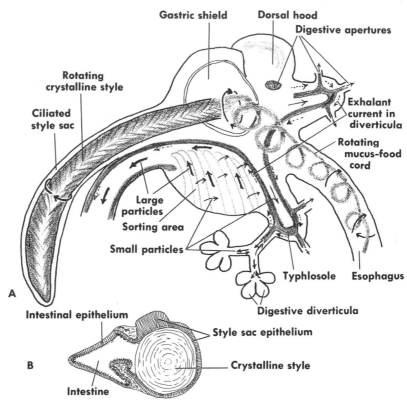

Fig. 26-10

A, Stomach and crystalline style of lamellibranch ciliary feeder. From volumes of water taken in, particles are engaged in cord of mucus, which is kept rotating by crystalline style. Ridged and ciliated sorting area directs large particles to intestine and small particles to digestive diverticula. **B,** Transverse section through straight portion of intestine of *Cardium* showing crystalline style. (**A** modified from Morton; **B** modified from Johnstone.)

the food particles are engulfed by the cells of the tubules. Food particles are drawn in by the lowered pressure within the lumen of the tubules induced by the progressive absorption of food or by the squeezing action of the muscles of the stomach. The digestive cells may also absorb products of extracellular digestion. In the digestive gland such enzymes as protease, lipase, and amylase are provided. Waste or rejected materials from the tubules are carried by excurrent ciliary tracts back to the intestinal groove and added to the feces of the intestine.

The dorsal heart is enclosed in the pericardium. Usually two auricles receive blood from the gills, and the single muscular ventricle pumps the blood through the body. The blood vessels are made up of arteries, veins, and sinuses. The integument of cephalopods may also contain capillaries. In some a single anterior aorta leaves the heart and breaks up into smaller arteries that pass to the mantle and viscera. The arteries form a network of vessels that pass into veins and sinuses. In its passage back to the heart the blood goes through the kidneys and gills for purification and gaseous exchange. The formed elements of the colorless blood are represented by a variety of amebocytes and corpuscles. Many mollusks have copper-bearing hemocyanin as a respiratory pigment although a few have hemoglobin.

Respiration takes place in mollusks through the surface of the mantle, by means of gills or ctenidia, or by a form of lung. The mantle gives rise to the ctenidia or the lung. A gill on each side of the body was the primitive plan. Each gill is an outgrowth at the side of the body and basically consists of a featherlike arrangement of filaments around a hollow vascular axis. The axis has an afferent and an efferent blood vessel, with branches for circulation of the blood through the gills. The afferent vessel receives its blood from a blood sinus, and the efferent vessel delivers its blood directly to that auricle on its side. Cilia cover the surface of all molluscan gills, except in the cephalopods. Cilia are used to keep the branchial current moving and, in some, to direct food particles to the mouth. In many gastropods, part of the mantle is modified to form a vascular cavity or lung for air breathing. There are many modifications of the respiratory system among the different mollusks.

The coelom is very much restricted in most mollusks, being confined mainly to the pericardium and gonadal cavity. Most of the body spaces represent the hemocoel, which is extensive in the Mollusca. In cephalopods the gonadal coelomic cavity is large and communicates directly with the pericardium. In most other mollusks the two cavities are separate. Closely connected to the coelomic cavities are the kidneys, which open internally into the pericardium in nearly all molluscans and may be considered a part of the coelom. In many the kidneys also serve as coelomoducts through which sperm and eggs are discharged; in the advanced cephalopods the genital ducts are separate from the kidneys. Each kidney is a tubelike structure that undergoes various differentiations, such as bladder and glandular regions in the higher mollusks. Its nephridiopore opens into some part of the mantle chamber.

The nervous system of mollusks is made up of certain ganglionic masses, nerve cords, and sense organs. Although there are several variations, in general the nervous system is simpler than that in other forms as advanced as this phylum. The primitive plan already described is followed to some extent by many mollusks, but there is a tendency to concentrate the ganglia in the head region, usually in the form of a circumesophageal ring. The longitudinal pallial and pedal cords on each side are connected by commissures but are modified here and there. The system is usually differentiated into paired ganglia, which are connected by nerve cords that do not bear ganglia. In cephalopods the nerves to the muscles of the mantle contain giant fibers for rapid escape. The chief ganglia are the cerebral, pallial, and pedal. From these ganglia the head region, mantle, viscera, and foot receive nerves. Sense organs are represented by a pair of eyes (variable in plan) on the head region, accessory eyes, statocysts, osphradia, and possibly others.

Most mollusks are dioecious, although the members of the subclasses Pulmonata, Opisthobranchia, and a few others are hermaphroditic. Pulmonates, however, like earthworms, usually practice cross-fertilization. Copulation with a penis occurs in cephalopods and certain gastropods. Fertilization may be external or internal when there is no penis, as in pelecypods. The eggs may be laid outside the body in some, but in others they are incubated in the parent's body. Certain types of viviparity occur only in some aquatic and pulmonate snails, but placental viviparity probably is never found. Parthenogenesis is almost nonexistent. Eggs vary in the amount of food they contain. The larvae of many aquatic mollusks pass through trochophore and veliger stages that are free swimming; but in all pulmonates and some others the trochophore and veliger stages are passed in the egg, and the young emerge as juvenile snails.

The embryologic development of mollusks resembles that of polychaete worms. Cleavage is spiral and total, although its pattern may be influenced by the amount of yolk present in the egg. According to those who have made a careful study of the embryology of certain mollusks, the first two cleavages produce about the same size of blastomeres, which then divide to form four small micromeres and four large macromeres. By further divisions, four quartets of cells are formed. Each quartet has about the same fate as those described in a previous section. Gastrulation occurs in several ways: some by invagination, some by epiboly, and others by ingression (Fig. 26-31). Much of the mesoderm arises from endoderm. The coelom may arise as a single cavity, with the renal and gonadal cavities

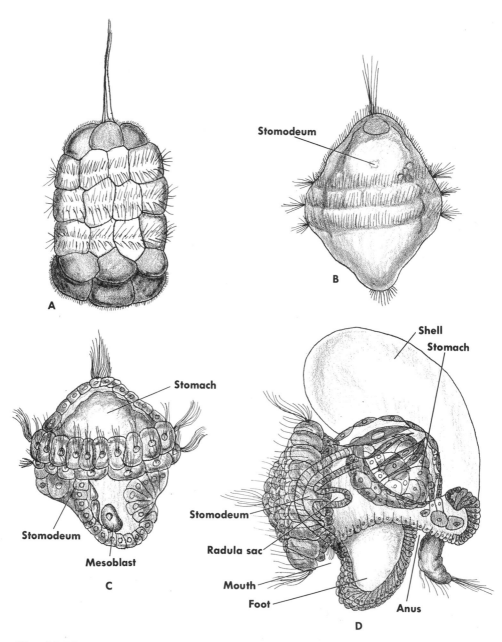

Fig. 26-11

Molluscan larvae. **A,** Trochophore of *Yoldia* (Pelecypoda). **B,** Trochophore of *Dentalium* (Scaphopoda). **C,** Young trochophore of limpet *Patella* (Gastropoda). **D,** Veliger of *Patella*. (Redrawn from MacBride: Textbook of embryology, The Macmillan Company.)

Fig. 26-12

Chaetopleura, a chiton (Polyplacophora). (From Hickman: Integrated principles of zoology, The C. V. Mosby Co.)

originating from its walls. A circlet of cilia forms around the equatorial region of the young embryo. One hemisphere remains small as growth takes place; the other enlarges. A mouth and anus appear in the larger hemisphere, and such a larval form is called the trochophore or trochosphere (Fig. 26-11, *A* to *C*). Later a second stage, the veliger (Fig. 26-11, *D*), which bears a velum of lobes for locomotion, appears.

CLASS AMPHINEURA

Amphineurans are elongated, bilaterally symmetric animals that represent the most primitive of existing mollusks. They vary in size from less than an inch to over 12 inches in length. They are divided into two subclasses, Polyplacophora and Aplacophora. Most of them live in rather shallow marine water and are sedentary in their habits. Some of them have a worldwide distribution, and their fossil record goes back to the Ordovician period. They have undergone little evolutionary change in their long history.

Subclass Polyplacophora

The most characteristic of the amphineurans belong to the subclass Polyplacophora, the most familiar members of which are the chitons. There are about 600 species existing at the present time. The chitons have a flattened, ovoid body with reduced head and no eyes or tentacles. The flat foot is broad, occupies the whole ventral surface of the body, and is fitted for close application to a substratum. The thick mantle or girdle may be scaly or fleshy and encircles the whole body. It is commonly provided with bristles and spines. The mantle bears embedded within it eight transverse and arched calcareous plates, so arranged that each plate overlaps the one behind (Fig. 26-12). The separate valves are articulated by means of anterior and posterior marginal projections and held in place by the reflexed mantle folds. This articulation enables the animal to roll up into a ball. In some chitons the entire shell is covered by the mantle. The reduced head and mouth are in front of the foot and beneath the mantle (Fig. 26-13, *A, B*). The anus lies on the ventral surface behind the foot. The mouth is usually provided with a radula. Each shell plate has a sculptured tegmentum, or upper layer, and an articulamentum, or lower layer. The upper layer is partly calcareous and partly organic matrix; the lower is entirely calcareous. The shell bears little branching canals through which nerves pass to sense organs or shell eyes.

Running completely around the animal is the shallow mantle groove between the mantle edge and the foot. This groove contains on each side a varying number (2 to 40 pairs) of gills which may be clustered close together or may extend along most of the groove on each side (Fig. 26-13, *A*, *B*). The large number of gills may be a multiplication of the single ancestral pair because a large mantle chamber is no longer available. The large marine limpets, such as *Lottia* (a West coast form), have passed through an evolution similar to that of chitons (parallel evolution); however, limpets lose their original gills and from mantle folds form secondary gills that project into the pallial groove along the side of the body. Each gill is made up of a central axis and many short filaments, which are held together by interlocking cilia. The inhalant chamber lies outside the row of gills and the exhalant chamber inside the gills. When the margin of the mantle is pressed close against the substratum, the mantle groove is a closed chamber. Inhalant apertures are formed by the mantle margins near the anterior end. Water entering at these openings passes through the gills into the dorsal exhalant chamber on each side. The two exhalant chambers may converge and discharge through single or paired exhalant apertures.

The chitons feed chiefly on algae and other plant life found on rocks. Food may be scraped off the rocks by the projection of the radula and odontophore to the substratum; when the radula is retracted, the food particles are carried back into the mouth where salivary glands empty a secretion for collecting the food and lubricating the radula. No digestion occurs in the mouth. The alimentary canal is differentiated into an esophagus, stomach, and intestine. The intestine may be coiled in some chitons and may be divided into anterior and posterior parts separated by an intestinal valve. The digestive gland discharges proteolytic enzymes into the stomach through paired ducts. Digestion is mostly extracellular and occurs in both the stomach and intestine. Phagocytic cells may play a minor role in some intracellular digestion. Ciliary tracts are present throughout the alimentary canal and aid in the passage of blood and fecal material.

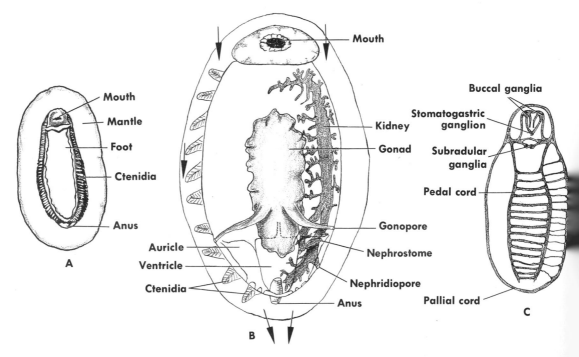

Fig. 26-13

Polyplacophora. **A**, Ventral view of *Acanthopleura*. **B**, Diagram of internal structure of chiton (gills and kidneys shown on one side only). **C**, Nervous system of *Acanthochiton*. (**A** and **C** modified from Pelseneer.)

The blood is discharged from the posterior heart through a single anterior aorta into a pair of sinuses. The blood passes to the gills for gaseous exchange and then is collected by a pair of auricles, which empty into the single ventricle. The two kidneys, one on each side, open into the pericardium, and the nephridiopores empty into the mantle groove near the posterior gills (Fig. 26-13, *B*). As the kidneys pass through the hemocoel, they form many diverticula and windings.

Amphineurans largely retain the primitive ancestral plan of nervous system with four main trunks and connecting commissures (Fig. 26-13, *C*). Nerve cells are distributed largely in the nerve cords, and ganglia are mainly absent. The esophageal nerve ring gives off nerves to the buccal region, radula, pedal region, mantle, and viscera. Besides the shell eyes already mentioned, sense organs are restricted chiefly to tactile and photoreceptor cells. The shell eyes, or aesthetes, vary. They may consist of bundles of sensory cells, or they may be made of cornea, lens, and retina. Chemoreceptors are also located in the epithelium around the mouth.

The sexes are separate in chitons. There is a single median gonad located in front of the pericardium, with which it has no communication. A pair of gonoducts opens by separated openings in the mantle cavity near the openings of the kidneys, and carries sperm or eggs to the outside. Fertilization may occur in the female mantle cavity where the sperm are carried by inhalant branchial currents. Eggs, either singly or in strings, are discharged into the sea. Usually the free-swimming pelagic larva, or trochophore, develops directly into the adult without an intervening veliger stage.

Subclass Aplacophora

The members of this subclass are commonly known as Solenogastres. They are wormlike forms without shell plates, but calcareous spicules may be embedded in the thick integument. The vestigial foot is represented by a median ridge in a small ventral groove (Fig. 26-14, *A*) in one of the two orders (Neomeniomorpha); in the other order (Chaetodermomorpha) this pedal groove is lacking.

In the Neomeniomorpha there is a large mucus gland that discharges its secretion into the anterior part of the pedal groove. The only remnant of the mantle cavity is represented by a deep posterior depression, the cloaca, into which the anus and the nephridiopores from the kidneys open. In the cloaca a circlet of epithelial folds, through which the blood circulates, serves as gills. There are no true blood vessels, but there is a ventral sinus between the foot and the gut; a posterior part of a tubular dorsal sinus serves as a contractile heart. A radula is sometimes present in the simple alimentary canal. The kidneys are represented by a pair of simple coelomoducts, each of which opens into the pericardium at the inner end and the cloaca at the outer end (nephridiopores). In this order a pair of hermaphroditic gonads opens separately into the pericardium, and the gametes are discharged through the coelomoducts, which serve as gonoducts. Glands at the terminal parts of the gonoducts secrete material for an eggshell. Seminal vesicles, or cecal outgrowths of the gonoducts, are also present. The eggs develop into free-swimming trochophore larvae. The nervous system is similar to that in chitons, with the same arrangement of the two sets of longitudinal nerve tracts—a dorsal pallial pair and a ventral pedal pair.

In the Chaetodermomorpha, besides the differences already mentioned, the margins of the mantle cavity have fused to form a bell-shaped, contractile cloaca, which bears a pair of bipectinate gills (Fig. 26-14, *B*). They also have separate sexes, each with a single dorsal gonad that opens into the pericardium. Gametes, however, are carried to the outside by the coelomoducts or renal tubules.

There are fewer than 100 species of these aberrant aplacophoran mollusks. All dwell in deep water, and some may burrow in the sand. They live upon small invertebrates and microorganisms. Some live upon corals and hydroids. Since some chitons have lost their shell, this might indicate how the aplacophorans could have originated from them. Several authorities consider the Solenogastres to be so aberrant that they are placed with such primitive worms as the flatworms.

The common genera are *Neomenia, Chae-* **499**

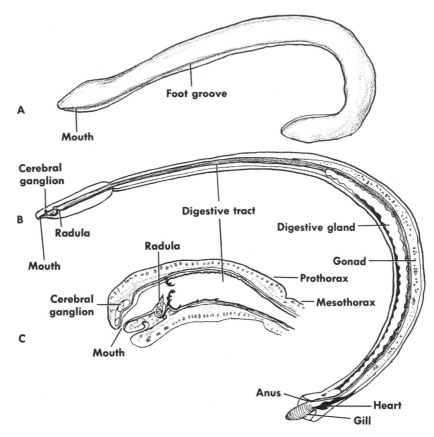

Fig. 26-14

Aplacophora. **A,** *Proneomenia* (Neomeniomorpha). **B,** Median sagittal section of *Chaetoderma* (Chaetodermomorpha). **C,** Enlarged anterior end of same. (Modified from Pelseneer.)

toderma, and *Proneomenia;* but since they live in deep water, they are most commonly found only in deep-sea dredgings.

CLASS GASTROPODA

This class is by far the largest of all molluscan classes in number of species and includes perhaps the most familiar members in the phylum. Often the members of the class because of their single shell are referred to as univalves in contrast to the bivalves. Their single shell, which is usually coiled, is one of their most distinguishing characteristics. The shell is very much modified, however, especially in the adult state, and assumes many forms. In some it is entirely absent. The gastropods also have a unique, asymmetric body organization brought about by a torsion process that is found no where else among the mollusks. A

well-defined head, which may be scanty or absent altogether in many other mollusks, is found in all gastropods.

This group has had an amazing adaptive radiation, which has enabled them to move into most kinds of ecologic niches and into nearly every area of the earth. They are found in marine and fresh water and on land. They exist from the greatest depths of the sea to mountainous altitudes of 15,000 to 20,000 feet. They are adapted to all types of aquatic bottoms, both littoral and bathyal. Some are pelagic and swim with ease. Some are adapted for living in desert regions, although most land forms prefer fairly moist habitats. They can occupy such specialized habitats as trees, exposed limestones, and coral formations; or they can live a parasitic existence. Their food habits are equally wide ranging; they feed on vegetation of all kinds, on other animals as predators, and on dead animals as scavangers.

Their fossil record is impressive, extending throughout the Paleozoic era and becoming increasingly abundant during the Mesozoic and Cenozoic eras (Fig. 26-3, A to C). Many families have become extinct, and there have been fluctuations in the relative abundance of the three subclasses—Prosobranchia, Opisthobranchia, and Pulmonata—during their long geologic history. It is generally agreed that the terrestrial forms evolved in a marine habitat, spread to fresh water, and then to land. As fossils the first nonmarine snails are known from the Pennsylvanian period. Gastropods are apparently enjoying the heyday of their evolutionary divergence at present.

Gastropods number between 35,000 and 40,000 species. In size they range from tiny species not more than 1 mm. long to the giant whelks that may be more than 2 feet long. Some fossil forms were much longer.

Within this extensive class are included the snails, slugs, whelks, periwinkles, nudibranchs, cowries, cones, and sea butterflies.

Significance of torsion

No aspect of gastropod organization and morphology has played a more important role in their evolutionary tendencies than the phenomenon of torsion and a related modification, the coiling of the shell. The body of a gastropod, like that of most mollusks, is composed of four parts—the visceral sac, the mantle, the head, and the foot. The basic plan of the molluscan body is bilaterally symmetric, with the mouth at one end and the anus at the other. In the gastropods, however, this bilateral symmetry is modified by a torsion, or twisting, of 180 degrees (Fig. 25-15), so that the anus is brought forward toward the mouth and the nervous system forms a figure eight. The body of most gastropods is generally wormlike, with the head and foot at one end and most of the body spirally coiled. The coiled visceral sac is covered by a mantle, which projects as a free fold at the anterior end and hangs down like a skirt around the head and foot. Thus the mantle cavity is in a position opposite to that in other mollusks. In the cavity between the mantle and head is the lung or gill. The site of the torsion is the neck behind the head-foot, through which the esophagus, rectum, aorta, visceral loop, and muscles of the shell pass. The actual twisting thus involves this neck tissue and the structures within it.

The development of the asymmetric condition begins in the veliger stage and may be very rapid (two to three minutes in *Acmaea*), although slow in some snails. In the aspidobranchian *Haliotis,* torsion occurs in two unequally timed phases of 90 degrees each. The initial cause of the torsion is the asymmetric growth of the right and left muscles attaching the shell to the head-foot, which forces the twisting process. During the first stage of torsion, there is a

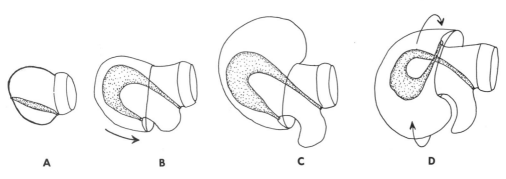

A   B   C   D

Fig. 26-15

Four basic stages in process of body torsion of gastropods. Alimentary canal is stippled in all figures. **A,** Embryo before torsion. **B** and **C,** Ventral flexure with anus and mantle cavity shifted to forward position. **D,** Embryo with lateral torsion in which organs on right have shifted to left, and vice versa.

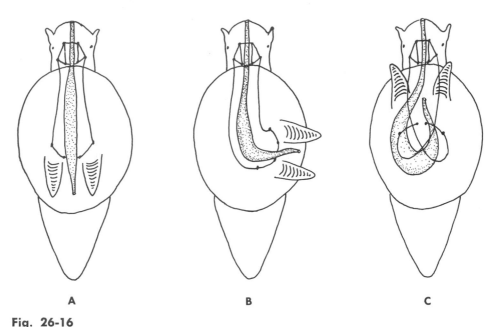

Fig. 26-16

Diagram showing effects of torsion upon position of gills, digestive tract, and nervous system. Note that nervous system in **C** has twisted into figure eight (streptoneury).

ventral flexure in the sagittal plane so that the anus and the openings of the mantle cavity are brought forward ventrally (Fig. 26-15, *A, B*). A second torsion movement at right angles to the first involves the rotation of the visceropallium 180 degrees upon the head-foot so that the mantle and other structures that were lying ventrally are shifted up the right side to a dorsal position where they face forward (Fig. 26-15, *C, D*). At the same time, structures that were dorsally located pass down the left side to lie ventrally. In this way the left structures (gill, renal organ, etc.) are shifted to the right and the right structures to the left (Fig. 26-16). The mantle cavity that originally faced backward now faces anteriorly. Such a torsion allows the sensitive head end of the animal to be drawn first into the protection of the mantle cavity and shell, with the tougher foot forming a barrier to the outside.

The torsion process as described applies to right-handed (dextral) snails, in which the organs on the left side eventually disappear, and to left-handed (sinistral) snails, in which the organs on the left side persist while those on the right side atrophy.

The spiral coiling of the shell and viscero-

pallium is an entirely separate process from that of torsion and does not seem to result from torsion. In fact, it is believed that coiling evolved before torsion. Some gastropods that have torsion exhibit no spiral coiling. There may be no causal relation between the two processes. Coiling is achieved by a more rapid growth of one side of the visceral mass than the other. When viewed from the apex of the shell, the direction of the coils is clockwise in dextral snails; counterclockwise in sinistral snails. In the spiral cleavage of the snail's egg during development the direction of the cleavage planes in dextral coiling is the reverse of that in the sinistral type. Early gastropods had a planospiral shell that was bilaterally symmetric instead of conically spiral (Fig. 26-17). Such a planospiral shell has certain disadvantages, such as a more unwieldly shape, some bilateral restriction of the mantle cavity, and a sharp reduction in the diameter of the inner coils with consequent reduction in available visceral space. Growth in an anteroposterior direction is restricted by the forward position of the anus; nor can it grow dorsally without becoming topheavy. Helical (conispiral) coiling provides better balance for the vis-

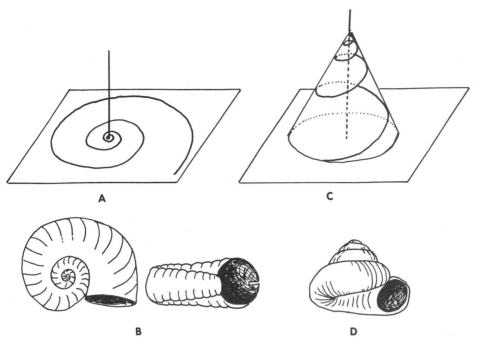

Fig. 26-17

Diagram showing types of coiling. **A,** Planospiral coiling with coils all in one plane. **B,** Plano-spirally coiled shell in (left) normal, upright position and (right) lying on side. Shell has bilateral symmetry but is topheavy and has limited visceral space. **C,** Helical (conispiral) coiling with spirals in different planes. **D,** Shell with helical coiling is asymmetric, compact, and easily balanced.

ceral sac as it grows. By twisting into a spiral, the shell and its contents acquire a more compact form and a diminished diameter, as well as better balance.

The effects of torsion are not equally evident in all gastropods. In the opistho-branchs and some others, although normal torsion takes place in the veliger larva, some detorsion occurs in later development, usually a juvenile stage. This frequently involves the carrying back of the anus and mantle cavity to a posterior position. In extreme cases, detorsion may involve a dis-appearance or reduction of the mantle and visceral mass, with the body becoming an elongated form (*Pterotrachea*). In the order Nudibranchia there is no mantle cav-ity or external shell in the adult, although they appear in the veliger. There are vari-ous degrees of detorsion, always accom-panied by some degeneration of the shell. Many different morphologic patterns are produced, according to the degree of de-torsion (e.g., 90 to 180 degrees). In the Opisthobranchia there is a marked evolu-tionary sequence of patterns, depending upon the amount of torsion. When detor-sion is only partial, the mantle aperture may be shifted to the right side. In *Aplysia*, in which there is more detorsion, the reduced shell is enclosed by the man-tle and moved backward along with the anus and the gill (Fig. 26-26, *A*). In the nu-dibranchs, where torsion is complete, the shell, mantle cavity, gill, and visceral hump all disappear; and the body assumes an elongated form with secondary bilateral symmetry (Fig. 26-26, *D*).

In pulmonates the detorsion is sup-pressed. They retain the posttorsion anus and mantle cavity but have no gills. The mantle cavity is modified into a lung. The secondary symmetry of the nervous sys-tem is due to a shortening of connectives and concentration of ganglia into a circum-esophageal ganglionic complex.

503

There are several theories as to the relative advantage or disadvantage of torsion to the gastropod. Some authorities feel that the main advantage must have been to the larva, while others feel that torsion would not have survived had it not been directly advantageous to the adult. One theory stresses the advantage of torsion to the larva in its adaptation to pelagic life. When the mantle cavity is twisted anteriorly, the larva is able to retract its head and its ciliary mechanism, the velum, into its mantle cavity and thus drop away from potential predators. Other pelagic larvae, however, such as those of the lamellibranchs, have no torsion; and in *Haliotis,* torsion is not completed until after the animal has left its pelagic life and settled to the bottom to live. According to another theory, the main advantage of torsion must be to the adult. Certainly torsion promotes stability in the adult by placing the bulky mass of the animal nearer the substratum. Other advantages may be obtained from facing the inhalant currents, which flush out the mantle cavity, and from the strategic forward placing of the sensory elements of the mantle cavity. Whatever the advantages are, torsion has undoubtedly also resulted in some problems to the adult. The diversity of gastropod morphologic patterns indicates some of the ways these difficulties have been met. For instance,

torsion has caused a tendency for the incurrent water to sweep the feces onto the gills, thus introducing a sanitation problem (Fig. 26-18, *A*). In primitive gastropods this was solved by a slit in the mantle and shell near the location of the anus. *Haliotis* and others have a series of holes for this purpose (Fig. 26-23). In pectinibranchs the problem is met by an arrangement of a single gill with a row of filaments that produce a lateral through current which carries the feces away from the gill (Fig. 26-18, *B*). Some have lost the gills altogether and use an adaptation of the mantle for respiration, such as the lung in pulmonates and the pallial gills in *Patella.*

General morphology
EXTERNAL ANATOMY

The major external features of a gastropod are the head, foot, mantle, and shell (which is absent in some). The head is one of the best developed among the mollusks. It usually bears one or two pairs of tentacles and is connected to the viscera by a mobile neck. When eyes are present, they are located on the tips of the tentacles or at their base. Provided with a snout and armed with a radula in the buccal cavity, the head is the active agent in food getting. When disturbed, the animal can retract its head and foot into the mantle cavity and shell.

The foot in most snails is usually elongated, flat, highly muscular, and fitted for creeping. However, it may be modified for digging or for swimming (Figs. 26-19, 26-20). Extension of the foot, as mentioned in a former section, is produced by blood pressure turgor in hemocoelic spaces with the cooperation of muscles; retraction of the foot is by powerful muscles. Muscles are of both the circular and longitudinal type and extend from columellar shell attachments into the foot. The foot is not only a locomoter organ (Fig. 26-8) but acts as an adhesive organ by suckerlike action. Ciliary movement also takes place over a slime sheet. In general the creeping movement occurs by locomotor waves which involve longitudinal muscle contraction followed by relaxation from behind to forward. Various modifications of the locomotor wave are also found. Some are able to produce

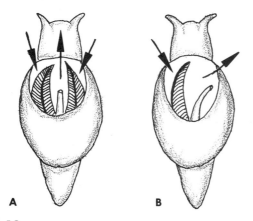

Fig. 26-18

Direction of currents in mantle cavity. **A,** Aspidobranch. **B,** Pectinibranch; one-way current carries feces away from gill. (Modified from Yonge.)

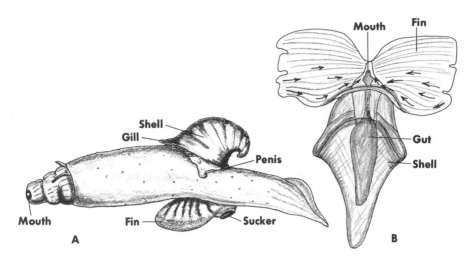

Fig. 26-19

A, *Carinaria,* a free-swimming, pelagic pteropod. Shell is reduced, and foot is modified into strong ventral fin. It swims ventral side up. **B,** *Cavolina,* the sea butterfly. Transparent shell is uncoiled and vase shaped. Ciliated filter tracts on fins direct small organisms to mouth where radula assists in swallowing. (**A** modified from Cambridge Natural History; **B** modified from Yonge.)

Fig. 26-20

Sea butterfly, a swimming pteropod. Long fins, or parapodia, are lateral projections of foot. (Photograph by Roman Vishniac, courtesy Encyclopaedia Britannica Films, Inc.)

forward movement by having the waves start at the front of the foot and pass posteriorly. Muscles involved in the locomotion of the sole also serve in the postural maintenance of the heavy shell and visceral mass. Leaping in the Strombidae may take place by extending the foot, attaching its opercular blade to a substratum, and then producing a quick, powerful contraction of the column muscles.

On the posterior surface of the foot in many snails there is a horny plate, the operculum, which forms a closing lid over the shell aperture when the head and foot are retracted into the shell. Certain gastropods also have a ridge or fold called the epipodium along the lower edge on each side of the foot. It bears appendages and sense organs and may be homologous to the funnel of cephalopods. The foot along with the head is connected to the visceral mass by the neck because there is no boundary between foot and head.

The mantle shows some variations that are correlated with the shape of the shell and the nature of respiration. The visceral coiled mass is enclosed in the mantle, which projects as a free fold at the anterior end down over the head and foot like a skirt. The cavity between the mantle and head serves to carry out respiration by gills or lungs. Those snails with gills usually have a wide opening to the outside, although in some a part of the mantle forms a siphon through which water is drawn by ciliary action for breathing. In air-breathing gastropods, where the cavity forms a lung, the edge of the mantle forms a small opening (pneumostome) for the admission of air by fitting tightly against the neck or foot. The mantle edge, by not fusing completely, may form a slit in some gastropods.

The mantle secretes the shell, which is of one piece but highly modified into many shapes. The typical shell is spirally coiled into more or less a cone shape. Such a shell is made of tubular whorls, with the smallest whorl at the apex and successively larger ones to the aperture of the shell (Fig. 26-21). The whorls are coiled around a central axis called the columella. If, when the shell is held with the spire pointed upward and the aperture facing the observer, the aperture is to the right of the columella or

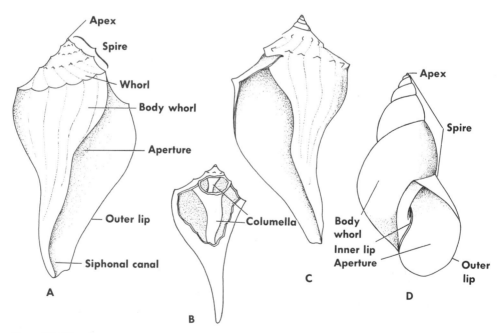

Fig. 26-21

Gastropod shell. **A** and **B**, *Busycon carica*, a dextral (right-handed) marine snail. **C**, *Busycon contrarium (perversum)*, a sinistral (left-handed) snail. **D**, *Lymnaea*, a freshwater snail.

shell axis, the shell is said to be right-handed or dextral (clockwise); if the aperture is to the left, it is said to be left-handed (sinistral, or counterclockwise) (Fig. 26-21, *A, C*). Only a relatively few shells are sinistral, although some species may have either a sinistral or dextral type.

The larval shell of gastropods, called a protoconch, is usually a plate or is caplike. The protoconch is represented in the adults by the small apex whorl and is usually smooth and not sculptured. In its development, the protoconch becomes coiled by the deposition of mineral salts round the mantle edge at the aperture end. The gastropod shell has the three layers character-

istic of most mollusk shells—the thin outer periostracum of horny, organic structure (conchiolin); the middle prismatic layer of vertical crystals of calcium carbonate; and the inner nacreous layer of calcium carbonate laid down in lamellar sheets.

Shells exist in a great variety of shape, color, and pattern (Fig. 26-22). Although primitively spiral, the shell in some has become uncoiled and cap shaped *(Patella).* Detorsion, or the untwisting of the original embryonic twisting, is always associated with reduced or complete loss of the shell (Tectibranchia, Pteropoda). The edges of the mantle may grow over the shell and cover most or all of its surface. This causes

Fig. 26-22

Some gastropod shells. **A,** *Gyraulus (Planorbis).* **B,** *Crepidula fornicata.* **C,** *Sinum perspectivum.* **D,** *Physa gyrina.* **E,** *Diodora.* **F,** *Urosalpinx.* **G,** *Littorina.* **H,** *Strombus.* **J,** *Murex.*

the shell to be internal and degenerate (slugs). Shell reduction is especially pronounced in opisthobranchs. In the nudibranchs and some others the shell may disappear completely. In *Vermicularia* the whorls are so arranged that the shell looks like a corkscrew. Sculpturing on the whorls also has many patterns; in some these patterns are quite rough and horny; in others very smooth. Many tree snails in the tropics are of a bright, uniform color, while others are striped and varicolored. Mollusk shells illustrate the principle of allometry, or disproportionate rate of growth of various parts of a structure in relation to the whole structure. Since the shell increases by marginal increments from the mantle, growth rates at different points on the margin vary during the shell's de-

velopment. Many ecologic factors can alter this allometric relationship of the shell's growth. In oysters *(Crassostrea)* the length-width ratio of the shell is greater when the animal grows on a soft bottom than when it grows on a hard substratum of the same area. When *Mytilus* lives below low-water levels, it has a narrower and thinner shell than when it is exposed between tides.

Most gastropods have aquatic respiration carried out by gills. Some aquatic mollusks have to rely upon cutaneous respiration because they have no gills. Some prosobranchs of a primitive nature have two gills of the bipectinate type, with two rows of filaments and cleft shell (Figs. 26-18, *A*, 26-23). In more specialized forms, only the left gill persists, with one row of filaments along the gill (Figs. 26-18, *B*,

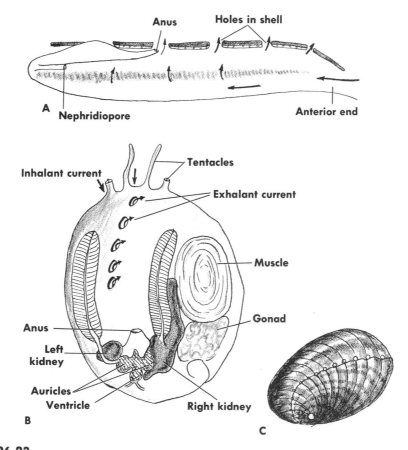

Fig. 26-23

Haliotis, the abalone (order Aspidobranchia). **A,** Diagram to show water current through mantle cavity. **B,** Diagram of mantle cavity. **C,** Shell. (**B** modified from Kerkut.)

26-27, *A*). The single pectinibranchiate gill pattern, with the inhalant current entering the mantle cavity at one side of the head and the exhalant current leaving on the other side where the anus is located, is often found in prosobranchs. This arrangement helps solve the problem of waste fouling caused by torsion. Many shore-dwelling prosobranchs have a mantle that can carry on aerial respiration. All kinds of modifications of respiration can be found between those snails with gills and those that are strictly aerial breathing (pulmonates). Aerial respiration may exist along with gill breathing. Some have eliminated regular gills altogether and have respiratory outgrowths; or true gills and outgrowths may be found together. *Littorina* has part of its gill modified into a vascular network over the mantle roof similar to that of pulmonates. Such snails can live out of water for long periods of time. The keyhole limpet *(Diodora)* (Fig. 26-22, *E*) has a cone-shaped shell with a slot at the summit of the shell that curves forward. Although the limpet begins life in a spiral shell with an elongated slit along the shell margin, the slit during growth gradually closes except at the apex. At the same time the apical spire becomes reduced or lost altogether. A siphon in the form of a modified mantle may project through the slot. Although the pulmonates have a mantle specialized for a lung, the pulmonate condition has also arisen separately in such groups as the Helicinidae and Cyclophoridae. Certain pulmonates (e.g., *Physa* and *Lymnaea*) have secondarily returned to fresh water;

they must come to the surface to expel a bubble of air from the lung and protrude the edge of the mantle around the pneumostome into a long, muscular siphon to take in a fresh supply of air.

INTERNAL ANATOMY

The alimentary canal varies somewhat with the food habits of gastropods, which are extremely varied. Modifications of the gut have thus been correlated with their nutrition. The alimentary canal usually consists of a mouth at the snoutlike end of the head; a buccal or pharyngeal cavity that is nearly always provided with a radula and often with cuticular mandibles; a long, slender esophagus, much folded within and sometimes provided with a muscular gizzard; a thin-walled stomach, which may have a cuticular lining, and a liver that opens into the stomach by two ducts; an intestine that may be long (herbivorous forms) or short (carnivorous forms) and bears a typhlosole ridge; and an anus that is usually found on the right side of the body near the head.

Because of torsion the stomach is turned around so that the esophagus enters at the posterior end and the intestine leaves at the anterior end. Digestion is mostly extracellular. Digestive enzymes are produced by the digestive glands and esophageal pouches. Salivary glands, which open on each side of the radula, mostly secrete mucus for lubricating the radula and for easing food passage.

The radula, one of the most characteristic organs of gastropods, is a bandlike or-

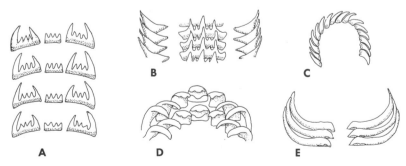

Fig. 26-24

Some patterns of radula teeth. **A,** *Busycon carica.* **B,** *Murex regius.* **C,** *Cypraea tigris.* **D,** *Elysia viridis* (side view). **E,** *Scaphander lignarius.* These represent only few of rows of teeth on radula and only few of types. (**B to E** modified from Cambridge Natural History.)

gan consisting of a horny basement membrane on which are rows of recurved teeth, usually arranged into two symmetric sets (Fig. 26-24). The number of teeth varies from a few to many thousands. The arrangement of the teeth is of great taxonomic value. The radula is located in a ventral diverticulum of the buccal cavity called the radula sac (Fig. 26-9). As old parts are worn away, new surfaces with teeth replace the old. A subradular membrane and odontophore cartilage support the radula. By special muscles and movement of an attached epithelial layer the radula moves forward continuously on the surface of the buccal cavity or pharynx (N. W. Runham) and may be used for a variety of purposes, such as raking, scraping, tearing, drilling holes, and macerating, depending upon the species. The radula is secreted continuously by permanent odontoblasts located posteriorly in the radula sac or gland. Runham (1963) has shown that in the pond snail *Lymnaea stagnalis* the radula moves forward at a rate of about 2.9 rows of teeth a day. At the anterior end of the radula the attached epithelium becomes detached from the radula, secretes a buccal cuticle, and disintegrates along with that end of the radula and its subradular membrane.

The stomach has no digestive function of its own but serves to hold the food that is being digested by enzymes from other sources. The products of digestion pass into the ducts of the digestive gland for absorption. The digestive gland is a bilobed structure, with the left lobe usually larger. It may be composed of ciliated tubes and glandular alveoli. In the alveoli are various cells that are secretory and resorptive in function. The secretory cells produce enzymes for digestion, and the resorptive cells also have proteolytic enzymes for intracellular digestion. In carnivorous gastropods (many prosobranchs and opisthobranchs) the radula has fewer but larger teeth. Jaws may be absent, but an extensible proboscis formed from the buccal cavity lies within a special proboscis sheath. With the aid of the radula, food is taken into the proboscis, which is retracted into the proboscis sheath. Digestion in carnivorous snails takes a different course from that in herbivorous forms. Proteolytic enzymes are discharged into the stomach, where digestion takes place rather than in the cells of the liver.

Prosobranchs such as *Urosalpinx* (Fig. 26-22, *F*) drill holes with their radula into the shells of bivalves such as oysters. The anterior part of the foot of these carnivorous forms contains an eversible gland that is applied to the region being drilled. Secretions of an unknown nature are produced by this gland and assist in the drilling process. The snail sucks out the contents of the prey with its proboscis after the radula has torn the tissues apart. Another prosobranch *Conus*, mainly a tropical form, has the radula teeth modified into long, hollow structures for stabbing its prey. A duct from a poison gland opens into the buccal cavity near the opening of the radula sac, and poison may flow into the wound made by the stabbing action of the tooth, which is attached by a slender tissue thread to the basement membrane and thrusts into the prey like a harpoon. The poison acts on the neuromuscular junction, thus paralyzing the prey. Some species of this genus are dangerous to man.

The carnivorous nudibranchs, which feed mainly upon hydroids and sea anemones, have digestive glands in the numerous papillae or cerata that cover their backs (Figs. 26-25, 26-26, *D*). The digestive tubule of each ceras joins that of others to form a branching, diffuse digestive gland, which

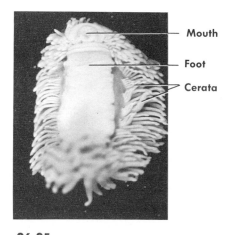

Fig. 26-25

Aeolis, a nudibranch; ventral view of preserved specimen.

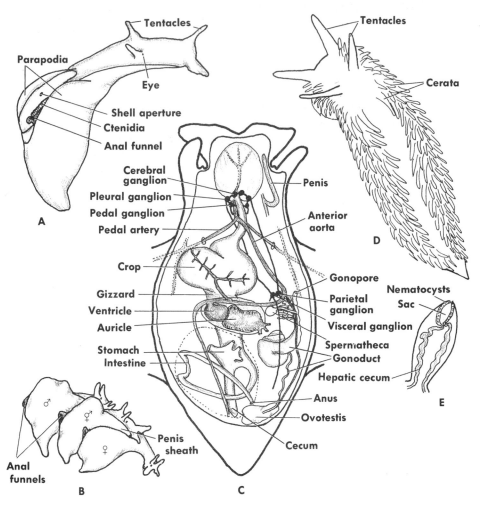

Fig. 26-26

Opisthobranchia. **A** to **C**, *Aplysia*, sea hare, a tectibranch. **A**, Living animal in expanded condition (dorsal side). Small thin shell lies between parapodia and is covered by mantle. **B**, Chain of three; middle one acts as male for female below and as female for male above. **C**, Internal structure. **D**, *Aeolis*, sea slug, a nudibranch snail; cerata contain branches of digestive gland. **E**, Section of ceras of *Aeolis*. (**A** to **C** modified from Eales; **E** modified from Lankester.)

opens into the stomach where digestive enzymes are discharged for extracellular digestion. The digested products are then absorbed by the stomach wall and digestive glands. Undischarged nematocysts from their coelenterate prey are carried by the digestive gland ducts to the tips (cnidosacs) of the cerata (Fig. 26-26, *E*) where they are discharged by the nudibranchs for their defense.

Ciliary feeders, such as the sessile form *Crepidula*, are provided with a crystalline style, a solid, gelatinous protein rod that is located in a style sac at the intestinal end of the stomach and projects into the other end of the stomach. (It is recalled that, owing to torsion, the stomach is turned around so that its anterior end is the intestinal one and its posterior end the esophageal.) The crystalline style (Fig. 26-10), which has evolved several times in the mollusks, is a special modification of the style sac. The rod contains amylolytic enzymes adsorbed on the protein rod. The rod is rotated by the ciliary action of the style sac, releasing the enzymes of the rod into the stomach and mixing the food contents. In such ciliary feeders the lengthened gill filaments aid in trapping the plankton as the water current passes through the mantle cavity. The particles of food are carried by gill cilia into a longitudinal groove alongside the gill filaments where they are formed into mucus strings. The strings of food are then pulled into the mouth by the radula and passed to the stomach. A special ciliary field in the floor of the stomach carries the food to the region of the gastric plate where the enzymes released by the crystalline rod digest the food. Digested products and small particles are carried into the ducts of the digestive gland where the digestion is completed intracellularly. The larger particles are passed directly by a ciliary groove to the intestine. Many other modifications of the style sac are found among the gastropods, depending upon feeding habits.

A few gastropods are parasitic on mollusks and echinoderms. Many of these ecto-parasites or endoparasites belong to the Pyramidellacea of the opisthobranchs.

The circulatory system in gastropods is well developed for a mollusk. The heart is usually in front of the visceral mass because of torsion (Figs. 26-27, 26-28), but may be located posteriorly in some of the Opisthobranchia that have complete detorsion (Fig. 26-26). The primitive members have two auricles (Fig. 26-23, *B*), but only the left auricle is found in other gastropods (Fig. 26-27). From the single ventricle an aorta arises and branches to form the posterior visceral artery to the viscera and an anterior cephalic artery to the head and foot. The venous blood is carried directly to the gills through sinuses, or it may first go to the kidneys and then into the branchial circulation before returning to the heart. The blood is usually colorless but may contain hemoglobin (*Planorbis*) or hemocyanin in a few genera.

The coelom in gastropods is restricted to the pericardium, kidneys, and to some extent, the reproductive gland. The large body cavity is the hemocoel. The kidneys

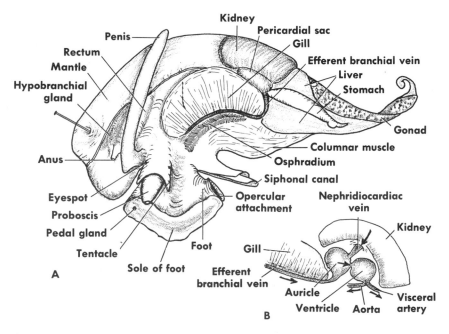

Fig. 26-27

A, Surface anatomy of male *Busycon* removed from shell. **B,** Dissection of heart and chief vessels of *Busycon*. (Drawn from life.)

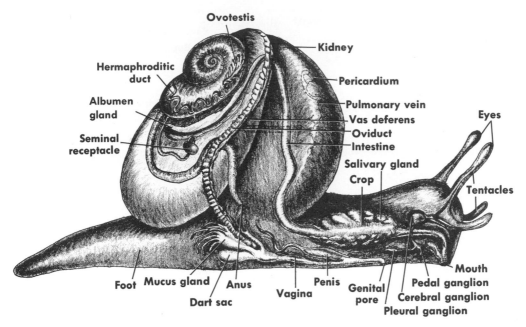

Ovotestis

Kidney

Hermaphroditic
duct

Pericardium

Albumen
gland

Pulmonary vein
Vas deferens
Oviduct
Intestine

Eyes

Seminal
receptacle

Salivary gland
Crop

Tentacles

Mouth

Foot   Mucus gland   Anus   Penis   Genital   Pedal ganglion
                                                pore   Cerebral ganglion
         Dart sac   Vagina   Pleural ganglion

Fig. 26-28

Side view of pulmonate land snail with shell removed (semidiagrammatic). (Modified from
Hegner.)

are mostly paired in the Aspidobranchia, but in the other gastropods only the left is functional. The kidney, or nephridium, connects with the pericardium and is much folded to increase its surface. The connection with the pericardial cavity may be made by a renopericardial canal that is ciliated. The waste from the kidney is carried away by a thin-walled ureter. In pectinibranchs the single left kidney has only an excretory function; whereas the former right kidney tube is now a gonoduct for genital products. In pulmonates the ureter opens to the outside behind the pneumostome and above the anus; in opisthobranchs and prosobranchs it opens inside the mantle cavity where waste is swept away by the branchial current. Aquatic gastropods excrete ammonia or its compounds as their chief waste, while land forms, in order to conserve water, excrete the insoluble uric acid. Terrestrial forms usually live in fairly humid surroundings, or they are nocturnal. Under very dry conditions they may aestivate in the soil and remain inactive. To protect themselves they may secrete a special calcareous membrane

over the shell aperture during the period of inactivity.

Gastropods in general have a well-developed nervous system consisting of nerves, ganglia, and sense organs. Its basic organization is the same as that of other mollusks although torsion has complicated certain aspects of it. The molluscan nervous system is mainly a diffuse one in its primitive plan (Fig. 26-13, *C*), and in many higher gastropods this plan has been little altered. Ganglionic nerve centers and commissures are the same as those in other mollusks (Figs. 26-26, *C*, 26-28, 26-29, *C*). A pair of cerebral ganglia lies over the posterior esophagus and sends nerves to the tentacles, eyes, and buccal ganglia. The buccal ganglia innervate the radula muscles and adjacent structures. From each cerebral ganglion a pedal nerve cord passes on each side of the esophagus to a pair of pedal ganglia in the middle of the foot. The pedal ganglia innervate the muscles of the foot. Also from the cerebral ganglia a pair of visceral nerves passes posteriorly to the paired visceral ganglia in the visceral mass. The visceral ganglia innervate the visceral

513

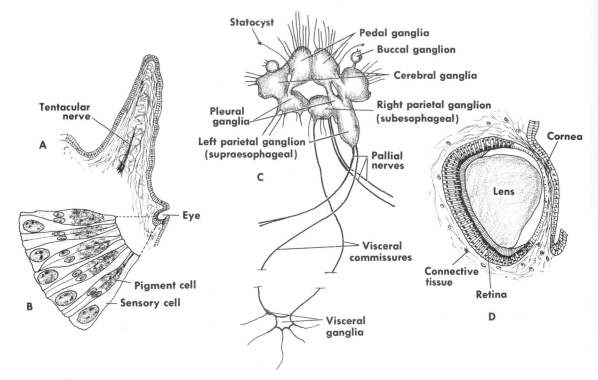

Fig. 26-29

Nervous and sensory organs. **A,** Cephalic tentacle of *Patella*, longitudinal section showing eye. **B,** Enlarged section of eye epithelium of *Patella*. **C,** Nerve centers of *Buccinum*. Commissure connecting cerebral ganglia has been severed and ganglia laid back. View is from inside nerve collar. **D,** Transverse section of eye of *Buccinum*. (**A** and **B** modified from Davis and Fleure; **C** and **D** modified from Dakin.)

mass. Along the visceral nerves are located two other pairs of ganglia, the pleural ganglia near the cerebral ganglia and the parietal ganglia more posteriorly toward the visceral ganglia. The pleural ganglia send nerves to the mantle and the muscles of the columella. Commissures from these ganglia also pass to the pedal ganglia. The parietal ganglia innervate the mantle, gills, and osphradia.

Torsion has produced a twisting of the basic molluscan type of nervous system into a figure eight (streptoneury) (Fig. 26-29, *C*). Because of their position the right parietal ganglion becomes the left or supraparietal ganglion, and the left ganglion the right or infraparietal ganglion after torsion (Figs. 26-16, 26-29, *C*). The locations of the pleural and cerebral ganglia are not changed by the torsion process. In most gastropods the ganglia tend to be

concentrated, and the commissures and connectives between ganglia shortened. A secondary bilateral symmetry of the nervous system is an evolutionary trend in most gastropods. In the whelks, such as *Busycon* and *Buccinum* (Fig. 26-29, *C*), most ganglia, except the visceral, are located close together around the esophagus just below the cerebral ganglia. In pulmonates there is an even greater concentration of ganglia, for the visceral ganglia have moved forward also.

The sense organs are represented by eyes, statocysts, osphradia, tactile organs, and chemoreceptors. The eyes may be located on the tips of the tentacles or at their bases. Eyes may be of two or three types. In the simplest or more primitive types (e.g., limpets) the eye is merely a cuplike invagination with a pigmented retinal layer that is exposed to the water through the open aperture (Fig. 26-29, *A*, *B*). In many gastropods the aperture is closed by a cornea and lens formed from the fusion of the edges of the aperture (Fig. 26-29, *D*). The photoreceptors are directed toward the source of light (direct eyes). Perhaps most of their eyes function merely to detect light. Tentacles also bear tactile and chemoreceptor organs. The tentacles (rhinophores) of nudibranchs may have olfactory as well as other functions. Usually the statocysts (Fig. 26-29, *C*) are found in the foot near the pedal ganglia, but in nudibranchs and some others they may be located near the cerebral ganglia. The Aspidobranchia have an osphradium located anterior to and above the attachment of each of its two gills; a single osphradium is found in most other gastropods that have only one gill (Fig. 26-27). This sense organ may test the chemical quality of the branchial water or the sediment that the water contains. In terrestrial gastropods the osphradia have been replaced by rhinophores on the tentacles.

Gastropods may be dioecious or monoecious. In all gastropods the gonad (ovary, testis, or ovotestis) is unpaired and located near the apex of the visceral hump. In the Aspidobranchia the kidney acts as a gonoduct for the discharge of the gametes into the mantle cavity. Fertilization in such a primitive condition takes place in sea water. In most other gastropods there is a separate gonoduct, which is partly made up of that part of the right kidney remaining after the kidney has degenerated. The gonoduct is lengthened by the addition of a pallial duct formed from the mantle. Differentiation of this pallial portion of the gonoduct provides for sperm storage and egg membrane formation. A gonoduct separate and distinct from the kidney, with its provision for forming membranes, has made possible internal fertilization in contrast to the external fertilization of the primitive Aspidobranchia. A penis is found in most prosobranchs other than the Aspidobranchia (Fig. 26-27). The penis is an elongated, tubular structure formed by a fold or extension of the body wall. In most gastropods with a penis the vas deferens is a closed tube and opens at the penial tip (Fig. 26-30, *A*). A prostate gland for the production of seminal fluid is formed by

part of the vas deferens. That part of the genital duct leading directly from the testis is usually very much coiled for the storage of sperm. The pallial section of the female oviduct is modified to form an albumen gland and a jelly or capsule gland. Some species lay their eggs enclosed in jelly from the jelly gland; others have the eggs within a capsule. A seminal receptacle for receiving sperm from the penis is found in that part of the oviduct proximal to the ovary (Fig. 26-28). At this place, the eggs are fertilized before they receive their accessory coats or membranes in the secretory parts of the oviduct. A more complicated method of sperm transfer to the seminal receptacles is found in some (e.g., *Urosalpinx*, *Busycon*), where the sperm are discharged first into a bursa at the distal end of the oviduct and then make their way posteriorly along a ventral groove to the seminal receptacle.

Most of the hermaphroditic species of gastropods (pulmonates and opisthobranchs) are simultaneously male- and female-gamete producing, although some are protandrous; i.e., they first form functional sperm and later produce the mature eggs (*Crepidula*, *Aplysia*, Fig. 26-26, *B*). The hermaphroditic system of the pulmonates may be taken as typical of such a system (Fig. 26-28). The single gonad, called an ovotestis, is located at the apex of the visceral mass. Both eggs and sperm are produced in the same follicle of the ovotestis. A common hermaphroditic duct, formed from the gonadal and renal portions of the genetic duct, carries both eggs and sperm to the albumen gland. At the terminal part of the hermaphroditic duct is a seminal receptacle or fertilization pouch where sperm is stored and fertilization may occur. In the region of the albumen gland the hermaphroditic gland begins to separate into two ducts, the oviduct and the sperm duct (vas deferens). This separation of the two ducts at first is only partly complete morphologically, but eventually the vas deferens breaks apart from the oviduct and passes to the tip of the penis; the oviduct continues straight to the vagina, which communicates with the common genital atrium on the right side of the snail's body. The anterior part of the female tract contains many accessory reproductive structures. First of all, **515**

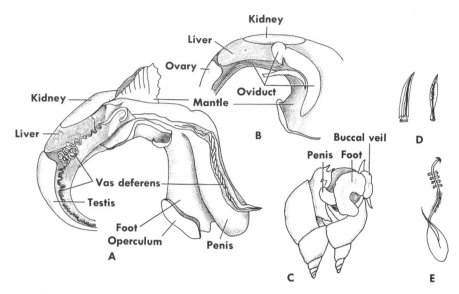

Fig. 26-30

Reproductive system. **A,** *Buccinum,* male. **B,** *Buccinum,* female. **C,** Copulation in *Lymnaea stagnalis,* left one acting as male. **D,** Darts of (left) *Helix hortensis* and (right) *Helix aspersa.* (About ⁵⁄₁₆ inch long.) **E,** Spermatophore of *Nanina.* (**A** and **B** modified from Dakin; **C** and **E** redrawn from Lankester: Treatise on zoology, Adam & Charles Black, Ltd.; **D** modified from Ashford.)

the female tract in this region is divided into the oviduct and a thick-walled vagina. The vagina communicates with an elongated spermatheca, which is supposed to receive sperm directly from the penis. Connected to the vagina region also is a mucus gland for lubricating purposes and a dart sac (Fig. 26-28) which secretes calcareous darts (Fig. 26-30, *D*) for sex-stimulating purposes.

Cross-fertilization is probably the rule in most pulmonates. When two snails prepare for mutual insemination, they approach each other with their genital atria everted and by muscular action of the dart sac each shoots a dart into the other. New darts are formed by the epithelium of the dart sac. The two snails then copulate (Fig. 26-30, *C*), each inserting its penis into the vagina of the other. The sperm are bound together as spermatophores (Fig. 26-30, *E*), and each snail discharges its spermatophores into the reproductive tract of the other. The spermatophores pass up the spermathecal duct to bulb-shaped spermatheca where the sperm are set free.

Later the sperm pass to the oviduct and up to the fertilization pouch where fertilization occurs. After fertilization the eggs take on large quantities of albumen before being discharged from the body.

Development

The eggs of primitive gastropods are fertilized externally and may be laid singly or in masses held together by gelatinous material. Higher gastropods usually have some form of membrane around their eggs. Fertilization is usually internal, and eggs are laid soon after fertilization. Some lay their eggs in a capsule containing many eggs imbedded in albumen (certain freshwater pulmonates). The eggs may be in a simple gelatinous mass (*Lymnaea*), or they may each have a shell enclosing the egg and albumen to prevent evaporation (terrestrial pulmonates). Most land snails lay their eggs in holes within the ground or under logs. Many prosobranchs attach their eggs to snail shells, their own or those of adjacent ones. Aquatic snails often attach their egg masses to vegetation.

Fig. 26-31

Cleavage and gastrulation in, **A,** *Patella* (ingression); **B,** *Littorina* (invagination); **C,** *Crepidula* (epiboly).

Cleavage in gastropods is spiral and total. The plan of this cleavage has already been described (see pp. 495-497). Quartets are formed in the usual way. Radial symmetry is characteristic of the 32-cell stage, and bilateral symmetry of the 64-cell stage (*Patella* Fig. 26-31, *A*). Gastrulation is usually by epiboly (Fig. 26-31, *C*), and the macromeres give rise to endoderm and mesoderm, while the ectoderm comes from the micromeres. Only in the primitive Aspidobranchia is the trochophore larval stage free swimming (Fig. 26-11, *C*). In others this stage is passed in the egg membrane. Most marine gastropods have a free-swimming veliger larva derived from the trochophore (Fig. 26-11, *D*). The veliger is provided with a special swimming structure of two ciliated lobes or folds, the velum. The velum has arisen as an outgrowth of the girdle of long cilia (the prototroch) characteristic of the trochophore. Structural details that started in the trochophore stage undergo a further development in the veliger, and some structures now appear for the first time. The foot, tentacles, and eyes now emerge; and the shell (cap shaped in the trochophore) assumes a spiral shape. Torsion also occurs in the late veliger stage,

in which the visceral mass twists about 180 degrees in relation to the foot and head (see pp. 501-504). Torsion may occur in a few minutes or it may involve many days of development. The growth of the foot is one of the characteristic aspects of the veliger stage, where the foot actually assumes a creeping form and the larva relies less upon the receding velum for locomotion. In the subclass Opisthobranchia, where detorsion is a marked tendency, the torsion occurs to a degree in the veliger before detorsion sets in. In the shell-less nudibranchs a shell appears in the veliger stage but is lost in its metamorphosis. All pulmonates and some prosobranchs (marine and freshwater) have no free-swimming larvae; but the trochophore and veliger stages occur, at least partly, within the egg. In these a small juvenile snail is hatched from the egg. Only a few gastropods are ovoviviparous, such as the freshwater prosobranchs (*Viviparus* and *Campeloma*) and certain species of *Littorina*.

CLASS PELECYPODA (LAMELLIBRANCHIATA, BIVALVIA)

The pelecypods represent one of the three largest classes of mollusks. They have a worldwide distribution and are mostly marine, although some have invaded brackish and fresh water. There are no terrestrial species. They number more than 10,000 living species and many thousands of fossil forms. They are characterized by a bilaterally symmetric body that is also laterally compressed. The body is completely enclosed in a mantle, which is subdivided into lateral lobes that secrete a shell of two calcareous valves joined together dorsally by an elastic cuticular ligament and hinge. Adductor muscles can close the shell ventrally and work in opposition to the elastic ligament that tends to open the valves. The head is reduced to a mouth without a radula or buccal mass. The mouth is surrounded by labial palps. The mantle cavity is unusually capacious and bears two large gills (ctenidia), one on each side of the body. The ventral foot is wedge shaped and adapted for locomotion through mud or sand. Most pelecypods are ciliary feeders, and feeding is accomplished mainly by the ciliated gills and labial palps, which form a mechanism of collecting mucus strands of food brought in by the incurrent water.

Although they have undergone some modifications of structure and habits, most pelecypods are somewhat sedentary and are found mainly in soft-bottom habitats. Their morphology has emphasized such a mode of living because their food of plankton and organic detritus is brought to them directly by water current rather than being sought.

The fossil record shows that they first appeared in the Early Cambrian period. During the Ordovician period they became differentiated and widely distributed. It is thought by some authorities that pelecypods arose from limpetlike monoplacophorans when calcifications occurred at two places in the shell and became hinged by the outer layer of periostracum. Their gill structure suggests that they may have come from a primitive gastropod such as *Haliotis*. By the Carboniferous period, bivalves became very numerous and displaced the brachiopods. Unlike the gastropods, pelecypods probably reached their peak in the ancient past and may be said now to be undergoing a slow decline. Fossil bivalves are important in the study of paleoecology

because the sensitivity of pelecypods to temperature and salinity gives a clue to ecologic conditions under which they flourished.

The evolution of the pelecypods is not so striking as that of the gastropods. The group has undergone adaptive radiation and convergence. Some show a tendency toward fusion of the mantle margins to produce long siphons for burrowing forms. Many seem to have acquired these trends independently. Each subclass usually has certain morphologic characteristics that are emphasized for a special function. Thus,

A

B

Fig. 26-32

A, *Lima,* the file shell. **B,** Posterior end of freshwater clam showing exhalant (dorsal) and inhalant (ventral) apertures formed by posterior edges of mantle lobes. (From Encyclopaedia Britannica films: **A,** "Pond Life"; **B,** "Adaptive Radiation—the Mollusks.")

the Protobranchia have become superficial burrowers, and the Filibranchia utilize byssal attachment to a substratum.

General morphology

EXTERNAL ANATOMY

The body of a pelecypod is composed of a mantle (with a shell), foot, and visceral mass. There is no head in a strict sense. The main axis of the bilaterally symmetric body is the visceral mass. The mouth and labial palps located at the anterior end of the visceral hump are usually not set off from the rest of the body. The visceral mass is found mainly in the dorsal part of the body and is covered by the mantle that hangs down on each side like a skirt and forms a sheet of tissue between the valves of the shell. Between the visceral mass and the free side of the mantle is the mantle

cavity, which is unusually large in most bivalves. The ventral margins of the two loose folds of the mantle may be free and unattached. In most bivalves the two mantle lobes are united with each other at one or more points below the ventral surface of the visceral mass. Some have only one posterior junction between the inhalant and exhalant orifices. In the freshwater clams *Anodonta* and *Unio* the mantle edges are not completely fused to form the inhalant aperture, although a functional orifice with frilled edges is present (Fig. 26-32, *B*). In many bivalves the orifices are prolonged as siphons so that the animal can retain communication with the water while burrowing beneath the surface of the mud (*Tagelus*, Figs. 26-33, 26-34, *Cumingia, Pholas,* Fig. 26-36, *C*). Shell impressions of sharply recurved, inward pallial

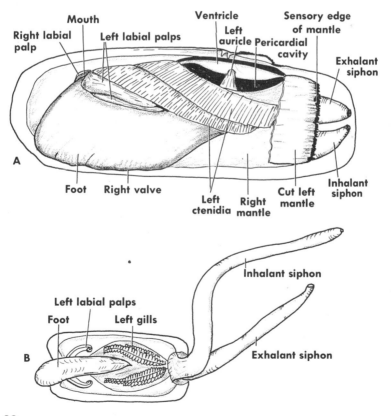

Fig. 26-33

A, *Tagelus gibbus;* left valve, mantle, and pericardial wall removed. **B,** *Tagelus,* ventral view with valves open, as seen in small aquarium where oxygenation was inadequate. Gaping valves afford good view of gills and siphons.

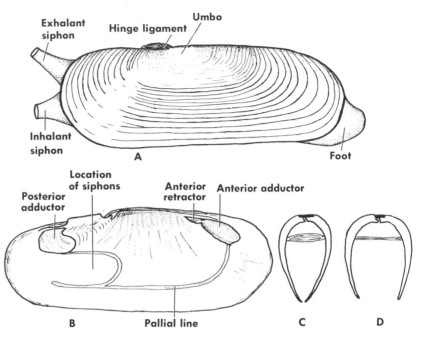

Fig. 26-34

A, *Tagelus gibbus,* the stubby razor clam, from right side. **B,** Inside of left valve of *Tagelus* showing muscle scars. **C** and **D,** Diagrammatic frontal sections of bivalve showing function of adductors and hinge ligament. **C,** Adductor is contracted, stretching hinge ligament and closing halves. **D,** Adductor is relaxed, allowing hinge ligament to pull valves apart.

lines often determine whether or not siphons have been present in the living animal (Fig. 26-34, *B*).

Many modifications of mantle fusion are found among pelecypods. In *Teredo* the siphons secrete a calcareous tube. The foot projects down as a highly muscular extension of the visceral mass and can be projected beyond the ventral margin of the valves. A common type of mantle fusion produces three apertures: the posterior or exhalant aperture, a posterior inhalant aperture, and a large anterior pedal orifice through which the foot protrudes (*Ensis, Cardium, Solemya*). A fourth orifice posterior to the pedal orifice is formed in some razor clams by a third fusion of the mantle edges.

The mantle and its derivatives are important in the basic organization plan of bivalves. Besides having its margins modified into apertures and siphons, the mantle secretes the shell, and its gills are modified chiefly for secondary feeding and develop-

mental functions. The margin of the mantle bears three folds: an outer secretory fold, a middle or sensory fold (sometimes with tentacles and eyes), and an inner muscular fold (Fig. 26-7). The outer fold contains an inner surface that secretes the noncalcareous periostracum and an outer surface that secretes the outer calcareous layer of the shell. The inner calcareous (nacreous) layer is also secreted by the outer surface of the mantle. The mantle is connected to the shell by pallial muscles (absent in gastropods) a short distance from the edge of the shell. This line of mantle attachment to the shell is represented on the inner surface of the shell as the pallial scar line (Fig. 26-34, *B*). The mantle margins have undergone a fusion pattern ventrally, posteriorly and dorsally in the evolution of the bivalves, although in the primitive condition they are free. The inner fold fuses first, followed by the middle fold, and then by the inner surface of the outer folds.

The shell of pelecypods is typically made

Fig. 26-35

Some pelecypod shells. **A,** *Dosinia discus.* **B,** *Chione cancellata.* **C,** *Dinocardium robustum.* **D,** *Tridacna gigas.* **E,** *Lampsilis ventricosa.* **F,** *Pecten irradiens.* **G,** *Atrina rigida.* **H,** *Yoldia.* **J,** *Mya.*

up of two convex valves of various shapes and contours (Fig. 26-35). It first appears in the embryo as a single shell. Later in its development, two separate calcareous plates are secreted by the left and right regions of the shell gland. The two valves of the shell are joined dorsally by an elastic hinge ligament, which acts as a spring by exerting tension upon the valves forcing them apart when the adductors relax (Fig. 26-34). The ligament (a persistent rudiment of the larval shell) is made up of conchiolin, or the horny substances of the periostracum. The valves are also usually articulated by a series of interlocking teeth located on the hinge line just beneath the hinge ligament. The shell is composed of the same three layers described in the dis-

521

cussion of gastropods—periostracum, prismatic, and nacreous (Fig. 26-7). The dorsal margin of each valve bears a prominence point near the hinge ligament called the umbo, or beak, which is the oldest part of the shell and around which are the concentric lines of shell growth. Each umbo may point slightly anteriorly so that it is usually possible to determine right and left valves. On the external surface of each valve the different areas may be called the anterior slope, the posterior slope, and the central disk. The shell valves are pulled together by two, usually transverse, adductor muscles (anterior and posterior) attached to the inner surfaces of the valves. Scars on the valves indicate where these adductor muscles are attached (Fig. 26-34, *B*). The adductor muscles act in opposition to the hinge ligament, which pulls the top edges of the two valves together, causing the lower edges of the valves to gape apart unless they are closed by the strong adductors (Fig. 26-34, *D*). Although in primitive bivalves both adductors are of about the same size, the anterior adductor in some becomes reduced (Fig. 26-42); and in oysters and scallops (Fig. 26-41) it is completely absent. To compensate for its absence the posterior adductor occupies a more central position. Adductor muscles have developed from the inner muscular fold of the mantle. In the scallop and some other bivalves the single adductor muscle consists of two kinds of fibers—quick striated fibers for quick closing of the valves and the catch smooth muscle fibers for holding the valves together.

Pelecypod shells are found in a great variety of shapes, sizes, colors, and surface sculpturings. In some genera the two valves are of unequal size and of different shape (*Ostrea, Pecten*). One of the valves may be permanently attached to a substratum. The shell is long and somewhat tubular in the razor clams (*Ensis, Tagelus*) (Fig. 26-34). In the shipworm the shell is rudimentary and adapted for drilling. In some the mantle may be reflected over the entire surface of the shell (*Scioberetia*). Ornamentation of the shell is often brought about through the interruption of growth lines by ribs radiating from the umbo. Shell size varies from certain tiny, freshwater forms smaller than a fingernail to the

giant clam *Tridacna* (Fig. 26-35, *D*), which may weigh several hundred pounds.

Whenever a foreign object becomes lodged between the mantle and the shell, concentric layers of nacreous shell are laid down around it. Pearls are formed in this manner. The most valuable pearls are produced by the pearl oysters (Pteriidae), with which artificial pearl culture is conducted by introducing a tiny piece of shell between the mantle and shell. Pearl buttons are made from shells of the freshwater family Unionidae.

The foot is highly muscular, and in a few protobranchs (*Yoldia, Nucula*) it may be used for creeping like a snail. However, most bivalves use it as a burrowing organ. The highly specialized *Solemya* uses its foot as both a burrowing and a swimming organ. Even in those bivalves that creep the foot can be folded to form a bladelike edge. In most cases the foot is bilaterally compressed, with the lower edge keeled to form a bladelike structure (hatchet-footed). Locomotion with such a foot is produced by thrusting the distal end of the foot forward, using blood pressure turgor in the sinuses of the foot and a pair of pedal protractor muscles. At its greatest expansion the distal end forms a bulb with all the blood flowing into it, which anchors the foot (Fig. 26-8, *E*). By contraction of a pair of anterior and a pair of posterior retractor muscles as well as muscles within the foot, the shell is pulled toward the swollen end of the foot. During retraction the blood of the foot is largely withdrawn into mantle spaces or sinuses.

Some clams, such as *Ensis* and *Laevicardium*, can leap and swim as well as burrow. The leaping movement is achieved by first extending the foot, looping it back beneath the shell, and suddenly straightening it (Fig. 26-8, *B*). Swimming is effected by alternately thrusting out and withdrawing the foot, with a simultaneous closing of the shell valves to expel water from the centrally closed valve through an anterior pedal gap. This modified version of jet propulsion forces the clam backward by jerks. The scallop *Pecten*, which swims by jerky movements, also uses jet propulsion. By rapidly shutting and opening its valves and forcing water out dorsally from each side of the hinge, the animal moves forward. File shells (Fig. 26-32, *A*) can swim slowly by clapping their valves, which are held vertically. Sometimes the water current passes out ventrally and the hinge joint becomes anterior. The adductor muscle in *Pecten* is single (Fig. 26-41), but it is divided into two unequal parts. The larger of these parts produces the rapid movement of swimming; the smaller keeps the valves closed by continual contraction. *Pecten* has a very reduced foot and cannot burrow.

Instead of being fastened down by the attachment of one valve, as in oysters, many marine bivalves are attached to the substratum by strong byssal threads (Fig. 26-36). These threads are secreted by a gland located in the middle line of the surface of the foot in a byssus pit (Fig. 26-36, *B*), which may correspond to the ventral pedal mucus gland of gastropods. The threads of *Mytilus* are composed of conchiolin and are pushed to the exterior singly when secreted. When the tip of the foot is in contact with the substratum, the fluidlike thread flows down a groove to the tip, hardens on contact with water, and attaches the clam to the substratum. The mussel withdraws its foot, changes its position, and attaches another thread in the same manner. In this way many threads are attached.

All pelecypods, except the Septibranchia, have a pair of gills. In some cases, the single gill on each side has been folded to form a double gill. The gills have in some ways kept pace with the formation of the large, lateral mantle cavity and have extended anteriorly toward the mouth with a great increase in number and length of filaments. The mantle cavity on each side of the body is divided into a small dorsal exhalant (suprabranchial) chamber and a large ventral inhalant chamber.

In the primitive Protobranchia (*Nucula*) each gill is composed of a central axis bearing on its opposite sides a series of filaments that are loosely connected by tufts of cilia (Fig. 26-37, *A*). Ciliary connections also lock the filaments to the sides of the foot and to the mantle. This basic plan has undergone many modifications among the different pelecypods. In one common type the rows of filaments become parallel to each other and hang downward in the man-

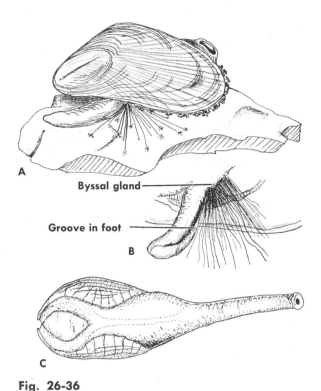

Byssal gland

Groove in foot

Fig. 26-36

A, *Mytilus* attached by byssal threads. B, Foot and byssal gland of *Mytilus*. C, *Pholas* (*Barnea*), a rock borer.

tle cavity, with the extremities of the filaments turned up at the ends to form the descending (attached to the axis) and ascending limbs for each filament. The gill is thus made up of four series (lamellae) of filaments, or each gill is a W-shaped structure with each half of two thin platelike lamellae (Fig. 26-37, *C*). At the ventral margin, where each filament is upturned, is a food groove. Adjacent limbs are connected by interlamellar junctions, and adjacent filaments are attached by tufts of cilia or disks. Each gill of two lamellae, one formed by the union of adjacent descending limbs and one formed by the union of ascending limbs, is called a demibranch.

The degree to which the gills are fused together to form continuous plates varies with the different subclasses, reaching its greatest development in the Eulamellibranchia. In this group, ciliary junctions between the filaments have been replaced by tissue fusion, and the lamellae are sheets of tissues (Fig. 26-38). The interlamellar junctions extend dorsoventrally the entire **523**

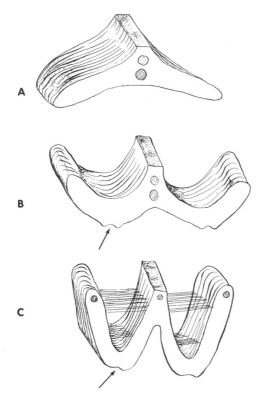

A

B

C

Fig. 26-37

Evolution of bivalve ctenidium by folding. **A,** Primitive protobranch gill. **B,** Hypothetical intermediate condition in which food grooves are formed (indicated by arrow). **C,** Gill in which filaments are folded at food groove to form ascending and descending limbs, connected by interlamellar junctions (filibranch condition) or interfilamentary tissue junctions (eulamellibranch condition).

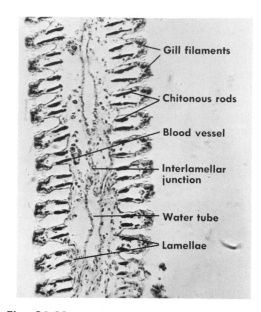

— Gill filaments

— Chitonous rods

— Blood vessel

— Interlamellar junction

— Water tube

— Lamellae

Fig. 26-38

Cross section through gill of mussel.

length of the lamellae and partition the interlamellar space into vertical water tubes (Fig. 26-38). Blood is carried through the afferent and efferent vessels in the interlamellar junctions for aeration. By fusing with the upper surface of the mantle on the outside and the foot on the inside, the tips of the ascending limbs have separated the mantle chamber horizontally into an upper suprabranchial (exhalant) chamber and a lower (inhalant) cavity. A current of water entering by the ventral aperture, or siphon, circulates among the original filaments and passes through ostia in the lamellae to the water tubes. Passing dorsally through the water tubes, the water then flows into the suprabranchial chamber and out the exhalant opening (aperture or

siphon) (Fig. 26-39). Some pelecypods, such as *Ensis*, have increased the lamellar surface area by secondary folds so that the gill surface has an undulated aspect.

Most oxygenation occurs in the gills, but some may take place in the inner mantle surface. The function of oxygenation is assumed entirely by the mantle surface in the subclass Septibranchia in which the gills are absent (Fig. 26-39, *C*).

The ecologic habits of bivalves have brought great changes to the basic primitive plan of water circulation through the mantle chamber. In the primitive protobranch *Nucula*, water passes through an anterior inhalant opening, then over the gills, and leaves the body by a posterior exhalant opening (Fig. 26-39, *A*). Lateral cilia sweep the water currents upward between the gill filaments into the dorsal exhalant chamber. Cleansing (frontal) cilia on the gill and mantle carry the heavier sediment to the ventral mantle edge where it is expelled from the inhalant cavity with other rejected particles by the sudden contraction of the adductor muscles.

Although *Nucula* is a burrowing form and a deposit feeder, its plan of water circulation is not sufficient for the filter-feeding bivalves. Burrowing in soft silt and mud involves the problem of bringing in much inorganic sediment with the inhalant current. Most pelecypods have the inhalant as well as the exhalant openings at the posterior end, so that the water current makes a U-turn as it passes through the gills into the suprabranchial chamber and out the exhalant opening. The mantle edges of *Nucula* are free and do not form distinct apertures for the inhalant and exhalant currents.

INTERNAL ANATOMY

Most bivalves are filter feeders, a process in which the gills play an important role. The primitive *Nucula* and related forms use what is called deposit feeding, by which they extend the two palp proboscides (Fig. 26-39,A) into the mud to pick up, by their ciliated grooves, organic deposits. From here the material is transferred to the base of the proboscis. It is then carried between the palp lamellae, the inner surfaces of which are ridged with ciliary tracts that form a sorting and rejecting device. Ingested particles are conveyed in a groove to the mouth, while rejected particles are swept by cilia to the tips of the palpal lamellae and transferred to the mantle cavity by way of the mantle surface. Helping in the circulation of water currents through the gill chamber is the "pumping" action of the gills and dorsal membrane. The gills in *Nucula* are formed of modified filaments united by extensive ciliary junctions which make them good pumping organs. Similar pumping devices are found in the Septibranchia, where the gills are converted into a muscular septum, perforated with ciliated pores, that can be raised and lowered to draw in the tiny animals on which the organism feeds (Fig. 26-39, C).

In the filter feeders the inhalant current, on entering the large mantle chamber, is checked somewhat to allow the large particles to sink to the bottom of the chamber, whence they are carried by cilia toward the posterior part of the mantle chamber. The inhalant current with the smaller food particles is drawn over the gills by the action of cilia covering the gills and mantle. The food is trapped by mucus on the gills and carried ventrally to the food groove along the ventral edge of the gill and thence

Fig. 26-39

Water currents in pelecypod types. **A**, Protobranchia. **B**, Lamellibranchia. **C**, Septibranchia; dotted lines indicate pumping movement of muscular septa.

to the palps around the mouth. The cilia involved in these processes differ in structure and function. Lateral cilia on the gills (Figs. 26-40, 26-41, D, E) draw the main current of water into the mantle cavity. The frontal cilia carry the trapped food down to the food groove by producing a constant stream over the surface of the gill toward its ventral margin. Laterofrontal cilia along the angles between the lateral and frontal cilia (Fig. 26-41, D) prevent large particles from clogging the gills and deflect the small food particles toward the frontal cilia. Trapped food is entangled in the mucus in stringlike masses and is directed by cilia partly into the food groove and toward the palps around the mouth (Fig. 26-42). In the labial palps the food may pass directly to the mouth, whereas rejected material may be carried posteriorly by ciliary paths toward the outgoing circulation.

525

Fig. 26-40

Simple gill filaments of *Donax variabilis* (Coquina). Epithelium has extremely long cilia to maintain currents of water. (×810.) (From Andrew: Textbook of comparative histology, Oxford University Press, Inc.)

In *Nucula* and a few related forms an enlarged buccal cavity with two lateral glandular pouches is present; but in most other pelecypods the mouth is a simple transverse aperture more or less compressed between a dorsoanterior and a ventroposterior lip. The lips are scalloped in *Pecten,* and the labial palps are really modifications of the lips.

Except in carnivorous forms, such as the Septibranchia, the alimentary canal of bivalves is adapted for dealing with a constant supply of small food particles, mostly of plant origin. There are some differences in the mechanism of handling food between the primitive protobranchs and the higher bivalves. The method in protobranchs will be considered first.

In protobranchs, after food enters the mouth, it is conducted by a short esophagus into a thin-walled and laterally compressed stomach. The stomach walls contain no muscle, except in the septibranchs, and may be partly buried in the visceropedal mass. The stomach is divided into a dorsal portion, into which the esophagus

and digestive glands open, and a ventral portion made up of the style sac. Surrounding the stomach is the liver or paired digestive glands made up of one kind of phagocytic cells. The dorsal part of the stomach is mainly a ciliated sorting organ, consisting of a series of longitudinal grooves formed by ridges (Fig. 26-43). It contains a semicircular, chitinous plate called the gastric shield that is provided with a toothlike elevation. When food enters the dorsal part of the stomach, it is carried along a ciliated tract to the cecum. In its transfer to the cecum the food passes the three ducts of the digestive glands, where some of the finer particles enter. After the rest of the food passes into and out of the cecum, it is entangled in a mass of feces and mucus called a protostyle, which is rotated counterclockwise by long cilia lining the walls of the style sac. As the protostyle with food at its anterior end rotates, it is pushed dorsally into the stomach by muscular contraction and by the action of the cilia. The food mass at the tip of the protostyle is now wound around the elevation of the gastric shield by the rotation of the protostyle. This process causes large particles of food to be freed and ground into smaller pieces by the pressure against the gastric shield. The smaller, freed particles are sent by the ciliated sorting grooves

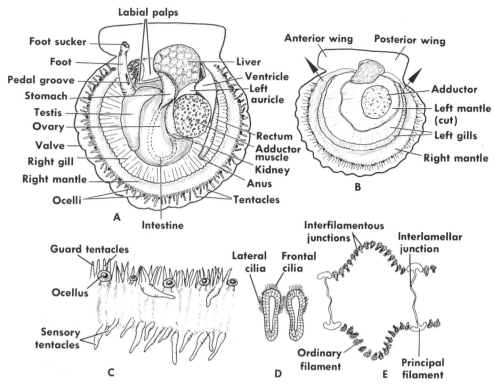

Fig. 26-41

Pecten irradiens (order Filibranchia). **A,** Structure as seen with left valve, mantle, and gills removed. **B,** Left valve and part of left mantle removed. **C,** Portion of velar fold showing tentacles and steely blue eyes. **D,** Two ordinary filaments of *Pecten* enlarged from **E. E,** Section of gill transverse to filaments at level of top ascending filaments. (×130.) (A to C drawn from life; D and E modified from Dakin.)

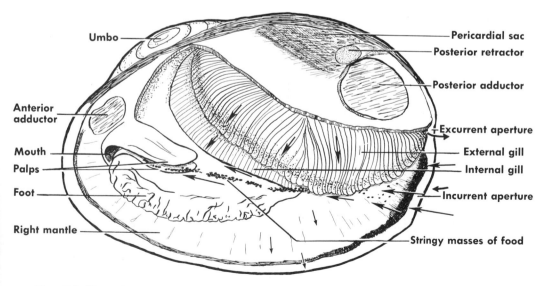

Fig. 26-42

Feeding mechanism of lamellibranch as seen in freshwater mussel. (From Hickman: Integrated principles of zoology, The C. V. Mosby Co.)

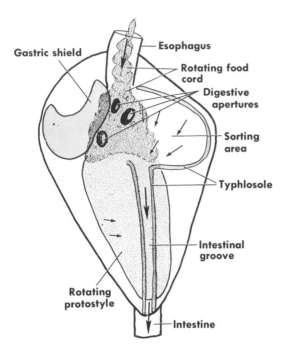

Gastric shield

Esophagus

Rotating food cord

Digestive apertures

Sorting area

Typhlosole

Intestinal groove

Rotating protostyle

Intestine

Fig. 26-43
Protobranch stomach, with protostyle (diagrammatic).
Compare with lamellibranch stomach, Fig. 26-10. (Modified from Owen.)

into the ducts of the digestive glands, while the larger particles are passed directly into the intestine by a groove from the anterior wall of the style sac. No extracellular digestion occurs by this method, but the food taken into the digestive gland is engulfed and digested intracellularly by cells in the tubular walls. Some digestion may also occur in phagocytic blood cells, which enter the gut. Wastes are returned by ciliary tracts to the stomach and thence to the style sac and intestine.

The long intestine forms a loop or two before passing dorsally between the anterior adductor muscle and the stomach. The posterior part of the intestine, or rectum, passes through the heart and pericardial chamber and over the posterior adductor muscle before opening by the anus into the suprabranchial chamber. An internal ridge (often called a typhlosole) extends the length of the intestine and is continuous with one of the ridges found beside the style sac groove. The intestine has no digestive or absorptive function, but is concerned only in forming the feces.

The more advanced pelecypods, such as the Eulamellibranchia, differ from the protobranchs by having a longer style sac, which is always provided with a crystalline style (Fig. 26-10). They also lack proboscides, characteristic of the deposit feeders. The advanced bivalves are strictly filter feeders living mainly on phytoplankton. The plankton is trapped by the mucus on the surface of the gills and passed by the frontal cilia to the food grooves along the ventral edge of the gills, as earlier described. There are several patterns of food currents over the gills among the different genera. Some may have both dorsal and ventral food grooves (*Pecten* and Unionidae). The palps have about the same function as in the protobranchs, sorting out the accepted food and passing it to the mouth; the rejected particles are carried by cilia to the ventral edge of the mantle, then posteriorly to be expelled just below the inhalant apertures.

The crystalline style consists of a protein matrix and bears at its anterior end the carbohydrate-splitting enzyme amylase (and in some a lipase or fat-splitting enzyme as well). Cilia in the style sac rotate the crystalline style several turns per minute and drive its free end against the gastric shield where the enzymes are rubbed off and mixed with the stomach contents. The style also forms a stirring mechanism for circulating the particles into the sorting areas. As the tip of the style in many pelecypods is eroded by rubbing against the gastric shield, the style at its base is continually being reformed. In some the style is replaced two or three times per day. The length of the crystalline style varies, usually between 1 and 2 inches, although it may be longer in large species.

The location of the style shows several variations. In some it is found in the intestine or in a sac derived from the intestine (Fig. 26-10), while in others it is derived as a pocket from the stomach. In oysters and some others the crystalline style acts as a capstan, and as it rotates, it draws in the mucus strings of food that are shed in the sorting areas of the stomach.

In the sorting areas of the stomach of higher bivalves, cilia pass the finer particles of food into the numerous digestive gland ducts that convey the food to the tubules of the gland. The digestion here is intracellular, and enzymes for all the classes of food may be found here. Some extracellular digestion occurs in the stomach when the crystalline style releases its enzymes, as already described.

The carnivorous septibranchs, with their muscular pumping septum, draw their prey into the mantle chamber and to the mouth (Fig. 26-39, *C*). Their stomach is muscular, lined with chitin, and acts as a gizzard to macerate the prey. Their reduced style may furnish mucus for coating sharp and injurious particles of food.

The circulatory system consists of a heart, arteries, and sinuses. The heart consists of a ventricle, wrapped around the rectum, and two auricles, each of which opens into

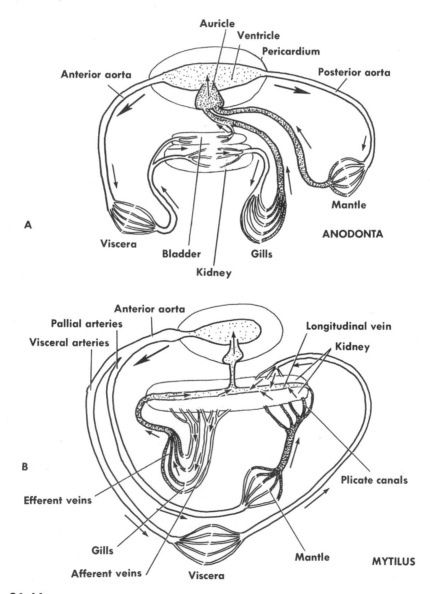

Fig. 26-44

Lamellibranch circulation. **A**, *Anodonta*. **B**, *Mytilus*. In *Anodonta*, most of blood from viscera goes to gills before returning to heart. In *Mytilus*, branchial circulation is less important and mantle circulation plays greater role.

the ventricle by a canal (Figs. 26-33, 26-41). Surrounding the heart and part of the digestive tract is the pericardial sac, to which the broad bases of the auricles are attached. Usually only the anterior aorta leaves the heart (Fig. 26-44, *B*), but in some (*Anodonta* and others) a posterior aorta is found (Fig. 26-44, *A*). After it leaves the heart, the anterior aorta enlarges into an aortic bulb, from which many arteries emerge. These include the pallial arteries to the mantle and the visceral arteries, the most important of which are the gastrointestinal to the digestive tract, the hepatic to the digestive glands, and the terminal arteries to the foot and anterior regions. In the different tissues the arteries break up into a network of sinuses, which join together to form larger sinuses mostly on the inner side of the mantle and superficial parts of the body. The course of the blood varies somewhat with different species. In some, such as *Mytilus,* the blood from the tissue sinuses flows through the kidneys; part of the blood from the kidney then passes to the auricles through a longitudinal vein; the other part of the blood circulates through the gills before returning to the auricles by the longitudinal vessel (Fig. 26-44, *B*). In *Anodonta,* most of the blood passes through the gills for oxygenation before returning to the heart, and only a small part of it goes directly from the kidneys to the heart (Fig. 26-44, *A*). Much oxygenation occurs in the mantle.

The blood is usually colorless, but hemoglobin is found in some (*Solen*) and hemocyanin in others (*Venus*).

In those bivalves with a well-developed foot, the blood plays an important part in the extension and manipulation of the foot. Blood is pumped into the foot sinuses and prevented from returning by a sphincter valve while the foot is being extended. When the foot is retracted, the blood retreats into the mantle sinuses.

Excretion in bivalves occurs through a pair of U-shaped nephridial tubules near the pericardium. The glandular part of each tubule opens into the anterior pericardium, while the bladder portion opens by a nephridiopore into the suprabranchial chamber. Modifications of the excretory system involve the absence of glandular and bladder differentiations in primitive

forms and many foldings and ramifications in higher pelecypods. In *Pecten* and other Filibranchia the reproductive ducts also open into the kidneys instead of having separate openings.

The nervous system has in general followed the simple basic plan of mollusks, such as three pairs of ganglia and two pairs of longitudinal nerve cords (Fig. 26-45). In the Protobranchia there are four distinct pairs of ganglia; in others the cerebral and pleural ganglia are fused. Commissures connect the members of paired ganglia with each other. The cerebropleural ganglia are located on each side of the esophagus and send paired nerve cords to the visceral ganglia below the posterior adductor muscle. A second pair of nerve cords from the cerebropleural ganglia runs to the pedal ganglia in the foot.

Sense organs are represented in the class as a whole by ocelli, tactile organs, statocysts, and osphradia (Figs. 26-41, 26-45, 26-46). Most sense organs are located on the edge of the mantle. The edge in some species bears pallial tentacles with tactile and chemoreceptor sense organs (*Pecten*) (Fig. 26-41, *C*). The ocelli are best represented in such forms as *Pecten,* where they each consist of cornea, lens, retina, and pigmented layer (Fig. 26-46). They are steel blue in color and are found along the edge of the mantle. Their retinal cells are directed away from the source of light. In most pelecypods the ocelli are simply pigment spots. Statocysts are usually located in or near the pedal ganglia. Osphradia, for testing incoming water or other functions, are located below the posterior adductor muscles in the exhalant canal.

Separate sexes are the rule in most pelecypods, although some species, e.g., *Ostrea* and *Pecten* as well as certain freshwater species (Sphaeriidae), are hermaphroditic. The paired gonads are practically fused together in their location around the intestinal loops. In the Protobranchia and some others the gonads open into the kidneys, which discharge the gametes to the exterior. In the Eulamellibranchia the gonoducts are separate from but close to the kidneys. The renal ducts and gonoducts may open on a common papilla (*Mercenaria*). In some hemaphroditic species the ovary and testis are separate from each

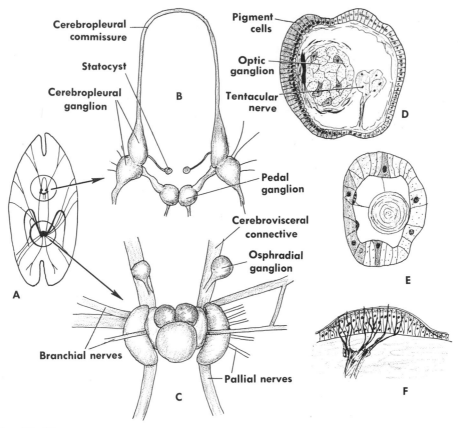

Fig. 26-45

Nervous and sensory system of pelecypods. **A,** General view of nervous system of *Pecten.* **B,** Cerebropleural and pedal ganglia of *Pecten.* **C,** Visceral ganglion of *Pecten;* this is largest ganglion in *Pecten* because posterior part of body is most developed and mantle (pallial) nerves arise from it. **D,** Section through tip of siphonal tentacle of *Cardium,* passing through an ocellus. **E,** Section through right statocyst of *Cardium.* **F,** Section through osphradium of *Pecten.* (**A** to **C** modified from Dakin; **D** and **E** modified from Johnstone.)

other and discharge their gametes by separate openings.

Fertilization occurs externally in the surrounding water in most marine pelecypods. After the gametes are shed into the suprabranchial chamber, they are carried through the exhalant aperture, or siphon, to the outside. In some marine species and freshwater forms the eggs are fertilized in the suprabranchial chamber by sperm that have entered by inhalant water currents. The fertilized eggs are then carried into the water tubes of the gills where they are incubated. Incubation is a feature of most freshwater bivalves. Self-fertilization in the gonoducts may occur in some hermaphroditic species, such as Sphaeriidae. Fertiliza-

tion of the eggs may also occur in the water tubes (e.g., Unionidae). In some species of *Ostrea* the incubation takes place in the mantle cavity outside of the gills.

Pelecypods have spiral cleavage, which may vary in certain details among the different groups. After the first two cleavage divisions and the formation of four macromeres, successive divisions of the macromeres produce quartets of micromeres. After the formation of certain bodily organs, a shell gland produces a dorsal horny plate, which grows in extent. Later, two calcareous plates are formed by the folding of the single plate and joined together by the hinge ligament, thus giving rise to the two valves of the shell. Around the proto-

531

Fig. 26-46

One of numerous eyes from margin of mantle of *Pecten*. Large lens, abundant pigment, and complex retina (here partly detached) are present. (×83.) (From Andrew: Textbook of comparative histology, Oxford University Press, Inc.)

Fig. 26-47

Bivalved glochidia larvae.

troch a girdle of long cilia arises with a tuft of cilia at the apex. This first free-swimming stage is called the trochophore (Fig. 26-11, A) and is followed by the veliger stage, which is usually of short duration. During the veliger stage many bodily structures are developed, such as the nervous system musculature, gills, and foot. The band of cilia (the velum) is lost; the larva musculature disappears; and the apex moves downward above the mouth, which assumes the characteristics of the adult mouth. In the Protobranchs the velum is unusually large with rows of ciliated cells,

the whole forming a sort of test. Inside this test the shell gland and shell develop. In the freshwater *Sphaerium* and *Unio* there is no free-swimming stage; development is direct, although both a reduced trochophore and veliger stage can be detected in their embryonic development. When development is completed, the young clam is discharged from the gills.

Development in the freshwater Unionidae is unique in having a veliger stage that is represented by a parasitic glochidium (Fig. 26-47). The glochidium (less than 0.5 mm. long) is a bivalve shell usually provided with hooks or teeth and a rudimentary foot bearing a long adhesive byssus thread. Its reduced digestive system is nonfunctional. When discharged from the gills through the suprabranchial chamber and exhalant aperture, the glochidium sinks to the bottom. Here it may by chance come in contact with a fish, to which it attaches itself by its hooks either to the fins or to other bodily parts. Those glochidia without hooks usually attach themselves to the gills to which they are carried by respiratory currents of water. The phagocytic cells of the larval mantle are able to obtain nutrition from the host tissues.

During the month or less of its parasitic existence the glochidium, in a cyst, undergoes considerable transformation, losing most of its larval structures and developing adult structures. When the immature clam breaks out of its cyst, it falls to the bottom mud where it takes up its existence for the rest of its life cycle. Infected fish can be detected by the small cysts of the glochidia, called "blackheads."

The number of glochidia produced by a freshwater clam may exceed two or three million, most of which die without an opportunity to parasitize a fish.

CLASS SCAPHOPODA

The class Scaphopoda or elephant's-tusk shells is represented by a small group of about 300 to 400 species. Many fossil species dating back to the Devonian period are known. Most of their evolutionary development has occurred, however, within the Cretaceous era.

The shell is an elongated, cylindric or tube-shaped structure, which may be slightly curved and open at both ends. It may resemble a miniature elephant's tusk or the canine tooth of a carnivore, with a gradual reduction in diameter posteriorly. The shell may also assume other shapes in a few species. It may be sculptured with longitudinal or annular ribs, or it may be smooth like a tooth. The size of the shell varies from 4 mm. to about 5 inches in length, although the average length is usually less than 2 inches. Fossil specimens reached a much greater size.

The class is divided into two families— Dentaliidae with pointed feet and Siphinodentaliidae with elongated feet terminating in a crenulated disk. They are exclusively marine and are adapted for burrowing. They are usually found buried in the sand, with the posterior end projecting from the surface (Fig. 26-48). The body fits snugly into its shell tube and is attached along the concave or dorsal side by special columellar muscles. The mantle cavity is continuous throughout the shell on the ventral side. The mantle, originally of two lobes, is fused into a tubelike structure to conform with the shell and forms an anterior aperture, into which the head can be protruded or withdrawn (Fig. 26-49). A narrow posterior aperture serves for the inhalant water current (by ciliary action) and the exhalant current (by muscular contraction).

The head is cylindric and made up of two lobes, each with several slender tentacles or captacula with adhesive knobs or prehensile disks at their ends. These captacula, along with the mantle cilia, aid the animal in getting its prey, mostly microscopic plankton. The head has no special

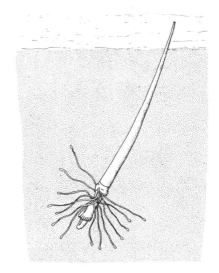

Fig. 26-48

Dentalium (class Scaphopoda) burrows into soft bottom to feed, leaving posterior end projecting into water. Its capitate oral tentacles (captacula) are used in feeding, and cilia in mantle cavity maintain water currents. (Modified from Light et al.)

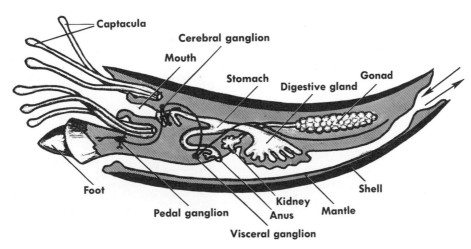

Fig. 26-49

Diagram of structure of *Dentalium*. (From Hickman: Integrated principles of zoology, The C. V. Mosby Co.)

sense organs except the captacula, which apparently have sensory functions.

Gills are lacking in this class; respiration takes place in ciliated folds lining a portion of the mantle cavity.

The mouth, which is located in a projection of the pharynx or proboscis, is found at the base of the foot. It contains a well-developed radula and mandibles. A narrow esophagus leads into the stomach, which receives the ducts of the bilobed digestive glands and a pyloric cecum. The V-shaped intestine leaves at the anterior end of the stomach and opens through the anus into the mantle cavity.

On each side of the anus is an opening, or nephridiopore, from each of the paired kidneys. Renopericardial openings are not present since there is no heart.

The blood system is made up of irregular sinuses, and the blood is kept circulating by the rhythmic protrusion and withdrawal of the foot.

The nervous system is typically molluscan (cerebral, pleural, and pedal ganglia with connectives). About the only sense organs besides the captacula are the subradula organ of taste and the statocysts in the foot.

The sexes are separate, and the gametes from the unpaired gonads are discharged through the right nephridium into the mantle cavity and to the outside. The eggs, which are laid singly, are fertilized externally.

Segmentation is irregular and unequal. Gastrulation is by invagination. A floating trochophore stage (Fig. 26-11, *B*) is followed by a bilaterally symmetric veliger larva, which is transformed after a few days into a creeping organism. Elongation of the body and shell takes place gradually.

Scaphopods are mostly sedentary animals and are chiefly found in fairly deep water, although a few species may live in shallow shore water. They burrow their way through the mud or sand with the foot, which is provided with retractor muscles that are fastened to the distal wall of the shell tube. Locomotion in the Siphinodentaliidae may take place by extending and anchoring the foot by means of the foot disk.

Dentalium is by far the most common genus and consists of several species in the coastal waters of North America, mostly in southern waters. Shells of this genus are easily found along the beaches where they have been washed ashore.

CLASS CEPHALOPODA

The cephalopods represent the most specialized of the molluscan group and in many ways are the most advanced of all the invertebrate groups. Although they possess the basic molluscan pattern of structure, they surpass all other mollusks in organization, cerebral development, more precise sensory information, learning processes, and locomotion. They include octopuses, cuttlefish, squids (Fig. 26-50), and nautiluses. Some have attained the largest size of all invertebrates. The giant squid *Architeuthis princeps* reaches a length of more than 50 feet (inclusive of the arms). On the other hand, the smallest cephalopod is probably the pigmy squid *Idiosepius*, which does not exceed a total length of 15 to 20 mm.

Their fossil record indicates that the peak of their evolutionary development was reached during the Paleozoic and Mesozoic eras, at which time they numbered thousands of species. At present there are only about 600 species of cephalopods found. In their early history they contained such important groups as the Ammonoidea (Figs. 26-3, *E*, 26-53) now wholly extinct. Only a single nautiloid, *Nautilus* (Fig. 26-51), now exists, although most of the fossil cephalopods belong to this subclass. In contrast to most mollusks the cephalopods are

Fig. 26-50

School of young squids in swimming formation. (Courtesy C. P. Hickman, Jr.)

chiefly active swimmers instead of bottom dwellers. They seem to be more closely related to the Gastropoda than to other classes of mollusks.

The cephalopods are bilaterally symmetric animals, but they have undergone profound rearrangement of their body axes in comparison with other mollusks. The anteroposterior axis has become greatly shortened and the dorsoventral axis lengthened. This causes the latter axis to become the dominant functional anteroposterior axis. As a result of this shift of axes the former ventral surface is now anterior, the anterior surface is dorsal, the dorsal surface is posterior, and the posterior surface is ventral. The posterior mantle cavity has become ventral. The mouth is now located in the middle of the foot, the edges of which are modified to form the tentacles or arms. Part of the foot (probably the region of the epipodium of gastropods) is represented by the funnel.

Most existing cephalopods have a very reduced shell (squids) or one that is vestigial or none at all (octopuses). The relict *Nautilus* has a completely developed shell that is also well represented by fossil cephalopods.

The evolutionary trends of the class have emphasized a vigorous, aggressive mode of life, fast locomotion, and predaceous habits. Molluscan body modifications have thus meant the elimination of the heavy calcareous shell and the formation, in many instances, of fins as an aid to active locomotion. By the forward movement of the foot the viscera forms a hump that is now posterior and covered by a dome-shaped mantle.

General morphology
EXTERNAL ANATOMY

Present-day cephalopods are divided into two chief groups—the Tetrabranchia (Nautiloidea) with an external shell and two pairs of gills and the Dibranchia (Coleoidea) with a shell that is internal or absent and a single pair of gills.

The tetrabranchs are represented today by a single genus, *Nautilus*. Their external shell is coiled in a planospiral and is partitioned into gas-filled chambers by successive, posterior, concave septa, except the last and largest chamber, which is occupied by the living animal (Fig. 26-51). Each of the chambers represents a stage in the animal's growth. In its growth and as

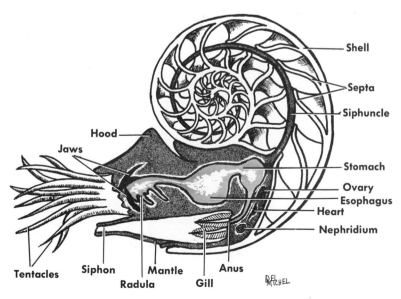

Fig. 26-51

Chambered nautilus in diagrammatic optical section. (From Hickman: Integrated principles of zoology, The C. V. Mosby Co.)

the shell is enlarged the animal moves forward while the mantle secretes a new septum, which is indicated on the shell wall by a suture. Each new successive chamber is larger than the preceding one. All the chambers, except the last, contain gas (mostly air with more nitrogen and less oxygen), which is secreted by a siphuncle or tubule extension of the visceral hump that extends through perforations in the middle of the septa. These gas-filled chambers make the heavy shell relatively buoyant so that the animal can swim more freely. The shell consists of an organic matrix, with an outer layer containing calcium carbonate crystals and an inner nacreous layer. The outer surface may bear alternating bands of orange and white, although in some the surface is a uniform pearly white.

The tetrabranchs are divided into the nautiloids and the ammonoids (extinct). The nautiloids probably reached their greatest development in the Paleozoic era. Many of them, such as *Orthoceras,* had straight cone-shaped or slightly curved shells. Some were 10 to 15 feet long. No general evolutionary pattern can be formulated about their coiling. Some forms tended to coil, culminating in the closely coiled *Nautilus.* Others tended to become uncoiled. All degrees of coiling are found among fossil forms (Fig. 26-52). The second group, the ammonoids (Fig. 26-53), reached their peak in the Mesozoic era and became extinct at the end of the Cretaceous period. They differed from the nautiloids mainly in the shape and sculpture of their whorls, the wrinkled septa, and the highly complex suture lines. Their morphology was highly varied. In some of these the shell may have been coiled at first and straightened later. Uncoiling was especially pronounced as they neared extinction. Their size ranges were equally varied, extending from tiny shells of ½ inch diameter to some with a diameter of 6 to 7 feet. The nature of the sutures forms an important index to the taxonomic studies of the group. Complex sutures may have been involved in the strengthening of the shell, and the abandonment of the coiling pattern may have been related to their return to a benthonic existence. Of course, nothing is known about the soft parts of these fossils.

The Coleoidea or Dibranchia, to which most of the existing cephalopods belong, have lost the rigid shell, which has become internal or absent. The mantle, which encloses the viscera and secretes the shell in the tetrabranchs, has assumed an active role in the locomotion of modern cephalo-

Fig. 26-52

Fossil cephalopod shells showing some varied shapes. Earliest fossil shells were slightly curved, and straight and coiled shells developed from these. (Modified from Moore, Lalicker, and Fischer.)

pods. With the loss of the shell and the presence of a highly muscular mantle the jet propulsion mechanism reaches its highest perfection.

The dibranchs may have evolved from the nautiloids; and in their evolution, the shell became enclosed in the mantle. As they evolved in the direction of an active swimming existence, the shell was partly or wholly discarded for more efficient locomotion. The fossil group Belemnites may represent a link between the nautiloids and dibranchs. These forms are considered dibranchs as they possessed the ink sac and the sucker type of tentacle. The belemnoids also possessed an anterior dorsal plate (proostracum), which projected from the anterior end of the shell for protection, and an external calcified sheath, the guard, at the apex of the shell. Modifications of this plan gave rise to several lines of descent leading to modern forms. Reduction of the guard and coiling of the shell led to the present-day *Spirula* (Fig. 26-63, *A, B*), in which the shell is still partly external. Another evolutionary line developed into the squids, in which all the shell has disappeared except for the horny pen. A third line of descent involves the cuttlefish *Sepia*, in which the uppermost side of the chambered shell with numerous septa persists (Fig. 26-63, *C, D.*). The cuttlefish has many thin chambers that are spaced and separated by numerous pillars and contain gas for buoyancy. In the octopuses, another evolutionary line, the shell has completely disappeared or is a mere vestige.

All cephalopods swim by some form of jet propulsion. They do this by taking water into the mantle cavity when the mantle circular muscles are relaxed and the longitudinal muscles contracted. Water enters the mantle cavity in the neck region between the mantle and head. When the mantle cavity is filled by the inhalant current, the longitudinal muscles relax, the circular muscles contract, draw the mantle margin tightly around the neck, and expel the water through the funnel. The snugness of the collar around the neck is furthered by mantle cartilage knobs that fit into sockets near the head (Fig. 26-54). As the water is expelled in one direction from the ventral funnel, the animal is propelled in the opposite direction. The funnel can be

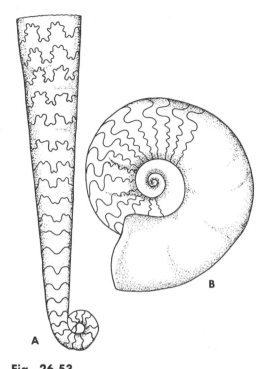

Fig. 26-53

Suture patterns in ammonoid shells. **A,** *Baculites*. **B,** *Ceratites*.

turned either forward or backward so that the animal can go in either direction. The body is stabilized during movement by lateral fins when such are present. Some animals perform slow swimming movements with their fins. Differentiated movements by jet propulsion are controlled by the force with which water is expelled from the mantle cavity.

In *Nautilus* the mantle is thin and plays no part in movement. Water is expelled from the funnel in these forms by drawing the body into the shell and contracting the funnel. The *Nautilus* shell is kept upright by the gas-filled chambers within it. Movement is slower because of the hindrance of the large shell.

Octopuses are more adapted for crawling and walking than for active swimming. They have no fins and their jet propulsion movements are jerky. They use their arms, which are provided with suction disks, to anchor and pull themselves along. Their movements in pursuing prey or escaping from enemies are skillfully and swiftly executed.

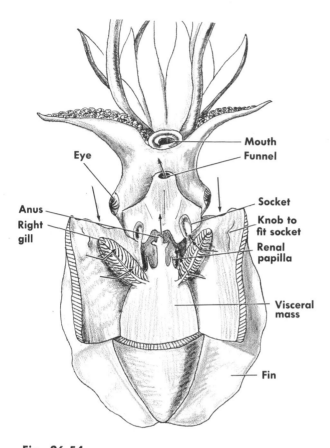

Fig. 26-54

Sepia, a cuttlefish. Arrows indicate direction of water current in mantle cavity.

As the water circulates through the mantle cavity, it provides power for movement and oxygen for the gills. *Nautilus* has four gills (ctenidia), and the dibranchs only two. The gills are featherlike, consisting of a central axis with numerous side filaments. Cilia are absent from the gills because nautiluses are not filter feeders, and the removal of sediment in such pelagic forms is no problem. Since the funnel is ventral, the exhalant current is ventral to the inhalant current—the reverse of that found in most other mollusks. Respiration may occur through the body surface in some cephalopods with vestigial gills.

INTERNAL ANATOMY

Dibranchs have an internal cartilaginous skeleton in the form of cartilage plates that are found around the brain, in the neck

region, at the base of the fin, in the gills, and often in the arms. In *Nautilus* the cartilaginous skeleton is not so prominent, although it does offer some cartilage support.

The digestive system (Fig. 26-55) is mainly a U-shaped tube that runs from the mouth to the anus, which opens into the mantle cavity near the siphon. The tract consists of a pair of chitinous jaws, a typical mollusk radula (Fig. 26-55, *B, C*), two pairs of salivary glands, a long esophagus, a stomach, a spiral cecum, an intestine, and a rectum. The jaws are located in the buccal mass in the center of the ring of arms. Modifications of the tract are found among the various groups of cephalopods. A crop or expanded portion of the esophagus occurs in the Octopoda. Some deep-sea forms lack a radula. Two pairs of salivary glands open into the buccal mass, except in *Nautilus.* The posterior pair of salivary glands opens by ducts just behind the lower jaw and often contains a poisonous secretion which is injected into the prey when seized. The muscular, nonglandular stomach has a spiral cecum attached near its anterior end. This unique organ is provided with a ciliary mechanism that removes solid particles from the cecal contents so that only fluid products are absorbed. The solid particles are carried back into the stomach and into the intestine by a cilated groove. The digestive gland is made up of two parts, a solid bilobed liver and a smaller spongy pancreas. Both parts of the digestive gland open by a common duct, which may be single or paired, into the cecum. In *Sepia* the liver portion of the digestive gland is paired. Enzymes from both the liver and pancreas are poured into the stomach when food is present there. Digestion, which is wholly extracellular, starts in the stomach and is completed in the cecum. Some absorption occurs in the intestine as well as in the cecum. The intestine discharges its waste into the mantle cavity through the anus.

A diverticulum of the intestine is located near the anus and forms the characteristic ink sac (absent in *Nautilus*) (Fig. 26-55). Its duct opens into the rectum behind the anus. The ink sac secretes a dark fluid of melanin pigment. Recent work on octopuses indicates that these animals when threatened by a predator (e.g., moray eel)

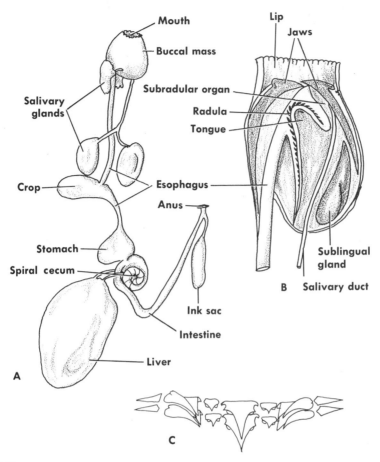

Fig. 26-55

Digestive system of *Eledone,* an octopod cuttlefish. **A,** Alimentary canal, ventral view; crop is turned to right, buccal mass to left, and liver forward. **B,** Buccal mass showing radula. **C,** Two rows of teeth from radula. (Redrawn from Isgrove: Eledone, L.M.B.C. Memoirs XVIII, Williams & Norgate, Ltd.)

give off a smoke screen of sepia that assumes roughly the shape of a large animal. Behind this screen the octopus takes off at right angles to its original direction. A product of the ink secretion is also thought to deaden the sense of smell of potential enemies.

Cephalopods are entirely carnivorous, feeding upon crustaceans, fishes, and even their own kind. The prey is seized by the suckers or clawlike hooks of the arms. The food is then bitten into pieces by the jaws and passed down the digestive tract to the stomach.

Squids have ten arms. Two from the dorsal side are much longer than the other eight and are called tentacles (Fig. 26-56).

The arms bear on their flattened inner surface many cup-shaped adhesive suckers, which are located on short stalks. Horny rims are often found around the suction cups for reinforcements. Muscle fibers in the floor of the cups can produce a suction effect on the seized object. The two longer tentacles have suckers only at the flattened ends and are mainly responsible for the active seizing of prey. Octopuses have only eight arms, all of which are equal in length. Their suckers are sessile and lack horny rims and hooks.

Nautilus has four kidneys, while the Dibranchia have only two. The kidneys are compact, spongy, saclike structures, each of which surrounds a large vein (Fig. 26-

Fig. 26-56

Loligo, dorsal view of preserved specimen. (From Hickman: Integrated principles of zoology, The C. V. Mosby Co.)

57). Within the outer wall of each kidney is the long renopericardial canal, which opens posteriorly into the visceropericardial cavity and anteriorly into the kidney cavity close to the renal papillae. Near the anus the nephridiopore or renal papilla of each nephridium opens into the mantle cavity. Excretory tissue around the vein selects waste from the blood and carries it to the kidney cavity. Nitrogenous waste is excreted by the kidneys mainly in the form of uric acid. The two kidneys (Decapoda) are connected anteriorly and usually communicate with each other. In *Nautilus* the four nephridia have no communication with each other or with the pericardium.

The circulatory system is mostly of the efficient closed type, except in *Nautilus,* where a great part of it is of the primitive lacunar type. The system consists of closed vessels and three hearts, two branchial and one systemic (Fig. 26-57). The systemic heart consists of a median ventricle and two lateral auricles. An anterior and a posterior aorta carry blood pumped by the ventricle to the various parts of the body. Blood is returned from the head by way of the vena cava which divides into two branches (branchial veins) near the kidney. Each branchial vein runs through a kidney to a branchial heart located at the base of a gill. The muscular branchial hearts facili-

tate unoxygenated blood flow through the capillaries of the gill. Oxygenated blood from the gills is returned to the auricles, which then pass the blood to the ventricle. The right branchial vein also receives blood from veins coming from the ink sac and gonads, while each of the branchial hearts receives blood from the mantle and abdominal veins.

The blood contains the respiratory pigment hemocyanin characteristic of the mollusks. Venous blood is blue in color, but becomes colorless when oxygenated.

The brain of cephalopods is the most complex among the invertebrates. It is made up of cerebral, branchial, pedal, and visceral ganglia, which are fused to form a ring around the esophagus (Fig. 26-58). Localized regions have been detected in the various ganglia so that certain areas or centers are linked with definite functions. Only a few ganglia lie outside the brain. Around the brain is a sort of skull in the form of cartilagelike tissues. The large cerebral ganglia make up the part of the brain lying above the esophagus. From them a pair of buccal nerves passes by way of the paired superior buccal ganglia and commissures around the esophagus to the paired inferior buccal ganglia just behind the buccal mass. From each side of the cerebral ganglia an optic nerve extends to the well-developed eye. The funnel is supplied with nerves from the infundibular center, and the tentacles by nerves from the branchial center of the pedal ganglia. The visceral ganglia have many centers that

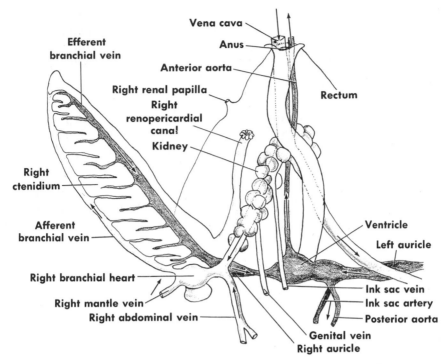

Fig. 26-57

Circulatory system in *Sepia* showing right gill, right gill heart, and systemic heart.

give off nerves to the gills, sympathetic nerves to the stomach, and a pair of large nerves to the mantle. Branchial and gastric ganglia have centers associated with localized functions in the organs they innervate.

In the mantle nerves are giant motor neurons that are involved in the rapid locomotion of such forms as the squids. These fibers are absent in the giant squid *Architeuthis* and are best developed in *Ommastrephes*. The giant fiber system of cephalopods involves a pair of giant cells in the visceral ganglia of the brain, processes from these cells that make synapse in the visceral part of the brain, and giant neurons that pass to the stellate or mantle ganglia where they synapse with other giant fibers. From the stellate ganglion, located anterior to each gill, many nerves containing giant axons, each made up of the fusion of processes from many stellate ganglionic cells, pass to the mantle. A single giant fiber may reach a diameter of 800 microns. Nerve impulses in the giant fiber are very rapid and ensure a quick contraction of the mantle in jet propulsion.

The best developed sense organs in cephalopods are the eyes, which are able to form images. They are similar in structure to the vertebrate type. The eye is provided with muscles for a limited amount of movement, a cornea, a lens suspended by a ciliary process, an iris diaphragm, a vitreous humor, and a retina with photoreceptors directed toward the source of light, not away from it as in vertebrates (Fig. 26-59). Focusing is performed by moving the lens forward and backward, not by changing the shape of the lens. Photoreceptors are connected to retinal cells which send processes to an optic ganglion at the outer ends of the optic nerve. The eye of *Nautilus* is of the pinhole camera type, with the optic cavity opened to the exterior (Fig. 26-60).

Other cephalopod sense organs are represented by statocysts on each side of the brain as well as tactile and chemoreceptor cells on the tentacles.

The sexes are separate in cephalopods; and sexual dimorphism, when it occurs, is chiefly a matter of size. Most males are dis-

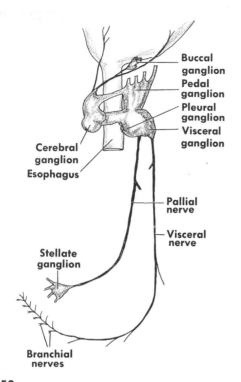

Fig. 26-58

Central nervous system of *Octopus,* from right side. (Modified from Lankester.)

tinguished by having one or more arms modified as copulatory organs; some males have longer prolongations of fins than females. The ovaries or testes are specialized parts of the coelomic wall and are located at the posterior end of the body.

The female system, which is simpler than that of the male, consists of a single, saccular ovary and a single (paired in *Octopus*) looped oviduct that opens into the mantle cavity. At the terminal end of the oviduct is an oviducal gland that furnishes part of the egg capsule. The eggs are fairly large (up to 15 mm. in diameter) and provided with a great deal of yolk. In the ovary the eggs are nourished by follicle cells that are derived from the peritoneum. After passing through the oviduct the eggs are covered by membranes from the oviducal gland and from the nidamental gland, which opens independently of the oviduct into the mantle cavity.

The male system (Fig. 26-61) consists of a saccular testis and a much-coiled sperm duct modified to form a seminal vesicle, a prostate gland joined to the seminal vesicle, and a storage reservoir (Needham's sac). Needham's sac opens into the left side of the mantle cavity. Sperm are produced in the wall of the testis, pass into the genital coelom, and

Fig. 26-59

Section through eyes of *Loligo.*

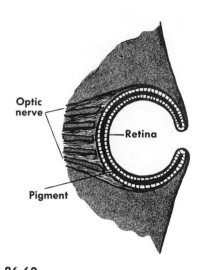

Fig. 26-60

Section through eye of *Nautilus*. (From Hickman: Integrated principles of zoology, The C. V. Mosby Co.)

enter the sperm duct through a small ciliated opening. In the seminal vesicle the sperm are encased or packed into the complicated spermatophores. From the seminal vesicle the spermatophores pass into the large Needham's sac where they are stored until copulation occurs. A spermatophore is an elongated structure, consisting of a sperm tube, a cement sac, a coiled ejaculatory apparatus, a cap, and an outer sheath with a terminal filament. It may attain a length of several inches although it is usually smaller.

In copulation the male makes use of a modified arm for the transference of spermatophores to the female (Figs. 26-61, 26-62). This arm, formerly thought to be a parasite, is called a hectocotylus ("the arm of a hundred suckers"). The arm modified for this purpose is the right or left fourth arm in squids (Fig. 26-61, *B*) and the right third arm in octopuses (Fig. 26-62, *A*). It varies in length and structure in different species. In some octopuses it may exceed 16 inches. When not in use the arm is coiled in a saclike sheath. Structural modifications usually involve some sort of groove with small suckers or a terminal depression or cavity. In the actual process of sperm transference the male withdraws a bundle of spermatophores from Needham's sac with his hectocotylus (Fig. 26-61, *B*),

which he then inserts into the mantle cavity of the female or into a fold (seminal receptacle) near the mouth (*Loligo*). In most species the spermatophores are deposited near the openings of the oviduct. The hectocotylus arm is completely detached and left in the mantle cavity of the female. Some cephalopods (*Vampyroteuthis*) have no hectocotylus. When the spermatophores are picked up by the hectocotylus, the cap is removed and the ejaculatory apparatus is loosened.

After deposition the spermatophores adhere to the seminal receptacles or the mantle walls. They can be discharged by mechanical pressure on the terminal filament or by imbibition of water. This results in an inversion of the ejaculatory apparatus, a process that pulls the sperm tube forward and releases the sperm. The sperm are activated by the sea water and are ready for fertilization, which may occur in the mantle or in the egg mass held by the arms.

The female grasps the strings of fertilized eggs as they emerge from her funnel and attaches them to a substratum in clusters of elongated capsules, each containing 50 to 100 eggs (Fig. 26-61, *C*). The gelatinous egg capsules absorb water and swell to several times their original size, forming what are called "deadman's fingers" (Figs. 26-61, *D*, 26-62, *B*). At the time of spawning the cephalopods are gregarious and often deposit their eggs in a common area. The primitive *Nautilus* has four tentacles modified as copulatory organs, and its eggs are laid singly on a substratum. *Vampyroteuthis* simply releases its eggs into the sea. The female of the paper nautilus (*Argonauta*) secretes a thin shell by means of two membranes on the dorsal pair of arms; in it, she lives and incubates her eggs. The smaller male without its own shell often lives in the shell with her. In some cases after the eggs have been deposited they are brooded over by the female (*Octopus*).

Development

The eggs of cephalopods contain a great deal of yolk and are telolecithal. Cleavage is, therefore, incomplete and restricted to one end of the egg (animal pole) (Fig. 26-61, *E*). This causes the embryo to be placed at one end with the ectoderm spread over

543

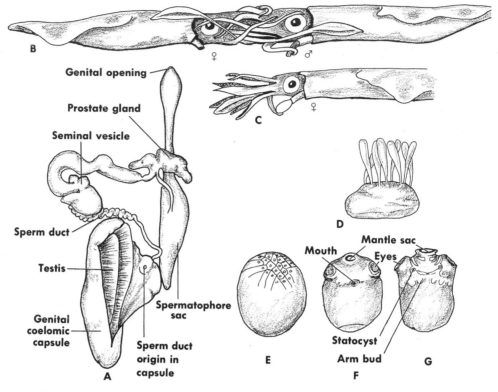

Fig. 26-61

A, Male reproductive organs of *Loligo*. B, *Loligo* in copulation. Male grasps spermatophores as they emerge through his funnel (as shown) and thrusts them between ventral arms of female where sperm reservoirs become attached to depression in buccal membrane. In another copulatory position, male inserts spermatophore into female's mantle chamber near end of oviduct. C, Female reaching for egg string as it emerges from funnel. D, Several egg strings attached to rock by female. E to G, Early cleavage and larval stages of *Loligo*. (A after Duvernoy; modified from Lankester; B to D modified from Drew.)

a large mass of yolk, forming a yolk sac. When the mouth is first formed, it is not surrounded by arms; these develop posteriorly and later migrate forward during development and encircle the mouth (Figs. 26-61, *F*, *G*, 26-62, *C*). The funnel is formed from double outgrowths, which remain separate in *Nautilus* but fuse in other cephalopods to form a single funnel. A trochophore or veliger stage is lacking; but eggs hatch into larvae, which at first may differ widely from adults in form. For a time the larvae may form a part of plankton populations. Embryologic development varies among cephalopods, but in every case it differs from that of other mollusks. In only a few cephalopods has it been completely explained.

Ecology

Cephalopods are exclusively marine forms and occupy most ecologic habitats, such as littoral, surface, pelagic, and abyssal. They are absent from brackish and fresh water and do not tolerate water of reduced salinity, although some are found in high salinity waters. The active squids are found mostly in the open sea, while the octopuses live in crevices along rocky shores. They have excellent protective devices against their potential enemies, mostly sperm whales and certain fish. In addition to the black secretions of their ink gland and their swift locomotion, they have remarkable powers to change colors.

The pigment cells are of two kinds, chromatophores and iridocytes, which are

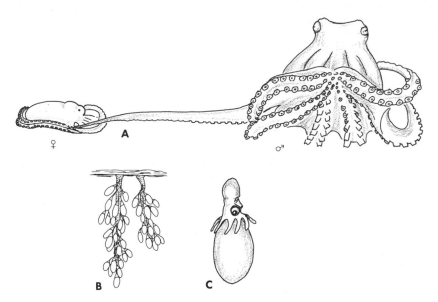

Fig. 26-62

A, Copulation in *Octopus.* Larger male uses third right hectocotylized arm to deposit spermatophores in mantle cavity of female in end of oviduct. **B,** Egg strings of cuttlefish *Eledone.* **C,** Unhatched embryo of *Eledone.* (**A** after Racovitza; redrawn from Lankester: Treatise on zoology, Adam & Charles Black, Ltd.; **B** and **C** modified from Isgrove.)

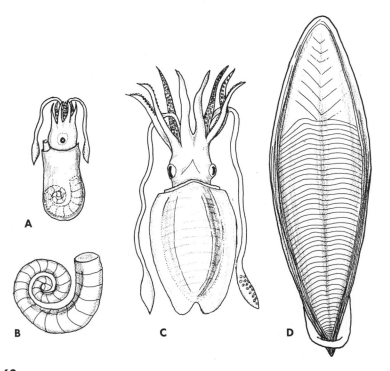

Fig. 26-63

A, *Spirula.* **B,** Internal shell of *Spirula.* **C,** *Sepia.* **D,** Internal shell (cuttlebone) of *Sepia.* (**A** and **B** modified from Cambridge Natural History; **C** and **D** modified from Lankester.)

found in the dermis. The method of changing color in the chromatophore has been described earlier. Pigment colors are represented by red, yellow, orange, red-brown, blue, violet, and black. Many cephalopods have a great variety of differently colored chromatophores. The ability of a chromatophore to change color is very rapid because of its quickness to contract and expand. Patterns of color often match the animal's surroundings in a highly effective way.

The cuttlefish (*Sepia*) is of special interest ecologically because of the buoyancy of its calcareous shell. The chambered shell (Fig. 26-63, *C, D*) is reminiscent of the great group of cephalopods that is now represented only by *Nautilus*. It has been demonstrated that the cuttlefish can vary its specific gravity by varying the proportions of liquid and gas in the cuttlebone. By pumping liquid out of the cuttlebone the cuttlefish increases its volume of gas space and becomes less dense. It becomes more dense by pumping liquid in again. A special membrane at the posterior ends of the cuttlebone chambers seems to be responsible for pumping the liquid in and out. The gas, mostly nitrogen, always retains its pressure of about 4/5 atmosphere at all depths. The cuttlefish can change depth by regulating the osmotic pressure difference between cuttlebone liquid and the blood; and it can reestablish as needed an equilibrium between the hydrostatic pressure of the sea and the osmotic difference that keeps the sea water from entering the cuttlebone. *Spirula*, which lives at much greater depths, uses its shell device in the same way (Fig. 26-63, *A, B*).

Annotated references

Abbott, R. T. 1954. American sea shells. Princeton, D. Van Nostrand Co., Inc. *More than a thousand marine shells are described in this semipopular treatise.*

Beadle, L. C., and J. B. Cragg. 1940. Studies on adaptation to salinity in *Gammarus* spp., part 1. Regulation of blood and tissues and the problem of adaptation to fresh water. J. Exp. Biol. **17**: 153-163.

Bidder, A. M. 1950. Digestive mechanism of European squids. Quart. J. Micr. Sci. **91**:1-43.

Carriker, M. R. 1959. Comparative functional morphology of the drilling mechanism in *Urosalopinx* and *Eupleura*. Proceedings of the 15th International Congress of Zoology, London. *This author describes how these forms bore their way into the shells of mollusks.*

Coe, W. R. 1942. Influence of natural and experimental conditions in determining shape of shell and rate of growth in gastropods of the genus *Crepidula*. J. Morphol. **71**:35-47.

Dakin, W. J. 1912. Buccinum (the whelk). L.M.B.C. Memoirs. London, Williams & Norgate, Ltd. *A technical treatise with numerous detailed illustrations.*

Davis, J. R. A., and H. J. Fleure. 1903. *Patella* (the common limpet). L.M.B.C. Memoirs. London, Williams & Norgate, Ltd. *A general description of the adult structures of the limpet and its development; well illustrated.*

Dehnel, P. A. 1955. Rates of growth of gastropods as a function of latitude. Physiol. Zool. **28**:115-144. *This paper shows how northern populations grow faster than southern ones at the same temperature. The author was one of the first to point out how poikilotherms vary physiologically with latitude at the interspecific and intraspecific level.*

Drew, G. A. 1911. Sexual activities of the squid. J. Morphol. **22**:327-359.

Eales, N. B. 1921. Aplysia. L.M.B.C. Memoirs. Liverpool, University Press of Liverpool.

Edmondson, W. T. (editor). 1959. Ward and Whipple's fresh-water biology, ed. 2. New York, John Wiley & Sons, Inc. *Keys are given of the freshwater mollusks of the United States.*

Evans, R. G. 1948. The lethal temperatures of some common British littoral molluscs. J. Anim. Ecol. **17**:165-173.

Fretter, V. 1937. The structure and function of the alimentary canal of some species of Polyplacophora, part 1. Trans. Roy. Soc. Edinburgh **59**:119-164. *A detailed description of the structure and physiology of the digestive tube in chitons.*

Graham, A. 1949. The molluscan stomach, part 3. Trans. Roy. Soc. Edinburgh **61**:737-778. *An especially fine treatise on the comparative morphology and histology of the complicated molluscan stomach.*

Gutsell, J. S. 1931. Natural history of the bay scallop. Bull. U. S. Bur. Fish. **46**:569-632.

Haas, F. Bivalvia (Pelecypoda). In Bronn, H. G. (editor). 1929-1935. Klassen und Ordnungen des Tierreichs, vol. 3, part 1. Leipzig, Akademische Verlagsgesellschaft. *One of the most comprehensive treatises ever published on this group of mollusks.*

Isgrove, A. 1909. Eledone. L.M.B.C. Memoirs. London, Williams & Norgate, Ltd.

Johnstone, J. 1899. Cardium. L.M.B.C. Memoirs. Liverpool, T. Dobb and Co.

Keen, A. M. 1963. Marine molluscan genera of western North America. Stanford, Stanford University Press. *An up-to-date systematic account of the mollusks in the western part of our continent.*

Lemche, H. 1957. A new living deep-sea mollusc of the Cambro-Devonian class Monoplacophora. Nature (London) **179**:413-416. *A description of the newly found* Neopilina, *a mollusk with internal segmentation.*

MacBride, E. W. 1914. Textbook of embryology; Invertebrata, vol. 1. London, The Macmillan Company.

MacGinitie, G. E., and N. MacGinitie. 1949. Natural history of marine animals. New York, McGraw-Hill Book Company. *A large section of this popular book is devoted to the mollusks of the Pacific coast.*

Moore, R. C., C. G. Lalicker, and A. G. Fischer. 1952. Invertebrate fossils. New York, McGraw-Hill Book Company. *About 200 pages are devoted to the mollusks in this excellent treatise on paleontology; well illustrated.*

Morton, J. E. 1960. Function of the gut in ciliary feeders. Biol. Rev. **35**:92-139. *An up-to-date treatise on this method of feeding in the different groups of animals. The author points out the convergent resemblances that have arisen because of similar problems facing animals which use this method. An excellent and comprehensive account is devoted to ciliary feeding in Mollusca, where this method reaches its greater complexity.*

Pelseneer, P. Mollusca. In Lankester, E. R. (editor). 1906. Treatise on zoology. vol. 5. London, Adam & Charles Black, Ltd. *In many respects this treatise will never become out of date.*

Pennak, R. W. 1953. Fresh-water invertebrates of the United States. New York, The Ronald Press Company. *Freshwater mollusks are discussed and keyed.*

Pilsbry, H. A. 1930. Land mollusks of North America (north of Mexico): Monograph 3, vol. 1, parts 1 and 2. Philadelphia, Academy of Natural Sciences. *The most important work on the land snails of North America.*

Raven, C. P. 1958. Morphogenesis; the analysis of molluscan development. New York, Pergamon Press, Inc. *This monograph is of great value in understanding the embryology of the mollusks. Extensive bibliography.*

Robin, G. C. 1932. A monograph of the recent Cephalopoda, 2 vols. London, The British Museum. *An outstanding account of this group.*

Runham, N. W. 1963. A study of the replacement mechanism of the pulmonate radula. Quart. J. Micr. Sci. **104**:271-277.

Segar, E. 1961. Acclimation in mollusks. Am. Zool. **1**:235-244.

Thiele, G. Solenogastres, Mollusca. In Kukenthal, W. and T. Krumbach (editors). 1924. Handbuch der Zoologie, vol. 5, pp. 1-256. Berlin, Walter De Gruyter & Co. *A complete account of this group.*

Wells, M. J. 1962. Brain and behavior in cephalopods. Stanford, Stanford University Press. *A fascinating study of this highly developed group of invertebrates.*

Wilbur, K. M., and C. M. Yonge (editors). 1964. The physiology of Mollusca, vol. 1. New York, Academic Press Inc. *This volume and a projected second one represent the most important recent treatise on mollusks.*

Yonge, C. M. 1932. The crystalline style of the Mollusca. Sci. Progr. **26**:643-653. *In this and other papers one of the greatest students of mollusks analyzes the functional aspects of molluscan structures.*

Young, J. Z. 1961. Learning and discrimination in the octopus. Biol. Rev. **36**:32-96. *An analysis of the learning ability of a form that is near the peak of learning capacity among the invertebrates.*

Phylum Echinodermata

This great group contains such familiar marine forms as sea stars, sea urchins, brittlestars, sea cucumbers, and sea lilies. The name means "spiny-skinned," which refers to the projecting spines or tubercles that give a rough, warty appearance to the surface of most echinoderms. Their morphologic organization is unique in the animal kingdom, and their structural peculiarities tend to separate them from all other phyla. However, they have certain basic structures that give them high ranking in the evolutionary pattern of the animal kingdom. Of all invertebrate groups, they are placed the closest to the chordates and represent the most advanced of the invertebrate phyla within the Deuterostomia, to which the chordates belong.

The primitive characteristic of radial symmetry is misleading because echinoderms do not belong to the Radiata (sponges, coelenterates, and ctenophores). Their primitive bilateral symmetry, which is characteristic of both fossil and living forms at certain stages, is more or less hidden by their adult radial symmetry because of their fivefold organization. Their pentamerous radial symmetry, with the body divided into five parts around a central axis, represents one of their most basic characteristics.

Other distinctive characteristics of echinoderms are an internal skeleton of numerous crystalline calcite plates and a water-vascular system of fluid-filled vessels and surface appendages or hollow tentacles. In some respects their physiologic processes are very simple because they have no head, no excretory system, no methods of copulation, and no internal fertilization. Many of their body systems, such as the respiratory, reproductive, circulatory, and nervous systems, are organized on a simple plan.

The fossil record of echinoderms is impressive, for it extends back to the early Cambrian period. During this time many structural patterns evolved, some of which were quite different from those of existing groups. Most echinoderm fossils that have been recovered were laid down in shallow sea deposits. There seems to be no doubt, however, that echinoderms were also laid down in deep-sea deposits that are unknown at present. Modern echinoderms have been dredged from great depths in recent times. From the Ordovician period, fossils of all the major classes of echinoderms, except holothurians, have been found. The earliest fossils were the stem-bearing echinoderms (Fig. 27-1, C, D), such as crinoids, most classes of which did not survive beyond the Mesozoic era. Fossils of the free-moving echinoderms are more common in later geologic formations. Echinoderms are well adapted for preservation as fossils because of their calcareous hard parts.

No other invertebrates surpass the echinoderms in the complexity of their skeleton, which has been responsible for an enormous range in their variations. The outstanding basic characteristic of the phylum, from the earliest fossils to present-

Fig. 27-1

Some fossil echinoderms. **A,** Heart urchins (spatangoids), past and present. Left, fossil type (from Florida) known from Eocene to Recent times; right, *Moira atropus,* present-day heart urchin that lives on our eastern shores. **B,** Devonian asteroid *Roemeraster,* Germany. **C,** Mississippian crinoid *Onychocrinus,* Indiana. **D,** Fossil crinoid stems.

day species, is their crystalline, calcareous endoskeleton. Each element of the skeleton consists of calcium carbonate laid down in the form of a fine honeycomb of crystalline calcite. All skeletal parts of ossicles, spines, and plates have this lattice arrangement of calcite crystals, each being a crystallographic unit. Interspersed through this lattice arrangement is the soft organic material that is replaced by calcite during fossil formation. Ossicles or plates may articulate with each other, or they may be fused to form a rigid test.

Many higher echinoderm taxa, including classes, are wholly extinct; others are represented by only a few modern types. It is customary to include these extinct echinoderms along with existing forms in many classifications of echinoderms because extinct groups may shed light on the phylogeny of present ones.

Except for a few planktonic forms, echinoderms are mostly bottom dwellers. They are strictly marine, and none is adapted to fresh water. Only a few are found in brackish water. In the ocean they are found in almost every conceivable habitat—in all depths and at all latitudes. Many are found in muddy bottoms (holothurians and echinoids), obtaining their organic food from the mud passed through their digestive tracts. Other echinoderms are found in sandy or rocky bottoms. Still others (asteroids and ophiuroids) are commonly found in littoral zones and also in fairly deep waters. In general, echinoderms are sluggish animals. The most rapid among them are the ophiuroids. Echinoderms range in size from less than 1 inch to 2 or 3 feet in diameter. Fossil forms were often much larger.

About 5,700 species of present-day echinoderms are recognized. Of the fossil echinoderms more than 5,000 crinoid fossil species have been found, in comparison with 600 to 650 living species of that class. The eleutherozoans are more numerous and varied today than those represented by the fossil record. Of the free-moving forms the echinoids make up more fossil species than all the other classes combined because of the rigid construction of their skeletons.

CLASSIFICATION OF EXISTING ECHINODERMS

Taxonomy is always in the process of revision, and the taxonomy of echinoderms is no exception to this rule. The fossil record has proved invaluable in showing the relationship of certain echinoderm groups. For instance, the sea stars and brittle stars are now known to be so closely related that many authorities place them together as subclasses in one class. Only the existing classes are represented in this scheme; some characteristic orders will be mentioned in the description of each class.

Phylum Echinodermata. Body of pentamerous radial symmetry, enterocoelous coelomate; bilateral symmetry as larvae; body usually of five ambulacra that bear tube feet (podia), alternating with interambulacra around an oral-aboral axis; calcareous endoskeleton of separate plates usually bearing spines; jawed pedicellariae (in some); coelomic canals forming a water-vascular system with projections to the exterior (tube feet or podia); definite head and brain absent; dioecious; external fertilization; entirely marine.

Subphylum Eleutherozoa. Free living and stemless; mouth usually downward and at middle of lower surface or at one side; mouth and anus (absent in some) usually at opposite ends of body; body globular, cylindric, or star shaped; mostly pentamerous organization; water-vascular system usually of tube feet with ampullae fitted for locomotion; chief nervous system oral; marine in all seas.

  Class Asterozoa. Body star shaped and dorsoventrally flattened; ambulacral canals open on oral surface, or closed by endoskeletal plates; tube feet restricted to lower surface of body; rays (five or more) merging gradually with central disk or sharply set off; madreporite in integument; anus present or absent.

  Subclass Asteroidea. Body star shaped or pentagonal; rays, five or more, not sharply set off from central disk; open ambulacral grooves on oral surface; tube feet with suckers; pedicellariae present. *Asterias* (Fig. 27-7), *Pteraster*, *Astropecten*.

  Subclass Ophiuroidea. Body flat and pentamerous; arms long and slender, sharply set off from central disk; ambulacral grooves absent or covered; intestine and anus absent; ceca of stomach usually do not extend into arms; tube feet without suckers; usually with ten genitorespiratory bursae projecting into interior between stomach outpouchings; no pedicellariae. *Ophiocoma, Amphipholis, Ophioderma.*

  Class Echinoidea. Body spheroidal, globular, or cordiform; endoskeleton in form of test of closely fitted plates arranged in ambulacral and interambulacral regions; ambulacral grooves covered; mouth usually centrally located with membranous peristome; anus with membranous periproct at or near the aboral pole; tube feet or podia with suckers extending through pores in ambulacral plates; body covered with movable spines; pedicellariae present. *Echinus, Strongylocentrotus* (Fig. 27-23, *B*), *Echinocardium.*

  Class Holothuroidea. Body elongated in the oral-aboral axis with secondary bilateral symmetry; ambulacral and interambulacral regions arranged meridionally around axis; side of body lying on substratum; endoskeleton reduced to microscopic ossicles embedded in body wall; ambulacral grooves covered; tube feet around mouth in form of tentacles; tube feet usually provided with suckers; spines and pedicellariae lacking. *Cucumaria, Thyone* (Fig. 27-35, *A*), *Holothuria.*

Subphylum Pelmatozoa. Sessile and usually stalked; oral surface directed upward with both oral and anal apertures; body with test of calcareous plates; ambulacra as food grooves usually extended into arms; tube feet chiefly food collecting.

  Class Crinoidea. Body may be attached by a stalk, but usually stalkless and free moving; theca formed into aboral, cup-shaped calyx; arms mostly branched and pentamerously arranged; ambulacra open; arms with or without pinnules; tube feet without suckers; madreporite, spines, and pedicellariae absent. *Neometra, Antedon* (Fig. 27-42), *Ptilocrinus.*

BASIC ADAPTIVE FEATURES

The two basic structural features that have guided the evolutionary divergence of the echinoderms more than any others are their endoskeleton and their water-vascular system. Echinoderms are primarily bottom-dwelling forms, and their adaptations have largely conformed to the requirements of such an ecologic existence. Within this sphere of activity they have exploited those adaptations that best meet the requirements of a sessile or sluggish mode of life. Their radiate type of symmetry, characteristic generally of all existing echinoderms, is not an original feature of the group. Some of the fossil forms had no radial symmetry, and others had a blending of bilateral and radial symmetry. All larval stages have bilateral symmetry. Whatever the primordial ancestor may have been like, the typical echinoderm form as we know it is an outcome of adaptations to a sessile, benthonic existence, and its basic morphologic structure has restricted its evolutionary divergence within the limits of such a pattern.

The one unique character shared by all echinoderms, both fossil and living, is their endoskeleton, which has the same basic structure in all instances. Each skeletal plate, or ossicle, is composed of a crystalline calcite, which is formed by the fusion of calcite spicules secreted by the stroma, or connective tissue matrix. The fenestrated or lattice structure of a plate is filled in life with the living stroma. The arrangement of the plates varies in the different groups of echinoderms. They usually form either radiate or bilaterally symmetric rows. The tendency to secrete and arrange a calcareous endoskeleton has been an important factor in echinoderm evolution. In the fossil noncrinoid Pelmatozoa the skeletal plates formed a closely fitting, heavy theca; but in the later evolution of echinoderms there is a marked tendency to reduce the endoskeleton in the interests of flexibility and mobility. This tendency is first evident in the crinoids, which have a flexible tegmen, or covering, of the oral disk replacing part of the theca. The strictly sessile nature of early echinoderms may have caused the protective demands of an endoskeleton to be overdone. Among the modern echinoderms only the echinoids have retained a test, while at the other extreme the holothurians have only calcite spicules scattered through the dermis.

The other basic adaptive feature, a water-vascular system, is a morphologic structure which the fossil record shows appeared early in echinoderm evolution. The original pattern may have been quite similar to that found in living crinoids today. This pattern usually consists of five ciliated oral grooves, each with a radial canal of the water-vascular system underneath. From this canal, podia or tube feet are given off as hollow projections of the body wall and lie along the margins of the food grooves. Here the podia provide a food-catching mechanism. Microscopic organisms captured by the podia are passed along the food grooves by a mucus-ciliary movement to the mouth. The open groove pattern is retained in the Eleutherozoa by the asteroids, but in the other freely movable classes the food grooves are closed to the exterior. It is clear that the podia were first concerned with food-getting, respiration, and sensory functions, although in the asteroids and echinoids they have acquired the secondary adaptation of locomotion. In the ophiuroids the podia have the original food-getting and sensory functions. The assumption of locomotor functions has made changes in the podia. Ampullae connected to the podia by pores through the endoskeleton furnished hydrostatic pressure. When the ambulacral grooves were closed and the podia became locomotor, filter feeding could no longer occur, and other methods of feeding had to be evolved.

PHYLOGENY AND EVOLUTION

It is not known from what group the echinoderms arose. Although their fossil record is outstanding, it throws no light on the nature of the first ancestor. Echinoderms are enterocoelous coelomate animals and belong to the Deuterostomia, the various groups of which may have sprung independently from coelenterate ancestors. The evolution and phylogeny of most major groups, however, have to be taken on trust without direct evidence to support them. By combining the evidence from many disciplines, such as anatomy, paleontology, and embryology, zoologists have tried to reconstruct a hypothetical ancestor of echinoderms that would help explain their basic characteristics. The similar embryonic development of the various echinoderms is widely employed to formulate an ancestral concept that would meet those requirements. Two such hypothetical echinoderm ancestors have been proposed by students

551

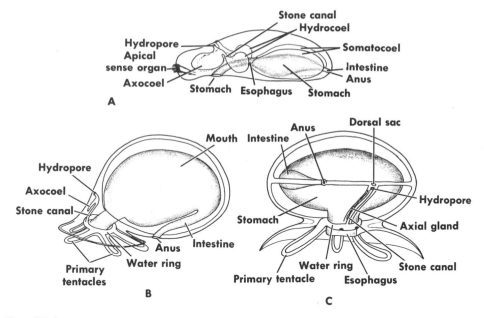

Fig. 27-2

Theories of echinoderm phylogeny. **A,** Dipleurula ancestor. **B,** Early bilateral pentactula ancestor. **C,** Later pentactula ancestor after assumption of radial condition. (**A** modified from Bather; **B** and **C** after Bury, from Hyman: The invertebrates; Echinodermata, McGraw-Hill Book Company.)

of the group—the dipleurula and the pentactula.

F. A. Bather, who wrote the classic account of echinoderms in Lankester's well-known *Treatise on Zoology,* developed the dipleurula concept. He considered such an ancestor as a bilateral, humpbacked, vermiform animal with a preoral lobe, a ventral anterior mouth, and a posterior anus (Fig. 27-2, *A*). On each side of the digestive tube were three coelomic sacs. These paired coelomic compartments were called the axocoels, hydrocoels, and somatocoels; and they correspond to the general adult terms "protocoel," "mesocoel," and "metacoel." Only the left axocoel and its dorsal pore (hydropore) persisted. The second pair of sacs, or hydrocoels, was connected to the first by the larval stone canal; and the third pair, or somatocoels, was independent. From these larval coelomic sacs there arose, by certain modifications, the coelomic sacs of the adult echinoderm condition. The water-vascular system is supposed to have arisen from three ciliated grooves in the mouth surface. Later two of these grooves

divided to form the characteristic five.

The pentactula concept is more commonly held by zoologists at present. According to this theory, the hypothetical ancestor had, in addition to the three pairs of coelomic sacs, a circlet of five tentacles around the mouth representing evaginations of the body wall and extensions of the two hydrocoels, or mesocoels (Fig. 27-2, *B*). From these tentacles the water-vascular system originated. The tentacles became connected around the mouth to a ring canal that opened to the surface by a stone canal and a hydroporic canal derived from the axocoel. The rest of the water-vascular system arose from the hydrocoels (mesocoels). From the side branches of the tentacles the podia or tube feet sprang, and along with them such accessory structures as radial nerves, hemal vessels, and food grooves. Possibly an endoskeleton of calcareous or cartilaginous plates evolved at this stage for the support of certain parts. Such a creature could crawl around in search of food. The real development of the echinoderm nature, however, revolves around a sessile existence at an early stage in their evolution. The evidence from embryologic development of existing echinoderms indicates that the pentactula became attached at the oral end where the mouth and sensory organs are located. As a logical consequence the animal assumed in time a shift of bodily structures in accordance with the radial symmetry of a sessile life (Fig. 27-2, *C*). The mouth and tentacles shifted to the left side, and the left hydrocoel became connected to the original right tentacles. A torsion of about 90 degrees in a clockwise direction caused the original left side to become the oral surface and the original right side to become the aboral surface. Since the shift of the right side to an aboral position deprived the coelomic sacs of their functions, the right axocoel (protocoel) and hydrocoel (mesocoel) degenerated. The passing of the mouth to the left side produced a curving of the left hydrocoel into a ring and the placing of the five tentacles around the mouth. The assumption of a true, pentamerous radial symmetry was perhaps a gradual one because some primitive echinoderms are not perfectly radially symmetric. The development of an endoskeleton for protection was also a logical outcome of a sessile existence. Attachment was made to a substratum by a stalk developed from the preoral region.

In the further evolution of the echinoderms some of the sessile forms became detached and assumed a free-moving life. Although they retained the radial symmetry, these forms brought the upper oral surface of the sessile pattern into contact with the substratum; and the aboral was shifted to an upper position. In this way the eleutherozoan classes may have evolved, although it is impossible to establish the direct relation of the eleutherozoans to their sessile ancestors by the fossil record. The free-moving radially symmetric existence has also tended to revert to a bilaterally symmetric one, as evidenced by such tendencies in sea cucumbers, sand dollars, and others.

Within the phylum, authorities are far from agreed on the relationships of the different classes. Larval similarities, which were formerly stressed, are now considered to be of doubtful validity. Convergent evolution is known to occur, and larval development among the different classes does not always coincide with the paleontologic record. Crinoids, the most primitive of existing echinoderms, cannot be related to any of the noncrinoid Pelmatozoa; nor is it possible to trace the origin of any other group to the crinoids. Just how the eleutherozoans arose from pelmatozoan ancestors is not known, but they may have derived from several different lines.

Holothurians have many primitive characteristics, such as the arrangement of the single gonad, hydropore, and gonopore and their reduced skeleton of microscopic calcareous bodies. They also show less radial symmetry than any other class of existing echinoderms, which some authorities think is an indication of a primitive feature inherited from the bilaterally symmetric ancestor. This pattern could have been secondarily acquired, however.

Although the larvae of ophiuroids and those of echinoids have a remarkable resemblance, the fossil record indicates that the ophiuroids and asteroids are closely related through a post-Cambrian ancestor, the extinct Somasteroidea, and are now placed in the same class (Asterozoa). That asterozoans and echinoids had a common ancestor is suggested by the general pattern of their skeleton. Of these, the asteroids appear to have had the more primitive structures, such as their attachment in early stages, open ambulacral groove, and arrangement of radial nerves and water canals.

The resemblance between the auricularia larva of holothurians and asteroids and the tornaria larva of enteropneusts (Hemichordata) has often been used as evidence of the relationship between the echinoderms and the chordates; but this evidence may well be questioned in the light of convergent larval evolution.

EMBRYOLOGY

Echinoderms have the radial and indeterminate cleavage characteristic of the deuterostomes. Eggs are mainly homolecithal and are fertilized in the sea water or in brood pouches. In radial cleavage the characteristic pattern is the formation of four equal blastomeres by two vertical cleavage planes (Fig. 27-16). The third

OPHIOPLUTEUS LARVA OF AN OPHIUROID (BRITTLE STAR)

BIPINNARIA LARVA OF AN ASTEROID (SEA STAR)

ECHINOPLUTEUS LARVA OF AN ECHINOID (SEA URCHIN)

AURICULARIA LARVA OF A HOLOTHUROID (SEA CUCUMBER)

DOLIOLARIA LARVA OF A CRINOID
No mouth or anus

Fig. 27-3

Larval types of different echinoderm classes. (From Hickman: Integrated principles of zoology, The C. V. Mosby Co.)

cleavage plane, horizontal and equatorial, divides the four blastomeres into eight equal blastomeres. The fourth cleavage plane is vertical and divides the embryo into 16 cells, eight of which are equal-sized mesomeres, four are small micromeres at the vegetal pole, and four are large macromeres. At the fifth cleavage, the blastomeres are divided about equally forming 32 cells. The succeeding cleavages are irregular, and the blastomeres do not all divide at the same time. As the blastomeres continue to divide, the blastula stage, a hollow sphere with a single layer of cells, occurs. By invagination at the center of the vegetal region a gastrula stage develops, with a narrow archenteron, or primitive gut. The blastopore, or a region near it, becomes the anus; and the mouth is formed by the breaking through of a stomodeum, a characteristic of the deuterostomes. Most cells of the archenteron are endodermal, but some mesodermal cells may also be found among them. The coelom is formed by outgrowth pockets or vesicles of the archenteron that separate and spread through the blastocoel. The cells of the coelomic walls are mesoderm. Such a method of mesoderm formation is described as enterocoelous, in contrast to the schizocoelous method of protostomes. The process of coelomic pouch formation varies among the different echinoderms, but eventually it gives rise to the three pairs of coelomic cavities that are called the axocoel (which opens dorsally by a hydropore), hydrocoel, and somatocoel. The mesenteries of the gut are formed by the meeting of the somatocoels above and below the gut. The free-swimming larva is bilateral and varies with the different classes. Among the eleutherozoans there are two well-marked larval types—the pluteus group with long arms and easel-shaped forms (ophiuroids and echinoids) and the auricularia group with barrel-shaped forms and lobe bands (holothurians and asteroids) (Fig. 27-3). A bipinnaria stage (Fig. 27-4) often follows the auricularia stage in asteroids. The ciliary bands, so characteristic of echinoderm larvae, have come from modifications and specializations of the cilia that are found on each of the blastomeres from the blastula stage on. These ciliary bands are for locomotion. The dolio-

Fig. 27-4

Bipinnaria larva. (Photograph by Roman Vishniac, courtesy Encyclopaedia Britannica Films, Inc.)

laria larva of crinoids has some of the characteristics of the auricularia larva, with its shape and ciliary bands, but it never feeds; it obtains all its nourishment during its brief swimming period from enteric yolk cells. After a planktonic existence as a free-swimming form the larva is transformed into an adult by a metamorphosis that varies with the different classes.

Subphylum Eleutherozoa
CLASS ASTEROZOA
Subclass Asteroidea

The familiar sea stars are star-shaped echinoderms composed of a central disk that merges gradually with the arms, of which there are typically five in number (but there may be more) (Fig. 27-5). They are also the only eleutherozoans that have open ambulacural grooves. These grooves are on the oral surface and are provided with two to four rows of locomotor podia (tube feet) with suckers and radial water canals on the outer side of the ambulacral plates.

Sea stars are usually brightly colored with carotenoid pigments that fade in most preservatives. They are found along the coasts of all the oceans and live in all types of bottoms, muddy, sandy, and rocky. A

Fig. 27-5

Some West coast asteroids. **A,** *Dermasterias.* **B,** *Pycnopodia.* **C,** *Pisaster.* (From Hickman: Integrated principles of zoology, The C. V. Mosby Co.)

few are found on sea algae. Several species occur at depths of 3 miles or more. They are most abundant and varied in tropical regions, especially coral reefs.

GENERAL MORPHOLOGIC FEATURES
EXTERNAL ANATOMY

Sea stars have a flattened, flexible body that is generally pentamerous in arrangement. Ciliated columnar epithelium with a thin cuticle covers the entire body (Fig. 27-6, *A*), and the body surface is rough be-

cause of projecting tubercles, spines, and ridges (Fig. 27-7). The mouth is located on the underside or oral surface in the center of the oral disk (Fig. 27-7, *B*). The upper or aboral surface bears the very small anus in the center of its disk (Fig. 27-7, *A*). At one side, between two of the arms, is the madreporite (Fig. 27-7, *A*), a small but conspicuous circular, grooved plate. Below each arm and lining the ambulacral groove are the two longitudinal series of ambulacral plates or ossicles, which meet in the midline (Fig. 27-8, *E*). They form a roof over the groove (Fig. 27-8, *A, G*) to protect the radial water vessel, the radial nerve, and podia. Along the margins of the grooves on each side are movable spines that can form a protective barrier over the grooves. Pincerlike pedicellariae of microscopic size are found on the skin or at the base of the spines (Fig. 27-6, *B, C, D*). These are protective in function. Six or seven major types are recognized and are useful in classification. Sea stars also have mucus gland cells in the epidermis (Fig. 27-6, *A*) that produce a gelatinous secretion for protection and cleansing. At the arm tip is the terminal tentacle (Fig. 27-7, *A*) with a red pigment spot where there are a number of ocelli. Most spines of the aboral surface are projections of the skeletal plates, but those on the oral side may articulate with their plates by a socket arrangement. Dermal gills or papulae, small delicate projections of the coelom, are scattered between the ossicles and function in respiration (Fig. 27-6, *D, E*).

Sea stars have a considerable size range. Some are not more than 1 cm. in greatest diameter; and others are almost a yard in diameter. Those species that have more than five rays tend to vary in the number of their rays.

INTERNAL ANATOMY

The endoskeleton (Fig. 27-8) consists of ossicles that have the characteristic crystalline calcite structure described in an earlier section. It is made up of a deep supporting part of calcareous plates bound together by connective tissue in the dermis of the body wall and a superficial part of spines and tubercles that project from or rest upon the ossicles of the deeper part. The super-

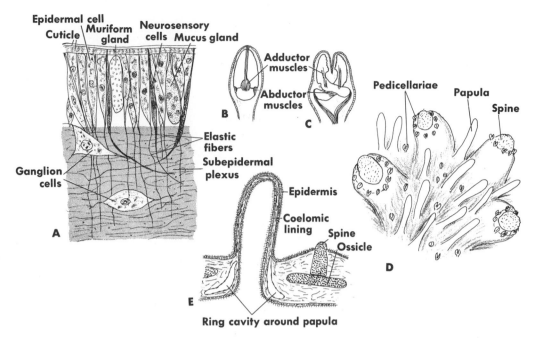

Fig. 27-6

A, Section through cuticle, epidermis, and underlying radial nerve of *Asterias*. B, Straight
forceps type of pedicellariae. C, Crossed scissors type of pedicellariae. D, Small portion of
aboral surface of live *Asterias* showing spines, papulae, and pedicellariae. E, Section through
papula (semidiagrammatic).

ficial part bears a thin covering of epidermis and dermis that is often worn off in
exposed places. The calcareous ossicles,
which make up the major part of the skeleton, may overlap or they may be further
apart. They are of various shapes and,
when bound together, form a closely knit or
reticulated skeleton with scattered spaces
for the emergence of papulae (Fig. 27-8,
B, D).

The body wall contains on its coelomic
side a thin muscular layer of outer circular
and inner longitudinal muscle fibers for
moving the arms. The ambulacral system
is provided with several muscles for manipulating its ossicles.

The water-vascular system follows the
general echinoderm pattern with certain
modifications. The system is derived from
parts of the coelomic sacs, and its canals
are lined with flagellated epithelium and
filled with fluid. In sea stars the system is
chiefly concerned with locomotion. The
canals are connected with sea water outside by means of a conspicuous madre-

porite located in an interradial position on
the aboral side (Fig. 27-7, A). It is a round
calcareous sieve plate with ciliated pores
located at the bottom of furrows (Fig.
27-9). Each pore leads into a pore canal, of
which there may be more than 200. The
pore canals unite to form collecting canals
that open into an ampulla beneath the
madreporite.

From the ampulla a vertical stone canal
(Figs. 27-9, 27-10, 27-12) passes in an oral
direction and opens into the water ring or
circular canal, which is located on the inner
side of the peristomial ring of ossicles
around the mouth region. The inner side
of the water ring gives rise interradially to
five pairs of small pouches called Tiedemann's bodies. One member of a pair may
be missing at the place where the stone
canal enters the ring, making a total of nine
Tiedemann's bodies (Fig. 27-10). In some
asteroids the ring canal also gives off interradially on its inner side one or more elongated polian vesicles suspended in the
coelom. The functions of the Tiedemann's

557

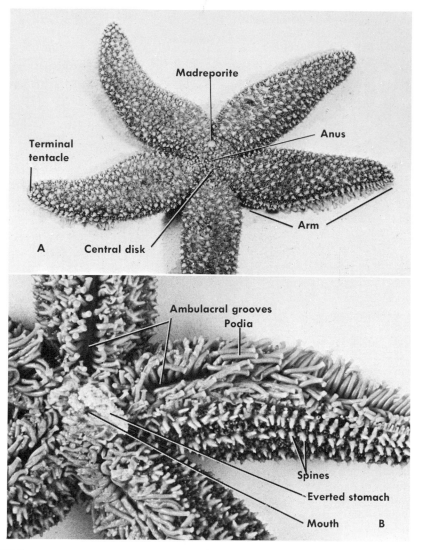

Fig. 27-7

A, Aboral view of sea star *Asterias*. B, Oral view of disk and arm of *Asterias*. (From Hickman: Integrated principles of zoology, The C. V. Mosby Co.)

bodies, as well as that of the polian vesicles (absent in the common *Asterias*), are unknown.

From the outer side of the water ring a radial water canal extends the length of each arm and ends in the terminal tentacle (Figs. 27-10, 27-12). This radial water canal runs on the oral side of the ambulacral ridge of ossicles that forms the center of the ambulacral groove (Fig. 27-11). From each side of the radial canal, lateral canals branch off and pass between the ambulacral ossicles on each side of the groove. Each lateral canal has a valve and runs to a podium provided with an expanded bulb (the ampulla) at its inner end in the coelomic cavity. Externally the podium forms a tubular projection of the body wall into the ambulacral groove. The outer end of the podium usually bears a sucker for attachment. The ampulla is a muscular sac consisting of peritoneum on

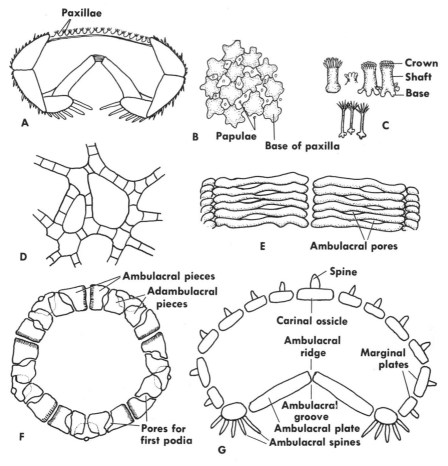

Fig. 27-8

Endoskeletal structure of asteroids. **A,** Schematic section through arm of *Astropecten* (order Phanerozonia) showing paxillae, or modified spines, found in some stars. **B,** Portion of endoskeleton from inside showing basal plates of paxillae. **C,** Several types of paxillae, each consisting of basal plate supporting rod crowned with minute spines. **D,** Reticular arrangement of aboral endoskeleton of *Asterias* (order Forcipulata). **E,** Ambulacral ossicles of *Asterias* showing pores for podia, staggered to form two rows of pores on each side of groove. **F,** Peristomial ring of ossicles of *Asterias*. **G,** Skeleton in schematic section through arm of forcipulate star. (**B, C,** and **G** modified from Hyman; **F** modified from Chadwick, 1923).

both its inside and outside surfaces, between which are circular and longitudinal muscle fibers and connective tissue. The podium is covered with flagellated epithelium on the outside and peritoneum on the inside. Between these layers are connective tissue and longitudinal muscle fibers. The number of podia varies in the different species. Those with a large number have the rows staggered so that there may be four rows instead of two along the ambulacral groove (Fig. 27-8, *E*). This dif-

ference is brought about by the alternate length of the lateral canals, some long and some short. Those species with only two rows of tube feet have lateral canals of the same length. The ring and radial canals have few muscles, but consist of a lining of flagellated coelomic epithelium with connective tissue in the wall.

The water-vascular system operates on the principle of a hydraulic system. Since each podium is a closed cylinder, when the valve in the lateral canal closes, the con-

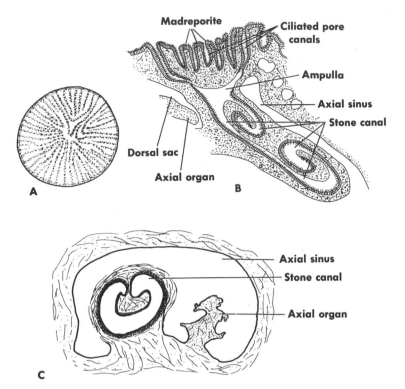

Fig. 27-9

A, External view of madreporite plate of *Asterias*. Furrows are perforated with ciliated pores. **B,** Vertical section of madreporite and aboral end of stone canal. **C,** Horizontal section through stone canal showing relative positions of stone canal and axial organ in axial sinus. (Modified from Chadwick, 1923.)

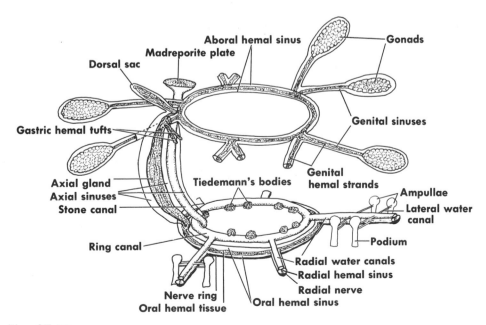

Fig. 27-10

Diagram of water-vascular and hemal systems of *Asterias*.

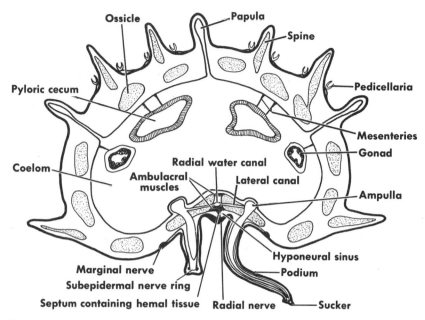

Fig. 27-11

Diagram of cross section through arm of young sea star.

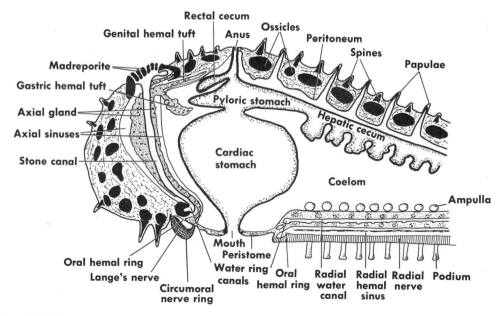

Fig. 27-12

Diagram of vertical section through disk and part of one arm of sea star.

traction of the bulblike ampulla at its inner end forces fluid into the podium and extends it as a flexible process that can be manipulated in any direction by the longitudinal muscles in its wall. When the tip of the podium touches a substratum, the withdrawal of the center of the terminal sucker lessens the pressure in the tip and causes the sucker to adhere. When the longitudinal muscles contract, fluid is forced back into the ampulla, and the animal is drawn forward by the shortening of the podia. Fluid pressure for the operation of the tube feet may be a function of all parts of the water-vascular system, such as the madreporite, stone canal, ring canal, and radial canals. Any slight fluid loss in the system is compensated by sea water intake through the madreporite. The podia can perform independently or in a coordinated manner. It is thought that coordination of the podia in movement is brought about chiefly by the presence of a nerve center at the junction of each radial nerve with the nerve ring, but an explanation of all the varied movements of the podia is still vague. Locomotion, especially on a soft substratum, makes little use of the suckers, the podia performing a stepping process that involves swinging of the podia followed by contraction that moves the animal forward. The coordinated action of the podia and their suckers is quite powerful and can draw the animal up a vertical sur-

Fig. 27-13

Oral view of large sun star, attached by podia to side of aquarium.

face without much effort (Fig. 27-13). When inverted, the sea star can right itself by twisting one or more arms until some of the suckers are attached to a substratum as an anchor and then slowly rolling over. Some asteroids do not have suckers but use only stepping motions with little or no gripping of the substratum.

Sea stars are carnivorous and feed on a variety of animals, such as crustaceans, mollusks, other echinoderms, fish, etc. Deep-sea forms feed on the organic detritus of mud by a filter-feeding method. Many have a decided preference for shellfish. *Asterias* is highly destructive to oyster beds.

The digestive system consists of a mouth, stomach, digestive glands, intestine, and anus and extends between the oral and aboral sides of the disk (Fig. 27-12). The mouth is in the middle of the peristomial membrane on the oral side and leads by a short esophagus into a large saclike stomach that is divided by a constriction into a lower cardiac stomach and a smaller, aboral pyloric stomach.

The cardiac stomach has pouched walls and is connected by paired mesenteries or gastric ligaments to the body wall. The star-shaped pyloric stomach lies above the cardiac stomach and is connected by ducts to a pair of large pyloric ceca in each arm (Figs. 27-12, 27-14). These ceca are digestive glands that are suspended in the coelom by dorsal mesenteries. Each cecum is made up of a longitudinal duct with many lateral ducts, into which secretory lobules open. The secretory lobules are lined with tall flagellated epithelium containing granular, storage, and mucus cells. Food reserves are found in the storage cells and enzymes in the granular or secretory cells. The longitudinal duct along each cecum may enter the pyloric stomach separately, or it may join with the other duct of the same arm before doing so. From the pyloric stomach a short intestine, provided with a varying number of rectal or intestinal ceca, ascends to the anus. An anus (and sometimes an intestine) is absent in many sea stars, and the feces are discharged through the mouth.

Histologically, the digestive tract is similar to the body wall, as it is lined with flagellated epithelium beneath which is a layer of muscle and connective tissue. Coe-

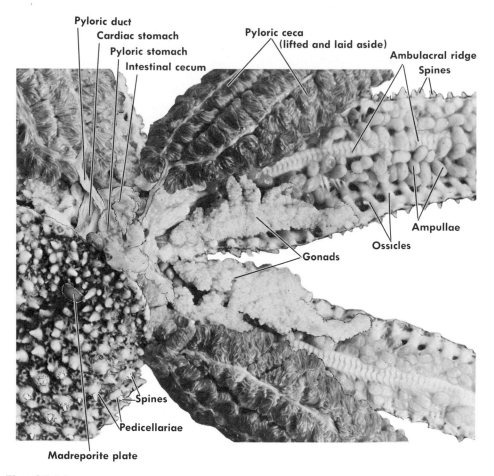

Pyloric duct
Cardiac stomach
Pyloric stomach
Intestinal cecum
Pyloric ceca
(lifted and laid aside)
Ambulacral ridge
Spines
Ampullae
Ossicles
Gonads
Spines
Pedicellariae
Madreporite plate

Fig. 27-14

Aboral view of *Asterias* showing portions of three arms dissected to expose internal structures. Parts of two undissected arms at left. (From Hickman: Integrated principles of zoology, The C. V. Mosby Co.)

lomic epithelium covers the coelomic side of the digestive tract.

Asteroids feed by two general methods. Those with short rays and suckerless podia swallow the prey whole (Phanerozonia) and digest it in the stomach, casting out the indigestible part through the mouth. *Asterias* and other sea stars with long flexible arms and podia with suckers feed by everting the cardiac stomach upon the prey, which is held enclosed by the arms. By contracting the body wall muscles they increase the pressure of the coelomic fluid, causing the cardiac stomach to be everted through the mouth. The gastric ligaments prevent the cardiac stomach from everting too far. The stomach engulfs the prey and pours upon it powerful digestive juice with enzymes from the pyloric ceca or stomach wall. This results in the digestion of the prey into a sort of broth, which is then sucked up into the body. Retraction of the stomach occurs when the stomach wall muscles contract and the body wall relaxes.

Since many sea stars feed upon bivalves (clams and oysters), the problem of opening the valves of the prey is involved. During feeding, the sea star humps itself over the bivalve and grasps it with its podia, while holding on to the substratum with the distal ends of its arms. By manipulating itself the sea star brings the gape of the bivalve close to its mouth. Opening the

563

valves was long thought to be brought about by the pull of the podia upon the valves with a force sufficient to overcome the adductor muscles of the bivalve or by a narcotic secretion that paralyzed the prey so that it was helpless against the pull. It has now been firmly established that minute gaps in the imperfectly closed valves offer an opening sufficient for the entrance of the sea star's stomach (A. L. Burnett and A. Christensen), although the pull of the sea star itself probably produces small gaps. It appears that the stomach of a sea star can squeeze through an opening as small as 0.1 mm. The sea star does not pull continuously with its podia upon the valves but only intermittently. If the valves close upon the stomach, it is not injured.

Digestion in sea stars is mostly extracellular, although some intracellular digestion may occur in the pyloric ceca. Such enzymes as protease, amylase, and lipase are found in the digestive juice produced by the ceca. Because of the nature of their food only a small amount of feces is produced. In those forms that feed by mucus-ciliary methods (e.g., *Porania*), ciliary currents and mucus entangle microscopic food and carry it to the mouth. J. M. Anderson (1960) has recently shown that the pyloric stomach of such asteroids is provided with five pairs of Tiedemann's pouches that act as flagellary pumping organs for sucking food from the stomach into the pyloric ceca.

The coelomic cavity of asteroids is very large and encloses the digestive system and reproductive organs. In addition, there are some other coelomic cavities, such as the axial sinus, genital sinus, marginal sinus, etc. (Figs. 27-10, 27-12). Coelomic spaces are lined with flagellated cuboidal epithelium. The coelom is filled with coelomic fluid, which has the composition of sea water, plus certain coelomocytes that are amebocytes with phagocytic properties. Coelomocytes originate from the coelomic epithelium and not from Tiedemann's bodies, as formerly supposed.

The hemal or blood system (Fig. 27-10), which is not so pronounced in asteroids as in some other echinoderms, is made up mostly of fine channels, or lacunae, enclosed in coelomic spaces (often called perihemal

sinuses). The principal hemal vessels are the oral hemal ring around the peristome; the radial hemal sinus (hyponeural canal) that runs into each arm from this ring along the midline of the ambulacral groove; and the axial sinus, which contains the stone canal and axial gland and arises from the oral hemal ring passing aborally into the genital sinus and ampulla of the stone canal. The axial gland, a brownish, spongy body of unknown function, may be the remnant of a heart (Figs. 27-10, 27-12). Coelomocytes are present in the fluid of the hemal system. The hemal system may be useful in distributing digested products, although its general functions are unknown.

Respiration in asteroids is effected by the papulae, or skin gills (Fig. 27-6, *D*, *E*), and by the tube feet; but general body surface may be used, especially in those species that lack papulae. The papulae are evaginations of the body wall that pass between the ossicles; their histologic structure is similar to that of the body wall, with flagellated epidermis on the outside and coelomic flagellated epithelium on the inside.

Asteroids have no excretory system. Coelomocytes may be responsible for getting rid of unwanted materials; and the pyloric ceca apparently are also used for the same purpose. Ammonia and urea appear to be the chief nitrogenous waste.

The nervous system, like that of all echinoderms, is a diffuse one, having a strong connection with the epidermis. It is commonly described as consisting of three interrelated systems. The chief one of these systems is the oral or ectoneural system just beneath the epidermis. It consists of a nerve ring, radial nerves (Figs. 27-10 to 27-12), and a subepidermal plexus. The nervous center is the pentagonal circumoral nerve ring near the periphery of the peristomial membrane. This nerve ring supplies nerves to the esophagus and to the peristomial membrane. At each radius it gives off a radial nerve that runs as a V-shaped mass along the bottom of the ambulacral groove in each arm to the terminal tentacle. The radial nerve, which has both bipolar and multipolar ganglion cells, sends nerve fibers to the podia and ampullae; and the radial nerves are connected to the subepidermal plexuses that innervate all the body wall appendages.

The second or entoneural nervous system consists mainly of a marginal cord (a thickened part of the subepidermal plexus) at the outer margin of the ambulacral groove along the length of the arm on each side. These marginal cords give off a pair of lateral motor nerves to the muscles of each pair of ambulacral ossicles. The nerves continue to the coelomic lining, beneath which they form a plexus that innervates the muscle layers of the wall.

The third or hyponeural system is a plate of nerve tissue (Lange's nerve) (Fig. 27-12) in the lateral oral wall of the hyponeural sinus beneath the coelomic epithelium. The system innervates the transverse muscles between the ambulacral ossicles in the roof of the hyponeural sinus.

Nerves from the same system pass to the peristomial region, where they form five interradial thickenings in the floor of the ring sinus, aboral to the main nerve ring.

The coordinated action of the podia depends upon the nerve ring and radial nerves. If a radial nerve of one arm is cut, the coordination of the podia in that arm is destroyed, and the podia do not work in unison with those of the other arms. A nervous center seems to exist at the junction of each radial nerve with the nerve ring; and when the sea star is progressing, the nerve center of the base of the leading arm has dominance over the nerve centers of the other arms and causes all their podia to move in harmony together.

The sensory system has few specialized sense organs. Sea stars cannot see, but they can detect differences in light intensities.

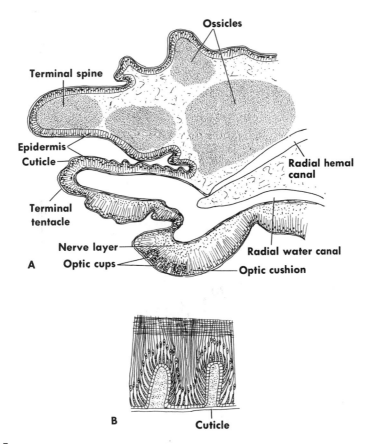

Fig. 27-15

A, Longitudinal and sagittal section through tip of sea star ray showing optic cushion and cups. B, Enlarged view of vertical section of two optic cups. (Modified from Chadwick, 1923.)

An eyespot is located at the base of the oral surface of each terminal tentacle of the arm (Fig. 27-15). It consists of many pigment-cup ocelli that together form an optic cushion. Each cup, or ocellus, is made up of epidermal cells with red pigment granules and is covered externally by a cuticle, beneath which in some species is a lens formed from the epidermis. The retinal cells, or photoreceptors with bulbous enlargements, project into the cavity of the cup. The number of ocelli in an optic cushion increases with age, but usually ranges between 50 and 200.

In addition to the eyespots, there are numerous neurosensory cells found everywhere in the epidermis. They are long, slender cells with distal threadlike processes that run to the cuticle and proximal fibers that join the subepidermal plexus (Fig. 27-6, A). They may serve for reception of contact and chemical stimuli and are especially abundant in the podial suckers, at the bases of the spines, and in the terminal tentacles. Some variations of the sense organs are found among the different species.

Asteroids are chiefly dioecious, although hermaphrodites may occasionally be found in those that normally have separate sexes. In this case the individual may be male at first and female later. Usually there is a pair of gonads for each arm, but there may be more in some species. Each gonad (Fig. 27-14) is a feathery cluster of tubules, the size of which varies with the seasons. At the spawning season they are very large; when inactive, they are only small tufts. Each gonad is enclosed in a genital coelomic sac, which is derived from the genital coelomic sinus and is attached at its proximal end near the junction of the arm and disk (Fig. 27-10). Each of the gonads has a small gonopore that usually opens aborally between the bases of the arms on the central disk; or in those with ventrally located gonads (e.g., *Asterina*) it opens orally. In the breeding season of some species the testes are pale in color, and the ovaries are pink or orange; but in general the sexes have no external sexual dimorphism.

A form of copulation may occur in a few species where the male lies on top of the female, his arms alternating with hers. Fertilization usually occurs in the sea, however, where the eggs and sperm are shed. Stimulation of gamete shedding appears to be brought about by several factors during the breeding season, which usually occurs once a year. Egg sea water will cause the male to shed his sperm; and sperm sea water will activate the female. It has recently been shown that the maturation and shedding of sea star eggs are stimulated by an identified secretion from neurosecretory cells in the radial nerves (H. Kanstani).

Brooding methods are found in some species. The female retains the fertilized egg mass in an oral concavity formed by the arching of her disk and the bending of the arms. Aboral brood chambers formed by spines also occur. Most asteroids, however, simply shed their gametes into the water and give no further attention to the fertilized egg. Sea stars usually become sexually mature in about a year, but they are known to grow for three or four years.

DEVELOPMENT

Asteroids have two types of development, indirect and direct. The indirect type has a free-swimming larval stage, and the eggs are homolecithal with little yolk. The direct type has large, yolky eggs, and the free-swimming stage is omitted. This type usually broods its eggs in some manner.

The development of the indirect type of egg (Fig. 27-16) may be described as follows: cleavage occurs soon after fertilization and is equal and indeterminate; by the second day a spherical, ciliated blastula is formed and becomes free swimming; by invagination an elongated gastrula is formed, the blastopore of which later becomes the anus, as is characteristic of deuterostomes. While forming, the archenteron gives off some mesenchyme into the inner blind end of the blastocoel. The archenteron gives rise to two outpocketings, or lateral pouches, that bud off, elongate, and lie on each side of the archenteron. Later, the two pouches connect anteriorly to form a U-shaped coelom. From the left pouch a narrow evagination forms a hydropore at the dorsal surface. The mouth originates from an ectodermal inpocketing (stomodeum), and the digestive system differentiates into the esophagus, stomach, and intestine, which are derived from the archenteron. The posterior ends of the lateral pouches are even-

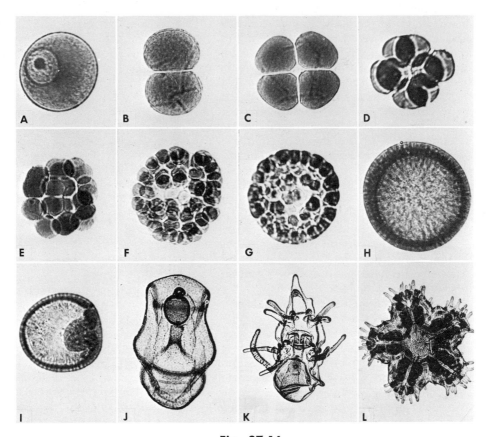

Fig. 27-16

Development of sea star *(Asterias)*. **A,** Unfertilized egg. **B** to **F,** Early cleavage stages. **G** and **H,** Blastula stages. **I,** Gastrula. **J,** Bipinnaria larva. **K,** Brachiolaria larva. **L,** Young sea star. (Courtesy Carolina Biological Supply Co., Burlington, N. C.)

tually pinched off and become the right and left somatocoels. In *Asterina,* the common European sea star, the anterior portion of the archenteron is cut off as a single coelomic sac to develop into a coelom, while the posterior archenteron becomes the digestive tract.

When the larva begins to swim, its body is covered with cilia; but later the cilia are restricted to an exterior band of many loops that are used in locomotion. Later, projections or arms arise on each side of the body. The locomotor bands extend along the arms, which often become long. At this stage the larva is called bipinnaria (Figs. 27-4, 27-16, *J*). The bilaterally symmetric larva swims in a clockwise rotation, with its anterior end foremost. It begins to feed, primarily on diatoms, as soon as its digestive tract is completed.

After a few weeks of free swimming, three additional lobes (brachiolar arms) appear at the anterior end, and the larva

is termed a "brachiolaria." The new arms differ from those of the bipinnaria in having a prolongation of the coelom in them and being tipped with adhesive cells. The arms, together with a suckerlike glandular region found between the bases of the three arms, forms an attachment device. When the brachiolaria settles to the bottom, it attaches itself by the sucker at the anterior end, which becomes a sort of stalk.

Metamorphosis now occurs. The anterior end degenerates and is absorbed, while the posterior end becomes enlarged. Five lobes appear on the right side of this posterior end, which becomes the aboral surface of the future sea star, while the left side becomes the oral surface. Arms are formed as extensions of the body. From the hydrocoel the water-vascular system develops, and two pairs of outgrowths from the hydrocoel in each lobe become the first tube feet. Skeletal elements begin to be formed as soon as the first lobes or arms appear. Most parts of the larval digestive system degenerate and are formed anew in the metamorphosis to the sea star condition. Most of the coelom arises from the somatocoel already described. Within two months after development starts and sufficient podia are formed for holding to a substratum, the young sea star (Fig. 27-16, *L*), not more than 1 mm. in diameter, is detached and begins a free existence. In this development the bilateral symmetry has gradually been replaced in most particulars by radial symmetry.

The larval stages of sea stars may form a considerable part of planktonic populations, especially in tropical and temperate seas. In the Arctic and Antarctic seas, however, where echinoderms tend to brood their young and have direct development, they form only a small part of the plankton. The same appears true of those that live in great depths of the ocean where most asteroids have large eggs and brood their young.

Regeneration of lost parts is common among asteroids. Some species are known to reproduce asexually by transverse division (*Allostichaster*). Almost any part of the arm can be regenerated. Some species can regenerate the whole animal from a severed arm (*Linckia*). In *Asterias* a complete regeneration of the animal will take place if part of the disk is attached to one arm, especially if the madreporite is included; but regeneration is a slow process, and many months may be required for complete replacement of parts.

Subclass Ophiuroidea

The members of this subclass of Asterozoa are commonly called brittle stars or sometimes basket stars and serpent stars. They are readily distinguished from the members of the other subclass (Asteroidea) by the arms, which are usually sharply demarcated from the central disk (Fig. 27-17). There are also many other differences between the two subclasses. Ophiuroids

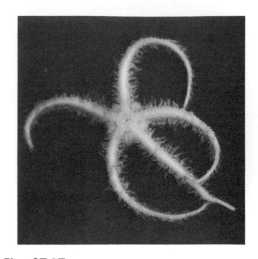

Fig. 27-17

Oral view of *Ophiothrix angulata*, a brittle star (Ophiuroidea).

have no ambulacral groove, their podia are small and without ampullae, and their arms are composed of jointed segments produced by the fusion of ambulacral ossicles. Ophiuroids do not use their podia for locomotion, but move by whiplike lashing movements of their arms, a process that resembles the vigorous action of serpent tails. They are found in all oceans at nearly all depths, from tidewater down. Many are shallow-water forms and hide in the algae or the mud with their arms protruding. They also frequently attach themselves to other animals by means of their twining arms. Because they are negative to light and positive to contact with a solid (stereotropism), they conceal themselves during the day and are active mainly at night.

There are about 1,900 living species of ophiuroids belonging to more than 200 genera. They all belong to one order, Ophiurida. Two suborders, Ophiurae and Euryalae, are recognized. Members of Ophiurae can move their arms (which do not branch) only sidewise in a horizontal plane. Those of Euryalae have flexible arms (often branched), which can coil upward or downward in a vertical plane. Their fossil record dates back to the Devonian period. It shows that many Paleozoic families had open ambulacral grooves.

GENERAL MORPHOLOGIC FEATURES
EXTERNAL ANATOMY

Most ophiuroids are five armed, but a few species are regularly six or seven armed. A five-armed species may have an extra arm as an abnormality. The general appearance of all ophiuroids is very similar. Their small flattened disk has a rounded, pentagonal, or scalloped contour (Fig. 27-17) and is usually not more than 1 inch in diameter (much smaller in many species). The basket stars (Gorgonocephalidae) may have disks of 3 or 4 inches in diameter and an arm spread of 20 inches. The aboral surface of the disk may be smooth, granular, or covered with small spines. In many cases it may have embedded plates. A pair of large radial shields is found at the base of each arm. There are no openings on the aboral surface, for an anus is lacking.

The arms may be smooth or provided with spines. Their interior is filled with a series of articulating ossicles. They have a jointed appearance because of four longitudinal series of calcareous plates, or shields, which may be concealed partly by the skin. Each arm joint corresponds to an internal skeletal ossicle and is covered aborally by an aboral shield, orally by an oral shield, and on each side by a lateral shield. Modifications of this plan may occur in which the aboral and oral shields are reduced with an enlargement of the lateral shields. The lateral arm shields correspond to the adambulacral ossicles of asteroids. Each lateral shield usually has about 3 to 15 spines in a vertical row. Many variations in size, shape, and arrangement of these spines occur in the different species. In some species there are poisonous spines, and in others the spines are transformed into hooks (*Ophiothrix*). Ambulacral grooves are totally lacking on the oral side.

There is a pair of small podia or tentacles on the oral surface of each joint. One member of each pair of podia emerges on each side between the lateral and oral arm shields. The podia in ophiuroids are mostly sensory in function, although they may play a minor role in locomotion by gripping objects. It is thus seen that the arm of ophiuroids consists of a series of jointed segments, each of which is made up of a "vertebra" that articulates with the others by means of ball-and-socket joints. In basket stars this articulation allows movement in all planes, but in serpent stars it permits only lateral mobility. The vertebrae are connected and manipulated by four sets of longitudinal muscles that are especially strong on the oral side of the arm, where they are inserted in muscle pits in the ossicle on the side toward the disk. Each vertebra is the result of the fusion of two ossicles lying side by side. On the aboral side of each vertebra is a dorsal groove; and on the oral side is an ambulacral channel that houses the radial water vessel, nerve, and blood vessel.

The skeleton of the disk is made up of the mouth frame, the genital plates between the genital pouches and arms, the buccal shields, and certain other plates or scales. In the center of the oral disk is the star-shaped mouth that is surrounded by five interradial triangular jaws made up of plates (Fig. 27-18). Each jaw consists of several plates, the most important of which are the half jaws and the oral or buccal shield. The oral ends of the half jaws are usually the exposed triangular part of the jaw. The oral shield covers most of the oral surface of the jaws. The jaws have teeth along their margin and also at their tip, where the teeth extend aborally in a vertical row. The jaw apparatus is manipulated by two concentric series of muscles—the external interradial and the oral internal interradial muscles. One of the buccal shields is commonly modified to form a madreporite, which has an oral location in ophiuroids. On the oral side the arms, with all their parts, except their aboral shields, are embedded in the oral disk and extend inward to the angles of the mouth.

The body surface of ophiuroids is covered with a cuticle, but cilia or flagella are restricted chiefly to the bursal slits and the surface of the disk. The syncytial epidermis is continuous with the dermis, which has embedded in it the endoskeletal shields along with a connective tissue matrix and scattered cells. Some ophiuroids are highly colored with pigments of carotenoid, melanin, riboflavin, and xanthophyll. Pigment spots sensitive to light are found on the aboral surface of the arm ossicles in some species. Melanin is a screen against radiation. Others have luminescent pigments, especially riboflavin. These pigments are

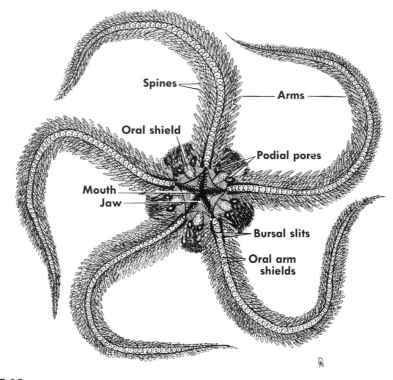

Fig. 27-18

Oral view of brittle star (Ophiuroidea). (From Hickman: Integrated principles of zoology, The C. V. Mosby Co.)

found in the dermis. There are no pedicellariae or papulae in the skin. External appendages are restricted to spines and podia. The larger spines are movable, like those of asteroids, and are mounted on tubercles.

Ophiuroids can move rapidly when disturbed. As already mentioned, the arms are well provided with longitudinal muscles that link the vertebrae together. Movement is produced either by trailing or by pushing ahead one of the arms while the others, by rowing movements against the substratum, thrust the body forward in a series of jerks. Movements show many variations. During locomotion the ophiuroid holds its disk above the substratum. Some move by grasping objects with their arms and pulling themselves along. A few apparently can swim by trailing one arm behind and performing stroking movements with the others (*Ophiacantha*). A sand-burrowing ophiuroid *(Amphiura)* can burrow directly downward by digging with its podia and remain covered in sand except for its arm tips.

INTERNAL ANATOMY

The ophiuroid water-vascular system is typical of the echinoderm group, with certain modifications (Fig. 27-19). The madreporite is usually single, although *Ophiactis* has five. The madreporite, which is found on the oral surface, usually has one pore canal, but may have more in some species. The stone canal ascends to the water ring, which occupies a groove on the aboral surface of the jaw apparatus. There are no Tiedemann's bodies, but usually four polian vesicles are borne by the water ring. From the water ring a radial canal descends toward the oral side, enters the arm base, and runs along the arm, aboral to the hyponeural canal, to the terminal tentacle. In each vertebral ossicle the radial canal gives off a pair of lateral or podial canals, which may pass directly or by a loop to the podia (Fig. 27-20). Ampullae are absent, but a valve is present where the podial canal enters the podium. The water-vascular system is lined throughout with flagellated coelomic epithelium.

The alimentary canal of ophiuroids is the simplest among the echinoderms. It consists of only a mouth and a large saclike stomach.

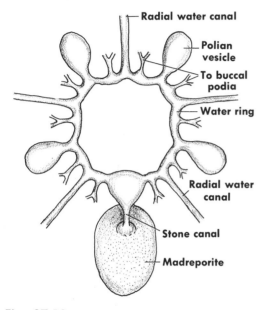

Fig. 27-19

Scheme of water-vascular ring of ophiuroid.

There is no intestine or anus. The stomach, usually with ten marginal pouches, is restricted to the disk (Fig. 27-21), except in the Ophiocanopidae, where it sends its blind ceca into the arms. The mouth, which is a circular opening in the center of the five-angled peristomial membrane, leads to a very short esophagus that may be provided with a smaller circular cavity on the inner side of a large one. Muscles from these cavities are involved in the opening and closing of the mouth. The esophagus opens into the sacciform stomach, which fills most of the interior of the disk. The peripheral pouches of the stomach are closely applied to the inner aboral surface of the disk, where they are attached by mesenteries. The bursae are placed between the pouches. The stomach wall consists of an internal lining of flagellated epithelium, a nervous stratum, a layer of connective tissue, circular muscle fibers, and an outer flagellated coelomic covering. Gland cells seem to be absent.

Ophiuroids live on bottom detritus and small organisms. They usually eat whatever they can find, although some are selective in their food habits. Certain predatory ophiuroids are known to live on coral polyps. When they feed, small food particles are passed to the mouth by the podia and by ciliary action, while large

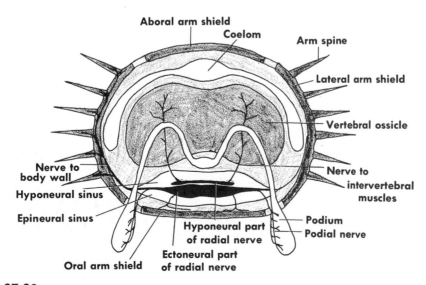

Fig. 27-20

Schematic cross section of arm of ophiuroid.

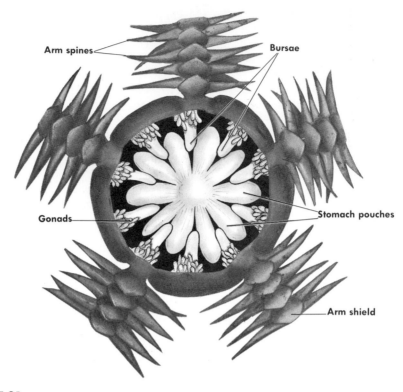

Fig. 27-21

Ophiuroid with aboral disk cut away to show principal internal structures. Only bases of arms shown. (From Hickman: Integrated principles of zoology, The C. V. Mosby Co.)

particles are carried toward the mouth by rhythmic sweeping of the arms.

The ophiuroid coelom is restricted to space in the disk around the organs, a narrow arm space between the vertebral ossicles and the arm shields, and certain minor coelomic cavities (hyponeural radial sinuses, axial sinus, and genital sinuses) (Figs. 27-20, 27-22). The coelomic fluid contains coelomocytes and certain ameboid cells. The axial complex is similar to that of the asteroids, except that it is turned orally because of the location of the madreporite. The axial sinus runs from the hyponeural ring sinus to the ampulla beneath the madreporite. Most of this sinus is filled with the axial gland and stone canal. The axial gland develops from the coelomic wall (the axocoel), which encloses the stone canal. The axial gland is considered a hemal center that connects the oral and aboral hemal rings, but its real function is largely a mystery.

Most of the hemal channels in ophiuroids are enclosed in coelomic channels. The oral hemal ring lies inside the hyponeural ring canal and gives off a radial hemal channel into each arm at the aboral side of the radial canal. The radial hemal channel sends hemal channels to the podia. The aboral hemal ring just mentioned sends channels to the bursae and gonads and receives gastric branches from the stomach. The hemal channels, or blood lacunae, have walls of nucleated membranes or a thin layer of connective tissue. The hemal fluid contains amebocytes. Some ophiuroids have coelomocytes containing hemoglobin.

Ophiuroids have special organs for respiration called bursae (Fig. 27-21). These are saclike invaginations of the oral wall of the disk near the arm bases. There are ten of these bursae, each one located between two stomach pouches. Each bursa opens to the outside by an elongated slit close to the arm base on the oral surface of the disk. In *Ophioderma* there are two openings to

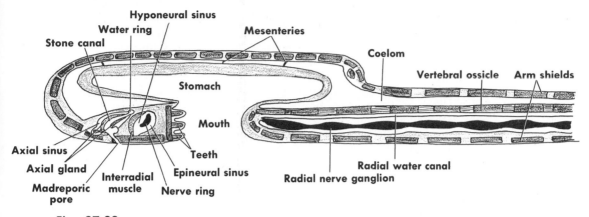

Fig. 27-22

Schematic longitudinal section of ophiuroid through interradius of disk and portion of one arm.

each bursa because the middle part of the slit has fused. The bursae are lined with flagellated epithelium, and on the outside they are covered with peritoneum. Calcareous deposits may be found in the dermis of the bursal wall. Water currents for gaseous exchange are constantly entering and leaving the bursae through the slits, a process faciliated by the beating of the flagellae. A pumping or suction action produced by the aboral disk wall may aid in the movement of the water in some species.

The nervous system of ophiuroids is similar to that of asteroids, consisting chiefly of an outer ectoneural system (sensory and motor) and an inner hyponeural system (motor) separated by only a thin membrane (Fig. 27-20). The two systems are actually superimposed; the nerve ring and radial nerves represent each system. The nerve ring is found in a groove near the aboral surface of the jaw apparatus between the outer water ring and the inner hemal ring. This nerve ring supplies nerves to the esophagus, to the buccal or first podia in the arm, and to the jaw apparatus and its teeth. From the nerve ring a radial nerve runs through each arm beneath the radial hemal channels and along the oral faces of the vertebral ossicles (Fig. 27-22). A ganglionic enlargement at the level of each vertebral ossicle is present in the radial nerve. A pair of motor nerves (from the hyponeural system) is given off at each ganglion in the arm to the interver-

tebral muscles. Between the ganglionic enlargements a podial nerve and a pair of lateral sensory nerves are given off and pass to the podia and body wall. A ring ganglion, formed by the podial nerve around the base of the podium, supplies the podium with a nerve. The chief coordinating center of the nervous system appears to be the nerve ring.

Most ophiuroids are dioecious, although some are known to be hermaphroditic (*Amphipholis*). Usually the sexes are very much alike, but in some species the female carries the dwarf male on her disk. The saclike gonads are confined to the disk, being attached to the coelomic side of the bursae (Fig. 27-21). Each gonad opens indirectly to the exterior by way of the bursa to which it is attached. When the gonads are ripe, the gametes are discharged into the bursae through a rupture or temporary opening and are carried out by the water currents. The number and arrangement of gonads vary. There may be one or more gonads per bursa. In some species they may be paired in the basal arm joints and discharged through the body wall. Fertilization occurs chiefly in the water, where development takes place. Brooding of the young in the bursae (where few or many embryos are present) is a common method of Arctic and Antarctic ophiuroids. The embryo of the viviparous *Amphipholis* has a nutritional attachment to the bursal wall. Most ophiuroids do not become sexually mature until they are three or four years old. Their life span has been estimated at five years, although some may live much longer.

Regeneration of lost parts is common in the class. Autotomy, or shedding of the arms, is also practiced. In some species the entire disk and at least one arm must be present for complete regeneration of the whole animal. Some species regularly reproduce asexually by transverse division, especially in the six-armed *Ophiactis*, so that such serpent stars may have one set of three large arms and one of three small arms.

DEVELOPMENT

Those ophiuroids with small eggs that are shed into the water pass through an indirect type of development (considered the most primitive), which involves a free-swimming larval form called an ophiopluteus (Fig. 27-3). Those with large eggs that are brooded have a direct type of development and omit the free-swimming stage. In indirect development the egg undergoes holoblastic and equal cleavage. A free-swimming and flagellated blastula stage is formed within 24 hours. The gastrula stage occurs (by embolic invagination) within two or three days. The coelomic sac is formed either as a separate sac from the tip of the archenteron or as a pouch on each side of the archenteron. The pluteus larva swims about during metamorphosis. Many aspects of development are similar to those in asteroids, although there are modifications of the basic echinoderm pattern here and there. There is no attachment stage during the development, and at the end of the metamorphosis the small brittle star sinks to the bottom to begin its adult existence.

CLASS ECHINOIDEA

These echinoderms are the sea urchins, sand dollars, and heart urchins. They are pentamerous echinoderms without arms, but with a compact body enclosed in an endoskeletal test or shell that is formed from fused plates bearing movable spines. Their general shape may be oval, globose, or a similar design, with the body flattened along the oral-aboral axis. Although they have no arms, their radii bear five double

rows of podia that are arranged as meridians between the oral and aboral poles. Some echinoids show a tendency toward secondary bilateral symmetry.

There are about 850 existing species divided among 225 genera. They are classified into two subclasses. The Regularia (Endocyclica), which are radial and have a centrally located aboral anus, are more or less spherical or globular and include the sea urchins (Figs. 27-23, 27-24). The Irregularia (Exocyclica) are bilateral, with a marginal anus, and may be oval or circular and flattened. They are represented by the heart urchins (Figs. 27-1, 27-28), sand dollars (Fig. 27-29), and cake urchins (Fig. 27-30). The class as a whole has left a very impressive fossil record (Figs. 27-1, *A*, 27-30, *A*).

Echinoids vary in size from a few millimeters to around 20 to 30 cm. in diameter. Although many species are darkish or dull in color, some have bright colors of red, green, orange, and purple. The pigment echinochrome (naphthaquinone), found in no other echinoderm and responsible for the red and purple colors of certain echinoids, is present both in the spines and the test.

Echinoids are found in all seas, but are absent from the deepest ocean depths. They are present from intertidal zones to depths of several thousand meters, but are most common in the littoral zone. Members of the subclass Irregularia are partial to sandy substrates, whereas the Regularia prefer rocky bottoms. The faunas of echinoids have regions of local distribution that vary greatly in the different seas. Some species (e.g., *Echinoneus* and *Echinocardium*) have a wide distribution, while others are very restricted. The littoral echinoids are most common in the Indo-Pacific region. Other regions with rich echinoderm faunas of interest to the new world are the West Indies–Florida area, the Panama area or eastern tropical Pacific region, the Gulf of California, and the Puget Sound region.

GENERAL MORPHOLOGIC FEATURES
EXTERNAL ANATOMY

As the names of the two subclasses Regularia (Endocyclica) and Irregularia (Exocyclica) suggest, echinoids are commonly divided into regular and irregular groups.

A   B

Fig. 27-23

Regular sea urchins. **A,** Oral view of *Arbacia punctulata,* an East coast urchin. **B,** Aboral view of *Strongylocentrotus franciscanus,* the giant red urchin of our Pacific shores.

A   B

Fig. 27-24

A, Group of regular sea urchins showing wide variety of spines. **B,** Cidaroid sea urchin (oral view) with large, paddle-shaped primary spines. (From Encyclopaedia Britannica film, "Echinoderms [Sea Stars and their Relatives].")

Regularia. Sea urchins (Figs. 27-23, 27-24) are characterized by a body that is globose or spherical in shape and an armature of many movable spines. Their oral and aboral surfaces are differentiated; they move upon their oral surface, which tends to be flattened as a consequence, while their aboral surface is somewhat

dome shaped. The sea urchin's body is thus radially arranged around a polar axis, with the oral pole bearing the mouth and peristome region and the aboral pole bearing the anus and periproct region. The body surface between the poles is divided into five ambulacral regions with rows of podia and five interambulacral regions without

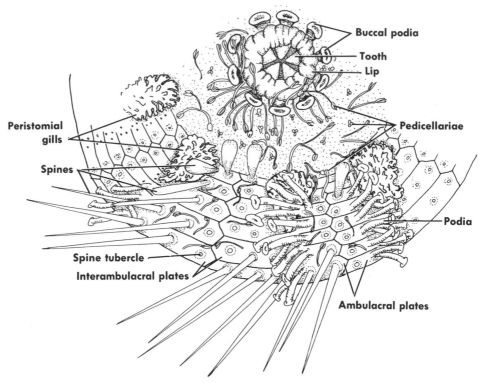

Fig. 27-25

Oral view of *Arbacia* showing peristome and related structures.

podia. These two types of regions alternate with each other as they run in a meridional direction between the two poles.

The mouth in the center of the oral surface is surrounded by a peristomial membrane, which is thickened along the mouth edge into a lip (Fig. 27-25). The membrane contains small embedded ossicles for support. Five pairs of modified podia (buccal podia) form a circlet near the mouth, and five pairs of little bushy gills are found at the edge of the peristome. The peristome usually bears on its surface small spines and pedicellariae. At the aboral pole is the periproct, which is a circular membrane also bearing embedded endoskeletal plates with small spines and pedicellariae (Fig. 27-26). The periproct contains the anus, usually near its center, but sometimes eccentric in position.

The spines are arranged in rows in both the ambulacral and interambulacral areas. The spines may be all the same size, but usually they are shortest at the poles and longest around the sides. Often the large and small spines are intermingled over the entire body. The length and size of spines vary greatly with different species (Figs. 27-23, 27-24).

Each spine has a concave socket that rotates over a tubercle on the test, thus forming a ball-and-socket joint (Fig. 27-25). The spine bears a milled ring at its base, to which muscles are attached. A circle of longitudinal muscles, which are attached at one end to the milled ring of the spine and at the other end to the marginal depression of the test around the tubercle, can point the spine in any direction. An inner set of muscles (the "catch" muscles) hold the spine in an erect position.

Spines are sometimes classified into primary, which are long for defense and walking; and secondary, which are short and may be used to protect the muscles around the primary spines. In the more familiar echinoids (*Echinus,* *Strongylocentrotus,* Fig. 27-23, *B*) the distinction between the

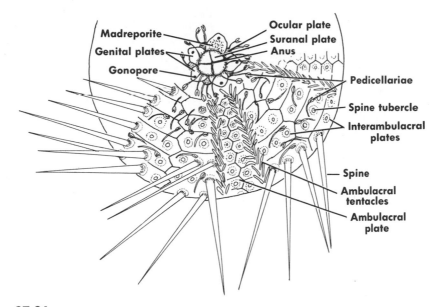

Fig. 27-26

Aboral view of *Arbacia* showing periproct and related structures.

two types is not evident. Spines are found in a variety of forms as well as sizes. Some are straight and circular in outline; others are flattened or triangular. Still others are curved. Poison spines, especially the secondary, occur in the genus *Asthenosoma* and are harmful to man.

The spines are composed of calcite, which is arranged in an inner axial zone and outer cortex. The entire spine behaves optically as a single crystal unit.

The pedicellariae are microscopic defense organs found only in the asteroids and echinoids (Fig. 27-25). They consist of a head, usually composed of three jaws (sometimes two, four, or five), set with flexible necks upon stalks. The stalk contains an internal skeletal rod that reaches to the flexible neck or sometimes to the head. An internal calcareous valve supports and determines the shape of each jaw. The jaws articulate against each other and are operated by muscles, which close and open them.

The purpose of pedicellariae is to discourage intruders and to catch small prey. They may also be used for cleaning the body surface. Some contain poison glands (globiferous, Fig. 27-27, *A*). Surrounding the outer side of each jaw are one or two

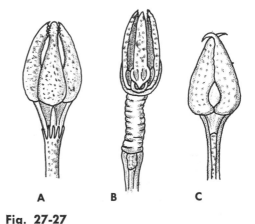

Fig. 27-27

Types of sea urchin pedicellariae. **A**, Globiferous (*Eucidaris*). **B**, Tridentate (*Arbacia*). **C**, Bidentate (sand dollar).

poison glands that open by ducts just below the terminal tooth of that jaw. The toxin paralyzes small prey. Other types of pedicellariae are the tridentate (Fig. 27-27, *B*), triphyllous, and ophiocephalous. Of these, the tridentate is the largest and most common. Its head has three elongated jaws that usually meet only distally.

On the ambulacral areas of most echinoids are hard, solid bodies, called sphae-

Anterior ambulacrum

Petaloid ambulacra

Anus

A

Anterior ambulacrum

Labrum

Plastron

Posterior ambulacra

B

Fig. 27-28

Moira atropos, the heart urchin (Irregularia). **A,** Aboral view. **B,** Oral view. Note large spoon-tipped spines on plastron used for burrowing. Long lateral spines are used to throw sand sidewise when burrowing. Spines in ambulacra are short. Minute spines (clavules), located in tract on aboral side, create water currents and help clean sand off test.

ridia. These may be organs of equilibrium. They are located on various regions of the body, such as the center of the ambulacra, on the oral side, or even on the aboral surface when numerous. In *Arbacia* there is one sphaeridium on each ambulacrum located near the edge of the peristome.

The podia in sea urchins (Fig. 27-25) are arranged in five double rows on the ambulacra and extend from the peristome to the periproct. In some sea urchins (e.g., Cidaroidea) the podia are even found on the peristome as far as the edge of the mouth. In these the special buccal podia are absent. Most podia are of the locomotor type just as they are in asteroids. They are usually long and slender and are provided with terminal suckers. Both the suckers and the stalk are supported by calcareous spicules, which are C-shaped in the stalk region. The podia (tentacles) of the

aboral side may lack terminal suckers (Fig. 27-26) and may have sensory functions.

The gills are thin-walled outgrowths that are attached to the edge of the peristome (Fig. 27-25). They are restricted to the sea urchins where they are found in all members, except one group (Cidaroidea). The gills open into the coelomic cavity around Aristotle's lantern.

Sea urchins use both the podia and spines in their locomotion. They can move in any direction with any ambulacral area forward. When placed on their aboral surface, they right themselves by attaching suitable podia to the substratum and contracting them. Righting may be assisted by using their long spines. Some can burrow by means of the Aristotle's lantern and by manipulating the spines around the circumference.

Irregularia. The irregular echinoids include the heart urchins and sand dollars. The heart urchins are commonly known as spatangoids (Figs. 27-1, *A,* 27-28), and the sand dollars as clypeastroids (Figs. 27-29, 27-30). They differ in many important respects from the regular sea urchins.

In the heart urchins the periproct and anus lie outside the apical system of plates, being displaced posteriorly along one interambulacrum or interradius, although the apical plates remain at the aboral pole. The mouth and peristome along with the center of the oral surface have moved anteriorly. The body is somewhat flattened and oval or rounded in shape. The circumference of the test (the ambitus), viewed orally or aborally, tends to be circular or somewhat angled. The oral surface is flat and the aboral surface hemispherical or convex.

The aboral ambulacral area is petal shaped, i.e., like petals radiating from a center, and is called petaloid. The oral ambulacral area is leaflike in arrangement and is known as a phyllode.

In the heart urchins the podia are not adapted for locomotion, which is done by the spines. Some of the aboral podia (petaloid region) are leaflike and branched, have no skeletal support, and are probably respiratory in function. Other types are found in this group, varying from slender tapering forms to those that have stellate disks. The oral ambulacral regions (phyllodes) of heart urchins bear special penicillate podia in place of the buccal podia of sea urchins. These podia are covered with erect club-shaped projections that are supported by an internal skeletal rod. They are chemoreceptive in function and also assist in food getting.

Spines in heart urchins are curved and held more or less parallel to the body. Spines vary in shape and size with the different regions of the body. Very minute spines called clavules, which are ciliated and flattened at the ends, are found in special tracts (fascioles). They function in maintaining water currents and in removing sand grains from the test. Other types of spines are specialized for burrowing (Fig. 27-28).

The sphaeridia in heart urchins are usually placed in shallow depressions on the plates of the phyllodes and along certain posterior ambulacra. Pedicellariae are usually of two types with only two jaws (Fig. 27-27, *C*) and scattered among the spines. No poisonous types of pedicellariae are found in this group.

The second group of irregular echinoids, called the clypeastroids, is made up of the sand dollars and cake urchins (Figs. 27-29, 27-30). They usually have a much-flattened body in the oral-aboral axis and a circular or oval ambitus. The aboral surface is frequently arched dorsally, which produces a cross-section profile of a convex aboral and a flattened oral side. The ambulacra are petaloid on the aboral side. Radiating

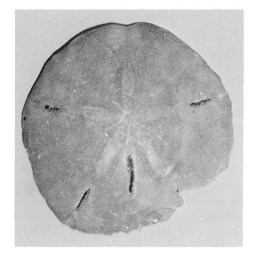

Fig. 27-29

Aboral view of test of sand dollar *Mellita quinquiesperforata,* a clypeastroid common to our East coast. Five slits or lunules (one broken) are basis for species name. Common West Indian sand dollar *M. sexiesperforata* has six lunules. Lunules may be useful in burrowing (Irregularia).

A   B

Fig. 27-30

Cake urchins, past and present (Irregularia). **A,** Fossil clypeastroid. Such fossil types date from Upper Cretaceous period to Recent time. **B,** Test of modern clypeastroid, the common West Indian sea biscuit.

grooves from the peristome to the ambitus occur on the oral surface and are used for transporting food to the mouth. Phyllodes, which are characteristic of the spatangoids, are absent in the clypeastroids. The mouth is midorally located, and the periproct and anus are usually also on the oral side in the posterior interambulacrum. The aboral and oral surfaces (except the ambulacral grooves containing tube feet) are densely covered with tiny spines, which give the animal a hairy appearance. Many sand dollars bear elongated slitlike holes (lunules) that perforate the test in a symmetric arrangement around the marginal area. They arise as marginal indentations and later are enclosed by the growth of the test. There are two or more of them wherever they occur. The keyhole sand dollar (*Mellita*) (Fig. 27-29) is a familiar example of a sand dollar in which there are five or six lunules. No real function has been assigned to the lunule, although some authorities think it may aid in burrowing. Several sand dollars also have indentations along the posterior margin (*Rotula*). Some sand dollars do not exceed 10 mm. in diameter, while others reach a diameter of 1 foot (*Sperosoma*).

In sand dollars there are chiefly two kinds of podia—the small suckered podia that are found all over the test in both ambulacral and interambulacral regions and help the spines in locomotion and the large simple or lobulated branchial podia found in the petaloids and used for respiration.

The irregular echinoids are especially well adapted for burrowing. They move only with their anterior end forward. Movements are restricted to the use of spines because their podia are specialized for a variety of other functions (sensory, respiratory, food getting, etc.) The spatangoids burrow by erecting themselves on their oral spines and tossing the sand sidewise by means of curved lateral spines. Most of the time the heart urchins remain buried in the sand with part of the aboral surface exposed to the outside. Water currents through the burrow are kept moving by the large spines on the aboral surface. Sand dollars, which lie buried just under the surface of the sand, in some instances pile up sand into mounds with their podia and then push themselves into the mound

with their spines. Other methods of burrowing are also employed.

INTERNAL ANATOMY

The body wall of echinoids has about the same organization as that of asteroids (Fig. 27-31). It consists of an external epidermis of one-layered epithelium covered with cilia, a dermis of connective tissue that includes the endoskeleton, and a flagellated coelomic lining. A cuticle may be present. Gland cells are found in the epidermis of some echinoids (*Diadema*). Pigment in the form of chromatophores or granules is found in the epidermis and dermis. Melanin is especially common in echinoids. A body wall musculature is absent. The external appendages have about the same histologic structure as the body wall, except that cilia tend to disappear from the spines with age and from the suckered terminals of podia. A layer of the ectoneural nervous system is present at the base of the epidermis. Poisonous pedicellariae occur in sand dollars.

The endoskeleton of echinoids is made up of closely fitting calcareous plates or ossicles so that the whole forms a solid, immovable test. Only the peristome and periproct plates are free and flexible. The skeletal plates (which can be seen to the best advantage in the cleaned test) are arranged in rows from the oral to the aboral pole (Figs. 27-25, 27-26). These plates are organized into five ambulacral areas of two plate rows alternating with five interambulacral areas of two plate rows. This arrangement produces twenty rows of plates, ten of which are ambulacral and ten interambulacral. The ambulacral areas are usually not so wide as the interambulacral areas, and they bear holes through which the podia pass. In all other echinoderms the podia pass between the plates, not through them.

Both ambulacral and interambulacral plates bear numerous tubercles on which the spines articulate in life. In the sea urchin test, there is usually one large, primary tubercle on each plate. These primary tubercles occur in meridional rows, with the smaller tubercles scattered among them. In the irregular echinoids (heart urchins and sand dollars) there is no such arrangement of large tubercles, but the plates bear many small tubercles, to which the tiny spines are attached.

The apical system of plates in regular echinoids surrounds the periproct. This system consists of five large genital plates, one of which serves as the madreporite, and five small ocular plates (Fig. 27-26). The genital plates, each with a gonopore, are in line with the interambulacra, and the ocular in line with the ambulacra. Each of the ocular plates has a pore for the emergence of the modified papillate podium (sensory). In the irregular echinoids the periproct lies outside the apical system, which usually has only four plates arranged close together with the madreporite shifted posteriorly, although there are many different arrangements of the apical system.

The water-vascular system is similar to that of other echinoderms (Fig. 27-33). It consists of a madreporite (a modified genital plate), a stone canal with an axial gland, a water ring with five polian vesicles above Aristotle's lantern, and five radial canals extending from the water ring and running under the five ambulacral areas of the test. These radial canals ascend to the inner surface of the test, where each gives off a terminal tentacle through a pore in an apical ambulacral plate. Each radial canal gives off, alternately to each side, lateral canals (with valves) for the ampulla of the podia (Fig. 27-31). From each ampulla two canals pass through the ambulacral plate (by a pore pair) and unite into a single canal on the outer surface of the test to form the lumen of the podium. In young stages and in some of the podia of irregular echinoids there is only a single canal connecting the podium to the ampulla. In older stages of some regular echinoids the ambulacral plates may fuse into compound plates with more than one pore pair. The arrangement of pore pairs has taxonomic value.

The spongy axial gland (Fig. 27-33) is not enclosed in the axial sinus, but is hollow and lined with coelomic epithelium. It represents a coelomic cavity of the right axo-

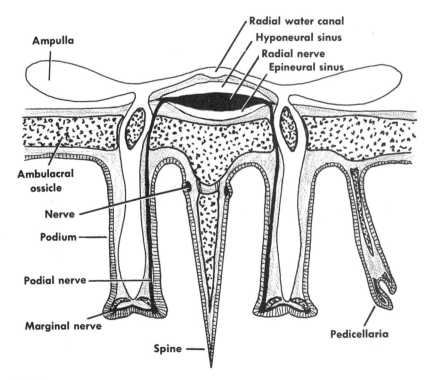

Fig. 27-31
Diagram of cross section of radius of echinoid.

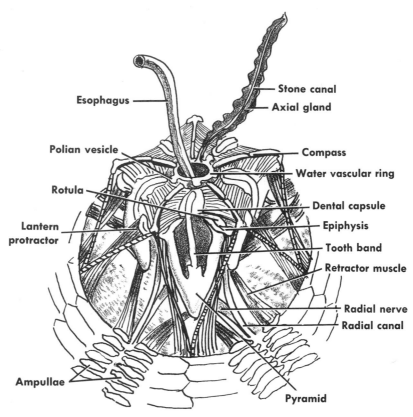

Fig. 27-32

Aboral-lateral view of dissected Aristotle's lantern of *Arbacia*.

coel. It is connected to the hemal ring; but little is known about its function, except that it may be excretory.

The mouth is located in the center of the peristome on the oral surface of the test in regular echinoids. In the irregular forms (spatangoids) it is shifted anteriorly and may lie opposite the interambulacrum, which contains the anus. The mouth is provided with a lip and passes into a small buccal cavity, where the teeth of the masticatory apparatus or Aristotle's lantern project. From the buccal cavity the pharynx or esophagus runs vertically through the lantern to the intestine. In all regular echinoids and in some of the irregular members the lantern of Aristotle, a unique chewing structure, is present (Fig. 27-33).

The lantern is an intricate complex of calcareous plates and muscles that is fitted

for seizing and chewing food (Fig. 27-32). It consists of five jaws in the form of calcareous plates (pyramids), each with a pointed tooth that projects into the mouth region. The pyramids are fanglike structures, composed of two half pyramids fused by a median suture. They are arranged radially in an interambulacral position. Each pyramid is connected by muscles to the adjacent pyramid on each side.

On the inner side along the midline of each pyramid is a calcareous band, the upper end of which is curled into a dental sac. This is the tooth band, the lower end of which is composed of hard calcareous material forming the tooth, which projects into the buccal cavity. When the teeth are worn away by usage, continuous growth of the tooth band replaces them.

At the aboral end of each pyramid is a cross bar (the epiphysis). The cross bars

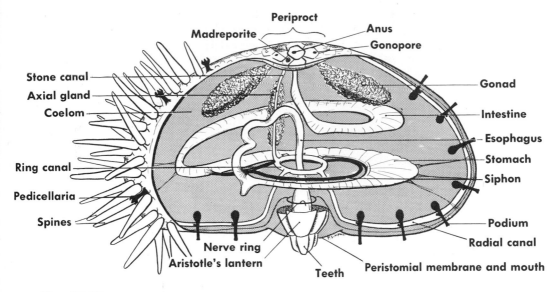

Fig. 27-33

Diagram of chief internal structures of echinoid. (From Hickman: Integrated principles of zoology, The C. V. Mosby Co.)

are sometimes joined to form a ring around the edge of the lantern. In the ambulacral positions five radial rotulas interlock with the epiphyses, and above these rodlike pieces are five arched rods, each composed of two ossicles (the compasses) and branched at the ends. An inturned flange of the test around the peristome forms the perignathic girdle to which the protractor muscles, which push the teeth through the mouth, are attached. Other muscles (retractors) pull the lantern back and open the teeth. Altogether, some 60 muscles operate the different parts of Aristotle's lantern. The variations in the structure of the lantern afford a basis for classification. Of the irregular echinoids the sand dollars have a modified Aristotle's lantern, and the heart urchins have none at all.

A cecum may be present at the junction of the esophagus and intestine. The intestine is fastened in place by mesenteries; first it makes an almost complete circuit around the inside of the test in a counterclockwise direction (seen aborally) and then another circuit in the opposite direction but aborally to the first (Fig. 27-33). The first circuit may be considered the small intestine and the second the large intestine. The large intestine joins the rectum, which empties through the anus located within the periproct.

In many echinoids a slender tube called the siphon (Fig. 27-33) runs along the intestine from the beginning of the small intestine to near the large intestine. This siphon enables the water removed from the food to bypass that part of the intestine where food is concentrated for digestion.

Sea urchins, or regular echinoids, will eat almost any kind of organic material. Some are mainly carnivorous and others herbivorous. Most are scavengers when the necessity arises. The irregular echinoids (heart urchins and sand dollars) feed mostly on organic particles in the sand where they lie buried.

In the sand dollar, sand and the organic material it contains are passed over the aboral surface by club-shaped spines. The finer food particles drop down between the spines and are carried to the oral surface. On the oral side special ciliated tracts convey the food to the ciliated ambulacral grooves and thence to the mouth. The modified Aristotle's lantern in sand dollars cannot be extended through the mouth. Their intestine makes but a single loop around the test, and the anus is located at the posterior ventral end.

583

The spatangoid, or heart urchin, makes use of its penicillate podia on the phyllodes in its feeding behavior. While it is buried in the sand these extensible podia are thrust out through the exposed aboral surface to explore the sand surface and pick up food particles with their adhesive ends. Then the podia contract and pass the food to the spines, which send it to the mouth. In the heart urchin the intestine makes two circuits, but the anus lies at the posterior ventral end.

Histologically, the digestive system of echinoids is lined with ciliated, tall epithelial cells. Muscle and connective tissue are found in the wall, which is covered on the outside with flagellated epithelium. Glands or glandular crypts are found in the lining epithelium of the pharynx but are absent from the intestine. Digestion and absorption probably occur in the intestine.

The coelomic cavity is spacious in regular echinoids, less so in the irregular echinoids. In addition to the major coelom, there are some minor coelomic cavities, such as the peripharyngeal cavity that encloses Aristotle's lantern. This cavity in some echinoids has five elongated sacs (Stewart's organs) that are expansion chambers for the fluid in the peripharyngeal cavity. The coelom is filled with a fluid that has about the same composition as sea water plus a large number of coelomocytes of about six types. Some of them are phagocytic with large pseudopodia, while others are nonphagocytic with short pseudopodia. The number of coelomocytes per unit volume of fluid varies greatly. Some have as many as 4,000 to 7,000 per cubic millimeter of fluid.

The hemal system consists of a hemal ring around the esophagus on the aboral side of Aristotle's lantern, radial sinuses beneath the radial canals of the water-vascular system (Fig. 27-31), the ventral marginal and the dorsal marginal sinuses on the ventral and dorsal sides of the intestine respectively, and small vessels that supply the organs or tissues directly. The sinuses do not have a definite lining, as they are made up of connective tissue and a covering of peritoneum. Little is known about the circulation in echinoids.

Some echinoids have five pairs of gills attached to the peristome (Fig. 27-25). The gills are outpockets of the body wall and communicate with the peripharyngeal coelomic cavity. On the aboral part of the lantern a special muscle (the elevator of the compasses) is attached to the compasses already described; and when this muscle contracts, the volume of the peripharyngeal cavity is increased and fluid is drawn out of the gills. Other muscles, the depressors of the compasses, pull the compasses down and force fluid into the gills. This pumping occurs only when the echinoid needs oxygen. Respiratory movements are controlled by the nerve ring, which is stimulated by an increase in carbon dioxide content of the fluid. Peristomial gills are lacking in the irregular echinoids, which use the modified podia of the petaloids for breathing.

The chief excretory products appear to be ammonia and urea. Coelomocytes ingest waste substances and carry them to the gills or body wall for elimination or deposit. The axial gland may also serve as an excretory organ, for coelomocytes laden with granules are numerous in it.

The nervous system has about the same pattern as the water-vascular system. The ectoneural is the chief nervous system. It consists of the circumoral ring that surrounds the pharynx within the lantern (Fig. 27-33); the five radial nerves that arise from the nerve ring, pass between the pyramids of the lantern, and follow the underside of the test in the midline of the ambulacra, just beneath the radial canals of the water-vascular system (Fig. 27-31); and nerves given off by the radial nerves that penetrate the test to the podia, body wall (where an extensive subepidermal plexus is formed), spines, and pedicellariae. Each of the podial nerves ends in a nerve network in the terminal sucker (Fig. 27-31), and the subepidermal plexus supplies the spines and pedicellariae with a network of nerves. A hyponeural nervous system of five plaques of nervous tissue on the aboral surface of the nerve ring sends nerves to the muscles of the lantern. Some regular echinoids may also have an entoneural nervous system in the form of a ring in the inner surface around the periproct, which gives off nerves to the gonads.

Sense organs are represented in the echinoids by tactile and taste organs in the spines, podia, and pedicellariae. The sphaeridia have functions of equilibrium. Some echinoids have photosensitive eye-spots in the aboral ectoderm, most of which are negatively phototropic.

The echinoids are dioecious, although hermaphrodites may occur as anomalies. Except in the case of brooding females, there is no sexual dimorphism. The regular echinoids have five gonads suspended by mesenteries along the interambulacra on the inner side of the test (Fig. 27-33). In the irregular echinoids the gonads may be reduced to three or four because the gonads of certain interambulacra are destroyed by the migration of the periproct. The gonads are quite large when ripe and may extend from the aboral center to the lantern. Each has a short gonoduct that opens through a gonopore in a plate of the apical system of the aboral end. Histologically, each hollow gonad is covered with coelomic peritoneum and lined with germinal epithelium with muscle and connective tissue between.

Both sperm and eggs are shed into the sea, and fertilization is external. Some echinoids of both subclasses brood their young, especially in the Antarctic (Fig. 27-34). The brood pouch may be a depression on the petaloids, around the periproct, or enclosed in spines on the peristome.

DEVELOPMENT

The eggs, mostly small except in brooding species, have a holoblastic, equal type of cleavage. After the eight-cell stage the four cells at the vegetal pole divide unequally into four small micromeres and four large macromeres. Further division of the micromeres and macromeres results in a coeloblastula of about 1,000 cells that are mostly equal in size, except for the micromeres at the vegetal pole. The blastula is flagellated and rotates within the fertilization membrane before the embryo is freed. The stage of the swimming blastula is reached about 12 hours after fertilization.

At the flattened vegetal pole the micromeres proliferate, sending mesenchymal cells into the interior. The invagination is embolic, and the resulting archenteron proliferates and produces secondary mesenchyme at its tip. At the inner end of the archenteron a double coelomic sac is formed and develops into the coelom. The conical gastrula develops into a character-

Brood pouch and young

Fig. 27-34

Cidaroid sea urchin with brood pouch full of young.

istic echinopluteus larva with four to six long arms and an easel-shaped form (Fig. 27-3). There are many varieties of the echinopluteus among the different species of echinoids. The echinopluteus is small and planktonic. Several months may elapse before the larva attains full development. The metamorphosis of the echinopluteus into a young urchin is rapid, requiring only an hour or so.

After metamorphosis, development continues. At metamorphosis only five pairs of podia are present, but additional pairs arise at the oral side, forcing the first ones aborally. At first the apical plates cover the entire aboral surface; but as the ambulacral and interambulacral plates form, the apical plates cover only a small surface. In echinoids that brood their young a free larval stage is omitted, and metamorphosis may occur in two or three days.

CLASS HOLOTHUROIDEA

Holothurians are commonly known as sea cucumbers because of their resemblance to the vegetable. In some ways they are the most aberrant group of echinoderms. They are elongated along an oral-aboral axis. Their shape forces them to lie on their side instead of on their oral surface, which leads to a differentiation of

Fig. 27-35

Holothuroidea. **A,** *Thyone briareus,* a common Atlantic coast sea cucumber. **B,** *Stichopus californicus,* the California cucumber.

Some 1,100 species and 170 genera of holothurians are recognized at present. They vary in size from 3 cm body length to 1.5 meters, with a diameter of several inches. Most common North American species are about 6 to 10 inches long. The largest forms are tropical. They display a wide range of color. Many species are of dull brown, black, or greenish coloration. Some are red, yellow, violet, and other shades. Striped patterns are common. The five orders of Holothuroidea are as follows:

Elasipoda. With scanty podia; shield-shaped tentacles; no respiratory tree; madreporite external; deep sea. *Benthodytes, Elpidia.*

Aspidochirota. With numerous locomotory and papillate podia; shield-shaped tentacles; paired respiratory trees. *Mesothuria, Stichopus* (Fig. 27-35, *B*).

Dendrochirota. With numerous podia; dendritic tentacles; respiratory tree. *Thyone* (Fig. 27-35, *A*), *Psolus.*

Molpadonia. With few podia; pinnate or unbranched tentacles; respiratory tree. *Caudina, Molpadia.*

Apoda. With no podia; vermiform; simple or pinnate tentacles; no respiratory tree. *Synapta, Leptosynapta.*

Because of the nature of their rather diffuse skeleton, holothurians have not left an impressive fossil record. Impressions of their bodies have been found in the Cambrian Burgess Shale of British Columbia, and their skeletal spicules and ossicles have been found in limestones and other rocks dating from the Mississipian period.

GENERAL MORPHOLOGIC FEATURES
EXTERNAL ANATOMY

The body varies in shape from globose to vermiform and cylindric. Since the side on which holothurians lie is usually flattened, it is called a sole and bears the locomotor podia. This gives the animal a secondary bilateral symmetry. On the dorsal surface the podia are usually represented by warts and papillae. The creeping sole consists of three ambulacral areas (the trivium) and two interambulacral areas; the dorsal surface has two ambulacral areas (the bivium) and three interambulacral areas. The podia of the sole may be arranged in three longitudinal rows, corresponding to the three ambulacral areas (*Stichopus*), or they may be scattered all

dorsal and ventral surfaces and a secondary bilateral symmetry. Their skeleton is reduced to microscopic ossicles embedded in the body wall. They have no arms and no pedicellariae. Ambulacral grooves are lacking, but ambulacral and interambulacral areas run from the anterior to the posterior end. Tube feet may or may not be present. The buccal podia are modified into a ring of five or more tentacles around the mouth.

The holothurians have worldwide distribution in all seas and at all depths. They have benthonic habits and are common in intertidal zones, where they are found on mucky bottoms, usually concealed from sight. Certain areas have much larger faunas than others, such as the Indo-West Pacific area, Australian coasts, Hawaiian Islands, Mediterranean Sea coasts, and many others. Along our Pacific coast the various species of *Stichopus* (Fig. 27-35, *B*), *Parastichopus,* and *Cucumaria* are among the most familiar. Along the Atlantic coast, common genera are *Cucumaria* and *Thyone* (Fig. 27-35, *A*).

over the sole (*Holothuria*). In the common *Thyone* and some others, podia are present on both sole and dorsal regions of the body although the suckers are best developed on the ventral podia. There is a tendency in many holothurians for the number of podia on the sole to be reduced and their radial distribution lessened. Podia are entirely absent in Apoda.

Sea cucumbers are able to move about but mostly at a slow rate. Those with differentiated creeping soles can perhaps move best of all, using their podia very much as asteroids do. Some use muscular waves of contraction much like those of a caterpillar. They can right themselves when placed on their dorsal sides by twisting the podia of the oral side around and attaching them to a substratum. Apodous holothurians can move by using their tentacles as holdfasts. Burrowing, which is common among the order Apoda, is accomplished by pushing into the sand with alternate contractions of their circular and longitudinal muscles, using their tentacles to shove the sand aside. Animals without tentacles cannot burrow. *Thyone* buries the middle part of its body, leaving both ends above the surface. Swimming is accomplished in young *Leptosynapta* by curving into a U shape and thrashing the ends of the body together in a sort of scissors kick. The deep-sea apodous form *Pelagothuria* has a sail or web formed by the papillae or modified podia for locomotion.

The body surface in most sea cucumbers is leathery and somewhat slimy, with microscopic endoskeletal ossicles embedded in the dermis (Fig. 27-36). In the family Psolidae the skin plates are large and overlap (imbricated), forming a sort of armor. The miscroscopic ossicles assume many shapes and sizes and are useful in taxonomic studies (Fig. 27-37). The ossicles are supposed to represent the persistent embryonic state of the skeleton (neoteny).

Fig. 27-36

Surface view of whole mount of skin of sea cucumber *Synapta* showing microscopic endoskeletal ossicles scattered through dermis. Compare with Fig. 23-37, *E*. (From Andrew: Textbook of comparative histology, The Oxford University Press, Inc.)

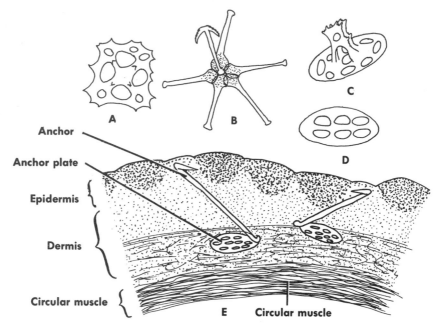

Fig. 27-37

Some types of ossicles in sea cucumbers. **A,** Radial piece *(Holothuria).* **B,** Anchor type *(Molpadia).* **C,** Table type *(Holothuria).* **D,** Biscuit type *(Holothuria).* **E,** Section through body wall of *Synapta* with anchors in place. Compare **E** with Fig. 27-36. (**B** after Danielsson and Koren; **E** after Woodland; both modified from Hyman.)

Ossicles are present in the tentacles, the papillate podia, the adhesive disks of the locomotor podia, and even in the internal structures.

The mouth may be terminal or displaced dorsally or ventrally. It is circular in outline and surrounded by a buccal membrane (Fig. 27-38, *A*). Around it in a single circlet are 10 to 30 modified buccal podia, known as tentacles. These podia contain extensions of the water-vascular system from the radial canals. They may or may not be of the same size. Both mouth and tentacles can be pulled into the body by retractor muscles, and the body wall made to close over them. In the order Dendrochirota the tentacles are much branched (dendritic) as in *Thyone* and *Cucumaria.* Sometimes they are attached to a short central stalk, which has horizontal branches (order Aspidochirota); or they may be fingerlike (order Molpadonia). The anus is terminal in the orders Molpadonia and Apoda, but is displaced in the other orders to the dorsal or ventral side. The anus may be encircled by small papillae or calcareous plates.

INTERNAL ANATOMY

The body wall varies in thickness among the different orders. Its surface has no cilia, and a thin cuticle covers the underlying epidermis. The epidermis consists of a single layer of tall epithelial cells that tend to merge with the dermis underneath. The epidermis also has sensory and gland cells, which are common in the Apoda.

The dermis makes up the greater part of the body wall and consists of connective tissue that encloses the calcareous ossicles (Fig. 27-37, *E*). The pigment, which gives color to the animal, may be in the form of chromatophores in the dermis or as free granules in both epidermis and dermis. A nerve plexus is contained in the dermis, and a subepidermal plexus may occur under the epidermis. Under the dermis is a layer of circular muscles that may form a complete cylinder, or the layer may be interrupted

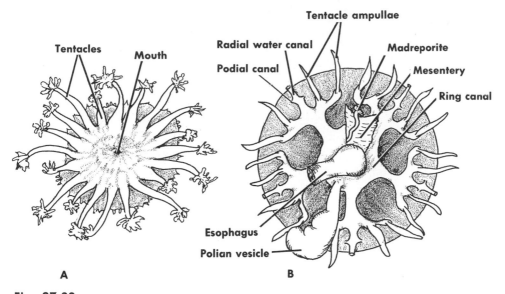

Fig. 27-38

A, Anterior or oral view of *Holothuria*. B, Diagram of water-vascular system of *Holothuria*. (Modified from Bather.)

by five single or double bands of longitudinal muscles that run along the ambulacral areas. The muscle fibers are of the smooth type. The inner surface of the body wall is lined with ciliated epithelium.

The water-vascular system is similar to that of other echinoderms in its basic plan (Fig. 27-38, *B*). It consists of a water ring around the proximal pharynx, five radial canals running the length of the body wall between the longitudinal and transverse muscles, small lateral canals to the podia, and a stone canal to an internal madreporite.

The water ring around the base of the pharynx bears one or more elongated or rounded polian vesicles that hang down in the coelomic cavity and open by a narrow neck into the ring canal (Fig. 27-38, *B*). As many as a dozen or more polian vesicles are found in the two common orders Dendrochirota and Aspidochirota, although some orders have the original condition of only one. The vesicle's wall is similar to that of the water ring. Polian vesicles may serve as expansion chambers for the maintenance of pressure in the water-vascular system. The stone canal, with calcified wall, arises from the water ring or ring canal and passes to the madreporite. There may

be more than one stone canal and more than one madreporite. The madreporites are internal (except in the order Elasipoda); and coelomic fluid, rather than sea water, enters the water-vascular system through them.

Of the five radial canals three lie in the trivium, or ventral side, and two in the bivium, or dorsal side (Fig. 27-39, *A*). After leaving the water ring, the radial canals pass upward through the outer wall of the aquapharyngeal bulb to the inner side of the calcareous ring, where the canals give off branches to the tentacles. Then proceeding through notches or holes in the radial plates of the calcareous ring, the radial canals run posteriorly along the inner surface of the ambulacral areas. Here the radial canals supply lateral or podial canals (with valves) to the podia and their ampullae (Fig. 27-39, *B*). Locomotor podia are projections of the body wall found chiefly on the sole. They may or may not have suckers. Their corresponding ampullae are sacs projecting into the coelom. The papillate podia on the dorsal surface are also provided with lateral canals from the radial canals, but these have nothing to do with locomotion. The radial canals terminate in the last podia or end podia of the

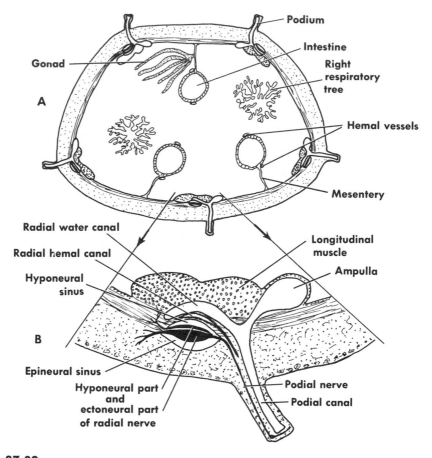

Fig. 27-39

A, Schematic section of holothurian. **B,** Enlarged section of one of radii shown in **A.** (Modified from Lang.)

ambulacral areas. The water-vascular system is poorly developed in the orders Molpadonia and Apoda.

The digestive system of holothurians consists typically of mouth, pharynx, esophagus, stomach, intestine, cloaca, and anus (Fig. 27-40). One or more of these divisions may be absent. The mouth, already described, leads into the pharynx, which is supported by mesenteric strands in a coelomic cavity, called the aquapharyngeal bulb. The beginning of the pharynx is encircled by a calcareous ring usually made up of five radial and five interradial plates bound together by connective tissue. This ring serves as an insertion point for the longitudinal muscle bands and retractor muscles of the tentacles and as a support for the pharynx and water ring. The

pharynx may lead into a slender esophagus, which opens into a short, muscular stomach; or, as in *Cucumaria*, it may pass directly to the intestine. The holothurian intestine may be three or four times the length of the body and is looped in a definite arrangement in the coelom. The last part of the intestine is sometimes called the large intestine. The terminal parts of the large intestine are called the cloaca in those forms that have respiratory trees. The cloaca is attached to the surrounding wall by radiating strands of connective tissue and muscle. The digestive system is supported by a mesentery that is continuous or else one that is divided into three portions.

The wall of the digestive tract is made up of a ciliated or nonciliated epithelial

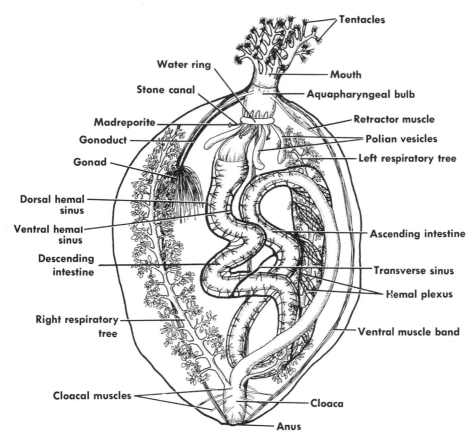

Fig. 27-40

Internal structure of common sea cucumber *Thyone* (schematic).

lining, an inner layer of connective tissue, a circular and longitudinal muscle layer, an outer thin layer of connective tissue, and a ciliated peritoneal covering. Gland cells may occur in the pharynx and stomach. Coelomocytes assist in digestion by carrying intestinal enzymes into the lumen and by distributing products of digestion.

Many holothurians, especially the dendrochirotes, are plankton feeders, making use of tentacles with mucus secretions for catching small organisms. The tentacles deliver their food catch by being thrust into the mouth and pharynx where the food is wiped off. Other holothurians feed on deposits that are passed into their mouths by their tentacles or are swallowed as the animals burrow in the deposits of the substratum. The organic part of the ingested material is digested, and the indigestible part is voided through the anus. A great

deal of substrate can pass through an animal in a short period of time.

Some members of the order Aspidochirota, such as *Holothuria* and *Actinopyga*, have small white or reddish tubules, called the organs or tubules of Cuvier, attached usually at the base of the respiratory tree. When irritated, the animal shoots slender sticky threads out by contractions of the body. These threads wrap around an intruder and render it helpless. When the sea cucumber breaks away, the threads are left behind and new ones are regenerated. These threads may also be used to trap small organisms as well as to repel predators.

The hemal system is well developed in holothurians (Fig. 27-40). It is made up of a hemal ring around the pharynx, radial hemal sinuses that parallel the water ring and radial canals of the water-vascular system, and a dorsal and ventral sinus along the small intestine and part of the large intestine. The intestinal sinuses give off a large number of small channels to the intestine. The hemal system is best developed in its relation to the intestine. From the ventral sinus, running along the descending intestine, a transverse connection crosses over to the ventral sinus running along the ascending intestine. The dorsal sinus is connected to the ascending small intestine by a network of lacunae, called the rete mirabile. A collecting vessel joins this network with the ascending small intestine by numerous branches. Part of the rete network runs to the terminal part of the left respiratory tree. There are variations in the distribution of the hemal system in the various species.

The hemal vessels do not have definite linings, but their walls contain coelomic epithelium, connective tissue, and muscle. The hemal fluid is about the same as that of coelomic cavities and contains coelomocytes that are formed in the walls of the hemal channels (C. L. Prosser and C. Judson), not in the polian vesicles as formerly supposed.

Respiration occurs in the skin, tube feet, and the respiratory trees. The respiratory trees (Fig. 27-40) represent a unique breathing device of tubules and are found in all orders except Apoda and Elasipoda. They are evaginations of the digestive tract at the anterior part of the cloaca near the entrance of the large intestine. Each respiratory tree consists of a main stem from which branches with terminal vesicles spring. There are two, left and right, and they occupy the space between the intestinal loops in the coelomic cavity. The two trees may enter the cloaca by a common stem or separately. Water is drawn into and out of the trees by rhythmic contractions of the cloaca and tree tubules. When the cloaca dilates, water flows in and fills it. The anal sphincters then close the anus, and the contraction of the cloacal wall forces water into the respiratory trees. Water is forced out by relaxation of the cloaca, contraction of the tubules, and opening of the anus. Several pumping cycles are required to fill the trees, but only one vigorous expulsion is necessary to expel all the water.

Experimental evidence indicates that oxygen in the inspired water diffuses through the terminal vesicles into the coelomic fluid and thence into the hemal system. Oxygen requirements of sea cucumbers are very low.

Excretion takes place by means of the coelomocytes and the respiratory trees. Most waste is in the form of ammonia compounds, although information about excretion is scanty. Urea and purine nitrogen have been identified in some. Nitrogenous waste in crystalline form is picked up and conveyed by coelomocytes to the respiratory tree, gonadal tubules, or to any hollow organ with an external opening.

Although the apodans lack respiratory trees, they possess ciliated funnels called urns that are found on various parts of the body, especially on the mesenteries. The urns are lined with ciliated columnar epithelium and covered with coelomic epithelium. They may be clustered together to form trees of urns. Their cavities contain coelomocytes, which have accumulated waste in them. Coelomocytes later carry this waste to the body wall, or they let it fall into the coelom to form masses called brown bodies.

The nervous system of holothurians follows the pattern of the water-vascular system, and is found between the canals and the body wall. The system consists of a nerve ring, radial nerves, and their numerous branches. The circumoral nerve ring is a flattened bandlike structure in the buccal membrane close to the base of the tentacles and usually within the calcareous ring. It supplies a nerve to each of the tentacles and also nerves to the buccal membrane and pharynx. Five radial nerves pass from the nerve ring, one to each of the ambulacral areas (Fig. 27-39, *B*). On leaving the ring, each radial nerve passes outward through a notch or hole in the plate of the calcareous ring. The radial nerves are located in the innermost dermal layer of the body as they pass through the ambulacral areas external to the radial water vessel. On the outer side of each radial nerve is the epineural sinus (noncoelomate), and on the inner side is the hyponeural sinus (coelomate) (Fig. 27-39, *B*). The radial nerves are ganglionated and divided into a thicker ectoneural part and a thinner hyponeural part. The ectoneural division furnishes ganglionated nerves to the podia and to a body wall plexus that supplies the sense organs. The hyponeural division (motor) innervates the body-wall muscles. The hyponeural division is found only on the middle course of the radial nerve, not at the ends. No aboral nervous system is found in holothurians. The nerve ring apparently does not have a dominant role in nervous integration.

Sense organs are restricted mainly to sensory cells in the epidermis. The whole body surface is sensitive to light, and in some synaptids (order Apoda) there are eyespots at the base of the tentacles. Like the eyespots of sea stars, these can detect shadow movements but cannot form images. The surface of synaptids also has warty elevations containing sensory buds surrounded by glands. These sense organs send nerves to ganglia of the dermal nerve plexus.

Statocysts have been demonstrated in a number of holothurians. These may be located on the radial nerves near their exit from the calcareous ring and are hollow spheres with lithocytes. Each statocyst sends a nerve to the adjacent radial nerve. Most statocysts are found around the nerve ring, but some are distributed along the ventrolateral radial nerves. All holothurians are negatively phototropic, and burrowing species are positively geotropic.

The power of autotomy is one of the most striking characteristics of the holothurians. This phenomenon is best shown in a process called evisceration, in which certain visceral organs are completely eliminated through a rupture in the cloacal region or in the body wall. Mention has already been made of the tubules of Cuvier by which these sticky structures are cast out in defense against predators or other invaders. Evisceration is a more drastic process. Under conditions of crowding, high temperatures, excessive irritation, foul water, and injuries to the body, the sea cucumber ruptures itself by a forceful contraction of the body (the coelom of which is filled with fluid) and, depending upon the species, emits one or both respiratory trees, the digestive tract (except the ends), and the gonads. Sometimes (e.g., *Thyone*) the anterior end is ruptured and the an-terior part of the viscera is shed. Such eviscerated individuals usually recover under normal conditions and undergo regeneration of the missing parts. The course of regeneration varies; but in many species studied the cloaca seems to be the center of regeneration. If the digestive tract has been shed in evisceration, the stubs of the esophagus and cloaca send outgrowths along the remnants of the mesentery, which meet to form a new tract in some 25 days. During the period of regeneration the animal does not feed. In *Stichopus*, regeneration of a new digestive tract is made from the cells along the torn edge of the mesentery. Although evisceration has been observed mostly in sea cucumbers under laboratory conditions, there is some evidence that it may occur in nature when the temperature is unusually high and the oxygen content of the water is low.

Usually each half of a transversely bisected animal forms a complete animal; in smaller sections only the section with a cloaca does so.

Most holothurians are dioecious, and sexual dimorphism is not evident, except in those females that brood their young. Hermaphroditic forms are sometimes found, especially in the order Apoda; but a hermaphroditic individual is not male and female at the same time; it is usually protandrous.

The reproductive system comprises a gonad and its duct (Fig. 27-40). The gonad is located in the anterior part of the coelom beneath a middorsal interambulacrum. It consists usually of a tuft or cluster of simple or branched tubules united basally. In some species, such as *Stichopus*, there may be two tufts, one on each side of the mesentery. Some authorities consider each tuft to be a separate gonad. From the common hollow base into which the tubules enter, a gonoduct passes in the mesentery to the gonopore, which may be mounted on a genital papilla. The gonopore is found either within or near the tentacles. The gonoduct sometimes divides so that more than one gonopore is present. The gonadal tubules are lined with germinal epithelium and covered with peritoneum. The gonoduct is lined with ciliated epithelium and covered with connective tissue.

Most species spawn during spring and **593**

summer. Fertilization is external in sea water. Dendrochirote and apodous species brood their young, especially in cold temperatures. Such brooding forms produce large yolky eggs. Brood pouches or positions are commonly found on the sole or dorsal body areas, where there may be depressions. The invaginated brood pouches may actually be internal in position. Spawning females catch the eggs released from the gonopore with their tentacles and transfer them, sometimes with the aid of special podia, to the brood depressions. In a few cases (e.g., *Synaptula*), eggs develop in the coelom where they are discharged from the gonads and fertilized in some unknown manner. The young are discharged from the female through an anal rupture.

Asexual reproduction occurs in a few species, such as *Cucumaria planci,* by transverse fission. Asexual reproduction seems to be restricted to young individuals.

DEVELOPMENT

Holothurians follow the deuterostome pattern of equal, holoblastic, and radial cleavage. Except in species that brood their young, where development is direct and the young hatch as juveniles, development occurs in the sea, where the embryo becomes a planktonic member.

The usual pattern of a coeloblastula with embolic gastrulation is followed. The gastrula becomes flagellated, escapes from the fertilization membrane, and develops into a free-swimming member. Mesenchyme is usually given off from the tip of the archenteron and fills the blastocoel with entomesoderm. The coelom is formed from the distal part of the archenteron, and the anlage of the digestive tract from the proximal part. The blastopore becomes the anus.

The coelomic sac separates from the archenteron and constricts, making an anterior hydrocoel and axocoel and a posterior somatocoel. The somatocoel later divides into the left and right somatocoels. Only the left hydrocoel and axocoel, which will form the definitive stone canal, are present. In the middle of the ventral surface a stomodeum forms and connects with the digestive tract.

About the third day of development, the embryo becomes the free-swimming auricularia larva (Fig. 27-3). The transparent

larva is provided with a flagellated band that makes a number of loops and curves similar to that of the bipinnaria of asteroids. The larva is usually about 1 mm. in length, but it may be longer. The auricularia is soon changed into a barrel-shaped larva (doliolaria), which has five hooplike rings that have arisen by the partial degeneration and reconstruction of the flagellated band of the auricularia. In some cases the embryo bypasses the auricularia stage altogether and becomes the doliolaria.

In the doliolaria the mouth, which is in the middle of the ventral surface of the auricularia, now has shifted to the anterior pole; and the anus has shifted to the posterior pole. In its metamorphosis to an adult the young sea cucumber has five tentacles and one or two functional podia and is sometimes referred to as a pentactula. Additional podia and tentacles appear later.

Subphylum Pelmatozoa
CLASS CRINOIDEA

Crinoids are stalked or unstalked and represent the most primitive of all classes of echinoderms. They have a flower-shaped body, which is placed at the tip of an attached stalk (sea lilies) or is free as an adult (feather stars). Most living crinoids belong to the stemless feather stars (Fig. 27-42). Crinoids are the sole surviving members of the Pelmatozoa, which flourished during the Paleozoic era (Fig. 27-1, C, D.). The oldest crinoids date from the lower Cambrian, but the origin of this group must lie somewhere in the Precambrian period.

Crinoids are distinguished from other echinoderms by their shape and by the structure of their skeleton (Fig. 27-41). The body is globular or disk shaped and is enclosed in an armor of symmetrically arranged calcareous plates. It bears a number of outspread appendages called arms that are usually subdivided into forks and many branches. The pinnulated arms and stem (when present) consist of many segments formed of calcareous ossicles, so joined that they permit a considerable degree of flexibility.

Although the crinoids gave rise to no other groups of echinoderms, the members of the subphylum Pelmatozoa, to which they belong, have laid down the basic plan of the modern echinoderms as we know them. The evidence from all disciplines indicates that the distinctive echinoderm characteristics of radial symmetry superimposed upon a bilateral symmetry, attachment usually at some stage of the life history, the coil of the gut, the development of the hydrocoel and the water-vascular system, the development of a free-swimming, ciliated bilateral larva, the pentamerous body of ambulacral and interambulacral plates, and the system of canals growing out of coelomic cavities are all features that can be traced back to the pelmatozoan ancestor.

The pelmatozoans were one of the earliest groups to exploit fully the sessile mode of existence. By having numerous arms provided with food grooves and sensory structures they were able to explore and to gather food from all directions. A heavy armor of plates ensured them of maximum protection against the dangers to which sessile forms are exposed. The arrangement of internal organs, such as nerves and blood vessels, was influenced by the above characteristics. Crinoids perhaps developed many of these tendencies to the fullest extent possible. By adaptive radiation the basic pelmatozoan pattern has been modified to form the various groups of modern echinoderms. Zoologists have been able to explain how some, but not all, of these changes could have occurred.

About 625 living species of crinoids are known, of which approximately 80 are stalked. This is a modest number compared with the more than 5,000 fossil species known to paleontologists. The heyday of the crinoids was the remote geologic past, and modern species represent only a remnant of their former greatness. The trend has been toward an unattached existence.

Crinoids live in all seas, except the Baltic and Black. None is found in fresh water. Feather stars are usually more common in shallow water and occur most abundantly in shallow tropical lagoons. More stalked forms (sea lilies) are found in deep water than stemless species (feather stars). Some sea lilies, for instance, have been dredged from depths as great as 5,000 meters. Many crinoids are also found in very

Fig. 27-41

General structure of stalked crinoid, or sea lily. (From Hickman: Integrated principles of zoology, The C. V. Mosby Co.)

cold water in Arctic and Antarctic seas. Their distribution is spotty, however, for they are scarce in certain regions of both the Atlantic and Pacific oceans. The genus *Antedon* (Fig. 27-42) has a wide range of distribution from cold water seas to warm. Feather stars prefer rocky bottoms; but sea lilies, especially those with long cirri, are often dredged from muddy sea floors. The same species may exhibit great variations in size range under different environmental conditions, being much larger in cold than in warm waters. Crinoids are often found in dense aggregations

Fig. 27-42

Feather star *Antedon* (suborder Comatulida), adult free-swimming stage, about natural size. **A,** At rest. **B,** Position of arms in swimming. (Modified from Chadwick, 1907.)

in a favorable location because of the feeble powers of dispersal of their free-swimming larvae.

Crinoids are often infested with large numbers of other animals. Some of these may establish symbiotic relationships of commensalism and parasitism. The curious polychaete myzostomes are ectoparasites on crinoids. These parasites live by inserting their pharynx into the food channels of the crinoids and sucking up the food. Carnivorous snails (*Stylina, Sabinella*) are able to bore with their proboscis through the theca and suck out the soft parts. Many crustaceans are harbored in some way by crinoids. Hydroids frequently attach themselves to a crinoid stem as a substratum.

Usually sea lilies, which are chiefly found in deeper waters, are bothered less by other animals than feather stars.

Crinoids range in size from 3 cm. across the outspread arms to more than 1 meter across. Most free-swimming crinoids are about 1 foot across the arms. In present stalked crinoids the average stalk rarely exceeds 2 feet, but in extinct species it was much longer (50 to 70 feet).

Feather stars may be highly colored because of conjugated carotenoids. They may be green, purple, yellow, or red. *Antedon bifida* owes its red color to echinochrome. The arms are frequently banded with different colors.

The class Crinoidea includes three orders or subclasses, which are wholly extinct, and one order or subclass of living crinoids. The three extinct groups are Inadunata, Flexibilia, and Camerata. All modern crinoids belong to the order (subclass) Articulata. Fossil crinoids had the general structural features of extant species, although differences in many details of these general features do exist. The calyx of fossil species tended to constitute more of the crown, and the tegmen included more plates and was less leathery than in modern crinoids. Stems were usually much longer in the fossils, and stemmed species were relatively more common. Many fossil crinoids had an asymmetric arrangement of plates, in contrast to the regular pentamerous organization of modern forms.

The Articulata, or existing crinoids, are comprised of the stalked orders or suborders (Isocrinida, Millericrinida, Cyrtocrinida) and the unstalked suborder (Comatulida). As already stated, the suborder Comatulida includes the vast majority of living crinoids.

GENERAL MORPHOLOGIC FEATURES
EXTERNAL ANATOMY

The crinoid has a pentamerous body proper, called the crown, and an attachment stalk. The stalk is characteristic of sessile sea lilies, but is vestigial or has disappeared in feather stars. The latter group is attached when young, but breaks off from its stalk when mature and swims away. The stalk has a cylindric or polygonal contour and its internal skeletal ossicles give it a jointed appearance. It is often fringed with small,

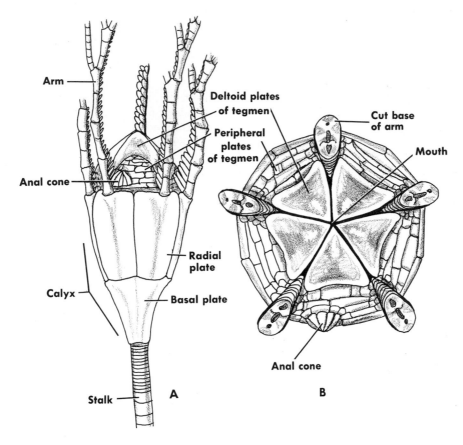

Fig. 27-43

A, *Hyocrinus,* a primitive existing crinoid with high calyx and deltoid plates. B, Oral view of tegmen of *Hyocrinus.* (After Carpenter; modified from Hyman.)

jointed cirri arranged in whorls around it (Fig. 27-41). Although the stem is lost in feather stars, some of the circlets of cirri persist at the aboral end of the crown (Fig. 27-42). The cirri, the terminal joint of which is claw shaped, are used for grasping a substratum when needed (feather stars) and when the stalk becomes dislodged (sea lilies). The stalk bears at its terminal end rootlike extensions or disklike enlargements for attachment.

The crown consists of the skeletal calyx or aboral body wall enclosing the viscera, the membranous tegmen or oral body wall, and a set of arms (brachia) that originate at the periphery between the calyx and the tegmen (Fig. 27-43). The calyx (theca) is composed of two circlets, each of five plates. The plates of the lower circlet are called basals and those of the upper circlet radials. Such a calyx is said to be monocyclic. When a third circlet of infrabasal plates is present below or aboral to the basal plates, the calyx is called dicyclic. The radials make up the skeletal elements at the beginnings of the arms.

The mouth is usually located near the center of the tegmen (Figs. 27-43, 27-44). From the mouth five ambulacral grooves run to the arms, thus dividing the tegmen into five ambulacral and five interambulacral areas. The anus, usually located at the tip of the anal cone, is present in one of the interambulacra.

Each of the five arms, the primitive number, is usually subdivided by one or more forks, forming at least 10 arms, and sometimes many more (up to 200 in some comat-

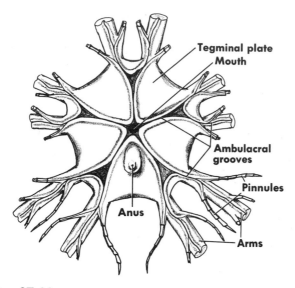

Fig. 27-44

Oral view of tegmen of *Antedon,* arms removed. (Modified from MacBride.)

ulids). The arms vary in length and shape. Some are long and slender; others are short and wide. They are usually shorter in cold water than in warm. The average length of an arm is 4 or 5 inches, but it may be shorter or longer. The arms may be of different lengths in the same animal. They are composed of brachial ossicles, which may be arranged in a single series (uniserial) or in a double series (biserial). They carry lateral appendages called pinnules. Pinnules have the same structure as the arms; and although their main function is to capture food and bear reproductive organs, they are differentiated into types with specialized functions (tactile and protective). The oral ambulacral grooves on the oral surface of the tegmen also extend along the arms and pinnules, so that each arm and pinnule has a ciliated groove along its center (Figs. 27-44, 27-45). A groove may be lacking in some of the specialized

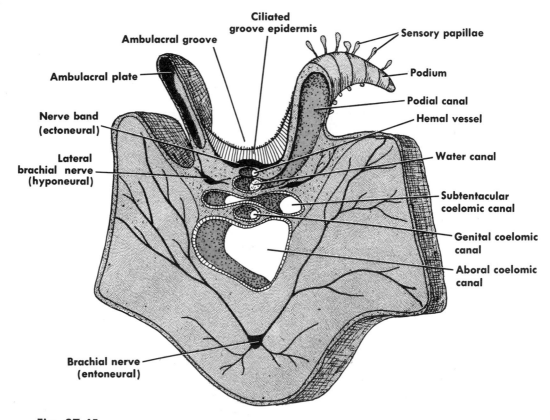

Fig. 27-45

Transverse section of crinoid arm. (After Bather; redrawn from Lankester, editor: A treatise on zoology, Adam & Charles Black, Ltd.)

pinnules. These ambulacral grooves bear raised edges that are scalloped into projections (lappets), which alternate on the two margins of a groove. On the inner side of the base of each lappet is a group of three podia. These lappets and podia are also found on the pinnules as well as on the arms. Small spherical bodies (saccules) are also located on the outer side of the lappets along the ambulacral grooves. Their function is not known, but pigment often collects in them in preserved specimens. Along the surface of the tegmen the ambulacral grooves bear reduced lappets with a single podium, not in groups of three.

The free-swimming comatulids, when inactive, are usually found attached by claws on certain cirri to some object. When detached they can swim by raising and lowering a set of arms alternately with others (Fig. 27-42). When the arms are raised, the pinnules of those arms are flexed against the arm axis; when lowered, the pinnules are fully extended. Comatulids can also crawl by catching hold of objects with the adhesive ends of the pinnules and pulling themselves along by contracting their arms. All have the oral surface uppermost when they swim or crawl. The well-known *Antedon* is a very active comatulid and is capable of diverse movements. The sessile sea lilies can swish their arms and pinnules and bend their stems for adjustment to the varying conditions of water currents.

INTERNAL ANATOMY

The endoskeleton composes most of the body wall, and its arrangement is of great importance in taxonomy. The endoskeletal ossicles are of the fenestrated calcite type characteristic of echinoderms. They are made up mostly of calcium carbonate and silicon dioxide. The ossicles are bound together by connective tissue ligaments. The stalk is made up of a single row of superimposed disk-shaped ossicles called columnals, which may be like or unlike throughout the stem. The end surfaces of the columnals are adapted for articulation with each other, and some flexibility is possible. The stem lacks muscles, but the columnals are bound together by elastic ligaments. The cirri, which are carried by the nodes of the stem, fit into articulating sockets, and consist of ossicles called cirrals held together by elastic ligaments. The cirri likewise have no muscles. The arms and pinnules also have a similar solid structure of superimposed ossicles held together by ligaments, but unlike the stem and cirri they are provided with muscles.

The body surface may or may not have a cuticle. The poorly developed epidermis is mostly a syncytial epithelium that is not sharply delineated from the underlying mesenchyme and may be lacking altogether. The ambulacral grooves are lined with tall, ciliated cells that are supporting and sensory in function. The mesenchyme of the body wall contains a gelatinous matrix together with stellate cells and fibers.

The muscular system consists chiefly of intersegmental muscle fibers that are restricted to the arms and pinnules. Flexor muscles enable the arms to bend inward toward the disk, and elastic ligaments enable them to be extended. Such an arrangement is also found in the pinnules. Muscle fibers appear to be a mixture of smooth and striated fibers.

The water-vascular system plan is similar to that of other echinoderms, consisting of a ring canal, radial vessels, and podia (Figs. 27-45, 27-46). The ambulacral grooves have already been described. Underneath each groove lies a canal of the water-vascular system. The water ring canal gives off a radial water canal into each arm, and the radial water canals send branches alternately on the side to each pinnule. Also in each arm and pinnule a group of three podia of the ambulacral groove receives alternately on each side a water canal that divides and sends a branch to the podium. The podia lack suckers and ampullae and are covered with cilia. They are well supplied with nerves, and their primary function is to serve as respiratory organs and for feeding, by producing food currents along the ambulacral grooves to the mouth. A madreporite is lacking, but the water ring canal around the mouth gives off at each interambulacral area about 30 short stone canals that open into the coelom. Many ciliated funnellike canals pass from the outside through the wall of the tegmen to the coelomic cavity. These little funnels, which may number as many as 1,500, al-

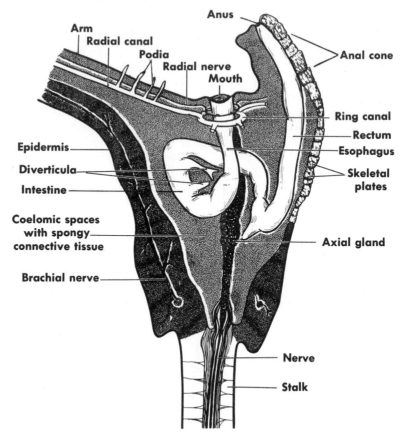

Fig. 27-46

Diagrammatic section through calyx of typical crinoid showing principal internal structure. (From Hickman: Integrated principles of zoology, The C. V. Mosby Co.)

low sea water to enter the coelom and maintain a proper fluid pressure in the body and in the water-vascular system.

The digestive system of crinoids consists of a mouth in or near the center of the tegmen; a short esophagus of tall ciliated cells provided with goblet cells; an intestine or midgut that first runs aborally and laterally, then makes a complete turn in a clockwise direction around the inner surface of the calyx before turning orally; and an anal cone with an anus through which the intestine or rectum opens (Fig. 27-46). A number of diverticula often branch off from the intestine on its inner side. The entire digestive system is lined with ciliated epithelium, and a reduced circular muscle layer and connective tissue are found in its walls. Gland cells are abundant in certain regions

of the digestive tract, but little is known about the digestive process itself.

Crinoids feed chiefly on small plankton organisms and organic detritus, which they collect on the feathery arms and podia, and toss into the ambulacral grooves. Mucus from the podia and ambulacral grooves entangles food particles, which are then carried along the grooves by ciliary action to the mouth. It is thought that a paralytic toxin is secreted by the pinnules and is used to narcotize small organisms nearby, thus facilitating their capture.

The coelom of crinoids is divided into spaces by the extensive strands of connective tissue (Fig. 27-46). Calcareous deposits are often found scattered through this connective tissue. The lining of the coelomic spaces, all of which communicate with each other, is a cuboidal epithelium. One of the coelomic spaces is the axial sinus that runs vertically through the center of the body and encircles the esophagus (Fig. 27-46). From the axial sinus a series of three single and one pair of coelomic canals, parallel to each other, extend into each arm. Some of these continue into the pinnules. At the aboral end of the axial sinus is a chambered organ composed of five radially arranged compartments and surrounded by nervous tissue. The five compartments end blindly at the oral end and become the canals of the cirri at the aboral end. The coelomic fluid and tissues contain many kinds of coelomocytes that wander freely in most places of the body.

The hemal system is mostly a network of sinuses or lacunae. The lacunae do not have a definite lining, but are enclosed in connective tissue with a coelomic epithelial covering. Part of the hemal system is formed into plexuses around the esophagus and beneath the tegmen. Branches from these plexuses extend into the spongy organ which lies along one side of the axial gland and which may form coelomocytes. A hemal space extends into each arm and carries sex cells (Fig. 27-45). The digestive tract is also supplied with hemal lacunae. The blood in the hemal system is not the same as coelomic fluid, but contains a high protein content. It contains no distinctive cells, except the ubiquitous coelomocytes.

Respiration can take place through the body surface, especially that of the extensive arm and pinnule system. The podia also are thought to play an important role in gaseous exchange.

There are no kidneys or other excretory organs, but coelomocytes may collect waste and deposit it in connective tissue.

The nervous system is made up of three systems at different body levels: (1) The ectoneural (oral) system consists of a subepidermal band running just under the epidermis of the ambulacral groove in each arm and its pinnules, where nerves supply the epidermis, the inner surface of the podia, and other parts (Fig. 27-45). The bands from all the grooves converge into five bands in the tegmen and in the mouth region form a nerve sheath around the esophagus and intestine. (2) The hyponeural (deeper oral) system forms a pentagon

lateral to the water ring of the water-vascular system (Fig. 27-46). From this pentagon, nerves are sent to the tegmen podia, anal canal, and other internal organs; and a pair of lateral brachial nerves is sent into each arm, one on each side (Fig. 27-45). These supply the musculature of the walls of the vessels in the water-vascular system and the outer surface of the podia. (3) The entoneural system (aboral) consists of a cup-shaped mass in the apex of the calyx and a series of nerves to the arms and the various aboral regions (Figs. 27-45, 27-46). The chief center of this system, or the cup-shaped mass, sends nerves directly to the cirri (comatulids) or forms a nervous sheath in the coelomic canal that runs through the columnals of the stem of stalked crinoids; from this sheath, nerves are sent to the cirri at the nodes. From the same mass center of the aboral system five brachial nerves pass through a pentagonal nerve ring in the radial plates of the calyx and then through canals in the arms. In each arm the brachial nerve gives off a pair of nerves to the flexor muscles and adjacent epidermis, a pair of nerves to the aboral part of the arm, a pair of commissure connectives to the lateral brachial nerves of the hyponeural system, and a pair of nerves to each pinnule. The entoneural system is the dominant system in crinoids, while in other echinoderm classes the ectoneural (oral) system is the dominant one.

Sense organs are represented only by the papillae of the podia (Fig. 27-45), by free nerve endings, and by sensory cells in the epidermis of the ambulacral regions. Crinoids so far as known are negatively phototropic.

The sexes in crinoids are separate, but sexual dimorphism is lacking. The gonads are usually found in the genital pinnules as masses of sex cells, although they may also occur in the arms. The sex cells develop within the genital canal (a coelomic extension within the arm, Fig. 27-45), which gives off a branch to each genital pinnule where the gametes are deposited. When the sex cells are mature, the walls of the pinnules rupture and release the eggs at spawning. In some (e.g., *Antedon*) the eggs may adhere to the pinnules by adhesive secretions; but they usually fall into the sea where they are fertilized. Development occurs in the membrane of the egg; and the stage in which a ciliated larva hatches and swims about before attachment follows that. A few Antarctic species brood the young in saclike invaginations of the pinnule walls. Regeneration of lost parts is rather well marked in crinoids. They can regenerate arms as well as pinnules and cirri. They can even regenerate four of the five pairs of arms that are lost simultaneously. The aboral nervous center is necessary for regeneration.

DEVELOPMENT

In development the egg undergoes a regular deuterostome type of holoblastic, radial cleavage, which produces a typical coeloblastula. Gastrulation occurs by a modified embolic type method. After the completion of gastrulation and the formation of the archenteron, the blastopore closes; and the archenteron becomes a closed, elongated sac in the blastocoel surrounded on three sides by entomesodermal mesenchyme. The archenteron sac now divides into an anterior vesicle (enterohydrocoel) and a posterior vesicle (somatocoel). The somatocoel divides into a right and left somatocoel. In the meantime the enterohydrocoel assumes a crescent shape and curls around the middle of the somatocoel at right angles to the long axis of the latter. The dorsal part of the crescent forms a process, which becomes the left axocoel; the ventral part of the crescent forms a process that separates as the hydrocoel (the left hydrocoel of other echinoderms). The right axocoel and right hydrocoel never form. The remaining portion of the enterohydrocoel, together with its two ends (horns), fuses to become the enteric sac or future intestine. The embryo elongates in an anteroposterior axis, and at its anterior end a tuft of cilia develops. Around the embryo by ectodermal differentiation, four or five ciliated bands about equally spaced appear along the axis.

The larva hatches as a free-swimming doliolaria (Fig. 27-3) without a bipinnaria stage. The larva has no mouth but lives off the yolk of the egg during its few days of swimming existence. It then attaches itself by a small adhesive pit located near the apical tuft of cilia, so that the anterior end becomes the attached aboral end and the posterior end becomes the oral end. The metamorphosis of the larva into a stalked sessile form involves a stalked larva known as the pentacrinoid stage (about 3 mm. long) which lasts for several months (*Antedon*). The stalk is produced by an elongation of the underpart (aboral) of the larva, which rests with its terminal plate on a substratum. Buds for the future arms appear on the upper or oral side of the calyx cup as five projections. Each of these splits into two forks later to form the ten arms common among comatulids. The pinnules, which are really miniature arms, are produced by the alternate forking of the arms to left and right. After the formation of cirri the pentacrinoid larva breaks loose from its stalk at the junction of the centrodorsal plate (formerly the top stem joint) with the top columnal of the stem and then leads a free existence.

Annotated references

Anderson, J. M. 1960. Histological studies on the digestive system of a starfish, *Henricia*, with notes on Tiedemann's pouches in starfishes. Bio. Bull. 119:371-393. *Tiedemann's pouches are used as pumping organs for drawing food from the stomach of the starfish into the pyloric ceca.*

Bather, F. A. The Echinoderma. In Lankester, E. R. (editor). 1900. A treatise on zoology, part 3, London, Adam & Charles Black, Ltd. *A work of great importance on the basic structures of echinoderms.*

Boolootian, R. A. 1963. The physiology of Echinodermata, Washington, D. C., vol. 3, pp. 113-138. XVI International Congress of Zoology. *A symposium represented by the following participants: J. M. Anderson—Aspects of digestive physiology among echinoderms. R. A. Boolootian—Reproductive physiology of echinoderms. A. Farmanfarmaian—Respiration in echinoderms. D. Nichols—Comparative histology of the echinoderm water-vascular system. J. E. Smith—The functions and properties of the echinoderm nervous system. G. Vevers—Pigmentation of the echinoderms. M. Yoshida—Photosensitivity in echinoids.*

Borradaile, L. A., and F. A. Potts. 1958. The Invertebrata, ed. 3. (Revised by G. A. Kerkut.) New York, Cambridge University Press. *A standard invertebrate text with fair coverage of the echinoderms.*

Buschbaum, R., and L. J. Milne. 1960. The lower animals; living invertebrates of the world. Garden City, Doubleday & Company, Inc. *Chapter*

19 is devoted to the echinoderms. Most of the superb illustrations are in full color.

Burnett, A. L. 1955. A demonstration of the efficacy of muscular force in the opening of clams by the starfish, *Asterias forbesi*. Biol. Bull. **109**:355-368. *No narcotic is used, but the starfish takes advantage of a small gape produced by an imperfectly sealed edge or by its own muscular force to insert its cardiac stomach.*

Clark, A. H. 1915-1950. A monograph of the existing crinoids, vol. 1, parts I to IV. U. S. Nat. Mus. Bull. **82**:1-700. *This incomplete monograph represents the most outstanding work on crinoids.*

Cuenot, L. Echinoderms. In Grasse, P. P. (editor). 1948. Traite de zoologie, vol. 11, pp. 1-363. Paris, Masson et Cie. *An authoritative work on echinoderms.*

Feder, H. M. 1955. On the methods used by the starfish, *Pisaster ochraceus*, in opening three types of bivalved mollusks. Ecology **36**:764-767.

Fisher, W. K. 1911-1930. Asteroidea of the North Pacific and adjacent waters, parts I to III. U. S. Nat. Mus. Bull. **76**:1-1020.

Galtsoff, P. S., and V. L. Loosanoff. 1950. Natural history and methods of controlling the starfish (*Asterias forbesi* Desor). U. S. Bur. Fisheries Bull. **49**:75-132.

Goodbody, I. 1960. The feeding mechanism in the sand dollar, *Mellita sexiesperforata*. Biol. Bull. **119**:80-86. *The author describes how small particles of food are carried by cilia and ciliated food tracts to the ambulacral grooves and mouth.*

Harvey, E. B. 1956. The American *Arbacia* and other sea urchins. Princeton, Princeton University Press.

Hyman, L. H. 1955. The invertebrates; Echinodermata, vol. 4. New York, McGraw-Hill Book Company. *The most up-to-date treatise on this group.*

Ikeda, H. 1941. Functions of the lunules of *Astriclypeus*. Annot. Zool. Japan **20**:1-24. *This paper* describes how the lunules function in burrowing by passing sand through them to the aboral surface.

Jennings, H. S. 1907. Behavior of the starfish *Asterias forreri* de Loriol. Univ. Calif. Pub. Zool. **4**:53-185. *The author describes several behavior patterns including the righting movement.*

Lavoie, M. 1956. How sea stars open bivalves. Biol. Bull. **111**:114-122.

MacGinitie, G. E., and N. MacGinitie, 1949. Natural history of marine animals. New York, McGraw-Hill Book Company. *The echinoderms included in this well-known work are mostly those of the Pacific coast.*

Marshall, A. 1884. Nervous system of *Antedon*. Quart. J. Micr. Sci. **24**:121-172. *A classic paper on the nervous system of crinoids.*

Mortensen, T. 1927. Handbook of the Echinoderms of the British Isles. New York, Oxford University Press, Inc.

Nicols, D. 1960. The histology and activities of the tube-feet of *Antedon bifida*. Quart. J. Micr. Sci. **101**:105-117.

Pearse, A. S. 1908. Behavior of *Thyone*. Biol. Bull. **15**:25-48. *A revealing study of a sea cucumber.*

Ricketts, E. F., and J. Calvin. 1952. Between Pacific tides, ed. 3. (Revised by J. W. Hedgpeth.) Stanford, Stanford University Press. *A unique book of seashore life. These authors with MacGinitie (see previous reference) are perhaps the most outstanding American students of marine life.*

Semon, R. 1888. Die Entwicklung der *Synapta digitata*. Z. Wiss. Zool. **22**:175-309. *A classic study on the embryology of a sea cucumber.*

Smith, R. I., et al. (editors). 1957. Intertidal invertebrates of the central California coast. Berkeley, University of California Press. *This treatise gives keys to the Pacific members of all echinoderm classes except the Crinoidea.*

Phylum Chaetognatha

The common name for members of this phylum is arrowworms. They belong to the Deuterostomia along with the echinoderms, hemichordates, pogonophorans, and chordates, although they lack most of the characteristics found among the other deuterostome members. Chaetognaths are among the most common forms found in planktonic populations in all oceans and at all latitudes. They are also found at considerable depths in the seas. Only one genus *(Spadella)* is an exception to their planktonic existence. This particular genus is benthonic, living mostly in shallow water, where it clings to plants and rocks by means of adhesive papillae. The abundance of chaetognaths in plankton is attested by the fact that as many as 1,000 or more specimens have been found in a cubic meter of sea water. Many of the species show a marked stratification of distribution. Some are found only in the limit of light penetration, living in depths not exceeding 200 meters (epiplanktonic). Other species are present in the zone of 200 to 1,000 meters' depth (mesoplanktonic), while still others live in depths below 1,000 meters (bathyplanktonic). It seems that each species is restricted to a definite depth zone for its habitat. Temperature may be the critical factor in their stratification. Their horizontal distribution, however, varies with latitude because of the variation in water temperatures between cold and warm regions. Most chaetognaths seem to belong to the warm-water, epiplanktonic zone. No one species is found in all depths and at all latitudes. However, the genus *Eukrohnia* has been found from the Arctic to the Antarctic by way of the colder water at considerable depths in the tropical regions. Some are restricted to zones of the continental shelf (neritic species) and others to areas normally far from shore (oceanic species). The degree of salinity may also be a factor in their distribution because shore water is sometimes diluted by fresh water from continental sources.

Little is known about the fossil record of chaetognaths because of their soft bodies. In the Burgess Shale deposits of the Middle Cambrian period of British Columbia, three fossil specimens of this group have been discovered *(Amiskwia)*. They were about 20 mm. long and had some of the typical features of chaetognaths, although there were some differences.

Chaetognaths are parasitized by several groups of animals. Protozoan parasites are represented by parasitic amebas, flagellates, ciliates, and sporozoans. Certain stages (metacercariae) of trematodes, the definitive hosts of which are fish, have been found in the intestine and coelom of chaetognaths. Some adult trematodes are also harbored. Copepods may serve as intermediate hosts in the life history of these parasites. Other parasites found in arrowworms are nematodes and copepods.

CLASSIFICATION

Phylum Chaetognatha. Bilaterally symmetric; coelomate and enterocoelic mesoderm formation; body divided into head, trunk, and tail; body with lateral and caudal fins; head with eyes and chitinous teeth and jaws (in some); cerebral and ventral ganglia connected by a pair of nerves; body wall musculature of longitudinal muscles arranged in four bands; digestive tract straight with muscular walls; no excretory, respiratory, or blood systems; hermaphroditic; self-fertilization; juvenile free-swimming larva; marine. Not divided into taxa higher than genera, about nine of which are recognized. The number of species does not exceed 50. *Sagitta* is most common genus. Other genera are *Spadella, Pterosagitta, Bathyspadella, Krohnitta, Zahonya, Eukrohnia,* and *Heterokrohnia.*

BASIC ADAPTIVE FEATURES

The small number of species in Chaetognatha indicates a very modest evolutionary divergence. Their general morphology and physiology are adapted for a planktonic existence. Their body structures are well suited for the floating life of plankton populations because their powers of active locomotion are feeble and restricted. Fins, which all of them possess, are excellent flotation devices, and little energy is required to keep them afloat. Some are provided with two pairs of fins and others with only one pair. *Spadella* is the only genus that has departed from a planktonic existence and developed a few adaptations for a benthonic existence, although retaining the basic morphology of the group. Such evolutionary divergence as one finds in the phylum is chiefly along physiologic lines. These differences are indicated in their distribution at different levels in the sea and their temperature preferences. Every chaetognath species has a habitat involving usually a certain depth in the water, which may be determined by its reactions to the temperature of the water at that particular depth. This evolutionary divergence has resulted in a widespread distribution of the different species. On this basis, they may be classified, as already mentioned, into warm-, cool-, and cold-water species. Since they are associated with certain types of water, chaetognaths are useful as indicator organisms in revealing the displacements of water masses. The few ecologic changes in such a uniform environment as that faced by planktonic populations does not tend to produce striking and radical adaptive radiation.

PHYLOGENETIC RELATIONSHIPS

It has been impossible to ally the chaetognaths with any other group, although they have certain resemblances to others either as adults or in their embryology. As adults they seem most closely to resemble the aschelminths. This resemblance is seen in the ring type of nervous system, the pharynx with its muscular end bulb, and the presence of only one muscular layer in the body wall. Much of the chaetognath structure is of the pseudocoel type of organization. However, their embryology indicates that they are true coelomate animals. Cleavage is total and equal, and their mesoderm is of the enterocoelous type, although the folding back of the two coelomic sacs is not in line with other enterocoelous animals. Present evidence seems to indicate that the chaetognaths have diverged quite early from the line of ancestry that leads to the deuterostomes (L. H. Hyman). This view seems to coincide with a more recent statement of P. P. Grasse, who believes that there is no place in the evolutionary scale where the chaetognaths fit.

GENERAL MORPHOLOGIC FEATURES
External anatomy

Chaetognaths range in size from 5 to over 100 mm. in length. Most species are between 12 and 25 mm. The body is fusiform or torpedo shaped (Fig. 28-1). It is divided into head, trunk, and tail. The anterior, ventral vestibule and mouth are almost surrounded by rows of lateral chitinous spines or hooks for catching prey. On the anterior end in *Sagitta,* the most common genus, are also two or four paired rows (anterior and posterior) of short chitinous teeth for holding the prey. Some species have only one row of teeth, and others none at all. The head and spines are covered by a hood (a fold of the body wall) when swimming and thus lessen the resistance of the head (Fig. 28-2). The head bears two dorsal eyes on the rear part. On the elongated trunk are one or two pairs of lateral, horizontal fins formed from the epidermal body wall. A large caudal or tail fin embraces the posterior end. The body is covered with a thin cuticle that overlies the single or stratified layer of epidermal cells.

Internal anatomy

Besides the epidermis and cuticle the body wall (Fig. 28-3) contains four bands of longitudinal muscles (two dorsolateral

605

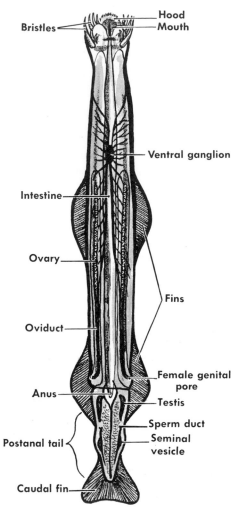

Bristles — Hood
— Mouth

Ventral ganglion

Intestine

Ovary

Fins

Oviduct

Female genital pore

Anus

Testis

Sperm duct
Seminal vesicle

Postanal tail

Caudal fin

Fig. 28-1

Ventral view of arrowworm *(Sagitta).* (From Hickman: Integrated principles of zoology, The C. V. Mosby Co.)

and two ventrolateral) and a basement membrane on which the epidermis rests and which also forms special plates in the head. The coelom is not lined with peritoneum but is divided into compartments represented by one coelomic space in the head, paired coelomic sacs in the trunk, and one or two (sometimes more) coelomic sacs in the tail region (Fig. 28-3, *A, B*). The coelomic spaces are separated by septa. The head musculature is complicated, being made up of special muscles for operating the hood, the teeth, and the spines.

Chaetognaths do not swim much, but drift passively most of the time. The fins are merely for flotation and play no role in swimming. Swimming is accomplished mostly by movements of the caudal fin and the contraction of the longitudinal body muscles. This enables them to dart forward in spurts with rest periods between. They cannot constrict their bodies because of the absence of circular muscles.

The simple digestive system consists of a cuticle-lined vestibule formed by the inturning of the center of the head, a mouth leading into a bulbous pharynx, a straight intestine with a pair of lateral diverticula at its anterior end, and an anus opening ventrally at the septum separating the trunk and tail (Fig. 28-1). The digestive tract contains muscle in its walls, especially in the pharynx where both longitudinal and circular muscles occur. The intestine is lined with columnar epithelium containing both granular secretory cells and absorptive cells (Fig. 28-3, *B*). The digestive tract

Fig. 28-2

Preserved specimen of arrowworm *(Sagitta)* with head mostly enclosed in hood. (From Hickman: Integrated principles of zoology, The C. V. Mosby Co.)

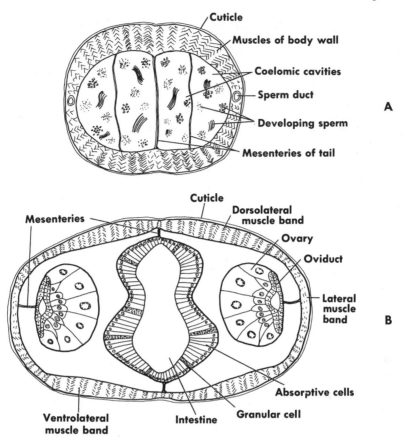

Fig. 28-3

A, Cross section of *Sagitta* through region of postanal tail showing four coelomic cavities. B, Cross section of *Sagitta* at level of ovaries. There are two coelomic spaces at this level. (Modified from Burfield, 1927.)

is supported by dorsal and ventral mesenteries formed by extensions of the basement membrane of the body wall.

Chaetognaths are mostly carnivorous, living on copepods, small worms, larva, eggs, crustaceans, and occasionally detrital particles. Prey is captured with the aid of the grasping spines or hooks and shoved into the mouth with the assistance of the small anterior and posterior teeth. Digestion is thought to be extracellular. The entire process is very rapid.

Specialized respiratory and excretory organs are absent. The coelomic fluid serves as a circulatory medium. It is a colorless fluid with small granules and is kept in movement by ciliary action, although there is no coelomic epithelium to bear cilia.

The nervous system consists of ganglia, connecting commissures, and nerves. The chief part of the nervous system is a circumenteric ring surrounding the pharynx. This ring is composed of a large dorsal cerebral ganglion which sends two frontal commissures to a pair of vestibular ganglia at the sides of the mouth. The vestibular ganglia, in turn, are connected to each other by a subpharyngeal commissure, thus completing the ring. The cerebral ganglion supplies nerves to the head region, such as the eyes, and from its sides sends two circumenteric connectives to the ventral subenteric ganglion (Fig. 28-1). The ventral ganglion supplies paired nerves to the trunk muscles and various sensory receptors.

Sense organs include the pair of eyes, the ciliary loop, tactile bristles, and ciliary pits. Each of the eyes consists of five combined pigment cell ocelli, one lateral and **607** four median. The eyes are inverse, with retinal cells facing the pigment cup. The ciliary loop is modified epidermis with cilia and is an oval body that extends from the head posteriorly, sometimes as far as the anterior region of the trunk. It is usually demonstrated only when stained. Its sensory function may be the detection of water currents or their chemical nature.

All chaetognaths are hermaphroditic, with a pair of tubular ovaries in the trunk just anterior to the trunk-tail septum and a bandlike testis on each side of the tail, just behind the septum (Fig. 28-1). An oviduct is found along the lateral side of each ovary and ends posteriorly in its own seminal receptacle. Each seminal receptacle opens through a vagina and gonopore in front of the trunk-tail septum. A sperm duct passes posteriorly from each testis to a seminal vesicle in the lateral body wall; along its course it opens by a funnel-shaped opening into the tail coelom. Spermatogonia leave the sperm duct through these funnel openings and pass into the coelom, where spermatogenesis is completed. When mature, the sperm pass back into the sperm duct and go to the seminal vesicle, where they are formed into spermatophores. There is no male gonopore, and the spermatophores are released by rupture of the seminal vesicle. The spermatophores adhere to the body surface or to the fins after their discharge. Sperm are then released and make their way to the female gonopore to enter the seminal receptacles. Fertilization is internal. Eggs mature in the ovaries at different times; and as they mature, they pass through an improvised channel formed by two special cells to the oviduct nearby (Fig. 28-3, *B*). Fertilization occurs when the sperm migrate up the oviduct from the seminal receptacle to the eggs. Self-fertilization occurs in *Sagitta*, but in *Spadella*, fertilization is reciprocal by exchange of sperm. In *Sagitta*, fertilized eggs

with a jelly coat are discharged singly into the sea, where they float as planktonic objects. In the genus *Krohnitta* the eggs are carried in packets attached to the back.

DEVELOPMENT

Chatognaths have radial and equal cleavage and form a coeloblastula. Gastrulation occurs at about the 50-blastomere stage and is embolic. The coelom is enterocoelous and is formed from two pairs of coelomic sacs that arise from two backward folds of the anterior wall of the archenteron. Embryology is mostly direct, and the young larvae (1 mm. long) hatch as juveniles within about 48 hours. *Sagitta* is noted for the early formation of its germ cells, which can be detected during gastrulation as a group of two cells in the anterior wall of the archenteron. The adult structures all appear within a week after hatching, and there is no metamorphosis.

Annotated references

de Beauchamp, P. Chaetognatha. In Grasse, P. P. (editor). 1960. Traite de zoologie, vol. 5, pp. 1500-1520. Paris, Masson et Cie. *The most recent description of the group.*

Bieri, R. 1959. The distribution of planktonic Chaetognatha in the Pacific and their relationship to the water masses. Limnol. Oceanogr. 4:1-28.

Burfield, S. 1927. Liverpool Marine Biological Commission, Memoir 28, Proceedings and Transactions of the Liverpool Biological Society, vol. 28, pp. 1-104. *An excellent monograph.*

Hyman, L. H. 1959. The invertebrates; smaller coelomate groups, vol. 5, pp. 1-71. New York, McGraw-Hill Book Company. *One of the best accounts of Chaetognatha.*

Kuhl, W. Chaetognatha. In Bronn, H. G. (editor). 1938. Klassen und Ordnungen des Tierreichs, vol. 4, part 4. Leipzig, Akademische Verlagsgesellschaft. *The most comprehensive treatment of the phylum.*

Shipley, A. E. *Sagitta*. In Harmer, S. F., and A. E. Shipley (editors). 1896. Cambridge natural history, vol. 2. London, The Macmillan Company. *A brief account.*

Phylum Hemichordata

The members of this group were formerly considered to be a subphylum of the phylum Chordata because of their unmistakable affinities with the chordates. As such they were judged to be the lowest of the chordates. However, the general organization of hemichordates is different from that of chordates, except that certain characteristics are common to each group. Among the common characteristics are the presence of gills and a short anterior structure considered to be a notochord. Many recent authorities, however, do not believe that the notochord in these animals is a true notochord but a stomochord instead. Many hemichordate features are invertebrate in type.

The hemichordates are vermiform, enterocoelous coelomate animals that are strictly marine, living usually in shallow water. Some members are colonial. The body and coelom are divided into three successive regions—proboscis, collar, and trunk. The first division has a single coelomic cavity, and the other two each have paired coelomic sacs. The two groups that make up the phylum are superficially very dissimilar, although they possess certain basic characters in common. General descriptions given here apply more to the enteropneusts than to the pterobranchs.

Enteropneusts live mostly in burrows or under stones, usually in the intertidal zones. Some have been collected at depths of several hundred meters. Burrowing is accomplished by thrusting the proboscis forward into the muck or mud and then by contract-

ing the longitudinal muscles, forming a peristaltic bulge that passes posteriorly. The bulge anchors the animal in preparation for another thrust. As the worm moves forward, grains of sand are carried backward by cilia to the collar, where a sand girdle is formed. By additions from the forward end the girdle is pushed posteriorly over the trunk. Not all members of the group form burrows, however.

Hemichordate distribution is not well known. Their secretive habits and fragile bodies make their collection difficult. They usually favor warm and temperate waters. In general their distribution is worldwide in particular regions, although none has been reported from the Antarctic regions. Several species are found around the British Isles. The genus *Saccoglossus (Dolichoglossus)* is found on both Atlantic and Pacific coasts. Other genera and species also occur on the Atlantic coast.

The size ranges of the class Enteropneusta (acorn worms) is from 20 to 2,500 mm. in length, with a breadth of from 3 to 200 mm. The members of the class Pterobranchia are much smaller, not exceeding 14 mm., and most are under 5 mm. (not including the stalk).

About 70 species of enteropneusts and three small genera of pterobranchs are recognized.

A few fossil pterobranchs have been described from the Cretaceous period and from the Paleocene epoch, but the wholly extinct graptolites, which closely resemble pterobranchs, have left a very good record. Other hemichordates have left little or no record.

CLASSIFICATION

Phylum Hemichordata. Body vermiform or vaselike; coelomate and enterocoelous; notochord (stomochord) restricted to preoral region; body typically divided into three unequal regions (proboscis, collar, trunk); no tail; three coelomic spaces corresponding to body divisions; paired gill slits, many, few, or none; nerve tissue both dorsal and ventral, partly hollow; with or without a lophophore bearing tentaculated arms; free living or sessile; some colonial; dioecious; asexual (in some); marine.

> **Class Enteropneusta.** Body vermiform, long, and contractile; many gill slits; straight intestine; tentaculated arms absent; dioecious, with saclike gonads in coelom along the trunk; tornaria larva (in some). Three families are recognized: Harrimaniidae *(Saccoglossus)*, Spengelidae *(Spengelia)*, Ptychoderidae *(Balanoglossus)*.

> **Class Pterobranchia.** Body small, vaselike; aggregated or colonial in secreted tubes (coenecia); one genus, *Atubaria*, without coenecium; tentaculated arms; gut U-shaped; dioecious and asexual reproduction; with or without gill slits.

>> **Order Rhabdopleurida.** True colonies with zooids in organic continuity; each zooid in a secreted tube; two tentaculated arms; gill slits absent; one gonad. *Rhabdopleura.*

>> **Order Cephalodiscida.** Aggregated in common coenecium; zooids unconnected; four to nine pairs of tentaculated arms; one pair of gill slits; two gonads. Two genera are recognized: *Cephalodiscus, Atubaria.*

BASIC ADAPTIVE FEATURES

The pterobranchs are the most primitive members of the phylum. Their sessile existence and tentaculated arms have enabled them to exploit one of the oldest methods of acquiring food, i.e., lophophore ciliary feeding. The uniformity of their habitat, mostly in secreted tubes in ocean bottoms where environmental conditions undergo few radical changes, has not promoted evolutionary divergence. On the other hand, the Enteropneusta, by losing the tentaculated arms and adopting a more active life in littoral zones, have tended to modify the primitive methods of feeding, although a form of mucus-ciliary feeding is retained by nonburrowing species. In place of the tentaculated arms the proboscis, with its mucus secretions, traps small organisms and passes them to the mouth. Burrowing species eat sand, from which they digest the organic material. Although they are sluggish animals, the nature of their habitat has enabled enteropneusts to undergo some modest evolutionary divergence while retaining some characteristics of their primitive ancestors at the same time.

PHYLOGENETIC RELATIONSHIPS

Hemichordates show affinities to both the echinoderms and the chordates. The resemblance between the tornaria larva of hemichordates and the bipinnaria larva of echinoderms is striking and cannot be due to evolutionary convergence. The formation of the coelomic sacs and the gastrula is similar in the embryology of the two groups. The behavior of the first coelomic pouch (protocoel) in sending a hydroporic canal to the surface hydropore in hemichordates is similar in many ways to the early development of the water-vascular system of echinoderms. The more primitive class of hemichordates, the pterobranchs, with their lophophore and tentaculated arms as well as their sessile existence, may represent a nearer approach to a common ancestor of the echinoderms and hemichordates than the larval forms of the two groups indicate. From this standpoint the enteropneusts have lost such structures as the tentaculated arms and the sessile mode of life characteristic of the more primitive class.

The relationship of hemichordates and chordates has long been recognized and emphasized, but the presence of a notochord in hemichordates seems now to rest on very flimsy evidence. Most authorities consider the formation of the buccal diverticulum of hemichordates to be entirely different from that of the true notochord of chordates, hence the term "stomochord." Certain resemblances between the two groups do exist, such as a dorsal nerve cord that is partly hollow in hemichordates (corresponding to the dorsal hollow nerve cord of chordates) and the presence of pharyngeal gill slits, which are restricted in the animal kingdom to these two groups. Because segmentation, a basic structure of chordates, is absent in hemichordates, and because there are other differences, it is not logical to include the two groups in the same phylum. Hemichordates apparently are close to a common ancestor of both echinoderms and chordates.

CLASS ENTEROPNEUSTA
General morphologic features
EXTERNAL ANATOMY

The elongated, wormlike forms are commonly called acorn or tongue worms. Some do not exceed 20 mm. in length, although others may reach a length of 2,500 mm. (*Balanoglossus gigas*). Their cyclindric, flaccid, mucus-covered body is divided into a tonguelike proboscis (protosome), a short cyclindric collar (mesosome), and an elongated trunk (metasome) (Fig. 29-1). The proboscis is connected to the collar by a narrow proboscis stalk. The short ringlike collar projects anteriorly (collarette) over the proboscis stalk and the posterior part of the proboscis and ventrally bears the mouth. The trunk, which makes up most of the body, bears along its length certain anatomic landmarks that correspond generally with various internal features. A middorsal and a midventral ridge indicate the location of median blood vessels and nerves (Figs. 29-1, 29-2). Just back of the

collar on each side of the middorsal ridge is the branchial region, which bears a longitudinal row of gill pores. The lateral region on each side of the anterior part of the trunk shows a genital ridge, or else two genital wings, underneath which are the gonads, whose gonopores to the exterior cannot be detected.

The postbranchial part of the trunk, which is relatively undifferentiated externally, may show the darkened outline of the intestine through the body wall, forming the hepatic region. In such a case the remaining part of the trunk is called the caudal region. In many genera these external divisions are not evident. The anus is found at the terminal end of the trunk.

The body is covered with ciliated columnar epithelium that bears many gland cells in certain areas of the body, especially in the trunk.

INTERNAL ANATOMY

In addition to the epidermis, the body wall contains a well-developed nervous layer in the base of the epidermis; a basement membrane that forms the proboscis skeleton composed of a median plate in the proboscis stalk and two posterior horns in the roof of the buccal cavity; a muscular sheath of outer circular and inner longitudinal fibers in the proboscis and collar regions or mostly longitudinal fibers in the trunk; and a connective tissue and muscle fiber layer that fills most of the coeolomic cavities. A peritoneum is lacking, except in the genus *Protoglossus*.

The coelom of hemichordates is divided into three segments: the proboscis, or protocoel, with a single cavity; the collar, or mesocoel, with two cavities; and the trunk, or metacoel, with two cavities. The protocoel is present in the posterior part of the proboscis and opens by a middorsal pore to the exterior (Fig. 29-2); the paired cavities of the mesocoel open by a pair of canals and pores on each side of the middorsal line; the paired metacoel cavities, separated by the mesenteries of the gut (Fig. 29-3), have no external openings. The three types of cavities are separated from each other by a transverse septum or by other tissue.

The muscular system, already described, consists of smooth muscle fibers of coelomic origin, which course through the coelomic

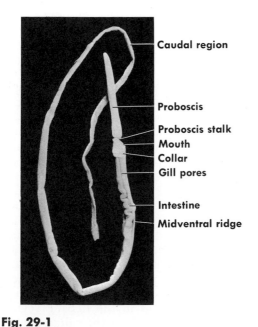

Fig. 29-1

Preserved specimen of tongue worm (*Dolicoglossus,* Enteropneusta).

Labels on figure:
- Caudal region
- Proboscis
- Proboscis stalk
- Mouth
- Collar
- Gill pores
- Intestine
- Midventral ridge

611

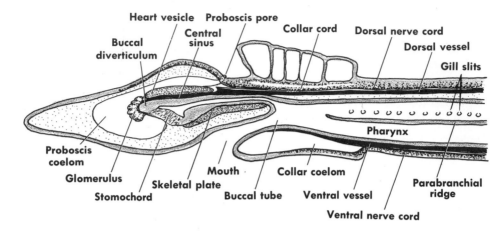

Fig. 29-2

Diagram of longitudinal section of anterior part of *Dolicoglossus*. (From Hickman: Integrated principles of zoology, The C. V. Mosby Co.)

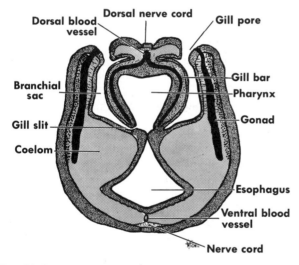

Fig. 29-3

Cross section of pharyngeal region of tongue worm. (From Hickman: Integrated principles of zoology, The C. V. Mosby Co.)

spaces and the inner surface of the epidermis. The muscular arrangement varies with the different regions of the body, especially in the proboscis and collar where the fibers may crisscross in complicated patterns, often filling up much of the coelomic spaces. The trunk musculature is composed of longitudinal fibers beneath the epidermis.

The digestive tract is a straight tube with little or no musculature in its walls. In the ventral region of the collar between the collarette and the proboscis is the large mouth, which passes to a buccal cavity in the center of the internal collar (Fig. 29-2). From the dorsal part of the buccal cavity projects anteriorly a buccal diverticulum, formerly thought to be a notochord, but now often called a stomochord. It is considered to be merely an extension of the gut. The buccal cavity opens posteriorly into the pharynx, in the dorsal half of which, on each side, are the U-shaped openings that connect with the gill pouches (Fig. 29-2). The ventral half of the pharynx is part of the digestive tract (Figs. 29-2, 29-3). These two regions of the pharynx may be separated by lateral constrictions. Following the pharynx in the digestive tract is the esophagus, which may be differentiated in certain regions. In some members of the families Harrimaniidae and Spengelidae the esophagus communicates with the exterior by canals and pores. The remaining part of the digestive system is the intestine, the posterior part of which is the rectum that opens to the outside by the anus. The anterior part, or darkish hepatic division of the intestine, has in some cases dorsal saccular differentations (Fig. 29-5) and can usually be distinguished from the posterior region by its dark brown or greenish inclusions. Glands for the production of enzymes are found in the hepatic region, but little is known about their digestion.

The circulatory system includes a mid-dorsal vessel, in which the blood is carried anteriorly; a midventral vessel; and a system of sinus channels (Fig. 29-2). Near the anterior level of the collar, the dorsal vessel, which runs in the dorsal mesentery of the digestive tract, expands into a venous sinus. The venous sinus then passes anteriorly into the central sinus, located below the heart vesicle, or pericardium, which has muscle fibers in its lower wall. The contraction of this lower wall drives blood through the central sinus into a special plexus organ, the glomerulus. The buccal diverticulum, central sinus, heart vesicle, and glomerulus together form a projection complex into the proboscis coelom. This complex is covered with peritoneum, the fingerlike evaginations of which contain blood sinuses and produce the organ known as the glomerulus. The sinuses in the glomerular evaginations contain blood from the central sinus. The glomerulus may free the blood from waste; hence it is called an excretory organ. From the glomerulus, vessels or arteries pass backward on each side to the ventral longitudinal vessel, which runs posteriorly beneath the digestive tract almost to the anus.

Blood from the longitudinal vessel passes through an extensive plexus of sinuses to the gut and body wall. From this plexus the blood goes to the dorsal vessel, thus completing the circuit.

The branchial apparatus is supposed to be concerned with gaseous exchange in breathing. The dorsal branchial region of the pharynx is placed just above the ventral digestive region and bears a longitudinal series of gill slits that vary in number from a few to a hundred or more on each side of the body (Fig. 29-2). New pairs are added as the animal grows older. The gill slits, or pharyngeal openings, do not open directly to the outside but into branchial sacs (Figs. 29-3, 29-4). The gill slits in the inner pharyngeal wall are U-shaped, produced by the downgrowth of tongue bars from the pharyngeal wall. Each slit opens into a separate branchial sac, which opens to the exterior by a dorsolateral gill pore that lies with the other gill pores in a longitudinal furrow along the branchial region of the body. The septa, or pharyngeal walls

Fig. 29-4

Diagram of optical section of two gill sacs of *Balanoglossus*. (Modified from Harmer.)

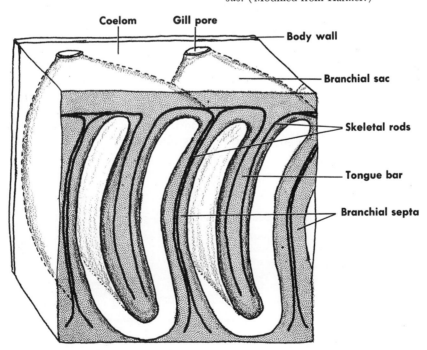

between clefts, and the tongue bars are ciliated and provided with a plexus of blood sinuses from the ventral longitudinal vessel. The cilia produce water currents through the mouth and through the gill slits. These water currents are important in pulling mucus strands of food into the mouth; but the gill apparatus does not capture food particles, which may have been its primitive function. Respiratory exchange of gases may occur between the blood sinuses of the septa and tongue bars and the water currents passing through the gills.

The nervous system consists of a net of nerve fibers in the base of the epidermis over the entire body and middorsal and midventral longitudinal cords formed from the thickening of the epidermal nervous layer (Fig. 29-2). These two longitudinal nerve trunks are connected at the anterior end of the trunk by a circumenteric ring. The dorsal cord continues into the collar as the collar cord, while the ventral cord terminates at the collar. In some the collar cord is hollow and may open to the outside by neuropores; in other acorn worms it may contain scattered cavities. The collar cord seems to represent the chief nervous center of enteropneusts. Conduction in the trunk can take place through the epidermal plexus as well as through the ventral and dorsal nerve cords. The collar cord is known to have giant nerve cells, the processes of which run posteriorly in the dorsal nerve trunk and to the ventral cord by way of the circumenteric ring.

Sense organs are represented by neurosensory cells throughout the epidermis. They are especially abundant in the proboscis. The preoral ciliary organ on the ventral side of the proboscis base may have chemoreceptor functions. W. N. Hess (1938) discovered photoreceptor cells in *Saccoglossus kowalevskii.*

The ·sexes are separate in enteropneusts and there is no sexual dimorphism. The gonads are saclike and lie on each side of the trunk in one or several longitudinal rows in the anterior region (Fig. 29-5). They may lie behind the gill slits in some species. The region containing the gonads may bulge to the outside as wings or ridges. Each gonad has a necklike extension, which opens to the outside by a pore that may be located in the same groove as the gill pores.

The eggs are large (1 mm.) and yolky in the family Harrimaniidae but are small in the other two families. In burrowing species, eggs are discharged from the burrows in coils that form masses of several thousand eggs. Shortly thereafter, sperm are emitted from the burrows of the males. The masses of fertilized eggs are disintegrated by tidal action, and the embryos are scattered in the sea.

Development

Indirect development involves a pelagic tornaria larva (Fig. 29-6), but in direct development there is no tornaria. The cleavage is holoblastic, equal, and of the radial type, producing a coeloblastula, which by embolic invagination forms the archenteron. Where the blastopore closes marks the location of the future posterior end of the animal. The animal elongates in the anteroposterior axis, forms cilia, rotates in the egg membrane for a time, and then hatches to

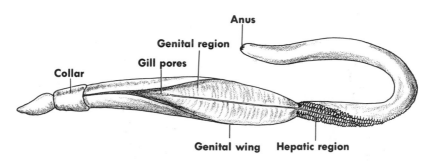

Fig. 29-5

Balanoglossus (Enteropneusta). (After Spengel; redrawn from Cambridge Natural History.)

begin a planktonic existence. Direct development usually has a free-swimming larva, as does indirect development; and up to the larval stage the major features are about the same in both types of development. In indirect development the larva gradually assumes the tornaria characteristics by forming sinuous ciliary bands and losing cilia elsewhere (Fig. 29-6). At a certain stage the tornaria resembles the bipinnaria larva of asteroids. Tornariae range in size from less than 1 mm. to 4 or 5 mm. in length. After a planktonic existence of several days or weeks the tornaria undergoes several changes, sinks to the bottom, and assumes an adult existence. In direct development the tornaria larva is bypassed, and the ciliated larva develops directly into the adult condition. Tornariae are found in *Balanoglossus*, *Ptychodera*, and some others. The common American species *Saccoglossus kowalevskii* has direct development without a tornaria.

CLASS PTEROBRANCHIA
General morphologic features

These small members of the hemichordates have many basic resemblances to the enteropneusts. Pterobranchs may or may not have gill slits. They inhabit both shallow and deep water, chiefly the latter. Most species occur in the southern hemisphere. Of the three genera, two live in aggregations or colonies in secreted tubes called coenecia, which are attached to various kinds of bottoms—rocky, muddy, sandy, or gravelly. They may also be attached to other sessile animals, such as sponges and bryozoans. Many species have been collected in the Antarctic and subantarctic regions. They are small animals, usually within the range of 1 to 5 mm. (not including the stalk). The members of *Cephalodiscus* are free living (Fig. 29-7), but many individuals live together in coenecia that may be joined together. In *Rhabdopleura* the individuals form true colonies, with the members in organic continuity, although each is enclosed within a tube. Individuals are provided on the belly with a stalk, which attaches the animal to its tube and which also bears buds. The individuals of a colony are called zooids. The body is divided into three regions of protosome (proboscis), mesosome (collar), and

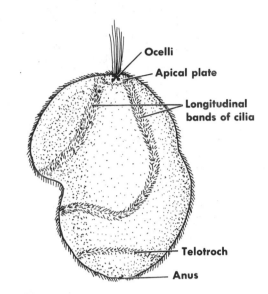

Fig. 29-6

Tornaria larva. This larva, which has remarkable resemblance to bipinnaria larva of sea stars, was first described by Johannes Müller, but Metschnikoff was first to point out its true systematic position in 1869.

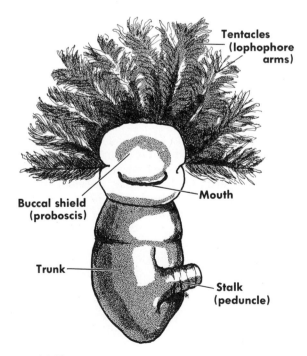

Fig. 29-7

Pterobranch *(Cephalodiscus)*. (From Hickman: Integrated principles of zoology, The C. V. Mosby Co.)

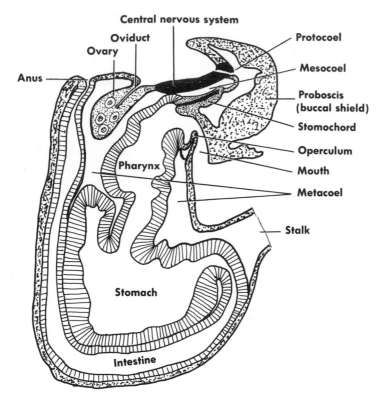

Fig. 29-8

Longitudinal median section of *Cephalodiscus*.

metasome (trunk). The corresponding body cavities of these divisions are protocoel, mesocoel, and metacoel (Fig. 29-8). The body is vase shaped, and the gut is a loop with the anus opening on the dorsal side of the collar (Fig. 29-8). The proboscis is shield shaped and is often called the buccal shield. It is tilted toward the ventral side and partially hides the crescent-shaped mouth. On its dorsal side the collar bears the tentaculated arms. In *Cephalodiscus* the collar bears five to nine pairs of arms; in *Rhabdopleura* a single pair. Each arm is composed of a single stem (containing a groove) with many side tentacles that increase in number with age. Food in the form of small organisms is caught by the adhesive secretions of the tentacles and arms and conveyed by ciliary grooves to the mouth.

Cephalodiscus has one pair of gill slits; *Rhabdopleura* has none. The gill apparatus contains no tongue bars, and the

pharyngeal region continues as the esophagus without marked demarcation. A slender diverticulum of the alimentary canal at the base of the proboscis is called a stomochord (Fig. 29-8).

The sexes are separate, but asexual reproduction from the stalk buds is common. A ciliated larva is found in *Cephalodiscus*. In *Rhabdopleura* new individuals are formed by budding from a creeping stolon; each young zooid buds off a new stolon from its stalk, thus resulting in colony formation.

Atubaria differs from the other two genera in having no coenecia, no bud formation, and in being solitary. Its structure is similar to that of *Cephalodiscus*. It uses its stalk to anchor itself to hydroids or other objects.

Annotated references

Bullock, T. H. 1940. Functional organization of the nervous system of Enteropneusta. Biol. Bull. **79**:91-113.

Dahlgren, U. 1917. Production of light by Enteropneusta. J. Franklin Inst. **183**:735-754. *Lumi-*

nescence is restricted to the family Ptycho-deridae. Photogenic cells are modified epidermal cells of the goblet type. These glands discharge the slime that produces the luminescence.

Dawydoff, C. Stomocordes. In Grasse, P. P. (editor). 1948. Traite de zoologie, vol. 11, pp. 367-532. Paris, Masson et Cie. *This is one of the outstanding treatises on the Hemichordata, although the author has proposed a different name for the group.*

Hess, W. N. 1936. Reaction to light in *Ptychodera*. Washington, D. C., Carnegie Institution of Washington, Papers Tortugas Laboratories 31:77-86.

Hess, W. N. 1937. Nervous system of *Dolicho-glossus kowalevskii*. J. Comp. Neurol. 68:161-171.

Hyman, L. H. 1959. The invertebrates; smaller coelomate groups, vol. 5, New York, McGraw-Hill Book Company. *The best account in English.*

Morgan, T. H. 1894. The development of *Balanoglossus*. J. Morphol. 9:1-86. *A classic description by the famous geneticist.*

Van der Horst, C. J. Hemichordata. In Bronn, H. G. (editor). 1927-1939. Klassen und Ordnungen des Tierreichs, vol. 4, part 4, pp. 1-737. Leipzig, Akademische Verlagsgesellschaft. *The most authoritative and comprehensive account of the Hemichordata.*

Phylum Pogonophora (Brachiata)

The latest phylum in the animal kingdom to be appraised is the Pogonophora, or beard worms, which were first discovered in the early part of this century in the deep sea off the coast of Indonesia. Although a number of French zoologists studied the animals in the years following their discovery, it remained for the Russian investigator A. V. Ivanov to establish them as a separate phylum, which he called Brachiata.

Since they were first found, their geographic range of discovery has been greatly extended; it is now believed that they inhabit all seas. The Bering Sea, the Sea of Okhotsk, and the seas of the Malay Archipelago seem to have the richest fauna and the greatest number of species at present. But new species are continually being discovered elsewhere, such as in the waters around New Zealand, Norway, and Africa. Recently, they have been found in great abundance off the coast of California.

Pogonophores are marine forms, usually but not exclusively found at abyssal depths of the sea. As new species are discovered, many have been found in relatively shallow water (22 meters). Some species are able to live in both shallow and abyssal waters. The greatest depth at which they have been found is about 10,000 meters, but most have been discovered in depths of from 3,000 to 6,000 meters. They are sessile animals. They live in closely fitting cylindric tubes that are much longer than the animal

(Fig. 30-1) and are made up of an organic complex of chitin and protein. The tubes may be uniformly smooth or made up of rings alternating with elastic interspaces. The diameter of the tube varies between 0.1 and 2.8 mm. and its length up to 150 cm., depending upon the species. Part of the tube usually projects above the surface of the seabed, while the remaining part is deeply embedded in the muddy ooze and sediment. However, the anterior part of the tube usually has thin walls and is so flimsy that it collapses and lies flat on the surface.

Pogonophores may be found in great abundance wherever they occur. Since they are filter feeders, their presence in any locality depends upon the abundance of food particles and bacterial fauna suspended in the water, plus a steady bottom current of water. In land-locked seas and deep trenches the pogonophore fauna seems to be more diversified than in the open ocean.

CLASSIFICATION

Order Athecanephria. Protosome separate from mesosome; pericardial sac close to dorsal part of heart; tentacles one or many, and always separate; coelomoducts divergent with lateral external pores; postannular portion of metasome without transverse ventral rows of adhesive papillae; spermatophores spindle shaped; two families; five genera. The chief genera are *Oligobrachia* and *Siboglinum*.
Order Thecanephria. Protosome may not be externally separate from mesosome; coelomoducts convergent with median pores; tentacles may be fused together; postannular region of metasome with transverse ventral rows of adhesive papillae; spermatophores flattened or leaf shaped; three families; nine genera. The chief genera are *Heptabrachia, Diplobrachia, Lamellisabella*.

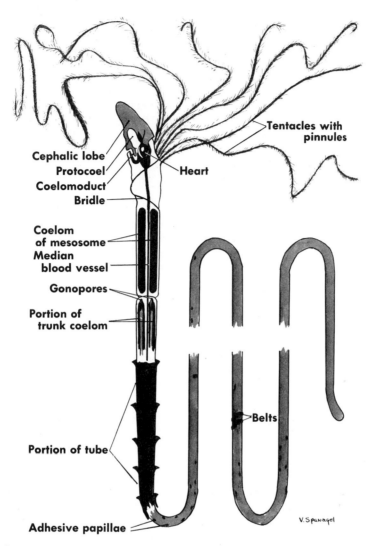

Cephalic lobe
Protocoel
Coelomoduct
Bridle

Heart

Tentacles with
pinnules

Coelom
of mesosome
Median
blood vessel

Gonopores

Portion of
trunk coelom

Belts

Portion of tube

Adhesive papillae

V. Spanagel

Fig. 30-1

Diagram of pogonophore, with tentacles separated from tentacular crown. (From Hickman: Integrated principles of zoology, The C. V. Mosby Co.)

Ivanov (1963) describes 71 species of the 80 or more that have been discovered.

BASIC ADAPTIVE FEATURES

Although the general body plan is uniform throughout the phylum, the tentacular apparatus shows much diversity among the different species. The number of tentacles fluctuates between 1 and 268 in the different species to date. Primitive species have few tentacles (e.g., *Oligobrachia* with 6 to 9), but reduction in the number of tentacles has also occurred in the evolution of the group. It is possible that the process of secondary oligomerization, in which many tentacles are fused or reduced to a few, accounts for certain evolutionary trends; but evolutionary trends also indicate the successive multiplication of tentacles and pinnules along with an increase in complexity of organization. The tentacular apparatus, therefore, may be considered the basic adaptive feature in guiding the evolution of the phylum.

PHYLOGENETIC RELATIONSHIPS

Pogonophores belong to the Deuterostomia; they have an enterocoelous method

619

of coelom formation as well as a typical subdivision of the coelomic cavity. Other deuterostome characteristics are the dorsal position of the nerve trunk and the trisegmental body plan.

Of all the Deuterostomia the Pogonophora seem to be most closely related to the Hemichordata, as evidenced by their trisegmental body plan, the unpaired first coelom, the paired coelomoducts in the first coelomic cavity, and the position of the gonads in the metasome. They cannot be placed with the hemichordates, however, because they lack a stomochord and gill slits as well as a digestive system. Their chief nervous mass is in the protosome and not in the mesosome, as in hemichordates.

Pogonophores have many unique features. Their embryology is unlike that of any other deuterostome. They have neither radial or spiral cleavage. Although holoblastic, their cleavage is unequal. It is also determinate, which is contrary to most deuterostomes which have indeterminate cleavage. No blastopore is formed, and the formation of the germ layers is atypical. The formation of the gastrula and archenteron is so vague and atypical that these structures are controversial points.

There are, therefore, ample reasons for placing the pogonophores in a phylum of their own. Perhaps the most amazing characteristic of this group, which shows considerable advancement in some systems (e.g., the vascular system) over those of deuterostomes, is the complete lack of a digestive system.

GENERAL MORPHOLOGIC FEATURES
External anatomy

Pogonophores are cylindric worms with long, slender bodies. They vary in length and diameter, with the length usually 100 to 600 times the breadth (Fig. 30-1). One species (*Siboglinum minutum*) is only 0.1 mm. in breadth, while some have a breadth of 2.5 mm. The length varies from 4 or 5 to 45 cm. The elongated body is composed of three sections: protosome, mesosome, and metasome. The two anterior sections (protosome and mesosome) may be more or less fused into an anterior region that is separated from the metasome or long trunk region by a diaphragm. The trunk

is subdivided into a preannular section that extends to the girdles or belts (annuli) and a postannular region posterior to the girdles. The two or three belts or girdles are elevated regions on muscular ridges and bear toothed platelets. The girdles may or may not encircle the body and help to anchor it in the tube. Dorsal and ventral sides are not evident, but the dorsal side is considered by some authorities to be the one on which the cephalic lobe with the brain is located and the ventral side the one to which the tentacles are attached.

The protosome is the first division of the body and carries the dorsal cephalic lobe and the ventral tentacles. In some species it may be divided from the mesosome by an annular groove. The ciliated tentacles are extensions of the body and coelomic cavities and are attached to the front end of the protosome, where they are usually arranged in the form of a crown. They number from 1 to 268. They may be fused to form a cylinder (Fig. 30-2) or even twisted to form a spiral. Each tentacle receives a single nerve from the brain. The tentacle contains a coelom (lined with peritoneum) in which afferent and efferent blood vessels run. Each tentacle bears on its inner surface a fringe of filiform pinnules arranged in rows. These may be lacking in some species. Capillaries from the tentacular blood vessels occur in the pinnules. Adhesive papillae, or oval protuberances with cuticular plaques, are found on ridges of the metasome, especially in the preannular regions. They help the animal cling to the inside of the tube as it moves up and down.

Pogonophores spend their entire lives in their tubes, which have already been described.

Internal anatomy

The body wall is made up of a cuticle, an epidermis of columnar epithelium with glands, and circular and longitudinal muscles (Fig. 30-3). The coelom (protocoel) in the protosome is single and opens to the surface by a pair of ciliated coelomoducts (Fig. 30-1). The coelomic canals of the tentacles originate from the protocoel. The coelomic sacs in the mesosome and metasome (mesocoel and metacoel) are paired. The mesocoel, unlike that of hemichordates,

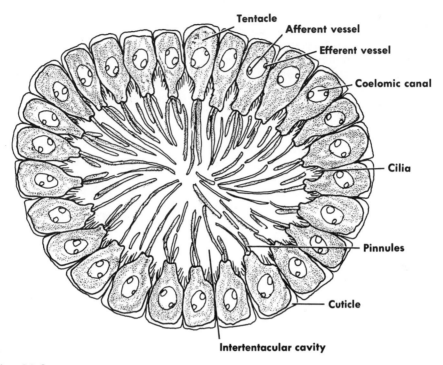

Fig. 30-2

Cross section of tentacular crown of pogonophore *Lamellisabella*. (Modified from Ivanov.)

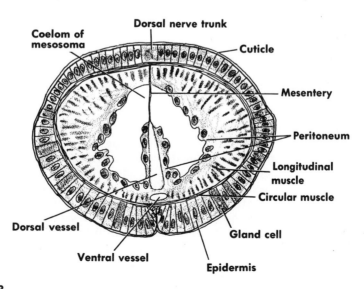

Fig. 30-3

Diagram of cross section in mesosomal region of pogonophore *Siboglinum* showing body wall and internal structure. (Modified from Ivanov.)

has no coelomoducts; but the metacoel has a pair, just as the protocoel does. A peritoneal membrane lines the coelomic cavities.

There is no digestive or respiratory system. Respiration is probably a function of the tentacular apparatus, where an extensive surface is exposed to water by the tentacles and their pinnules. Nutrition is carried on by the tentacular apparatus. Pogonophores have external and extracellular digestion. Digestive enzymes, secreted by the epidermis of the tentacles or glands at the base of the pinnules, act on the food collected by the tentacular ciliary bands and digest the food within the intertentacular cavity. Absorption of the food takes place through the walls of the tentacles.

Excretion takes place through the coelomoducts of the protocoel (Fig. 30-1). Certain cells in the mesosome and metasome may store excretory products.

Pogonophores have a closed vascular system, which is well developed. A dorsal and a ventral blood vessel (Fig. 30-3), running the entire length of the body, are connected at the anterior end by blood vessels of the tentacular system and at the posterior end by transverse commissural vessels. A ventral heart, differentiated from the ventral vessels, is found in the mesosome. Blood flows forward in the ventral vessel and backward in the dorsal vessel.

The nervous system is located within the epidermis (Fig. 30-3). In the cephalic lobe of the protosome is a ganglionic mass (brain), from which arises a dorsal nerve trunk with nerves to the tentacles. Neurocords, or giant nerve fibers, are found in the dorsal nerve trunk. Little is known about the innervation of the internal organs.

Pogonophores are dioecious. The gonads are located in the metacoel. The male system consists of a pair of testes and a pair of sperm ducts. The testes are large and, with their ducts, fill most of the posterior half of the metasome. The mature sperm are packed in spermatophores to which filaments are attached that may be used in the transfer of the spermatophore (Fig. 30-4) to the female. The female system consists of a pair of long ovaries, which lie in the anterior end of the metacoel, and a

Fig. 30-4

Spermatophore of *Lamellisabella*, with long attached filament. (Modified from Ivanov.)

pair of oviducts. The oviducts are actually a pair of U-shaped coelomoducts that have a funnellike opening to the outside.

DEVELOPMENT

Eggs are laid by the female in the anterior part of the tube in which she lives, where fertilization takes place and the entire development occurs. A clutch may consist of 10 to 45 eggs laid in a row in front of the animal. Eggs are rich in yolk and, after fertilization, are surrounded by a fertilization membrane.

The irregular nature of cleavage and gastrulation has already been noted. The first cleavage plane runs obliquely across the eggs and divides it into two equal blastomeres. At the second cleavage both blastomeres divide unequally, with the two larger ones lying at the anterior and posterior poles and the two smaller ones between. Many subsequent cleavages are unknown at present; but there is a distribution of the larger blastomeres to the hind end of the embryo, which early shows a bilateral symmetry. Although there is no trace of an enteric cavity, the coelomic cavities arise as a pair of sacs from a central cell mass, which may be considered the endodermal gut primordium. The coelom is thus considered enterocoelous in its formation. The coelomic pouches arise in very much the same manner as those of the hemichordates. The complete embryo is provided with a ciliary band on the protosome, and part of the mesosome bears a ciliated tract. On the metasome are also some ciliated bands and bundles of short bristles. When removed from the maternal tube, the larva can swim around; but normally it remains in the tube and is not free swimming; its locomotor devices are simply a remnant of ancestral conditions.

When fully formed, the young pogonophore leaves the tube and begins to make a tube of its own. Little is known about its subsequent differentiation of structures.

Annotated references

De Beer, G. 1955. The Pogonophora. Nature (London) **176**:888. *An early appraisal of the group.*

Hartman, O. 1954. Pogonophora Johansson, 1938. Syst. Zool. 3:183-185.

Hyman, L. H. 1959. The invertebrates; smaller coelomate groups, vol. 5. New York, McGraw-Hill Book Company. *An excellent account of the group, although many new species have been discovered since Hyman's volume was published.*

Ivanov, A. V. 1963. Pogonophora. (Translated and edited by D. B. Carlisle.) New York, Consultants Bureau. *This treatise by the most active investigator of the phylum gives a fine evaluation of its present status. Seventy-one of the eighty known species are described in it. Illustrated, with up-to-date bibliography.*

Manton, S. M. 1958. Embryology of Pogonophora and classification of animals. Nature (London) **181**:748-751.

Southward, A. J., and E. C. Southward. 1963. Biology of some Pogonophora. Washington, D. C. Proceedings of the Sixteenth International Congress of Zoology 1:96. *In this and other accounts these investigators have discussed the ecology and distribution of this newly described phylum. Pogonophores are found chiefly in muddy sand at depths of from 150 to 1,500 meters and are very spotty in their distribution because of the absence of mobile stages in their life cycle.*

Chapter 31

Phylum Chordata: the urochordates and cephalochordates

The phylum Chordata is considered the highest and most advanced group in the animal kingdom. It includes the tunicates, or urochordates, the cephalochordates, and the vertebrates. All these possess the three most distinguishing characteristics of the phylum—a notochord, or gelatinous supporting rod above the gut; a dorsal hollow nerve cord; and paired pharyngeal gill slits on the sides of the pharynx. All these characteristics are found at some stage in the life history of a chordate animal, although they may be restricted to an embryonic stage. The phylum is divided into three subphyla: Urochordata, Cephalochordata, and Vertebrata. The Vertebrata, or vertebrate animals, make up the great bulk of the phylum. They include animals that have a backbone (vertebral column) and are represented by the important classes of fishes, reptiles, birds, and mammals, which in a large measure dominate land and sea. The other two subphyla of Urochordata and Cephalochordata are small groups of marine animals of much more lowly organization and of little economic importance. Their chief interest to zoologists is the light that they throw upon the possible early origin of the phylum, especially the great vertebrate group. The urochordates and cephalochordates, however, lack a backbone or vertebral column and are, therefore, invertebrates and lie within the scope of this work.

Subphylum Urochordata (Tunicata)

Urochordates, or tunicates, differ from other chordates in the following ways: the notochord is chiefly restricted to the tail and posterior region of the body of the larval form and disappears during metamorphosis; no typical chordate metamerism is present; the typical coelom of chordates is reduced, and the main cavity is a kind of hemocoel characteristic of arthropods; an atrium developed from dorsal lateral invaginations of the epidermis is found around the pharynx in many; a secreted tunic of living cells that contain supporting structures of calcareous deposits and cellulose forms an encasement for the body; and although they are deuterostomes, they have determinate instead of indeterminate cleavage.

Tunicates are strictly marine animals of cosmopolitan distribution throughout all seas from the intertidal zones to the great depths. The most common and primitive group of tunicates is the sea squirts. Some tunicate species have a wide distribution through all latitudes; others have a restricted, local distribution.

About 2,000 species of tunicates are known to zoologists. They are usually classified in accordance with the position of their reproductive glands and the nature of their gill apparatus. Three classes are recognized—Ascidiacea, Thaliacea, and Larvacea (Copelata).

The class Ascidiacea is by far the largest and best known. Ascidians are sedentary animals with typical life histories and metamorphosis. The other two classes, Thaliacea and Larvacea (100 species), are pelagic or free-swimming groups and are specialized for a planktonic existence. Although the three classes have differences from each other, many characteristics of both morphology and function are shared by all of them.

Tunicates are of great interest in the evolutionary interpretation of the chordates. Formerly, the adult sessile or attached form of tunicates was considered to be degenerate and the tadpole stage a recapitulation of a primitive condition. It is now thought that the attached ascidians are the primitive ancestral condition, and that the chordate-vertebrate group arose from ocean-bottom forms. A plausible theory, widely accepted at present, is that vertebrates arose from tunicate tadpoles that became neotenous (retention of larval characteristics) by mutation and eliminated the sessile stage. Such tadpoles, by swimming up continental streams to exploit the rich organic detritus, developed structures such as muscles, nerves, segmentation, and sense organs, which are largely lacking in the primitive sessile ancestors. The class Larvacea of existing tunicates may well be considered neotenous, with later stages omitted in its evolution. The early divergence of the urochordates from the chordate line of descent may explain the lack of segmentation in that group.

CLASS ASCIDIACEA

A common name for the ascidians is sea squirts. They are common in marine littoral waters, where they may be found attached to rocks, piers, shells, seaweed, and other objects. A few species live at considerable depths in the water. Common genera of ascidians along our coasts are *Ciona*, *Styela*, *Molgula*, and *Botryllus*. Most ascidians are attached, but *Polycarpa* and some others are free living.

External anatomy

The body of ascidians is cylindric or globose in shape and attached at one end by a stalk to a substratum (Fig. 31-1). It is enclosed by a test or tunic, which is lined by a membranous mantle with muscle fibers and blood vessels. The tunic contains tunicin (cellulose). Cellulose is found in only a few other metazoans, such

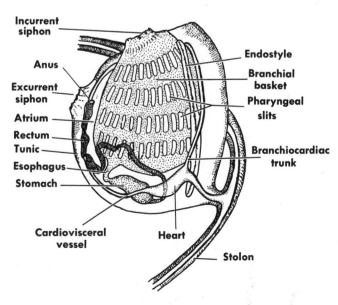

Fig. 31-1

Perophora viridis, a small colonial ascidian. Zooids are 2.5 to 4 mm. long. (From life.)

625

as sessile hemichordates and (recently) in the skin of man. At the end opposite the one attached to the substratum are two external openings that can be extended as siphons, the top incurrent siphon and the side excurrent siphon. The incurrent or oral siphon leads into the pharynx or branchial region, and the excurrent or atrial siphon (dorsal side of animal) leads away from the atrium. Water currents are kept moving in and out of the two siphons by the beating of cilia on the gill slits of the pharynx. The striated muscle of the body wall muscles can produce contraction of the body, causing the familiar squirts from the siphons.

Internal anatomy

Surrounding the pharynx (except where the pharynx is attached to the midventral body wall) is the atrium, which opens through the excurrent or atrial siphon (Figs. 31-1, 31-4). The atrium is lined with ectodermal epithelium, which also lines

the atrial siphon, and is continuous with the epidermis on the outside. The atrium contains strands of tissue or muscle to prevent overexpansion, and the siphons are provided with sphincters to regulate intake and outflow of water currents. Below the atrial cavity is the visceral or abdominal cavity, which contains the digestive tract and other visceral organs.

The pharyngeal chamber is often barrel-shaped and occupies a large part of the animal (Figs. 31-1, 31-2). It is lined with endoderm and covered by ectoderm with a mesenchymal framework between. Its entrance is guarded by a ring of tentacles for selecting food particles. The walls of the pharynx are pierced by small slits, through which water passes from the pharyngeal region into the atrium and thence through the atrial siphon to the outside. On the ventral side of the pharynx and extending through its whole length is a groove, the endostyle, the lateral walls of which are ciliated and the bottom of which contains mucus-secreting cells and long flagella

Fig. 31-2

Diagrammatic cross section through pharyngeal region of tunicate.

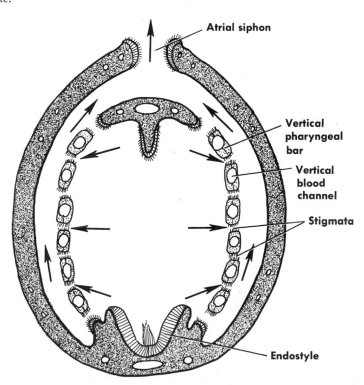

(Figs. 31-1, 31-2). From a pit at its posterior end the endostyle sends ciliated peripharyngeal grooves or ridges anteriorly, where the ridges form a band of glandular tissue just behind the anterior ring of tentacles. This band is a glandular tissue and secretes mucus. A dorsal membrane (dorsal lamina) runs posteriorly to the esophagus along the dorsal side. This membrane bears languets, or fingerlike projections involved in the feeding mechanism.

The pharyngeal cavity between the dorsal membrane and the ventral endostyle bears the specialized gill slits called stigmata. The stigmata are curved or spiral shaped and represent subdivided gill slits (Fig. 31-3). They are arranged in horizontal rows that are separated by horizontal and vertical bars, thus producing a grid pattern for greater surface area.

Ascidians are mucus-ciliary feeders and live upon the plankton organisms brought into the pharynx by water currents. The feeding mechanism involves the coordinating action of the two components—the water currents and the mucus entanglement of the food particles. An enormous amount of water for the size of the animal is strained for food. The principal sites of mucus formation are the endostyle and the anterior band of glandular tissue. Strands of mucus secreted by the endostyle are carried upward or anteriorly on each side by cilia on the pharyngeal wall and by the ciliated peripharyngeal grooves, As the strands of mucus cross the pharynx, the

food particles carried by the water currents through the stigmata are trapped on the mucus cords and passed to the dorsal midline of the pharynx. Here the food is rolled into cords by the ciliated dorsal membrane with the aid of the languets and tentacles. The mucus strands, now laden with trapped food, are passed posteriorly in the direction of the esophageal opening on the dorsal side of the pharynx, toward which the dorsal membrane is directed.

The digestive system of sea squirts varies, but consists of a ciliated tube or narrow esophagus, enlarged stomach with glandular outgrowths (liver), and intestine more or less looped (Figs. 31-1, 31-4). In certain ascidians (*Ciona*) a tube arises as a double evagination at the base of the pharynx and runs parallel to the intestine, which it may surround. It is called an epicardium. The anus opens into the cloacal region of the atrium. Digestion is extracellular. A pyloric gland composed of a network of vesicles occurs on the outer wall of the intestine and opens into the stomach. It may have excretory functions.

Some waste substances are excreted at the surface of the tunic, and some are carried by specialized cells (nephrocytes) to certain regions (intestine and gonads), where they accumulate to form vesicles or excretory storage organs.

The blood-vascular system is open, and capillaries are absent (Fig. 31-1). The tubular heart, with pacemakers at each end, alternates the direction of blood flow, resulting in a periodic reversal of blood flow. The reversal is independent of nervous control. The heart is a specialized part of the pericardium and is located near the stomach. Each end of the heart opens into a large sinus channel. Blood is carried by the subendostylar channel to the endostyle region and to the gill slits where respiratory exchange occurs. From the pharyngeal region the blood is carried by a channel beneath the dorsal membrane back to the digestive tract and other organs, and from there it is carried to the dorsal end of the heart by a dorsal abdominal sinus. This pattern of the blood channels is similar in some ways to that of fishes.

No respiratory pigment is found in the blood plasma, the osmotic pressure of

Fig. 31-3

Spiral stigmata in *Corella*. In most tunicates, stigmata are straight or curved. (Modified from Herdman.)

which is slightly higher than sea water. The plasma contains blood cells of several types. In some ascidians, oxides of vanadium and free sulfuric acid are found in the plasma and in certain cells. The function of these two substances is unknown, although the sulphuric acid tends to keep the vanadium in a reduced state.

The nervous system consists of a cerebral ganglion (brain), located in the body wall between the two siphons, and a variable number of nerves that originate in the ganglion and run to the siphons, gill slits, and visceral organs. A neural gland lying near the brain communicates by a duct with the dorsal corner of the gill chamber. This structure is thought by some investigators to be homologous with part of the vertebrate pituitary gland.

Sensory cells of tactile and chemorecep-

tive functions are abundant around the siphons (both inside and out), around the buccal tentacles, and in the atrium. These are probably used in sampling the water.

Tunicates are nearly all hermaphroditic, although the male gonads may develop before the ovaries. Usually, there is a single testis and a single ovary, which are located within, or posterior to, the intestinal loop (Fig. 31-4, *B*). Both gonads are attached to the atrial wall, with the testis below the ovary. The ovary is a saccular structure with germinal areas and follicles for the developing eggs. Mature eggs are carried by a single oviduct, which runs along the intestine and opens into the cloacal region in front of the anus. A sperm duct leads from the testis alongside the oviduct and opens into the cloaca. *Molgula, Styela,* and

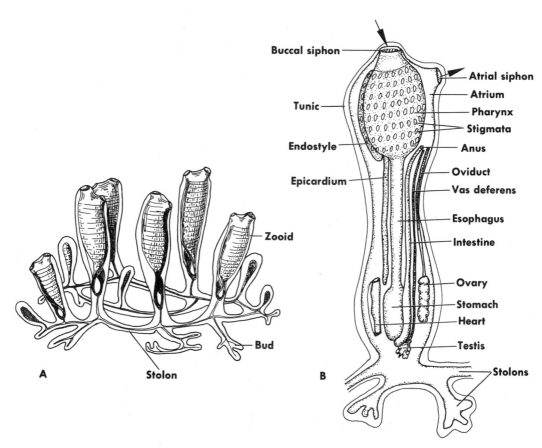

Fig. 31-4

A, Colony of *Clavelina.* All members of colony are connected by common blood system, and buds on stolons are vascular outgrowths of body and epicardium. **B,** *Clavelina* showing thorax and long abdominal region. (**A** modified from Herdman; **B** modified from Brien.)

some others have paired gonads of each sex, with one set consisting of a male and female gonad located in the right body wall of the branchial region and the other set within the digestive loop. In such cases the gonoducts are also paired. Fertilization may be internal or external, with some forms viviparous and others oviparous. Some species are solitary (*Molgula, Styela*, and others), and some are colonial or compound. Solitary ascidians are generally large; but colonial individuals are usually small, although the colony may be large. In some colonies the individuals are separate entities but are united by stolons that may be long and trailing; in others the stolons are short, and the individuals form compact groups (Fig. 31-4, *A*). In some colonial forms the basal parts of the individuals are joined together (*Clavelina*), and in the highly specialized or compound forms many individuals share the same test (*Botryllus*, Fig. 31-5). In some of these compound ascidians each member has its own inhalant siphon, but the excurrent opening is a common cloacal chamber with one aperture in the center of the colony. Many other arrangements occur in compound ascidians. In the so-called social ascidians a peculiar type of colony is formed by the grouping together of two entirely different genera, such as *Clavelina* and *Stolonica*.

Tunicates, with few exceptions, have a high capacity for regeneration of missing parts. A related phenomenon is budding, or asexual reproduction, which has been much studied, especially by N. J. Berrill, in recent years. Budding is chiefly a separation of a fragment or part of an individual and the subsequent growth and maturation of the fragment. Buds may detach and form independent individuals, or they may stay together and produce a colony. The nature of budding in tunicates is highly variable and complex. Usually it involves some form of constriction by the epidermis in which the tissues are divided into separate masses, the nature of which depends upon the part separated. In some a bud or blastozooid first appears on the stolon as a growth with food reserves. When the stolon and bud are separated from the parent, or the parent degenerates, the bud develops (*Clavelina*, Fig. 31-4, *A*). In others, after the thorax degenerates, the abdomen breaks up into buds. Nearly all colonies are formed by budding in some way, although not all budding results in colonies. It may be simply a method for increasing the number of independent individuals; nor is it restricted to the adult condition, for it often occurs in the larval stage.

Development

The embryologic development of tunicates has largely revealed the true status of the group, which was formerly placed among the Mollusca. The eggs of the solitary species tend to be smaller than those of the colonial forms, which have more yolk. Fertilization in most solitary species occurs in sea water; in colonial species internal fertilization is the rule. In *Botrylloides* the eggs are fertilized in the ovary, and development to the tadpole stage occurs there or in the atrium. The tadpole finally escapes through the body wall. Most colonial forms brood their young in the atrium.

There are many variations in the development of the different species of tunicates. In the common genus *Styela* the egg has a yellow-pigmented, a gray yolky, and a clear yolk-free area. The cleavage is holoblastic and radial but determinate (contrary to most other deuterostomes in which it is indeterminate). In the 16-cell stage the blastomeres are arranged in two tiers of eight cells, each with the yellow-pig-

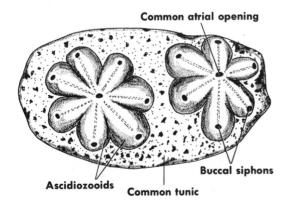

Common atrial opening

Buccal siphons

Ascidiozooids **Common tunic**

Fig. 31-5

Colony of *Botryllus* with common excurrent siphon and separate incurrent siphons. (Modified from Milne-Edwards.)

mented region located in four of the vegetal cells. A flattened coeloblastula appears in about the 40-cell stage. The future ectoderm of the animal side is made up of thick cells, while the future endoderm of the vegetal side is flat. Gastrulation is epibolic and produced by an invagination of the vegetal pole cells followed by an overgrowth of the prospective ectoderm. Within the archenteron the yellow-pigmented cells make up the mesoderm, which is not formed by an enterocoelous method, and the other vegetal cells produce the endoderm. The blastopore, which later closes, marks the posterior end of the embryo. The dorsal layer of ectoderm anterior to the blastopore gives rise to the neural tube, which becomes the brain and spinal cord along the middorsal line. Beneath the neural tube the mesoderm forms the noto-

chord, which is the forerunner of the vertebral column in vertebrates. The notochord enlarges to become the future axis of the tail, and the larva is hatched.

During later development, the larva elongates and becomes an appendicularia larva, commonly called the ascidian tadpole (Fig. 31-6, *A*). At this stage the tadpole has a nonfunctional digestive tract, two pairs of gill slits, a cerebral eye, statocyst, and three anterior adhesive papillae by which it can fasten itself to a substratum. The mouth, which later becomes the inhalant siphon, is located anteriorly but may not be opened during the larval stage. The mouth passes into the pharynx, which is followed by a looped digestive tract. A ventral endostyle occurs along the pharynx, and the atrium is represented by a small pocket. A

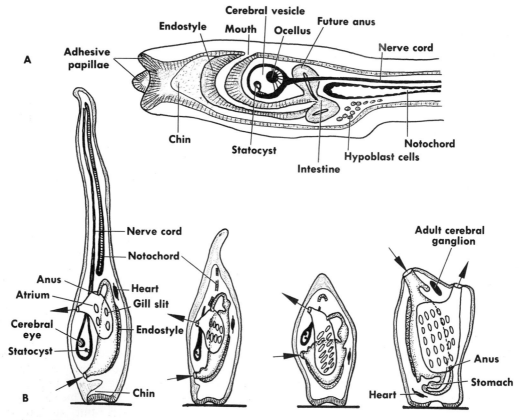

Fig. 31-6

A, Sagittal section of anterior end of free-swimming ascidian tadpole (*Ciona*). **B,** Four stages in metamorphosis of simple ascidian tadpole from attachment of tadpole to sessile adult stage. See text for description of process. (Modified from Kowalevsky and others.)

tunic secreted by the ectoderm covers the entire larva and, in the dorsal and ventral tail region, forms a fin.

Metamorphosis begins after a short free-swimming but nonfeeding existence when the larva sinks to the bottom and attaches itself to a substratum by the adhesive papillae (Fig. 31-6, *B*). The tail ectoderm contracts and breaks up the notochord, nerve cord, and tail muscles, which are then reabosrbed by phagocytosis. A rapid growth of the chin region near the adhesive papillae and the mouth results in the mouth being carried upward until it is opposite the point of attachment. Internal organs undergo a similar rotation of 90 to 180 degrees. A new nervous system replaces the old larval one. A differentiation of the intestine forms a stomach and liver. The circulatory system, which was started during the larval stage, now forms a heart. The number of gill slits increases, and the gonads are laid down. The final stages involve a functional use of the siphons.

CLASS THALIACEA

The tunicates of this class are pelagic and form part of the plankton population of the ocean, especially in tropical and semitropical waters. They are characterized by having no tail, inhalant and exhalant siphons opening at opposite ends of the body, a degenerate nervous system, and gill clefts not divided by external longitudinal bars. In many the body is barrel- or lemon-shaped and encircled by rings of muscle strands. These circular muscle bands are complete in *Doliolum;* incomplete in *Salpa.* Contractions of these muscles drive water through the exhalant (atrial) opening and aid in locomotion by a sort of jet propulsion. In *Pyrosoma* the gill clefts are numerous and tall dorsoventrally; in *Salpa* there are only two, each occupying most of a side of the pharynx. Many, including *Pyrosoma,* have brilliant luminescence.

Asexual budding occurs in all thaliaceans. The sexually reproducing stages are derived as blastozooid buds from the individual (oozooid) formed from the egg. In the colonial *Pyrosoma* there is no larval stage. Each member produces a meroblastic egg, which develops in the parent atrium into an oozooid embryo. The oozo-oid gives rise to four buds along a stolon, which are liberated by the rupture of the parent atrium. When the oozooid degenerates, the four buds on the stolon form a new colony by secondary budding. In the solitary *Salpa* the single egg in the atrium develops by a placental attachment, and the oozooid breaks free from the parent to form a chain of buds that later separates to form the sexual individual. In *Doliolum* (also solitary) there is a tailed larval stage. Three eggs produced by the parent are shed into the water where each develops into a tailed larva. The larva metamorphoses into an oozooid bearing a stolon with buds. These prebuds form several generations of blastozooids, which are attached to the parent oozooid and which form individuals of three kinds: gastrozooids, for nutrition, phorozooids, for carrying the third type, and gonozooids. The gonozooids are later liberated and become the sexual-reproducing individuals.

CLASS LARVACEA (COPELATA)

These small transparent tunicates are also pelagic and planktonic. They represent sexually mature forms that have retained the larval organization in many respects. Their body has a resemblance to the ascidian tadpole described in an earlier section. They have a permanent tail and a much simplified internal structure. Their test, or "house," does not contain tunicin and encloses or is loosely attached to the body. From time to time the animal disengages itself from the house and secretes a new one. The house, which is formed of gelatinous material secreted by the epidermis, is provided with an incurrent and an excurrent orifice. The incurrent orifice has a water-intake filter in the form of a screen of fine fibers. A food-concentrating apparatus, which strains out plankton from the water current, is also present in the test and serves as a second filter. The food from this second screening is carried to the mouth by the water current, which is created by the beating of the tail.

The body is a small compact structure, with the tail attached to the ventral side. The mouth is located at the anterior end of the body, which bears two simple gill clefts opening directly to the outside. The **631** pharynx is also provided with a food filter, and the intestine opens to the exterior ventrally or to one side.

The nervous system is composed of a brain (a compact ganglion) and a nerve cord. There is no eye, but a statocyst lies near the brain. The Larvacea are hermaphroditic, and the gonads are located in the posterior end of the body. A notochord and a caudal ganglion are found in the tail.

Oikopleura is one of the most familiar genera in the Larvacea, of which there are about 60 species.

Subphylum Cephalochordata

The members of this subphylum are commonly called lancelets. Another name for them is Leptocardii or amphioxus. Lancelets are small fishlike animals that rarely exceed 2½ inches in length, although there is one species in southern China that reaches 6 inches. Perhaps no animal is better known to zoologists than this little form because of its basic chordate characteristics and its evolutionary implications. It has the three chief chordate characteristics of dorsal hollow nerve cord, notochord, and well-developed pharyngeal gill slits, which are atypical in some respects.

The adults are found burrowing in coarse sand in shore water of the subtemperate and tropical oceans of the world. They burrow rapidly, anterior end first, in the sand by means of the vibrating action of the body and assume a resting condition with the anterior end exposed to the water. They are good swimmers and swim mostly at night, by lateral movements of their body. They select sandy regions of certain specifications and are partial to rounded sand grains coated with microorganisms and free from organic decay. Many are often found together in favorable regions, especially when spawning.

Only two genera and 29 species are recognized in the Cephalochordata.

Asymmetron. Gonads present on right side only; asymmetric metapleural folds, the right one continuous with the ventral fin; may or may not have a caudal appendage.
Branchiostoma. Gonads paired; both metapleural folds similar and ending behind the atriopore; no caudal appendage.

Branchiostoma virginiae is a common species along the southern Atlantic coast (United States); *Branchiostoma californiense* is common along the Pacific coast south of the San Diego region. *Branchiostoma lanceolatum* is a familiar European species.

External anatomy

The body of the lancelet is laterally compressed and tapered at each end like a lance (Fig. 31-7). The tail is more pointed than the anterior end. There is no head or paired fins. A low median dorsal fin occurs along the body, passes around the tail as the tail fin, and continues part way anteriorly along the ventral side as the ventral fin. A pair of metapleural folds extends along the anterior two thirds of the ventral surface of the body, which is flattened anterior to the ventral fin (Figs. 31-8, 31-10).

Fig. 31-7

Mature specimen of *Branchiostoma*, the cephalochordate commonly known as amphioxus. Gonads appear as row of block-shaped structures beneath myotomes. (From Hickman: Integrated principles of zoology, The C. V. Mosby Co.)

Just posterior to the metapleural folds is the ventral opening, the atriopore. The anus is on the left side near the base of the tail fin. The buccal cavity or oral hood (vestibule) is on the ventral anterior end just under the snout, or rostrum, and is fringed with about twenty sensory cirri that are provided with jointed internal skeletons. These cirri can spread out to open the buccal cavity, or bend inward to form a protective grating over the cavity. The body is covered by a single layer of epidermis composed of tall columnar cells, some of which are sensory with tactile processes. A thin, cuticular border, which may be a thin layer of mucus, is found in the adult. In the young amphioxus the epidermal cells are cuboidal and ciliated. Beneath the epidermis are the dermis of connective tissue and some cells. There are no glands or chromatophores in the integument, although some pigment is present in the epidermis near the anterior end.

Internal anatomy

Internally, amphioxus has a notochord extending the length of the body above the alimentary canal (Figs. 31-8, 31-10). It is a solid, elastic cord of gelatinous material and vacuolated cells filled with fluid, and surrounded by a connective tissue sheath (Fig. 31-9, *A*). Other skeletal or supporting structures are the circular cartilagelike reinforcement of the oral hood, the cross-

connection rods in the gill bars, and the delicate fin rays, in addition to those of the cirri. On each side of the body and tail are longitudinal muscles that are divided into chevronlike segments called myotomes (about 60 to 70 on each side) (Fig. 31-7). The myotomes of the two sides alternate with each other, and adjacent myotomes of a side are separated from each other by septa (myosepta or myocomma) of connective tissue (Fig. 31-10). Contraction of these muscles produces the lateral movements for burrowing and swimming. There are also some transverse muscles in the floor of the atrial cavity between the metapleural folds. These muscles serve to compress the atrial cavity in the discharge of the water.

Above the notochord lies the dorsal nerve cord (Figs. 31-8, 31-10) with a small central canal (neurocoel). The nerve cord is slightly dilated anteriorly to form the median cerebral vesicle, with a middorsal olfactory pit. An eyespot of black pigment may be present, and usually two pairs of so-called cranial nerves are given off from the anterior region of the cord. The nerve cord is connected to the myotomes by pairs of ventral motor nerves, one to each myotome (Figs. 31-9, *B*, 31-10). Alternately with the ventral nerves, pairs of sensory nerves originate at the dorsal edge of the nerve cord and pass to the skin and gut.

The straight digestive system starts with

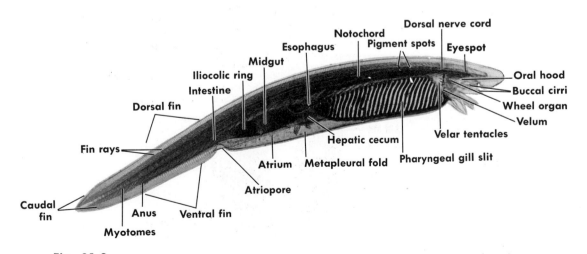

Fig. 31-8

Structure of young amphioxus *(Branchiostoma).* (From Hickman: Integrated principles of zoology, The C. V. Mosby Co.)

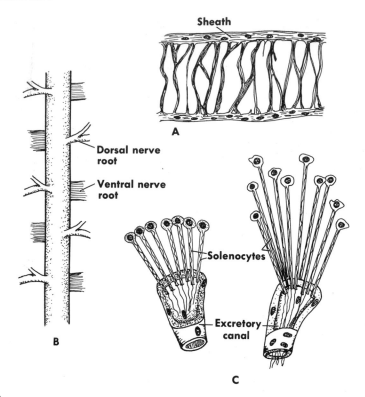

Fig. 31-9

A, Section of notochord of *Branchiostoma* showing vacuolated cell structure. **B,** Portion of nerve cord of *Branchiostoma* showing arrangement of dorsal and ventral nerve roots. **C,** Comparison of nephridia (in part) of marine polychaete (left) and amphioxus (right) showing solenocytes and their flagella. (**A** modified from Herdman; **C** modified from Goodrich.)

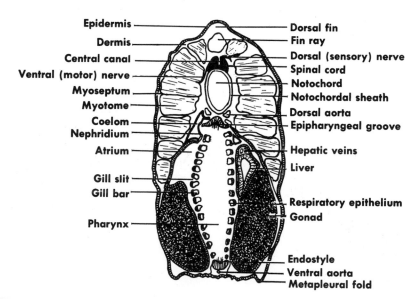

Fig. 31-10

Cross section of amphioxus through pharynx and gonads. (From Hickman and Hickman: Laboratory studies in integrated zoology, The C. V. Mosby Co.)

the oral hood or vestibule, which, as already described, is surrounded by the cirri (Fig. 31-8). At the posterior bottom end of the hood is the membranous velum to which are attached twelve velar tentacles, which are sensory and which also exclude large particles in the water current. The mouth proper is a circular opening in the velum and is guarded by the velar tentacles (Fig. 31-8). On the lateral walls of the oral hood are parallel ciliated patches that originate from a pair of dorsolateral ridges. Because of the rotating effect of its cilia, the entire structure is called the wheel organ. Its ciliary action directs the water current and food particles toward the mouth. The mouth opens into the large compressed pharynx with more than a hundred pairs of diagonal gill slits running more than half the length of the body (Fig. 31-8). The slits are separated by bars containing skeletal rods (Fig. 31-10) and subdivided by cross bars called synapticulae. The edges and inner surfaces of the gill bars bear cilia for drawing water from the mouth and driving it outward through the atrium. The branchial basket of gill slits is protected by two metapleural folds, which grow down on each side of the body and join midventrally to form the atrium, which opens posteriorly at the atriopore. The pharynx is suspended dorsally and hangs free in the atrium, which is within the body wall muscles (Fig. 31-10). The pharynx contains a ventral groove, the endostyle, with gland cells between which is a median tract of long flagella. The lateral margins of the endostyle diverge anteriorly to form a pair of ciliated peripharyngeal bands or grooves that encircle the pharynx inside the mouth. These bands bend back dorsally to join the ciliated hyperbranchial or epipharyngeal groove located middorsally in the pharynx.

From the hyperbranchial groove of the narrow hind end of the pharynx a short esophagus leads into the straight intestine (Fig. 31-8). There is no stomach or gastric glands. A blind fingerlike diverticulum of the intestine, the hepatic cecum, passes anteriorly to lie on the right side of the pharynx. This diverticulum is often called the liver, but it appears to be the seat for the production of digestive enzymes. Food does not enter the hepatic cecum. Near the hind end of the intestine is a ciliated iliocolic ring where the cord of food and mucus is rotated (Fig. 31-8). The rotation of the food-mucus cord assists the action of the enzymes on the food. Digestion is extracellular. The enzymes—amylase, protease, and lipase—have been detected in various regions of the gut. Behind the iliocolic ring, the intestine passes to the anus. Absorption of the food takes places in the intestine.

Feeding occurs in lancelets by a filter-feeding or mucus-ciliary method. When the animal is at rest in its burrow with its anterior end protruding and mouth open, the cilia on the inner surface and sides of the numerous gill bars draw the feeding current of water, laden with minute organisms, into the mouth and pharynx. As the water passes through the pharynx and between the gill bars into the atrium, the endostyle (Fig. 31-10) secretes a stream of mucus, which is swept up the side walls of the pharynx in the form of longitudinal strings by the frontal cilia of the gill bars. The food in the water currents is strained off by the gill bars, trapped in the mucus strings on the walls of the pharynx, and rolled upward into the hyperbranchial groove. Mucus and food are also carried up the peripharyngeal ciliated tracts to the hyperbranchial groove, which concentrates the mucus strings of food into a continuous food strand that passes into the intestine.

The circulatory system of amphioxus has no heart, but is similar in basic plan to that of higher chordates (Fig. 31-11). Blood is driven by the muscular contraction of the walls of the larger vessels. A subintestinal vein collects blood from the digestive tract and passes it to the hepatic portal vein from the hepatic cecum. From here the blood goes to the hepatic vein, which empties into the sinus venosus that also receives blood from other posterior parts of the body. From the sinus venosus just back of the pharynx a ventral aorta runs forward beneath the endostyle and distributes blood to the branchial arches of the gill bars. At the base of each primary gill bar is a little bulb that functions as a branchial heart. The blood is aerated as it passes through the gill bars and collects in the paired dorsal aortae, which join be-

Fig. 31-11

Scheme of circulation in amphioxus. (From Hickman and Hickman: Laboratory studies in integrated zoology, The C. V. Mosby Co.)

hind the pharynx to form the single dorsal aorta. The dorsal aorta furnishes blood to a system of lacunae, which supply the body tissues. Capillaries are absent. From the lacunae the blood passes into the venous system of caudal and cardinal veins and a gut plexus. The paired cardinal veins in the dorsal wall of the coelom collect blood from the muscles and body wall. They empty into the sinus venosus by way of the ducts of Cuvier. The caudal veins join the gut plexus, from which the blood is collected by the subintestinel vein already mentioned. An endothelial lining is found only in the dorsal aorta.

The blood of cephalochordates is colorless and has no respiratory pigment. Some investigators doubt the oxygenation of blood in the gills (although there are lamellae on bars of the gill clefts), but believe that this process occurs in the lacunae of the metapleural folds.

The excretory system consists of many protonephridia (100 or more) in the coelom above the pharynx (Fig. 31-10). Each protonephridium is a short, curved tube-like structure, closed at one end but opening at the other by a pore into a gill slit. The protonephridium bears along its curved side several tufts of solenocytes, or specialized flame cells, which project into the reduced coelom of *Branchiostoma* (Fig. 31-9, *C*). A solenocyte is an elongated tubular cell with a long flagellum extending down its interior from a protoplasmic mass. By diffusion through the solenocyte wall induced by the undulatory movement of its flagellum, waste and excess fluids are excreted from the coelom to the atrium. The solenocytes are in close contact with the blood vessels. Each protonephridium may bear as many as 500 solenocytes. Elsewhere in the animal kingdom, solenocytes are found only in some polychaete worms and a few others. This has posed difficult phylogenetic relationships.

The sexes are separate in amphioxus and there is no sexual dimorphism. The gonads arise as pouches from the lower ends of the myotomes and form bulges into the atrium near the base of the metapleural folds (Fig. 31-10). There are usually 25 to 33 gonads (depending on the species) on each side (Fig. 31-7). The testes usually bear yellow concretions, which are often absent in the ovaries. The mature gametes are shed by bursting through the wall into the atrium and thence to the exterior. Fertilization is external in the sea water. Breeding usually occurs in the early spring.

Development

The eggs of amphioxus have so little yolk, or else it is so uniformly distributed in them (isolecithal), that they represent a classic example of regular cleavage and gastrula formation. Development occurs in the water. In general, amphioxus has the deuterostome pattern of embryology, involving radial cleavage and enterocoelous formation of mesoderm (Fig. 31-12). Cleavage is rapid and a blastula, composed of a floor of large cells and a dome of smaller cells, is formed. Invagination is very

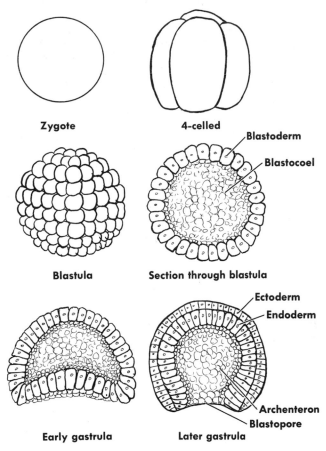

Zygote

4-celled

Blastoderm

Blastocoel

Blastula

Section through blastula

Ectoderm

Endoderm

Archenteron

Blastopore

Early gastrula

Later gastrula

Fig. 31-12

Early stages in embryology of amphioxus. (From Hickman: Integrated principles of zoology, The C. V. Mosby Co.)

regular in the formation of the archenteron, which has a large blastopore (the future anus). The gastrula is covered with cilia and rotates within the egg membrane. After the embryo elongates, the neural tube is formed by the sinking in of the flattened dorsal side as in the typical lower vertebrates. Near the anterior end of the archenteron a pair of lateral pouches is formed by evaginations. The walls of these pouches are to become the future mesoderm, and their cavities the future coelom. The notochord is formed by a middorsal evagination of the roof of the archenteron. After the formation of the coelomic pouches and the notochord, the remaining part of the archenteron becomes the definitive gut lined with endoderm. Other bilateral mesodermal pouches arise from the gut endoderm and lose their connections with the

gut. The pouches fuse to each other, with their outer walls applied to the body wall of the embryo to form the somatopleure and their inner walls to the gut to form the splanchnopleure. Between the two is the coelomic cavity. On each side of the dorsal nerve cord the inner wall of the mesoderm forms the myotome, which becomes segmented into blocks, the somites. The upper part of the coelomic cavity, the myocoel, becomes separated from the ventral part, the splanchnocoel. By expansion of the splanchnocoel the adult coelom is formed.

The first two coelomic pouches differentiate into a right coelomic cavity of the head and a reduced left cavity (Hatschek's pit of the adult mouth region) with an external opening (homologue of the probos-

637

cis pore of hemichordates) and a ciliated surface.

Branchiostoma hatches about eight hours after fertilization at the two-somite stage and swims around. At this time it has no mouth or anus. It elongates rapidly with the formation of new somites, perforation of the mouth and anus, and the first gill slits. The larva is very asymmetric. The mouth, which first appeared in the mid-ventral line, now shifts to the left side and the gill slit to the right side. Additional gill slits are added to the right side, but later some degenerate and others move to the left side until there is a symmetric arrangement. Further slits are then added by pairs; and metapleural folds grow over them to form the atrium. The reason for this early asymmetric development is not clear. The larva completes its development while resting on the sea bottom. The transformation and shifting of the gills from an asymmetric to a symmetric condition is often referred to as the metamorphosis stage.

Evolutionary status of amphioxus

Although amphioxus shows many basic features common to all chordate animals, it can hardly be called a generalized ancestral type because of such unique characters as the many gill slits, the presence of solenocytes, atrium, and some others. The animal apparently arose from sessile ancestors that had a tadpole stage which, by a loss of fixation and a retention of larval characters with certain adaptive modifications for its present existence, evolved into its present form. Some of its characters have been retained from an early sessile form, such as the employment of the large pharynx with its numerous gills for a food-catching mechanism, its lack of a brain, and its behavior of remaining stationary in a burrow for a large part of its existence, as well as other features. It may be considered a divergent line from the early ancestral line leading to the vertebrates.

Annotated references

Barrington, E. J. W. 1937. The digestive system of *Amphioxus*. Phil. Trans. Roy. Soc., London **228**:269-312.

Berrill, N. J. 1936. The evolution and classification of ascidians. Phil. Trans. Roy. Soc., London **226**:43-70.

Berrill, N. J. 1955. The origin of vertebrates. New York, Oxford University Press, Inc. *This author stresses the ascidian tadpole theory.*

Bigelow, H. B., and I. P. Farfante. Lancelets, cyclostomes, and sharks. In Tee-Van, J., et al. (editor). 1948. Fishes of the western North Atlantic. New Haven, Yale University Press, Sears Foundation for Marine Research, part 1, pp. 1-28.

Brien, P., and P. Drach. Procordes. In Grasse, P. P. (editor). 1948. Traite de zoologie, vol. 11, pp. 535-1040. Paris, Masson et Cie. *A comprehensive treatise on the lower chordates. One of the best accounts of this group.*

Bullough, W. S. 1950. Practical invertebrate anatomy. The Macmillan Company, London. *This author gives practical dissection methods for members of all three subclasses of tunicates and for amphioxus.*

Garstang, W. 1928. The morphology of Tunicata. Quart. J. Micr. Sci. **72**:51-187.

Hatschek, B. 1882. Studien ueber der Entwicklung des *Amphioxus*. Arbeiten aus dem zoologischen Institute der Universitat Wien. **4**:1-88. *A classic work by the great German investigator.*

Herdman, W. A. Ascidians and Amphioxus. In Harmer, S. F., and A. E. Shipley (editors). 1904. Cambridge natural history, vol. 7, London, The MacMillan Company.

Huus, J., H. Lohmann, and I. F. W. Ihle. Tunicata. In Kukenthal, W., and T. Krumbach (editors). 1933. Handbuch der Zoologie, vol. 5, part 2. Berlin, Walter De Gruyter & Co.

Van Name, W. G. 1945. The North and South American ascidians. Am. Mus. Natur. Hist. Bull. **84**:1-476. *The best American treatise on the group. Keys to species are given.*

Willey, A. 1894. Amphioxus and the ancestry of the vertebrates. New York, Columbia University Press. *A classic study of the famous animal.*

Young, J. Z. 1962. The life of vertebrates. New York, Oxford University Press, Inc. *The author believes that amphioxus has retained the ciliary feeding behavior of the early chordate ancestors and that it has undergone little change since the Silurian time. A good description of its structural features.*

Glossary

acetabulum True sucker in trematodes, usually of circular shape and raised rim.

aciculum (**pl. acicula**) Special strong seta for stiffening parapodium in polychaetes.

acontium Fine thread originating as a septal filament at the edge of a mesentery in the anthozoan gastrovascular cavity.

actinotroch (*actinotrocha*) Modified trochophore larva in the phoronids.

aerobic Requiring oxygen in respiration.

aesthetascs Slim, minute sensory processes on the antennae of certain crustaceans.

aesthetes Small light-sensitive structures on the calcareous plates of certain Amphineura.

afferent Leading toward a given position.

agamete Single germ cell that develops into an individual.

aliform Wing shaped.

ambulacra. Radially arranged series of plates that bear the rows of tube feet, or podia, in echinoderms.

ameboid movement Process of putting forth pseudopodia, as in an ameba or white blood corpuscle.

amictic Pertaining to the diploid egg of rotifers or the females that produce such eggs.

amphiblastula Larval stage of certain marine sponges in which the animal pole has flagellated cells and the vegetal pole unflagellated cells.

amphid Anterior chemoreceptor sense organ in certain nematodes.

amplexus Clasping process of copulation in certain animals.

ampulla Bulblike internal end of a tube foot in echinoderms.

anabiosis State of suspended animation, especially in the tardigrades.

anaerobic Oxygen-independent type of respiration.

anamorphic Having fewer segments in young stages than in the adult.

anastomosis Union of two or more hollow organs, such as blood vessels.

androgenic gland Sex-regulating gland in the amphipod *Orchestia* and some others.

anisogametes Unlike gametes in fertilization.

annulus Ringlike part, often mistaken for a true segment in leeches.

antennae Long, sensory, paired appendages on the head of many arthropods.

antennule One of the first pair of antennae on the head of crustaceans; usually smaller than the second pair of antennae.

antrum Chamber at the end of the male or female system in flatworms; opens into the gonopore.

apodeme Internal projection in an arthropod skeleton; usually for the attachment of muscles.

apopyle Pore between radial canals or flagellated chambers and the spongocoel in sponges.

archenteron Primitive gut of a metazoan embryo, formed by the process of gastrulation.

areoles Irregular, rounded, and thickened cuticular areas in some Nematomorpha.

athecate Absence of a hydrotheca around hydranths in certain hydrozoans.

atrium Large anterior chamber containing the pharynx in cephalochordates and tunicates; the peribranchial chamber.

autotomy Self-amputation of a body structure by reflex action.

autotrophic nutrition Ability to use simple inorganic substances for synthesis of more complex compounds, as in chlorophyll-bearing organisms.

avicularium Differentiated individual, or zooid, in a colony of ectoprocts; of the general shape of a bird's head and beak.

axoneme Fibril extending from the flagellum to its basal granule.

axopodium Pseudopodium containing an axial rod and a cytoplasmic envelope, as in Heliozoida.

benthonic Referring to the bottom of lakes and seas.

biramus Having two branches.

blastomere Early cleavage cell of an embryo before the gastrula stage.

blastopore In embryology, the mouthlike opening of a gastrula.

blastula In embryology, an early stage of a mass (usually hollow) of cells just before the gastrula stage.

639

blepharoplast *(kinetosome)* Intracellular granule of the flagellum from which the axoneme extends; may be fused with the basal granule.

bothrium One of two or four shallow sucking grooves on the scolex of certain tapeworms and characterized by weak muscularity and lack of inner muscle layer; variable in shape and form as a holdfast organ.

botryoidal tissue Loosely arranged mesenchyme tissue in certain leeches.

brachial Referring to the forelimb or arm.

branchial Referring to gills.

branchiostegite Expanded lateral part of the carapace, serving as a gill covering or gill chamber in certain crustaceans.

buccal cavity Mouth cavity; the region just inside the mouth opening.

bursa Saclike cavity or pouch forming part of the female reproductive system. The pouchlike bodies with genitorespiratory functions in ophiuroids.

byssus Anchorage fibers produced by many marine bivales.

calotte Anterior cap of cells in certain Mesozoa.

calyx Visceral body of certain invertebrates; the cup-shaped central part of the body.

capitate Referring to short tentacles with the nematocysts packed in terminal knobs.

capitulum Part of a barnacle enclosed in the mantle. The swollen end of a hair or antenna.

capsule Cluster of ganglia in annelids, sometimes called the follicle. An investing sheath of connective tissue.

captacula Tentacles with suckerlike tips on the head of certain scaphopods for sensory functions and food getting.

carcinology Study of crustaceans.

cephalization Tendency to concentrate in the head region.

cephalon Head region.

ceras (pl. **cerata**) Club-shaped projection containing tubules of the digestive glands and nematocysts on the back of certain nudibranchs.

cercaria In the life history of trematodes, the tadpole-shaped larva that breaks out of the snail or other intermediate host.

cercopod One of a pair of long filamentous projections of the posterior end of certain crustaceans.

cervical groove Transverse groove indicating the general boundary between the head and thoracic areas of the carapace of certain crustaceans.

chela Pincer claw on an arthropod appendage.

chelicerae First pair of appendages in arachnids; for seizing and crushing prey.

chilarium One of the pair of appendages at the posteior end of the cephalothorax in certain arachnids.

chitin Horny substance of a nitrogenous polysaccharide forming the hard part of the outer integument in arthropods, mollusks, and other invertebrates.

chloragogue Special spongy tissue that envelops the intestine of certain annelids; probably aids in excretion.

chlorocruorin Green, iron-bearing respiratory pigment in certain polychaetes.

cingulum Outer, ciliated, girdlelike band, or zone, on the corona of a rotifer.

cirrus Any slender appendage of various forms, such as the featherlike arm of a crinoid, the filamentous appendage of a barnacle, etc. Temporary projection formed by the turning inside out of the ejaculatory duct and serving as a male copulatory organ in many invertebrate phyla.

clitellum Saddlelike glandular structure on some midbody segments of certain annelids; forms mucus for cocoon formation and copulation.

clypeus Median anterior plate on an insect's head.

coeloblastula Simple blastula with cavity (blastocoel).

coelomocyte Corpuscle or amebocyte in the coelomic or pseudocoelomic fluid of invertebrates.

coelomoduct Duct that carries gametes or excretory products from the coelom to the exterior.

coenenchyme Common tissue connecting adjacent polyps in alcyonarian coelenterates.

coenosarc Axial living part of certain hydrozoan coelenterates; often surrounded by a perisarc.

coenosteum Calcareous skeleton of colonial corals.

collenchyma Undifferentiated mesenchyme with loosely scattered cells.

colloblasts Adhesive cells found on the tentacles of ctenophores.

collum Collar or neck region.

commensalism Symbiotic relationship between two different species whereby one member of a species derives an advantage and the member of the other species derives no advantage or disadvantage.

conchiolin Albuminoid organic matrix of a mollusk shell.

coracidium Early larval stage of certain tapeworms.

corona Ciliated zone surrounding the anterior end of a rotifer, often called the wheel organ.

coxal gland Excretory gland at the base of the leg in some arthropods.

coxopodite Basal segment of a pereiopod in crustaceans.

craspedote Pertaining to a coelenterate medusa with a velum.

crystalline style Cylindric proteinaceous rod in a cecum of the stomach or intestine of certain bivalves and gastropods; releases enzymes as it rotates.

cyclomorphosis Gradual changes in gross morphology during successive seasonal generations, as in Cladocera.

cypris larva Free-swimming stage developed from the nauplius in barnacles.

cysticercoid Larval stage in certain tapeworms; resembles the cysticercus but has a tail.

cytopharynx Funnel-shaped food canal leading from the cytostome into the cell of ciliates.

cytopyge Area in the body wall of ciliates which serves as an anus for the discharge of undigested materials.

cytosome Cell body inside the plasma membrane.

cytostome Mouth of certain holozoic protozoans.

dactylozooid Type of polyp specialized for a tactile role in hydrozoan coelenterate colonies.

Desor larva Modified pilidium larva that remains inside the egg membrane and lacks certain pilidium charatceristics.

determinate cleavage Fate of blastomeres is fixed early in development; mosaic cleavage in which all the blastomeres are required for complete development.

detritus Any fine particulate debris of organic or inorganic origin.

dextral Right-handed; in gastropods, when facing the aperture, the coils turn to the right; having the aperture to the right of the shell axis.

diapause Period of suspended development or growth in certain insects and other invertebrates during stages of their life cycle.

diaxial Movable at right angles to the long axis of the body.

dioecious Pertaining to an organism in which the male and female reproductive systems are in different individuals.

dipleurula Hypothetical ancestral form of echinoderms; a general term for various types of ciliated echinoderm larvae.

doublura In horseshoe crabs, the ventral surface of the marginal reflected carapace of the prosoma.

ecdysis Periodic molting or shedding of the exoskeleton to permit increase in size of arthropods, nematodes, and others.

ectolecithal Pertaining to zygotes with peripheral yolk granules.

elytra Pair of anterior heavy wings of beetles.

embolus Anterior end of the palp in male spiders through which sperm is injected into the female.

endite Basal median lobe of many arachnid and crustacean appendages.

endolecithal Pertaining to zygotes with enclosed yolk granules.

endopodite Median branch of a biramus appendage.

endosome Intranuclear body, other than chromatin granules, within the nuclear membrane.

endosternite Sclerotized process on the inner surface of the cephalothoracic exoskelton in certain arthropods for muscle attachment.

endostyle Ciliated ventral groove in the pharynx of tunicates, cephalochordates, and some others; collects food particles and passes them on.

enterocoelous formation of coelom Type of mesoderm formation that involves the pouchlike outfolding of the archenteron.

enteron Part of the digestive tract derived from the endoderm; sometimes used as a general term for the alimentary canal.

ephippium Posterodorsal egg pouch in certain Cladocera.

ephyra Immature, free-swimming jellyfish from asexual division of the strobila.

epiboly Growth of ectodermal cells downward to cover the vegetal cells during gastrulation.

epicuticle Outermost, hardened waxy layer in an arthropod cuticle.

epigastric furrow Groove separating the region of the book lungs from the posterior part of the abdomen.

epigynum Flap covering the genital pore in female spiders.

epimeron Posterior lateral part of a pleuron in certain arthropods.

epimorphic Having a full complement of segments in the young.

epiphysis Small peripheral bar in Aristotle's lantern.

epipodite Respiratory process attached at the base of the trunk appendage in certain arthropods.

epistome Flap that covers the mouth of ectoprocts.

epitoky Seasonal modification in posterior part of marine polychaete; posterior part becomes swollen with gonads and eggs or sperm.

erythrocruorin Invertebrate hemoglobin of several varieties found in annelids, echinoderms, mollusks, and some others.

eutely Constant number of cells in all adult members of a single species.

exite Lobe on the outer margin of a foliaceous appendage in certain crustaceans.

exopodite Lateral branch of biramous appendage.

filopodium Pseudopodium in the form of filamentous projections that may branch but do not anastomose, as in *Amoeba radiosa*.

flame bulb Hollow bulb-shaped structure of one or more cells provided with one or many cilia (flagella) and forming part of the protonephridial system in many invertebrates; excretory and osmoregulatory in function.

foliaceous appendage Flat, leaflike subdivided appendage in certain crustaceans.

frustule Nonciliated planulalike bud that develops into a polyp in some hydrozoans.

funiculus Fibrous strand connecting the lower end of the digestive tract to the body wall in Ectoprocta.

furca Any forked process.

gamont Gametocyte that develops into sporoblasts in sporozoan life histories.

gastrolith Calcareous body in the cardiac stomach wall of certain crustaceans.

gastrula In embryology, an invaginated blastula; in some cases, it is hollow and sometimes a solid sphere of cells.

gemmule Cystlike body of freshwater sponges able to withstand winter conditions and to germinate new sponge when conditions are favorable.

giant fiber Large nerve fiber that can transmit impulses faster than normal fibers; refers especially to those in the nerve cord of annelids, arthropods, and squids.

glabella Median part of the head of a trilobite and some others.

glochidium Bivalve larval stage in freshwater mussels.

gnathobase Basal process on the appendages of certain arachnids; usually for crushing or handling food.

gnathochilarium Appendage of united second maxillae, or the lower lip, of millipedes.

641

gnathosoma Anterior part of the body of ticks and mites, chiefly the mouth and mouthparts.

gonangium Asexual reproductive polyp in certain coelenterates.

gonophore Asexual bud of a polyp or polypoid colony in certain hydroids; produces medusae or gametes.

gonotheca Vaselike sheath around the blastostyle of certain coelenterates.

gonozooid Polyp specialized for reproduction in certain hydrozoans.

hectocotylus Modified arm in certain cephalopod mollusks for use as a copulatory organ.

hematochrome Bright red pigment occuring in some plantlike flagellates; allied to chlorophyll.

hemocoel Blood cavity consisting of spaces between tissues; found in arthropods and some others with reduced coeloms.

heterogamy Condition in which two unlike gametes unite to form a zygote.

heterotrophic nutrition Type of nutrition that depends upon complex organic food materials originating in other plants and animals.

holoblastic cleavage Complete and nearly equal cleavage of cells in early embryology.

holophytic nutrition Type of nutrition by which green plants are able to make food from simple inorganic substances.

holozoic nutrition Animallike nutrition that involves ingestion and metabolic utilization of solid food particles or living prey.

hydatid Fluid-filled cyst that produces scolices and daughter cysts in the life history of some tapeworms.

hydrotheca Vaselike sheath around the hydranth, or terminal portion, of certain hydroid polyps.

hypertonic Condition in which a concentration of dissolved materials gains solvent through a differentially permeable membrane from a solution with a lower solute concentration.

hypodermic impregnation Injection or passage of sperm, often in packets (spermatophores), directly through the epidermis.

hypodermis Epidermis that secretes an overlying cuticle.

hypostoma Median anterior mouthpart in certain arachnids; in Hemiptera, the lower part of the anterior surface of the head.

hypotonic Condition in which a concentration of dissolved materials loses solvent through a differentially permeable membrane to a solution with a concentration of greater dissolved materials.

idiosoma Posterior part of ticks and mites, making up most of the body in these forms.

indeterminate cleavage Type of cleavage in which the early blastomeres do not have a predetermined fate in forming tissues and organs; if separated, early blastomeres will each give rise to a complete larva.

infraciliature System of granules and fibrils lying beneath the pellicle and underlying the cilia in ciliates.

infusorigen Hermaphroditic cell cluster in the rhombogen of Mesozoa.

inquiline Organism living in the nest or burrow of another animal; may or may not be a commensal.

insemination Introduction of sperm into the female.

integument Outer covering, or skin and its derivatives, of an animal.

introvert In sipunculids, the anterior part, or proboscis, which may be withdrawn into the trunk.

isogamy Condition in which the two gametes of a union are alike morphologically.

Johnston's organ Auditory organ on the second segment of each antenna in certain insects.

kinetosome Small body or basal granule underlying the cilium or flagellum and capable of self-reproduction; may be involved in controlling the motion of the flagellum or cilium.

kinety Row of basal granules, or kinetosomes, with their associated fibrils (kinetodesmas).

labium Lower lip of the mouth in insects; sometimes bilobed.

labrum Fleshy upper lip of the mouth in insects.

lacinia mobilis Movable process near the mandibular teeth in certain crustaceans and insects.

lacuna Space in the tissues, serving as part of the circulatory system.

larva Early feeding stage in the life cycle of an animal; unlike the adult.

Laurer's canal In some trematodes, a narrow canal running from the oviduct to the dorsal body surface where it may open; may function in copulation.

lemnisci Pair of bodies in the neck or pseudocoel of Acanthocephala, serving as reservoirs for the lacunar fluid when the proboscis is retracted.

littoral Shallow part of lakes and seas along the coast; the sea floor from the shore to the edge of the continental shelf.

lobopodium Blunt, fingerlike pseudopodium, as in *Amoeba proteus.*

lophophore Anterior ridge bearing ciliated tentacles in Ectoprocta, Brachiopoda, and Phoronida.

lorica Rigid case or exoskeleton of certain protozoans and rotifers.

macromere One of the larger cells resulting from unequal cleavage during embryology.

macronucleus Polyploid nucleus in ciliates produced by repeated divisions of chromosomes; the larger vegetative nucleus of the two types of nuclei in ciliates.

macroplacoid Small sclerotized plate embedded in the pharyngeal muscles of a tardigrade.

madreporite Sievelike porous plate (usually on the surface) which enables the fluid to pass in and out of the water-vascular system in echinoderms.

Malpighian tubule Excretory, blind tubular glands opening into the anterior part of the hindgut of many terrestrial arthropods.

mantle Extension of the body wall in mollusks and brachiopods; involved in secreting the shell and many other functions.

marsupium External brood pouch.

mastax Muscular portion of a rotifer pharynx containing the trophi.

mastigonemes Branching fibrils extending from the flagella in some flagellates.

maxilla Head appendage (one or two pairs) modified in various ways for food handling in many arthropods.

maxillary glands Two small glands posterior to the mouth in certain crustaceans; probably excretory in function.

medusa Free-swimming stage or form in the life history of many coelenterates; jellyfish.

megalops Larval stage just before the adult stage of marine crabs.

Mehlis' gland Cluster of unicellular glands surrounding the ootype in some trematodes and cestodes; formerly called the shell gland.

membranelle Compound ciliary organelle made up of several fused transverse rows of cilia, usually occurring in a buccal cavity leading to the cytostome.

merozoite Cell resulting from multiple fission, or schizogony, of a schizont in certain Sporozoa.

mesenteron Midgut.

mesoglea Amorphous jellylike material between the epidermis and gastrodermis in sponges and coelenterates; when it has cells and fibers, it is considered a third germ layer (mesoderm).

metacercaria Larval stage in trematodes in which the larva loses its tail and becomes encysted on an intermediate host.

metagenesis Alternation of generations; the succession of asexual and sexual individuals in a life history.

metamerism Linear repetition of body parts (metameres or segments) at regular intervals along the anteroposterior axis.

metanephridium Type of nephridium with open inner ends; the inner end called the nephrostome and the external opening the nephridiopore; common in annelids, sipunculids, mollusks, and others.

metasoma Posterior part of the body in arachnids.

metastoma Labium.

micromere One of the smaller cells resulting from unequal cleavage during embryology; contrast with the macromere.

micropyle Small pore in the chorion of an insect egg through which sperm enter.

microthriches Fingerlike projections of the outer surface of the tegument in certain cestodes, which may interdigitate with the microvilli of the host's intestine.

mictic Pertains to the haploid eggs of rotifers or the female that produces such eggs.

miracidium Ciliated free-swimming larva that hatches from a trematode egg; the first larva in the life cycle of trematodes.

mosaic Type of development in which each blastomere is fated to become a definite part of the whole embryo after fertilization.

motorium Ciliate organelle with its connecting fibers, serving as a motor-coordinating center.

myochordotonal organ Small proprioceptor in the third segment of each leg of decapod crustaceans.

myoneme Contractile filament in the cytoplasm of protozoans.

mysis One of the first three larval stages of certain decapods; has 13 pairs of appendages.

myxopodium Condition of anastomosing rhizopods in certain ameboid protozoans.

nacreous layer Innermost lustrous layer of a mollusk shell.

nauplius Free-swimming larval form typically of three pairs of appendages; characteristic of many crustaceans.

nauplius eye Unpaired median eye of crustaceans.

nectochaeta Type of free-swimming larva in some polychaetes.

nectophore Swimming, bell-shaped medusa of a siphonophore colony.

nematogen Individual dicyemid mesozoan found in young cephalopods; gives rise to vermiform larvae.

nephridiopore External opening of a nephridium.

nephridium Tubular organ for excretion and osmoregulation in annelids, mollusks, arthropods, and other invertebrates.

nephromixium Combination of coelomoduct and nephridium into a compound organ with both genital and excretory functions.

nephrostome Ciliated internal opening of a nephridium as in a metanephridium.

neritic Pertaining to that part of the continental shelf between the low-tide line and depths of about 600 feet, including both bottom and water.

neuron Nerve cell, including cell body, dendrites, and axons.

notochord Longitudinal elastic rod lying between the nervous system and the digestive tract in the embryos of all chordates and in the adults of some.

nuchal organ Glandular pit on the head of certain polychaetes; may have sensory functions.

ocellus Complex photoreceptor with a lenslike body enclosed in pigment.

ommatidium One of the slender visual units of the compound eye, made up of a complex of structures.

oncosphere Six-hooked larva that hatches from the eggs of certain tapeworms.

oostegites Flat plates extending medially from the thoracic appendage of certain crustaceans (Peracarida).

ootype Thickened portion of the oviduct surrounded by Mehlis' glands in trematodes and cestodes; formerly considered the place where the shell is formed.

operculum Flaplike covering of many types, such as the gill cover of crayfish, the plates of a barnacle shell, the horny covering of the aperture in gastropods, etc.

opisthaptor Sucker at the posterior end of certain trematodes (Monogenea).

opisthosoma Abdomen, or posterior part of body, in arachnids.

opsiblastic Referring to the heavy-shelled gastrotrich egg that may delay hatching if weather conditions are unfavorable.

organelle Specialized part of a cell having a specific function.

643

sclerite Hard plate forming part of the exoskeleton of arthropods, especially in insects.

scleroprotein Fibrous protein found in connective tissue.

sclerotized Pertaining to specially hardened areas of the arthropod exoskeleton.

scolex Anterior end of a tapeworm; usually provided with holdfast structures.

scutellum Part of the dorsal thoracic exoskeleton in some insects.

scyphistoma Polyp stage of a scyphozoan jellyfish with tetramerous symmetry and a gastrovascular cavity of four divisions.

seminal vesicle Enlarged part of the male reproductive system where sperm are stored; sometimes a fluid is secreted here also.

sensillum Cell or group of cells associated with chitinous structures and functioning as a sense organ.

septum Membranous partition separating two cavities.

seta Type of hairlike projection of the exoskeleton, or integument, of arthropods and annelids.

setosal Bearing bristles.

setule Threadlike bristle.

sinistral Left-handed; in gastropods, when facing the aperture, the coils turn to the left; having the aperture to the left of the shell axis.

sinus Cavity, recess, or depression; an expanded blood vessel or blood cavity.

sinus gland Ductless gland in the eyestalk of certain crustaceans and associated with the X organ; regulates molting and controls the physiology of chromatophores.

siphon Specialized tube of the mantle of certain pelecypods and cephalopods, or in the test of tunicates; for the entrance and exit of water.

siphonoglyph Groovelike, ciliated lip of an anthozoan stomodeum.

solenia Gastrodermal tubes, or continuations of the gastrovascular walls of adjacent polyps, by which the polyps communicate with each other in the colonies of Alcyonaria.

solenocyte Type of flame cell, or bulb, with a single long flagellum.

specialized Adapted by structure or function for a particular mode of life in its evolutionary development as contrasted with its early ancestral condition.

spermaducal gland Small gland associated with the vas deferens of oligochaetes.

spinneret Conical posterior structure bearing openings to silk glands in spiders.

spiracle External opening to the tracheae or book lungs in arthropods.

spiral cleavage Type of cleavage in which the cleavage spindles are diagonal to the polar axis, resulting in successive alternating tiers of cells or a spiral arrangement.

spongin Fibrous network skeleton of certain sponges, consisting of a sulfur-containing protein.

spore Cell encased in a resistant covering and capable of developing into an organism.

sporocyst Saclike larval stage in many trematodes; usually embedded in the viscera of an interme-

diate host. In certain protozoans, a sac in which spores are formed.

sporogony Process of spore formation resulting in the production of sporozoites.

sporozoite Last stage in the sexual cycle of Sporozoa.

statocyst Sense organ of equilibration; usually consists of a vesicle with lithocytes and a movable statolith.

stercoral pocket Cecum connecting with the rectum in many arachnids and serving as storage place for feces.

stereogastrula Any type of solid gastrula; a parenchymula.

stigma Light-perceiving organelle in green flagellates and some colorless ones; usually contains reddish pigments. A spiracle or breathing pore in certain arthropods.

stigmata Breathing pores. Slits in the pharyngeal wall of tunicates.

stolon Horizontal stemlike attachment of certain invertebrates; gives rise to individuals at intervals.

stoma Mouthlike opening, or mouth cavity, in some invertebrates.

stomochord Anterior diverticulum of the buccal cavity in hemichordates; may be considered a type of notochord.

stomodeum In embryology, the ectoderm-lined mouth and foregut of the enteron; in class Anthozoa of coelenterates and phylum Ctenophora, the ectodermal-lined pharynx.

streptoneury Visceral loop (especially the nervous system) in the form of a figure eight in certain mollusks.

stridulate Producing sound by rubbing parts of the body together.

strobila Scyphistoma stage of scyphozoan jellyfish made up of a stack of potential jellyfish (ephyrae). The main body of a tapeworm, not including the anterior scolex; the chain of proglottids.

symbiosis Intimate association of two organisms of different species, which may be expressed as commensalism, mutualism, or parasitism.

syncytium Mass of protopasm or a cell containing several nuclei not separated by cell boundaries.

syngamy Formation of a zygote by the union of male and female gametes; fertilization or conjugation.

synkaryon Fertilization nucleus formed by the union of two pronuclei.

tapetum Iridescent pigmented area of the choroid coat and retina of the eye for reflecting the light rays.

tectin Substance similar to chitin (pseudochitin) in the shells of forams.

tegmen Covering of the oral disk of crinoids.

tegument External covering, formerly called the cuticle, in cestodes.

telopodite Segmented appendage of the trilobite trunk; also those segments of an insect limb distal to the coxa.

telotroch Preanal tuft of cilia in certain larval forms (e.g., a trochophore).

telson Posterior projection of the last body segment in some arthropods; also the terminal stinging segment of a scorpion.

tentaculocyst Small club-shaped sense organ along the margin of certain medusae; rhopalium.

tergum Dorsal surface of a body segment in arthropods; may consist of one or more sclerites.

theca Sheath such as the test, or armor, of a protozoan.

thecate Having a hydrotheca around the hydranth in coelenterates.

Tiedemann's bodies Small ceca of the ring canal in many echinoderms and supposed by some authorities to furnish coelomocytes.

torsion Twisting process in certain gastropods which alters the position of the viscera and other structures through 180 degrees from the primitive plan.

tracheae Air tube respiratory system in insects and other arthropods.

trichites Rodlike bodies forming an internal skeleton around the mouth and gullet of certain ciliates; similar to trichocysts, but are not discharged.

trichobothrium Sensory hair in certain arthropods.

trochal disk One of the ciliated disks of which the corona is composed in certain rotifers.

trochophore larva Type of larva common (with some modifications) to several invertebrate groups.

trochus Inner ciliated ring at the anterior end of a rotifer.

trophi Set of sclerotized jaws embedded in the mastax of rotifers.

trophozoite Growing or vegetative stage in the protozoan (especially in the Sporoza) life cycle.

urosome Posterior or abdominal region of an arthropod.

velarium Subumbrella extension in certain scyphozoan medusae, analogous to a true velum.

veliger larva Free-swimming larva that develops from the trochophore in many marine mollusks; has the beginning of a shell, mantle, and foot.

vibraculum Type of modified zooid of whiplike shape that aids in keeping the bryozoan colony free from debris in certain marine species.

X organ Ductless gland closely associated with the sinus gland, the secretions of which prevent or delay molting.

Y organ Ductless gland in the head of crustaceans; apparently accelerates molting.

zoarium Colony of ectoprocts.

zoea One of the early larval stages of marine crabs.

zonite Body segment in Kinorhyncha and millipedes.

zooecium Secreted covering of the individual making up a colony of ectoprocts.

zooid Individual member of a colony of animals.

Index

Illustrations are indicated by boldface page numbers.

Index